Solid

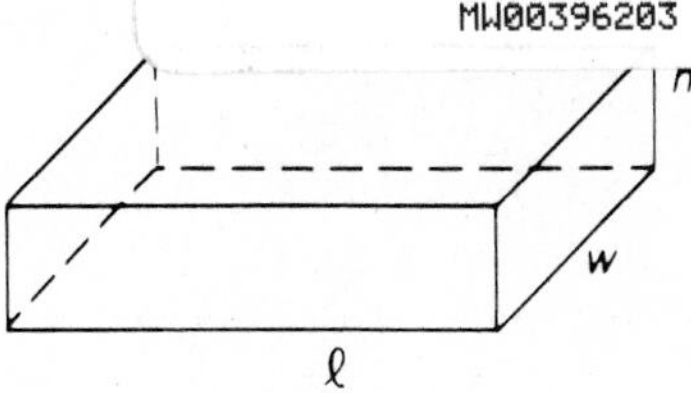

Rectangular Solid (Parallelepiped)

Surface Area $S = 2\ell w + 2wh + 2\ell h$
Volume $V = \ell wh$

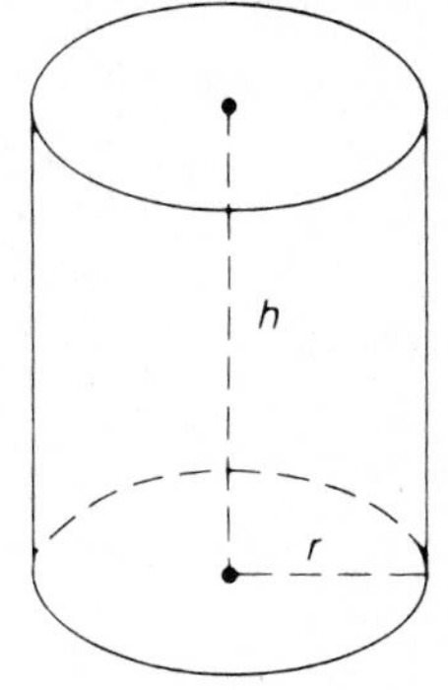

Right Circular Cylinder

Surface Area $S = 2\pi rh + 2\pi r^2$
Volume $V = \pi r^2 h$

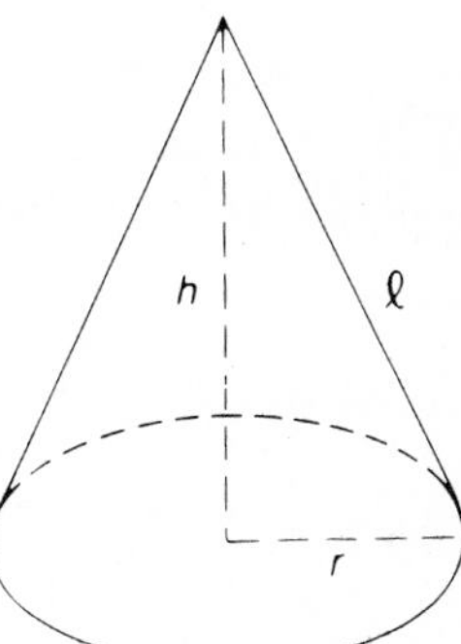

Right Circular Cone

Surface Area $S = \pi r\ell + \pi r^2$
Volume $V = \frac{1}{3}\pi r^2 h$

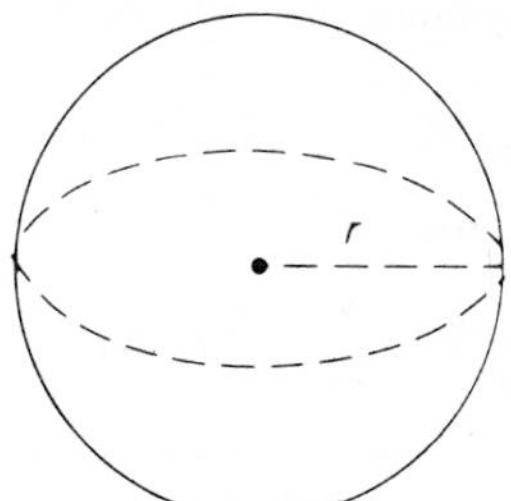

Sphere

Surface Area $S = 4\pi r^2$
Volume $V = \frac{4}{3}\pi r^3$

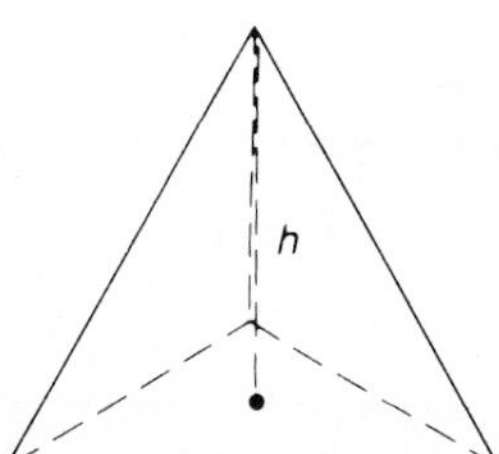

Right Pyramid

Volume $V = \frac{1}{3}bh$
(b is the area of the base)

Principles of

Elementary Algebra with Applications

Second Edition

Principles of

Elementary Algebra

with Applications

Second Edition

Harry L. Nustad

Terry H. Wesner
Henry Ford Community College

Wm. C. Brown Publishers

Book Team

Editor *Earl McPeek*
Developmental Editor *Theresa Grutz*
Production Editor *Eugenia M. Collins*
Designer *K. Wayne Harms*
Photo Editor *Carrie Burger*

Wm. C. Brown Publishers

President *G. Franklin Lewis*
Vice President, Publisher *George Wm. Bergquist*
Vice President, Publisher *Thomas E. Doran*
Vice President, Operations and Production *Beverly Kolz*
National Sales Manager *Virginia S. Moffat*
Advertising Manager *Ann M. Knepper*
Marketing Manager *John W. Calhoun*
Editor in Chief *Edward G. Jaffe*
Managing Editor, Production *Colleen A. Yonda*
Production Editorial Manager *Julie A. Kennedy*
Production Editorial Manager *Ann Fuerste*
Publishing Services Manager *Karen J. Slaght*
Manager of Visuals and Design *Faye M. Schilling*

Cover photo by Bob Coyle; Woodwork by Herbert F. Hanselmann

Photo Credits: R.1: © Jim Pickerell/Comstock; Chapter Opener 1, 2: © Bob Coyle; Chapter Opener 3: © Jon Feingersch/Stock Boston; Chapter Opener 4: © Mark Antman/The Image Works, Inc.; Chapter Opener 5: © Bob Coyle; Chapter Opener 6: © Holt Confer/The Image Works, Inc.; Chapter Opener 7: © Bob Daemmrich/The Image Works, Inc.; Chapter Opener 8: © Bob Coyle; Chapter Opener 9: © Peter Vandermark/Stock Boston; Chapter Opener 10: © Mike Mitchell/Photo Researchers, Inc.

Library of Congress Catalog Card Number: 90-56202

ISBN 0-697-01351-0

Printed in the United States of America by Wm. C. Brown Publishers, 2460 Kerper Boulevard, Dubuque, IA 52001

10 9 8 7 6 5 4 3 2 1

To my wife Dene
Harry

To my wife Mary Ann
Terry

Contents

2 Solving Equations and Inequalities

3 Algebraic Expressions

4 Factoring and Solution of Quadratic Equations by Factoring

5 Rational Expressions, Ratio and Proportion

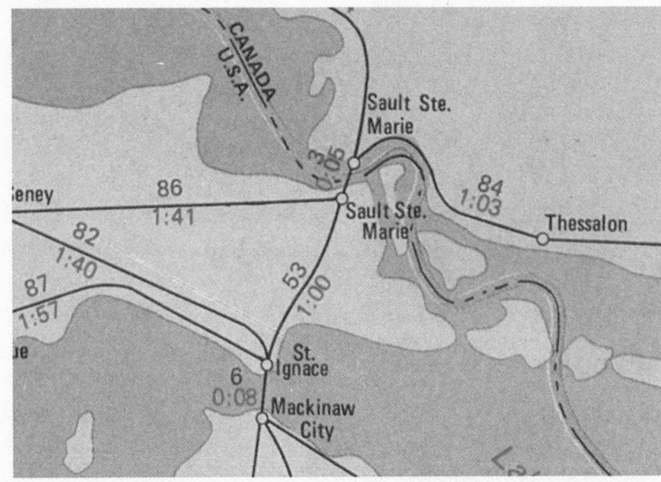

6 Operations with Rational Expressions

7 Linear Equations in Two Variables

8 Systems of Linear Equations

9 Roots and Radicals

10 Solutions of Quadratic Equations

Nustad and Wesner's

20 Point Learning System

Students will count on Harry Nustad and Terry Wesner's integrated learning system. The product of over 50 years of combined teaching experience, this system has been developed with the help of feedback from many of our tens of thousands of users—both professors and students—through various texts and editions by this author team. The authors have fine-tuned and enhanced their learning system for this second edition of *Principles of Elementary Algebra.* ▣ A full-color design makes an already superb learning system even better. The pedagogical color scheme is used consistently throughout, providing a road map to guide students through the key points of each section. Much more than just adding visual appeal, the color in this text is an integral part of the learning system. Let's take a look at examples of the 20 points that make up the learning system.

1. Chapter Lead-in Problem
2. Proficiency Check
3. Explanations
4. Examples
5. Margin Exercises
6. Procedure Boxes
7. Definitions
8. Concepts
9. Notes
10. Problem Solving
11. Mastery Points
12. Section Exercises
13. Quick-Reference Examples
14. Trial Problems
15. Core Exercise Problems
16. Section Review Exercises
17. Solution to Chapter Lead-in Problem
18. Chapter Summary
19. Chapter Review Exercises
20. Cumulative Test

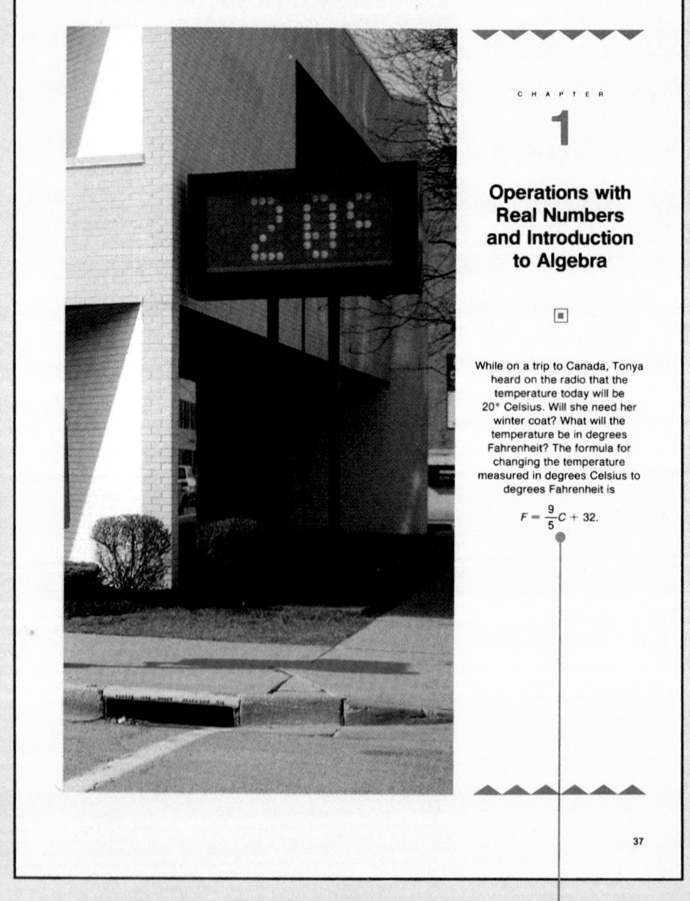

CHAPTER

1

Operations with Real Numbers and Introduction to Algebra

▣

While on a trip to Canada, Tonya heard on the radio that the temperature today will be 20° Celsius. Will she need her winter coat? What will the temperature be in degrees Fahrenheit? The formula for changing the temperature measured in degrees Celsius to degrees Fahrenheit is

$$F = \frac{9}{5}C + 32.$$

37

A **chapter-opening application** problem with full-color photo poses a problem that students will learn to solve as they progress through the chapter.

A **proficiency check,** appearing at the beginning of each chapter and keyed to chapter and section, allows students to check their mastery of the chapter's necessary prerequisite skills.

38 Chapter 1 Operations with Real Numbers and Introduction to Algebra

Proficiency check

[R-1] **1.** $\frac{3}{4} \cdot \frac{2}{9}$ [R-1] **2.** $2\frac{2}{3} \cdot 2\frac{1}{4}$ [R-1] **3.** $\frac{6}{5} \div \frac{3}{10}$

[R-1] **4.** $\frac{1}{2} + \frac{1}{6}$ [R-1] **5.** $\frac{3}{4} - \frac{2}{3}$ [R-2] **6.** $4.7 + 0.39 + 5.16$

[R-2] **7.** $(8.7)(4.3)$ [R-2] **8.** $10.32 \div 1.2$ [R-2] **9.** $27.3 - 8.19$

[R-2] **10.** $(2.7)(0.13)$

1–1 Numbers and the number line

Natural numbers and whole numbers

The most basic use of our number system is that of counting. We use 1, 2, 3, 4, 5, and so on, as symbols to represent the **natural** or **counting numbers.**

Natural numbers 1,2,3,4,5, . . .

The three dots tell us to continue this counting pattern indefinitely. If we include 0 with the natural numbers, we have the **whole numbers.**

Whole numbers 0,1,2,3,4,5, . . .

Integers

We shall start by giving the natural numbers another name, the **positive integers.** We then form the *opposites*, or *negatives*, of the positive integers as follows: −1, −2, −3, ... Combining the positive integers, the negative integers, and 0, we have the integers.

Integers . . . , −3, −2, −1, 0, 1, 2, 3, . . .

Example 1–1 A

Use integers to represent each of the following.

1. Bromine melts at seven degrees below zero Celsius.
−7 degrees Celsius — Less than zero is a negative value

You are now ready to do **A_1**.

A_1 A debt of nine dollars

Procedure boxes clearly state step-by-step processes for working problems.

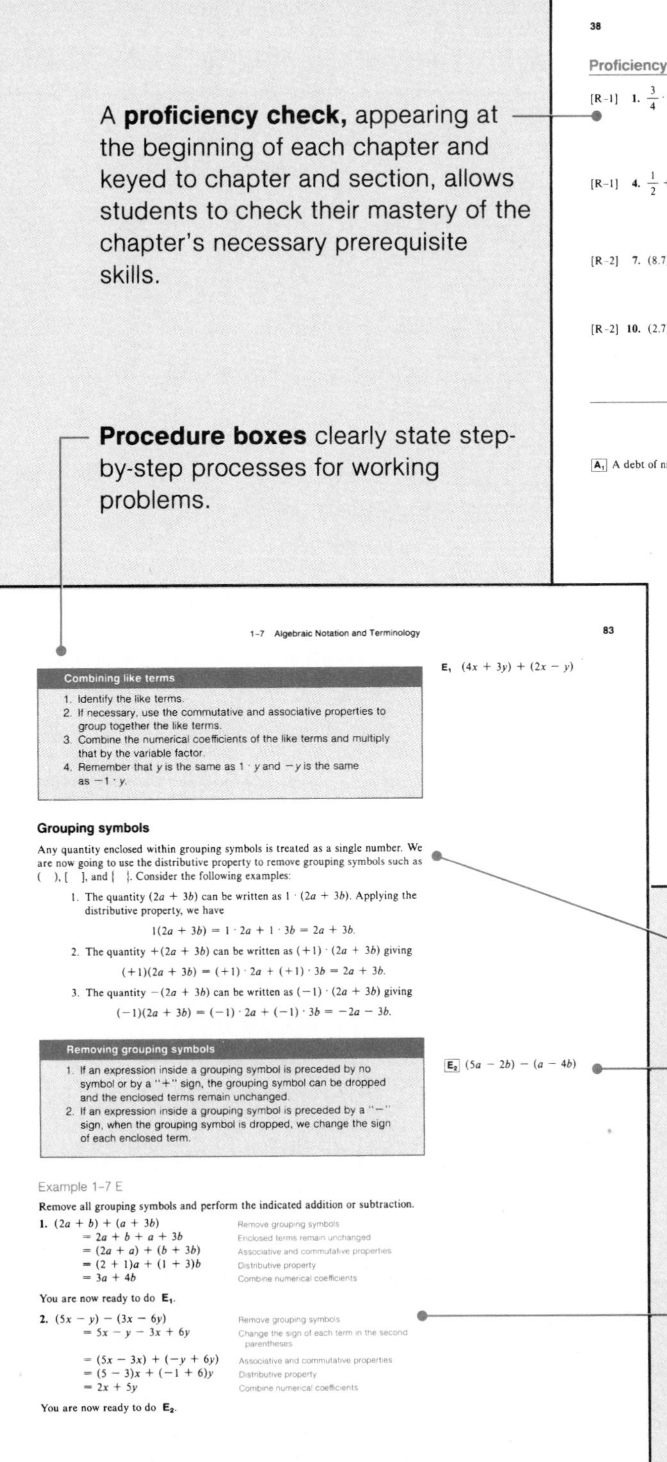

1–7 Algebraic Notation and Terminology 83

Combining like terms

1. Identify the like terms.
2. If necessary, use the commutative and associative properties to group together the like terms.
3. Combine the numerical coefficients of the like terms and multiply that by the variable factor.
4. Remember that y is the same as $1 \cdot y$ and $-y$ is the same as $-1 \cdot y$.

Grouping symbols

Any quantity enclosed within grouping symbols is treated as a single number. We are now going to use the distributive property to remove grouping symbols such as ( ), [ ], and { }. Consider the following examples:

1. The quantity $(2a + 3b)$ can be written as $1 \cdot (2a + 3b)$. Applying the distributive property, we have
$$1(2a + 3b) = 1 \cdot 2a + 1 \cdot 3b = 2a + 3b.$$
2. The quantity $+(2a + 3b)$ can be written as $(+1) \cdot (2a + 3b)$ giving
$$(+1)(2a + 3b) = (+1) \cdot 2a + (+1) \cdot 3b = 2a + 3b.$$
3. The quantity $-(2a + 3b)$ can be written as $(-1) \cdot (2a + 3b)$ giving
$$(-1)(2a + 3b) = (-1) \cdot 2a + (-1) \cdot 3b = -2a - 3b.$$

Removing grouping symbols

1. If an expression inside a grouping symbol is preceded by no symbol or by a "+" sign, the grouping symbol can be dropped and the enclosed terms remain unchanged.
2. If an expression inside a grouping symbol is preceded by a "−" sign, when the grouping symbol is dropped, we change the sign of each enclosed term.

Example 1–7 E

Remove all grouping symbols and perform the indicated addition or subtraction.

1. $(2a + b) + (a + 3b)$ — Remove grouping symbols
$= 2a + b + a + 3b$ — Enclosed terms remain unchanged
$= (2a + a) + (b + 3b)$ — Associative and commutative properties
$= (2 + 1)a + (1 + 3)b$ — Distributive property
$= 3a + 4b$ — Combine numerical coefficients

You are now ready to do **E_1**.

2. $(5x - y) - (3x - 6y)$ — Remove grouping symbols
$= 5x - y - 3x + 6y$ — Change the sign of each term in the second parentheses
$= (5x - 3x) + (-y + 6y)$ — Associative and commutative properties
$= (5 - 3)x + (-1 + 6)y$ — Distributive property
$= 2x + 5y$ — Combine numerical coefficients

You are now ready to do **E_2**.

E_1 $(4x + 3y) + (2x - y)$

E_2 $(5a - 2b) - (a - 4b)$

Explanations are written as if the authors are talking directly to students.

Margin exercises parallel the development of examples within the text and allow students to immediately test their understanding of the material being studied. Notice that E_2 becomes a quick-reference example on page 87.

Examples include arrows that visually guide students through steps needed to solve the problem. A detailed explanation to the right of each step ensures student understanding of the correct solution method.

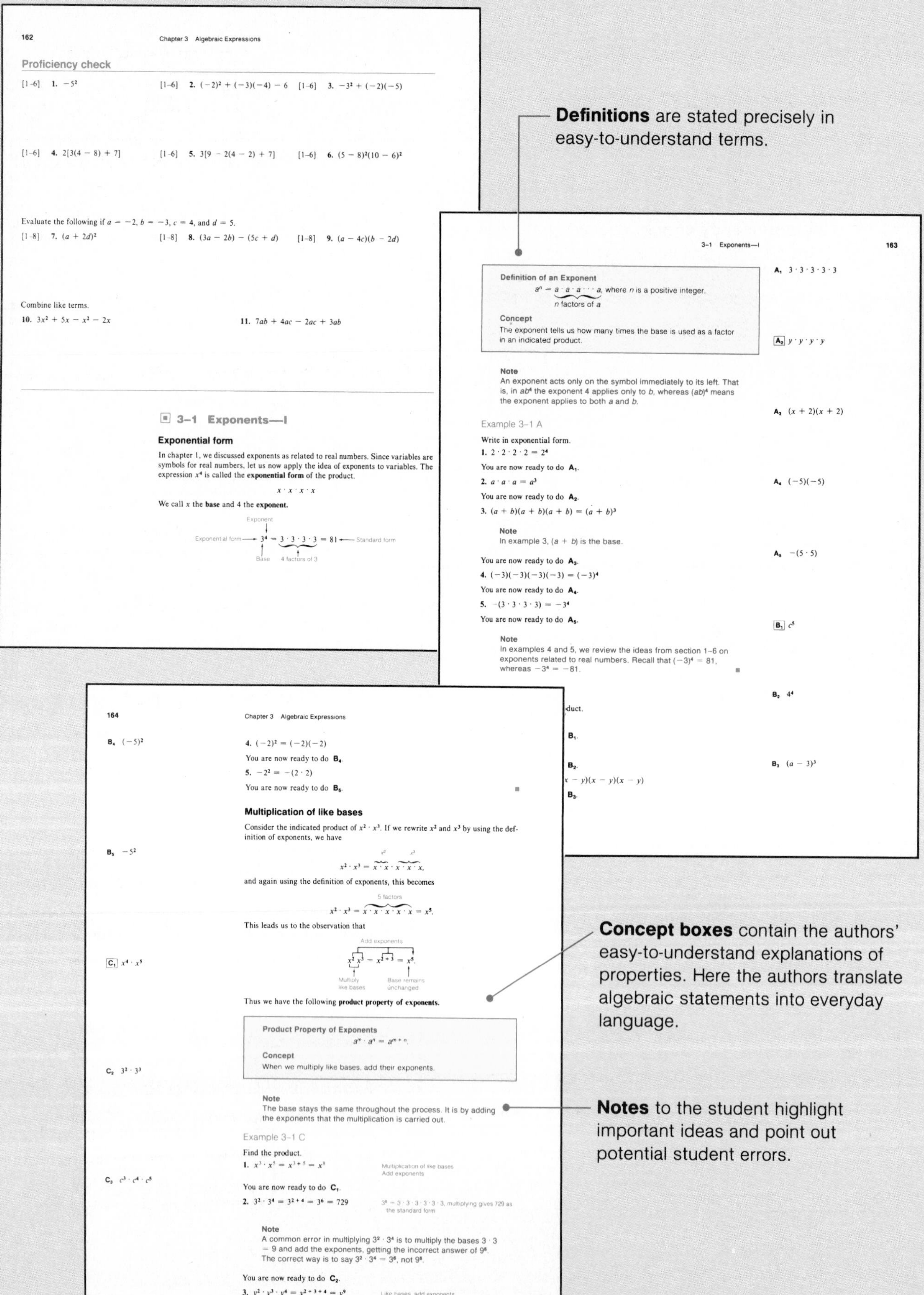

Definitions are stated precisely in easy-to-understand terms.

Concept boxes contain the authors' easy-to-understand explanations of properties. Here the authors translate algebraic statements into everyday language.

Notes to the student highlight important ideas and point out potential student errors.

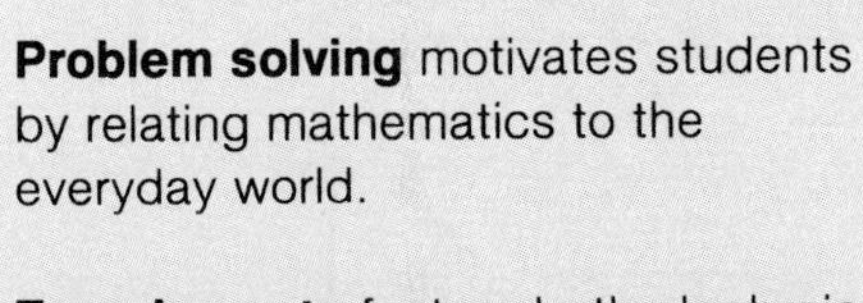
Problem solving motivates students by relating mathematics to the everyday world.

Exercise sets feature both algebraic and word problems that give students ample opportunity to practice their skills.

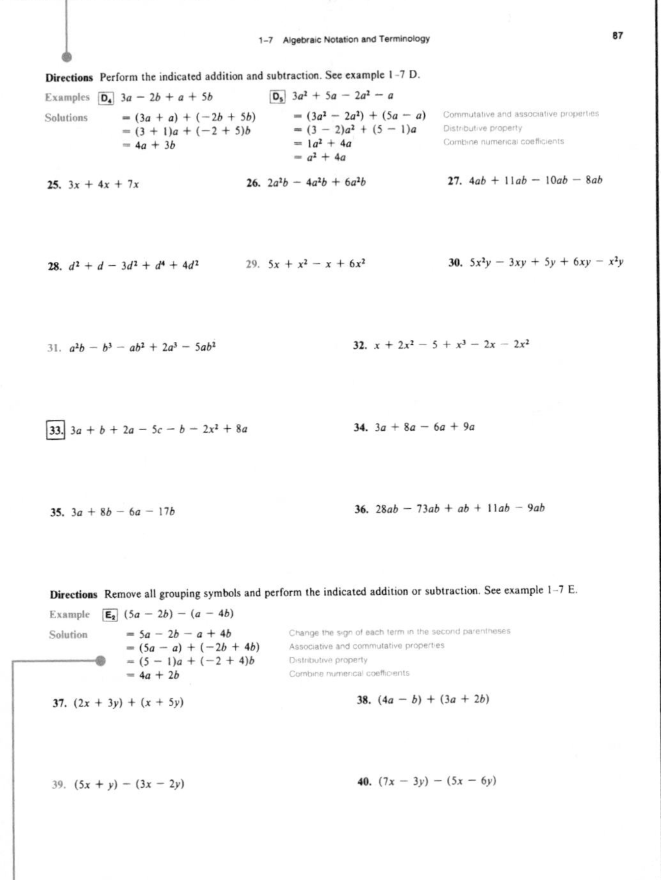
1–7 Algebraic Notation and Terminology 87

Directions Perform the indicated addition and subtraction. See example 1–7 D.

Examples $\boxed{D_4}$ $3a - 2b + a + 5b$ $\boxed{D_5}$ $3a^2 + 5a - 2a^2 - a$

Solutions
$= (3a + a) + (-2b + 5b)$
$= (3 + 1)a + (-2 + 5)b$
$= 4a + 3b$

$= (3a^2 - 2a^2) + (5a - a)$ Commutative and associative properties
$= (3 - 2)a^2 + (5 - 1)a$ Distributive property
$= 1a^2 + 4a$ Combine numerical coefficients
$= a^2 + 4a$

25. $3x + 4x + 7x$ **26.** $2a^2b - 4a^2b + 6a^2b$ **27.** $4ab + 11ab - 10ab - 8ab$

28. $d^2 + d - 3d^2 + d^4 + 4d^2$ 29. $5x + x^2 - x + 6x^2$ **30.** $5x^2y - 3xy + 5y + 6xy - x^2y$

31. $a^2b - b^3 - ab^2 + 2a^3 - 5ab^2$ **32.** $x + 2x^2 - 5 + x^3 - 2x - 2x^2$

$\boxed{33.}$ $3a + b + 2a - 5c - b - 2x^2 + 8a$ **34.** $3a + 8a - 6a + 9a$

35. $3a + 8b - 6a - 17b$ **36.** $28ab - 73ab + ab + 11ab - 9ab$

Directions Remove all grouping symbols and perform the indicated addition or subtraction. See example 1–7 E.

Example $\boxed{E_2}$ $(5a - 2b) - (a - 4b)$

Solution
$= 5a - 2b - a + 4b$ Change the sign of each term in the second parentheses
$= (5a - a) + (-2b + 4b)$ Associative and commutative properties
$= (5 - 1)a + (-2 + 4)b$ Distributive property
$= 4a + 2b$ Combine numerical coefficients

37. $(2x + 3y) + (x + 5y)$ **38.** $(4a - b) + (3a + 2b)$

39. $(5x + y) - (3x - 2y)$ **40.** $(7x - 3y) - (5x - 6y)$

168 Chapter 3 Algebraic Expressions

G_3 $(5xy^2)(2x^3y^3)$

3. $(2a^2b)(3ab^3) = (2 \cdot 3)(a^2a)(bb^3)$ Regroup to multiply like factors
$= 6a^3b^4$ Multiply like bases, add exponents

Note
When multiplying two quantities together, first multiply their coefficients, then multiply like bases.

You are now ready to do **G_3**.

G_4 $\left(\frac{3x^2y}{z^4}\right)^2$

4. $\left(\frac{2a^2b^3}{c^5}\right)^3 = \frac{(2a^2b^3)^3}{(c^5)^3}$ Both the numerator and the denominator are raised to the 3rd power
$= \frac{2^3(a^2)^3(b^3)^3}{(c^5)^3}$ Each factor in the numerator is raised to the 3rd power
$= \frac{8a^6b^9}{c^{15}}$ Power of a power, multiply exponents

You are now ready to do **G_4**.

Problem solving

The following problems require us to write algebraic expressions involving the use of exponents.

Example 3–1 H

Write an algebraic expression for each of the following verbal statements.

The area, A, of a square is found by using the length of the equal side, s, as a factor twice. Write an expression for the area of a square.

1. The volume of a cube is found by using the length of the edge, e, as a factor 3 times. Write an expression for the volume of a cube.
We write e as a factor 3 times as $e \cdot e \cdot e = e^3$. Then the volume, V, of a cube is given by
$V = e^3$.

You are now ready to do **H_1**.

Write an expression for 2 times the square of t.

2. Write an expression for the square of a number less 5.
The square of a number, n, is given as n^2, and since "less" means to subtract, the expression is given by
$n^2 - 5$.

You are now ready to do **H_2**.

Answers to section 3–1 margin exercises

A_1 3^5 A_2 y^4 A_3 $(x + 2)^2$ A_4 $(-5)^2$ A_5 -5^2 B_1 $c \cdot c \cdot c \cdot c \cdot c$ B_2 $4 \cdot 4 \cdot 4 \cdot 4$ B_3 $(a - 3)(a - 3)(a - 3)$ B_4 $(-5)(-5)$ B_5 $-(5 \cdot 5)$ C_1 x^8 C_2 $3^5 = 243$ C_3 c^{12} C_4 b^{11} C_5 $(a - 4)^5$ C_6 $(-3)^3 = -27$ D_1 x^3y^3 D_2 $81x^4y^4$ D_3 216 E_1 $6^6 = 46{,}656$ E_2 $3^6 = 729$ E_3 a^{12} F_1 $\frac{8}{125}$ F_2 $\frac{x^7}{y^7}$ F_3 $\frac{x^3}{27y^3}$ G_1 $27x^{12}y^6$ G_2 $8a^{12}b^9$ G_3 $10x^4y^5$ G_4 $\frac{9x^4y^2}{z^8}$ H_1 $A = s^2$ H_2 $2t^2$

Mastery points

Can you
- Write a product in exponential form?
- Multiply factors with like bases?
- Raise a group of factors to a power?
- Raise a power to a power?
- Raise a fraction to a power?

Mastery points are listed before each section's exercise set to alert students to the skills they must have mastered to successfully work the problems.

-erations with Real Numbers and Introduction to Algebra

42. $(4x - 3y - 2z) - (3x - 4y - z)$

44. $(7a - b - 3c) - (5a - 4b + 3c)$

Directions Write an algebraic expression for each of the following. See example 1–7 F.

Examples $\boxed{F_1}$ The product of x and y $\boxed{F_2}$ A number increased by 8

Solutions $x \cdot y$ Let x represent the number; hence $x + 8$

45. The sum of a and b **46.** 3 times a, subtracted from b

47. 7 less than x **48.** 5 more than y

49. The sum of x and y, divided by z **50.** x times the sum of y and z

51. a decreased by 5 **52.** a decreased by b

$\boxed{53.}$ $\frac{1}{2}$ of x, decreased by 2 times x **54.** A number decreased by 12

$\boxed{55.}$ 3 times a number and that product increased by 1 **56.** A number added to 4

57. A number divided by 5 58. 2 times the sum of a number and 4

Fully worked-out **quick-reference examples** (selected margin exercises) are included for students to use as a line-by-line check of their work or as an example.

Trial exercise problems are located in the exercise sets and are denoted with a box around the problem number indicating that the solution is completely worked out in the answer appendix. The problem can be used as an example or a line-by-line check of the problem.

Core exercise problems address the major ideas of the section. The problem numbers for these exercises appear in green type for easy identification.

Review exercises at the end of each section help students prepare for the following section and keep in touch with previous material.

A chapter **summary** synthesizes important concepts.

The completely worked-out solution for the **chapter-opening word problem** appears at the end of the chapter prior to the chapter summary.

Chapter review exercises feature problems to help students determine if they need further work on a particular section. The problems are keyed to refer students back to the section from which they were drawn.

Cumulative tests emphasize the "building-block" nature of mathematics and help students retain knowledge and skills from previous chapters.

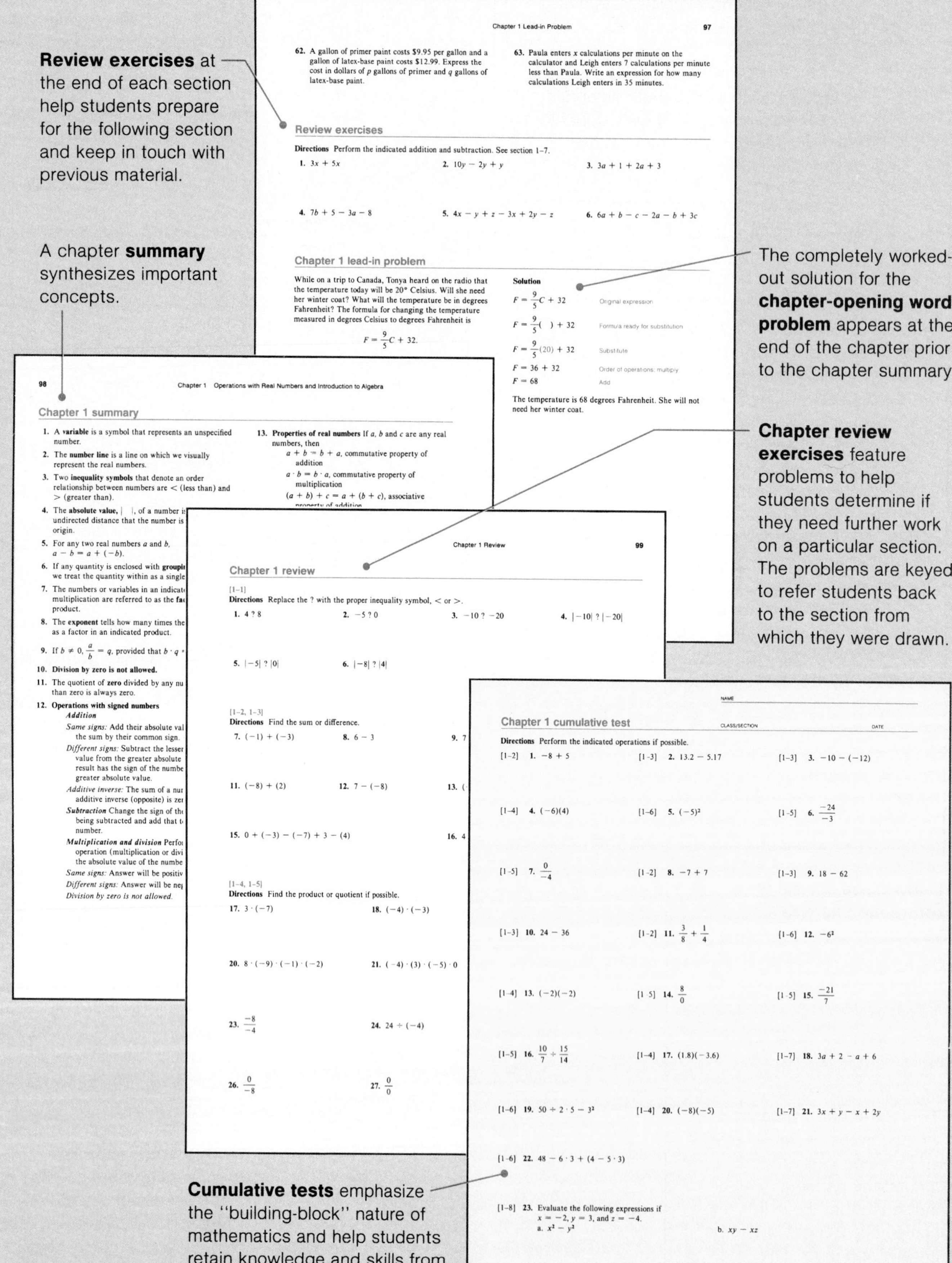

Chapter 1 Lead-in Problem 97

62. A gallon of primer paint costs $9.95 per gallon and a gallon of latex-base paint costs $12.99. Express the cost in dollars of p gallons of primer and q gallons of latex-base paint.

63. Paula enters x calculations per minute on the calculator and Leigh enters 7 calculations per minute less than Paula. Write an expression for how many calculations Leigh enters in 35 minutes.

Review exercises

Directions Perform the indicated addition and subtraction. See section 1–7.

1. $3x + 5x$ 2. $10y - 2y + y$ 3. $3a + 1 + 2a + 3$

4. $7b + 5 - 3a - 8$ 5. $4x - y + z - 3x + 2y - z$ 6. $6a + b - c - 2a - b + 3c$

Chapter 1 lead-in problem

While on a trip to Canada, Tonya heard on the radio that the temperature today will be 20° Celsius. Will she need her winter coat? What will the temperature be in degrees Fahrenheit? The formula for changing the temperature measured in degrees Celsius to degrees Fahrenheit is

$$F = \frac{9}{5}C + 32.$$

Solution

$F = \frac{9}{5}C + 32$ Original expression

$F = \frac{9}{5}(\quad) + 32$ Formula ready for substitution

$F = \frac{9}{5}(20) + 32$ Substitute

$F = 36 + 32$ Order of operations: multiply

$F = 68$ Add

The temperature is 68 degrees Fahrenheit. She will not need her winter coat.

98 Chapter 1 Operations with Real Numbers and Introduction to Algebra

Chapter 1 summary

1. A **variable** is a symbol that represents an unspecified number.
2. The **number line** is a line on which we visually represent the real numbers.
3. Two **inequality symbols** that denote an order relationship between numbers are < (less than) and > (greater than).
4. The **absolute value**, | |, of a number i… undirected distance that the number is … origin.
5. For any two real numbers a and b, $a - b = a + (-b)$.
6. If any quantity is enclosed with **groupi…** we treat the quantity within as a single…
7. The numbers or variables in an indicat… multiplication are referred to as the **fa…** product.
8. The **exponent** tells how many times the… as a factor in an indicated product.
9. If $b \neq 0$, $\frac{a}{b} = q$, provided that $b \cdot q$ …
10. **Division by zero is not allowed.**
11. The quotient of **zero** divided by any nu… than zero is always zero.
12. **Operations with signed numbers**
    Addition
    Same signs: Add their absolute val… the sum by their common sign.
    Different signs: Subtract the lesser… value from the greater absolute… result has the sign of the numbe… greater absolute value.
    Additive inverse: The sum of a nu… additive inverse (opposite) is ze…
    Subtraction Change the sign of th… being subtracted and add that t… number.
    Multiplication and division Perfo… operation (multiplication or divi… the absolute value of the numbe…
    Same signs: Answer will be positiv…
    Different signs: Answer will be ne…
    Division by zero is not allowed.
13. **Properties of real numbers** If a, b and c are any real numbers, then
    $a + b = b + a$, commutative property of addition
    $a \cdot b = b \cdot a$, commutative property of multiplication
    $(a + b) + c = a + (b + c)$, associative property of addition

Chapter 1 Review 99

Chapter 1 review

[1–1]
Directions Replace the ? with the proper inequality symbol, < or >.

1. 4 ? 8 2. −5 ? 0 3. −10 ? −20 4. |−10| ? |−20|

5. |−5| ? |0| 6. |−8| ? |4|

[1–2, 1–3]
Directions Find the sum or difference.

7. $(-1) + (-3)$ 8. $6 - 3$ 9. 7…

11. $(-8) + (2)$ 12. $7 - (-8)$ 13. (…

15. $0 + (-3) - (-7) + 3 - (4)$ 16. 4…

[1–4, 1–5]
Directions Find the product or quotient if possible.

17. $3 \cdot (-7)$ 18. $(-4) \cdot (-3)$

20. $8 \cdot (-9) \cdot (-1) \cdot (-2)$ 21. $(-4) \cdot (3) \cdot (-5) \cdot 0$

23. $\frac{-8}{-4}$ 24. $24 \div (-4)$

26. $\frac{0}{-8}$ 27. $\frac{0}{0}$

NAME

Chapter 1 cumulative test CLASS/SECTION DATE

Directions Perform the indicated operations if possible.

[1–2] 1. $-8 + 5$ [1–3] 2. $13.2 - 5.17$ [1–3] 3. $-10 - (-12)$

[1–4] 4. $(-6)(4)$ [1–6] 5. $(-5)^2$ [1–5] 6. $\frac{-24}{-3}$

[1–5] 7. $\frac{0}{-4}$ [1–2] 8. $-7 + 7$ [1–3] 9. $18 - 62$

[1–3] 10. $24 - 36$ [1–2] 11. $\frac{3}{8} + \frac{1}{4}$ [1–6] 12. -6^2

[1–4] 13. $(-2)(-2)$ [1–5] 14. $\frac{8}{0}$ [1–5] 15. $\frac{-21}{7}$

[1–5] 16. $\frac{10}{7} \div \frac{15}{14}$ [1–4] 17. $(1.8)(-3.6)$ [1–7] 18. $3a + 2 - a + 6$

[1–6] 19. $50 \div 2 \cdot 5 - 3^2$ [1–4] 20. $(-8)(-5)$ [1–7] 21. $3x + y - x + 2y$

[1–6] 22. $48 - 6 \cdot 3 + (4 - 5 \cdot 3)$

[1–8] 23. Evaluate the following expressions if $x = -2$, $y = 3$, and $z = -4$.
a. $x^2 - y^2$ b. $xy - xz$

103

Preface

Principles of Elementary Algebra with Applications is a beginning level text designed specifically for students who have not had a previous course in algebra. The book can be used in lecture-discussion classes, self-paced classes, or math labs.

Problem-solving orientation The skill of problem solving has been integrated throughout the text. The emphasis on problem solving begins in chapter 1 with word problems that have simple arithmetic solutions. The student also learns to change word phrases into algebraic expressions. In chapter 2 and throughout the rest of the text, the student is shown how to form and solve equations from word problems. **Diagrams** are used to show how the words are translated into mathematical symbols. **Tables** are provided to illustrate how several different word phrases become the same mathematical expression.

Readability We have attempted to make the text as readable and accessible to students as possible by presenting the material in a manner similar to that which the instructor might use in the classroom. The amount of reading the student is required to do has been kept to a minimum.

Applications We have tried to provide a cross section of applications, mainly in the exercises. These are provided to help answer the perennial question "Why am I studying this stuff?" and to make the learning process itself more interesting. In particular, we have tried to show that algebra has become more important than ever in this age of the digital computer. Most ideas are supported by real-life applications relative to that concept.

Functional use of color In this second edition, color has been used to guide students through the text and clearly show the hierarchy of the text's elements. The effective use of color for each particular text element is described in this preface and is illustrated in the 20 Point Learning System.

Highlights of the learning aids

Proficiency checks The proficiency checks are short sets of exercises that students can use to determine whether they have acquired the skills necessary to succeed with the material within a chapter. Proficiency checks are located at the beginning of every chapter except chapter R. Each problem has the section number from which it is drawn so the student can refer to the appropriate section.

Examples Examples present all aspects of the material being studied with a step-by-step development showing how the problem is worked. Examples have short phrase statements in blue type next to each step stating exactly what has been done. The examples solidify in the student's mind the correct approach for working a problem that is detailed in the procedure boxes. The student is able to develop a clear understanding of how a problem is worked without having to guess what went on in a particular step. After finishing an example, the student immediately interacts with the material by doing the appropriate problem in the margin.

Margin exercises The exercises in the margin are designed to involve the student with the material while studying it. Margin exercises directly parallel the development and examples in the text and are worked according to the same directions as that group of examples. As each new idea or procedure is illustrated with an example, the student is asked to work a similar problem. This direct correspondence between the margin problem and the example allows students to immediately reinforce their understanding of the example or to quickly identify any difficulty or misunderstanding they might have. Answers to all margin problems are placed at the end of each section just before the mastery points, and selected margin problems denoted by a '□' are worked step-by-step as quick-reference examples within the exercise set.

Procedure boxes Procedure boxes clearly state a step-by-step process by which types of problems are to be worked. Color has been consistently used for all procedure boxes to emphasize their importance to students.

Concept boxes Concept boxes include properties, theorems, or definitions along with an explanation in easy-to-understand language.

Notes Notes to the student highlight important ideas and point out potential errors that students might make. The notes are printed in green type to attract the student's attention.

Mastery points Mastery points are listed before each exercise set. In essence, they are objectives for that section. They are specifically placed in this location to alert students to the particular skills they must know to successfully work the problems. When students have completed the section, the objectives have more meaning.

The green outlined box is used to draw the students' attention to the mastery points before they begin the exercise set.

Exercise sets Exercise sets provide abundant opportunities for students to check their understanding of the concepts being presented. The problems in the exercise sets are carefully graded by level of difficulty to guide the students easily from straightforward computations to more challenging, multi-step problems. Rather than grouping similar problems in pairs, similar problems are grouped by fours, providing greater practice with each skill and concept.

Problem numbers that appear in green type identify the key problems in each exercise set. These problems concisely address the major ideas of the section. Students can use these problems as a quick review, while instructors can quickly structure basic assignments around these **core exercise problems.**

The directions for each group of problems refer the student to a specific group of parallel examples. After each set of directions is a **quick-reference example.** This example is a specifically chosen margin problem from the section and is worked and explained step-by-step. Students can use this as a line-by-line check of their solution, if they worked the problem while studying the material, or as an example they can refer to while working the exercise set. Keying the directions to specific examples and solving margin problems as quick-reference examples give students specific places to return to within the text if they have any difficulty. They also serve as an invitation to read the material for those students who try to jump right into the exercise set without studying the material first.

Review exercises At the end of each section is a group of review problems that relate to the next section. These exercises help reinforce the skills necessary for success in the following section. Answers are provided for all the review exercises.

Trial exercise problems Trial exercise problems appear throughout each exercise set and are denoted by a box around the problem number. This indicates that the solution is shown in its entirety in the answer appendix. The trial exercise problems can serve as additional examples to enhance the student's understanding of the concept or as a step-by-step check of the student's own solution. The student can immediately verify that his or her procedure is correct or identify the specific point at which an error has occurred.

Chapter summaries End-of-chapter summaries synthesize the important ideas of each chapter.

Chapter review A chapter review is placed at the end of each chapter. This problem set follows the same organization as the chapter. Each problem is keyed to the section from which it was drawn. It is designed to help students determine whether they need additional study on any section of the chapter. Answers to all review problems are provided in the appendix.

Cumulative tests Cumulative tests give students the opportunity to work problems that are drawn from the chapter and from preceding chapters. Not only do students demonstrate their full understanding of the particular chapter, but they get to show their ability to retain information from previous chapters. If students need refreshing, they can use the section references to review the concept.

Answers Answers are given for section exercise problems whose problem number is not a multiple of four. This provides 50 percent more answers than the traditional listing of answers to odd-numbered problems only. Students can check their progress while one of every type of problem is retained for the instructor to work as an example in class or to include on a quiz or exam. These added problems with answers can also be used as a secondary assignment when students study for a test. The answers to all problems in the chapter reviews and cumulative tests are provided in the appendix.

New to this edition

Content

1. The arithmetic review has been moved from the appendix and is now in the opening chapter (chapter R).
2. Chapter 1 no longer discusses sets—sets are introduced only in chapter 4 in listing elements in solutions sets.
3. Solving equations, verbal problems, formulas, and linear equalities have been moved from chapter 3 in the first edition to chapter 2 in the second edition to start the student on these concepts earlier.
4. Introduction to exponents has been moved to chapter 3 from chapter 2 in the first edition.
5. The quotient of two polynomials has been moved from chapter 2 in the first edition to chapter 5 in the second edition to accompany operations on rational expressions.
6. Solving quadratic equations *by factoring* has been moved from chapter 5 in the first edition to chapter 4 in the second edition to accompany the work on factoring.
7. Chapter 6 in the first edition is broken into two chapters—chapters 5 and 6 on rational expressions to make this material more manageable.
8. Graphing linear inequalities in two variables has been added to chapter 7 in the second edition.
9. Graphing quadratic equations in two variables has been added to chapter 10.

Learning aids

1. Some margin exercises become quick-reference examples that are worked out in the exercise sets to serve as further examples for the students and as an invitation to read the material. This is especially important for those students who tend to jump into the exercise sets without studying the material first.
2. Review exercises at the end of each section help prepare the student for the work of the following section.
3. Cumulative tests at the end of each chapter help the student keep in touch with past work.
4. Step-by-step development of examples is accompanied by explanations in blue type of the manipulation performed at each step.
5. Arrows are used to clearly show the important steps taken in the development of examples.
6. All step-by-step procedures are outlined for the major concepts and placed in colored boxes for emphasis.
7. Each chapter is introduced with a lead-in application problem (and accompanying related photo) that can be solved using the procedures studied in the chapter. The application problem is worked out in detail at the end of the chapter, just prior to the chapter summary.

For the instructor

The ***Annotated Instructor's Edition*** provides a convenient source for answers to all exercise and margin problems. Each answer is placed directly below the problem in boldface red type. The *Annotated Instructor's Edition* eliminates the need to search through a separate answer key.

The ***Instructor's Manual*** has been expanded to include a guide to the supplements that accompany *Principles of Elementary Algebra with Applications,* Second Edition. Also included are a complete listing of all mastery points, suggested course schedules based on the mastery points and reproducible quizzes, tests, and extension problems. The final section of the *Instructor's Manual* contains answers to the reproducible materials.

The ***Educator's Notebook*** is designed to assist you in formatting and presenting the concepts of *Principles of Elementary Algebra with Applications,* Second Edition to your students. Reproducible transparency masters are provided for each section of the textbook. Included are all major concepts for each topic and illustrative examples to complement your lecture. The transparency masters are stored in a three-ring binder, tabbed by chapter for easy access.

The ***Test Item File/Quiz Item File*** is a printed version of the computerized *TestPak* and *QuizPak* that allows you to choose test items based on chapter, section, or objective. The objectives are taken directly from the mastery points in *Principles of Elementary Algebra with Applications,* Second Edition. The items in the *Test Item File* and *Quiz Item File* are different from those in the prepared tests in the *Instructor's Manual.* Hence, you will have even more items to choose from for your tests.

WCB ***TestPak 3.0,*** our computerized testing service, provides you with a call-in/mail-in testing program and the complete *Test Item File* on diskette for use with IBM PC, Apple or Macintosh computers. WCB *TestPak* requires no programming experience. Tests can be generated randomly, by selecting specific test items, or by choosing mastery points/objectives. In addition, new test items can be added and existing test items can be edited.

WCB *TestPak 3.0* disks and the WCB call-in service are available free to instructors adopting *Principles of Elementary Algebra with Applications,* Second Edition.

WCB ***GradePak,*** also a part of *TestPak 3.0,* is a computerized grade management system for instructors. This program allows you to track students' performance on examinations and assignments. It will compute each student's percentage and corresponding letter grade, as well as the class average. Printouts can be made utilizing both text and graphics.

For the student

The ***Student's Solutions Manual*** contains overviews of every chapter of the text, chapter self-tests with solutions, and solutions to all proficiency checks, every other odd-numbered section exercise, and odd-numbered chapter review exercise problems. It is available for student purchase.

On the **Videotapes,** the instructor introduces a concept, provides detailed explanations of example problems that illustrate the concept, including applications, and concludes with a summary. The tapes are available free to qualified adopters.

The **Audiotapes** have been developed specifically to accompany *Principles of Elementary Algebra with Applications,* Second Edition. They begin with a brief synopsis of the section, followed by clear discussions of examples with warnings and hints where appropriate. Exercises are solved for each section of the text: students are directed to turn off the tape and solve a specific problem and turn the tape on again for a complete explanation of the correct solution.

The concepts and skills developed in *Principles of Elementary Algebra with Applications,* Second Edition are reinforced through the interactive **Algebra Problem Solver.** Students practice solving problems generated by the computer or they may input their own problems from the text. Step-by-step solutions with complete explanations guide students to mastery of the major concepts and skills of elementary algebra.

WCB ***QuizPak,*** a part of *TestPak 3.0,* provides students with true/false and matching questions from the *Quiz Item File* for each chapter in the text. Using this portion of the program will help your students prepare for examinations. Also included with the WCB *QuizPak* is an on-line testing option that allows professors to prepare tests for students to take using the computer. The computer will automatically grade the test and update the gradebook file.

Acknowledgments

We wish to express our heartfelt thanks and grateful appreciation for the many comments and suggestions given to us during the preparation of the first edition. In particular, we wish to thank George Gullen III, Lynne Hensel, Terry Baker, Harry Datsun, and Robert Olsen for their excellent effort in reviewing each stage of the book and supplying us with numerous valuable comments, suggestions, and constructive criticisms.

We also wish to thank Lisa Miyazaki for her superb help in preparing the manuscript and working all of the problems.

A very special thank you goes out to the memory of the former Mathematics Division Head, Raymond L. Spencer, for the frequent talks, advice, and encouragement.

The authors would like to acknowledge the contribution of Philip Mahler, who introduced to them the idea of using the tabular format to list all possible combinations of factors in factoring trinomials. Mr. Mahler was also responsible for the idea of using the sign of the product "mn" as an operation in the second column of the table. The chief virtue of this method is that it is algorithmic. The authors have modified the method slightly by listing the greater factor first.

The authors would also like to thank Louise Dyson who checked the wording of the concepts and properties for accuracy and clarity. Her suggestions are very much appreciated.

Throughout the development, writing, and production of this text, two people have been of such great value that we are truly indebted to them for their excellent work on our behalf. We wish to express our utmost thanks to Suresh Ailawadi and Eugenia M. Collins.

We would like to thank the following reviewers of the second edition of *Principles of Elementary Algebra with Applications:*

Joe Albree
Austin University at Montgomery

Alice Grandgeorge
Manchester Community College

Michele Greenfield
Middlesex County College

T. Henry Jablonski, Jr.
East Tennessee State University

Joanne F. Korsmo
New Mexico State University

Thomas McGannon
Chicago City College

Kelly Wyatt
Umpaqua Community College

In addition, we would like to thank the reviewers of *Principles of Elementary Algebra with Applications,* First Edition and *Elementary Algebra with Applications,* Second Edition, whose comments have positively influenced this edition.

Neil Aiken
Milwaukee Area Technical College

Ann Anderson
Broward Community College

Robert Baer
Miami University–Hamilton Branch

Pat Barbalich
Jefferson Community College

Charles Beals
Hartnell College

Don Bellairs
Grossmont College

John P. Bibbo
Southwestern College

Nancy Bray
San Diego Mesa College

Daniel Burns
Sierra College

P. M. Commons
Florida Junior College–South Campus

Ben Cornelius
Oregon Institute of Technology

Lena Dexter
Faulkner State Junior College

Louise Dyson
Clark College

Gail Earles
St. Cloud University

George Gullen III
Henry Ford Community College

Ray Haertel
Central Oregon Community College

Pam Hager
College of the Sequoias

Harry Hayward
Westmoreland County Community College

Lynne Hensel
Henry Ford Community College

Angela Hernandez
University of Montevallo

Tom Householder
Muskingham Area Technical College

Roe Hurst
Central Virginia Community College

Elizabeth Huttenlock
Pennsylvania State University

Martha Jordan
Okaloosa–Walton Junior College

Glen Just
Mount St. Clare

Judy Kasabian
El Camino College

Margaret A. Kimbell
Texas State Technical Institute Waco Campus

Henry Kubo
West Los Angeles College

Theodore Lai
Hudson County Community College

Howard B. Lambert
East Texas State University

Calvin Lathan
Monroe Community College

Jeri Vorwerk Love
Florida Junior College

Phil Mahler
Middlesex Community College

Gerald Marlette
Cuyahoga Community College

Hank Martel
Broward Community College Samuels Campus

Jerry J. Maxwell
Olney Central College

Donald Mazukelli
Los Angeles Valley College

Michael Montemuro
Westchester University

Robert Olsen
Dearborn Public Schools

Robert Pearce
South Plains College

Gus Pekara
Oklahoma City Community College

Hadley Pobst
Virginia Highlands Community College

Jack Porter

Johnsie Posey
Southern University

A. K. Rajappa
Walsh College

Suzanne Reid
Virginia Highlands Community College

J. Doug Richey
Henderson County Junior College

Kenneth Ross
Broward Community College

John Samoylo
Delaware County Community College

Phyllis Schott
Catonsville Community College

Erik Schreiner
Western Michigan University

Dwain E. Small
Valencia Community College

John Snyder
Sinclair Community College

J. Bryan Sperry
Pittsburg State University

Ara Sullenberger
Tarrant County Junior College

Molly Sumner
Pikes Peak Community College

Lou Sutton
Central Texas College

Paul Till
Jefferson Junior High School

George T. Wales
Ferris State College

John F. Weiler
University of Wisconsin/ Stevens Point

Hettie Williams
Broward Community College–North Campus

Ruth Young
George C. Wallace State Community College

Finally, we are grateful to our "book team," for without them there would be no book. In particular, we would like to express our sincere thanks to Earl McPeek, Gene Collins, Theresa Grutz, K. Wayne Harms, and Carrie Burger.

Study tips

When you work to your full capacity, you can hope to attain the knowledge and skills that will enable you to create your future and control your destiny. If you do not, you will have your future thrust upon you by others.

*A Nation at Risk**

There are certain study skills that you as an algebra student need to have, or develop, to assure your success in this course. In addition to the following items listed, acquaint yourself with the text by reading the preface material that precedes these study tips. Then–

1. For every hour spent in class, plan to spend at least two hours studying outside class.
2. Before going to class, read the material to be covered. This will help you more easily understand the instructor's presentation.
3. Review the material related to each exercise set *before* attempting to work the problems. Be sure you understand the underlying concepts in the worked-out examples and the reason for each step.
4. Carefully read the instructions to the exercise set. Look at the examples and determine what is being asked. Remember, these same instructions will most likely appear on tests.
5. When working the exercise set, take your time, think about what you are doing in each step, and ask yourself why you are performing that step. As you become more confident, increase your speed to better prepare yourself for test situations.
6. When working the exercise sets, compare examples to see in what ways they are alike and in what ways they are different. Problems often *look* similar but are not.

If you do not know how to begin a problem, or you get partway through and are unable to proceed, (a) look back through your notes or (b) look for an exercise you can do that has the answer given and try to analyze the similarities. If doing these things does not work, put the problem aside. Often getting away from it for a time will "open the door" when you try it again. Finally, if you need to, consult your instructor and show him/her the work you have done.

The fact that you will be "using tomorrow what you are doing today" makes it imperative that you learn each concept as you go along. Most concepts, especially the ones that give you the most difficulty, need constant review.

*The National Commission on Excellence in Education. *A Nation at Risk.* Washington, D.C.: U.S. Government Printing Office, 1983.

The practice of checking your work will aid you in two ways:

1. It will develop confidence, knowing you have done the problem correctly.
2. It will help you discover your errors on an exam that might otherwise have gone undetected had you not checked your work.

When checking your work, use a different method from the one you used to solve the problem. If the same procedure is used, a tendency to make the same mistake exists. Develop methods for checking your work as you do the practice exercises. This checking then becomes automatic when taking a test.

The following hints will aid you in preparing for an exam:

1. Begin studying and reviewing a number of days prior to the exam. This will enable you to contact your instructor for help if you need it. "All-night" sessions the night before the exam seldom (if ever) yield good results.
2. Take periodic breaks—10 to 15 minutes for each hour of study. Study for no longer than four hours at a time.
3. Work to develop understanding as well as skills. Memorization is seldom useful in an algebra course, so concentrate on understanding the methods and concepts. However do not ignore skill development, since doing so can often lead to what students call "stupid mistakes."

Prior to taking an exam, use the exercise sets, chapter reviews, and/or *Student's Solutions Manual* to make out a practice test, determine where your errors lie, and retake the test to be sure that you have corrected the mistakes. Allot the same amount of time you will be allowed on test day.

When taking the algebra exam you should:

1. Look over the exam to locate the easiest problems.
2. Work these problems first.
3. Work the more difficult and time-consuming problems next. Remember, when stuck on a problem, go on to other problems and return to those giving you difficulty *only after* completing all that you can.
4. Use what time remains to check your answers or to rework those problems that you found most difficult.

Don't panic should you "draw a blank." Avoid thoughts of failure. Should you feel this happening, relax and try to clear your mind. Search out the problems you feel most confident about and begin again. Should you be unable to complete the exam, be sure to check the problems that you have completed. Always be aware of the time remaining. *Do not hurry* and do not be intimidated by other students completing the exam early.

One final bit of advice. Show your work neatly. Develop this habit when working on your practice problems. There is a close correlation between neatly laid-out work and the correct answer. Your instructor will appreciate this and be more inclined to give you more credit if the answer is wrong.

CHAPTER

R

Review of Fractions, Decimals, and Percent

Each week Sarah Christie puts 5% of her paycheck into savings and uses 9% of her paycheck to pay off her credit card debt. Sarah earns $500 each week. How much money does Sarah (a) put into savings each week and (b) use to pay off her credit card debt each week?

A_1 21

▣ R–1 Operations with fractions

Fractions

In day-to-day living, the numbers we use most often are the whole numbers,

$$0, 1, 2, 3, 4, \text{ and so on,}$$

for counting and the fractions, such as

$$\frac{1}{2}, \frac{3}{4}, \text{ and } \frac{9}{10},$$

when talking about parts of a whole. Two whole numbers placed one above the other and separated by a line form a *fraction.* The top number is called the **numerator** and the bottom number is called the **denominator.**

$$\frac{9}{10} \quad \begin{array}{l} \leftarrow \text{Numerator} \\ \leftarrow \text{Denominator} \end{array}$$

There are two types of fractions:

1. Proper fractions: the numerator is less than the denominator; for example, $\frac{9}{10}$.
2. Improper fractions: the numerator is greater than or equal to the denominator; for example, $\frac{10}{9}$ or $\frac{9}{9}$.

Prime numbers and factorization

Any whole number can be stated as a product of two or more whole numbers, called **factors** of the number. For example,

$12 = 2 \cdot 6$	2 and 6 are factors
$12 = 1 \cdot 12$	1 and 12 are factors
$12 = 4 \cdot 3$	4 and 3 are factors
$12 = 2 \cdot 2 \cdot 3$	2, 2, and 3 are factors

To factor a whole number is to write the number as a product of factors. In future work, it will be necessary to factor whole numbers such that the factors are **prime numbers.**

> **Prime numbers**
>
> A prime number is any whole number greater than 1 whose only factors are the number itself and 1.

The first ten prime numbers are

$$2, 3, 5, 7, 11, 13, 17, 19, 23, \text{ and } 29.$$

Thus when we factored 12 as $12 = 2 \cdot 2 \cdot 3$, the number was stated as a product of prime factors.

Example R–1 A

Write each number as a product of prime numbers.

1. 15

Since the prime factors of 15 are 3 and 5, then

$15 = 3 \cdot 5.$

You are now ready to do $\mathbf{A_1}$.

2. 36

$$\begin{aligned} 36 &= 2 \cdot 18 && \text{Divide } 36 \div 2 = 18 \\ &= 2 \cdot 2 \cdot 9 && \text{Divide } 18 \div 2 = 9 \\ &= 2 \cdot 2 \cdot 3 \cdot 3 && 9 = 3 \cdot 3 \end{aligned}$$

Thus $36 = 2 \cdot 2 \cdot 3 \cdot 3$.

You are now ready to do $\mathbf{A_2}$.

$\mathbf{A_2}$ 42

Note
This could have been done in the following way.

② ⌊36	Divide 36 ÷ 2 = 18
② ⌊18	Divide 18 ÷ 2 = 9
③ ⌊9	Divide 9 ÷ 3 = 3
③	

We successively divide by prime numbers, starting with 2 if possible, until the quotient is a prime number.

3. 54

$\mathbf{A_3}$ 100

② ⌊54	Divide 54 ÷ 2 = 27
③ ⌊27	Divide 27 ÷ 3 = 9
③ ⌊9	Divide 9 ÷ 3 = 3
③	

Thus $54 = 2 \cdot 3 \cdot 3 \cdot 3$.

You are now ready to do $\mathbf{A_3}$. ■

When working with fractions, we usually want them written in lowest terms where the numerator and the denominator are the least possible numbers. To do this, we use factorization (write as a product of factors).

Reducing fractions to lowest terms

A fraction is **reduced to lowest terms** when the only factor common to the numerator and the denominator is 1.

$\mathbf{B_1}$ $\dfrac{10}{15}$

Reducing a fraction to lowest terms

1. Write the numerator and the denominator as a product of prime factors.
2. Divide the numerator and the denominator by all common factors.

Example R–1 B

Reduce each fraction to lowest terms.

1. $\dfrac{14}{21} = \dfrac{2 \cdot 7}{3 \cdot 7}$ Write as a product of prime numbers

$= \dfrac{2}{3}$ Divide numerator and denominator by common factor 7

$\dfrac{2}{3}$ is the answer since 2 and 3 have only 1 as a common factor.

You are now ready to do $\mathbf{B_1}$.

B₂ $\frac{25}{45}$

2. $\frac{45}{60} = \frac{3 \cdot 3 \cdot 5}{2 \cdot 2 \cdot 3 \cdot 5}$ Write as a product of prime numbers

$= \frac{3}{2 \cdot 2}$ Divide numerator and denominator by $3 \cdot 5$

$= \frac{3}{4}$ Multiply in denominator

You are now ready to do **B_2**. ■

Products and quotients of fractions

To multiply two or more fractions, we use the following procedure.

> **To multiply fractions**
>
> 1. Multiply the numerators and place this product over the product of the denominators.
> 2. Reduce the resulting fraction to lowest terms.

C_1 $\frac{7}{8} \cdot \frac{3}{5}$

Example R–1 C

Multiply the following fractions and reduce to lowest terms.

1. $\frac{2}{3} \cdot \frac{5}{7} = \frac{2 \cdot 5}{3 \cdot 7}$ Multiply numerators / Multiply denominators

$= \frac{10}{21}$ Perform multiplications

You are now ready to do **C_1**.

2. $\frac{5}{6} \cdot \frac{3}{4} = \frac{5 \cdot 3}{6 \cdot 4}$ Multiply numerators / Multiply denominators

$= \frac{5 \cdot 3}{2 \cdot 3 \cdot 4}$ Factor $6 = 2 \cdot 3$

$= \frac{5}{2 \cdot 4}$ Divide numerator and denominator by 3

$= \frac{5}{8}$ Multiply in denominator

C_2 $\frac{8}{9} \cdot \frac{3}{10}$

You are now ready to do **C_2**. ■

Suppose we multiply the fractions

$$\frac{5}{6} \cdot \frac{6}{5} = \frac{5 \cdot 6}{6 \cdot 5}$$ Multiply numerators / Multiply denominators

$$= \frac{30}{30}$$ Multiply as indicated

$$= 1.$$ $30 \div 30 = 1$

When the product of two numbers is 1, we call the numbers **reciprocals** of each other. Thus

$$\frac{5}{6} \text{ and } \frac{6}{5} \text{ are reciprocals,}$$
$$\frac{2}{7} \text{ and } \frac{7}{2} \text{ are reciprocals,}$$
$$\frac{14}{13} \text{ and } \frac{13}{14} \text{ are reciprocals.}$$

We can see that the reciprocal of any fraction is obtained by interchanging the numerator and the denominator. The reciprocal of a fraction is used to divide fractions.

D₁ $\frac{5}{8} \div \frac{2}{9}$

To divide fractions

1. Multiply the first fraction by the **reciprocal** of the second fraction.
2. Reduce the resulting product to lowest terms.

Example R–1 D

Divide the following fractions and reduce to lowest terms.

1. $\frac{7}{8} \div \frac{6}{7} = \frac{7}{8} \cdot \frac{7}{6}$ Multiply by the reciprocal of $\frac{6}{7}$

$= \frac{7 \cdot 7}{8 \cdot 6}$ Multiply numerators / Multiply denominators

$= \frac{49}{48}$ Perform indicated operations

Note

The improper fraction $\frac{49}{48}$ can be written as the **mixed number** $1\frac{1}{48}$, which is the sum of a whole number and a proper fraction. This is obtained by dividing the numerator by the denominator.

$$48\overline{)49} = 1\frac{1}{48}$$

quotient 1; 48; 1 Remainder

You are now ready to do **D₁**.

D₂ $\dfrac{\frac{5}{6}}{\frac{5}{8}}$

2. $\dfrac{\frac{4}{5}}{\frac{3}{7}} = \frac{4}{5} \cdot \frac{7}{3}$ Multiply by the reciprocal of $\frac{3}{7}$

$= \frac{4 \cdot 7}{5 \cdot 3}$ Multiply numerators / Multiply denominators

$= \frac{28}{15}$ or $1\frac{13}{15}$ Perform indicated operations

You are now ready to do **D₂**.

Note

The improper fraction answer is usually the one preferred in algebra, so we will henceforth leave our answers in this form when they occur.

D₃ $\left(2\frac{1}{2}\right) \div \left(1\frac{3}{4}\right)$

3. $3\frac{1}{4} \div 5\frac{2}{3}$

We change the mixed numbers to improper fractions.

$$\text{mixed number} = \frac{(\text{denominator} \cdot \text{whole number}) + \text{numerator}}{\text{denominator}}$$

$$3\frac{1}{4} = \frac{(4 \cdot 3) + 1}{4} = \frac{12 + 1}{4} = \frac{13}{4}$$

$$5\frac{2}{3} = \frac{(3 \cdot 5) + 2}{3} = \frac{15 + 2}{3} = \frac{17}{3}$$

We now divide as indicated.

$$3\frac{1}{4} \div 5\frac{2}{3} = \frac{13}{4} \div \frac{17}{3}$$

$= \frac{13}{4} \cdot \frac{3}{17}$ Multiply by reciprocal of $\frac{17}{3}$

$= \frac{13 \cdot 3}{4 \cdot 17}$ Multiply numerators / Multiply denominators

$= \frac{39}{68}$ Perform indicated operations

D₄ $\frac{5}{9} \div 2$

You are now ready to do **D₃**.

4. $\frac{7}{8} \div 3 = \frac{7}{8} \div \frac{3}{1}$ $3 = \frac{3}{1}$

$= \frac{7}{8} \cdot \frac{1}{3}$ Multiply by reciprocal of $\frac{3}{1}$

$= \frac{7 \cdot 1}{8 \cdot 3}$ Multiply numerators / Multiply denominators

$= \frac{7}{24}$ Perform indicated operations

You are now ready to do **D₄**.

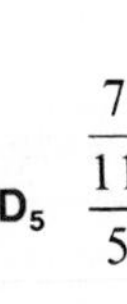

D₅ $\dfrac{\frac{7}{11}}{5}$

5. $\dfrac{\frac{9}{10}}{4} = \dfrac{\frac{9}{10}}{\frac{4}{1}}$ $4 = \frac{4}{1}$

$= \frac{9}{10} \cdot \frac{1}{4}$ Multiply by reciprocal of $\frac{4}{1}$

$= \frac{9 \cdot 1}{10 \cdot 4}$ Multiply numerators / Multiply denominators

$= \frac{9}{40}$ Perform indicated operations

You are now ready to do **D₅**.

6. The area of a rectangle is found by multiplying the length of the rectangle by the width of the rectangle. Find the area of a rectangle that is $2\frac{1}{2}$ feet long and $1\frac{5}{6}$ feet wide.

We multiply the given dimensions.

$$\text{Area} = 2\frac{1}{2} \cdot 1\frac{5}{6}$$

$$= \frac{5}{2} \cdot \frac{11}{6}$$ Change mixed numbers to improper fractions

$$= \frac{5 \cdot 11}{2 \cdot 6}$$ Multiply numerators; Multiply denominators

$$= \frac{55}{12}$$ Perform indicated operations

The area of the rectangle is $\frac{55}{12}$ square feet $\left(\text{or } 4\frac{7}{12} \text{ square feet}\right)$.

You are now ready to do $\mathbf{D_6}$. ■

$\mathbf{D_6}$ Find the area of a rectangle that is $5\frac{1}{4}$ yards long and $3\frac{1}{2}$ yards wide.

Addition and subtraction of fractions

To add or subtract a pair of fractions, the fractions must have a *common* (same) *denominator.*

$\mathbf{E_1}$ $\frac{5}{11} + \frac{3}{11}$

To add or subtract fractions with common denominators

1. Add or subtract the numerators.
2. Place the sum or difference over the common denominator.
3. Reduce the resulting fraction to lowest terms.

Example R–1 E

Add or subtract the following fractions as indicated. Reduce to lowest terms.

1. $\frac{3}{7} + \frac{2}{7} = \frac{3 + 2}{7}$ Add numerators

$= \frac{5}{7}$ Combine in numerator

You are now ready to do $\mathbf{E_1}$.

$\mathbf{E_2}$ $\frac{1}{6} + \frac{1}{6}$

2. $\frac{3}{8} + \frac{1}{8} = \frac{3 + 1}{8}$ Add numerators

$= \frac{4}{8}$ Combine in numerator

$= \frac{1}{2}$ Reduce to lowest terms

You are now ready to do $\mathbf{E_2}$.

$\mathbf{E_3}$ $\frac{7}{12} - \frac{5}{12}$

3. $\frac{7}{16} - \frac{5}{16} = \frac{7 - 5}{16}$ Subtract numerators

$= \frac{2}{16}$ Combine in numerator

$= \frac{1}{8}$ Reduce to lowest terms

You are now ready to do $\mathbf{E_3}$. ■

F_1 12 and 10

When the fractions have different denominators, we must rewrite all of the fractions with new common denominators. Many numbers can satisfy the condition for any set of denominators, but we want the *least* of these numbers, called the **least common denominator** (denoted by LCD). For example, 24 is the least common denominator of the denominators 6 and 8 in the fractions

$$\frac{7}{8} \text{ and } \frac{5}{6}$$

since it is the least (smallest) number that can be divided by 6 and 8 exactly. The procedure for finding the LCD is outlined next.

To find the least common denominator (LCD)

1. Express each denominator as a product of prime factors.
2. List all the *different* prime factors.
3. State each prime factor the *greatest* number of times it appears in any of the prime factorizations in step 1.
4. The least common denominator is the product of all factors from step 3.

Example R–1 F

Find the least common denominator (LCD) of the fractions with following denominators.

1. 24 and 18

a. Express 24 and 18 as products of prime numbers.

$$24 = 2 \cdot 2 \cdot 2 \cdot 3$$
$$18 = 2 \cdot 3 \cdot 3$$

F_2 6, 9, and 12

b. The different prime factors are 2 and 3.

c. 2 is a factor three times in 24 and 3 is a factor two times in 18 (the greatest number of times).

d. The LCD is $2 \cdot 2 \cdot 2 \cdot 3 \cdot 3 = 72$.

You are now ready to do F_1.

2. 6, 8, and 14

a.
$$6 = 2 \cdot 3$$
$$8 = 2 \cdot 2 \cdot 2$$
$$14 = 2 \cdot 7$$

b. The different prime factors are 2, 3, and 7.

c. 2 is a factor three times in 8, 3 is a factor once in 6, and 7 is a factor once in 14.

d. The LCD is $2 \cdot 2 \cdot 2 \cdot 3 \cdot 7 = 168$.

You are now ready to do F_2. ■

Building fractions

To write the fraction $\frac{5}{6}$ as an equivalent fraction with new denominator 24, we find the number that is multiplied by 6 to get 24. Since

$$24 \div 6 = 4$$

we use the factor 4. Now multiply the given fraction $\frac{5}{6}$ by the fraction $\frac{4}{4}$ (which is equal to 1). Thus

$$\frac{5}{6} = \frac{5}{6} \cdot \frac{4}{4} = \frac{5 \cdot 4}{6 \cdot 4} = \frac{20}{24}.$$

Multiplication by 1

We use the following procedure to write equivalent fractions.

To find equivalent fractions

1. Divide the original denominator into the new denominator.
2. Multiply the numerator and the denominator of the given fraction by the number obtained in step 1.

Example R–1 G

Write equivalent fractions having the new denominator.

1. $\frac{3}{5} = \frac{?}{30}$

Since $30 \div 5 = 6$, multiply $\frac{3}{5}$ by $\frac{6}{6}$.

$$\frac{3}{5} = \frac{3}{5} \cdot \frac{6}{6}$$ Multiply by $\frac{6}{6}$

$$= \frac{3 \cdot 6}{5 \cdot 6}$$ Multiply numerators / Multiply denominators

$$= \frac{18}{30}$$

You are now ready to do $\mathbf{G_1}$.

$\mathbf{G_1}$ $\frac{2}{9} = \frac{?}{27}$

2. $\frac{7}{9} = \frac{?}{72}$

Since $72 \div 9 = 8$, multiply $\frac{7}{9}$ by $\frac{8}{8}$.

$$\frac{7}{9} = \frac{7}{9} \cdot \frac{8}{8}$$ Multiply by $\frac{8}{8}$

$$= \frac{7 \cdot 8}{9 \cdot 8}$$ Multiply numerators / Multiply denominators

$$= \frac{56}{72}$$

You are now ready to do $\mathbf{G_2}$. ■

$\mathbf{G_2}$ $\frac{11}{12} = \frac{?}{72}$

To add or subtract fractions having different denominators, we use the following procedure.

To add or subtract fractions having different denominators

1. Find the LCD of the fractions.
2. Write each fraction as an equivalent fraction with the LCD as the denominator.
3. Perform the addition or subtraction as before.
4. Reduce the resulting fractions to lowest terms.

H_1 $\frac{6}{7} + \frac{4}{14}$

Example R–1 H

Add or subtract the following fractions as indicated. Reduce the resulting fraction to lowest terms.

1. $\frac{7}{8} + \frac{5}{6}$

a. The LCD of 8 and 6 is 24.

b. Since $24 \div 8 = 3$, then

$$\frac{7}{8} = \frac{7}{8} \cdot \frac{3}{3} = \frac{7 \cdot 3}{8 \cdot 3} = \frac{21}{24}. \qquad \text{Multiply by } \frac{3}{3}$$

Since $24 \div 6 = 4$, then

$$\frac{5}{6} = \frac{5}{6} \cdot \frac{4}{4} = \frac{5 \cdot 4}{6 \cdot 4} = \frac{20}{24}. \qquad \text{Multiply by } \frac{4}{4}$$

c. $\frac{7}{8} + \frac{5}{6} = \frac{21}{24} + \frac{20}{24}$ Add fractions with LCD

$= \frac{21 + 20}{24}$ Add numerators

$= \frac{41}{24}$ or $1\frac{17}{24}$

You are now ready to do **H_1**.

H_2 $\frac{3}{8} + \frac{5}{12}$

2. $\frac{5}{24} + \frac{7}{18}$

a. The LCD of 24 and 18 is 72.

b. Since $72 \div 24 = 3$, then

$$\frac{5}{24} = \frac{5}{24} \cdot \frac{3}{3} = \frac{15}{72}. \qquad \text{Multiply by } \frac{3}{3}$$

Since $72 \div 18 = 4$, then

$$\frac{7}{18} = \frac{7}{18} \cdot \frac{4}{4} = \frac{28}{72}. \qquad \text{Multiply by } \frac{4}{4}$$

c. $\frac{5}{24} + \frac{7}{18} = \frac{15}{72} + \frac{28}{72}$ Add fractions with LCD

$= \frac{15 + 28}{72}$ Add numerators

$= \frac{43}{72}$

You are now ready to do **H_2**.

3. $\frac{7}{8} - \frac{1}{3}$

a. The LCD of 8 and 3 is 24.

b. Since $24 \div 8 = 3$, then

$$\frac{7}{8} = \frac{7}{8} \cdot \frac{3}{3} = \frac{21}{24}. \qquad \text{Multiply by } \frac{3}{3}$$

Since $24 \div 3 = 8$, then

$$\frac{1}{3} = \frac{1}{3} \cdot \frac{8}{8} = \frac{8}{24}. \qquad \text{Multiply by } \frac{8}{8}$$

c. $\frac{7}{8} - \frac{1}{3} = \frac{21}{24} - \frac{8}{24}$ Subtract fractions with LCD

$= \frac{21 - 8}{24}$ Subtract numerators

$= \frac{13}{24}$

H_3 $\frac{7}{9} - \frac{1}{3}$

You are now ready to do H_3.

4. $3\frac{7}{8} - 2\frac{3}{4}$

Change each of the mixed numbers to an improper fraction.

$3\frac{7}{8} = \frac{(8 \cdot 3) + 7}{8} = \frac{31}{8}$; $2\frac{3}{4} = \frac{(4 \cdot 2) + 3}{4} = \frac{11}{4}$

a. The LCD of 8 and 4 is 8.

b. $\frac{31}{8}$ already has the LCD in its denominator.

Since $8 \div 4 = 2$, then

$\frac{11}{4} = \frac{11 \cdot 2}{4 \cdot 2} = \frac{22}{8}$. Multiply by $\frac{2}{2}$

H_4 $4\frac{1}{2} - 2\frac{3}{4}$

c. $3\frac{7}{8} - 2\frac{3}{4} = \frac{31}{8} - \frac{11}{4}$ Subtract improper fractions

$= \frac{31}{8} - \frac{22}{8}$ Subtract fractions with LCD

$= \frac{31 - 22}{8}$ Subtract numerators

$= \frac{9}{8}$ or $1\frac{1}{8}$

You are now ready to do H_4.

5. The perimeter (distance around) of a rectangle is found by *adding* the lengths of the four sides of the rectangle. Find the perimeter of a rectangle that is $\frac{5}{4}$ yards long and $\frac{5}{6}$ of a yard wide.

H_5 Find the perimeter of a rectangle that is $\frac{7}{8}$ feet long and $\frac{2}{3}$ feet wide.

perimeter = length + length + width + width

$= \frac{5}{4} + \frac{5}{4} + \frac{5}{6} + \frac{5}{6}$ Add four sides

$= \frac{10}{4} + \frac{10}{6}$ Add like fractions

$= \frac{30}{12} + \frac{20}{12}$ LCD is 12—restate each fraction with common denominator

$= \frac{30 + 20}{12}$ Add numerators

$= \frac{25}{6}$ or $4\frac{1}{6}$

The perimeter of the rectangle is $\frac{25}{6}$ yards $\left(\text{or } 4\frac{1}{6} \text{ yards}\right)$.

You are now ready to do H_5. ■

Answers to section R–1 margin exercises

A_1 $3 \cdot 7$ **A_2** $2 \cdot 3 \cdot 7$ **A_3** $2 \cdot 2 \cdot 5 \cdot 5$ **B_1** $\frac{2}{3}$ **B_2** $\frac{5}{9}$ **C_1** $\frac{21}{40}$ **C_2** $\frac{4}{15}$ **D_1** $\frac{45}{16}$
D_2 $\frac{4}{3}$ or $1\frac{1}{3}$ **D_3** $\frac{10}{7}$ **D_4** $\frac{5}{18}$ **D_5** $\frac{7}{55}$ **D_6** $18\frac{3}{8}$ square yards **E_1** $\frac{8}{11}$ **E_2** $\frac{1}{3}$
E_3 $\frac{1}{6}$ **F_1** LCD = 60 **F_2** LCD = 36 **G_1** 6 **G_2** 66 **H_1** $\frac{8}{7}$ or $1\frac{1}{7}$ **H_2** $\frac{19}{24}$
H_3 $\frac{4}{9}$ **H_4** $\frac{7}{4}$ or $1\frac{3}{4}$ **H_5** $3\frac{1}{12}$ ft

Mastery points

Can you

- Reduce a fraction to lowest terms?
- Multiply and divide fractions?
- Find the least common denominator (LCD) of two or more fractions?
- Add and subtract fractions?

Exercise R–1

Directions Reduce the following fractions to lowest terms. See example R–1 B.

Example [B_2] $\frac{25}{45}$

Solution

$$\frac{25}{45} = \frac{5 \cdot 5}{5 \cdot 3 \cdot 3}$$ Factor numerator, Factor denominator

$$= \frac{5}{3 \cdot 3}$$ Divide numerator and denominator by 5

$$= \frac{5}{9}$$ Multiply in denominator

1. $\frac{4}{8}$ **2.** $\frac{3}{9}$ **3.** $\frac{10}{12}$ **4.** $\frac{8}{14}$

5. $\frac{16}{18}$ **6.** $\frac{14}{21}$ [**7.**] $\frac{28}{36}$ **8.** $\frac{50}{75}$

9. $\frac{32}{64}$ **10.** $\frac{72}{96}$ **11.** $\frac{85}{100}$ **12.** $\frac{84}{120}$

Directions Multiply or divide the fractions as indicated. Reduce to lowest terms. See example R–1 C and D.

Example D2 $\dfrac{\frac{5}{6}}{\frac{5}{8}}$

Solution

$$\dfrac{\frac{5}{6}}{\frac{5}{8}} = \frac{5}{6} \div \frac{5}{8} = \frac{5}{6} \cdot \frac{8}{5}$$ Multiply by reciprocal of $\frac{5}{8}$

$$= \frac{5 \cdot 8}{6 \cdot 5}$$ Multiply numerators / Multiply denominators

$$= \frac{8}{6}$$ Reduce by common factor 5

$$= \frac{2 \cdot 2 \cdot 2}{2 \cdot 3}$$ Write numerator and denominator as prime factors

$$= \frac{2 \cdot 2}{3}$$ Reduce by common factor 2

$$= \frac{4}{3} \text{ or } 1\frac{1}{3}$$ Multiply in denominator

13. $\frac{5}{6} \cdot \frac{3}{5}$ **14.** $\frac{2}{3} \cdot \frac{5}{6}$ **15.** $\frac{7}{8} \cdot \frac{7}{12}$ **16.** $\frac{7}{5} \cdot \frac{3}{2}$ **17.** $\frac{7}{9} \cdot \frac{3}{4}$

18. $\frac{3}{4} \cdot 6$ **19.** $\frac{3}{7} \div \frac{4}{5}$ **20.** $\frac{12}{25} \div \frac{8}{15}$ **21.** $\frac{6}{7} \div 3$ **22.** $4 \div \frac{3}{8}$

23. $\frac{15}{17} \div \frac{3}{5}$ **24.** $4 \div \frac{7}{2}$ **25.** $17 \div 2\frac{1}{3}$ **26.** $12 \cdot 1\frac{5}{6}$ **27.** $7\frac{1}{3} \cdot 2\frac{4}{7}$

28. $1\frac{1}{5} \cdot 2\frac{1}{2}$ **29.** $4\frac{4}{5} \cdot 2\frac{1}{2}$ **30.** $7\frac{1}{2} \div 5\frac{1}{4}$ **31.** $\dfrac{8}{\frac{2}{3}}$ **32.** $\dfrac{\frac{17}{3}}{4}$

33. $\dfrac{\frac{7}{8}}{\frac{4}{3}}$

34. $\dfrac{\frac{15}{64}}{\frac{45}{8}}$

35. $\frac{4}{5} \cdot \frac{2}{3} \cdot \frac{3}{8}$

36. $\frac{9}{8} \cdot \frac{2}{3} \cdot \frac{3}{8}$

37. $\frac{8}{3} \cdot \frac{4}{7} \div \frac{15}{4}$
(*Hint:* Perform operations from left to right.)

38. $\frac{8}{3} \div \frac{15}{14} \cdot \frac{4}{7}$

39. $\frac{8}{3} \cdot \frac{15}{14} \div \frac{4}{7}$

See example R–1 D–6.

40. What is the total length of 25 pieces of steel, each $5\frac{1}{2}$ inches long?

41. The volume of a rectangular block is found by multiplying the length times the width times the height.

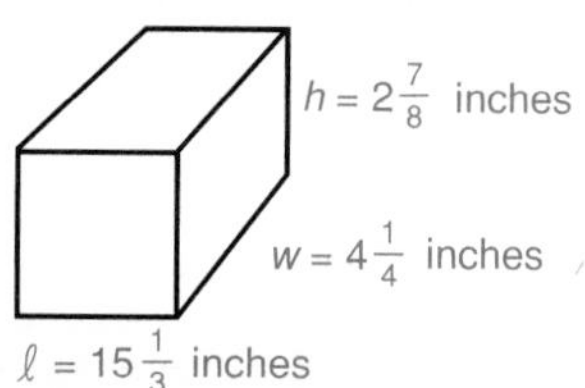

a. What is the volume in cubic inches of a rectangular block of wood $15\frac{1}{3}$ inches long, $4\frac{1}{4}$ inches wide, and $2\frac{7}{8}$ inches high?

b. What is the volume in cubic inches of a block of steel $8\frac{1}{2}$ inches long, $2\frac{1}{8}$ inches wide, and $1\frac{3}{4}$ inches high?

42. A space $61\frac{1}{2}$ inches long is divided into 14 equal parts. What is the length of each part?

Directions Find the LCD of sets of fractions with the following denominators. See example R–1 F.

Example $\boxed{F_2}$ 6, 9, and 12

Solution

1. Express 6, 9, and 12 as a product of prime factors.
   $6 = 2 \cdot 3$
   $9 = 3 \cdot 3$
   $12 = 2 \cdot 2 \cdot 3$
2. The different prime factors are 2 and 3.
3. 2 is a factor twice in 12 and 3 is a factor twice in 9.
4. The LCD is $2 \cdot 2 \cdot 3 \cdot 3 = 36$.

43. 3, 8, 10 **44.** 9, 15, 21 **45.** 6, 14, 18 **46.** 5, 10, 12

47. 16, 24, 36 **48.** 12, 16, 24 **49.** 5, 7, 11 **50.** 10, 20, 30

51. 8, 10, 12 **52.** 10, 14, 18 **53.** 10, 15, 20 **54.** 10, 15, 24

Directions Add or subtract the following fractions as indicated. Reduce to lowest terms. See example R–1 H.

Example $\boxed{H_4}$ $4\frac{1}{2} - 2\frac{3}{4}$

Solution We first change the mixed numbers to improper fractions.

$$4\frac{1}{2} = \frac{(4 \cdot 2) + 1}{2} = \frac{9}{2};\quad 2\frac{3}{4} = \frac{(4 \cdot 2) + 3}{4} = \frac{11}{4}$$

$$4\frac{1}{2} - 2\frac{3}{4} = \frac{9}{2} - \frac{11}{4}$$ Replace mixed numbers with improper fractions

The LCD is 4.

$$= \frac{18}{4} - \frac{11}{4}$$ Write $\frac{9}{2}$ as an equivalent fraction with denominator 4

$$= \frac{18 - 11}{4}$$ Subtract numerators

$$= \frac{7}{4} \text{ or } 1\frac{3}{4}$$

55. $\frac{1}{3} + \frac{1}{3}$ **56.** $\frac{2}{5} + \frac{3}{10}$ **57.** $\frac{1}{3} + \frac{1}{4}$ **58.** $\frac{5}{6} - \frac{1}{6}$

59. $\frac{4}{5} - \frac{2}{10}$ **60.** $\frac{5}{6} - \frac{3}{8}$ **61.** $1 + \frac{5}{8}$ **62.** $3 + \frac{5}{6}$

63. $4 - \frac{3}{5}$

64. $\frac{2}{3} + \frac{3}{4}$

65. $\frac{3}{5} + \frac{7}{15}$

66. $\frac{5}{6} - \frac{1}{3}$

67. $\frac{3}{8} - \frac{1}{12}$

68. $\frac{7}{24} - \frac{3}{16}$

69. $\frac{7}{54} + \frac{19}{45}$

70. $\frac{1}{2} + \frac{1}{5} + \frac{1}{10}$

71. $\frac{7}{15} + \frac{5}{6} - \frac{3}{4}$

72. $\frac{9}{16} + \frac{5}{18} - \frac{2}{15}$

73. $8\frac{3}{16} - 4\frac{5}{8}$

74. $7\frac{1}{2} + 2\frac{3}{4}$

75. $\frac{2}{7} + \frac{2}{3} + \frac{5}{7}$

See example R–1 H–5.

76. Jane owed Joan some money. If she paid Joan $\frac{1}{4}$ of the debt on June 15, $\frac{1}{3}$ of the original debt on July 1, and $\frac{3}{8}$ of the original debt on August 10, how much of her debt had Jane paid by August 10?

77. A flower garden in the form of a rectangle has two sides that are $24\frac{1}{2}$ feet long and two sides that are $18\frac{3}{4}$ feet long. Find the perimeter (total distance around) of the rectangle.

78. On a given day, Mrs. Jones purchased $\frac{5}{6}$ yard of one material, $\frac{3}{4}$ yard of another material, and $\frac{2}{3}$ yard of a third material. How many yards of material did she purchase altogether?

79. Butcher John has $32\frac{1}{4}$ pounds of pork chops. If he sells $21\frac{1}{3}$ pounds of the pork chops on a given day, how many pounds of pork chops does he have left?

80. A machinist has a piece of steel stock that weighs $12\frac{7}{8}$ kilograms. If he cuts off $5\frac{1}{5}$ kilograms, how many kilograms does he have left?

R–2 Operations with decimals

A_1 0.4

In R–1, we discussed fractions that represent parts of a whole. A **decimal number** is a special fraction with a denominator that is a 10, 100, 1,000, and so on. The **decimal point** is a shorthand symbol used to indicate which of these numbers is the denominator.

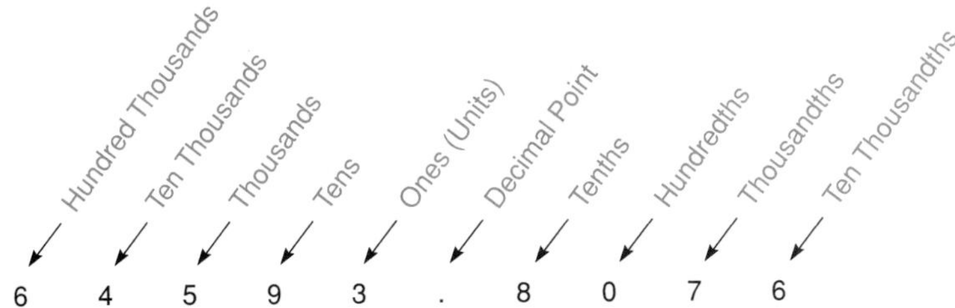

We use place value to write a decimal number as a fraction. For example, 0.27, which is read "twenty-seven *hundredths,*" is written

$$0.27 = \frac{27}{100}. \leftarrow \text{Hundred}$$

A_2 0.42

0.149, which is read "one hundred forty-nine *thousandths,*" is written

$$0.149 = \frac{149}{1{,}000}. \leftarrow \text{Thousand}$$

The last digit in the number is the key to the denominator of the fraction.

Example R–2 A

Write the following decimal numbers as fractions reduced to lowest terms.

1. 0.8 (read "eight *tenths*")

$$0.8 = \frac{8}{10} \leftarrow \text{Ten}$$

$$= \frac{4}{5} \quad \text{Reduce to lowest terms}$$

You are now ready to do A_1.

2. 0.57 (read "fifty-seven *hundredths*")

A_3 0.5012

$$0.57 = \frac{57}{100} \leftarrow \text{Hundred}$$

You are now ready to do A_2.

3. 0.1234 (read "one thousand two hundred thirty-four *ten thousandths*")

$$0.1234 = \frac{1{,}234}{10{,}000} \leftarrow \text{Ten thousand}$$

$$= \frac{617}{5{,}000} \quad \text{Reduce to lowest terms}$$

You are now ready to do A_3.

Note
A decimal number that is written as a fraction will reduce *only if* the numerator is divisible by 2 or 5. This was the case in examples 1 and 3. ■

B$_1$ $1.09 + 23.6 + 401.79 + 0.45 + 6.0946$

Addition and subtraction of decimal numbers

To add or subtract decimal numbers, we place the numbers under one another so that the decimal points line up vertically and then proceed as in adding or subtracting whole numbers.

Example R–2 B

Add or subtract the following numbers as indicated.

1. $5.67 + 32.046 + 251.7367 + 0.92$

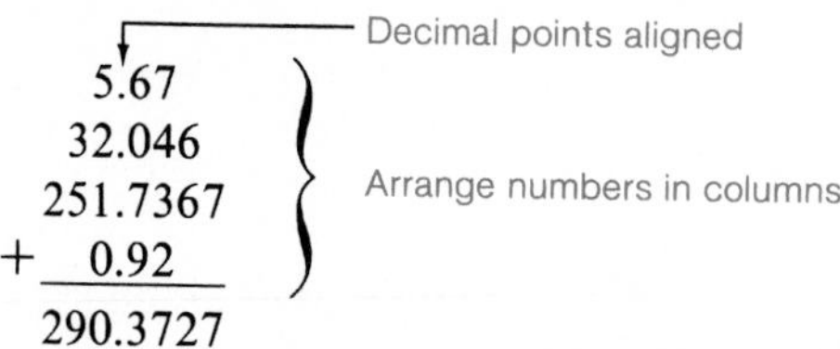

B$_2$ $68.95 - 23.12$

Note
To avoid possible errors, it is often a good idea to insert *zeros* so that you have all columns filled in to the right of the decimal point.

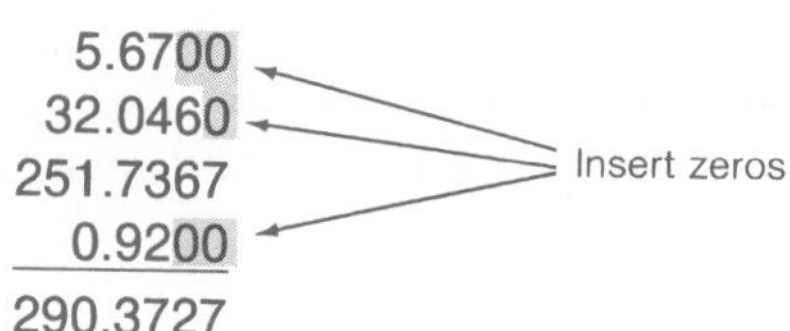

B$_3$ Subtract 14.9 from 83.42.

You are now ready to do **B$_1$**.

2. $53.67 - 22.07$

```
    53.67      Decimal points aligned
  − 22.07      Arrange numbers in columns
    31.60
```

You are now ready to do **B$_2$**.

3. Subtract (a) 18.7 from 39.62, (b) 4.38 from 19.2.

B$_4$ Find the perimeter of a triangle whose sides are 8.43 inches, 9.57 inches, and 12.13 inches.

```
a.   39.62   (3 crossed out to 8)
   − 18.70  ← Insert zero
     20.92
```

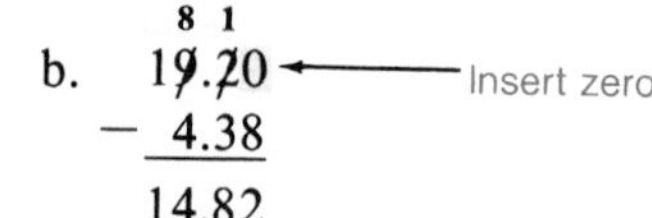

You are now ready to do **B$_3$**.

4. What is the perimeter of the figure in the diagram? (Recall that the perimeter is the total distance around the figure.)

```
    3.97 ft
    7.39 ft
    3.18 ft
  + 7.83 ft
   22.37 ft
```

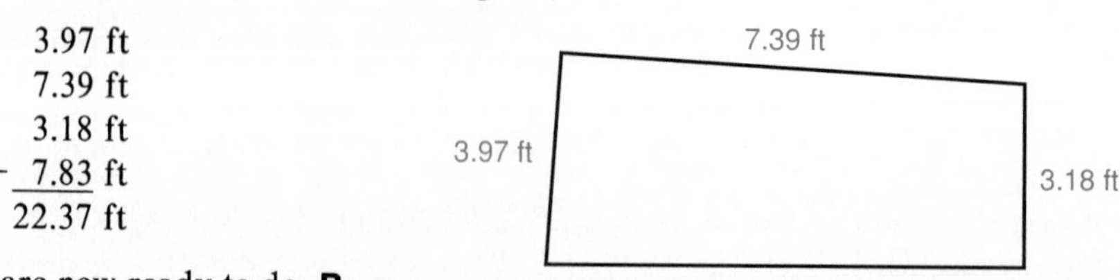

You are now ready to do **B$_4$**. ■

To multiply decimal numbers

1. Multiply the numbers as if they are whole numbers (ignore the decimal points).
2. Count the number of decimal places in both factors. That is, count the number of digits to the right of the decimal point in each factor. This total is the number of decimal places the product must have.
3. Beginning at the right in the product, count off to the left the number of decimal places from step 2. Insert the decimal point. If necessary, zeros are inserted so there are enough decimal places.

C_1 1.43×0.916

Example R–2 C

Multiply the following.

1. 2.36×0.403

```
    2.36 ←— 2 decimal places
   0.403 ←— 3 decimal places   (2 + 3 = 5)
     708
    944
 0.95108 ←— 5 decimal places
```

You are now ready to do C_1.

2. (18.14)(106.4)

```
     18.14 ←— 2 decimal places
     106.4 ←— 1 decimal place   (2 + 1 = 3)
      7256
    10884
    1814
 1,930.096 ←— 3 decimal places
```

C_2 (206.1)(9.36)

You are now ready to do C_2.

Note
We need not write the problem in column form with the decimal points in the same column, since the arrangement of the numbers being multiplied does not help determine our answer. When multiplying, *do not* insert extra zeros. ■

To divide decimal numbers, we must identify the divisor, the dividend, and the quotient in an indicated division.

```
   10  ←— Quotient
25)250 ←— Dividend
↑
└———— Divisor
```

We now outline the procedure for dividing decimal numbers.

D_1 51.076 ÷ 4.52

To divide decimal numbers

1. Change the *divisor* to a whole number by moving the decimal point to the *right* as many places as is necessary.
2. Move the decimal point in the *dividend* to the right this same number of places. If necessary, zeros are inserted so there are enough decimal places.
3. Insert the decimal point in the *quotient* directly above the new position of the decimal point in the dividend.
4. Divide as with whole numbers.

Example R–2 D

Divide the following.

1. 30.814 ÷ 2.17

a. Write the problem $2.17\overline{)30.814}$.

b. Move the decimal point *two* places to the right in 2.17 and 30.814.

$$217\overline{)3{,}081.4}$$

c. Now divide as with whole numbers.

```
        14.2
217)3,081.4
    2 17
      911
      868
       434
       434
         0
```

D_2 4,950.3 ÷ 5.69

You are now ready to do **D_1**.

2. 360.5 ÷ 1.03

a. Write the problem $1.03\overline{)360.5}$.

b. Move the decimal point *two* places to the right in 1.03 and 360.5.

$103\overline{)36{,}050.}$ ← Zero inserted as placeholder

c. Now divide as with whole numbers.

```
       350.
103)36,050.
    30 9
     5 15
     5 15
        0
```

The answer is 350.

You are now ready to do **D_2**.

3. If an automobile travels 429.76 miles and uses 15.8 gallons of gas, how many miles per gallon did the automobile achieve?

To determine the fuel economy, we divide the total number of miles traveled by the amount of gasoline used.

429.76 ÷ 15.8

```
       27.2
158)4,297.6
    316
    1137
    1106
      316
      316
        0
```

The automobile achieved 27.2 miles per gallon.

You are now ready to do **D_3**.

D_3 If a car travels 393.25 miles on 12.1 gallons of gas, how many miles per gallon did the car achieve?

We can change a fraction into its decimal number equivalent using the following procedure.

To change a fraction to a decimal number

Divide the denominator into the numerator.

Example R-2 E

Convert each fraction to a decimal number.

E_1 $\frac{3}{8}$

1. $\frac{3}{4}$

We divide 3 by 4. To do this, we must add zero placeholders.

```
  0.75
4)3.00  ←Annex zeros
  2 8
    20
    20
     0
```

Thus $\frac{3}{4} = 0.75$.

You are now ready to do **E_1**.

2. $\frac{1}{3}$

We divide $1 \div 3$. We must add zero placeholders.

E_2 $\frac{2}{3}$

```
       ┌── Continues indefinitely
  0.333̄
3)1.000 ←Add zeros
   9
   10
    9
    10
     9
     10
```

We can see that no matter how many zero placeholders we add, the quotient will continue to add digits of 3. This is called a **repeating decimal** (denoted by the bar placed over the last digit, or digits, that are repeating). We can round a repeating decimal to as many places as are needed. We can say that $\frac{1}{3}$ is *approximately equal* to $0.33\overline{3}$, denoted by

$$\frac{1}{3} \approx 0.33\overline{3}.$$

Answers to section R–2 margin exercises

A_1 $\frac{2}{5}$ A_2 $\frac{21}{50}$ A_3 $\frac{1{,}253}{2{,}500}$ B_1 433.0246 B_2 45.83 B_3 68.52 B_4 30.13 in.
C_1 1.30988 C_2 1,929.096 D_1 11.3 D_2 870 D_3 32.5 mpg E_1 0.375 E_2 $0.66\overline{6}$

Mastery points

Can you

- Write decimal numbers as fractions?
- Add and subtract decimal numbers?
- Multiply and divide decimal numbers?
- Write fractions as decimal numbers?

Exercise R–2

Directions Write each decimal number as a fraction reduced to lowest terms. See example R–2 A.

Example A_2 0.42

Solution 0.42 is read "forty-two *hundredths*."

$$0.42 = \frac{42}{100} \quad \leftarrow \text{Hundred}$$
$$= \frac{21}{50} \quad \text{Reduce to lowest terms}$$

1. 0.4 **2.** 0.8 **3.** 0.15 **4.** 0.36

5. 0.125 **6.** 0.248 **7.** 0.875 **8.** 0.625

Directions Add or subtract the following as indicated. See example R–2 B.

Example B_3 Subtract 14.9 from 83.42.

Solution We want 83.42 − 14.9.

$$\begin{array}{r} 83.42 \\ -\underline{14.90} \\ 68.52 \end{array} \quad \leftarrow \text{Add zero placeholder}$$

9. 6.8 + 0.354 + 2.78 + 7.083 + 2.002

10. 4.76 + 0.573 + 3.57 + 40.09 + 13

11. 8.0007 + 360.01 + 25.72 + 6.362 + 140.2

12. 7.0001 + 8 + 7.067 + 803.1 + 5.25

13. 10.03 + 3.113 + 0.3342 + 0.0763 + 0.005

14. 27.376 − 14.007

15. 367.0076 − 210.02

16. 836 − 0.367

17. 1.07 − 0.00036

18. 4,563.2 − 274.063

19. 19.07 + 2.736 − 8.007 − 4.1
(*Hint:* Perform operations in order from left to right.)

20. 0.00436 + 2.63 + 0.127 − 1.36

21. 14 − 0.07 + 7.3 − 8.0073

22. 363.45 − 43.606 − 120.6 + 42

23. 9.631 − 0.73 + 57.0008 − 42.6 − 0.079

Directions Multiply the following. See example R–2 C.

Example C_2 (206.1)(9.36)

Solution

```
     206.1  ←—— 1 decimal place
      9.36  ←—— 2 decimal places   (1 + 2 = 3)
     12366
     6183
   18549
 1,929.096  ←—— 3 decimal places
```

24. 0.375 × 100

25. 42.63 × 1,000

26. 246.37 × 10

27. (5.6076)(10,000)

28. (42.6)(73)

29. (7.006)(1.36)

30. 703.6 × 1.7

31. (56.37)(0.0076)

32. 346.137 × 0.07743

33. 30.0303 × 0.030303

34. 2.456 × 0.00012

Directions Divide the following. See example R–2 D.

Example **D₂** 4,950.3 ÷ 5.69

Solution

1. Write the problem $5.69\overline{)4,950.3}$.
2. Move the decimal point *two* places in 5.69 and 4,950.3.

$569\overline{)495,030.}$ ← Add zero placeholder

3. Divide as whole numbers.

```
          870.  ← Add zero placeholder
569)495,030.
     4552
      3983
      3983
         0
```

Thus 4,950.3 ÷ 5.69 = 870.

35. 0.84 ÷ 0.7 **36.** 0.525 ÷ 0.5 **37.** 10.4 ÷ 0.26 **38.** 21.681 ÷ 8.03

39. 6,125.1 ÷ 60.05 **40.** 166.279 ÷ 64.7 **41.** 31.50 ÷ 0.0126 **42.** 2.9868 ÷ 0.057

Directions Convert each fraction to a decimal number. See example R–2 E.

Example **E₁** $\frac{3}{8}$

Solution We divide 3 ÷ 8, adding zero placeholders where necessary.

```
   0.375
8)3.000  ← Zero placeholders
  2 4
    60
    56
     40
     40
      0
```

The decimal equivalent of $\frac{3}{8}$ is 0.375.

43. $\frac{3}{20}$ **44.** $\frac{5}{8}$ **45.** $\frac{13}{20}$ **46.** $\frac{7}{8}$ **47.** $\frac{1}{8}$

48. $\frac{17}{50}$ **49.** $\frac{2}{9}$ **50.** $\frac{5}{9}$ **51.** $1\frac{3}{5}$

52. A carpenter has three pieces of 2 by 4s which are 24.5 inches, 35.25 inches, and 62.375 inches long, respectively. How many inches of wood does she have all together?

53. A wood craftsman has 74.75 inches of a particular stock. He needs 5.75 inches of the stock to carve out a cardinal bird. How many cardinals can he make?

54. Gasoline costs 89.9 cents per gallon. What is the total cost of 14.36 gallons, correct to the nearest cent?

55. A rectangular field is 21.3 yards long and 15.75 yards wide. Find the area (length × width) of the field.

56. A student bought a book for $21.68. If she gave the cashier $25, how much change did she receive?

57. The 500-meter speed-skating event was won in a time of 43.33 seconds in the 1972 olympics. The winning time in 1976 was 42.76 seconds. How much faster was the 1976 time?

58. An airline pilot flew distances of 210.6 kilometers, 504.3 kilometers, 319.6 kilometers, 780.32 kilometers, and 421.75 kilometers on five flights. How many kilometers did he fly all together?

59. On a 4-day trip, the Adams family used 32.5 gallons, 28.36 gallons, 41.87 gallons, and 19.55 gallons of gasoline. How many gallons of gasoline did they use all together?

60. If a cubic foot of water weighs 62.5 pounds, how many pounds of water are there in a tank containing 506.3 cubic feet?

61. Gasoline costs 92.9 cents per gallon. What is the total cost of 13.15 gallons, correct to the nearest cent?

62. A rectangular field is 43.3 yards long and 25.34 yards wide. Find the area (length × width) of the field.

A_1 7%

R–3 Percent

We use decimal numbers extensively in our work with **percent.** The word percent means "per one hundred."

> Percent is defined to be parts per one hundred.

We use the symbol "%" to represent percent. Thus

3% means "three parts per one hundred"

or

3% means "three one hundredths."

From the above discussion,

$$3\% = \frac{3}{100} = 0.03.$$

A_2 73%

That is, we can write a percent as

1. a decimal number and
2. a fraction with denominator 100.

Example R–3 A

Write each percent as a fraction and as a decimal number.

1. 7%
7% means "seven one hundredths."

$$7\% = \frac{7}{100} = 0.07$$

You are now ready to do $\mathbf{A_1}$.

2. 39%
39% means "thirty-nine one hundredths."

$$39\% = \frac{39}{100} = 0.39$$

A_3 241%

You are now ready to do $\mathbf{A_2}$.

3. 123%
123% means "one hundred twenty-three one hundredths."

$$123\% = \frac{123}{100} = 1.23$$

You are now ready to do $\mathbf{A_3}$. ■

From these examples, we can see how to write a percent as a decimal number.

> **To write a percent as a decimal number**
>
> Move the decimal point two places to the *left* and drop the % symbol.

To write a fraction or decimal number as a percent, we reverse the procedure.

B$_1$ 0.44

To write a decimal number as a percent

Move the decimal point two places to the *right* and affix the % symbol.

To write a fraction as a percent

Find the decimal number equivalent of the fraction and change this decimal number to a percent.

Example R–3 B

B$_2$ 0.7

Write the following as decimal numbers, fractions, and percents.

1. 0.32

$0.32 = 32\%$ — Move decimal point two places to the right and affix % symbol

Since $0.32 = \frac{32}{100}$ — Write as a fraction

$= \frac{8}{25}$ — Reduce to lowest terms

then $0.32 = \frac{8}{25} = 32\%.$

You are now ready to do **B$_1$**.

2. 0.9

B$_3$ 1.75

$0.9 = 90\%$ — Move decimal point two places to the right and affix % symbol (Add a zero placeholder)

Since $0.9 = \frac{9}{10}$ — Write as a fraction

then $0.9 = \frac{9}{10} = 90\%.$

You are now ready to do **B$_2$**.

3. 1.25

$1.25 = 125\%$ — Move decimal point two places to the right and affix % symbol

Since $1.25 = \frac{125}{100}$ — Write as a fraction

$= \frac{5}{4}$ — Reduce to lowest terms

B$_4$ $\frac{1}{8}$

then $1.25 = \frac{5}{4} = 125\%.$

You are now ready to do **B$_3$**.

4. $\frac{7}{8}$

Divide $7 \div 8$ to obtain the decimal equivalent. Doing this we find that

$\frac{7}{8} = 0.875.$

Then $\frac{7}{8} = 0.875 = 87.5\%.$ — Move decimal point two places to the right and affix % symbol

You are now ready to do **B$_4$**. ■

C_1 43% of 200

Percentage

When we find 60% of 500, we find the **percentage.** In the language of mathematics, "of" usually means the operation multiplication. Thus

60% of 500 means 60% · 500.

However, we cannot multiply 60% times 500. We must first change 60% to a decimal number (or a fraction) before we can perform the multiplication.

$$\begin{aligned} 60\% \text{ of } 500 &= 60\% \cdot 500 \\ &= 0.60 \cdot 500 \quad \text{Change 60\% to 0.60} \\ &= 300 \quad \text{Percentage} \end{aligned}$$

Therefore 60% · 500 = 300.
(percent) · (whole) = (percentage)

C_2 3% of 230

Example R–3 C

Find the following percentages.

1. 52% of 300

52% = 0.52 — Change percent to a decimal number

52% of 300 = 0.52 · 300 — Multiply
= 156

Thus 52% of 300 = 156.

You are now ready to do C_1.

2. 8% of 35

8% = 0.08 — Change percent to a decimal number

8% of 35 = 0.08 · 35 — Multiply
= 28

Thus 8% of 35 = 28.

You are now ready to do C_2.

C_3 236% of 20

3. 224% of 50

224% = 2.24 — Change percent to a decimal number

224% of 50 = 2.24 · 50 — Multiply
= 112

Thus 224% of 50 = 112.

You are now ready to do C_3.

C_4 $5\frac{1}{4}\%$ of 360

4. $3\frac{1}{2}\%$ of 270

$3\frac{1}{2}\% = 3.5\%$ — $\frac{1}{2} = 0.5$ as a decimal number
$= 0.035$ — Change percent to a decimal number

$3\frac{1}{2}\%$ of 270 $= 0.035 \cdot 270$ — Multiply
$= 9.45$

Thus $3\frac{1}{2}\%$ of 270 = 9.45.

You are now ready to do C_4. ■

Often it is necessary to find what percent one number is of another number. From the previous examples, we learned

$$(\text{percent}) \cdot (\text{whole}) = (\text{percentage}).$$

We are now looking for the percent when we know the whole and the percentage. To find the percent, divide the percentage by the whole.

$$(\text{percent}) = \frac{(\text{percentage})}{(\text{whole})}.$$

To illustrate, suppose we wish to know

7 is what percent of 25?

The percentage is 7 and the whole is 25.

Then

$$\begin{aligned} \text{percent} &= \frac{7}{25} && \begin{array}{l}\leftarrow \text{Percentage}\\ \leftarrow \text{Whole}\end{array} \\ &= 0.28 && \text{Write fraction as a decimal number} \\ &= 28\% && \text{Change decimal number to percent} \end{aligned}$$

Therefore 7 is 28% of 25.

Example R–3 D

Find the percent in the following problems.

1. 24 is what percent of 96?

We are asked (what percent) of 96 is 24?

$$\begin{aligned} \text{percent} &= \frac{24}{96} && \begin{array}{l}\leftarrow \text{Percentage}\\ \leftarrow \text{Whole}\end{array} \\ &= 0.25 && \text{Write fraction as a decimal number} \\ &= 25\% && \text{Write decimal number as a percent} \end{aligned}$$

Thus 24 is 25% of 96.

You are now ready to do **D_1**.

2. What percent of 90 is 72?

$$\begin{aligned} \text{percent} &= \frac{72}{90} && \begin{array}{l}\leftarrow \text{Percentage}\\ \leftarrow \text{Whole}\end{array} \\ &= 0.80 && \text{Write fraction as a decimal number} \\ &= 80\% && \text{Write decimal number as a percent} \end{aligned}$$

Thus 80% of 90 is 72.

You are now ready to do **D_2**.

3. The sales tax on $250 is $10. What percent of the price of the article was charged in sales tax?

We want $10 is what percent of $250?

$$\begin{aligned} \text{percent} &= \frac{10}{250} && \begin{array}{l}\leftarrow \text{Percentage}\\ \leftarrow \text{Whole}\end{array} \\ &= 0.04 && \text{Write fraction as a decimal number} \\ &= 4\% && \text{Write decimal number as a percent} \end{aligned}$$

Thus $10 in sales tax is 4% of $250.

You are now ready to do **D_3**. ■

D_1 30 is what percent of 50?

D_2 What percent of 84 is 21?

D_3 The sales tax on $36 is $2.16. What percent of the price of the article is the sales tax that was charged?

Answers to section R–3 margin exercises

A_1 0.03 A_2 0.73 A_3 2.41 B_1 $\frac{11}{25} = 44\%$ B_2 $\frac{7}{10} = 70\%$ B_3 $\frac{7}{4} = 175\%$
B_4 $0.125 = 12.5\%$ C_1 86 C_2 6.9 C_3 47.2 C_4 18.9 D_1 60%
D_2 25% D_3 6%

Mastery points

Can you

- Change a percent to a decimal number?
- Change a decimal number to a percent?
- Change a percent to a fraction?
- Find the percentage?
- Find what percent one number is of another number?

Exercise R–3

Directions Write each percent as a fraction and as a decimal number. See example R–3 A.

Example  241%

Solution 241% means "two hundred forty-one one hundredths."

$$241\% = \frac{241}{100} = 2.41$$

1. 5% **2.** 1% **3.** 12% **4.** 64%

5. 135% **6.** 150% **7.** 325% **8.** 570%

Directions Write exercises 9–14 as a fraction and a percent and exercises 15 and 16 as a decimal and a percent. See example R–3 B.

Example  1.75

Solution $1.75 = 175\%$ Move decimal point two places to the right and affix % symbol

$1.75 = \frac{175}{100}$ Write as a fraction

$= \frac{7}{4}$ Reduce fraction to lowest terms

Thus $1.75 = \frac{7}{4} = 175\%$.

9. 0.8 **10.** 0.9 **11.** 0.54 **12.** 0.80

13. 1.15 **14.** 2.40 **15.** $\frac{3}{4}$ **16.** $\frac{5}{2}$

Directions Find the following percentages. See example R–3 C.

Example $\boxed{C_3}$ 236% of 20

Solution 236% = 2.36 Change percent to a decimal number

236% of 20 = 2.36 · 20 Multiply
= 47.2

Thus 236% of 20 = 47.2.

17. 5% of 40

18. 8% of 45

19. 26% of 130

20. 78% of 900

21. 110% of 500

22. 240% of 60

23. City Bank pays 5.7% interest per year on its savings accounts. What is the annual interest on a savings account that has $4,500? (*Hint:* Interest = Percent · Amount in savings.)

24. The sales tax on retail sales in Michigan is 4%. How much sales tax does John pay on a purchase of $250?

25. If Jane pays 5% of her weekly salary in state income tax, how much state tax does she pay if her weekly salary is $460?

26. The local shoe store is giving a 25% discount on clearance items. How much discount is there on a pair of shoes costing $34? What is the price of the shoes *after* the discount excluding sales tax?

27. A local retailer predicts his profit in a given year will be 116% of the previous year. What is his predicted profit for this year if last year's profit was $42,500?

28. A company charges $4\frac{1}{2}$% shipping and handling charges on all items shipped. What are the shipping and handling charges on goods that cost $70? What is the total cost for the goods?

29. A bottle of solution is 4% salt. How much salt is there in a 24-fluidounce bottle of solution?

30. Self-employed persons must pay a Social Security tax of about 12%. What is the Social Security tax on earnings of $25,000? If the person is in the 28% federal income tax bracket, how much federal income tax does he pay?

Directions Find the percent in the following problems. See example R–3 D.

Example D₂ What percent of 84 is 21?

Solution

$$\text{percent} = \frac{21}{84} \begin{matrix} \leftarrow \text{Percentage} \\ \leftarrow \text{Whole} \end{matrix}$$

$= 0.25$ Write fraction as a decimal number

$= 25\%$ Write decimal number as a percent

Thus 25% of 84 is 21.

31. 6 is what percent of 20?

32. 15 is what percent of 50?

33. 35 is what percent of 42?

34. 36 is what percent of 27?

35. What percent of 60 is 45?

36. What percent of 150 is 75?

37. What percent of 16 is 48?

38. What percent of 11 is 55?

39. 42 is what percent of 105?

40. What percent of 424 is 106?

41. If John James earned $120 on his investment of $2,400, what percent did he earn on his investment?

42. Marcia made a trip of 2,500 miles, part by airplane and part by boat. If she flew 1,200 miles by airplane, what percent of the trip was by airplane? What percent of the trip was by boat?

43. Pamela spends an average of 6 hours each day watching TV. What percent of the 24-hour day does she spend watching TV?

44. A particular light bulb has a "life" of about 150 hours of burning. If the bulb has burned a total of 60 hours, what percent of its "life" has been used?

45. A 20-fluidounce container of solution has 7 ounces of salt. What percent of the solution is salt?

46. Sarah is presently earning $480 per week. If her employer promises her a weekly raise of $24, what percent of increase in pay will she receive?

47. A dress that has a marked price of \$56 is reduced by \$14. What percent of the marked price has the dress been reduced?

48. If Kelly spends \$80 each week for groceries and her weekly income is \$400, what percent of her weekly income is spent on groceries?

Chapter R lead-in problem

Each week Sarah Christie puts 5% of her paycheck into savings and uses 9% of her paycheck to pay off her credit card debt. Sarah earns \$500 each week. How much money does Sarah (a) put into savings each week and (b) use to pay off her credit card debt each week?

Solution

a. Sarah puts 5% of \$500 into savings.

$$\begin{aligned} 5\% \text{ of } \$500 &= 5\% \cdot 500 \\ &= 0.05 \cdot 500 \\ &= 25 \end{aligned}$$

Sarah puts \$25 into savings each week.

b. Sarah pays 9% of \$500 to pay off her debt.

$$\begin{aligned} 9\% \text{ of } 500 &= 9\% \cdot \$500 \\ &= 0.09 \cdot 500 \\ &= 45 \end{aligned}$$

Sarah pays \$45 toward her debt each week.

Chapter R summary

1. A **prime number** is any whole number greater than 1 whose only factors are the number itself and 1.
2. All whole numbers except 0 and 1 that are not prime can be written as a **product of two or more prime numbers.**
3. To **reduce a fraction** to lowest terms,
   a. write the numerator and the denominator as a product of prime numbers.
   b. divide the numerator and the denominator by the common factors.
4. To **multiply** fractions,
   a. multiply the numerators and the denominators and place the product of the numerators over the product of the denominators.
   b. reduce the resulting fraction to lowest terms.
5. To **divide** fractions, multiply the first fraction by the reciprocal of the second fraction and reduce to lowest terms.
6. To **add** or **subtract** fractions having the same denominator, add or subtract the numerators and place this sum or difference over the common denominator.
7. The **least common denominator** (LCD) of two or more fractions is the least (smallest) number that is exactly divisible by the denominators.
8. A **decimal number** represents a part of a whole.
9. **Percent** is defined to be parts per one hundred.
10. The symbol for percent is %.
11. To change **percent to a decimal number,** move the decimal point two places to the left and drop the % symbol.
12. To change from a **decimal number to a percent,** move the decimal point two places to the right and affix the % symbol.
13. To change a **fraction to percent,** change the fraction to a decimal number and then to a percent.
14. To change a percent to a fraction, write the percent as a decimal number and then write the decimal number as a percent.

Chapter R review

R–1

Directions Reduce each fraction to lowest terms.

1. $\frac{10}{14}$

2. $\frac{36}{48}$

3. $\frac{120}{180}$

Directions Multiply or divide the following as indicated. Reduce to lowest terms.

4. $\frac{6}{7} \cdot \frac{5}{3}$

5. $\frac{2}{3} \cdot \frac{9}{10}$

6. $\frac{7}{8} \div \frac{5}{6}$

7. $\frac{5}{12} \div \frac{10}{21}$

8. $3\frac{3}{4} \div 1\frac{1}{5}$

9. $2\frac{1}{2} \cdot 3\frac{1}{3}$

10. Hannah rents $\frac{3}{4}$ of a plot of land. If the plot is $\frac{5}{6}$ of an acre in size, how many acres does Hannah rent?

11. A recipe calls for $\frac{4}{5}$ of a cup of sugar. If Dene wishes to make $\frac{1}{2}$ of the recipe, how many cups of sugar should she use?

Directions Add or subtract the following fractions as indicated. Reduce to lowest terms.

12. $\frac{3}{7} + \frac{5}{7}$

13. $\frac{5}{8} + \frac{1}{6}$

14. $\frac{11}{12} - \frac{1}{12}$

15. $\frac{8}{9} - \frac{2}{3}$

16. $4\frac{1}{4} + 2\frac{3}{5}$

17. $\frac{1}{5} - \frac{2}{3} + \frac{5}{6}$

18. Paula paid $\frac{1}{3}$ of her debt one week and $\frac{1}{4}$ of her debt the second week. At the end of the second week, how much of her debt had she paid off?

19. Bob Burger owns $3\frac{1}{8}$ acres of land. If he sells $2\frac{1}{4}$ acres to his friend Eric Hand, how many acres does he have left?

R–2

Directions Perform the indicated operations on decimal numbers.

20. 20.6 + 1.373 + 210.42 + 0.027 + 31.09

21. 42.5 − 10.705

22. 213.4 × 6.35

23. 316.03 ÷ 22.1

24. Peter purchased an automobile for $3,450.63 and sold it for $4,016.12. How much profit did Peter make on the sale?

26. An automobile uses 15.2 gallons of gasoline to travel 188.8 miles. How many miles per gallon did the automobile average?

25. Linda owns 3 pieces of property 2.34, 3.61, and 1.91 acres in size. How many total acres of property does she own?

R–3

Directions Find the following percentages.

27. 4% of 250

28. 57% of 120

29. 62.5% of 40

30. 131.2% of 60

Directions Find the following percents.

31. 15 is what percent of 120?

32. What percent of 20 is 45?

33. In California, the state sales tax on purchases is 7.1%. What is the sales tax on a purchase of $150? What is the total cost to the consumer?

34. John and Jane took an automobile trip of 1,260 miles. If Jane drove 315 miles of the trip, what percent of the trip did Jane drive?

CHAPTER

1

Operations with Real Numbers and Introduction to Algebra

While on a trip to Canada, Tonya heard on the radio that the temperature today will be 20° Celsius. Will she need her winter coat? What will the temperature be in degrees Fahrenheit? The formula for changing the temperature measured in degrees Celsius to degrees Fahrenheit is

$$F = \frac{9}{5}C + 32.$$

Proficiency check

[R–1] **1.** $\frac{3}{4} \cdot \frac{2}{9}$

[R–1] **2.** $2\frac{2}{3} \cdot 2\frac{1}{4}$

[R–1] **3.** $\frac{6}{5} \div \frac{3}{10}$

[R–1] **4.** $\frac{1}{2} + \frac{1}{6}$

[R–1] **5.** $\frac{3}{4} - \frac{2}{3}$

[R–2] **6.** $4.7 + 0.39 + 5.16$

[R–2] **7.** $(8.7)(4.3)$

[R–2] **8.** $10.32 \div 1.2$

[R–2] **9.** $27.3 - 8.19$

[R–2] **10.** $(2.7)(0.13)$

1–1 Numbers and the number line

A_1 A debt of nine dollars

Natural numbers and whole numbers

The most basic use of our number system is that of counting. We use 1, 2, 3, 4, 5, and so on, as symbols to represent the **natural** or **counting numbers.**

Natural numbers 1,2,3,4,5, . . .

The three dots tell us to continue this counting pattern indefinitely. If we include 0 with the natural numbers, we have the **whole numbers.**

Whole numbers 0,1,2,3,4,5, . . .

Integers

We shall start by giving the natural numbers another name, the **positive integers.** We then form the *opposites,* or *negatives,* of the positive integers as follows: −1, −2, −3, ... Combining the positive integers, the negative integers, and 0, we have the integers.

Integers . . . , −3, −2, −1,0,1,2,3, . . .

Example 1–1 A

Use integers to represent each of the following.

1. Bromine melts at seven degrees below zero Celsius.
−7 degrees Celsius — Less than zero is a negative value

You are now ready to do $\mathbf{A_1}$.

2. Bromine boils at fifty-nine degrees Celsius.
59 degrees Celsius — Greater than zero is a positive value

You are now ready to do **A$_2$**. ■

A$_2$ A balance of ten dollars in a savings account

The number line

To picture the integers, we shall use a number line. We begin by drawing a line where the arrowhead at each end of the line indicates that the line continues on indefinitely in both directions. Next we choose any point on the line to represent 0. This point is called the **origin** of the number line. Numbers to the right of zero are positive and numbers to the left of zero are negative (figure 1–1).

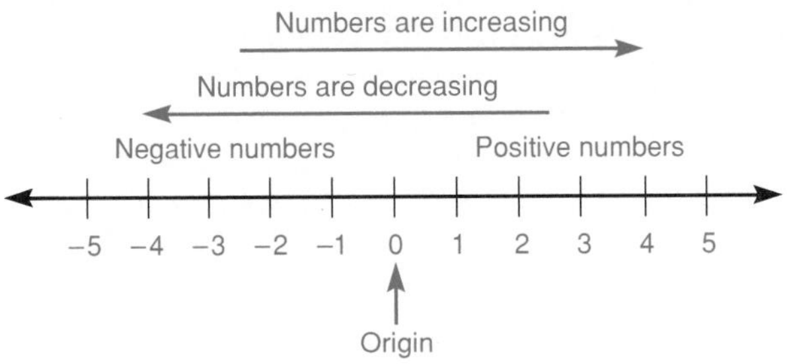

Figure 1–1

The direction in which we move on the number line is important. If we move to the right, we are moving in a positive direction and the numbers are *increasing.* If we move to the left, we are moving in a negative direction and the numbers are *decreasing* (figure 1–1).

Order on the number line

So that the discussion can be more general, we will now introduce the concept of a **variable. A variable is a symbol (generally a lowercase letter) that represents an unspecified number.** A variable holds a position for a number. If we choose any two points on the number line and represent them by a and b, where a and b represent some **unspecified** numbers, we observe that there is an **order** relationship between a and b (figure 1–2).

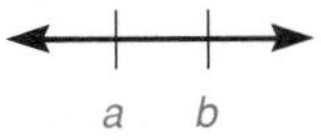

Figure 1–2

Since the point associated with a is to the left of the point associated with b, we say that a is **less than** b, which in symbols is $a < b$. We might also say that b is **greater than** a, which in symbols is $b > a$. The symbols $<$ (less than) and $>$ (greater than) are inequality symbols called **strict inequalities** and denote an **order relationship** between numbers.

Example 1–1 B

Replace the ? with the proper inequality symbol, $<$ or $>$.

1. 5 ? 7

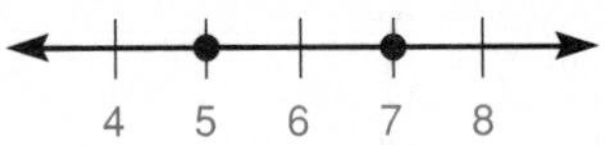

Answer: $5 < 7$ because 5 is to the left of 7 on the number line

You are now ready to do **B$_1$**.

B$_1$ 2 ? 4

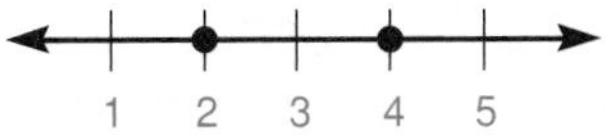

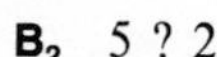
B_2 5 ? 2

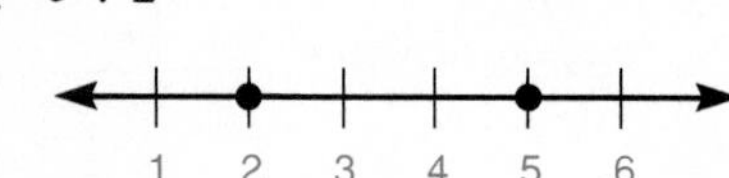

2. 8 ? 3

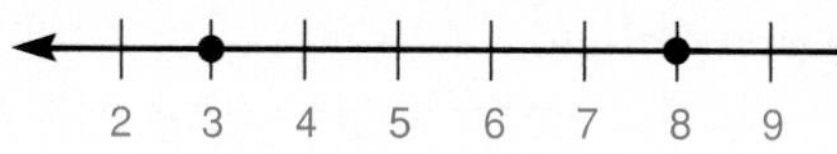

Answer: $8 > 3$ because 8 is to the right of 3 on the number line

Note
No matter which inequality symbol you use, the arrow *always* points at the lesser number.

You are now ready to do B_2.

3. -5 ? -3

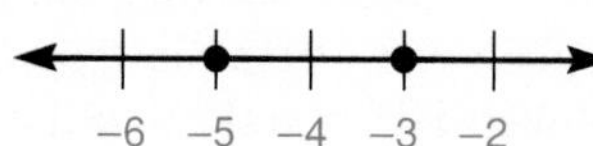

Answer: $-5 < -3$ because -5 is to the left of -3

B_3 -4 ? -2

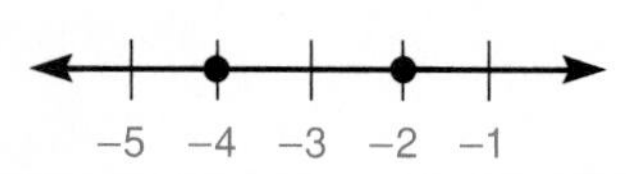

Note
If you have difficulty deciding which of two numbers is greater, think of the numbers as representing temperature readings. In example 3, the -5 would be thought of as 5 degrees below zero and the -3 would be 3 degrees below zero. It is easy to realize that -3 is the greater (warmer) temperature and the inequality would be $-5 < -3$.

You are now ready to do B_3.

4. -9 ? -12

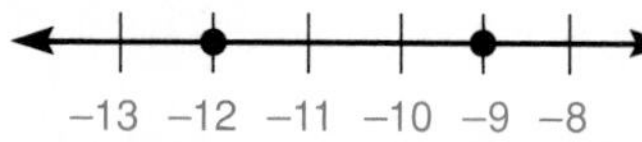

Answer: $-9 > -12$ because -9 is to the right of -12

B_4 -3 ? -6

You are now ready to do B_4.

5. 0 ? -4

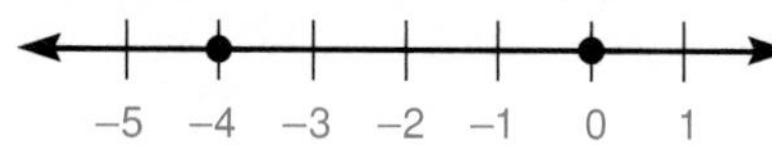

Answer: $0 > -4$ because 0 is to the right of -4

You are now ready to do B_5.

6. 0 ? 3

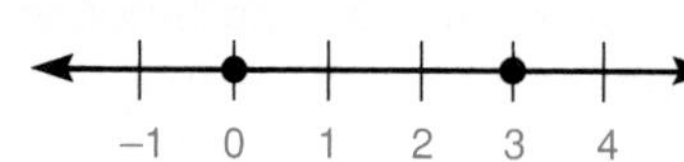

Answer: $0 < 3$ because 0 is to the left of 3

You are now ready to do B_6. ■

B_5 2 ? 0

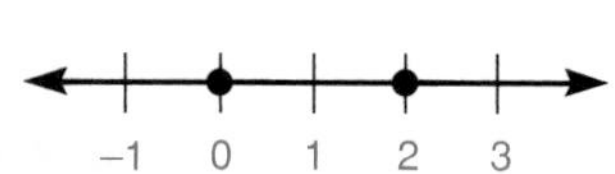

Rational numbers

If we want to determine the miles per gallon (mpg) that our car is getting, and we find that 8 gallons of gas enable us to travel 325 miles, then our miles per gallon can be computed by dividing the number of miles by the number of gallons used.

$$\frac{325 \text{ miles}}{8 \text{ gallons}} = \frac{325}{8} \text{ mpg} = 40\frac{5}{8} \text{ mpg}$$

This number is not an integer. We call such numbers **rational numbers.**

B_6 -2 ? 0

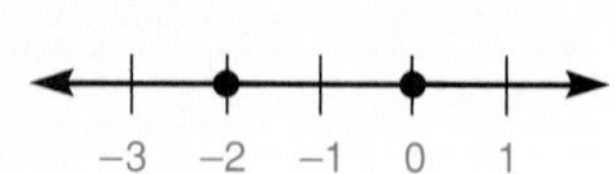

> **Definition**
> A rational number is any number that can be expressed as a quotient of two integers such that the divisor is not zero.*

*Division involving zero will be discussed in section 1–5.

Other examples of rational numbers are

$$\frac{2}{3}, \quad -\frac{1}{2}, \quad \frac{6}{1}, \quad \frac{19}{5}, \quad -\frac{23}{7}, \quad \frac{15}{3}.$$

The decimal representation of a rational number is either a terminating or a repeating decimal. Some examples of terminating or repeating decimals are

$$\frac{1}{2} = 0.5, \quad \frac{1}{3} = 0.\overline{3}, \quad -\frac{1}{6} = -0.1\overline{6}, \quad -\frac{5}{4} = -1.25,$$

where a bar placed over a number or group of numbers indicates that the number(s) repeat indefinitely.

Irrational numbers

At this point, we might feel that we now have numbers that will answer all possible physical situations. However, that is not the case. Consider the following question: What is the exact length of a side of a square whose area is 10 square units (figure 1–3)?

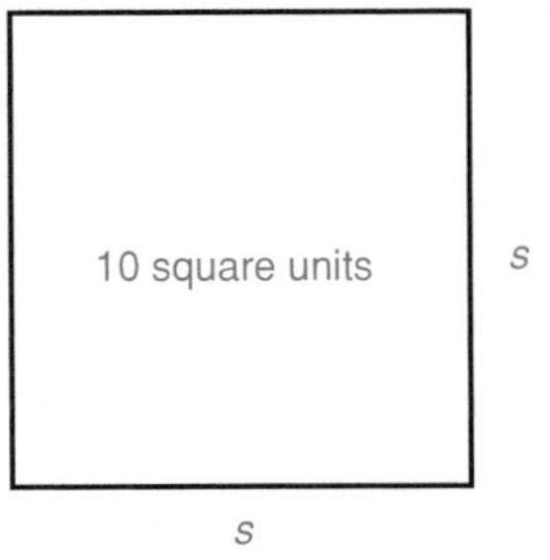

10 square units

s

s

Figure 1–3

To answer this question, we need to find the number that when multiplied by itself gives a product of 10. If we use 3.16, the result would be $(3.16) \times (3.16) = 9.9856$. This is close to 10 but is not equal to 10.

It can be shown that there is no rational value that when multiplied by itself has a product of 10. The answer to this question and many others is not a rational number. In chapter 9, we will see that the answer to this question is $\sqrt{10}$ (read "the square root of 10"). Such numbers that cannot be expressed as the quotient of two integers are **irrational numbers.**

Examples of irrational numbers are

$$\sqrt{3}, \quad -\sqrt{5}, \quad \pi, \quad \frac{\sqrt{2}}{2}.$$

The decimal representation of an irrational number will never terminate. We cannot find a repeating pattern of digits, no matter how many digits we write past the decimal point.

Note

By using a calculator, the previous numbers can be represented by the following approximations to three decimal places:

$$\sqrt{3} \approx 1.732, \quad -\sqrt{5} \approx -2.236, \quad \pi \approx 3.142, \quad \frac{\sqrt{2}}{2} \approx 0.707.$$

The symbol $\approx$ is read "is approximately equal to." π is the distance around a circle (circumference) divided by the distance across the circle through the center (diameter). Common approximations for π are 3.14 and $\frac{22}{7}$.

Real numbers

The real numbers consist of all the rational numbers and all the irrational numbers. We can illustrate the relationship among the numbers that make up the real numbers as in figure 1–4.

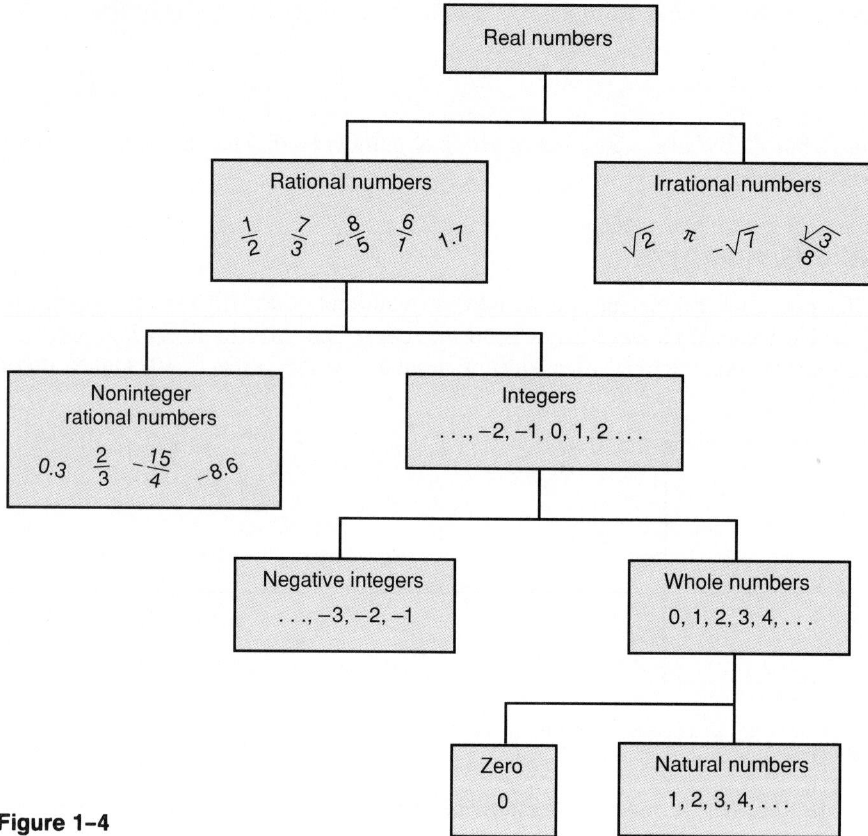

Figure 1–4

Absolute value

As we study the number line, we observe a very useful property called **symmetry.** The numbers are symmetrical with respect to the origin. That is, if we go four units to the right of 0, we come to the number 4. If we go four units to the left of 0, we come to the *opposite* of 4, which is -4 (figure 1–5).

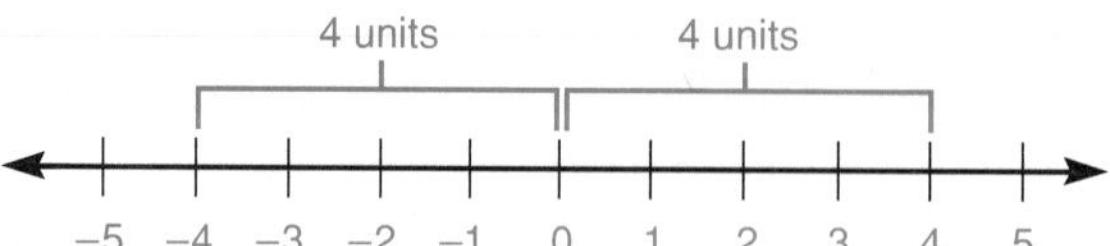

Figure 1–5

Each of these numbers is four units away from the origin. How far a given number is from the origin is called the **absolute value** of the number. **The absolute value of a number is the undirected distance that the number is from the origin.** The symbol for absolute value is $|\ |$

C_1 $|-3|$

Example 1–1 C

Evaluate the following expressions.

1. $|-7| = 7$ $\quad$ -7 is 7 units from the origin

You are now ready to do C_1.

2. $|3| = 3$ 3 is 3 units from the origin

You are now ready to do **C_2**.

3. $|0| = 0$ 0 is the origin, therefore 0 units from the origin

You are now ready to do **C_3**.

4. $\left|\frac{2}{3}\right| = \frac{2}{3}$ $\frac{2}{3}$ is $\frac{2}{3}$ of a unit from the origin

You are now ready to do **C_4**.

5. $|-3.7| = 3.7$ -3.7 is 3.7 units from the origin

You are now ready to do **C_5**.

6. $|\sqrt{10}| = \sqrt{10}$ $\sqrt{10}$ is $\sqrt{10}$ units from the origin

You are now ready to do **C_6**.

7. $-|-6| = -6$ -6 is 6 units from the origin. The problem is to find the opposite of the absolute value

Note
The absolute value bars are only applied to the symbol contained within them. The $-$ sign in front of the absolute value bars is not affected by the absolute value bars. The problem would be read "the opposite of the absolute value of -6."

You are now ready to do **C_7**. ■

C_2 $|12|$

C_3 $|\sqrt{2}|$

C_4 $\left|-1\frac{1}{2}\right|$

C_5 $|-7.4|$

C_6 $|-\sqrt{7}|$

C_7 $-|-4|$

Answers to section 1–1 margin exercises
A_1 -9 dollars A_2 $+10$ dollars B_1 $2 < 4$ B_2 $5 > 2$ B_3 $-4 < -2$ B_4 $-3 > -6$ B_5 $2 > 0$ B_6 $-2 < 0$ C_1 3 C_2 12 C_3 $\sqrt{2}$ C_4 $1\frac{1}{2}$ C_5 7.4 C_6 $\sqrt{7}$ C_7 -4

Mastery points

Can you
- Identify natural numbers, whole numbers, integers, rational numbers, irrational numbers, and real numbers?
- Determine which of two real numbers is greater?
- Find absolute values?

Exercise 1–1

Directions Use integers to represent each of the following. See example 1–1 A.

Example A_1 A debt of nine dollars

Solution -9 dollars A debt is a negative value

1. Hydrogen's melting point is 259 degrees below zero Celsius. Water boils at 100 degrees Celsius.
2. A man is ten dollars overdrawn on his checking account; a woman has 150 dollars in her savings account.

3. Mercury's melting point is 39 degrees below zero Celsius. Its boiling point is 357 degrees Celsius.

4. There is a loss of 10 yards on a football play; there is a gain of 16 yards.

5. Mt. Everest rises 29,028 feet above sea level; the Dead Sea has a depth of 1,290 feet below sea level.

6. The Dow Jones Industrial Stock Average fell 14 points; it rose 8 points.

Directions Replace the ? with the proper inequality symbol, $<$ or $>$. See example 1–1 B.

Examples $\boxed{B_1}$ 2 ? 4 — $\boxed{B_4}$ -3 ? -6

Solutions $2 < 4$ because 2 is to the left of 4 on the number line — $-3 > -6$ because -3 is to the right of -6 on the number line

7. 5 ? 7

8. 9 ? 2

$\boxed{9.}$ -2 ? -4

10. -3 ? -8

11. -9 ? -6

12. -10 ? -5

$\boxed{13.}$ -3 ? 0

14. 0 ? -6

15. 0 ? 8

Directions Evaluate the following expressions. See example 1–1 C.

Examples $\boxed{C_1}$ $|-3|$ — $\boxed{C_2}$ $|12|$ — $\boxed{C_7}$ $-|-4|$

Solutions 3 — -3 is 3 units from the origin; 12 — 12 is 12 units from the origin; -4 — -4 is 4 units from the origin. The problem is to find the opposite of the absolute value

16. $|-4|$

17. $|0|$

18. $|-5|$

19. $|-7|$

20. $\left|-\frac{1}{2}\right|$

21. $\left|-\frac{3}{4}\right|$

22. $\left|1\frac{1}{2}\right|$

23. $|5.6|$

24. $|-11.2|$

$\boxed{25.}$ $-|-2|$

26. $-\left|-2\frac{3}{4}\right|$

27. $-\left|\frac{5}{8}\right|$

Directions Replace the ? with the proper inequality symbol, $<$ or $>$. See examples 1–1 B and C.

Examples **a.** $|-6|$? $|-3|$

Solutions 6 ? 3 — $|-6|$ is 6 and $|-3|$ is 3

$6 > 3$ — 6 is to the right of 3 on the number line

then $|-6| > |-3|$

b. $|4|$? $|-7|$

4 ? 7 — $|4|$ is 4 and $|-7|$ is 7

$4 < 7$ — 4 is to the left of 7 on the number line

then $|4| < |-7|$

28. $|10| \ ? \ |12|$

29. $|-6| \ ? \ |-3|$

30. $|5| \ ? \ |-7|$

31. $|0| \ ? \ |-2|$

32. $|-3| \ ? \ |4|$

33. $|-8| \ ? \ |-5|$

34. $|-9| \ ? \ |7|$

35. $|-6| \ ? \ |-2|$

Directions Use absolute value to write each of the following. See example 1–1 C.

Example The distance between -8 and 0

Solution $|-8|$ The absolute value of a number is the distance from the number to the origin.

36. The distance between 14 and 0

37. The distance between -27 and 0

38. The distance between 18 and 0

39. The distance between -9 and 0

40. The distance between -19 and 0

Review exercises

Directions Perform the indicated addition. See sections R–1 and R–2.

1. $3.7 + 1.6 + 9$

2. $3\frac{1}{4} + 4\frac{1}{2}$

3. $5\frac{1}{2} + 8\frac{1}{3}$

4. $3.4 + 5.7$

5. $3.08 + 4.17$

6. $\frac{5}{6} + \frac{3}{4}$

▣ 1–2 Addition of real numbers

Addition of two positive numbers

When we perform the operations of addition and subtraction with integers, we will refer to this as operations with **signed numbers.** We use the minus sign ($-$) to indicate a negative number and the plus sign ($+$) to indicate a positive number. We should realize that the minus sign is identical to the symbol used for subtraction, and the plus sign is identical to the symbol used for addition. The meanings of these symbols will depend on their use in the context of the problem. In the case of a positive number, the plus sign need only be used if we wish to emphasize the fact that the number is positive. **When there is no sign, the number is understood to be positive.**

So the discussion can be more general, we will use variables to state the process of addition on the number line. Recall that a variable represents an unspecified number. It is a placeholder for a number.

A_1 $(+7) + (+3)$

Addition on the number line

To add a and b, that is $a + b$, we locate a on the number line and move from there according to b.

1. If b is positive, we move to the right b units.
2. If b is negative, we move to the left the absolute value of b units.
3. If b is 0, we stay at a. Zero is called the **identity element of addition.**

To add 5 and 4, that is $5 + 4$, we locate the 5 and from there we move 4 units to the right (figure 1–6).

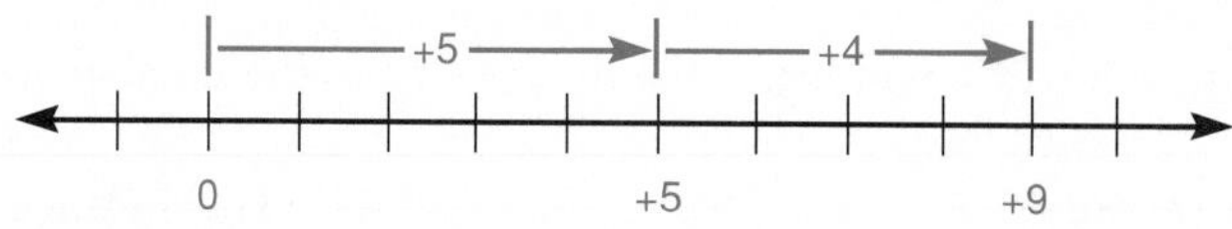

Figure 1–6

A_2 $(+11) + (+8)$

Performing the addition, we have $(+5) + (+4) = (+9)$. Notice that the sum, $(+9)$, has the same sign as the 5 and the 4.

Example 1–2 A

Add the following numbers.

1. $(+4) + (+5) = +9$ 4 and 5 are called addends, 9 is the sum

You are now ready to do A_1.

2. $(+3) + (+8) = +11$ The sum of 3 and 8 is 11

You are now ready to do A_2.

3. $(+6) + (0) = +6$ 6 plus 0 equals 6

You are now ready to do A_3. ■

We have used the plus $(+)$ sign in front of a number to emphasize the fact that the number was positive. In future examples, we will omit the plus sign from a positive number and it will be understood that 3 means $+3$.

A_3 $(+4) + (0)$

From example 3, we see that when zero and some number are added, the sum is the given number. For this reason, zero is called the **identity element of addition.** We now state this property.

Identity property of addition

For every real number a,

$$a + 0 = 0 + a = a.$$

Concept

Adding zero to a number leaves the number.

Observe that our example in figure 1–6 and example 1 in example 1–2 A are the same addition problem with the order of the numbers reversed. That is, $5 + 4 = 9$ and $4 + 5 = 9$. This observation illustrates an important mathematical principle called the **commutative property of addition.**

> **Commutative property of addition**
>
> For every real number a and b,
>
> $$a + b = b + a.$$
>
> **Concept**
>
> This property says that when we are *adding* numbers, changing the order in which the numbers are added will not change the answer (sum).

To add -6 and -5, we locate -6 and from there we move $|-5|$, which is 5 units to the left. The answer is -11 (figure 1–7).

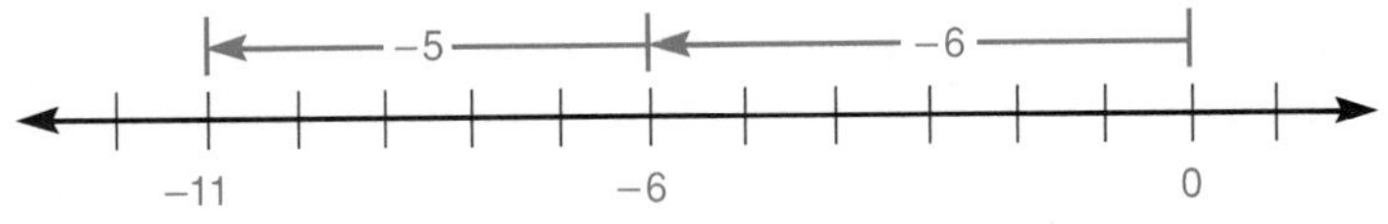

Figure 1–7

We can summarize what we have done by saying: **When we add two negative numbers, we add their absolute values and prefix the sum with their common sign, $-$.**

Example 1–2 B

Add the following numbers.

1. $(-2) + (-7) = -9$ The sum of -2 and -7 is -9

You are now ready to do $\mathbf{B_1}$.

2. $(-9) + (-4) = -13$ -9 plus -4 equals -13

You are now ready to do $\mathbf{B_2}$.

3. $(-20) + (-30) = -50$ -20 added to -30 is -50

You are now ready to do $\mathbf{B_3}$.

4. $(-6) + (-11) = -17$ -6 combined with -11 is -17

You are now ready to do $\mathbf{B_4}$. ■

$\boxed{\mathbf{B_1}}$ $(-5) + (-7)$

$\mathbf{B_2}$ $(-5) + (-5)$

$\mathbf{B_3}$ $(-11) + (-9)$

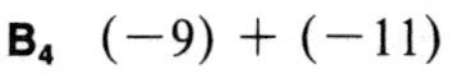

$\mathbf{B_4}$ $(-9) + (-11)$

Addition of two numbers with different signs

To add 15 and -10, that is $15 + (-10)$, we locate 15 and from there we move 10 units to the left because 10 is negative. The answer is 5.

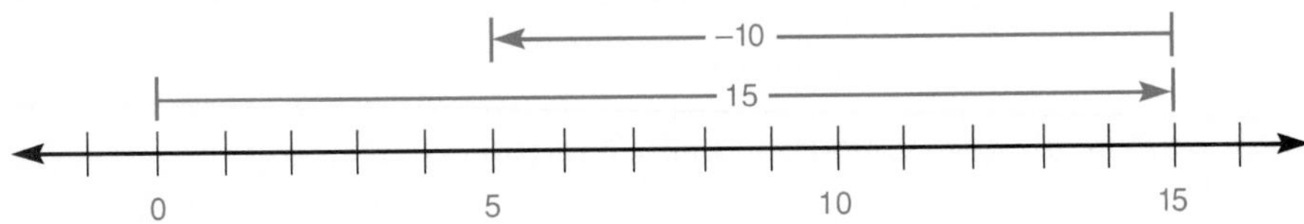

Figure 1–8

To add 10 and -15, we locate 10 and from there we move $|-15|$ units to the left. The answer is -5.

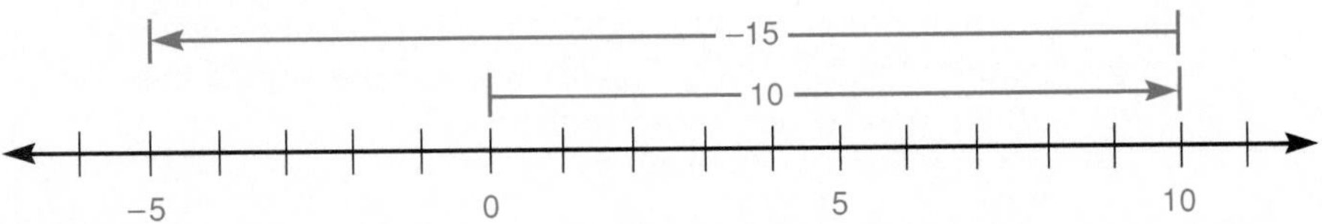

Figure 1–9

C_1 $(-8) + (-4)$

We now summarize the procedure for adding two numbers of different signs. **The sum of a positive number and a negative number can be found by subtracting the lesser absolute value from the greater absolute value. The answer has the sign of the number with the greater absolute value.**

Example 1–2 C

Add the following numbers.

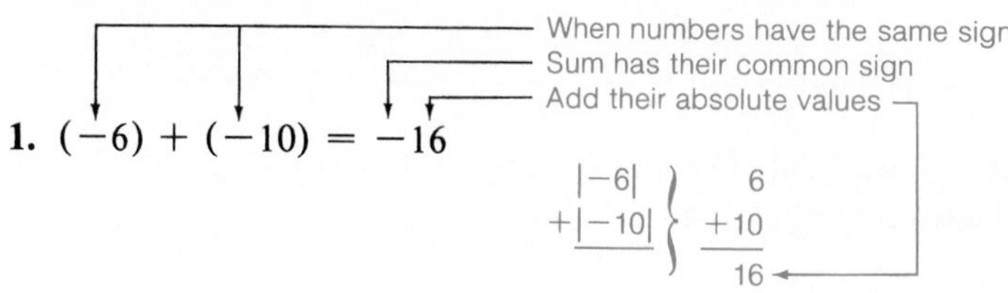

1. $(-6) + (-10) = -16$

C_2 $(3) + (-8)$

You are now ready to do **C_1**.

When numbers have different signs
Sum has sign of number with the greater absolute value, -8
Subtract the lesser absolute value from the greater absolute value

2. $(-8) + (5) = -3$

$|-8|$
$-|5|$

8
-5
3

You are now ready to do **C_2**.

3. $(-4) + (6) = 2$ — Difference of the absolute values and the sign comes from the $+6$

C_3 $(5) + (-7)$

You are now ready to do **C_3**.

4. $(10) + (-10) = 0$ — The sum of a number and its opposite is zero

You are now ready to do **C_4**. ■

We observe from example 4 that $(10) + (-10) = 0$. That is, a number added to its opposite gives a sum equal to zero. The opposite of a number is also called the **additive inverse** of that number. We now state this property.

C_4 $(-8) + (8)$

> **Additive inverse property**
> For every real number a,
>
> $$a + (-a) = (-a) + a = 0.$$
>
> **Concept**
> The sum of a number and its opposite is zero. The opposite is also called its additive inverse.

We can summarize our procedure for addition of two real numbers.

> **Addition of two real numbers**
>
> 1. If the signs are the same, we add their absolute values and prefix the sum by their common sign.
> 2. If the signs are different, we subtract the lesser absolute value from the greater absolute value. The answer has the sign of the number with the greater absolute value.
> 3. The sum of a number and its opposite (additive inverse) is zero.

In many problems, there will be more than two numbers being added together. In those situations, as long as the operation involved is *strictly addition,* we can add the numbers in any order we wish.

D₁ $(4) + (-6) + (-7)$

Example 1–2 D

Find the sum.

1. $(-2) + (-7) + (12) = (-9) + (12)$ First $(-2) + (-7)$ is -9
   $= 3$ Then $(-9) + (12)$ is 3

You are now ready to do **D₁**.

> **Note**
> For convenience, we simply add the numbers as they appear, reading them from left to right.

2. $(14) + (-4) + (4) = (10) + (4)$ First $(14) + (-4)$ is 10
   $= 14$ Then $(10) + (4)$ is 14

You are now ready to do **D₂**. ■

D₂ $(-11) + (7) + (4)$

Since the numbers can be added in any order, we might feel that it would be easier to add the (-4) and (4) first.

$$(14) + (-4) + (4) = (14) + 0 = 14$$

Therefore we observe the following:

$$[(14) + (-4)] + (4) = (14) + [(-4) + (4)] = 14.$$

This illustrates a mathematical principle called the **associative property of addition.**

> **Associative property of addition**
> For every real number *a*, *b*, and *c*,
> $$(a + b) + c = a + (b + c).$$
> **Concept**
> Changing the grouping of the numbers will not change the sum.

Problem solving

To solve the following word problems, we must find the sum of the given quantities. Represent gains by positive integers and losses by negative integers.

E₁ Tim Wesner received money for his birthday from 4 different people. He received $10, $8, $7, and $5. How much money did Tim receive for his birthday?

Example 1–2 E

Choose a variable to represent the unknown quantity and find its value.

1. A pipe that is 4 feet long is joined with a pipe that is 6 feet long. What is the total length of the pipe?

   Let ℓ = the total length of the pipe. To find the total length, we must *add* the individual lengths.

total length	is	4-foot pipe	joined with	6-foot pipe
ℓ	$=$	4	$+$	6

$\ell = 4 + 6$
$\ell = 10$

The total length of the pipe is 10 feet.

You are now ready to do **E₁**.

E_2 If a man borrows \$1,800 and has \$700 in savings, what is his net worth?

2. The quarterback of the Detroit Lions attempted 4 passes with the following results: a 12-yard gain, an incomplete pass, a 5-yard loss (tackled behind the line), and a 15-yard gain. What was his total gain (or loss)?

Let t = the total gain (or loss). To find the total gain (or loss), we must *add* the results of the 4 plays. Then

total gain (or loss)	is	12-yard gain		incomplete pass		5-yard loss		15-yard gain
t	$=$	(12)	$+$	(0)	$+$	(-5)	$+$	(15)

$t = (12) + (0) + (-5) + (15)$
$t = (12) + (-5) + (15) = (7) + (15) = 22$

The total *gain* was 22 yards after the 4 plays.

You are now ready to do **E_2**. ■

Answers to section 1–2 margin exercises

A_1 $+10$ **A_2** $+19$ **A_3** $+4$ **B_1** -12 **B_2** -10 **B_3** -20 **B_4** -20 **C_1** -12 **C_2** -5 **C_3** -2 **C_4** 0 **D_1** -9 **D_2** 0 **E_1** \$30 **E_2** $-\$1,100$

Mastery points

Can you

- Add real numbers on the number line?
- Add real numbers mentally?
- Use the commutative and associative properties of addition?

Exercise 1–2

Directions Find each sum. See examples 1–2 A, B, C, and D.

Examples **B_1** $(-5) + (-7)$

Solutions -12 Signs are the same, add their absolute values and prefix the sum by their common sign

C_2 $(3) + (-8)$

-5 Signs are different, subtract lesser absolute value from greater, sign comes from number with greater absolute value

1. $(-9) + (-4)$
2. $(+3) + (-5)$
3. $(+7) + (-2)$
4. $(-14) + (-10)$

5. $(-8) + 3$
6. $(+12) + (-8)$
7. $4 + (-9)$
8. $(-11) + 7$

9. $4 + (-4)$
10. $(-3) + 3$
11. $(-8.7) + (-4.9)$
12. $(-12.1) + 8.6$

13. $(-3.7) + (-7.4)$
14. $(-8.3) + (15.8)$
15. $\left(-\frac{1}{6}\right) + \left(-\frac{1}{3}\right)$

16. $\frac{3}{4} + \left(-\frac{7}{8}\right)$

17. $\frac{1}{5} + \left(-\frac{1}{10}\right)$

18. $\left(-1\frac{1}{2}\right) + \left(-1\frac{1}{4}\right)$

19. $\left(2\frac{1}{2}\right) + \left(-3\frac{1}{4}\right)$

20. $\left(5\frac{3}{8}\right) + \left(-2\frac{1}{4}\right)$

21. $10 + (-5) + (-2)$

22. $3 + (-4) + 1$

23. $(-12) + (-10) + (+8) + (+24)$

24. $(-24) + (+12) + (+12)$

25. $(-30) + 14 + (-8) + (-20)$

26. $(-2) + (+3) + (-4) + (-5)$

27. $(-25) + 4 + (-32) + 28 + 3$

28. $(+11) + (-12) + (-14) + (-9)$

Directions Find the sum.

Example The sum of -6, 2, and -9

Solution $(-6) + 2 + (-9) = (-4) + (-9)$ First add -6 and 2. We get -4

$= -13$ Then add -4 and -9

29. The sum of 7, -11, and -6

30. The sum of -16, -6, and -5

31. 18 plus -14 plus -4

32. -9 plus 15 plus -17

33. The sum of -5 and 12 increased by 4

34. The sum of 15 and -18 increased by 10

35. 15 added to the sum of -9 and 9

36. 9 added to the sum of -6 and -11

Directions Choose a variable to represent the unknown quantity and find its value. See example 1–2 E.

Example E_2 If a man borrows $1,800 and has $700 in savings, what is his net worth?

Solution We represent the borrowed amount as (−1,800) dollars and his savings as (+700) dollars. Let n = his net worth. His net worth is then represented by $n = (-1{,}800)$ dollars + (+700) dollars = (−1,100) dollars.

37. Jane Balch made profits of $5, $7, $2, $3, and $15 in five days of selling Kool Aid. How much did she receive in profits from her five-day sale?

38. The temperature in Sault Ste. Marie was −13° F at 8 A.M. By 1 P.M. that day, it had risen by 39° F. What was the temperature at 1 P.M.?

39. The stock market rose by 23 points on Monday, fell by 10 points on Tuesday, rose by 8 points on Wednesday, rose by 31 points on Thursday, and fell by 19 points on Friday. What was the total gain (or loss) during the 5 days?

40. The temperature on a given day in Anchorage, Alaska, was −19° F. The temperature then went down by 22° F. What was the final temperature that day?

41. The barometric pressure rose 6 mb (millibars), then dropped 9 mb. Later that day the pressure dropped another 3 mb and then rose 8 mb. What was the total rise (or fall) in barometric pressure that day?

42. A TWA plane is flying at an altitude of 33,000 feet. It suddenly hits an air pocket and drops 4,200 feet. What is its new altitude?

43. A small business showed profits of $15, $25, $10, $9, and $27 on five consecutive days. What was the total profit?

44. Mack Wooten has $35 in his checking account. He deposits $52, $25, and $32; he then writes checks for $18 and $62. What is the final balance in his checking account?

45. A temperature of (−18)° C is increased by 25° C. What is the resulting temperature?

46. A football team has the ball on its 25-yard line. On three successive plays, the team gains 6 yards, loses 3 yards, and then gains 4 yards. Where does the ball rest for the fourth play?

Review exercises

Directions Perform the indicated subtraction. See sections R–1 and R–2.

1. $9 - 1.7$ **2.** $7\frac{1}{2} - 2\frac{1}{4}$ **3.** $12\frac{1}{5} - 6\frac{1}{10}$ **4.** $18.4 - 9.7$ **5.** $11.08 - 6.4$ **6.** $17 - 6.49$

1–3 Subtraction of real numbers

A_1 (10) − (2)

Subtraction of two real numbers

We are already familiar with the operation of subtraction in problems such as 15 − 10 = 5. From the definition of subtraction, we know that 15 − 10 = 5 since 5 + 10 = 15. In figure 1–8 of section 1–2, we see that 15 + (−10) is also equal to 5. That is:

Subtraction: $15 - 10 = 5$ and Addition: $15 + (-10) = 5$

From this example, we see that we obtain the same results if we change the operation from subtraction to addition and change the sign of the number that we are subtracting. We would have an addition problem and could proceed as we did in section 1–2.

To summarize our procedure for subtracting real numbers, we can state algebraically:

Definition of subtraction

For any two real numbers *a* and *b*,

$$a - b = a + (-b).$$

That is, $a - b = a +$ (opposite of *b*).

Concept

"*a* minus *b*" means the same as "*a* plus the opposite of *b*."

$$(a) - (b) = (a) + (-b)$$

Opposite of *b*

Change to addition

A_2 (7) − (13)

Our steps to carry out the subtraction would be as follows:

Subtraction of two real numbers

Step 1 We change the operation from subtraction to addition.
Step 2 We change the sign of the number that follows the subtraction symbol.
Step 3 We perform the addition, using our rules for adding signed numbers.

Example 1–3 A

Subtract the following numbers.

		Step 1 Subtraction to addition	***Step 2*** Change sign of number being subtracted		***Step 3*** Add
1. (9) − (5) =	(9)	+	(−5)	=	4

You are now ready to do **A_1**.

2. (4) − (11) =	(4)	+	(−11)	=	−7

You are now ready to do **A_2**.

A₃ $(-8) - (12)$

	Step 1 Subtraction to addition		*Step 2* Change sign of number being subtracted		*Step 3* Add
3. $(-9) - (5) =$	(-9)	$+$	(-5)	$=$	-14
You are now ready to do **A₃**.					
4. $(6) - (-8) =$	(6)	$+$	(8)	$=$	14
You are now ready to do **A₄**.					
5. $(-12) - (-8) =$	(-12)	$+$	(8)	$=$	-4
You are now ready to do **A₅**.					
6. $(-5) - (-14) =$	(-5)	$+$	(14)	$=$	9
You are now ready to do **A₆**.					
7. $(8) - (5) =$	(8)	$+$	(-5)	$=$	3
You are now ready to do **A₇**.					
8. $(5) - (8) =$	(5)	$+$	(-8)	$=$	-3
You are now ready to do **A₈**.					

A₄ $(4) - (-6)$

A₅ $(-13) - (-7)$

Note

From examples 7 and 8, we see that the operation of subtraction is *not* commutative. That is,

$$(8) - (5) \neq (5) - (8). \quad \blacksquare$$

A₆ $(-2) - (-8)$

Addition and subtraction of more than two real numbers

When several numbers are being added and subtracted in a horizontal line, do the problem in order from left to right. For example,

$$\begin{aligned} &9 - 3 + 4 + 3 - 6 - 1 + 4 \\ &= \underline{9 - 3} + 4 + 3 - 6 - 1 + 4 \\ &= \underline{6 + 4} + 3 - 6 - 1 + 4 \\ &= \underline{10 + 3} - 6 - 1 + 4 \\ &= \underline{13 - 6} - 1 + 4 \\ &= \underline{7 - 1} + 4 \\ &= \underline{6 + 4} \\ &= 10. \end{aligned}$$

Operation being performed

$9 - 3 = 6$
$6 + 4 = 10$
$10 + 3 = 13$
$13 - 6 = 7$
$7 - 1 = 6$
$6 + 4 = 10$

A₇ $(11) - (6)$

Note

If we had changed each of the indicated subtractions to addition, $9 + (-3) + 4 + 3 + (-6) + (-1) + 4$, then the order in which the problem was carried out would not change the answer. For example, $9 - 3 \neq 3 - 9$, but $9 + (-3) = (-3) + 9$.

A₈ $(6) - (11)$

Grouping symbols

Many times, part of the problem will have a group of numbers enclosed with grouping symbols, such as parentheses ( ), brackets [ ], or braces { }. **If any quantity is enclosed with grouping symbols, we treat the quantity within as a single number.** Thus in

$$9 - (3 + 2) + (6 - 2) - (5 - 4),$$

we perform operations within parentheses first to get — *Operation being performed*

$= 9 - 5 + 4 - 1$	$3 + 2 = 5$, $6 - 2 = 4$, and $5 - 4 = 1$
$= 4 + 4 - 1$	$9 - 5 = 4$
$= 8 - 1$	$4 + 4 = 8$
$= 7.$	$8 - 1 = 7$

B₁ $10 - 7 + 8 - 6 - 2$

Example 1-3 B

Perform the indicated operations. — Operation being performed

1. $8 - 3 + 2 - 5 - 1$ — $8 - 3 = 5$
   $= 5 + 2 - 5 - 1$ — $5 + 2 = 7$
   $= 7 - 5 - 1$ — $7 - 5 = 2$
   $= 2 - 1$ — $2 - 1 = 1$
   $= 1$

You are now ready to do **B₁**.

B₂ $14 - 11 + 18 - (7 - 12) + 2$

2. $(6 + 1) - (2 - 5) + 7 + (9 - 6)$ — $6 + 1 = 7$, $2 - 5 = -3$, and $9 - 6 = 3$
   $= 7 - (-3) + 7 + 3$ — $7 - (-3) = 10$
   $= 10 + 7 + 3$ — $10 + 7 = 17$
   $= 17 + 3$ — $17 + 3 = 20$
   $= 20$

You are now ready to do **B₂**.

B₃ $(18 - 9) - 4$

3. $(14 - 7) - 2$ — $14 - 7 = 7$
   $= 7 - 2$ — $7 - 2 = 5$
   $= 5$

You are now ready to do **B₃**.

4. $14 - (7 - 2)$ — $7 - 2 = 5$
   $= 14 - 5$ — $14 - 5 = 9$
   $= 9$

B₄ $18 - (9 - 4)$

You are now ready to do **B₄**.

Note
We observe from examples 3 and 4 that the operation of subtraction is *not* associative. That is,

$$(14 - 7) - 2 \neq 14 - (7 - 2).$$ ■

Problem solving

To solve the following word problems, we must find the difference between two quantities. To find the difference, we must **subtract.**

C₁ A temperature of $(+14)°$ Celsius is decreased by 18 degrees Celsius. What is the resulting temperature?

Example 1-3 C

Choose a variable for the unknown quantity and find its value by subtracting.

1. On a given winter's day in Detroit, Michigan, the temperature was 31° F in the afternoon. By 9 P.M. the temperature was −12° F. How many degrees did the temperature drop from afternoon to 9 P.M.?

   Let t = the number of degrees fall in temperature. We must find the difference between 31° and −12°. Thus

degrees fall	is	difference between 31° and −12°
t	$=$	$31 - (-12)$

   $t = 31 - (-12) = 31 + 12 = 43.$

   There was a 43° F drop in temperature.

You are now ready to do **C₁**.

2. From a board that is 16 feet long, John must cut a board that is 7 feet long. How much is left of the original board?

Let $f =$ the number of feet of board left. We must find the difference between 16 and 7. Thus

feet left	is	difference between 16 and 7
f	$=$	$16 - 7$

$f = 16 - 7 = 9.$

John has 9 feet of the original board left.

You are now ready to do **C_2**. ■

C_2 A piece of wood 24 feet long is cut into three pieces so that two of the pieces measure 8 feet and 10 feet. What is the length of the third piece?

Answers to section 1–3 margin exercises

A_1 8 **A_2** -6 **A_3** -20 **A_4** 10 **A_5** -6 **A_6** 6 **A_7** 5 **A_8** -5 **B_1** 3 **B_2** 28 **B_3** 5 **B_4** 13 **C_1** $-4°$ C **C_2** 6 ft

Mastery points

Can you

- Subtract real numbers?
- Add and subtract in order from left to right?
- Remember that subtraction is *not* commutative or associative?
- Remember that quantities within grouping symbols represent a single number?

Exercise 1–3

Directions Find each sum or difference. See example 1–3 A.

Examples $\boxed{A_4}$ $(4) - (-6)$

Solutions

	Step 1	Step 2	Step 3
$= (4)$	$+$	(6)	$= 10$

$\boxed{A_6}$ $(-2) - (-8)$

	Step 1	Step 2	Step 3
$= (-2)$	$+$	(8)	$= 6$

1. $(4) - (5)$

2. $(-6) - (2)$

3. $(4) - (-2)$

4. $(-3) - (-7)$

5. $(-8) - (4)$

6. $(4) - (-8)$

7. $(4) - (9)$

8. $(-8) - (-5)$

9. $(-8) - (-4)$

10. $(-12) - (-16)$

11. $(8) - (-6)$

12. $(14) - (4)$

13. $(-6) + 0$

14. $(9) - (11)$

15. $(+7) - 0$

16. $(6) + (-10)$

17. $\left(-\frac{1}{2}\right) - \left(-\frac{1}{4}\right)$

18. $\left(-\frac{2}{3}\right) - \left(-\frac{1}{4}\right)$

19. $1\frac{3}{8} - \left(-1\frac{1}{4}\right)$

20. $5\frac{5}{6} - \left(-2\frac{1}{3}\right)$

21. $-18.7 - (-9.3)$

22. $107.4 - (-12.6)$

23. $-215.8 - 96.2$

24. $-119.1 - 218.8$

25. $-512.7 - (-814.5)$

26. $(-12) - (-10) - (8)$

27. $(-30) + (14) - (8)$

28. $(-25) + (4) - (32) + (28)$

29. $(-24) - (-12) - (12) + (-13)$

30. $(-2) - (3) + (-4) - (-5) + (-6)$

31. $(-15) - (13) - (-7) - (32)$

32. $(-17) - (11) - (-12) - (-5)$

Directions Find each sum or difference. See example 1–3 B.

Example $\boxed{B_2}$ $14 - 11 + 18 - (7 - 12) + 2$

Solution $14 - 11 + 18 - (-5) + 2$ Perform operations within parentheses first, then add and subtract from left to right

$= 3 + 18 - (-5) + 2$
$= 21 - (-5) + 2$
$= 26 + 2$
$= 28$

33. $17 + 4 - (7 - 2)$

34. $(25 - 2) - (12 - 3)$

35. $(-6) - 4 + 8 - (8 - 7)$

36. $32 - 5 + 7 - 4 - (11 - 8)$

37. $10 - 10 + (10 + 10) - 10$

38. $12 + 3 - 16 - 10 - (12 + 5)$

39. $10 + (2 - 21) - (7 - 8)$

40. $(12 + 3) - 16 - 10 + (12 - 5)$

41. $(18 - 14) - (12 - 17) - 16$

42. $8 - 4 + 7 - (5 - 2) - 3$

Example C_1 A temperature of $(+14)°$ Celsius is decreased by 18 degrees Celsius. What is the resulting temperature?

Solution

$$(+14) - (+18) = (+14) + (-18) = (-4)° \text{ Celsius}$$

43. A temperature of $(-6)°$ C is decreased by 32° C. What is the resulting temperature?

44. An electronics supply house has 432 resistors of a certain type. If 36 are sold during the first week, 72 during the second week, 29 during the third week, and 58 during the fourth week, how many are left at the end of the fourth week?

45. Tim owes Tom and Rob \$343 and \$205, respectively, and Terry owes Tim \$176. In terms of positive and negative symbols, how does Tim stand monetarily?

46. If a person has \$78 after paying off a debt of \$23, how much money did he have before paying off the debt? Write a statement involving the operation subtraction of integers to show your answer.

47. Express the temperature change using signed numbers.

a. 3° C to 34° C

b. $(-8)°$ C to 47° C

c. $(-37)°$ C to $(-46)°$ C

d. $(-78)°$ C to $(-21)°$ C

e. 5° C to $(-49)°$ C

f. 86° C to 35° C

Directions Find the difference.

Example 12 diminished by 20

Solution $12 - 20$ Diminished by 20 means subtract 20
$= 12 + (-20)$ Change to addition
$= -8$

48. -8 diminished by 11

49. -15 diminished by 7

50. -6 diminished by -21

51. -18 diminished by -9

52. Subtract -26 from -18.

53. Subtract -19 from 41.

54. Subtract -17 from 28.

55. From -26 subtract -45.

56. From -43 subtract -16.

Directions Choose a variable for the unknown quantity and find the indicated difference. See example 1–3 C.

57. Rob has $23 in his savings account. If he spends $15 to buy a game, how much is left in his savings account?

58. Tom has $44 in his savings account. He wishes to buy a baseball glove for $21. How much is left in his savings account?

59. The temperature was $-15°$ F at 6 A.M. but by noon the temperature has risen to 23° F. How many degrees did it rise from 6 A.M. to noon?

60. The temperature dropped 22° F from $-7°$ F at midnight to just before daybreak at 7 A.M. What was the temperature at 7 A.M.?

61. Erin Nustad was born in 1986. How old will she be in the year 2000?

62. A chemist now has 100 ml of acid and she needs 368 ml of the acid. How much more is needed?

63. Amy has $450 in assets and she wants to borrow enough money to buy a stereo system for $695. How much will she owe?

64. The top of Mt. Everest in Asia is 29,028 feet above sea level and the top of Mt. McKinley in Alaska is 20,320 feet above sea level. How much higher is the top of Mt. Everest than the top of Mt. McKinley?

65. Death Valley in California is 282 feet below sea level (-282). What is the difference in the altitude between Mt. McKinley and Death Valley? (See exercise 64.)

66. Mt. Whitney in California is 14,494 feet above sea level and the Salton Sea in California is 235 feet below sea level. What is the difference in the altitude between Mt. Whitney and Salton Sea?

67. Jim owes John \$25. He paid back \$13 and then had to borrow another \$7. How much does Jim owe John now?

68. Sheila won \$10 in a poker game, then lost \$9, then lost \$14, and finally lost \$6 on 4 successive hands. What is her financial position after the 4 hands?

Review exercises

Directions Perform the indicated multiplication. See sections R–1 and R–2.

1. $38 \cdot 12$

2. $14.3 \cdot 26.7$

3. $9.04 \cdot 1.3$

4. $0.23 \cdot 6.5$

5. $34 \cdot 1.6$

6. $\frac{3}{8} \cdot \frac{4}{9}$

7. $\frac{15}{16} \cdot \frac{24}{25}$

1–4 Multiplication of real numbers

Multiplication of two positive numbers

We are already familiar with the fact that the product of two positive numbers is positive. We can see this fact by considering multiplication as repeated addition. For example, if we wish to add four 3s, then $3 + 3 + 3 + 3 = 12$. Another way of expressing this repeated addition is $4 \cdot 3 = 12$, in which case the raised dot, $\cdot$, means multiply or times. We could also have added three 4s: $4 + 4 + 4 = 12$, which could be written as $3 \cdot 4 = 12$. This observation illustrates an important mathematics principle called the **commutative property of multiplication.**

Commutative property of multiplication

For every real number a and b,

$$a \cdot b = b \cdot a.$$

Concept

This property tells us that changing the order of the numbers when we multiply will not change the answer (product).

In the previous paragraph, the number 12 is called the **product** of 4 and 3, and 4 and 3 are called **factors** of 12. *The numbers or variables in an indicated multiplication are referred to as the factors of the product.*

In our example, we used a raised dot to indicate the operation of multiplication. The cross, $\times$, is used in arithmetic to indicate multiplication. We avoid using it in algebra because it may become confused with the variable x. Another way to indicate multiplication is the absence of any operation symbol between factors. The following are other examples of how we can express multiplication.

Example 1–4 A

1. $5 \cdot 7$ is read 5 times 7. The raised dot indicates multiplication.
2. (4)(6) is read 4 times 6. The parentheses separate the numbers; the absence of any operation symbol between the numbers indicates multiplication.
3. $3a$ is read 3 times a.
4. ab is read a times b.
5. 6(8) is read 6 times 8.

Note

34 does not mean $3 \cdot 4$ and $3\frac{1}{2}$ does not mean $3 \cdot \frac{1}{2}$. ■

Multiplication of two numbers with different signs

As an illustration of multiplying a positive number times a negative number, consider the following pattern:

$$
\begin{aligned}
3 \cdot 3 &= 9 \\
2 \cdot 3 &= 6 \\
1 \cdot 3 &= 3 \\
0 \cdot 3 &= 0 \\
(-1) \cdot 3 &= -3 \\
(-2) \cdot 3 &= -6 \\
(-3) \cdot 3 &= -9
\end{aligned}
$$

The answers decrease by 3

The product of a negative and a positive is a negative

We observe from this pattern that our answers decrease by 3 each time. It logically follows that **the product of a negative number and a positive number is a negative number.**

A second observation from this pattern is that zero times a number has a product of zero. This is called the **zero factor property.**

Zero factor property

For every real number a,

$$a \cdot 0 = 0 \cdot a = 0.$$

Concept

Multiplying any number by zero always gives zero as the answer. That is, whenever we are multiplying and zero is one of the factors, our product will be zero.

A third observation from this pattern is that 1 times a number is equal to the number. For this reason, 1 is called the **identity element of multiplication.**

Identity property of multiplication

For every real number a,

$$a \cdot 1 = 1 \cdot a = a.$$

Concept

Multiplying a number by 1 leaves the number unchanged.

B_1 $(-5)\cdot 4$

Multiplication of two negative numbers

We will observe another pattern when we consider the following.

$$\begin{aligned} 3(-3) &= -9 \\ 2(-3) &= -6 \\ 1(-3) &= -3 \\ 0(-3) &= 0 \\ (-1)(-3) &= +3 \\ (-2)(-3) &= +6 \\ (-3)(-3) &= +9 \end{aligned}$$

The answers increase by 3

The product of two negatives is a positive

From this pattern, we can see that our answers increase by 3 each time. It logically follows that **the product of two negative numbers is a positive number.**

We can summarize our procedures for multiplication of two real numbers as follows:

B_2 $(-4)(-3)$

Multiplication of two real numbers

1. Multiply their absolute values and the product will be positive if the numbers have the same signs.
2. Multiply their absolute values and the product will be negative if the numbers have different signs.

Example 1–4 B

Multiply the following numbers.

1. $(-2)\cdot 3 = -6$

Product of their absolute values: $2 \cdot 3 = 6$
Product is negative because the numbers have different signs

B_3 $4(-7)$

You are now ready to do **B_1**.

2. $(-2)(-4) = 8$

Product of their absolute values: $2 \cdot 4 = 8$
Product is positive because the numbers have the same signs

You are now ready to do **B_2**.

3. $4(-4) = -16$ Negative because signs are different

You are now ready to do **B_3**.

4. $(-5)(-5) = 25$ Positive because signs are the same

B_4 $(-4)(-6)$

You are now ready to do **B_4**. ■

We can determine the sign of our answer when we multiply three or more real numbers. Consider the following examples.

1. $(-1)(2)(3)(4) = (-2)(3)(4) = (-6)(4) = -24$ Odd number of negative factors
2. $(-1)(2)(-3)(4) = (-2)(-3)(4) = (6)(4) = 24$ Even number of negative factors
3. $(-1)(2)(-3)(-4) = (-2)(-3)(-4) = (6)(-4) = -24$ Odd number of negative factors
4. $(-1)(-2)(-3)(-4) = (2)(-3)(-4) = (-6)(-4) = 24$ Even number of negative factors

Multiplication of two or more real numbers

1. If in the numbers being multiplied there is an **odd** number of negative factors, the answer will be negative.
2. If in the numbers being multiplied there is an **even** number of negative factors, the answer will be positive.

C_1 $(-3)(-2) \cdot 4$

Example 1–4 C

Multiply the following numbers.

1. $(-7)(-2)(5) = (14)(5) = 70$ — Even number of negative factors

You are now ready to do C_1.

2. $(-6)(2)(-4) = (-12)(-4) = 48$ — Even number of negative factors

You are now ready to do C_2.

3. $[(-3)(5)](4) = (-15)(4) = -60$ — Odd number of negative factors

You are now ready to do C_3.

4. $(-3)[(5)(4)] = (-3)(20) = -60$ — Odd number of negative factors

You are now ready to do C_4. ■

C_2 $(4)(-3)(-3)$

C_3 $[(-2)(-5)](3)$

Examples 3 and 4 lead us to an important mathematical principle called the **associative property of multiplication.**

Associative property of multiplication

For every real number *a*, *b*, and *c*,

$$(a \cdot b)c = a(b \cdot c).$$

Concept

Changing the grouping of the numbers will not change the product.

C_4 $(-2)[(-5)(3)]$

Problem solving

To solve the following problems, we must multiply the quantities.

Example 1–4 D

Choose a variable for the unknown and find the indicated product.

1. What is the cost of 7 VHS tapes if each tape costs \$5.95?

Let c = the cost of the 7 tapes. We must multiply to find the total cost of all 7 tapes. Thus

total cost	is	7 tapes	at	\$5.95 each
c	$=$	7	$\cdot$	(5.95)

$c = 7 \cdot (5.95) = 41.65.$

The 7 tapes cost \$41.65.

You are now ready to do D_1.

D_1 A clothier ordered 15 suits, each costing him \$65. What was the total cost of the 15 suits?

D_2 Jim Johnson lost \$23 per hand in 4 successive poker games. What were his total losses? (Represent this by a negative answer.)

2. On 4 successive days, the stock market dropped 9 points (represented by a negative number) each day. How many points did the market change in the 4 days?

Let d = the total drop. Represent the 9-point drop by -9. We multiply to obtain

total drop	is	4 days	at	9-point drop each day
d	$=$	4	$\cdot$	(-9)

$d = 4 \cdot (-9) = -36.$

The stock market dropped 36 points (-36) in the 4 days.

You are now ready to do **D_2**.

Answers to section 1–4 margin exercises

B_1 -20 **B_2** 12 **B_3** -28 **B_4** 24 **C_1** 24 **C_2** 36 **C_3** 30 **C_4** 30
D_1 \$975 **D_2** $-$\$92

Mastery points

Can you

- Use the commutative and associative properties of multiplication and the zero factor property?
- Multiply real numbers?

Exercise 1–4

Directions Perform the indicated operations. See examples 1–4 B and C.

Examples $\boxed{B_2}$ $(-4)(-3)$

Solutions $= 12$ Product is positive because the numbers have the same signs

$\boxed{C_1}$ $(-3)(-2) \cdot 4$

$= 6 \cdot 4$ $(-3)(-2) = 6$ because the numbers have the same signs

$= 24$ 6 times 4 is 24

1. $(-3)(-5)$ **2.** $0 \cdot (-6)$ **3.** $4 \cdot (-7)$ **4.** $(-8) \cdot 3$

5. $4 \cdot (-3) \cdot 5$ **6.** $(-2)(2)(-2)$ **7.** $4 \cdot (-9)$ **8.** $(-3)(-2)(-8)$

9. $(-1)(-4)(5)$ **10.** $(-5)(2)(4)(3)$ $\boxed{\textbf{11.}}$ $7 \cdot (-1)(-3)(-5)$ **12.** $2 \cdot (-3)(-1)(2)(-2)(3)$

13. $(-1.8)(2.4)$ **14.** $(-5.7)(-6.12)$ **15.** $(0.49)(-28.1)$ **16.** $(-8.9)(-8.9)$

17. $(-27)(0.08)$ $\boxed{\textbf{18.}}$ $\left(-\frac{1}{3}\right)\left(\frac{3}{5}\right)$ **19.** $\left(-\frac{3}{4}\right)\left(-\frac{3}{4}\right)$ **20.** $\left(-\frac{3}{4}\right)\left(\frac{8}{9}\right)$

21. $\left(-\frac{5}{8}\right)\left(-\frac{2}{5}\right)$ **22.** $\left(\frac{5}{12}\right)\left(-\frac{9}{10}\right)$ 23. $(-5)(-4)(-3)(2)$ **24.** $(-2)(-7)(7)(4)$

25. $(-3)(3)(-4)(4)$ **26.** $(-1)(-1)(-1)(-1)$ **27.** $(-2)(0)(3)(-4)$ **28.** $(-3)(-2)(4)(0)$

29. $(-5)(0)(-4)$

Directions Find two integers such that their product is the first number and their sum is the second number.

Examples **a.** 4, −4

Solutions Since $(-2)(-2) = 4$ and $(-2) + (-2) = -4$, then −2 and −2 are the integers.

b. −27, −6

Since $(-9)(3) = -27$ and $(-9) + (3) = -6$, then −9 and 3 are the integers.

30. −30, 1 **31.** −16, 0 **32.** 20, −9 **33.** −11, 10

34. −72, −21 35. −12, −1 **36.** 48, 16 **37.** 35, 12

38. 9, −6 **39.** −8, 7 **40.** −12, 1 **41.** −15, 2

42. −18, 3 43. 25, 10

Directions Choose a variable for the unknown and multiply to find the value. See example 1–4 D.

44. Over a five-day period, the price of a particular stock suffered losses of \$3 on each of the first two days and \$2 on each of the last three days. If the stock originally sold for \$88, what was its price after the five-day period?

45. A man acquires a debt of \$6 each day for five days. If we represent a \$6 debt by (−6), write a statement of the change in his assets after five days. What is the change?

46. An auditorium contains 42 rows of seats. If each row contains 25 seats, how many people can be seated in the auditorium?

47. There are 7 rows of desks in a classroom. If each row contains 8 desks, how many students will the classroom hold?

48. A department store averages a loss of \$75, due to thefts, each day. How much is lost in a month of 31 days?

49. Mrs. Jones purchased two dozen (24) cans of frozen orange juice concentrate on sale for 57¢ per can. How much did the orange juice cost her?

50. If a bank advertises that a person can double his investment in a savings account in 9 years, how much will \$120 grow to in 9 years?

51. Joanie sold 35 glasses of lemonade at her corner stand. If she charged 15¢ a glass, how much did she make in sales?

52. Berkeley Gossett deposits his weekly allowance of \$3 in a savings account at the bank. How much has he deposited in 3 years? (*Hint:* 52 weeks = 1 year.)

53. A grocer averages selling 25 gallons of milk each day. How many gallons of milk does he sell in 4 weeks? (Assume the grocery is open 7 days per week.)

Review exercises

Directions Perform the indicated division. See sections R–1 and R–2.

1. $56 \div 7$

2. $576 \div 24$

3. $27 \div 4$

4. $3{,}780 \div 36$

5. $10.26 \div 2.7$

6. $96.24 \div 1.2$

1–5 Division of real numbers

Division of numbers

Recall that when we divide a number (called the **dividend**) by another number (called the **divisor**), we compute an answer (called the **quotient**). We define the operation of division as follows:

> **Definition of division**
>
> If $b \neq 0$*, $\dfrac{a}{b} = q$ provided that $b \cdot q = a$, where a is the dividend, b is the divisor, and q is the quotient.

The second part of our definition shows how to check the problem. We multiply the divisor by the quotient to get the dividend ($b \cdot q = a$).

By definition, the quotient of the two negative numbers $(-20) \div (-5)$, or $\dfrac{-20}{-5}$, must be that number which multiplied by -5 gives -20. That number is 4,

*The reason for this restriction will be explained on page 68.

since $(-5)(4) = -20$. Therefore $\frac{-20}{-5} = 4$. We observe that **the quotient of two negative numbers is a positive number.**

A₁ $\frac{-18}{-9}$

To divide a positive number by a negative number, or a negative number by a positive number, consider the following divisions:

$$(-14) \div (+2) = \frac{-14}{+2} = -7$$

since

$$(+2)(-7) = -14$$

and

$$(+24) \div (-6) = \frac{+24}{-6} = -4$$

A₂ $\frac{-12}{-1}$

because

$$(-6)(-4) = +24.$$

We find that **the quotient of a positive number and a negative number is always a negative number.**

We can summarize our procedures for multiplication and division of real numbers as follows:

Multiplication or division of two real numbers

To multiply or divide two real numbers, perform the operation (multiplication or division) using the absolute value of the numbers and

1. the answer will be positive if the numbers have the same signs;
2. the answer will be negative if the numbers have different signs.

A₃ $\frac{-15}{3}$

Example 1–5 A

Divide the following numbers.

1. $\frac{-14}{-7} = 2$, since $(-7)(2) = -14$.

You are now ready to do **A₁**.

2. $\frac{-36}{-6} = 6$, since $(-6)(6) = -36$.

You are now ready to do **A₂**.

A₄ $\frac{32}{-2}$

3. $\frac{-24}{+3} = -8$, since $(+3)(-8) = -24$.

You are now ready to do **A₃**.

4. $\frac{+15}{-5} = -3$, since $(-5)(-3) = +15$.

You are now ready to do **A₄**. ■

In section 1–4, we developed a rule for determining the sign of our answer when we multiply three or more signed numbers. This same rule can be extended to apply to division. Consider the following examples.

B_1 $\dfrac{(-1)(24)}{(2)(3)}$

B_2 $\dfrac{(1)(-24)}{(-2)(3)}$

B_3 $\dfrac{(1)(-24)}{(-2)(-3)}$

B_4 $\dfrac{(-1)(-24)}{(-2)(-3)}$

C_1 $\dfrac{0}{11}$

Example 1–5 B

1. $\dfrac{(-1)(12)}{(2)(3)} = \dfrac{(-12)}{(6)} = -2$ Odd number of negative numbers

You are now ready to do **B_1**.

2. $\dfrac{(-1)(12)}{(2)(-3)} = \dfrac{(-12)}{(-6)} = 2$ Even number of negative numbers

You are now ready to do **B_2**.

3. $\dfrac{(-1)(12)}{(-2)(-3)} = \dfrac{(-12)}{(6)} = -2$ Odd number of negative numbers

You are now ready to do **B_3**.

4. $\dfrac{(-1)(-12)}{(-2)(-3)} = \dfrac{(12)}{(6)} = 2$ Even number of negative numbers

You are now ready to do **B_4**. ■

We can summarize the procedure for three or more real numbers in a multiplication or division problem as follows:

Multiplication or division of two or more real numbers

When we multiply or divide, if we have an odd number of negative numbers, our answer will be negative; otherwise it will be positive.

Division involving zero

In section 1–1, we defined a rational number to be any number that can be expressed as a quotient of two integers in which the divisor is not zero. The number zero, 0, is the only number that we cannot use as a divisor. To see why we exclude zero as a divisor, recall that we check a division problem by multiplying the divisor times the quotient to get the dividend. If we apply this idea in connection with zero as a divisor, we observe the following situations. Suppose there were a number q, such that $3 \div 0 = q$. Then $q \cdot 0$ would have to be equal to 3 for our answer to check, but this product is zero regardless of the value of q. Therefore we cannot find an answer for this problem. We say that the answer is **undefined.** If we try to divide zero by zero and again call our answer q, we have $0 \div 0 = q$. When we check our work, $0 \cdot q = 0$, we see that any value for q will work. Since any value for q will work, we say our answer is **indeterminate.** We therefore decide that **division by zero is not allowed.**

It is important to note that although division by zero is not allowed, this does not extend to the division of zero by some other number. We can see that $\dfrac{0}{-4} = 0$ since $(-4) \cdot 0 = 0$. Thus **the quotient of zero divided by any number other than zero is always zero.**

Example 1–5 C

Perform the division, if possible.

1. $\dfrac{0}{5} = 0$ The quotient of zero divided by any number other than zero is zero

You are now ready to do **C_1**.

2. $\frac{2}{0}$ is undefined.

You are now ready to do **C₂**.

3. $\frac{0}{0}$ is indeterminate.

You are now ready to do **C₃**. ■

Problem solving

To solve the following problems, we will have to divide the given quantities.

Example 1–5 D

Choose a variable for the unknown quantity and find the indicated quotient.

1. If \$7.68 is spent on 6 three-way light bulbs, how much did each light bulb cost?

   Let c = the cost of each light bulb. We must divide \$7.68 by 6. Thus

cost per bulb	is equal to	total cost	divided	by 6 identical items
c	$=$	(7.68)	$\div$	6

   $c = (7.68) \div 6 = 1.28.$

   Each light bulb cost \$1.28.

You are now ready to do **D₁**.

2. There are 400 people seated in a full auditorium. If there are 25 identical rows of seats, how many people are there in each row?

   Let x = the number of people in each row. We must divide 400 by 25. Thus

people per row	is equal to	total number of people	divided	by 25 identical rows
x	$=$	400	$\div$	25

   $x = 400 \div 25 = 16.$

   There are 16 people seated in each row.

You are now ready to do **D₂**. ■

Answers to section 1–5 margin exercises

A_1 2 **A_2** 12 **A_3** −5 **A_4** −16 **B_1** −4 **B_2** 4 **B_3** −4 **B_4** 4 **C_1** 0
C_2 undefined **C_3** undefined **D_1** 24 bushels per acre
D_2 45 words per minute

Mastery points

Can you

- Perform division with real numbers?
- Remember the results of division involving zero?

C_2 $\frac{11}{0}$

C_3 $\frac{-11}{0}$

D_1 A farmer got 720 bushels of wheat from a 30-acre field. How many bushels did he get per acre?

D_2 Mary Ann typed 1,350 words in 30 minutes. How many words did she type per minute?

Exercise 1–5

Directions Perform the indicated operations, if possible. See examples 1–5 A, B, C.

Examples **A₁** $\frac{-18}{-9}$ **A₃** $\frac{-15}{3}$ **C₂** $\frac{11}{0}$

Solutions $= 2$ Quotient of two negatives is a positive; $= -5$ Quotient of a positive and a negative is a negative; Is undefined

1. $\frac{-14}{-7}$ 2. $\frac{-15}{5}$ 3. $\frac{32}{-4}$ 4. $\frac{18}{3}$ 5. $\frac{-22}{-11}$

6. $\frac{18}{-3}$ 7. $\frac{-16}{2}$ 8. $\frac{-25}{-5}$ 9. $\frac{7}{0}$ 10. $\frac{-4}{0}$

11. $\frac{0}{-9}$ 12. $\frac{0}{5}$ 13. $\frac{0}{0}$ 14. $\frac{-24}{-6}$ 15. $\frac{49}{-7}$

16. $\frac{36}{-6}$ 17. $\frac{-25}{5}$ 18. $\frac{-64}{8}$ **19.** $\frac{(-4)(-3)}{-6}$ 20. $\frac{(-18)(2)}{-4}$

21. $\frac{(16)(2)}{-8}$ **22.** $\frac{(-4)(0)}{-8}$ 23. $\frac{(-16)(0)}{-8}$ 24. $\frac{(-5)(-2)}{(-1)(-10)}$ 25. $\frac{(-18)(3)}{(-2)(-9)}$

26. $\frac{(-2)(-4)}{(0)(4)}$ 27. $\frac{(-3)(6)}{(0)(-2)}$ 28. $\frac{8-8}{3+4}$ **29.** $\frac{(-6)(0)}{(-3)(0)}$ 30. $\frac{6-6}{6-6}$

Example A football player carried the ball eight times, making the following yardages: gain of 6 yards (yd), loss of 3 yd, loss of 4 yd, gain of 4 yd, gain of 3 yd, loss of 1 yd, loss of 2 yd, gain of 5 yd. Show his gains and losses by positive and negative integers. What was his average gain or loss?

Solution Since a gain is positive and a loss is negative, we have (6) yd, (−3) yd, (−4) yd, (4) yd, (3) yd, (−1) yd, (−2) yd, (5) yd. To find the average gain or loss, we find the sum of the yardages and divide by 8, the number of carries.

$$\frac{(6)\text{ yd} + (-3)\text{ yd} + (-4)\text{ yd} + (4)\text{ yd} + (3)\text{ yd} + (-1)\text{ yd} + (-2)\text{ yd} + (5)\text{ yd}}{8} = \frac{(8)\text{ yd}}{8} = 1\text{ yd}$$

31. The temperature at 1 P.M. for seven consecutive days in January was 5° C, −8° C, −7° C, −1° C, 10° C, −6° C, and 0° C. What was the average temperature for the seven days?

32. If the stock market showed the following gains and losses during six consecutive hours of trading on a given day, determine the average gain or loss during that six-hour period. Gain 36 points, loss 23 points, loss 72 points, gain 25 points, loss 31 points, loss 21 points.

33. Between Chicago and Detroit, a distance of 282 miles, a driver averages 47 miles per hour. How long will it take the driver to make the trip?

34. A trip of 369 miles takes nine hours to complete. What was the average rate of speed?

35. Light travels at a rate of 186,000 miles per second. How long will it take to travel 1,674,000 miles?

36. How long does it take light from the sun to reach earth if the sun is approximately 93,000,000 miles away? (Refer to exercise 35.)

Directions Choose a variable for the unknown quantity and find the value by dividing. See example 1–5D.

37. Mrs. Smith paid $36 for 9 crates of peaches for her fruit market. How much did each crate cost her?

38. A carpenter wishes to cut a 12-foot board into 3 pieces that are all the same length. Find the length of each piece.

39. A man drove 350 miles and used 14 gallons of gasoline. How many miles did he drive on each gallon of gasoline?

40. Irene drove 424 miles in 8 hours. How many miles did she travel each hour (in miles per hour) if she drove at a constant speed?

41. During a recent cold wave, the temperature fell 28° over a 7-day period. What was the average fall per day?

42. Alice took part in a 26-mile marathon run. If she ran the marathon in 5 hours and 12 minutes, how long did it take her to run 1 mile (in minutes) if she ran at a constant speed?

43. The college bookstore purchased 480 mathematics textbooks. If the books came in 15 boxes of the same size, how many books were in each box?

44. Jim, John, Pete, and Mike worked together painting farmer John's barn. If he gave them $124 to split evenly among them, how much did each boy receive?

Review exercises

Directions Perform the indicated operations. See sections 1–2 and 1–3.

1. $(-12) + 6$ **2.** $4 + (-8)$ **3.** $10 - 18$ **4.** $9 - (-9)$

5. $-6 - (-6)$ **6.** $(-14) + (-7)$

1–6 Properties of real numbers and order of operations

In the previous four sections, we introduced some of the properties of real numbers. We also saw how these properties are used when performing fundamental operations with numbers. Since variables represent numbers, we will be using these and other properties throughout our study of algebra. The properties that we have covered so far are listed in the following box. The page number where the property was first introduced is listed for reference.

> **Properties of real numbers**
>
> If a, b, and c are any real numbers, then
>
> $a + b = b + a$, commutative property of addition (page 47)
> $a \cdot b = b \cdot a$, commutative property of multiplication (page 60)
> $(a + b) + c = a + (b + c)$, associative property of addition (page 49)
> $(a \cdot b)c = a(b \cdot c)$, associative property of multiplication (page 63)
> $a \cdot 1 = 1 \cdot a = a$, identity property of multiplication (page 61)
> $a + 0 = 0 + a = a$, identity property of addition (page 46)
> $a + (-a) = (-a) + a = 0$, additive inverse property (page 48)
> $a \cdot 0 = 0 \cdot a = 0$, zero factor property (page 61)

Exponents

Consider the indicated products

$$4 \cdot 4 \cdot 4 = 64$$

and

$$3 \cdot 3 \cdot 3 \cdot 3 = 81.$$

A more convenient way of writing $4 \cdot 4 \cdot 4$ is 4^3, which is read "4 to the third power" or "4 cubed." We call the number 4 the **base** of the expression and the number 3, to the upper right of 4, the **exponent.**

Thus

$$4 \cdot 4 \cdot 4 = 4^3 = 64.$$

In like fashion, $3 \cdot 3 \cdot 3 \cdot 3$ may be written 3^4, where 3 is the base and 4 is the exponent. The expression is read "3 to the fourth power." Then

$$3 \cdot 3 \cdot 3 \cdot 3 = 3^4 = 81.$$

Notice that **the exponent tells how many times the base is used as a factor in an indicated product.** We call this form of a product the **exponential form.** That is, the exponential form of the product $3 \cdot 3 \cdot 3 \cdot 3$ is 3^4.

A₁ $(-4)^3$

Note
The exponent is understood to be 1 when a number has no exponent. That is, $5 = 5^1$.

Remember that when we have a negative number, we place it inside parentheses. With this fact in mind, we can see that there is a definite difference between $(-2)^4$, which is read "-2 to the fourth power," and -2^4, which is read "the opposite of 2 to the fourth power." In the first case, the parentheses denote that this is a negative number to a power: $(-2)^4 = (-2)(-2)(-2)(-2) = +16$. In the second case, since there are no parentheses around the number, we understand that this is *not* (-2) to a power. It is, rather, the opposite of the answer when we raise 2^4. Therefore $-2^4 = -(2)^4 = -(2 \cdot 2 \cdot 2 \cdot 2) = -(16)$.

A₂ -4^3

Example 1–6 A

Perform the indicated multiplication.

1. $(-3)^3 = (-3)(-3)(-3) = -27$

You are now ready to do **A₁**.

2. $-3^3 = -(3 \cdot 3 \cdot 3) = -27$

You are now ready to do **A₂**.

3. $(-3)^4 = (-3)(-3)(-3)(-3) = +81$

You are now ready to do **A₃**.

A₃ $(-3)^2$

4. $-3^4 = -(3 \cdot 3 \cdot 3 \cdot 3) = -81$

You are now ready to do **A₄**. ■

When we are performing several different types of arithmetic operations within an expression, we need to agree on an order in which the operations will be performed.

Order of operations, or priorities

1. **Groups:** Perform any operations within a grouping symbol such as ( ) parentheses, [ ] brackets, { } braces, | | absolute value, or in the numerator or the denominator of a fraction.

Note
a. Within a grouping symbol, the order of operations will still apply.
b. If there are several grouping symbols intermixed, remove them by starting with the innermost one and working outward.

2. **Exponents:** Perform operations indicated by exponents.
3. **Multiply and divide:** Perform multiplication and division in order from left to right.
4. **Add and subtract:** Perform addition and subtraction in order from left to right.

A₄ -3^2

Example 1–6 B

Perform the indicated operations in the proper order and simplify.

1. $6 + 5(7 - 3) - 2^2$

$= 6 + 5(4) - 2^2$ We first evaluate within the grouping symbol, Priority 1
$= 6 + 5(4) - 4$ Perform the indicated exponent, Priority 2
$= 6 + 20 - 4$ Carry out the multiplication, Priority 3
$= 26 - 4$ Perform the addition and subtraction
$= 22$ In order from left to right, Priority 4

You are now ready to do **B_1**.

2. $7 + 8 \cdot 3 \div 2 = 7 + 24 \div 2$ Priority 3, multiply
$= 7 + 12$ Priority 3, divide
$= 19$ Priority 4, add

You are now ready to do **B_2**.

3. $(7 - 1) \div 2 + 3 \cdot 4 = 6 \div 2 + 3 \cdot 4$ Priority 1, parentheses
$= 3 + 12$ Priority 3, divide and multiply
$= 15$ Priority 4, add

You are now ready to do **B_3**.

4. $\frac{1}{2} + \frac{3}{4} \div \frac{5}{8} = \frac{1}{2} + \frac{\overset{1}{\cancel{3}}}{\cancel{4}_1}\cdot\frac{\overset{2}{\cancel{8}}}{5}$ Invert and divide out common factors

$= \frac{1}{2} + \frac{6}{5}$ Priority 3, multiply

$= \frac{5}{10} + \frac{12}{10}$ Common denominator

$= \frac{5 + 12}{10}$ Priority 4, add

$= \frac{17}{10}$ or $1\frac{7}{10}$

You are now ready to do **B_4**.

5. $2^2 \cdot 3 - 3 \cdot 4 = 4 \cdot 3 - 3 \cdot 4$ Priority 2, exponent
$= 12 - 12$ Priority 3, multiply
$= 0$ Priority 4, subtract

You are now ready to do **B_5**.

6. $\frac{3}{4} - \frac{1}{2} \cdot \frac{2}{3} = \frac{3}{4} - \frac{1}{\cancel{2}_1} \cdot \frac{\overset{1}{\cancel{2}}}{3} = \frac{3}{4} - \frac{1}{3}$ Priority 3, multiply

$= \frac{9}{12} - \frac{4}{12}$ Common denominator

$= \frac{9 - 4}{12} = \frac{5}{12}$ Priority 4, subtract

You are now ready to do **B_6**.

7. $(7.28 + 1.6) \div 2.4 - (6.1)(3.8)$

$= (8.88) \div 2.4 - (6.1)(3.8)$ Priority 1, parentheses
$= 3.7 - 23.18$ Priority 3, divide and multiply
$= -19.48$ Priority 4, subtract

You are now ready to do **B_7**.

B_1 $28 - 6 \cdot 5 \div 3$

B_2 $10 \div (7 - 5) + 4 \cdot 6$

$\boxed{B_3}$ $18 \div 6 \cdot 3 + 10 - (4 + 5)$

B_4 $\frac{3}{4} + \frac{1}{3} \div \frac{5}{6}$

B_5 $2 \cdot 3^2 - 7 \cdot 5$

B_6 $\frac{7}{8} - \frac{2}{3} \cdot \frac{3}{4}$

B_7 $(13.12 + 11.2) \div 3.2 - (8.6)(9.7)$

8. $\left(\frac{2}{3}+\frac{7}{8}\right) \div \frac{5}{6} = \left(\frac{16}{24}+\frac{21}{24}\right) \div \frac{5}{6}$

$= \left(\frac{16+21}{24}\right) \div \frac{5}{6}$ Priority 1, parentheses

$= \frac{37}{24} \div \frac{5}{6}$

$= \frac{37}{\cancel{24}_{4}} \cdot \frac{\cancel{6}^{1}}{5}$ Invert and divide out common factors

$= \frac{37}{20}$ or $1\frac{17}{20}$ Priority 3, multiply

You are now ready to do **B₈**.

9. $(5.4)^2 - 4(3.1)(2.8)$

$= 29.16 - 4(3.1)(2.8)$ Priority 2, exponent

$= 29.16 - 34.72$ Priority 3, multiply

$= -5.56$ Priority 4, subtract

You are now ready to do **B₉**.

10. $\frac{3(2+4)}{4-2} - \frac{4+6}{5} = \frac{3(6)}{4-2} - \frac{4+6}{5}$ Priority 1, groups: numerator and denominator

$= \frac{18}{2} - \frac{10}{5}$ Priority 1, numerator and denominator

$= 9 - 2$ Priority 3, divide

$= 7$ Priority 4, subtract

You are now ready to do **B₁₀**.

11. $5[7 + 3(10 - 4)]$

We first evaluate within the grouping symbol, starting with the innermost one, applying the order of operations.

$5[7 + 3(6)] = 5[7 + 18]$ Priority 1, groups

$= 5[25]$ Priority 1, groups

$= 125.$ Priority 3, multiply

You are now ready to do **B₁₁**. ■

B₈ $\left(\frac{1}{2}+\frac{5}{8}\right) \div \frac{6}{5}$

B₉ $(9.5)^2 - 4(1.6)(4.7)$

B₁₀ $\frac{2(3+4)}{9-2} - \frac{2^2+6}{5}$

B₁₁ $2[15 - 2 \cdot 6 + 1]$

Problem solving

Solve the following word problems using the order of operations.

Example 1–6 C

Choose a variable to represent the unknown quantity and find its value by performing the indicated operations.

1. Mrs. Hansen purchased 6 boxes of cereal at $1.25 per box and 7 cans of tuna fish at 70¢ per can. What was her total bill?

Let t = Mrs. Hansen's total bill. 6 boxes at $1.25 per box cost $6 \cdot \$1.25$ and 7 cans at 70¢ per can cost $7 \cdot \$0.70$. The total cost is given by

total bill	is equal to	6 boxes of cereal	at	$1.25 per box	and	7 cans of tuna	at	$0.70 per can
t	$=$	6	$\cdot$	(1.25)	$+$	7	$\cdot$	(0.70)

$t = 6 \cdot (1.25) + 7 \cdot (0.70)$

$= 7.50 + 4.90$ Priority 3

$= 12.40.$ Priority 4

Mrs. Hansen's total bill was $12.40.

You are now ready to do **C₁**.

C₁ A woman purchased a case of pop (24 bottles) at 15¢ per bottle, 5 pounds of candy at 49¢ per pound, and 20 jars of baby food at 75¢ per jar. What was her total bill in dollars and cents?

C_2 Colleen Meadow is a typist in a law firm. Her base pay is \$7 per hour for a 40-hour week and she receives time and a half for every hour she works over 40 hours in a week. How much will she earn if she works 49 hours in one week?

2. A man works a 40-hour week at \$12 per hour. If he works 11 hours of overtime at time and a half, how much will he receive for the 51 hours of work?

Let w = the man's total wages for the week. 40 hours at \$12 per hour is $40 \cdot \$12$. Hourly rate at time and a half is $\left(1\frac{1}{2} \cdot \$12 = \$18\right)$ and 11 hours at time and a half is $11 \cdot \$18$. Thus

total wages	is equal to	40 hours	at	\$12 per hour	and	11 hours	at	\$18 per hour
w	$=$	40	$\cdot$	12	$+$	11	$\cdot$	18

$$\begin{aligned} w &= 40 \cdot 12 + 11 \cdot 18 \\ &= 480 + 198 && \text{Priority 3} \\ &= 678. && \text{Priority 4} \end{aligned}$$

The man's total wages for the week was \$678.

You are now ready to do **C_2**. ■

Answers to section 1–6 margin exercises

A_1 -64 **A_2** -64 **A_3** 9 **A_4** -9 **B_1** 18 **B_2** 29 **B_3** 10 **B_4** $\frac{23}{20}$ or $1\frac{3}{20}$ **B_5** -17 **B_6** $\frac{3}{8}$ **B_7** -75.82 **B_8** $\frac{15}{16}$ **B_9** 60.17 **B_{10}** 0 **B_{11}** 8 **C_1** \$21.05 **C_2** \$374.50

Mastery points

Can you

- Perform multiple operations in the proper order?
- Use exponents?

Exercise 1–6

Directions Perform the indicated operations. See example 1–6 A.

Example **A_4** -3^2

Solution

$$\begin{aligned} -3^2 &= -(3^2) && -3^2 \text{ is not the same as } (-3)^2 \\ &= -9 && \text{The opposite of } 3^2 \end{aligned}$$

1. $(-4)^2$ **2.** $(-5)^4$ 3. $(-3)^3$ **4.** -4^2 5. -6^2 **6.** -2^4

Directions Perform the indicated operations and simplify. See example 1–6 B.

Example **B_3** $18 \div 6 \cdot 3 + 10 - (4 + 5)$

Solution

$$\begin{aligned} &= 18 \div 6 \cdot 3 + 10 - 9 && \text{Priority 1, parentheses} \\ &= 3 \cdot 3 + 10 - 9 && \text{Priority 3, division} \\ &= 9 + 10 - 9 && \text{Priority 3, multiplication} \\ &= 19 - 9 && \text{Priority 4, addition} \\ &= 10 && \text{Priority 4, subtraction} \end{aligned}$$

7. $\frac{4+2}{3}+2$ 8. $-6 \cdot 7+8$ 9. $6+5 \cdot 4$ 10. $\frac{1}{5} \cdot 5+6$ 11. $-2+10 \cdot \frac{1}{5}$

12. $4(3-2)(2+1)$ **13.** $0(5+2)+3$ 14. $\frac{24 \cdot 3}{9}-6$ 15. $(24-6) \div 3$ 16. $(37-4) \div 11$

17. $\frac{2}{3} \div \left(\frac{5}{6}-\frac{4}{9}\right)$ 18. $12 \cdot 4+2$ 19. $15 \cdot 3^2-14$ 20. $(8-3)(5+3)$ 21. $\frac{7}{8}-\frac{1}{2} \div \frac{3}{4}$

22. $\frac{3}{8}+\frac{7}{12} \cdot \frac{3}{14}$ 23. $3(6-2)(7+1)$ 24. $12+3 \cdot 16 \div 4^2-2$ 25. $10-3 \cdot 4 \div 6-5$

26. $8-(12+3)-4 \cdot 3$ **27.** $4(2-5)^2-2(3-4)$ 28. $6(-8+10)-5(4-7)$ **29.** $\frac{5(3-5)}{2}-\frac{27}{-3}$

30. $\frac{3(8-6)}{2}-\frac{8}{-2}$ 31. $\frac{5(6-3)}{3}-\frac{(-14)}{2}$ 32. $(14.13+11.4) \div 3.7-(2.4)(7.8)$

33. $(5.1+2.2)(4.8)-(6.3)(8.1)$ 34. $(5.1)^2 \cdot 3-(14.64) \div (6.1)$ 35. $(1.9)^2+4(3.3)^2-8.7$

36. $18+[14-5(6-4)+7]$ **37.** $5[10-2(4-3)+1]$ 38. $(8-2)[16+4(5-7)]$

39. $(9 - 6)[21 + 5(4 - 6)]$

40. $\left(\frac{3}{12} - \frac{1}{6}\right)\left(\frac{2}{3} + \frac{1}{8}\right)$

41. $\left(\frac{6-3}{7-4}\right)\left(\frac{14 + 2 \cdot 3}{5}\right)$

42. $\left(\frac{1}{4} - \frac{1}{6}\right) \div \left(\frac{2}{3} - \frac{1}{8}\right)$

Directions Perform the indicated operations and simplify. See example 1–6 B.

43. To convert 74° Fahrenheit (F) to Celsius (C), we use the expression

$C = \frac{5}{9}(F - 32)$; thus in this case,

$C = \frac{5}{9}(74 - 32)$.

Find C.

44. A Murray Loop is used to determine the point at which a telephone line is grounded. The unknown distance to the point of the ground, x, for a length of the loop of 32 miles and resistances of 222 and 384 ohms is given by

$$x = \frac{384}{222 + 384} \cdot 32.$$

Find x.

45. The surface area of a flat ring whose inside radius is 2 inches and whose outside radius is 3 inches is approximately

$$\frac{22}{7} \cdot 3^2 - \frac{22}{7} \cdot 2^2.$$

Find the area of this surface in square inches.

46. The surface area of a ring section whose inside diameter is 18 inches and whose outside diameter is 26 inches is approximately

$$\frac{22}{7} \cdot \frac{26 + 18}{2} \cdot \frac{26 - 18}{2}.$$

Find the area of this surface in square inches.

47. To find the pitch diameter, D, of a gear with 36 teeth and an outside diameter of 8 inches, we use

$$D = \frac{36(8)}{38 + 3}.$$

Find D in inches.

Directions Choose a variable for the unknown quantity and use order of operations to find its value. See example 1–6 C.

48. In a series of poker games, Ace McGee won \$4,000 in each of 3 games, lost \$1,500 in each of 4 games, and won \$2,000 in each of 2 games. How much did Ace win (or lose) in the 9 games?

49. A carpenter must cut a 16-foot long board into 4-foot lengths and a 12-foot long board into 3-foot lengths. How many pieces of lumber will he have?

50. Jane, Joan, and Mary are typists in an office. Joan can type 75 words per minute, Jane can type 80 words per minute, and Mary can type 95 words per minute. How many words can they type together in 15 minutes?

51. The stock market opened at 1,725 points on a given day. If it lost 9 points per hour during the first 3 hours after opening and then gained 6 points per hour during the next 5 hours, what did the stock market close at?

Review exercises

Directions Perform the indicated operations. See sections 1–4 and 1–5.

1. $(-40)(-6)$

2. $5 \cdot (-3)$

3. $\frac{0}{7}$

4. $\frac{-24}{-6}$

5. $\frac{-54}{14}$

6. $\frac{-8}{0}$

7. $(-8) \cdot 5$

8. $(-3)(0)(-2)(4)$

1–7 Algebraic notation and terminology

Algebraic terminology

In section 1–1, we defined a variable to be a symbol that represents an unspecified number. A variable is able to take on any one of the different values that it represents. In the relationship

$$y = 2x,$$

y and x are variables since they both can assume various numerical values.

A constant is a symbol that does not change its value. In the relationship

$$y = 2x,$$

2 is a constant. A number is a constant. If a symbol represents only one value, that symbol is a constant.

A₁ $5 + x^2y - z$

Any meaningful collection of variables, constants, grouping symbols, and signs of operations is called an algebraic expression. Examples of algebraic expressions would be

$$5xy, \quad \frac{xy}{z}, \quad 2\ell + 2w, \quad \frac{x^2 - 1}{x^2 + 1}, \quad 3x^2 + 2x - 1, \quad 5(a + 2b).$$

In an algebraic expression, terms are any constants, variables, or products or quotients of these. Terms are separated by plus or minus signs.

A₂ $a^2 + 1$

Example 1–7 A

Identify the number of terms in the algebraic expression.

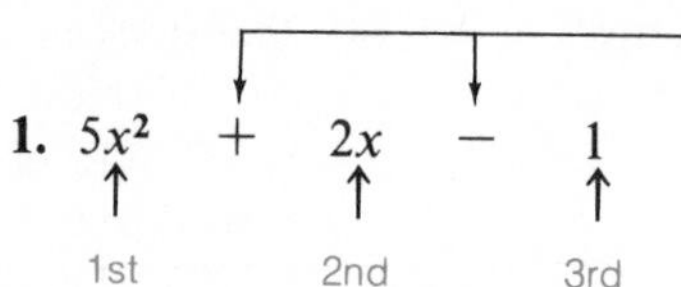

The plus and minus signs separate the algebraic expression into three terms

You are now ready to do **A₁**.

A₃ $6a^2b + 7ab^2 - 3a^2b^2 + 5$

2. $x^2 + y^2$ (1st: x^2; 2nd: y^2)

There are two terms

You are now ready to do **A₂**.

3. $4x^5y^2z^4$ (1st)

There is one term

You are now ready to do **A₃**.

A₄ $4x^2 - \dfrac{2x + z}{y^2}$

4. $a^2 + \dfrac{b + c^2}{d}$ (1st: a^2; 2nd: $\frac{b+c^2}{d}$)

There are two terms since the fraction bar forms a group

You are now ready to do **A₄**. ■

In the expression $5xy$, *each factor or grouping of factors is called the* **coefficient** *of the remaining factors.* That is, 5 is the coefficient of xy; x is the coefficient of $5y$; $5x$ is the coefficient of y; and so on. The 5 is called the **numerical coefficient,** and it tells us how many xy's we have in the expression.

Since we most often talk about the numerical coefficients of a term, we will eliminate the word "numerical" and just say "coefficient." It will be understood that we are referring to the numerical coefficient. If no numerical coefficient appears in a term, the coefficient is *understood* to be 1.

B₁ Determine the numerical coefficients in the algebraic expression $a^2 - 2a + 4b$?

Example 1–7 B

The algebraic expression $6x - 3y + z$ is thought of as the sum of terms $6x + (-3y) + z$. Therefore, 6 is the coefficient of x, -3 is the coefficient of y, and 1 is understood to be the coefficient of z.

You are now ready to do **B₁**. ■

Distributive property

When multiplying and one or more of the factors contains more than one term, we must use the **distributive property** to carry out the multiplication.

Distributive property

For every real number *a*, *b*, and *c*,

$$a(b + c) = ab + ac \text{ and } a(b - c) = ab - ac.$$

Concept

If a number is being used to multiply the sum or difference of two others, it is "distributed" to them both. That is, it multiplies them both.

C_1 Are $3a^2b$ and $-2a^2b$ like terms?

The following is an application of the distributive property.

Each term inside the parentheses is multiplied by 3

$$\begin{aligned} 3(4 + 5) &= (3 \cdot 4) + (3 \cdot 5) \\ &= 12 + 15 \\ &= 27 \end{aligned}$$

Note

Since we are able to add the numbers inside the parentheses, our solution without using the distributive property would be

$$3(4 + 5) = 3(9) = 27.$$

We are now going to use the distributive property to carry out addition and subtraction of algebraic expressions.

Like terms

C_2 Are $4a^2b^2$ and $4a^3b^3$ like terms?

We first need to define the types of quantities that can be added or subtracted. We can add or subtract only like, or similar, quantities.

Like terms or similar terms are terms whose variable factors are the same.

Note

For two or more terms to be called like terms, the variable factors of the terms, along with their respective exponents, must be identical. However the numerical coefficients of these identical variable factors may be different.

Example 1–7 C

1. $3a^2b^3$ and $-2a^2b^3$ are like terms because the variables (a and b) are the same and the respective exponents are the same (a is to the second power in each term and b is to the third power).

You are now ready to do C_1.

2. $2x^2y$ and $2xy^2$ both contain the same variables but are *not* like terms because the exponents of the respective variables are not the same.

You are now ready to do C_2. ■

Addition and subtraction

Using the definition of like terms and the distributive property, we are ready to carry out addition and subtraction of algebraic expressions. Consider the following example:

$$3a + 4a.$$

Using the distributive property, the expression can be written

$$3a + 4a = (3 + 4)a = 7a.$$

Note
The process of addition or subtraction is performed only with the numerical coefficients. **The variable factor and its exponent remain unchanged.**

Example 1–7 D

Perform the indicated addition and subtraction.

1. $5x + 7x$ — Identify like terms
$= (5 + 7)x$ — Distributive property
$= 12x$ — Add numerical coefficients

You are now ready to do **D_1**.

2. $4ab + 3ab$ — Identify like terms
$= (4 + 3)ab$ — Distributive property
$= 7ab$ — Add numerical coefficients

You are now ready to do **D_2**.

3. $y + 3y - 2y$ — Identify like terms
$= (1 + 3 - 2)y$ — Distributive property
$= 2y$ — Combine numerical coefficients

Note
Recall that y is the same as $1 \cdot y$. The coefficient is understood to be 1 when it is not written. Also, $-y$ is the same as $-1 \cdot y$.

You are now ready to do **D_3**.

4. $2x + 6y + 5x - 3y$ — Identify like terms
$= 2x + 5x + 6y - 3y$ — Commutative property
$= (2x + 5x) + (6y - 3y)$ — Associative property
$= (2 + 5)x + (6 - 3)y$ — Distributive property
$= 7x + 3y$ — Combine numerical coefficients

Note
Because of the commutative and associative properties, we can rearrange the expression and combine like terms.

You are now ready to do **D_4**.

5. $7a^2 + 2a + 5a + 4a^2$ — Identify like terms
$= (7a^2 + 4a^2) + (2a + 5a)$ — Commutative and associative properties
$= (7 + 4)a^2 + (2 + 5)a$ — Distributive property
$= 11a^2 + 7a$ — Combine numerical coefficients

You are now ready to do **D_5**.

6. $3ab^2 + 5ab + 4ab + 2ab^2$ — Identify like terms
$= (3ab^2 + 2ab^2) + (5ab + 4ab)$ — Commutative and associative properties
$= (3 + 2)ab^2 + (5 + 4)ab$ — Distributive property
$= 5ab^2 + 9ab$ — Combine numerical coefficients

You are now ready to do **D_6**. ■

D_1 $7a + 4a$

D_2 $5xy + 8xy$

D_3 $8x - 3x + x$

D_4 $3a - 2b + a + 5b$

D_5 $3a^2 + 5a - 2a^2 - a$

D_6 $x^2y + 4x^2y^2 - 3x^2y^2 - x^2y$

E_1 $(4x + 3y) + (2x - y)$

Combining like terms

1. Identify the like terms.
2. If necessary, use the commutative and associative properties to group together the like terms.
3. Combine the numerical coefficients of the like terms and multiply that by the variable factor.
4. Remember that y is the same as $1 \cdot y$ and $-y$ is the same as $-1 \cdot y$.

Grouping symbols

Any quantity enclosed within grouping symbols is treated as a single number. We are now going to use the distributive property to remove grouping symbols such as ( ), [ ], and { }. Consider the following examples:

1. The quantity $(2a + 3b)$ can be written as $1 \cdot (2a + 3b)$. Applying the distributive property, we have
$$1(2a + 3b) = 1 \cdot 2a + 1 \cdot 3b = 2a + 3b.$$
2. The quantity $+(2a + 3b)$ can be written as $(+1) \cdot (2a + 3b)$ giving
$$(+1)(2a + 3b) = (+1) \cdot 2a + (+1) \cdot 3b = 2a + 3b.$$
3. The quantity $-(2a + 3b)$ can be written as $(-1) \cdot (2a + 3b)$ giving
$$(-1)(2a + 3b) = (-1) \cdot 2a + (-1) \cdot 3b = -2a - 3b.$$

Removing grouping symbols

1. If an expression inside a grouping symbol is preceded by no symbol or by a "+" sign, the grouping symbol can be dropped and the enclosed terms remain unchanged.
2. If an expression inside a grouping symbol is preceded by a "−" sign, when the grouping symbol is dropped, we change the sign of each enclosed term.

E_2 $(5a - 2b) - (a - 4b)$

Example 1–7 E

Remove all grouping symbols and perform the indicated addition or subtraction.

1. $(2a + b) + (a + 3b)$ — Remove grouping symbols
$= 2a + b + a + 3b$ — Enclosed terms remain unchanged
$= (2a + a) + (b + 3b)$ — Associative and commutative properties
$= (2 + 1)a + (1 + 3)b$ — Distributive property
$= 3a + 4b$ — Combine numerical coefficients

You are now ready to do E_1.

2. $(5x - y) - (3x - 6y)$ — Remove grouping symbols
$= 5x - y - 3x + 6y$ — Change the sign of each term in the second parentheses
$= (5x - 3x) + (-y + 6y)$ — Associative and commutative properties
$= (5 - 3)x + (-1 + 6)y$ — Distributive property
$= 2x + 5y$ — Combine numerical coefficients

You are now ready to do E_2.

E₃ $(2x - y + 3z) - (x - 4y + 2z)$

3. $(5a + 2b - 4c) - (a - 3b - c)$ — Remove grouping symbols

$= 5a + 2b - 4c - a + 3b + c$ — Change the sign of each term in the second parentheses

$= (5 - 1)a + (2 + 3)b + (-4 + 1)c$ — Associative and commutative properties

$= 4a + 5b - 3c$ — Combine numerical coefficients

You are now ready to do **E_3**. ■

Algebraic notation

Many problems that we encounter will be stated verbally. These will need to be translated into algebraic expressions. While there is no standard procedure for changing a verbal phrase into an algebraic expression, the following guidelines should be of use.

1. Read the problem carefully, determining useful prior knowledge. Note what information is given and what information we are asked to find.
2. Let some letter represent one of the unknowns. Then express any other unknowns in terms of it.
3. Use the given conditions in the problem, the useful prior knowledge from step 1, and the unknowns from step 2 to write an algebraic expression.

When translating verbal phrases into an algebraic expression, we should be looking for phrases that involve the basic operations of addition, subtraction, multiplication, and division. Table 1.1 shows some examples of phrases that are commonly encountered. We will let x represent the unknown number.

Phrase		**Algebraic expression**
Addition	· 6 more than a number · the sum of a number and 6 · 6 plus a number · a number increased by 6 · 6 added to a number	$x + 6$
Subtraction	· 6 less than a number · a number diminished by 6 · the difference of a number and 6 · a number minus 6 · a number less 6 · a number decreased by 6 · 6 subtracted from a number · a number reduced by 6	$x - 6$
Multiplication	· a number multiplied by 6 · 6 times a number · the product of a number and 6	$6x$
Division	· a number divided by 6 · the quotient of a number and 6 · $\frac{1}{6}$ of a number	$\frac{x}{6}$

Table 1–1

Example 1–7 F

Write an algebraic expression for each of the following.

1. The *product* of a and b — $a \cdot b$

You are now ready to do **F_1**.

2. The *sum* of a and 4 — $a + 4$

You are now ready to do **F_2**.

3. x *decreased by* 9 — $x - 9$

You are now ready to do **F_3**.

4. y *divided by* 3 — $\frac{y}{3}$

You are now ready to do **F_4**.

5. A number *increased by* 6 — $n + 6$

   Let n represent the number.

You are now ready to do **F_5**.

6. *Two times* a number and that product *decreased by* 5 — $2n - 5$

   Let n represent the number.

You are now ready to do **F_6**.

7. A number *divided by* 3 and that quotient *increased by* 2 — $\frac{n}{3} + 2$

   Let n represent the number.

You are now ready to do **F_7**.

8. *Twice* the *sum* of x and 4 — $2(x + 4)$

   Let x represent the number.

You are now ready to do **F_8**. ■

F_1 The product of x and y

F_2 The sum of x and z

F_3 4 decreased by a

F_4 a divided by 7

F_5 A number increased by 8

F_6 The product of x and y, decreased by 9

F_7 The sum of a number and 3, divided by 5

F_8 Twice the sum of y and z

Answers to section 1–7 margin exercises

A_1 3 terms **A_2** 2 terms **A_3** 4 terms **A_4** 2 terms **B_1** 1 is the coefficient of a^2, -2 is the coefficient of a, 4 is the coefficient of b **C_1** yes **C_2** no **D_1** $11a$ **D_2** $13xy$ **D_3** $6x$ **D_4** $4a + 3b$ **D_5** $a^2 + 4a$ **D_6** x^2y^2 **E_1** $6x + 2y$ **E_2** $4a + 2b$ **E_3** $x + 3y + z$ **F_1** $x \cdot y$ **F_2** $x + z$ **F_3** $4 - a$ **F_4** $\frac{a}{7}$ **F_5** $x + 8$ **F_6** $xy - 9$ **F_7** $\frac{x+3}{5}$ **F_8** $2(y + z)$

Mastery points

Can you

- Identify terms in an expression?
- Identify like terms?
- Use the distributive property?
- Combine like terms?
- Write an algebraic expression?
- Remove grouping symbols?

Exercise 1–7

Directions Specify the number of terms in each expression. See example 1–7 A.

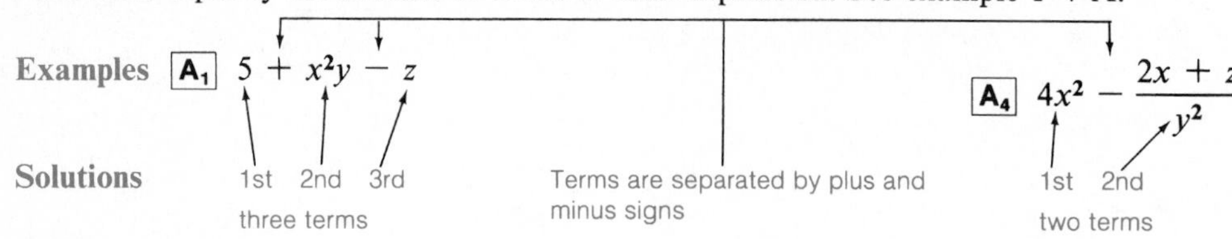

1. $3x + 4y$

2. $5xyz$

3. $4x^2 + 3x - 1$

4. $x^3 - 4x + 7$

5. $\frac{6x}{5}$

6. $\frac{x}{3}$

7. $8xy + \frac{5y}{2} - 6x$

8. $x^2 + a^2(y^2 - z)$

9. $5x^3 + (3x^2 - 4)$

10. $\frac{15x^2 + y}{8}$

11. $(x + y + z)$

12. 7

13. $a^2(b + c) - x^2(y + z)$

14. $x^2 + \frac{y - z}{a} + c$

Directions Determine the numerical coefficents of the following algebraic expressions. See example 1–7 B.

Example B1 $a^2 - 2a + 4b$

Solution 1 is understood to be the coefficient of a^2
-2 is the coefficient of a
4 is the coefficient of b

15. $5x^2 + x - 4z$

16. $a^2b + 4ab^2 - ab$

17. $x - y - 3z$

18. $-2a - b + c$

Directions For the groups of terms, write like or unlike. See example 1–7 C.

Example C2 $4a^2b^2$ and $4a^3b^3$

Solution Both contain the same variables but are **unlike** because the exponents of the respective variable are not the same.

19. $3a, -2a$

20. $5x, 7x$

21. $4a^2, a^2$

22. $b^3, -2b^3$

23. $2a^2, 2a^3$

24. $4x, 4x^2$

Directions Perform the indicated addition and subtraction. See example 1–7 D.

Examples D4 $3a - 2b + a + 5b$ | D5 $3a^2 + 5a - 2a^2 - a$

Solutions

$= (3a + a) + (-2b + 5b)$
$= (3 + 1)a + (-2 + 5)b$
$= 4a + 3b$

$= (3a^2 - 2a^2) + (5a - a)$ — Commutative and associative properties
$= (3 - 2)a^2 + (5 - 1)a$ — Distributive property
$= 1a^2 + 4a$ — Combine numerical coefficients
$= a^2 + 4a$

25. $3x + 4x + 7x$

26. $2a^2b - 4a^2b + 6a^2b$

27. $4ab + 11ab - 10ab - 8ab$

28. $d^2 + d - 3d^2 + d^4 + 4d^2$

29. $5x + x^2 - x + 6x^2$

30. $5x^2y - 3xy + 5y + 6xy - x^2y$

31. $a^2b - b^3 - ab^2 + 2a^3 - 5ab^2$

32. $x + 2x^2 - 5 + x^3 - 2x - 2x^2$

33. $3a + b + 2a - 5c - b - 2x^2 + 8a$

34. $3a + 8a - 6a + 9a$

35. $3a + 8b - 6a - 17b$

36. $28ab - 73ab + ab + 11ab - 9ab$

Directions Remove all grouping symbols and perform the indicated addition or subtraction. See example 1–7 E.

Example E2 $(5a - 2b) - (a - 4b)$

Solution

$= 5a - 2b - a + 4b$ — Change the sign of each term in the second parentheses
$= (5a - a) + (-2b + 4b)$ — Associative and commutative properties
$= (5 - 1)a + (-2 + 4)b$ — Distributive property
$= 4a + 2b$ — Combine numerical coefficients

37. $(2x + 3y) + (x + 5y)$

38. $(4a - b) + (3a + 2b)$

39. $(5x + y) - (3x - 2y)$

40. $(7x - 3y) - (5x - 6y)$

41. $(3a - b + 4c) - (a - 2b - c)$

42. $(4x - 3y - 2z) - (3x - 4y - z)$

43. $(8x + 3y - 4z) - (6x - y - 4z)$

44. $(7a - b - 3c) - (5a - 4b + 3c)$

Directions Write an algebraic expression for each of the following. See example 1–7 F.

Examples F₁ The product of x and y

Solutions $x \cdot y$

F₅ A number increased by 8

Let x represent the number; hence $x + 8$

45. The sum of a and b

46. 3 times a, subtracted from b

47. 7 less than x

48. 5 more than y

49. The sum of x and y, divided by z

50. x times the sum of y and z

51. a decreased by 5

52. a decreased by b

53. $\frac{1}{2}$ of x, decreased by 2 times x

54. A number decreased by 12

55. 3 times a number and that product increased by 1

56. A number added to 4

57. A number divided by 5

58. 2 times the sum of a number and 4

59. A number decreased by 6 and that difference divided by 11

Review exercises

Perform the indicated operations. See section 1–6.

1. -5^2 **2.** $(-8)^2$ **3.** $10 - 6 \cdot 2$ **4.** $25 - 5 \cdot 2$

5. $100 \div 10 \cdot 2 + 2$ **6.** $28 - (8 - 12) - 3^2$

1–8 Evaluating algebraic expressions

Substitution property

An extremely important process in algebra is that of calculating the numerical value of an expression when we are given specific replacement values for the variables. This process is called **evaluation.** To perform evaluation, we need the following **property of substitution.**

> **Property of substitution**
>
> If $a = b$, then a may be replaced by b or b may be replaced by a in any expression without altering the value of the expression.
>
> **Concept**
>
> When two things are equal, they can replace each other in any expression.

Example 1–8 A

Evaluate the following expressions for the given real number replacement for the variable or variables.

1. $x^2 + 2x - 7$, when $x = 4$

The expression would be $(\quad)^2 + 2(\quad) - 7$ without the x.

Substituting 4 for each x, we have $(4)^2 + 2(4) - 7$. Using the order of operations, we have

$= 16 + 2(4) - 7$ Exponents

$= 16 + 8 - 7$ Multiply

$= 24 - 7$ Add

$= 17$ Subtract

Therefore the expression $x^2 + 2x - 7$ evaluated for $x = 4$ is 17.

You are now ready to do **A_1**.

A_1 $y^2 - y - 4$, when $y = 2$

A₂ $3a - 2(c - d) + b$ when $a = 2$, $b = 3$, $c = -2$, and $d = -3$

2. $5a - b + 2(c + d)$ when $a = 2$, $b = 3$, $c = -2$, and $d = -3$

$5a - b + 2(c + d)$	Original expression
$= 5(\ ) - (\ ) + 2[(\ ) + (\ )]$	Expression ready for substitution
$= 5(2) - (3) + 2[(-2) + (-3)]$	Substitute
$= 5(2) - (3) + 2[-5]$	Order of operations: groups
$= 10 - (3) + (-10)$	Multiply
$= 7 + (-10)$	Subtract
$= -3$	Add

You are now ready to do **A₂**.

A₃ $a^2b - b^2a$ when $a = -3$ and $b = 2$

3. $4ab - c^2 + 3d$ when $a = 2$, $b = 3$, $c = -2$, and $d = -3$

$4ab - c^2 + 3d$	Original expression
$= 4(\ )(\ ) - (\ )^2 + 3(\ )$	Expression ready for substitution
$= 4(2)(3) - (-2)^2 + 3(-3)$	Substitute
$= 4(2)(3) - (4) + 3(-3)$	Order of operations: exponents
$= 8(3) - 4 + 3(-3)$	Multiply
$= 24 - 4 + 3(-3)$	Multiply
$= 24 - 4 + (-9)$	Multiply
$= 20 + (-9)$	Subtract
$= 11$	Add

You are now ready to do **A₃**. ■

To evaluate an algebraic expression

1. Write parentheses in place of each variable.
2. Place the value that the variable is representing into the parentheses.
3. Perform the indicated operations according to the order of operations.

Formulas

A type of algebraic expression that we most frequently use is a **formula.** A formula expresses a relationship between quantities in the physical world. For example, $d = rt$ (distance traveled is equal to the rate multiplied by the time).

B₁ $V = \ell wh$ when $\ell = 6$ yards, $w = 3$ yards, and $h = 4$ yards

Example 1–8 B

Evaluate the following formulas for the real number replacements of the variables.

1. The volume (V) of a rectangular solid is found by multiplying length (ℓ) times width (w) times height (h). The formula then reads $V = \ell wh$. Find the volume in cubic feet if $\ell = 12$ feet, $w = 4$ feet, and $h = 5$ feet.

$V = \ell wh$	Original formula
$V = (\ )(\ )(\ )$	Formula ready for substitution
$V = (12)(4)(5)$	Substitute
$V = (48)(5)$	Order of operations: multiply
$V = 240$	Multiply

The volume is 240 cubic feet.

You are now ready to do **B₁**.

2. If we know the temperature in degrees Fahrenheit (F), the temperature in degrees Celsius (C) can be found by the formula $C = \frac{5}{9}(F - 32)$. Find the temperature in degrees Celsius if the temperature is 86 degrees Fahrenheit.

$C = \frac{5}{9}(F - 32)$ Original formula

$C = \frac{5}{9}[(\quad) - 32]$ Formula ready for substitution

$C = \frac{5}{9}[(86) - 32]$ Substitute

$C = \frac{5}{9}(54)$ Order of operations: groups first

$C = 30$ Multiply

The temperature is 30 degrees Celsius.

You are now ready to do **B_2**.

B_2 $C = \frac{5}{9}(F - 32)$ when $F = 77$

3. The perimeter* (P) of a rectangle is found by the formula $P = 2\ell + 2w$, where ℓ is the length of the rectangle and w is the width. Find the perimeter of the rectangle in meters if $\ell = 8$ meters and $w = 5$ meters.

$P = 2\ell + 2w$ Original formula
$P = 2(\quad) + 2(\quad)$ Formula ready for substitution
$P = 2(8) + 2(5)$ Substitute
$P = 16 + 10$ Order of operations: multiply
$P = 26$ Add

The perimeter of the rectangle is 26 meters.

You are now ready to do **B_3**.

B_3 $P = 2\ell + 2w$ when $\ell = 7$ inches and $w = 5$ inches

4. A formula in electricity is $I = \frac{E}{R}$, where I represents the current measured in amperes in a certain part of a circuit, E represents the potential difference in volts across that part of the circuit, and R represents the resistance in ohms of that part of the circuit. Find I in amperes if $E = 110$ volts and $R = 44$ ohms.

$I = \frac{E}{R}$ Original formula

$I = \frac{(\quad)}{(\quad)}$ Formula ready for substitution

$I = \frac{(110)}{(44)}$ Substitute

$I = \frac{5}{2} = 2\frac{1}{2}$ Reduce and change to a mixed number

The current is $2\frac{1}{2}$ amperes.

You are now ready to do **B_4**. ■

B_4 $I = \frac{E}{R}$ when $E = 220$ volts and $R = 11$ ohms

Problem solving

The following word problems are designed to help us interpret verbal phrases and write expressions for them in algebraic symbols.

*The perimeter is the distance around a closed geometric figure.

C_1 Jim enters 85 keystrokes per minute on the computer. How many keystrokes can he enter in m minutes?

C_2 Express the cost in dollars of x cassette tapes if each tape costs $2.95.

C_3 A 10-pound box of candy costs y dollars. How much does the candy cost per pound?

Example 1–8 C

Write an algebraic expression for each of the following verbal phrases.

1. Nancy can type 90 words per minute. How many words can she type in n minutes?

If Nancy can type 90 words in one minute, then we multiply

$90 \cdot n$ or $90n$

to obtain the number of words she can type in n minutes.

You are now ready to do $\mathbf{C_1}$.

2. If John has n dollars in his savings account and on successive days he deposits $15 and then withdraws $34 to make a purchase, write an expression for the balance in his savings account.

We *add* the deposits and *subtract* the withdrawals. Thus

$n + 15 - 34 = n - 19$

represents the balance in John's savings account after the two transactions.

You are now ready to do $\mathbf{C_2}$.

3. A woman paid d dollars for a 30-pound bag of dog food. How much did the dog food cost her per pound?

The price per pound is found by dividing the total cost by the number of pounds. Thus the price per pound of the dog food is represented by $\frac{d}{30}$ dollars.

You are now ready to do $\mathbf{C_3}$. ■

Answers to section 1–8 margin exercises

A_1 −2 A_2 7 A_3 30 B_1 72 yd³ B_2 25° C B_3 24 in. B_4 20 amps C_1 $85m$ C_2 $2.95x$ C_3 $\frac{y}{10}$

Mastery points

Can you

- Evaluate an algebraic expression?
- Evaluate a formula?
- Write an algebraic expression?

Exercise 1–8

Directions Evaluate the following expressions if $a = 2$, $b = 3$, $c = -2$, $d = -3$. See example 1–8 A.

Example [A₂] $3a - 2(c - d) + b$

Solution

$= 3(\ \ ) - 2[(\ \ ) - (\ \ )] + (\ \ )$	Expression ready for substitution
$= 3(2) - 2[(-2) - (-3)] + (3)$	Substitute
$= 3(2) - 2(1) + 3$	Order of operations: groups
$= 6 - 2 + 3$	Multiply
$= 7$	Subtract and add

1. $2a + b - c$
2. $(a + b)$
3. $3a - 2b - (c + d)$
4. $a - 3(c + b)$
5. $(3a + 2b)(a - c)$
6. $2ab(c + d)$
7. $ac - bd$
8. $3c - 2(3a + b)$
9. $7a - d(6b + c)$
10. $(3a - 5c)(2b - 4d)$
11. $(5c - 3a)(4d - 2b)$
12. $(5c - d)4a$
13. $5a + 7b - 3c(a - d)$
14. $(4a + b) - (3a - b)(c + 2d)$
15. $a^2 - c^2$
16. $b^2 + 2d^2$
17. $3ab - 4c^2 + d$
18. $(c + d)^2$
19. $(c - d)^2$
20. $a^2b^2 + c^2d^2$
21. $3ac - 2a^2c^2$

22. $ab - ac$

23. $(ab)^2 - (ac)^2$

24. $(c - d)^2(a + b)$

25. $a^3b - c^3d$

26. $c^2 - d^3$

27. $3d^2 - 2c^3$

28. $(3d - 5c)^3$

Directions Evaluate the following formulas. See examples 1–8 B.

Example B4 $I = \frac{E}{R}$ when $E = 220$ and $R = 11$

Solution

$I = \frac{(\ )}{(\ )}$ Formula ready for substitution

$= \frac{(220)}{(11)}$ Substitute

$= 20$ Order of operations

29. $I = \frac{E}{R}$, $E = 220$ and $R = 33$

30. $V = \ell wh$, $\ell = 7$, $w = 5$, and $h = 6$

31. $I = prt$, $p = 1{,}000$; $r = 0.08$; and $t = 2$

32. $F = ma$, $m = 18$ and $a = 6$

33. $W = I^2R$, $I = 12$ and $R = 2$

34. $V = k + gt$, $k = 24$, $g = 9$, and $t = 4$

35. $A = \frac{1}{2}h(b + c)$, $h = 6$, $b = 8$, and $c = 10$

36. $\ell = a + (n - 1)d$, $a = 2$, $n = 14$, and $d = 3$

37. $A = p + pr$, $p = 2{,}000$ and $r = 0.07$

38. $H = \frac{D^2N}{2}$, $D = 4$ and $N = 6$

39. $A = \frac{I^2R - 120E^2}{R}$, $E = 5$, $I = 12$, and $R = 100$

40. $S = \frac{1}{2}gt^2$, $g = 32$ and $t = 4$

Directions Evaluate the following formulas. See examples 1–8 B.

41. Find the horsepower (h) required by a hydraulic pump when it needs to pump 10 gallons per minute (g) and the pounds per square inch (p) equal 3,000. Use $h = \frac{g \cdot p}{1{,}714}$.

42. The required ratio of gearing (R) of a milling machine is given by $R = (A - N) \cdot \frac{40}{A}$, where N = required number of divisions and A = approximate number of divisions. Find R when $A = 280$ and $N = 271$.

43. In a gear system, the velocity (V) of the driving gear is defined by $V = \frac{vn}{N}$, where v = velocity of follower gear, n = number of teeth of follower gear, and N = number of teeth of driving gear. Find V when $v = 90$ revolutions per minute, $n = 30$ teeth, $N = 65$ teeth.

44. The tap drill size (T) of a drill needed to drill threads in a nut is given by $T = D - \frac{1}{N}$, where D = diameter of the tap and N = number of threads per inch. Find T with a $\frac{1}{2}$-inch tap and 13 threads per inch.

45. It is necessary to drag a box 600 feet across a level lot in 3 minutes. The force required to pull the box is 2,000 pounds. What is the horsepower (h) needed to do this if horsepower is defined by $h = \frac{\ell \cdot w}{33{,}000 \cdot t}$, where ℓ = length to be moved, w = force exerted through distance ℓ, and t = time in minutes required to move the box through ℓ?

46. A pulley 12 inches in diameter that is running at 320 revolutions per minute is connected by a belt to a pulley 9 inches in diameter. How many revolutions per minute will the smaller pulley make if $s = \frac{SD}{d}$, where s = speed of smaller pulley and d = diameter of smaller pulley, S = speed of larger pulley and D = diameter of larger pulley?

Directions Write an algebraic expression for the following verbal statements. See example 1–8 C.

Example C_2 Express the cost in dollars of x cassette tapes if each tape costs $2.95.

Solution If we are buying x tapes at $2.95 each, then we must multiply x by $2.95. The algebraic expression in terms of dollars would be $2.95 \cdot x = 2.95x$.

47. Bill's savings account has a current balance of $258. He makes a withdrawal of n dollars and then makes a deposit of m dollars. Express his new balance in terms of n and m.

48. Paula has a balance of n dollars in her checking account. She makes a deposit of $36 and then writes 3 checks for m dollars each. Express her new balance in terms of n and m.

49. Pete has c cents, all in half-dollars. Write an expression for the number of half-dollars Pete has.

50. If x represents a whole number, write an expression for the next greater whole number.

51. If z represents an odd integer, write an expression for the next greater odd integer.

52. If y represents an even integer, write an expression for the next greater even integer.

53. If Larry is f feet and t inches tall, how tall is Larry in inches?

54. Mike paid $25 for a ticket to a play. If the play lasted h hours, what did it cost him per hour to see the play?

55. Arlene has n nickels and d dimes in her purse. Express in cents the amount of money she has in her purse. (*Hint:* n nickels is represented by $5n$.)

56. Jack has q quarters, d dimes, and n nickels. Express in cents the amount of money Jack has.

57. Susan is p years old now. Express her age (a) 12 years from now, (b) 5 years ago.

58. Ann is 3 years old. If Jan is n times as old as Ann, express Jan's age. Express Jan's age 8 years ago.

59. John earns $1,000 more than twice what Terry earns in a year. If Terry earns d dollars, write an expression for John's annual salary.

60. Jean's annual salary is $2,000 less than n times Lisa's annual salary. If Lisa earns $25,000 per year, express Jean's annual salary.

61. Express the total cost in cents of purchasing x cans of tuna at 69¢ per can on Friday and y cans of the same tuna at 57¢ per can on Saturday.

62. A gallon of primer paint costs \$9.95 per gallon and a gallon of latex-base paint costs \$12.99. Express the cost in dollars of p gallons of primer and q gallons of latex-base paint.

63. Paula enters x calculations per minute on the calculator and Leigh enters 7 calculations per minute less than Paula. Write an expression for how many calculations Leigh enters in 35 minutes.

Review exercises

Directions Perform the indicated addition and subtraction. See section 1–7.

1. $3x + 5x$

2. $10y - 2y + y$

3. $3a + 1 + 2a + 3$

4. $7b + 5 - 3a - 8$

5. $4x - y + z - 3x + 2y - z$

6. $6a + b - c - 2a - b + 3c$

Chapter 1 lead-in problem

While on a trip to Canada, Tonya heard on the radio that the temperature today will be 20° Celsius. Will she need her winter coat? What will the temperature be in degrees Fahrenheit? The formula for changing the temperature measured in degrees Celsius to degrees Fahrenheit is

$$F = \frac{9}{5}C + 32.$$

Solution

$F = \frac{9}{5}C + 32$	Original expression
$F = \frac{9}{5}(\quad) + 32$	Formula ready for substitution
$F = \frac{9}{5}(20) + 32$	Substitute
$F = 36 + 32$	Order of operations: multiply
$F = 68$	Add

The temperature is 68 degrees Fahrenheit. She will not need her winter coat.

Chapter 1 summary

1. A **variable** is a symbol that represents an unspecified number.
2. The **number line** is a line on which we visually represent the real numbers.
3. Two **inequality symbols** that denote an order relationship between numbers are $<$ (less than) and $>$ (greater than).
4. The **absolute value,** $| \quad |$, of a number is the undirected distance that the number is from the origin.
5. For any two real numbers a and b, $a - b = a + (-b)$.
6. If any quantity is enclosed with **grouping symbols,** we treat the quantity within as a single number.
7. The numbers or variables in an indicated multiplication are referred to as the **factors** of the product.
8. The **exponent** tells how many times the base is used as a factor in an indicated product.
9. If $b \neq 0$, $\frac{a}{b} = q$, provided that $b \cdot q = a$.
10. **Division by zero is not allowed.**
11. The quotient of **zero** divided by any number other than zero is always zero.
12. **Operations with signed numbers**

    Addition

    Same signs: Add their absolute values and prefix the sum by their common sign.

    Different signs: Subtract the lesser absolute value from the greater absolute value. The result has the sign of the number with the greater absolute value.

    Additive inverse: The sum of a number and its additive inverse (opposite) is zero.

    Subtraction Change the sign of the number being subtracted and add that to the first number.

    Multiplication and division Perform the operation (multiplication or division) using the absolute value of the numbers.

    Same signs: Answer will be positive.

    Different signs: Answer will be negative.

    Division by zero is not allowed.
13. **Properties of real numbers** If a, b and c are any real numbers, then

    $a + b = b + a$, commutative property of addition

    $a \cdot b = b \cdot a$, commutative property of multiplication

    $(a + b) + c = a + (b + c)$, associative property of addition

    $(a \cdot b)c = a(b \cdot c)$, associative property of multiplication

    $a \cdot 1 = 1 \cdot a = a$, identity property of multiplication

    $a + 0 = 0 + a = a$, identity property of addition

    $a + (-a) = (-a) + a = 0$, additive inverse property

    $a \cdot 0 = 0 \cdot a = 0$, zero factor property

    $a(b + c) = ab + ac$, distributive property
14. **Order of operations**
    1. ***Groups:*** Perform any operations within a grouping symbol such as ( ) parentheses, [ ] brackets, { } braces, $| \quad |$ absolute value, or in the numerator or the denominator of a fraction.
    2. ***Exponents:*** Perform operation indicated by exponents.
    3. ***Multiplication and Division:*** Perform multiplication and division in order from left to right.
    4. ***Addition and Subtraction:*** Perform addition and subtraction in order from left to right.
15. A **constant** is a symbol that does not change its value.
16. An **algebraic expression** is any meaningful collection of variables, constants, grouping symbols, and signs of operations.
17. The **terms** in an algebraic expression are any constants, variables, or products or quotients of these. They are separated by plus or minus signs.
18. In the expression $8x$, 8 is called the **numerical coefficient** or just the coefficient.
19. We use the **property of substitution** to evaluate algebraic expressions.

Chapter 1 review

[1–1]

Directions Replace the ? with the proper inequality symbol, $<$ or $>$.

1. $4 ? 8$

2. $-5 ? 0$

3. $-10 ? -20$

4. $|-10| ? |-20|$

5. $|-5| ? |0|$

6. $|-8| ? |4|$

[1–2, 1–3]

Directions Find the sum or difference.

7. $(-1) + (-3)$

8. $6 - 3$

9. $7 - 13$

10. $(-4) + (5)$

11. $(-8) + (2)$

12. $7 - (-8)$

13. $(-8) - (-4)$

14. $(-3) - (6)$

15. $0 + (-3) - (-7) + 3 - (4)$

16. $4 - 3 + 7 - 8 + 12 - (-3)$

[1–4, 1–5]

Directions Find the product or quotient if possible.

17. $3 \cdot (-7)$

18. $(-4) \cdot (-3)$

19. $(-8) \cdot (3) \cdot (-1)$

20. $8 \cdot (-9) \cdot (-1) \cdot (-2)$

21. $(-4) \cdot (3) \cdot (-5) \cdot 0$

22. $\frac{-14}{2}$

23. $\frac{-8}{-4}$

24. $24 \div (-4)$

25. $\frac{7}{0}$

26. $\frac{0}{-8}$

27. $\frac{0}{0}$

28. $\frac{(-2)(-3)}{(-6)}$

29. Find two integer factors of 36 whose sum is -13.

30. A man suffers successive financial losses of \$3,000, \$2,560, and \$3,300 on three business transactions. A loss is denoted by a negative number and the man originally had \$52,000.

a. Write a statement using integers representing his assets after the losses.

b. Find the total assets after the losses.

31. The temperature readings in degrees Fahrenheit during a five-hour period were 63°, 72°, 80°, 75°, and 69°.

a. Represent by positive and negative integers how much rise (+) and fall (−) there was from hour to hour.

b. Was the absolute value of the total rise greater than, equal to, or less than that of the total fall? How much? (Represent by a positive or negative integer.)

c. If the sixth hour showed a drop of 11° F, what was the temperature? Write a statement involving a negative integer representing this answer.

[1–6]

Directions Perform the indicated operations and simplify.

32. -4^3

33. -4^2

34. -3^3

35. $(-5)^2$

36. $100 - 4 \cdot 5 + 18$

37. $-7 + 14 \div 7 + 2$

38. $18 + 3 \cdot 12 \div 2^2 - 7$

39. $19 - (14 - 6) + 7^2 - 11$

40. $\dfrac{8(2 - 4)}{4} - \dfrac{35}{7}$

41. $4[8 - 2(5 - 3) + 1]$

42. $10 - 10 \div 10 \cdot 10 - 10^2$

43. $3[5(8 - 4) - 6 + 3]$

44. $46 - 18 \div 6 + 3 - 4^2$

45. If a person makes \$8 per hour straight time and \$12 per hour overtime, what would be her total pay if she worked 40 hours straight time and 11 hours overtime?

[1–7]

Directions Specify the number of terms in each expression.

46. $4x^2 + 3x + 2$

47. $5a^2b$

48. $7xy + 5$

49. $(ab + cd) + xy$

Directions Determine the numerical coefficients of the terms in the following algebraic expressions.

50. $5a^2 + a - b$

51. $x^2 + 7x - y$

52. $-6a^2b - 4ab^2 + ab$

Directions For the group of terms write like or unlike.

53. $9x, -2x$

54. $2a^2, 2a^3$

55. $-4x^2, 3x^2$

Directions Perform the indicated addition or subtraction.

56. $8x + 9x$

57. $8y + 9y$

58. $8a + a + 4a$

59. $b + 9b$

60. $8z - 2z$

61. $8c - 11c$

62. $5x + 3x + 14 + 9$

63. $8a + 6a + 12 - 17$

64. $4x - 13x + 8x - 7 + 3$

65. $(9y + 3z) - (6y - 2z)$

66. $(4x - 3y) - (3x - 5y)$

67. $(3a - 2b + 4c) - (a - 5b - 6c)$

Directions Write an algebraic expression for each of the following.

68. 5 times x

69. 7 less than y

70. 4 more than z

71. 2 times a number, plus 6

Directions Evaluate the following expressions if $a = 3$, $b = 4$, $c = -4$, and $d = -3$.

72. $3a - b + c$

73. $d - 2(a + c)$

74. $a^2b - a^2c$

75. $(2a + c)(b + 2d)$

76. $(c - 2d)^2$

77. $c^2 - d^2$

78. Evaluate R when $R = \dfrac{P \cdot L}{D^2}$ given (a) $P = 6$, $L = 8$, $D = 4$; (b) $P = 7$, $L = 3$, $D = \dfrac{2}{3}$.

79. The volume of a gas V is given by $V = \dfrac{RS}{P}$. Find V when $R = 780$, $S = 80$, and $P = 60$.

NAME

Chapter 1 cumulative test

CLASS/SECTION DATE

Directions Perform the indicated operations if possible.

[1–2] **1.** $-8 + 5$

[1–3] **2.** $13.2 - 5.17$

[1–3] **3.** $-10 - (-12)$

[1–4] **4.** $(-6)(4)$

[1–6] **5.** $(-5)^2$

[1–5] **6.** $\frac{-24}{-3}$

[1–5] **7.** $\frac{0}{-4}$

[1–2] **8.** $-7 + 7$

[1–3] **9.** $18 - 62$

[1–3] **10.** $24 - 36$

[1–2] **11.** $\frac{3}{8} + \frac{1}{4}$

[1–6] **12.** -6^2

[1–4] **13.** $(-2)(-2)$

[1–5] **14.** $\frac{8}{0}$

[1–5] **15.** $\frac{-21}{7}$

[1–5] **16.** $\frac{10}{7} \div \frac{15}{14}$

[1–4] **17.** $(1.8)(-3.6)$

[1–7] **18.** $3a + 2 - a + 6$

[1–6] **19.** $50 \div 2 \cdot 5 - 3^2$

[1–4] **20.** $(-8)(-5)$

[1–7] **21.** $3x + y - x + 2y$

[1–6] **22.** $48 - 6 \cdot 3 + (4 - 5 \cdot 3)$

[1–8] **23.** Evaluate the following expressions if $x = -2$, $y = 3$, and $z = -4$.

a. $x^2 - y^2$

b. $xy - xz$

[1–7] **24.** Write an algebraic expression for each of the following.

a. x increased by 6

b. y diminished by 4

c. Twice a number, plus 4

CHAPTER

2

Solving Equations and Inequalities

Bonnie has $3,000 invested at 8% simple interest per year. How much more money must she invest at 7% simple interest if she wants an income of $660 per year ($55 per month) from her investments?

Proficiency check

[1–2] **1.** $(-6) + (-3)$

[1–3] **2.** $(-4) - (-8)$

[1–4] **3.** $(-5)(-2)$

[1–5] **4.** $\dfrac{7 - 14}{(-5) - (-5)}$

[1–6] **5.** $18 - (6 - 3) - 4 - 9$

[1–6] **6.** $(-3)^2 + (-7)(-2) - 19$

[1–6] **7.** $-4^2 + (-8)(-2) + 5$

[1–7] **8.** Combine like terms.
a. $4ab - 3ac + 6ac + ab$
b. $3xy - xy + 2xy - xy$

[1–7] **9.** Write an algebraic expression for each of the following.
a. The sum of x and 7
b. A number decreased by 4
c. Three times a number, decreased by 6

▣ 2–1 The addition and subtraction property of equality

Equations

An **equation** is a statement of equality. If two expressions represent the same number, then placing an equality sign, =, between them forms an equation. The following diagram is used to show the parts of an equation.

$$\underbrace{3x - 7}_{\text{Left member of the equation}} = \underbrace{2x + 5}_{\text{Right member of the equation}}$$

Equality sign (pointing to =)

A **mathematical statement** is a mathematical sentence that can be labeled true or false. $2 + 3 = 5$ is a true statement, and $3 + 4 = 8$ is a false statement. An equation that is true for some values of the variable and false for other values of the variable is called a **conditional equation.** The equation $x + 2 = 8$ is a conditional equation since it is true when $x = 6$ and false otherwise.

If the equation is true for every permissible value of the variable, it is called an **identical equation,** or **identity.** For example,

$$2(x + 3) = 2x + 6$$

is true for any real number replacement for x and is thus an identity. Properties such as

$$a + (b + c) = (a + b) + c \quad \text{and} \quad a \cdot b = b \cdot a$$

are further examples of identities.

Solution

A replacement value for the variable that forms a true statement is called a **root,** or a **solution,** of the equation. We say that a root of the given equation *satisfies* that equation.

$\boxed{A_1}$ Determine if the statement is true or false for the given replacement value of the variable. $3x + 3 = 6$; 1

Example 2–1 A

Determine if the statement is true or false for the given value of the variable.

1. If we replace x by 6 in the equation

$$2 + x = 8$$

and simplify each member

$$\begin{aligned} 2 + (6) &= 8 \\ 8 &= 8, \end{aligned}$$

the equation is true. Then 6 is the root of the equation. The only solution to this equation is 6.

You are now ready to do $\mathbf{A_1}$.

2. If we replace x by -3 in the equation

$$4 - x = 7$$

and simplify each member

$$\begin{aligned} 4 - (-3) &= 7 \\ 7 &= 7, \end{aligned}$$

the equation is true and -3 is the root of the equation.

You are now ready to do $\mathbf{A_2}$. ■

$\boxed{A_2}$ Determine if the statement is true or false for the given replacement value of the variable. $2x - 1 = 3$; 4

To check the solution of an equation

1. **Substitute:** Replace the variable in the original equation with the solution.
2. **Order of operations:** Perform the indicated operations.
3. **True statement:** If step 2 produces a true statement, the solution is correct.

Equivalent equations

So far we have looked at **linear equations,** such as $2 + x = 8$ and $4 - x = 7$, for which the solution could be found by inspection. Unfortunately, the majority of equations cannot be solved by inspection. We must develop a procedure for finding the solution.

If we wish to solve a more complicated equation, such as

$$2 + x + 3x - 4 = 2x + 4 + x,$$

the solution is not so obvious. To solve such an equation, we go through a series of steps whereby we form equations that are equivalent to the original equation until we have the equation in the form $x = n$, n being some real number. These equations that we form are called **equivalent equations. Equivalent equations are equations whose solution is the same.**

C₁ $x - 7 = 12$

C₂ $a + 7 = 10$

C₃ $b - 7 = -10$

C₄ $5 = x + 9$

Example 2–1 B

The following are equivalent equations whose solution is 6.

1. $2 + x + 3x - 4 = 2x + 4 + x$
2. $4x - 2 = 3x + 4$
3. $x - 2 = 4$
4. $x = 6$

■

Addition and subtraction property of equality

Since an equation is a statement of equality between two expressions, identical quantities added to or subtracted from each expression will produce an equivalent equation. We can state this property as follows:

> **Addition and subtraction property of equality**
> For any algebraic expressions a, b, and c,
>
> if $a = b$, then $a + c = b + c$ and $a - c = b - c$.
>
> **Concept**
> We can add or subtract the same quantity in each member of an equation and the result will be an equivalent equation.

Example 2–1 C

Find the solution and check the answer.

1.
$$x - 5 = 7$$
$$x - 5 + 5 = 7 + 5 \quad \text{Add 5 to both members}$$
$$x + 0 = 12 \quad \text{Additive inverse}$$
$$x = 12 \quad \text{Solution}$$

Check:
$(12) - 5 = 7$
$7 = 7$ True

You are now ready to do **C₁**.

2.
$$x + 4 = 12$$
$$x + 4 - 4 = 12 - 4 \quad \text{Subtract 4 from both members}$$
$$x = 8 \quad \text{Solution}$$

Check:
$(8) + 4 = 12$
$12 = 12$ True

Note
The operation of subtracting 4 could also have been accomplished by adding (-4) to both members.

You are now ready to do **C₂**.

3.
$$x - 8 = -11$$
$$x - 8 + 8 = -11 + 8 \quad \text{Add 8 to both members}$$
$$x = -3 \quad \text{Solution}$$

Check:
$(-3) - 8 = -11$
$-11 = -11$ True

You are now ready to do **C₃**.

4.
$$2 = x + 7$$
$$2 - 7 = x + 7 - 7 \quad \text{Subtract 7 from both members}$$
$$-5 = x \quad \text{Solution}$$

Check:
$2 = (-5) + 7$
$2 = 2$ True

You are now ready to do **C₄**. ■

Symmetric property of equality

The **symmetric property of equality** is also useful in finding the solution of equations.

D_1 $4y - 3 = 5y - 8$

Symmetric property of equality

If $a = b$, then $b = a$.

Concept

This property allows us to interchange the right and left members of the equation.

In example 2–1 C–4, instead of leaving the equation as $-5 = x$, we could use the symmetric property and write the equation as $x = -5$.

Sometimes it is necessary to use the associative, commutative, and distributive properties to perform indicated operations in one or both members of an equation. This will **simplify** the equation before the addition and subtraction property of equality is used.

D_2 $4x - 2 = 3x + 5$

Example 2–1 D

Find the solution.

1. $6x - 4 = 7x + 2$

$6x - 6x - 4 = 7x - 6x + 2$	Subtract 6x from both members
$-4 = x + 2$	Combine like terms
$-4 - 2 = x + 2 - 2$	Subtract 2 from both members
$-6 = x$	Solution
$x = -6$	Symmetric property

You are now ready to do D_1.

D_3 $3a + 2 - a = 6a - 5a + 4$

2. $3x + 5 - x = x + 4$

$2x + 5 = x + 4$	Simplify. Combine like terms
$2x - x + 5 = x - x + 4$	Subtract x from both members
$x + 5 = 4$	Combine like terms
$x + 5 - 5 = 4 - 5$	Subtract 5 from both members
$x = -1$	Solution

You are now ready to do D_2.

3. $5x - 4 + 2x = 6x - 6 + 11$

$7x - 4 = 6x + 5$	Simplify. Combine like terms
$7x - 6x - 4 = 6x - 6x + 5$	Subtract 6x from both members
$x - 4 = 5$	Combine like terms
$x - 4 + 4 = 5 + 4$	Add 4 to both members
$x = 9$	Solution

You are now ready to do D_3.

D_4 $5x + 2x - 4 = 6x + 7$

4. $2 + x + 3x - 4 = 2x + 4 + x$

$4x - 2 = 3x + 4$	Simplify. Combine like terms
$4x - 3x - 2 = 3x - 3x + 4$	Subtract 3x from both members
$x - 2 = 4$	Combine like terms
$x - 2 + 2 = 4 + 2$	Add 2 to both members
$x = 6$	Solution

You are now ready to do D_4.

D₅ $3(2x + 1) = x + 4x - 2$

5.

$$
\begin{aligned}
3x &= 2(2x - 4) \\
3x &= 4x - 8 && \text{Simplify (distributive property)} \\
3x - 3x &= 4x - 3x - 8 && \text{Subtract } 3x \text{ from both members} \\
0 &= x - 8 && \text{Combine like terms} \\
0 + 8 &= x - 8 + 8 && \text{Add 8 to both members} \\
8 &= x && \text{Solution} \\
x &= 8 && \text{Symmetric property}
\end{aligned}
$$

You are now ready to do $\mathbf{D_5}$.

6.

$$
\begin{aligned}
3(3x - 1) + 4 &= 2(4x + 3) \\
9x - 3 + 4 &= 8x + 6 && \text{Simplify (distributive property)} \\
9x + 1 &= 8x + 6 && \text{Simplify, combine like terms} \\
9x - 8x + 1 &= 8x - 8x + 6 && \text{Subtract } 8x \text{ from both members} \\
x + 1 &= 6 && \text{Combine like terms} \\
x + 1 - 1 &= 6 - 1 && \text{Subtract 1 from both members} \\
x &= 5 && \text{Solution}
\end{aligned}
$$

You are now ready to do $\mathbf{D_6}$. ■

D₆ $2(3a - 4) + 2 = 4(a + 1) + a$

Problem solving

We are now ready to combine our ability to write an expression and our ability to solve an equation and apply them to solve a verbal problem. While there is no standard procedure for solving a verbal problem, the following guidelines should be useful.

Solving verbal problems

1. Read the problem carefully. Determine useful prior knowledge and note what information is given and what information you are asked to find.
2. Choose a variable to represent one of the unknowns and then express other unknowns in terms of it.
3. Use the given conditions in the problem and the unknowns from step 2 to write an algebraic equation.
4. Solve the equation for the unknown. Relate this answer to any other unknowns in the problem.
5. Check your results in the original statement of the problem.

E₁ A number increased by 11 yields 37. Find the number.

Example 2–1 E

Solve each of the verbal problems by setting up an equation and solving it.

1. A number increased by 16 gives 24. Find the number.

Let n = the number we are looking for. The key words to use are "increased by," which means *add,* and "gives," which means *equals.* The equation is then

a number	increased by	16	gives	24
n	$+$	16	$=$	24

$$
\begin{aligned}
n + 16 &= 24 \\
n &= 8. && \text{Subtract 16 from each member}
\end{aligned}
$$

The number is 8.

You are now ready to do $\mathbf{E_1}$.

2. Joan earned \$15 less than Mary did last week. If Joan earned \$342, how much did Mary earn?

Let d = the amount that Mary earned last week. The key words are "less than." Since Joan earned \$15 less than Mary, the equation is given by

Mary's salary	less \$15	is	Joan's salary
d	-15	$=$	342

$$d - 15 = 342$$
$$d = 357. \quad \text{Add 15 to each member}$$

Mary earned \$357 last week.

You are now ready to do **E_2**. ■

E_2 If a number is decreased by 16, the result is 52. Find the number.

Answers to section 2–1 margin exercises

A_1 true **A_2** false **C_1** $x = 19$ **C_2** $a = 3$ **C_3** $b = -3$ **C_4** $-4 = x$ **D_1** $y = 5$
D_2 $x = 7$ **D_3** $a = 2$ **D_4** $x = 11$ **D_5** $x = -5$ **D_6** $a = 10$ **E_1** 26 **E_2** 68

Mastery points

Can you

- Determine if a given number is a root of an equation?
- Use the addition and subtraction property of equality?
- Simplify equations?
- Solve for an unknown?
- Check your answer?

Exercise 2–1

Directions Determine if the statement is true or false for the given replacement value of the variable. See example 2–1 A.

Examples $\boxed{A_1}$ $3x + 3 = 6; 1$

Solutions

$$3(1) + 3 = 6$$
$$3 + 3 = 6$$
$$6 = 6 \quad \text{True}$$

$\boxed{A_2}$ $2x - 1 = 3; 4$

$$2(4) - 1 = 3$$
$$8 - 1 = 3$$
$$7 = 3 \quad \text{False}$$

1. $4 + x = 8; 4$

2. $3 - x = 4; -1$

3. $x + 7 = 10; 3$

4. $3x - 2 = 4; 2$

5. $8x + 6 = 2x - 6; -2$

6. $\frac{4}{5}x + 2 = 10; 10$

7. $7x - 3 = 2x + 2; -2$

8. $5x - 1 = 11x - 1; 0$

9. $2(x - 1) = 4x + 5; -\frac{7}{2}$

10. $3x + 2 = 5x - 1; \frac{3}{2}$

11. $\frac{x}{5} - 2 = 3x + 1; 1$

12. $\frac{2x}{3} - 1 = \frac{x}{4} + 3; 2$

Directions Find the solution by using the addition and subtraction property of equality. Check each solution. See examples 2–1 C and D.

Examples $\boxed{C_1}$ $x - 7 = 12$

Solutions
$x - 7 + 7 = 12 + 7$ Add 7
$x = 19$ Solution

Check $(19) - 7 = 12$
$12 = 12$ True

$\boxed{D_2}$ $4x - 2 = 3x + 5$

$4x - 3x - 2 = 3x - 3x + 5$ Subtract 3x
$x - 2 = 5$ Combine like terms
$x - 2 + 2 = 5 + 2$ Add 2
$x = 7$ Solution

Check $4(7) - 2 = 3(7) + 5$
$28 - 2 = 21 + 5$
$26 = 26$ True

13. $x - 4 = 12$ **14.** $y - 7 = 11$ **15.** $a + 5 = 2$ **16.** $b + 5 = 7$

17. $y - 6 = -8$ **18.** $5 = x + 7$ **19.** $9 = x + 14$ **20.** $a - 5 = -2$

21. $-10 = x - 4$ **22.** $a - 18 = -14$ **23.** $b + 7 = 0$ **24.** $y - 14 = 0$

25. $3x - 4 = 2x + 10$ **26.** $-y - 6 = -2y + 1$ **27.** $b + 4 = 2b + 5$

28. $6x - 5 = 5x + 11$ **29.** $-z - 8 = -2z - 4$ **30.** $5 - 3x = 7 - 4x$

31. $9 - 7a = 14 - 6a$ **32.** $3a - 5 = 2a - 2$

Directions Find the solution. See examples 2–1 C and D.

Examples $\boxed{D_4}$ $5x + 2x - 4 = 6x + 7$

Solutions
$7x - 4 = 6x + 7$ Combine like terms
$7x - 6x - 4 = 6x - 6x + 7$ Subtract 6x
$x - 4 = 7$ Combine like terms
$x - 4 + 4 = 7 + 4$ Add 4
$x = 11$ Solution

$\boxed{D_5}$ $3(2x + 1) = x + 4x - 2$

$6x + 3 = 5x - 2$ Distributive property
Combine like terms
$6x - 5x + 3 = 5x - 5x - 2$ Subtract 5x
$x + 3 = -2$ Combine like terms
$x + 3 - 3 = -2 - 3$ Subtract 3
$x = -5$ Solution

33. $6a - 3a + 7 = 9a - 5a + 2$ **34.** $-4x - 2x + 1 = -5x + 7$ **35.** $7b - 2b + 5 - 4b = 11$

36. $12 = 6x + 3 - 4x - x$

37. $-4 - x = 4x + 2 - 6x$

38. $5(x + 2) = 4(x - 1)$

39. $2(2y - 1) = 3(y + 2)$

40. $5(3x + 2) = 7(2x + 3)$

41. $5x - 4 + x = 5(x - 2)$

42. $3(2x + 1) - 7 = 5x - 4$

43. $(4a + 5) - (2 + 3a) = 8$

44. $(9b + 7) - (8b + 2) = -4$

45. $3(z + 7) - (8 + 2z) = 6$

46. $4(x - 5) - (3x + 4) = -2$

47. $2(a - 3) - (a - 2) = 8$

48. $5(a + 1) - (4a + 3) = 14$

49. $2(3x - 1) + 3(x + 2) = 4(2x + 5)$

50. $3(4x - 5) + 2(x - 4) = 3(5x + 2)$

51. $-2(b + 1) + 3(b - 4) = -5$

52. $-3(x - 2) + 4(x - 5) = -7$

Directions Solve the following problems by setting up an equation and solving for the unknown. See example 2–1 E.

53. Harry is 6 years older than Dene. If Dene is 54 years old, how old is Harry?

54. If Jake withdraws \$340 from his savings account, his balance will be \$395. How much does Jake have in his savings account now?

55. Pam deposits \$42.50 in her checking account. If her new balance is \$125.30, how much did she have in her account originally?

56. Mr. Johnson took in \$560 on a given day in his grocery store. If he paid out \$195 in expenses, how much profit did he realize?

57. Marsha can groom 11 more dogs per day than Margaret can. If Marsha can groom 24 dogs per day, how many dogs per day can Margaret groom?

58. If Gary's age is increased by 4 years, he would be 37 years old. How old is Gary now?

Review exercises

Directions Perform the indicated operations. See sections 1–4 and 1–5.

1. $(-2)(-8)$

2. $(-4)(3)$

3. $\frac{-8}{-8}$

4. $\frac{6}{6}$

5. $\left(\frac{1}{3}\right)(3)$

6. $\left(-\frac{1}{4}\right)(-4)$

2–2 The multiplication and division property of equality

Multiplication and division property of equality

In section 2–1, we used the associative, commutative, and distributive properties to simplify equations. We then used the addition and subtraction property of equality to solve for the unknown. These properties are sufficient to solve many of the equations that we encounter. However we cannot use them to solve such equations as

$$3x = 21 \quad \text{or} \quad \frac{2}{3}x = 12.$$

Recall that we want our equation to be of the form $x = n$. This means that the coefficient of x must be 1. To achieve this, we make use of the multiplication and division property of equality.

> **The multiplication and division property of equality**
> For any algebraic expressions a, b, and c $(c \neq 0)$,
>
> $$\text{if } a = b, \text{ then } a \cdot c = b \cdot c \text{ and } a \div c = b \div c.$$
>
> **Concept**
> An equivalent equation is obtained when we multiply or divide both members of the equation by the same nonzero quantity.

The multiplication and division property of equality enables us to multiply or divide both members of an equation by the same nonzero quantity. In the equation $3x = 21$, we use the multiplication and division property of equality to divide both members of the equation by 3. This forms an equivalent equation where x has a coefficient of 1, that is, $x = n$.

$$3x = 21$$

$$\frac{3x}{3} = \frac{21}{3} \qquad \text{Divide both members by 3}$$

$$x = 7 \qquad \text{Solution}$$

For the example $\frac{2}{3}x = 12$, recall that when we divide by a fraction, we invert and multiply. Therefore, if the coefficient is a fraction, we will multiply both members of the equation by the **reciprocal,** or **multiplicative inverse,** of the coefficient.

Multiplicative inverse

The **multiplicative inverse** of a number, also called the **reciprocal** of the number, is such that when we multiply a number times its reciprocal, the answer will be 1.

> **Multiplicative inverse property**
>
> For every real number a, $a \neq 0$,
>
> $$a \cdot \frac{1}{a} = 1.$$
>
> **Concept**
>
> Every real number except zero has a multiplicative inverse, and the product of a number and its multiplicative inverse is always 1.

Note

Zero is the only number that does not have a reciprocal. From the zero factor property, we know that zero times any number is zero. Therefore there can be no number such that zero times that number gives 1 as an answer.

$$a \cdot 0 = 0$$

The following examples are illustrations of the multiplicative inverse property, where the second number can be considered the reciprocal of the first, and the first can be considered the reciprocal of the second.

1. $5 \cdot \frac{1}{5} = 1$
2. $\frac{1}{2} \cdot 2 = 1$
3. $b \cdot \frac{1}{b} = 1, b \neq 0$
4. $\frac{3}{4} \cdot \frac{4}{3} = 1$
5. $\left(-\frac{5}{7}\right)\left(-\frac{7}{5}\right) = 1$

We will now use the multiplicative inverse property to solve the equation $\frac{2}{3}x = 12$.

$$\frac{2}{3}x = 12$$

$$\frac{3}{2} \cdot \frac{2}{3}x = \frac{3}{2} \cdot 12 \quad \text{Multiply both members by the reciprocal of the coefficient}$$

$$x = 18 \quad \text{Solution}$$

Note

In the earlier example $3x = 21$, we could have multiplied by the reciprocal of 3 to solve the equation. That is,

$$3x = 21$$

$$\frac{1}{3} \cdot 3x = \frac{1}{3} \cdot 21. \text{ Multiply both members by the reciprocal } \frac{1}{3}.$$

$$x = 7.$$

Remember that to divide by a number is the same operation as to multiply by the reciprocal of that number.

Example 2–2 A

Find the solution.

1. $5x = 30$

$\frac{5x}{5} = \frac{30}{5}$ Divide both members by the coefficient 5

$x = 6$ Solution

You are now ready to do **A_1**.

A_1 $5x = 35$

2. $\frac{3}{4}x = 9$

$\frac{4}{3} \cdot \frac{3}{4}x = \frac{4}{3} \cdot 9$ Multiply both members by the reciprocal $\frac{4}{3}$

$x = 12$ Solution

You are now ready to do **A_2**.

A_2 $\frac{2}{3}x = 8$

3. $7x = -14$

$\frac{7x}{7} = \frac{-14}{7}$ Divide both members by the coefficient 7

$x = -2$ Solution

You are now ready to do **A_3**.

A_3 $5y = -10$

4. $-3x = 15$

$\frac{-3x}{-3} = \frac{15}{-3}$ Divide both members by the coefficient -3

$x = -5$ Solution

You are now ready to do **A_4**.

A_4 $-3z = 18$

5. $-x = -10$

$-1 \cdot x = -10$ -1 is the coefficient

$\frac{-1 \cdot x}{-1} = \frac{-10}{-1}$ Divide both members by the coefficient -1

$x = 10$ Solution

You are now ready to do **A_5**.

A_5 $-6y = -24$

6. $6x = 10$

$\frac{6x}{6} = \frac{10}{6}$ Divide both members by the coefficient 6

$x = \frac{5}{3}$ Reduce the fraction—solution

You are now ready to do **A_6**.

A_6 $9a = -24$

7. $\frac{x}{4} = 6$ We can rewrite the left member to show that the coefficient is $\frac{1}{4}$

$\frac{1}{4}x = 6$ $\frac{x}{4}$ is the same as $\frac{1}{4} \cdot x$

$4 \cdot \frac{1}{4}x = 4 \cdot 6$ Multiply both members by the reciprocal 4

$x = 24$ Solution

You are now ready to do **A_7**.

A_7 $\frac{b}{3} = 5$

8. $1.2x = 4.8$

$\frac{1.2x}{1.2} = \frac{4.8}{1.2}$ Divide both members by 1.2

$x = 4$ Solution

You are now ready to do **A_8**.

A_8 $1.7x = 10.2$

9. $\frac{2}{5}x = \frac{4}{9}$

$\frac{5}{2} \cdot \frac{2}{5}x = \frac{5}{2} \cdot \frac{4}{9}$ Multiply both members by the reciprocal $\frac{5}{2}$

$x = \frac{10}{9}$ Solution

You are now ready to do **A_9**. ■

A_9 $\frac{3}{4}y = \frac{9}{10}$

Problem solving

Now we will translate some verbal statements into equations and solve the resulting equations.

Example 2–2 B

Write an equation for each problem and then solve the equation.

1. When a number is multiplied by -6, the result is 48. Find the number.

   Let n = the number we are looking for. Then the equation would be

a number	multiplied by (-6)	result is	48
n	$\cdot(-6)$	$=$	48

$n \cdot (-6) = 48$

$\frac{n(-6)}{-6} = \frac{48}{-6}$ Divide both members by -6

$n = -8.$ Solution

The number is -8.

You are now ready to do **B_1**.

B_1 When a number is multiplied by 6, the result is 54. Find the number.

2. Alice makes \$4.50 per hour. If her pay was \$108, how many hours did she work?

   Let n = the number of hours that she worked. Then the equation would be

hourly rate	times	number of hours worked	gives	total pay
(4.50)	$\cdot$	n	$=$	108

$(4.50) \cdot n = 108$

$\frac{(4.50)n}{4.50} = \frac{108}{4.50}$ Divide both members by 4.50

$n = 24.$ Solution

Alice worked 24 hours.

You are now ready to do **B_2**. ■

B_2 Adam worked for 14 hours and received \$52.50. Find his hourly wage.

Answers to section 2–2 margin exercises

A_1 $x = 7$ **A_2** $x = 12$ **A_3** $y = -2$ **A_4** $z = -6$ **A_5** $y = 4$ **A_6** $a = -\frac{8}{3}$

A_7 $b = 15$ **A_8** $x = 6$ **A_9** $y = \frac{6}{5}$ **B_1** 9 **B_2** \$3.75 per hour

Mastery points

Can you

- Use the multiplication and division property of equality to form equivalent equations where the coefficient of the unknown is 1?
- Check your answer?

Exercise 2–2

Directions Find the solution by using the multiplication and division property of equality. Check each solution. See example 2–2 A.

Examples

A₁ $5x = 35$

Solutions $\frac{5x}{5} = \frac{35}{5}$ Divide by 5

$x = 7$ Solution

Check $5(7) = 35$

$35 = 35$ True

A₂ $\frac{2}{3}x = 8$

$\frac{3}{2} \cdot \frac{2}{3}x = \frac{3}{2} \cdot 8$ Multiply by $\frac{3}{2}$

$x = 12$ Solution

Check $\frac{2}{3}(12) = 8$

$8 = 8$ True

A₃ $1.7x = 10.2$

$\frac{1.7x}{1.7} = \frac{10.2}{1.7}$ Divide by 1.7

$x = 6$ Solution

Check $1.7(6) = 10.2$

$10.2 = 10.2$ True

1. $2x = 8$ **2.** $3x = 18$ **3.** $6x = 36$ **4.** $9x = 45$

5. $\frac{3}{4}x = 12$ **6.** $\frac{2}{5}x = 10$ **7.** $\frac{1}{7}x = 5$ **8.** $\frac{1}{5}x = 9$

9. $\frac{3}{2}x = 18$ **10.** $14 = \frac{7}{3}x$ **11.** $5x = -15$ **12.** $-8 = 2x$

13. $-24 = 6x$ **14.** $-5x = 30$ **15.** $-4x = -28$ **16.** $-30 = -6x$

17. $-x = 4$ **18.** $-x = -11$ **19.** $6x = 14$ **20.** $5x = 9$

21. $4x = 6$ **22.** $3x = -8$ **23.** $5x = 0$ **24.** $0 = 7x$

25. $-3x = 0$ **26.** $-2x = 0$ **27.** $\frac{x}{3} = 5$ **28.** $\frac{x}{4} = 8$

29. $\frac{x}{-2} = 7$ **30.** $-2 = \frac{x}{-3}$ **31.** $2.6x = 10.4$ **32.** $3.1x = 21.7$

33. $-4.8x = 33.6$

34. $-7.1x = 35.5$

35. $-42.9 = -3.9x$

36. $(0.4)x = 7.2$

37. $(0.3)x = -7.8$

38. $\frac{5}{7}x = 8$

39. $\frac{3}{8}x = 14$

40. $\frac{2}{9}x = 11$

Directions Write an equation for each exercise and then solve the equation. See example 2–2 B.

41. When a number is multiplied by -4, the result is 36. Find the number.

42. When a number is divided by 9, the result is -7. Find the number.

43. When a number is divided by -8, the result is -8. Find the number.

44. Four friends shared equally in the expenses for a party. If each person's share was $32.50, what was the total cost of the party?

45. Nancy worked for 30 hours and received $135. Find her hourly wage.

46. Six friends shared equally in the cost of dinner. If the cost of the dinner was $51, what was each person's share?

47. If $\frac{3}{4}$ of a number is 48, find the number.

48. If $\frac{2}{3}$ of a number is 26, find the number.

Review exercises

Directions Perform all indicated operations. See section 1–7.

1. $3x + 2x + 1 - 3$

2. $7x - 5x - 3 + 4$

3. $8x - 5 + 4x + 7$

4. $6x + 3 - 3x - 8$

5. $2(3x + 1) + 4x - 3$

6. $3(x - 1) + 2(x + 2)$

2–3 Solving linear equations

Review of properties

We now are ready to combine the properties from the previous sections to help us solve more involved equations. The process consists of forming equivalent equations until we have our equation in the form of $x = n$. The properties that we will use are the following:

1. We can add or subtract the same number in both members of the equation.
2. We can multiply or divide both members of the equation by the same nonzero number.

Procedure for solving a linear equation

Using these properties, there are four basic steps to solve a linear equation. We shall now apply the properties to the equation $6(x + 1) = 4x + 10$.

Solving a linear equation

$$6(x + 1) = 4x + 10$$

Step 1 *Simplify each member of the equation.* Perform all indicated addition, subtraction, multiplication, and division. Remove all grouping symbols. In our example, step 1 would be to carry out the indicated multiplication in the left member as follows:

$$6(x + 1) = 4x + 10$$
$$6x + 6 = 4x + 10. \quad \text{Distributive property}$$

Step 2 *Use the addition and subtraction property of equality to form an equivalent equation where all the terms involving the unknown are in one member of the equation.* By subtracting $4x$ from *both* members of the equation, we have

$$6x + 6 = 4x + 10$$
$$6x - 4x + 6 = 4x - 4x + 10 \quad \text{Subtract } 4x$$
$$2x + 6 = 10. \quad \text{Combine like terms}$$

Step 3 *Use the addition and subtraction property of equality to form an equivalent equation where all the terms not involving the unknown are in the other member of the equation.* Subtracting 6 from *both* members of the equation, we have

$$2x + 6 = 10$$
$$2x + 6 - 6 = 10 - 6 \quad \text{Subtract 6}$$
$$2x = 4. \quad \text{Combine like terms}$$

Step 4 *Use the multiplication and division property of equality to form an equivalent equation where the coefficient of the unknown is 1.* That is, $x = n$. By dividing *both* members of the equation by 2, we have

$$2x = 4$$
$$\frac{2x}{2} = \frac{4}{2} \quad \text{Divide by 2}$$
$$x = 2. \quad \text{Solution}$$

To check our answer, we substitute the solution in place of the unknown in the original equation. If we get a true statement, we say that the solution "satisfies" the equation. For the equation $6(x + 1) = 4x + 10$, we found that $x = 2$. We can check the answer by substituting 2 in place of x in the original equation.

$$6[(2) + 1] = 4(2) + 10 \quad \text{Substitute 2 for } x$$
$$6[3] = 8 + 10 \quad \text{Order of operations}$$
$$18 = 18 \quad \text{True}$$

We see that $x = 2$ satisfies the equation.

Example 2–3 A

Find the solution and check.

1. $8y + 5 - 7y = 10 - 2y + 3$

$$5 + y = 13 - 2y \quad \text{Combine like terms (step 1)}$$
$$5 + y + 2y = 13 - 2y + 2y \quad \text{Add } 2y \text{ (step 2)}$$
$$5 + 3y = 13 \quad \text{Combine like terms}$$
$$5 + 3y - 5 = 13 - 5 \quad \text{Subtract 5 (step 3)}$$
$$3y = 8 \quad \text{Combine like terms}$$
$$\frac{3y}{3} = \frac{8}{3} \quad \text{Divide by 3 (step 4)}$$
$$y = \frac{8}{3} \quad \text{Solution}$$

Check: $8\left(\frac{8}{3}\right) + 5 - 7\left(\frac{8}{3}\right) = 10 - 2\left(\frac{8}{3}\right) + 3$ Substitute $\frac{8}{3}$ for y

$$\frac{64}{3} + \frac{15}{3} - \frac{56}{3} = \frac{30}{3} - \frac{16}{3} + \frac{9}{3} \quad \text{Multiply, change to common denominator}$$
$$\frac{64 + 15 - 56}{3} = \frac{30 - 16 + 9}{3} \quad \text{Add and subtract in numerators}$$
$$\frac{23}{3} = \frac{23}{3} \quad \text{True}$$

You are now ready to do **A₁**.

2. $\frac{4x + x}{3} = 10$

$$\frac{5x}{3} = 10 \quad \text{Combine like terms in numerator}$$
$$\frac{5}{3} \cdot x = 10 \quad \frac{5x}{3} \text{ is the same as } \frac{5}{3} \cdot x$$
$$\frac{3}{5} \cdot \frac{5}{3} \cdot x = \frac{3}{5} \cdot 10 \quad \text{Multiply both members by } \frac{3}{5}$$
$$x = 6 \quad \text{Solution}$$

Check: $\frac{4(6) + (6)}{3} = 10$ Substitute 6 for x

$$\frac{24 + 6}{3} = 10 \quad \text{Multiply}$$
$$\frac{30}{3} = 10 \quad \text{Add}$$
$$10 = 10 \quad \text{True}$$

You are now ready to do **A₂**.

A_1 $13a + 7 + a = 15 + 10a$

A_2 $\frac{5a + a}{7} = 12$

$\boxed{A_3}$ $5x + 2(x - 1) = 4 - 3x$

Observe from the last example that although we have four basic steps in solving a linear equation, we do not always use all four steps in each problem.

3.
$$
\begin{aligned}
4(5x - 2) + 7 &= 5(3x + 1) \\
20x - 8 + 7 &= 15x + 5 && \text{Distributive property} \\
20x - 1 &= 15x + 5 && \text{Combine like terms} \\
20x - 15x - 1 &= 15x - 15x + 5 && \text{Subtract } 15x \\
5x - 1 &= 5 && \text{Combine like terms} \\
5x - 1 + 1 &= 5 + 1 && \text{Add 1} \\
5x &= 6 && \text{Combine like terms} \\
\frac{5x}{5} &= \frac{6}{5} && \text{Divide by 5} \\
x &= \frac{6}{5} && \text{Solution}
\end{aligned}
$$

Check:
$$
\begin{aligned}
4\left[5\left(\frac{6}{5}\right) - 2\right] + 7 &= 5\left[3\left(\frac{6}{5}\right) + 1\right] && \text{Substitute } \frac{6}{5} \text{ for } x \\
4[6 - 2] + 7 &= 5\left[\frac{18}{5} + 1\right] && \text{Order of operations} \\
4[4] + 7 &= 5\left[\frac{18}{5} + \frac{5}{5}\right] \\
16 + 7 &= 5\left[\frac{23}{5}\right] \\
23 &= 23 && \text{True}
\end{aligned}
$$

You are now ready to do $\mathbf{A_3}$. ■

At this point, we will no longer show the check of our solution, but we should realize that a check of our solution is an important final step.

$\mathbf{B_1}$ $\frac{1}{3}x - 1 = \frac{1}{6}$

The following equations contain several fractions. When this occurs, it is usually easier to **clear the equation of all fractions.** We do this by **multiplying both members of the equation by the least common denominator of all the fractions.** Clearing all of the fractions is considered a means of simplifying the equation and will be done as a first step when necessary. Equations containing fractions will be studied more completely in chapter 6.

Example 2–3 B

Find the solution.

1.
$$
\begin{aligned}
\frac{1}{4}x + 2 &= \frac{1}{2} \\
4\left(\frac{1}{4}x + 2\right) &= 4\left(\frac{1}{2}\right) && \text{The least common denominator of the fractions is 4, multiply \textbf{both members} by 4} \\
4\left(\frac{1}{4}x\right) + 4(2) &= 4\left(\frac{1}{2}\right) && \text{Simplify (distributive property)} \\
x + 8 &= 2 && \text{All fractions have been cleared} \\
x + 8 - 8 &= 2 - 8 && \text{Subtract 8} \\
x &= -6 && \text{Solution}
\end{aligned}
$$

You are now ready to do $\mathbf{B_1}$.

2.

$$\frac{5}{6}x - \frac{2}{3} = \frac{3}{4}x + 2$$

$$12\left(\frac{5}{6}x - \frac{2}{3}\right) = 12\left(\frac{3}{4}x + 2\right)$$ The least common denominator of 3, 4, and 6 is 12, multiply by 12

$$12\left(\frac{5}{6}x\right) - 12\left(\frac{2}{3}\right) = 12\left(\frac{3}{4}x\right) + 12(2)$$ Simplify (distributive property)

$$10x - 8 = 9x + 24$$ Multiply

$$10x - 9x - 8 = 9x - 9x + 24$$ Subtract $9x$

$$x - 8 = 24$$ Combine like terms

$$x - 8 + 8 = 24 + 8$$ Add 8

$$x = 32$$ Solution

You are now ready to do **B_2**. ■

B_2 $\frac{3}{4}x + \frac{1}{2} = \frac{2}{3}x + \frac{5}{6}$

Answers to section 2–3 margin exercises

A_1 $a = 2$ **A_2** $a = 14$ **A_3** $x = \frac{3}{5}$ **B_1** $x = \frac{7}{2}$ **B_2** $x = 4$

Mastery points

Can you

- Solve linear equations?
- Check your answers?

Exercise 2–3

Directions Find the solutions of the following equations and check the answers. See examples 2–3 A, B.

Example $\boxed{A_3}$ $5x + 2(x - 1) = 4 - 3x$

Solution

Step 1 $5x + 2x - 2 = 4 - 3x$ Simplify (distributive property)

$7x - 2 = 4 - 3x$ Combine like terms

Step 2 $7x + 3x - 2 = 4 - 3x + 3x$ Add $3x$

$10x - 2 = 4$ Combine like terms

Step 3 $10x - 2 + 2 = 4 + 2$ Add 2

$10x = 6$ Combine like terms

Step 4 $\frac{10x}{10} = \frac{6}{10}$ Divide by 10 and reduce

$x = \frac{3}{5}$ Solution

Check

$$5\left(\frac{3}{5}\right) + 2\left[\left(\frac{3}{5}\right) - 1\right] = 4 - 3\left(\frac{3}{5}\right)$$ Substitute $\frac{3}{5}$ for x

$$5\left(\frac{3}{5}\right) + 2\left[\frac{3}{5} - \frac{5}{5}\right] = 4 - \frac{9}{5}$$ Order of operations

$$5\left(\frac{3}{5}\right) + 2\left[\frac{-2}{5}\right] = \frac{20}{5} - \frac{9}{5}$$

$$\frac{15}{5} + \frac{-4}{5} = \frac{11}{5}$$

$$\frac{11}{5} = \frac{11}{5}$$ True

1. $2x = 4$ **2.** $3x = 11$ **3.** $5x = -10$ **4.** $-2x = 8$

5. $\frac{x}{2} = 18$

6. $\frac{x}{4} = 24$

7. $\frac{3x}{2} = 8$

8. $\frac{5x}{3} = 18$

9. $x + 7 = 11$

10. $x - 4 = 9$

11. $x + 5 = 5$

12. $x - 4 = -4$

13. $3x + 1 = 10$

14. $5x - 2 = 13$

15. $4x + 7 = 7$

16. $6x + 2 = 2$

17. $5x + 2x = x + 6$

18. $2x + (3x - 1) = 4 - x$

19. $2x + 3x - 6x = 4x - 8$

20. $\frac{x}{2} + 7 = 14$

21. $5 - \frac{3x}{5} = 11$

22. $\frac{5x + 2x}{6} = 10$

23. $\frac{1}{2}x + 3 = \frac{3}{4}$

24. $\frac{1}{5}x - 1 = \frac{7}{10}$

25. $\frac{1}{3}x + 2 = \frac{1}{2}x - 1$

26. $\frac{1}{4}x - 3 = \frac{1}{8}x + 1$

27. $\frac{2}{3}x + 5 = \frac{3}{4}$

28. $\frac{3}{5}x - 3 = \frac{3}{10}$

29. $\frac{3}{8}x + \frac{1}{2} = \frac{1}{4}x + 2$

30. $\frac{7}{12}x + 1 = \frac{2}{3}x - 1$

31. $3(2x - 1) = 4x + 3$

32. $5(7x - 3) = 30x + 11$

33. $12x - 8 = 5x + 2$

34. $3(2x + 5) = 4(x - 3)$

35. $8 - 2(3x + 4) = 5x - 16$

36. $(3x + 2) - 2(2x - 5) = 7$

37. $(7x - 6) - 3(4 - 3x) = 27$

38. $2(x - 4) - 3(5 - 2x) = 16$

39. $3(2x + 3) = 5 - 4(x - 2)$

40. $6(3x - 2) = 7(x - 3) - 2$

41. $2(x + 5) = 16$

42. $6 = 2(2x - 1)$

43. $2x - 2(3 - x) = 0$

44. $3(7 - 2x) = 30 - 7(x + 1)$

45. To convert Celsius temperature to Fahrenheit, we use $F = \frac{9}{5}C + 32$.

a. Find C when $F = 18$.

b. Find C when $F = -27$.

c. Find C when $F = 2$.

46. The Stefan-Boltzmann Law in metallurgy, which is the temperature scale of radiation pyrometers, is given by $W = KT^4$.

a. Find K when $W = 36$, $T = 2$.

b. Find K when $W = 243$, $T = -3$.

47. The total creep of a metal (E) at time t is given by $E = C + Vt$, where C = original creep, t = time, and V = the original volume. Find V when $E = 16$, $C = 9$, and $t = 3$.

48. In a gear system, the speed, in number of revolutions, of two gears and the number of teeth in the gears are related by $S \cdot T = D \cdot E$, where S is the speed of the driver, T is the number of teeth in the driver, D is the speed of the driven gear, and E is the number of teeth in the driven gear.

a. If $S = 240$, $T = 40$, and $D = 360$, find E.

b. If $S = 120$, $D = 90$, and $E = 18$, find T.

Review exercises

Directions Evaluate the following formulas. See section 1–8.

1. $W = I^2R$, $I = 6$ and $R = 3$

2. $S = \frac{1}{2}gt^2$, $g = 32$ and $t = 3$

3. $A = \frac{1}{2}h(b + c)$, $h = 8$, $b = 10$, and $c = 12$

4. $I = prt$; $p = 2{,}000$; $r = 0.06$; and $t = 3$

5. $V = \ell wh$, $\ell = 10$, $w = 4$, and $h = 7$

6. $V = k + gt$, $k = 12$, $g = 16$, and $t = 5$

▣ 2–4 Verbal problems

Many problems that you encounter will be stated verbally. These will need to be translated into algebraic equations. In chapter 1, we saw how to take a verbal phrase and write an algebraic expression for it.

We are now ready to combine our ability to write an expression and our ability to solve an equation and apply them to solve a verbal problem. While there is no standard procedure for solving a verbal problem, the following guidelines should be useful.

1. Read the problem carefully. Determine useful prior knowledge and note what information is given and what information you are asked to find.
2. Let some letter represent one of the unknowns, and then express other unknowns in terms of it.
3. Use the given conditions in the problem and the unknowns from step 2 to write an algebraic equation.
4. Solve the equation for the unknown. Relate this answer to any other unknowns in the problem.
5. Check your results in the original statement of the problem.

Example 2–4 A

Write an equation for the problem and solve for the unknown quantities.

1. One number is 4 more than a second number. If their sum is 38, find the two numbers.

Note
In problems where you are finding more than one value, it is usually easiest to let the unknown represent the smallest unknown value.

Let x = the smaller number (the second number). Then $x + 4$, which is 4 more than the smaller number, represents the other number. The parts that make up the equation are

smaller number	sum	larger number	is	38
x	$+$	$(x + 4)$	$=$	38

$x + (x + 4) = 38$	Original equation
$x + x + 4 = 38$	Remove grouping symbol
$2x + 4 = 38$	Combine like terms
$2x = 34$	Subtract 4
$x = 17$	Divide by 2

Therefore the smaller number is 17 and the larger number is 4 more than the smaller number and is $17 + 4 = 21$.

You are now ready to do **A_1**.

A_1 What number added to its double gives 24?

2. One number is 6 times a second number and their sum is 21. Find the numbers.

Let x = the smaller number. Then six times the smaller number or $6x$ = the other number. The parts that make up the equation are

smaller number	sum	larger number	is	21
x	$+$	$6x$	$=$	21

$x + 6x = 21$	Original equation
$7x = 21$	Combine like terms
$x = 3$	Divide by 7

Hence the smaller number is 3 and the larger number is 6 times the smaller number and is $6 \cdot (3) = 18$.

You are now ready to do **A_2**.

A_2 One natural number is 5 times another natural number and their sum is 36. Find the numbers.

3. If the first of two consecutive integers is multiplied by 3, this product is 4 more than the sum of the two integers. Find the integers.

Note
Prior knowledge that is needed for this problem is that consecutive integers differ by 1. Therefore we add 1 to the first to get the second, we would add 2 to the first to get a third, and so on.

first	second	third	fourth	fifth
x	$x + 1$	$x + 2$	$x + 3$	$x + 4$

A₃ The sum of three consecutive integers is 36. Find the integers.

first integer	second integer
x	$x + 1$

The parts that make up the equation are

three times the first integer	this product is	4	more than	the sum
$3x$	$=$	4	$+$	$x + (x + 1)$

$$3x = 4 + x + (x + 1) \quad \text{Original equation}$$
$$3x = 4 + x + x + 1 \quad \text{Remove grouping symbol}$$
$$3x = 2x + 5 \quad \text{Combine like terms}$$
$$x = 5 \quad \text{Subtract } 2x$$

Therefore the first consecutive integer is 5 and the second integer is one more than the first and is $5 + 1 = 6$.

You are now ready to do $\mathbf{A_3}$. ■

Answers to section 2–4 margin exercises

$\mathbf{A_1}$ 8 $\mathbf{A_2}$ 6, 30 $\mathbf{A_3}$ 11, 12, 13

Mastery points

Can you

- Write an equation for a verbal problem?
- Solve for the unknown quantities?

Exercise 2–4

Directions Write an equation for the problem and solve for the unknown quantities. See example 2–4 A.

Example $\mathbf{A_2}$ One natural number is 5 times another natural number and their sum is 36. Find the numbers.

Solution Let $x =$ the smaller number. Then five times the smaller number or $5x =$ the other number. The parts that make up the equation are

smaller number	sum	larger number	is	36
x	$+$	$5x$	$=$	36

$$x + 5x = 36 \quad \text{Original equation}$$
$$6x = 36 \quad \text{Combine like terms}$$
$$x = 6 \quad \text{Divide by 6}$$

Therefore the smaller number is 6 and the larger number is 5 times the smaller number and is $5 \cdot (6) = 30$.

1. One number is 18 more than a second number. If their sum is 62, find the two numbers.

2. One number is 9 less than another number. If their sum is 47, find the two numbers.

3. The difference of two numbers is 17. Find the numbers if their sum is 87.

4. If three times a number is increased by 11 and the result is 47, what is the number?

5. If a number is divided by 4 and that result is then increased by 6, the answer is 13. Find the number.

6. If a number is decreased by 14 and that result is then divided by 5, the answer is 15. Find the number.

7. Nine times a number is decreased by 4, leaving 59. What is the number?

8. One-third of a number is 8 less than one-half of the number. Find the number.

9. The difference between one-half of a number and one-third of the number is 9. Find the number.

Example A_3 The sum of three consecutive integers is 36. Find the integers.

Solution

first integer	second integer	third integer
x	$(x+1)$	$(x+2)$

The parts that make up the equation are

the sum of three consecutive integers	is	36
$x + (x+1) + (x+2)$	$=$	36

$$x + (x+1) + (x+2) = 36 \quad \text{Original equation}$$
$$x + x + 1 + x + 2 = 36 \quad \text{Remove grouping symbols}$$
$$3x + 3 = 36 \quad \text{Combine like terms}$$
$$3x = 33 \quad \text{Subtract 3}$$
$$x = 11 \quad \text{Divide by 3}$$

Hence the first integer is $x = 11$, the second integer is $x + 1 = (11) + 1 = 12$, and the third integer is $x + 2 = (11) + 2 = 13$.

10. The sum of three consecutive even integers is 72. Find the integers.

11. The sum of three consecutive odd integers is 51. Find the integers.

12. One number is 4 times a second number and their sum is 65. Find the numbers.

13. One number is 9 times a second number and their sum is 120. Find the numbers.

14. The sum of three numbers is 44. The second number is three times the first number and the third number is 6 less than the first number. Find the three numbers.

15. The sum of three numbers is 63. The first number is twice the second number and the third number is three times the first number. Find the three numbers.

16. One number is 7 more than another number. Find the two numbers if three times the larger number exceeds four times the smaller number by 5.

17. One number is 4 more than another number. Find the two numbers if two times the larger number is 7 less than five times the smaller number.

Example The length of a rectangle is 3 times its width and its perimeter is 40 feet. Find the dimensions.

Note
We need the prior knowledge that the perimeter of a rectangle is given by the formula $P = 2w + 2\ell$.

Solution Let $x =$ the width, then 3 times the width or $3x =$ the length.

$P = 2w + 2\ell$	Formula for perimeter
$40 = 2(x) + 2(3x)$	Substitute
$40 = 2x + 6x$	Multiply
$40 = 8x$	Combine like terms
$5 = x$	Divide by 8

Therefore the width is $x = 5$ feet and the length is $3x = 3(5) = 15$ feet.

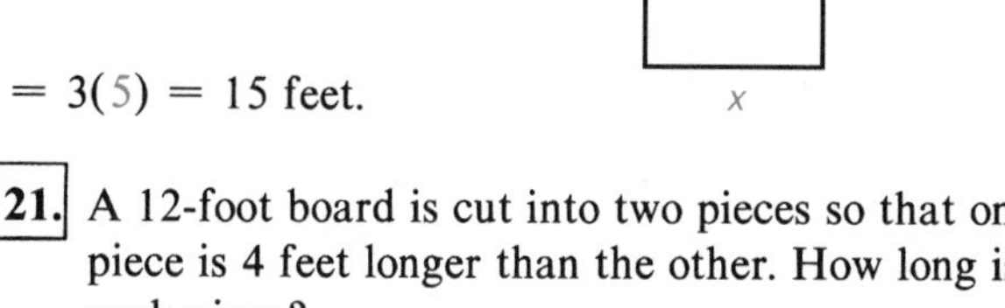

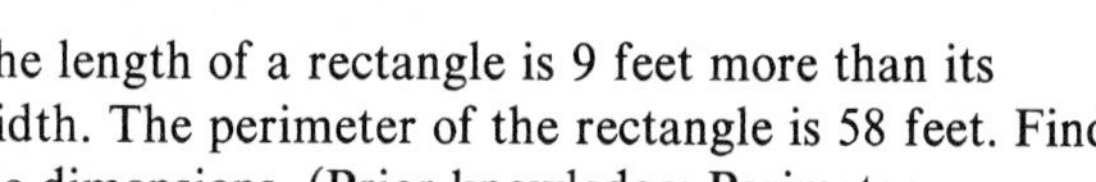

18. The length of a rectangle is 9 feet more than its width. The perimeter of the rectangle is 58 feet. Find the dimensions. (Prior knowledge: Perimeter = 2 times the length plus 2 times the width.)

19. The width of a rectangle is 3 feet less than its length. The perimeter of the rectangle is 70 feet. Find the dimensions. (See exercise 18.)

20. The width of a rectangle is $\frac{1}{3}$ of its length. If the perimeter is 96 feet, find the dimensions.

21. A 12-foot board is cut into two pieces so that one piece is 4 feet longer than the other. How long is each piece?

22. A 24-foot rope is cut into two pieces so that one piece is twice as long as the other. How long is each piece?

23. A 50-foot extension cord is cut into two pieces so that one piece is 12 feet longer than the other piece. How long is each piece?

24. The sum of two currents is 80 amperes. If the greater current is 24 amperes more than the lesser current, find their values.

Example A man has $10,000, part of which he invests at 11% and the rest at 8%. If his total income from the two investments for one year is $980, how much does he have invested at each rate?

Solution

Note

All interest problems in this textbook will be simple interest and the prior knowledge that is needed for these problems is that Interest = principal · rate · time. Time will be equal to 1 year in the following problems.

11% investment	8% investment
x	$10{,}000 - x$

equation

$$x(0.11) + (10{,}000 - x)(0.08) = 980$$

If we have a total amount of $10,000 to invest and we invest x dollars at 11%, then the amount left to invest at 8% would be the total amount minus what we have already invested, $10{,}000 - x$.

$x(0.11) + (10{,}000 - x)(0.08) = 980$	Original equation
$0.11x + 800 - 0.08x = 980$	Distributive property
$0.03x + 800 = 980$	Combine like terms
$0.03x = 180$	Subtract 800
$x = 6{,}000$	Divide by 0.03

Hence he has $x = 6{,}000$ dollars at 11% and $10{,}000 - x = 10{,}000 - (6{,}000) = 4{,}000$ dollars at 8%.

25. Phil has $20,000, part of which he invests at 8% interest and the rest at 6%. If his total income was $1,460 from the two investments, how much did he invest at each rate?

26. Nancy has $18,000. She invests part of her money at 7½% interest and the rest at 9%. If her income from the two investments was $1,560, how much did she invest at each rate?

27. Rich has $18,000, part of which he invests at 10% interest and the rest at 8%. If his income from each investment was the same, how much did he invest at each rate?

28. Barb has $30,000, part of which she invests at 9% interest and the rest at 7%. If her income from the 7% investment was $820 more than that from the 9% investment, how much did she invest at each rate?

29. Lynne made two investments totaling \$25,000. On one investment she made an 18% profit, but on the other investment she took an 11% loss. If her net gain was \$2,180, how much was each investment?

30. Larry made two investments totaling \$21,000. One investment made him a 13% profit, but on the other investment, he took a 9% loss. If his net loss was \$196, how much was each investment?

31. Jennifer has \$14,000 invested at 7% and is going to invest an additional amount at 11% so that her total investment will make 9%. How much does she need to invest at 11% to achieve this?

Review exercises

Directions Evaluate the following formulas. See section 1–8.

1. $I = prt$, $p = 2{,}000$; $r = 0.05$; $t = 1$

2. $V = \ell wh$, $\ell = 7$, $w = 4$, $h = 3$

3. $F = ma$, $m = 34$, $a = 6$

4. $V = k + gt$, $k = 12$, $g = 32$, $t = 3$

5. $A = p + pr$, $p = 3{,}000$; $r = 0.06$

6. $A = \frac{1}{2}(b + c)$, $b = 20$, $c = 12$

7. $S = \frac{1}{2}gt^2$, $g = 32$, $t = 4$

8. $\ell = a + (n - 1)d$, $a = 4$, $n = 10$, $d = 4$

▣ 2–5 Solving literal equations and formulas

A₁ $V = \ell wh$; solve for ℓ.

Literal equations and formulas

Equations that contain two or more variables are called **literal equations.** In a literal equation, we generally solve the equation for one variable in terms of the remaining variables and constants. **The procedure for solving a literal equation is the same as the procedure for solving linear equations.** A **formula** is a mathematical equation that states the relationship between two or more physical conditions.

The following list is a restatement of the procedure for solving linear equations that we will now apply to literal equations.

Solving a literal equation or a formula

Step 1 Simplify each member of the equation.
Step 2 Collect all the terms with the variable for which we are solving in one member of the equation. (Addition and subtraction property)
Step 3 Collect all the terms not involving the variable for which we are solving in the other member of the equation. (Addition and subtraction property)
Step 4 Divide each member of the equation by the coefficient of the variable for which we are solving. (Multiplication and division property)

Example 2–5 A

Solve for the specified variable.

A₂ $I = prt$; solve for t.

1. The volume of a rectangular solid is found by multiplying length (ℓ) times width (w) times height (h), $V = \ell wh$. Solve the equation for h.

$V = \ell wh$	Original equation
$V = (\ell w)h$	Coefficient of h is ℓw
$\frac{V}{\ell w} = \frac{\ell wh}{\ell w}$	Divide by ℓw
$\frac{V}{\ell w} = h$	Equation is solved for h in terms of V, ℓ, and w
$h = \frac{V}{\ell w}$	Symmetric property

You are now ready to do **A₁**.

2. The simple interest (I) earned on the principal (p) over a time period (t) at an interest rate (r) is given by $I = prt$. Solve for r.

$I = prt$	Original equation
$I = (pt)r$	pt is the coefficient of r
$\frac{I}{pt} = \frac{ptr}{pt}$	Divide by pt
$\frac{I}{pt} = r$	Equation is solved for r in terms of I, p, and t
$r = \frac{I}{pt}$	Symmetric property

You are now ready to do **A₂**.

A₃ $P = 2\ell + 2w$, for ℓ

3. If we know the temperature in degrees Fahrenheit (F), the temperature in degrees Celsius (C) can be found by the equation $C = \frac{5}{9}(F - 32)$. Solve the formula for F.

$C = \frac{5}{9}(F - 32)$	Original equation
$9C = 9 \cdot \frac{5}{9}(F - 32)$	Clear the fraction
$9C = 5(F - 32)$	Multiply
$9C = 5F - 160$	Distributive property
$9C + 160 = 5F$	Add 160
$\frac{9C + 160}{5} = F$	Divide by 5
$F = \frac{9C + 160}{5}$	Symmetric property

If the temperature is given in degrees Celsius, we use this form of the equation to determine the temperature in degrees Fahrenheit.

You are now ready to do **A₃**.

Note
Although we have not stated any restrictions on the variables, it is understood that the values that the variables can take on must be such that no denominator is ever zero. That is, in example 1, $\ell \neq 0$ and $w \neq 0$; in example 2, $p \neq 0$, $t \neq 0$. ■

Whether we are solving a linear equation or a literal equation, the procedure is the same.

Linear equation	**Literal equation**	
$5(x + 1) = 2x + 7$	$5(x + y) = 2x + 7y$	Original equation
$5x + 5 = 2x + 7$	$5x + 5y = 2x + 7y$	Simplify (distributive property)
$3x + 5 = 7$	$3x + 5y = 7y$	All x in one member
$3x = 2$	$3x = 2y$	Terms not containing x in other member
$x = \frac{2}{3}$	$x = \frac{2y}{3}$	Divide by the coefficient

In the linear equation, we have a solution for x, and in the literal equation, we have solved for x in terms of y.

Answers to section 2–5 margin exercises

A₁ $\ell = \frac{V}{wh}$ **A₂** $t = \frac{I}{pr}$ **A₃** $\ell = \frac{P - 2w}{2}$

Mastery points

Can you

- Solve literal equations and formulas for a specified variable?

Exercise 2–5

Directions Solve for the specified variable. See example 2–5 A.

Example A3 $P = 2\ell + 2w$ for ℓ

Solution

$$P - 2w = 2\ell \quad \text{Subtract } 2w$$

$$\frac{P - 2w}{2} = \ell \quad \text{Divide by 2}$$

$$\ell = \frac{P - 2w}{2} \quad \text{Symmetric property}$$

1. $V = \ell wh$, for w

2. $V = \ell wh$, for ℓ

3. $I = Prt$, for P

4. $I = prt$, for t

5. $F = ma$, for m

6. $E = IR$, for R

7. $K = PV$, for V

8. $E = mc^2$, for m

9. $W = I^2R$, for R

10. $A = \ell w$, for w

11. $P = 2\ell + 2w$, for w

12. $C = \pi D$, for π

13. $P = a + b + c$, for a

14. $A = \frac{1}{2}bh$, for b

15. $ay - 3 = by + c$, for a

16. $ay - 3 = by + c$, for b

17. $V = k + gt$, for k

18. $V = k + gt$, for t

19. $A = \frac{1}{2}h(b + c)$, for b

20. $A = \frac{1}{2}h(b + c)$, for h

21. $\ell = a + (n - 1)d$, for a

22. $\ell = a + (n - 1)d$, for d

23. $A = p(1 + r)$, for p

24. $\ell = a + (n - 1)d$, for n

25. $T = 2f + g$, for f

26. $i = \frac{prm}{12}$, for r

27. $D = dq + R$, for q

28. $M = -P(\ell - x)$, for x

29. $R = W - b(2c + b)$, for c

30. $A = p(1 + rt)$, for p

31. $A = p(1 + rt)$, for r

32. $V = r^2(a - b)$, for a

33. $3x - y = 4x + 5y$, for x

34. $3x - y = 4x + 5y$, for y

35. $2S = 2vt - gt^2$, for g

36. $ax + by = c$, for y

Directions Solve the following formulas or literal equations for the specified variable. See example 2–5 A.

37. The distance s that a body projected downward with an initial velocity of v falls in t seconds because of the force of gravity is given by $s = \frac{1}{2}gt^2 + vt$. Solve for g.

38. Solve the formula in exercise 37 for v.

39. The net profit P on sales of n identical tape decks is given by $P = n(S - C) - e$, where S is the selling price, C is the cost to the dealer, and e is the operating expense. Solve for S.

40. Solve the formula in exercise 39 for C.

41. Solve the formula in exercise 39 for e.

Review Exercise

Directions Perform the indicated operations. See section 1–6.

1. -5^2 **2.** $(-5)^2$ **3.** -3^4 **4.** $(-3)^3$

Directions Write an algebraic expression for each of the following. See section 1–7.

5. x raised to the fourth power

6. A number squared

7. The product of a and b

8. x multiplied by y

2–6 Solving linear inequalities—The addition and subtraction property of inequalities

Inequality symbols

In chapter 1, we studied the meaning of the *strict inequality* symbols.

$<$ is less than
$>$ is greater than

There are two other inequality symbols, called *weak inequalities*. They are

$\leq$ is less than or equal to,
$\geq$ is greater than or equal to.

The weak inequality symbol $\geq$, is greater than or equal to, denotes that one number could either be greater than a second number or equal to that second number. The inequality $x \geq 3$ means that x **is at least** 3. That is, x represents all numbers that are 3 or more.

The other weak inequality symbol, $\leq$, is less than or equal to, denotes that one number could either be less than a second number or equal to that second number. The inequality $x \leq 5$ means that x **is at most** 5. That is, x represents all numbers that are 5 or less.

These symbols define order, or sense, between real numbers.

1. If we want to state symbolically that 4 is less than 7, we write $4 < 7$.
2. If we wish to denote that the variable x represents 5 or any number greater than 5, we write $x \geq 5$.

Note
$x \geq 5$ represents *any* real number that is greater than or equal to 5, and not just any integer greater than or equal to 5. Remember that 5.1, 5.004, and so on, are also greater than 5.

3. If we wish to denote that the variable T represents any number less than 3, but not 3 itself, we write $T < 3$.

A₁ $x < 2$

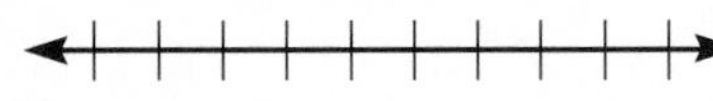

Linear inequalities

We now study **linear inequalities.** These are statements that relate algebraic expressions by order (inequality) symbols. To illustrate,

$$3x - 2 < x + 7$$

Left member — Inequality symbol — Right member

is a linear inequality in one variable (x). Recall that a linear equation in one variable has at most *one* solution. Linear inequalities in one variable have an interval of solutions that satisfy the inequality.

Consider the inequality

$$2x \geq 6.$$

We can, by inspection, see that if we replace x by 3, $\frac{7}{2}$, 4, or 5, we have a true statement. In fact, replacing x by *any* number that is 3 or greater will produce a true statement. That is, $x \geq 3$.

Another way to indicate the solution of an inequality is by graphing. To graph the solution, we simply draw a real number line (as we did in chapter 1), place a solid circle at 3 on the number line, and draw an arrow extending from the solid circle to the right (figure 2–1).

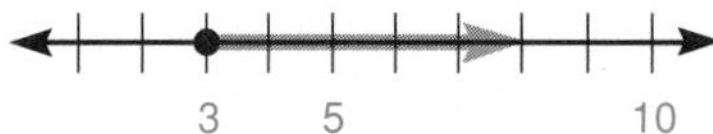

Figure 2–1

A₂ $x \geq 0$

The solid line indicates that *all* numbers greater than or equal to 3 are part of the graph.

Example 2–6 A

Graph the following linear inequalities on the real number line.

1. $x < 4$

Here x represents all real numbers less than 4, but not 4 itself. To denote the fact that x cannot equal 4, we put a **hollow circle** at 4.

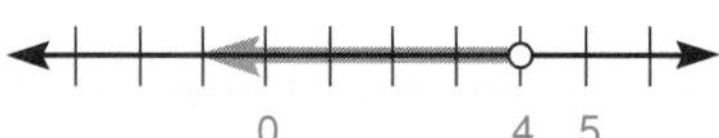

You are now ready to do **A₁**.

2. $x \geq -3$

The greater than or equal to symbol, $\geq$, indicates that the graph will contain the number -3, and we place a **solid circle** at -3.

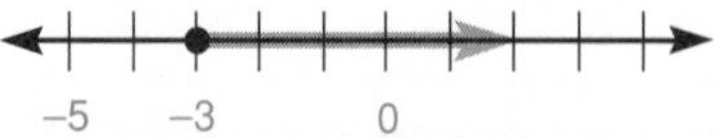

> **Note**
> When we graph inequalities, a strict inequality ($<$ or $>$) is represented by a hollow circle at the number. A weak inequality ($\leq$ or $\geq$) is represented by a solid circle at the number.

You are now ready to do **A₂**.

3. $-3 \leq x < 4$

This statement is called a **compound inequality.** It is read "-3 is less than or equal to x **and** x is less than 4." We place a solid circle at -3 to show that -3 is included and place a hollow circle at 4 to show that 4 is not included. We then draw a line segment between the two circles.

−5 −3 0 4 5

You are now ready to do **A₃**.

A₃ $-7 < x \leq -4$

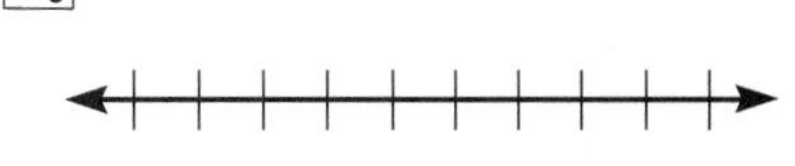

The addition and subtraction property of inequalities

The properties that we will be using to solve inequalities are similar to those that we used to solve linear equations.

> **Addition and subtraction property of inequalities**
>
> For all real numbers a, b, and c, if $a < b$, then
>
> $$a + c < b + c \text{ and } a - c < b - c.$$
>
> **Concept**
>
> The same number can be added to or subtracted from both members of an inequality without changing the direction of the inequality symbol.

Note

The property is stated in terms of the less than ($<$) symbol. The property also applies to any of the other inequality symbols ($>$, $\leq$, or $\geq$).

B₁ $y - 3 < -1$

The following examples demonstrate how the addition and subtraction property of inequalities is used to find the solution of linear inequalities in one variable.

Example 2–6 B

Find the solution of the following inequalities and graph the solution on the real number line.

1. $x - 6 < 1$

As with equations, the objective is to get the variable alone in one member and the numbers in the other member.

$x - 6 + 6 < 1 + 6$ Add 6 to each member

$x < 7$ Combine in each member

Thus $x < 7$ and the solutions are all real numbers *less than 7.*

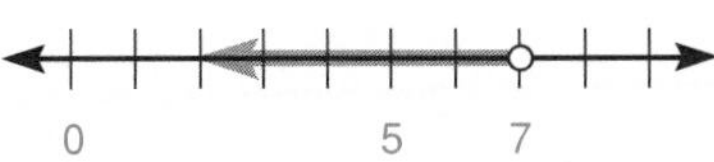

You are now ready to do **B₁**.

B₂ $4x - 1 \geq 3x + 1$

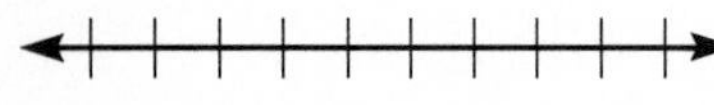

2. $3x + 4 \geq 2x - 1$

We must apply the addition and subtraction property twice.

$$\begin{aligned} 3x + 4 - 2x &\geq 2x - 1 - 2x && \text{Subtract } 2x \text{ from each member} \\ x + 4 &\geq -1 && \text{Combine in each member} \\ x + 4 - 4 &\geq -1 - 4 && \text{Subtract 4 from each member} \\ x &\geq -5 && \text{Combine in each member} \end{aligned}$$

Thus $x \geq -5$ and the solutions are all real numbers greater than or equal to -5.

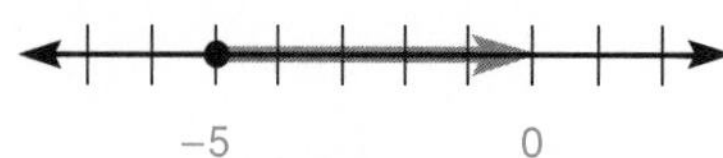

You are now ready to do **B_2**.

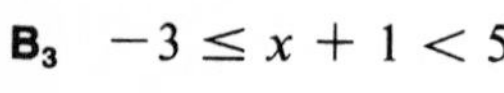

B_3 $-3 \leq x + 1 < 5$

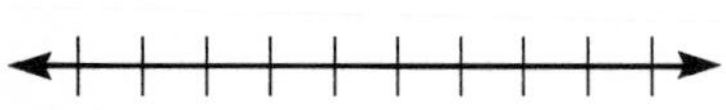

Note

When subtracting the term containing the variable from each member, *always* subtract the term whose coefficient is the least. We subtracted $2x$ in the previous example rather than $3x$. Doing this will give a positive coefficient for the variable.

3. $-2 \leq x - 5 < 1$

We now have a compound inequality. What we do to one member of the inequality we must do to each of the other two members. The objective is to get the variable by itself in the middle member with a coefficient of 1.

$$\begin{aligned} -2 + 5 \leq x - 5 + 5 &< 1 + 5 && \text{Add 5 to each member} \\ 3 \leq x &< 6 && \text{Combine in each member} \end{aligned}$$

Thus $3 \leq x < 6$ and the solutions are all real numbers *between* 3 and 6, *including 3 but not 6.*

0 3 5 6

You are now ready to do **B_3**.

B₄ To complete an order for cement, a company needs at least 3 trucks. Write an inequality for the number of trucks needed.

4. Write an inequality for the following statement: A student's test grade, G, must be at least 75 to have a passing grade.

If the student's grade must be *at least* 75, the grade must be 75 or greater. Thus

$G \geq 75$.

You are now ready to do **B_4**.

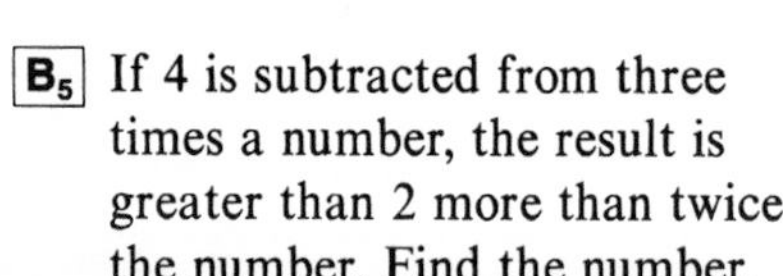

B₅ If 4 is subtracted from three times a number, the result is greater than 2 more than twice the number. Find the number.

5. Four times a number less 5 is to be no more than three times the number increased by 2. Find the number.

Let x represent the number.

4 times a number	less	5	is no more than	3 times the number	increased by	2
$4x$	$-$	5	$\leq$	$3x$	$+$	2

The inequality is

$$\begin{aligned} 4x - 5 &\leq 3x + 2 \\ 4x - 5 - 3x &\leq 3x + 2 - 3x && \text{Subtract } 3x \text{ from each member} \\ x - 5 &\leq 2 && \text{Combine in each member} \\ x - 5 + 5 &\leq 2 + 5 && \text{Add 5 to each member} \\ x &\leq 7 && \text{Combine in each member} \end{aligned}$$

The number is any real number x such that $x \leq 7$.

You are now ready to do **B_5**. ■

Answers to section 2–6 margin exercises

A₁ 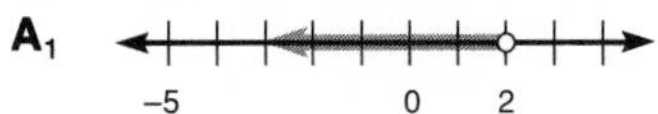

A₂ 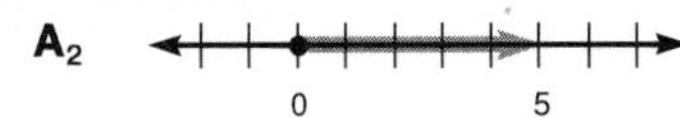

A₃

−7 −4 0

B₁ $y < 2$

−5 0 2

B₂ $x \geq 2$

0 2 5

B₃ $-4 \leq x < 4$

−4 0 4

B₄ $x \geq 3$ **B₅** $x > 6$

Mastery points

Can you

- Graph inequalities and compound inequalities?
- Solve inequalities and compound inequalities?
- Write inequality statements for word statements?

Exercise 2–6

Directions Graph the following on the real number line. See example 2–6 A.

Example **A₃** $-7 < x \leq -4$

Solution We want all real numbers between -7 and -4, *including* -4 (since $x \leq -4$) and *excluding* -7 (since $-7 < x$).

1. $x > 2$

2. $x \geq -1$

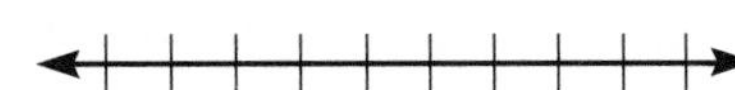

3. $x < 0$

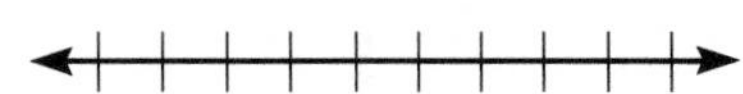

4. $x > 0$

5. $x \leq -4$

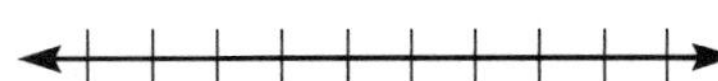

6. $-1 < x < 2$

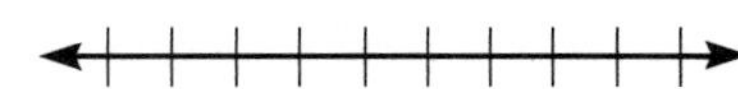

7. $0 \leq x \leq 5$

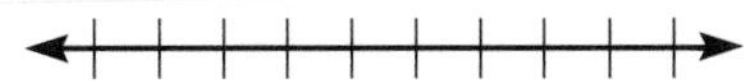

8. $-1 < x \leq 3$

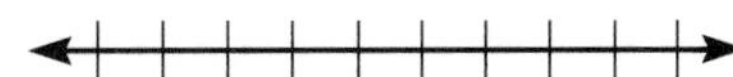

9. $-2 \leq x < 2$

Directions Solve each inequality for the variable and graph the solution on the real number line. See example 2–6 B–1, 2, 3.

Example $\boxed{B_2}$ $4x - 1 \geq 3x + 1$

Solution

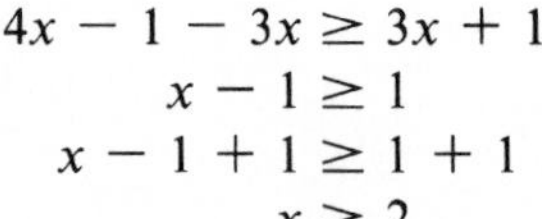

$$4x - 1 - 3x \geq 3x + 1 - 3x \quad \text{Subtract } 3x \text{ from each member}$$
$$x - 1 \geq 1 \quad \text{Combine in each member}$$
$$x - 1 + 1 \geq 1 + 1 \quad \text{Add 1 to each member}$$
$$x \geq 2 \quad \text{Combine in each member}$$

Thus $x \geq 2$ and the solutions are all real numbers greater than or equal to 2.

10. $x + 7 \geq 9$

11. $x + 5 < 0$

12. $x + 4 > -1$

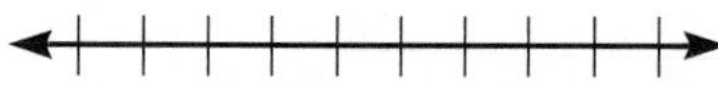

13. $x + 1 \leq -3$

14. $5x \geq 4x - 1$

15. $3x < 2x + 3$

16. $4x - 2 \leq 3x + 1$

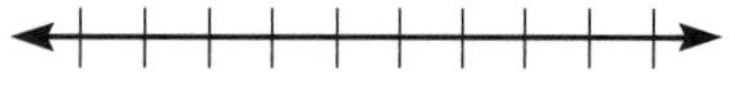

17. $2x + 5 > 3x + 2$

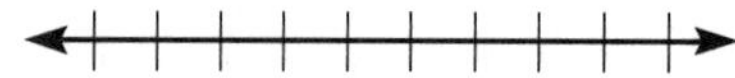

18. $8y + 3 \geq 9y + 6$

19. $3 \leq y + 1 \leq 5$

20. $0 < y + 3 < 4$

21. $-8 \leq x - 4 < 1$

22. $-3 < x - 6 \leq 0$

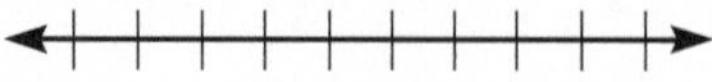

Directions Write an inequality for each of the following statements. See example 2–6 B–4.

Example B₄ To complete an order for cement, a company needs at least 3 trucks.

Solution The words *at least* 3 trucks means that the company will need *3 or more* trucks. If x is the number of trucks needed, then

$x \geq 3.$

23. The student's score must be at least 72 on the final exam to pass the course.

24. The temperature today will be less than 38.

25. A company needs to order at least 8 new lift trucks.

26. The selling price (P) must be at least twice the cost (C).

27. A company will hire at least 2 new employees, but not more than 7.

28. A student's score must be below 65 to fail the examination.

Directions Translate each of the following word problems into an inequality and solve the problem. See example 2–6 B–5.

Example B₅ If 4 is subtracted from three times a number, the result is greater than 2 more than twice the number. Find the number.

Solution Let x be the unknown number. Then $3x - 4$ is "4 subtracted from three times the number," $2x + 2$ is "2 more than twice the number."

Since the two expressions are related by "is greater than," the inequality is

$$3x - 4 > 2x + 2$$
$$3x - 4 - 2x > 2x + 2 - 2x \quad \text{Subtract } 2x \text{ from each member}$$
$$x - 4 > 2 \quad \text{Combine in each member}$$
$$x - 4 + 4 > 2 + 4 \quad \text{Add 4 to each member}$$
$$x > 6 \quad \text{Combine in each member}$$

The number is any number that is greater than 6.

29. Three times a number is less than the sum of 5 and two times the number. Find the numbers that satisfy this condition.

30. The product of 6 times a number added to 2 is greater than or equal to 1 subtracted from five times the number. What are the numbers that satisfy these conditions?

31. Twice a number increased by 7 is no more than three times the number decreased by 5. Find the numbers that satisfy these conditions.

32. The perimeter (the sum of the sides) of a triangle is more than 52 cm. If two sides of the triangle are 18 cm and 16 cm, respectively, what are the possible values for the length of the third side?

33. Two sides of a triangle are 10 ft and 12 ft long, respectively. If the perimeter must be at least 31 ft, what are the possible values for the length of the third side?

Review exercises

Directions Perform the indicated operations.

1. Simplify the expression $-3 + 2(-4) - 6(3 - 5)$. See section 1–6.

2. Evaluate the expression $3x - 2y - 4(y - x)$ when $x = 3$ and $y = -2$. See section 1–8.

3. Solve the following equations. See section 2–3.

a. $-4x = 24$

b. $5y + 2 = y - 8$

c. $\frac{3}{2}y - \frac{2}{3}y = 26$

4. Given $n = 10$, $a = 2$, and $\ell = 26$, find S when $S = \frac{n}{2}(a + \ell)$. See section 2–4.

2-7 Solving linear inequalities—The multiplication and division property of inequalities

A linear inequality such as $3x < 12$ cannot be solved using the addition or subtraction property. Such an inequality requires the use of the **multiplication** and **division property of inequalities.**

> **Multiplication and division property of inequalities**
>
> For all real numbers a, b, and c, if $a < b$, then
>
> 1. If $c > 0$ (c represents a positive number), then
>
> $$a \cdot c < b \cdot c \text{ and } \frac{a}{c} < \frac{b}{c}.$$
>
> **Concept**
>
> We can multiply or divide *both* members of the inequality by the same positive number without changing the direction of the inequality symbol.
>
> 2. If $c < 0$ (c represents a negative number), then
>
> $$a \cdot c > b \cdot c \text{ and } \frac{a}{c} > \frac{b}{c}.$$
>
> **Concept**
>
> We can multiply or divide *both* members of an inequality by the same *negative* number, provided that we **reverse** the direction of the inequality symbol.

To demonstrate these properties, consider the inequality $6 < 12$.

1. Multiplying by a positive number: multiply by 4.

$$6 < 12$$
$$4 \cdot 6 < 4 \cdot 12 \quad \text{Multiply each member by 4}$$
$$24 < 48 \quad \text{True}$$

2. Dividing by a positive number: divide by 3.

$$6 < 12$$
$$\frac{6}{3} < \frac{12}{3} \quad \text{Divide each member by 3}$$
$$2 < 4 \quad \text{True}$$

3. Multiplying by a negative number: multiply by -2.

$$6 < 12$$
$$-2 \cdot 6 < -2 \cdot 12 \quad \text{Multiply each member by } -2$$
$$-12 < -24 \quad \text{False}$$

We must change the direction of the inequality symbol to obtain a true statement. Thus

$$-12 > -24 \quad \text{True}$$

A₁ $4y \geq 20$

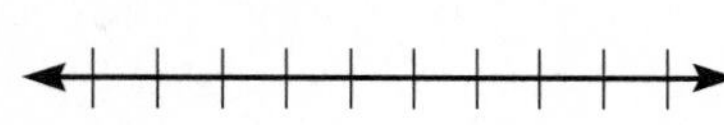

4. Dividing by a negative number: divide by -2.

$6 < 12$

$\frac{6}{-2} < \frac{12}{-2}$ Divide each member by -2

$-3 < -6$ False

We must change the direction of the inequality symbol.

$-3 > -6$ True

Note
This property also holds true for the inequality symbols $\leq$, $>$, and $\geq$.

Example 2–7 A

Find the solution of the following inequalities and graph the solution on the real number line.

1. $3x \leq 12$
To isolate the variable in the left member, divide each member by 3.

$\frac{3x}{3} \leq \frac{12}{3}$ Divide each member by 3

$x \leq 4$ Direction of the inequality symbol does not change since 3 is positive

Thus $x \leq 4$ and the solutions are all real numbers less than or equal to 4.

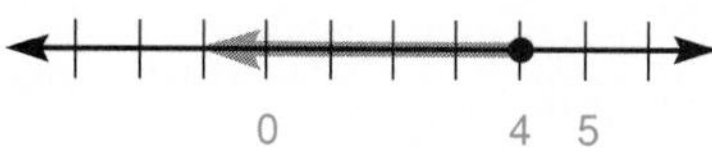

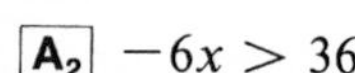

A₂ $-6x > 36$

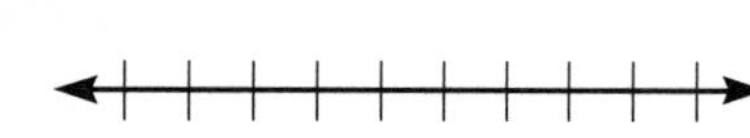

You are now ready to do **A₁**.

2. $-5x < 35$
Divide each member by -5 to isolate the variable.

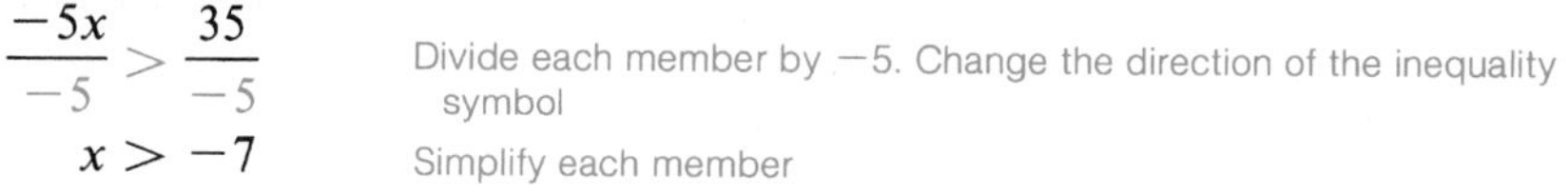

$\frac{-5x}{-5} > \frac{35}{-5}$ Divide each member by -5. Change the direction of the inequality symbol

$x > -7$ Simplify each member

Thus $x > -7$ and the solutions are all real numbers greater than -7.

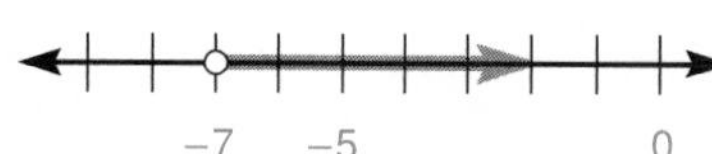

You are now ready to do **A₂**. ■

In the following examples, we use the addition and subtraction along with multiplication and division properties to find the solutions. The steps used to solve these inequalities are as follows:

Solving a linear inequality

1. Simplify in each member, where necessary, by performing the indicated operations.
2. Use the addition and subtraction property of inequalities to get all terms containing the unknown in one member of the inequality.
3. Use the addition and subtraction property of inequalities to get all terms *not* containing the unknown in the other member of the inequality.
4. Use the multiplication and division property of inequalities to obtain a coefficient of 1 for the unknown. **Remember, when multiplying or dividing by a negative number, always change the direction of the inequality symbol.**

Example 2–7 B

Find the solution of the following inequalities and graph the solution on the real number line.

1. $2x + 5x - 1 < 4x + 2$

$7x - 1 < 4x + 2$	Combine like terms in left member
$7x - 1 - 4x < 4x + 2 - 4x$	Subtract $4x$ from each member
$3x - 1 < 2$	Combine like terms
$3x - 1 + 1 < 2 + 1$	Add 1 to each member
$3x < 3$	Combine like terms
$x < 1$	Divide each member by 3

Thus $x < 1$ and the solutions are all real numbers less than 1.

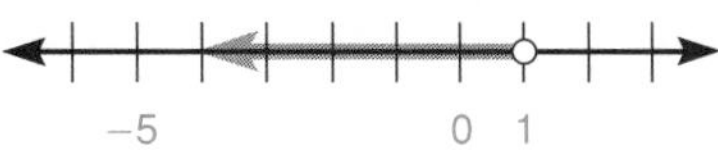

You are now ready to do **B_1**.

2. $5(2x + 1) \geq 7x - 4x - 9$

$10x + 5 \geq 3x - 9$	Simplify by multiplying in left member and combining like terms in right member
$10x + 5 - 3x \geq 3x - 9 - 3x$	Subtract $3x$ from each member
$7x + 5 \geq -9$	Combine like terms
$7x + 5 - 5 \geq -9 - 5$	Subtract 5 from each member
$7x \geq -14$	Combine like terms
$\frac{7x}{7} \geq \frac{-14}{7}$	Divide each member by 7
$x \geq -2$	Simplify

Thus $x \geq -2$ and the solutions are all real numbers greater than or equal to -2.

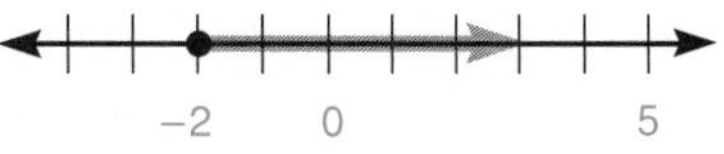

You are now ready to do **B_2**.

B_1 $3y + 2y - 5 < y + 3$

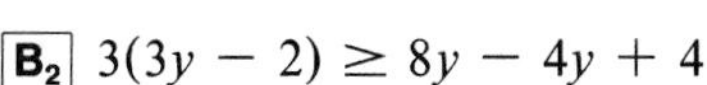

B_2 $3(3y - 2) \geq 8y - 4y + 4$

B₃ $-4 < 3x - 1 \le 8$

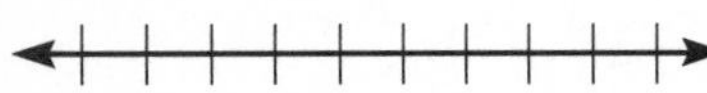

3. $-3 \le 2x + 1 < 5$

We have a compound inequality. So what we do to one member (part) of the inequality, we must do to the other two members (parts). We work to isolate the unknown in the middle member with a coefficient of 1.

$-3 - 1 \le 2x + 1 - 1 < 5 - 1$	Subtract 1 from all three members
$-4 \le 2x < 4$	Combine in each member
$\frac{-4}{2} \le \frac{2x}{2} < \frac{4}{2}$	Divide all three members by 2
$-2 \le x < 2$	Simplify

Thus $-2 \le x < 2$ and the solutions are all real numbers between -2 and 2, including -2 but excluding 2.

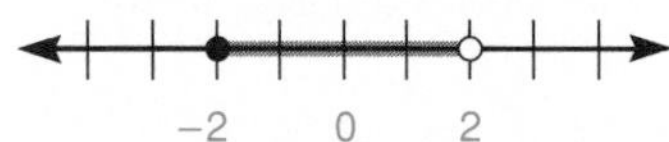

You are now ready to do **B₃**.

B₄ $-2 \le 4 - 3x < 13$

4. $2 < 5 - 3y \le 11$

$2 - 5 < 5 - 3y - 5 \le 11 - 5$	Subtract 5 from each member
$-3 < -3y \le 6$	Combine in each member
$\frac{-3}{-3} > \frac{-3y}{-3} \ge \frac{6}{-3}$	Divide each member by -3 Change the direction of the inequality symbols
$1 > y \ge -2$	Simplify

The solution is all real numbers y such that 1 is greater than y and y is greater than or equal to -2 (or $-2 \le y < 1$ which is read -2 is less than or equal to y and y is less than 1. This is the preferred way to write the compound inequality where values increase from left to right).

In symbols, we have

$$1 > y \ge -2 \quad \text{or} \quad -2 \le y < 1.$$

−2 0 1

You are now ready to do **B₄**.

B₅ The sum of 8 and four times a number is no more than 24. Find all numbers that satisfy this condition.

5. If five times a number is added to 3, the result is no more than 18. Find all numbers that satisfy this condition.

Let x represent the number. Then

five times a number	is added to	3	the result is no more than	18
$5x$	$+$	3	$\le$	18

The inequality is

$5x + 3 \le 18$	
$5x + 3 - 3 \le 18 - 3$	Subtract 3 from each member
$5x \le 15$	Combine in each member
$\frac{5x}{5} \le \frac{15}{5}$	Divide each member by 5
$x \le 3$	Simplify

The answer is all real numbers that are 3 or less.

You are now ready to do **B₅**. ■

The following table shows a number of different ways to state the inequality symbols.

Symbol	$<$	$\leq$	$>$	$\geq$
In words	is less than is fewer than	is at most is no more than is no greater than is less than or equal to	is greater than is more than exceeds	is at least is no less than is no fewer than is greater than or equal to

Answers to section 2–7 margin exercises

A_1 $y \geq 5$

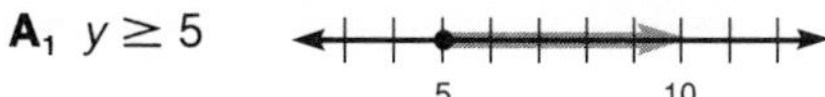

A_2 $x < -6$

B_1 $y < 2$

B_2 $y \geq 2$

B_3 $-1 < x \leq 3$

B_4 $-3 < x \leq 2$

B_5 $x \leq 4$

Mastery points

Can you

- Solve linear inequalities in one variable using the multiplication and division property of inequalities?
- Solve linear inequalities in one variable using the addition and subtraction along with the multiplication and division properties of inequalities?
- Set up an inequality for a word problem and then solve it?

Exercise 2–7

Directions Find the solution and graph the solution on the real number line. See example 2–7 A.

Example A₂ $-6x > 36$

Solution $\dfrac{-6x}{-6} < \dfrac{36}{-6}$ Divide each member by -6. Change the direction of the inequality symbol since we divided by a negative number

$x < -6$ Reduce in each member

Thus $x < -6$ and the solutions are all real numbers less than -6.

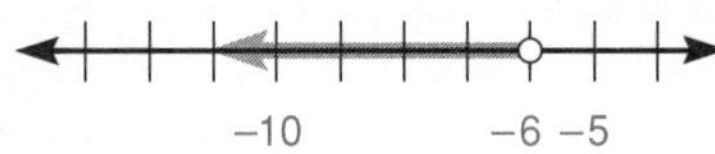

1. $2x > 10$

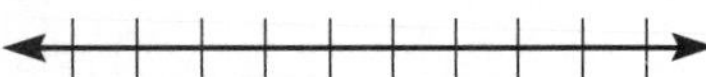

2. $4x \leq -12$

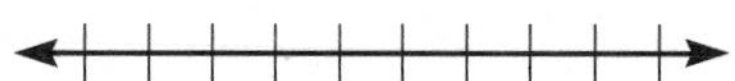

3. $3x \geq 15$

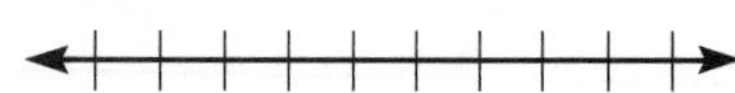

4. $5x < 30$

5. $\dfrac{3}{4}x < -3$

6. $\dfrac{2}{3}x \geq 4$

7. $-4x < 12$

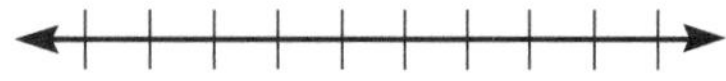

8. $-6x \geq 18$

9. $-2x \leq -10$

10. $-\dfrac{5}{3}x > 25$

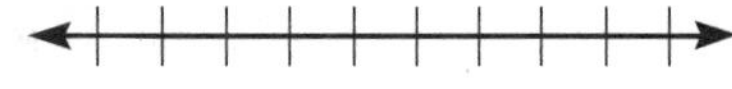

See example 2–7 B.

Example **B₂** $3(3y - 2) \geq 8y - 4y + 4$

Solution

$9y - 6 \geq 4y + 4$	Multiply in left member and combine in right member
$9y - 4y - 6 \geq 4y - 4y + 4$	Subtract $4y$ from each member
$5y - 6 \geq 4$	Combine in each member
$5y - 6 + 6 \geq 4 + 6$	Add 6 to each member
$5y \geq 10$	Combine in each member
$\dfrac{5y}{5} \geq \dfrac{10}{5}$	Divide each member by 5
$y \geq 2$	Simplify

Thus $y \geq 2$ and the solutions are all real numbers greater than or equal to 2.

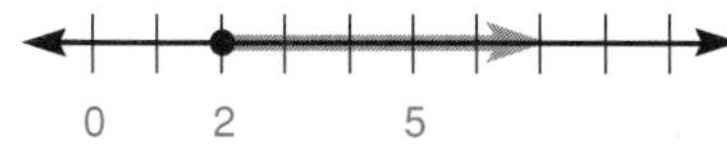

11. $8x - 2x > 4x - 5$

12. $3x + 2x < x + 6$

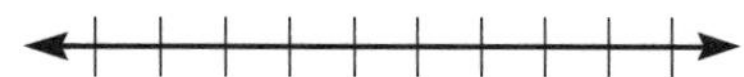

13. $12x - 8 > 5x + 2$

14. $4y + 3 \geq 2y - 5$

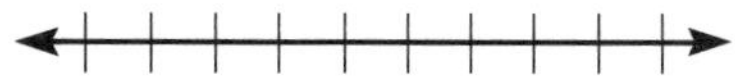

15. $3 - 5y \leq 2y + 10$

16. $4 - x < 3x - 4$

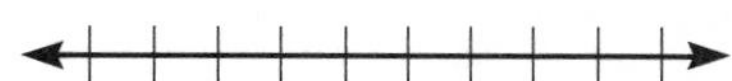

17. $2 + 5x - 16 < 6x - 4$

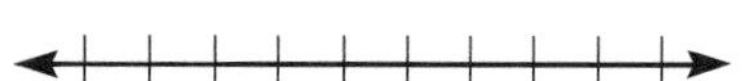

18. $8 - 2(3x + 4) > 5x - 16$

19. $3(1 - 2x) \geq 2(4 - 4x)$

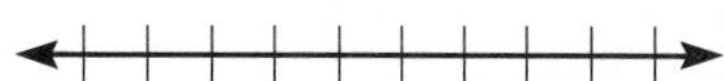

20. $3(2x - 3) \geq -4(x - 4)$

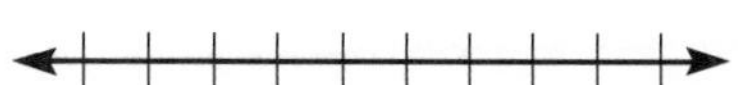

21. $-1 < 2x + 3 < 4$

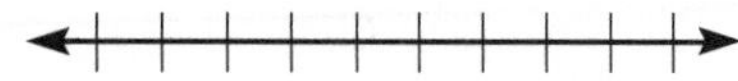

22. $-2 \leq 5x + 2 \leq 3$

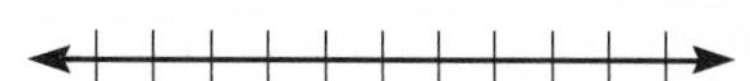

23. $-5 < 4x + 3 \leq 8$

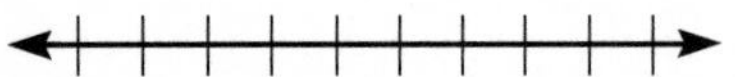

24. $-1 \leq -x < 4$

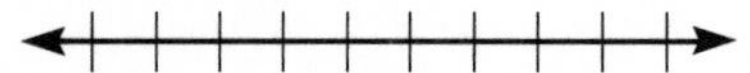

25. $-2 < -x \leq 3$

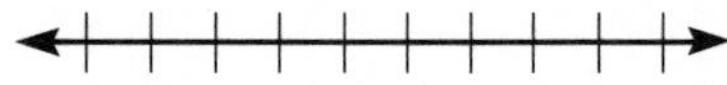

26. $-3 < 4 - x \leq 5$

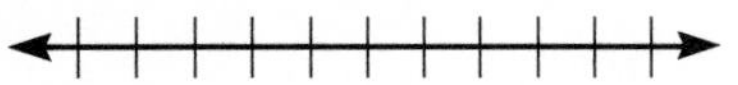

27. $0 \leq 1 - 3x < 7$

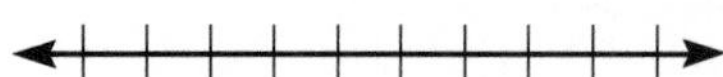

28. $-16 \leq 8 - 4x \leq 0$

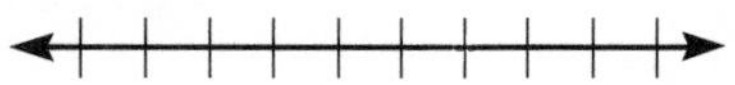

Directions Set up an inequality and solve each word problem. See example 2–7 B–5.

Example B5 The sum of 8 and four times a number is no more than 24. Find all numbers that satisfy these conditions.

Solution Let x represent the number. Then

8	the sum of	four times a number	is no more than	24
8	$+$	$4x$	$\leq$	24

The inequality is

$$8 + 4x \leq 24$$
$$8 + 4x - 8 \leq 24 - 8 \quad \text{Subtract 8 from each member}$$
$$4x \leq 16 \quad \text{Combine in each member}$$
$$\frac{4x}{4} \leq \frac{16}{4} \quad \text{Divide each member by 4}$$
$$x \leq 4 \quad \text{Simplify}$$

All real numbers such that $x \leq 4$ satisfy the conditions of the problem.

29. When 6 is subtracted from five times a number, the result is no more than 14. Find all numbers that satisfy these conditions.

30. When 7 is added to six times a number, the result is at least 25. What numbers satisfy these conditions?

31. Eight times a number less 1 is at least three times the number increased by 9. What numbers satisfy these conditions?

32. The perimeter of a square must be greater than 20 inches but less than 108 inches. Find all values of a side that satisfy these conditions. (*Note:* Perimeter equals four times the length of side.)

33. Twice a number increased by 4 is at least 8 and is less than 16. Find all numbers that satisfy these conditions.

34. Two times a number plus 4 is greater than 6 but less than 14. Find all numbers that satisfy these conditions.

35. Four times a number minus 7 is greater than 17 but less than 25. Find all numbers that satisfy these conditions.

36. The perimeter of a square must be at least 24 inches but at most 144 inches. Find all values of a side that satisfy these conditions.

37. The perimeter of a rectangle must be less than 100 feet. If the length is known to be 30 feet, find all numbers that the width could be. (*Note:* The width of a real rectangle must be a positive number.)

38. Sam has scores of 72, 67, and 81 on three tests. If an average of 70 is required to pass the course, what is the minimum score he must have on the fourth test to pass? $\left(\textit{Hint: } \text{average} = \dfrac{\text{sum of the quiz scores}}{\text{number of quizzes}}\right)$

39. Eugenia has scores of 7, 6, and 8 on three quizzes. What must she score on the fourth quiz to have an average of 7 or higher? (See exercise 38.)

Review exercises

1. Perform the indicated operations.
$5(-5) - (4 + 10) + 2(5 - 1)$. See section 1–6.

2. Simplify the expression $(2x + 4) - (x - 3)$. See section 1–7.

3. Solve the following equations for y. See section 2–5.

a. $3x + y = 5$

b. $4x - y = 6$

4. Perform the indicated operations on fractions. See section R–1.

a. $\dfrac{9}{10} - \dfrac{2}{5}$

b. $\dfrac{7}{8} \div \dfrac{21}{20}$

Chapter 2 lead-in problem

Bonnie has \$3,000 invested at 8% simple interest per year. How much more money must she invest at 7% simple interest if she wants an income of \$660 per year (\$55 per month) from her investments?

Solution

Let x = the number of dollars invested at 7%.

income from 8% investment + income from 7% investment = total income

$$3{,}000(0.08) + x(0.07) = 660 \quad \text{Original equation}$$
$$240 + 0.07x = 660 \quad \text{Simplify}$$
$$0.07x = 420 \quad \text{Subtract 240}$$
$$x = 6{,}000 \quad \text{Divide by 0.07}$$

Therefore Bonnie needs to invest \$6,000 at 7% so that her total income from both investments is \$660 per year.

Chapter 2 summary

1. A **mathematical statement** can be labeled true or false.
2. An equation that is true for every permissible value of the variable is called an **identical equation,** or **identity.**
3. A replacement value for the variable that forms a true statement (satisfies that equation) is called a **root,** or a **solution,** of the equation.
4. The **addition and subtraction property of equality** enables us to add or subtract the same quantity in each member of an equation and the result will be an equivalent equation.
5. The **symmetric property of equality** allows us to interchange right and left members of an equation.
6. The **multiplication and division property of equality** enables us to multiply or divide both members of an equation by the same nonzero quantity.
7. We use the same procedures for solving **literal equations** that we use to solve linear equations in one variable.
8. A **linear inequality** involves the symbols $<$, $\leq$, $>$, and $\geq$.
9. The **addition and subtraction property of inequalities** states that the same number can be added to or subtracted from both members of an inequality without changing the direction of the inequality symbol.
10. The **multiplication and division property of inequalities** states that
    a. Both members of an inequality can be multiplied or divided by the same **positive** number without changing the direction of the inequality symbol.
    b. When both members of an inequality are multiplied or divided by the same **negative** number, the direction of the inequality symbol *must be reversed.*

Chapter 2 review

[2–1]

Directions Determine whether the given statement is true or false when we replace the variable in each equation with the given number.

1. $x + 7 = 11; 4$
2. $2x + 1 = 9; 2$
3. $5x - 1 = 21; 5$
4. $\frac{x}{2} + 5 = 12; 14$

[2–1, 2–2, 2–3]

Directions Find the solution.

5. $x + 5 = 12$
6. $x - 4 = 17$
7. $a + 7 = -4$
8. $b - 3 = -9$
9. $5z + 3z - 7z + 3 = 7$
10. $2(3x - 4) - 5x = 11$
11. $3(2y + 3) = 7 + 5y$
12. $3(x - 1) - 2(x + 1) = 4$
13. $3x = 9$
14. $4x = 12$
15. $-2x = 14$
16. $-3x = 21$
17. $\frac{x}{3} = 4$
18. $\frac{x}{2} = 7$
19. $\frac{3x}{5} = 9$
20. $\frac{2x}{7} = 6$
21. $\frac{1}{3}x - 1 = \frac{3}{4}$
22. $\frac{1}{3}x + 1 = \frac{1}{6}x - 2$

23. $\frac{3}{4}x + 4 = \frac{5}{8}$

24. $\frac{3}{5}x + \frac{1}{2} = \frac{7}{10}x - 3$

25. $3x = 0$

26. $-x = -4$

27. $3.7a = 22.2$

28. $32.8 = -4.1x$

29. $2x + 5 = 11$

30. $3b - 8 = 6$

31. $y + (2y - 1) = 6$

32. $x + 3x = 5 + 7$

33. $3(2a - 1) = 4a - 2$

34. $5(x + 3) = 2x - 7$

35. $(3x - 2) - (4x - 1) = 3x$

36. $2a + 5a - 4 = 3(1 - 2a)$

37. $8 - 3x + 7 = 5(x + 7)$

38. $2y - 3(y + 1) = 11$

39. $7x - 4(2x + 3) = 12$

40. $8x - 14 = 14 - 8x$

41. $5b + 4 = 4 - 2b$

42. $-3(2x + 1) = 4x - 5$

43. $3(c + 2) - 2(c + 1) = 5c + 11$

44. $4x - 2(1 - 3x) = 8x + 2$

[2–4]

Directions Write an equation for the problem and solve for the unknown quantities.

45. The difference between two numbers is 23. Find the two numbers if their sum is 105.

46. If a number is divided by 9 and that result is then increased by 7, the answer is 11. Find the number.

47. The difference between one-third of a number and one-fifth of a number is 6. Find the number.

48. John invested part of \$20,000 at 8% and the rest at 7%. If his income from the 8% investment was \$250 more than that from the 7% investment, how much was invested at each rate?

49. Anne made two investments totaling \$25,000. On one investment, she made a 12% profit but on the other, she took a 19% loss. If her net loss was \$1,030, how much was in each investment?

[2–5]

Directions Solve for the specified variable.

50. $F = ma$, for a

51. $E = IR$, for I

52. $k = PV$, for P

53. $V = k + g + t$, for g

54. $A = \frac{1}{2}h(b + c)$, for c

55. $5x - y = 2x + 3y$, for x

[2–6, 2–7]

Directions Find the solution and graph each solution on the real number line.

56. $3x > 12$

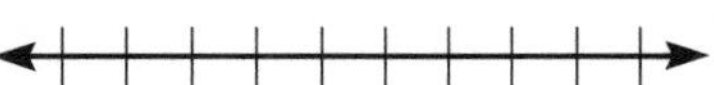

57. $-2x < 14$

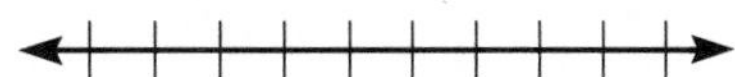

58. $2x + 1 < 5$

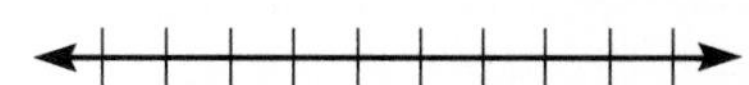

59. $3x + 7 < 5x - 2$

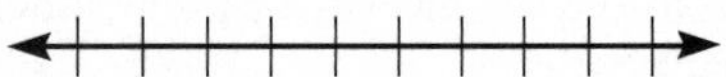

60. $6(2x - 1) \le 3x - 4$

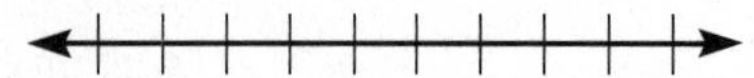

61. $-4 < 5x + 7 < 10$

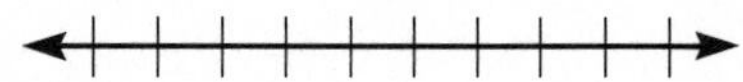

62. $0 \le 1 - 5x < 6$

63. $5 < 4x + 3 < 12$

NAME

Chapter 2 cumulative test

CLASS/SECTION DATE

Directions Perform the indicated operations, if possible, and simplify.

[1–2] **1.** $(-8) + (-4)$

[1–6] **2.** -5^2

[1–6] **3.** $14 + 2 \cdot 15 \div 6 - 3 + 4$

[1–5] **4.** $\frac{8}{0}$

[1–3] **5.** $(-10) - (-14)$

[1–7] **6.** $5a + 3a^2 - 4a - a^2 + 5 + a^3 - 6$

[1–5] **7.** $\frac{-24}{-8}$

[1–6] **8.** $5(-4 + 7) - 3(8 - 5)$

Directions Two numbers are listed. Find two integers such that their product is the first number and their sum is the second number.

[1–4] **9.** $-30, 1$

[1–4] **10.** $24, -10$

[1–4] **11.** $30, -17$

[1–4] **12.** $48, 19$

Directions Find the solution.

[2–3] **13.** $10x - 7 = 4x + 3$

[2–3] **14.** $3x + (x - 1) = 7 - x$

[2–3] **15.** $16 - 2(4x - 1) = 3x - 12$

[2–3] **16.** $2x + 3 = 11$

[2–4] **17.** Phil has $10,000, part of which he invests at 6% and the rest at 5%. If his total income from the two investments was $560, how much did he invest at each rate?

[2–4] **18.** The sum of three consecutive even integers is 48. Find the integers.

[2–6] **19.** $3x - 4 \leq 2x + 5$

[2–6] **20.** $4 \leq y + 1 \leq 7$

[2–7] **21.** $-3x > 9$

[2–7] **22.** $6x - 3 > 2x + 9$

[2–7] **23.** Twice a number decreased by 2 is at most 10. Find all numbers that satisfy this condition.

CHAPTER

3

Algebraic Expressions

If Diane makes $13 per hour and works 40 hours per week, she will earn more than one million dollars over the next 40 years. How much money will Diane earn? Perform the computations using scientific notation.

Proficiency check

[1–6] **1.** -5^2

[1–6] **2.** $(-2)^2 + (-3)(-4) - 6$

[1–6] **3.** $-3^2 + (-2)(-5)$

[1–6] **4.** $2[3(4 - 8) + 7]$

[1–6] **5.** $3[9 - 2(4 - 2) + 7]$

[1–6] **6.** $(5 - 8)^2(10 - 6)^2$

Evaluate the following if $a = -2$, $b = -3$, $c = 4$, and $d = 5$.

[1–8] **7.** $(a + 2d)^2$

[1–8] **8.** $(3a - 2b) - (5c + d)$

[1–8] **9.** $(a - 4c)(b - 2d)$

Combine like terms.

10. $3x^2 + 5x - x^2 - 2x$

11. $7ab + 4ac - 2ac + 3ab$

▣ 3–1 Exponents—I

Exponential form

In chapter 1, we discussed exponents as related to real numbers. Since variables are symbols for real numbers, let us now apply the idea of exponents to variables. The expression x^4 is called the **exponential form** of the product.

$$x \cdot x \cdot x \cdot x$$

We call x the **base** and 4 the **exponent.**

Exponent

Exponential form → $3^4 = \underbrace{3 \cdot 3 \cdot 3 \cdot 3}_{\text{4 factors of 3}} = 81$ ← Standard form

Base

Definition of an Exponent

$a^n = \underbrace{a \cdot a \cdot a \cdots a}_{n \text{ factors of } a}$, where n is a positive integer.

Concept

The exponent tells us how many times the base is used as a factor in an indicated product.

Note

An exponent acts only on the symbol immediately to its left. That is, in ab^4 the exponent 4 applies only to b, whereas $(ab)^4$ means the exponent applies to both a and b.

Example 3–1 A

Write in exponential form.

1. $2 \cdot 2 \cdot 2 \cdot 2 = 2^4$

You are now ready to do **A_1**.

2. $a \cdot a \cdot a = a^3$

You are now ready to do **A_2**.

3. $(a + b)(a + b)(a + b) = (a + b)^3$

Note

In example 3, $(a + b)$ is the base.

You are now ready to do **A_3**.

4. $(-3)(-3)(-3)(-3) = (-3)^4$

You are now ready to do **A_4**.

5. $-(3 \cdot 3 \cdot 3 \cdot 3) = -3^4$

You are now ready to do **A_5**.

Note

In examples 4 and 5, we review the ideas from section 1–6 on exponents related to real numbers. Recall that $(-3)^4 = 81$, whereas $-3^4 = -81$. ■

Example 3–1 B

Write as an indicated product.

1. $b^4 = b \cdot b \cdot b \cdot b$

You are now ready to do **B_1**.

2. $5^3 = 5 \cdot 5 \cdot 5$

You are now ready to do **B_2**.

3. $(x - y)^4 = (x - y)(x - y)(x - y)(x - y)$

You are now ready to do **B_3**.

A_1 $3 \cdot 3 \cdot 3 \cdot 3 \cdot 3$

A_2 $y \cdot y \cdot y \cdot y$

A_3 $(x + 2)(x + 2)$

A_4 $(-5)(-5)$

A_5 $-(5 \cdot 5)$

B_1 c^5

B_2 4^4

B_3 $(a - 3)^3$

B₄ $(-5)^2$

4. $(-2)^2 = (-2)(-2)$

You are now ready to do **B₄**.

5. $-2^2 = -(2 \cdot 2)$

You are now ready to do **B₅**. ■

Multiplication of like bases

Consider the indicated product of $x^2 \cdot x^3$. If we rewrite x^2 and x^3 by using the definition of exponents, we have

B₅ -5^2

$$x^2 \cdot x^3 = \overbrace{x \cdot x}^{x^2} \cdot \overbrace{x \cdot x \cdot x}^{x^3},$$

and again using the definition of exponents, this becomes

$$x^2 \cdot x^3 = \overbrace{x \cdot x \cdot x \cdot x \cdot x}^{\text{5 factors}} = x^5.$$

This leads us to the observation that

$$x^2 x^3 = x^{2+3} = x^5.$$

C₁ $x^4 \cdot x^5$

Thus we have the following **product property of exponents.**

> **Product Property of Exponents**
>
> $$a^m \cdot a^n = a^{m+n}.$$
>
> **Concept**
>
> When we multiply like bases, add their exponents.

C₂ $3^2 \cdot 3^3$

Note

The base stays the same throughout the process. It is by adding the exponents that the multiplication is carried out.

Example 3–1 C

Find the product.

1. $x^3 \cdot x^5 = x^{3+5} = x^8$ — Multiplication of like bases; Add exponents

C₃ $c^3 \cdot c^4 \cdot c^5$

You are now ready to do **C₁**.

2. $3^2 \cdot 3^4 = 3^{2+4} = 3^6 = 729$ — $3^6 = 3 \cdot 3 \cdot 3 \cdot 3 \cdot 3 \cdot 3$, multiplying gives 729 as the standard form

Note

A common error in multiplying $3^2 \cdot 3^4$ is to multiply the bases $3 \cdot 3 = 9$ and add the exponents, getting the incorrect answer of 9^6. The correct way is to say $3^2 \cdot 3^4 = 3^6$, not 9^6.

You are now ready to do **C₂**.

3. $y^2 \cdot y^3 \cdot y^4 = y^{2+3+4} = y^9$ — Like bases, add exponents

You are now ready to do **C₃**.

4. $a^2 \cdot a \cdot a^3 = a^{2+1+3} = a^6$. *a* means a^1

C_4 $b^5 \cdot b \cdot b^5$

Note
If there is no exponent associated with a numeral or a variable, the exponent is understood to be 1, that is, $a = a^1$.

You are now ready to do **C_4**.

5. $(a + b)^3(a + b)^4 = (a + b)^{3+4}$ Base is $(a + b)$
$= (a + b)^7$

C_5 $(a - 4)^2(a - 4)^3$

You are now ready to do **C_5**.

6. $(-2)^3(-2)^2 = (-2)^{3+2} = (-2)^5$ Base is -2
$= -32$ Standard form

You are now ready to do **C_6**. ■

Group of factors to a power property of exponents

Several additional properties of exponents can be derived using the definition of exponents and the commutative and associative properties of multiplication. Observe the following:

C_6 $(-3)(-3)^2$

$$(xy)^3 = \overbrace{xy \cdot xy \cdot xy}^{\text{3 factors of } xy}$$

$$= \overbrace{x \cdot x \cdot x}^{\text{3 factors of } x} \cdot \overbrace{y \cdot y \cdot y}^{\text{3 factors of } y}$$

$$= x^3y^3.$$

D_1 $(xy)^3$

This leads us to the following property of exponents.

> **Group of factors to a power property of exponents**
> $$(ab)^n = a^nb^n.$$
> **Concept**
> When a group of **factors** is raised to a power, we can raise each of the factors in the group to this power.

D_2 $(3xy)^4$

Example 3–1 D

Simplify.

1. $(ab)^4 = a^4b^4$ Both *a* and *b* are raised to the 4th power

You are now ready to do **D_1**.

D_3 $(2 \cdot 3)^3$

2. $(2ab)^3 = 2^3a^3b^3$ 2, *a*, and *b* are all raised to the 3rd power
$= 8a^3b^3$ 8 is the standard form of 2^3

Note
The number 2 is a factor in the group. Therefore it is raised to the indicated power.

You are now ready to do **D_2**.

3. $(3 \cdot 4)^3 = 3^3 \cdot 4^3 = 27 \cdot 64 = 1{,}728$ $(3 \cdot 4)^3$ also is $(12)^3 = 1{,}728$

You are now ready to do **D_3**.

E₁ $(6^3)^2$

Note
The quantity $(a + b)^3 \neq a^3 + b^3$ because a and b are *terms,* not factors as the property specified. If we consider $(a + b)$ to be a single factor, then by the definition of exponents, we have

$$(a + b)^3 = (a + b)(a + b)(a + b).$$

We will see the method of multiplying this later in this chapter. ■

Power of a power

Consider the expression $(x^4)^3$. Applying the definition of exponents and the multiplication property of exponents, we have

$$(x^4)^3 = \overbrace{x^4 \cdot x^4 \cdot x^4}^{\text{3 factors of } x^4} = \overbrace{x^{4+4+4}}^{\text{Adding the exponents}} = x^{12}.$$

In chapter 1, we reviewed the idea that multiplication is repeated addition of the same number. Therefore adding the exponent 4 three times is the same as $3 \cdot 4$. Thus

E₂ $(3^2)^3$

$$\underset{\text{Power of a power}}{(x^4)^3} = \underset{\text{Multiply exponents}}{x^{3 \cdot 4}} = x^{12}$$

Therefore we have the following property of exponents.

> **Power of a power property of exponents**
>
> $$(a^m)^n = a^{n \cdot m}$$
>
> **Concept**
>
> A power of a power is found by multiplying the exponents.

Example 3–1 E

Simplify.

1. $(y^3)^2 = y^{2 \cdot 3} = y^6$ — Power of a power, multiply exponents

E₃ $(a^4)^3$

You are now ready to do **E₁**.

2. $(4^2)^5 = 4^{5 \cdot 2} = 4^{10} = 1{,}048{,}576$ — $(4^2)^5$ also is $(16)^5 = 1{,}048{,}576$

You are now ready to do **E₂**.

3. $(x^5)^4 = x^{4 \cdot 5} = x^{20}$ — Multiply exponents

You are now ready to do **E₃**. ■

Fraction to a power property of exponents

Our last property of exponents can be derived from the definition of exponents. Consider the expression $\left(\frac{a}{b}\right)^3$.

$$\left(\frac{a}{b}\right)^3 = \underbrace{\frac{a}{b} \cdot \frac{a}{b} \cdot \frac{a}{b}}_{\text{3 factors of } \frac{a}{b}} = \frac{\overbrace{a \cdot a \cdot a}^{\text{3 factors of } a}}{\underbrace{b \cdot b \cdot b}_{\text{3 factors of } b}} = \frac{a^3}{b^3}$$

Thus

Fraction raised to a power → $\left(\frac{a}{b}\right)^3 = \frac{a^3}{b^3}$. ← Numerator raised to the power; ← Denominator raised to the power

Fraction to a power property of exponents

$$\left(\frac{a}{b}\right)^n = \frac{a^n}{b^n},\ b \neq 0.$$

Concept

Whenever a fraction is raised to a power, the numerator and the denominator are *both* raised to that power.

Example 3–1 F

Perform the indicated operations and simplify.

1. $\left(\frac{3}{4}\right)^3 = \frac{3^3}{4^3}$ — Both the numerator and the denominator are raised to the 3rd power

   $= \frac{27}{64}$ — $3^3 = 27$ and $4^3 = 64$

You are now ready to do **F_1**.

2. $\left(\frac{a}{b}\right)^5 = \frac{a^5}{b^5}$ — Both the numerator and the denominator are raised to the 5th power

You are now ready to do **F_2**.

3. $\left(\frac{2a}{b}\right)^3 = \frac{(2a)^3}{b^3}$ — Both the numerator and the denominator are raised to the 3rd power

   $= \frac{2^3a^3}{b^3}$ — Each factor in the numerator is raised to the 3rd power

   $= \frac{8a^3}{b^3}$ — 2^3 in standard form is 8

You are now ready to do **F_3**. ■

The following examples illustrate some problems in which more than one property of exponents is applied within the problem.

Example 3–1 G

Simplify

1. $(2a^2b^3)^3 = 2^3(a^2)^3(b^3)^3$ — Each factor in the group is raised to the 3rd power

   $= 2^3a^6b^9$ — Power of a power, multiply exponents

   $= 8a^6b^9$ — 8 is the standard form of 2^3

You are now ready to do **G_1**.

2. $(5a^4b^2)^4 = 5^4(a^4)^4(b^2)^4$ — Each factor in the group is raised to the 4th power

   $= 5^4a^{16}b^8$ — Power of a power, multiply exponents

   $= 625a^{16}b^8$ — 625 is the standard form of 5^4

You are now ready to do **G_2**.

F_1 $\left(\frac{2}{5}\right)^3$

F_2 $\left(\frac{x}{y}\right)^7$

F_3 $\left(\frac{x}{3y}\right)^3$

G_1 $(3x^4y^2)^3$

G_2 $(2a^4b^3)^3$

G_3 $(5xy^2)(2x^3y^3)$

3. $(2a^2b)(3ab^3) = (2 \cdot 3)(a^2a)(bb^3)$ Regroup to multiply like factors
$= 6a^3b^4$ Multiply like bases, add exponents

Note
When multiplying two quantities together, first multiply their coefficients, then multiply like bases.

You are now ready to do **G_3**.

G_4 $\left(\dfrac{3x^2y}{z^4}\right)^2$

4. $\left(\dfrac{2a^2b^3}{c^5}\right)^3 = \dfrac{(2a^2b^3)^3}{(c^5)^3}$ Both the numerator and the denominator are raised to the 3rd power

$= \dfrac{2^3(a^2)^3(b^3)^3}{(c^5)^3}$ Each factor in the numerator is raised to the 3rd power

$= \dfrac{8a^6b^9}{c^{15}}$ Power of a power, multiply exponents

You are now ready to do **G_4**. ■

Problem solving

The following problems require us to write algebraic expressions involving the use of exponents.

Example 3–1 H

Write an algebraic expression for each of the following verbal statements.

1. The volume of a cube is found by using the length of the edge, e, as a factor 3 times. Write an expression for the volume of a cube.

   We write e as a factor 3 times as $e \cdot e \cdot e = e^3$. Then the volume, V, of a cube is given by

   $V = e^3$.

H_1 The area, A, of a square is found by using the length of the equal side, s, as a factor twice. Write an expression for the area of a square.

You are now ready to do **H_1**.

2. Write an expression for the square of a number less 5.

   The square of a number, n, is given as n^2, and since "less" means to subtract, the expression is given by

   $n^2 - 5$.

You are now ready to do **H_2**. ■

H_2 Write an expression for 2 times the square of t.

Answers to section 3–1 margin exercises

A_1 3^5 A_2 y^4 A_3 $(x+2)^2$ A_4 $(-5)^2$ A_5 -5^2 B_1 $c \cdot c \cdot c \cdot c \cdot c$ B_2 $4 \cdot 4 \cdot 4 \cdot 4$ B_3 $(a-3)(a-3)(a-3)$ B_4 $(-5)(-5)$ B_5 $-(5 \cdot 5)$ C_1 x^9 C_2 $3^5 = 243$ C_3 c^{12} C_4 b^{11} C_5 $(a-4)^5$ C_6 $(-3)^3 = -27$ D_1 x^3y^3 D_2 $81x^4y^4$ D_3 216 E_1 $6^6 = 46{,}656$ E_2 $3^6 = 729$ E_3 a^{12} F_1 $\frac{8}{125}$ F_2 $\frac{x^7}{y^7}$ F_3 $\frac{x^3}{27y^3}$ G_1 $27x^{12}y^6$ G_2 $8a^{12}b^9$ G_3 $10x^4y^5$ G_4 $\frac{9x^4y^2}{z^8}$ H_1 $A = s^2$ H_2 $2t^2$

Mastery points

Can you

- Write a product in exponential form?
- Multiply factors with like bases?
- Raise a group of factors to a power?
- Raise a power to a power?
- Raise a fraction to a power?

Exercise 3–1

Directions Write the following expressions in exponential form. See example 3–1 A.

Example $\boxed{A_2}$ $y \cdot y \cdot y \cdot y$

Solution $= y^4$ *y* to the 4th power

1. $a \cdot a \cdot a \cdot a \cdot a$ **2.** $b \cdot b \cdot b \cdot b$ **3.** $(-2)(-2)(-2)(-2)$

4. $-(2 \cdot 2 \cdot 2 \cdot 2)$ **5.** $x \cdot x \cdot x \cdot x \cdot x \cdot x$ **6.** $(a + b)(a + b)$

7. $(x - y)(x - y)(x - y)$

Directions Write as an indicated product. See example 3–1 B.

Example $\boxed{B_1}$ c^5

Solution $= c \cdot c \cdot c \cdot c \cdot c$ *c* written as a factor 5 times

8. x^4 **9.** y^5 **10.** $(-2)^3$

11. -2^4 **12.** $(a + b)^3$ **13.** $(x - y)^2$

Directions Simplify by using the properties of exponents. See examples 3–1 C, D, E, F, and G.

Examples $\boxed{C_1}$ $x^4 \cdot x^5$

Solutions
$= x^{4+5}$ Like bases
$= x^9$ Add exponents

$\boxed{E_3}$ $(a^4)^3$
$= a^{3 \cdot 4}$ Power of a power
$= a^{12}$ Multiply exponents

$\boxed{G_2}$ $(2a^4b^3)^3$
$= 2^3(a^4)^3(b^3)^3$ Group of factors to a power
$= 2^3a^{12}b^9$ Power of a power
$= 8a^{12}b^9$ Standard form

14. $x^4 \cdot x^7$ **15.** $a^5 \cdot a^5$ **16.** $a \cdot a^4$ **[17.]** $R^2 \cdot R$

18. $a^2 \cdot a^3 \cdot a^4$ **19.** $x^5 \cdot x \cdot x^3$ **20.** $6 \cdot 6^3$ **[21.]** $5^2 \cdot 5^3$

22. $4 \cdot 4^2 \cdot 4^4$ **23.** $(ab)^5$ **24.** $(xy)^4$ **25.** $(2abc)^3$

26. $(4xyz)^3$

27. $(a^2)^4$

28. $(x^5)^3$

29. $(y^2)^2$

30. $(b^5)^5$

31. $(c^9)^3$

32. $(4x^2y^3)(5xy^4)$

33. $(2xy^2)(3x^3y)$

34. $(a^2b^3)(a^5b^2)$

35. $(x^2y^2)(x^4y^3)$

36. $(2a^3b^4c)(6a^4b^3)$

37. $(a^3b^2)^3$

38. $(x^4y^3z)^4$

39. $(2a^5b^2c)^3$

40. $(5a^5b^2c^4)^2$

41. $\left(\frac{a}{b}\right)^6$

42. $\left(\frac{x}{y}\right)^4$

43. $\left(\frac{2}{3}\right)^3$

44. $\left(\frac{1}{2}\right)^4$

45. $\left(\frac{2x}{y}\right)^4$

46. $\left(\frac{3a}{b}\right)^3$

47. $\left(\frac{2x^2}{y^3}\right)^3$

48. $\left(\frac{ab^2}{c^4}\right)^4$

49. $\left(\frac{2x^3y^3}{z^5}\right)^2$

50. $\left(\frac{a^5bc^4}{d^2e}\right)^5$

51. The formula for finding the volume of a cube is $V = e^3$, where V represents volume in some cubic units of measure and e represents the length of the edge of the cube. Write an expression for the volume in expanded form, and then determine the number of cubic units in the figure for each of the following values of e: (a) $e = 5$, (b) $e = 4$, (c) $e = 6$.

Directions Using exponents, write an expression for each of the following verbal statements. See example 3–1 H.

52. The distance a falling object will fall in time, t, seconds is found by multiplying $\frac{1}{2}$ times the acceleration due to gravity, g, times the square of t. Write an expression for the distance the object will fall.

53. The area of a circle is found by multiplying the constant π times the length of the radius, r, used as a factor 2 times. Write an expression for the area of a circle.

54. The volume of a sphere is found by multiplying $\frac{4}{3}\pi$ times the radius, r, used as a factor 3 times. Write an expression for the volume of a sphere.

55. Johnny is n years old. His mother says that she is 6 years more than the cube of Johnny's age. Write an expression for his mother's age.

56. Jane is m years old. Her father is 8 years less than Jane's age used as a factor 4 times. Write an expression for her father's age.

57. Write an expression for twice the square of x less the cube of y.

58. A number can be written in the form a multiplied by the product of 10 used as a factor 8 times, where a is a number between 1 and 10. Write an expression for the number in terms of a.

59. Write an expression for the quotient of the cube of p divided by the square of q.

Review exercises

Directions Perform the indicated addition and subtraction. See section 1–7.

1. $2a + 3a + 4a$

2. $5x + x + 2x$

3. $3ab - 2ab + 5ab$

4. $9xy + 4xy - 6xy$

5. $4a^2 + 3a^2 - 2a + 7a$

6. $6x^2 + 3x - x^2 + 2x$

7. $2x^2y - x^2y + 3xy^2 + 4xy^2$

8. $5ab^2 + 3a^2b - 2ab^2 - a^2b$

A_1 $4x - 3x + x$

3–2 Algebraic addition and subtraction

Addition and subtraction of like terms

In section 1–7, we learned that we can add or subtract only like or similar terms and that like terms or similar terms are terms whose variable factors are the same. Unlike terms have different variables or different exponents on the same variables.

Example 3–2 A

Perform the indicated addition and subtraction.

1. $6a + a - 2a$ — Identify like terms

$= (6 + 1 - 2)a$ — Distributive property

$= 5a$ — Combine numerical coefficients

A_2 $7a - 2b - 4a + 5b$

You are now ready to do A_1.

2. $3x + 7y - x + 5y$ — Identify like terms

$= 3x - x + 7y + 5y$ — Commutative property

$= (3x - x) + (7y + 5y)$ — Associative property

$= (3 - 1)x + (7 + 5)y$ — Distributive property

$= 2x + 12y$ — Combine numerical coefficients

You are now ready to do A_2.

3. $x^2y + 3xy^2 + 4x^2y - 2xy^2$ — Identify like terms

$= (x^2y + 4x^2y) + (3xy^2 - 2xy^2)$ — Commutative and associative properties

$= (1 + 4)x^2y + (3 - 2)xy^2$ — Distributive property

$= 5x^2y + xy^2$ — Combine numerical coefficients

A_3 $ab^2 + 3a^2b + ab^2 - 2a^2b$

You are now ready to do A_3. ■

Grouping symbols

In chapter 1, we learned how to use the distributive property to remove grouping symbols such as ( ), [ ], and { }. The following is a restatement of that procedure.

Removing grouping symbols

1. If an expression inside a grouping symbol is preceded by no symbol or by a "+" sign, the grouping symbol can be dropped and the enclosed terms remain unchanged.
2. If an expression inside a grouping symbol is preceded by a "−" sign, when the grouping symbol is dropped, we change the sign of each enclosed term.

B_1 $(2a^2 - a + 5) + (a^2 + 3a - 2)$

Example 3–2 B

Remove all grouping symbols and perform the indicated addition or subtraction.

1. $(3x^2 + 2x + 5) + (4x^2 + 3x + 6)$ — Remove grouping symbols

$= 3x^2 + 2x + 5 + 4x^2 + 3x + 6$ — Enclosed terms remain unchanged

$= (3x^2 + 4x^2) + (2x + 3x) + (5 + 6)$ — Associative and commutative properties

$= (3 + 4)x^2 + (2 + 3)x + 11$ — Distributive property

$= 7x^2 + 5x + 11$ — Combine numerical coefficients

You are now ready to do B_1.

2. $(3x^2 - x + 4) - (2x^2 - 5x - 7)$ — Remove grouping symbols

$= 3x^2 - x + 4 - 2x^2 + 5x + 7$ — Change the sign of each term in the second parentheses

$= (3x^2 - 2x^2) + (-x + 5x) + (4 + 7)$ — Associative and commutative properties

$= (3 - 2)x^2 + (-1 + 5)x + 11$ — Distributive property

$= 1x^2 + 4x + 11$ — Combine numerical coefficients

$= x^2 + 4x + 11$ — x^2 is the same as $1x^2$

You are now ready to do **B_2**.

B_2 $(5x^2 + 2x - 1) - (3x^2 - 4x + 3)$

Note
In the following examples, we will mentally add or subtract the like terms.

B_3 $(4y^2z - 5yz + 4) - (3y^2z - 6yz - 7)$

3. $(a^2 + 2ab + b^2) - (3a^2 - 4ab + b^2)$ — Remove grouping symbols

$= a^2 + 2ab + b^2 - 3a^2 + 4ab - b^2$ — Change the sign of each term in the second parentheses

$= (a^2 - 3a^2) + (2ab + 4ab) + (b^2 - b^2)$ — Associative and commutative properties

$= -2a^2 + 6ab + 0$ — Combine like terms

$= -2a^2 + 6ab$ — No b^2 are left

You are now ready to do **B_3**.

4. $(8R^2 - 2R + 3) - (6R^2 + 6R - 1)$ — Remove grouping symbols

$= 8R^2 - 2R + 3 - 6R^2 - 6R + 1$ — Change the sign of each term in the second parentheses

$= (8R^2 - 6R^2) + (-2R - 6R) + (3 + 1)$ — Associative and commutative properties

$= 2R^2 - 8R + 4$ — Combine like terms

You are now ready to do **B_4**. ■

B_4 $(6a^2 + 2a - 4) - (6a^2 - 2a + 4)$

There are many situations where there will be grouping symbols within grouping symbols. In these situations, **it is usually easier to remove the innermost grouping symbol first.**

Example 3–2 C

Remove all grouping symbols and perform the indicated addition or subtraction.

C_1 $3a - [5a + (b - c)]$

1. $2x - [y + (x - z)] = 2x - [y + x - z]$ — Remove parentheses first

$= 2x - y - x + z$ — Next remove brackets

$= x - y + z$ — Combine like terms

You are now ready to do **C_1**.

2. $2a - [3b - (2a - b)] = 2a - [3b - 2a + b]$ — Remove parentheses first

$= 2a - [4b - 2a]$ — Combine like terms within brackets

$= 2a - 4b + 2a$ — Remove brackets

$= 4a - 4b$ — Combine like terms

C_2 $5a - \{2a + [5b - 3a]\}$

Note
After removing the parentheses, we added the like terms before removing the brackets. **Simplify within a group whenever possible.**

You are now ready to do **C_2**.

C_3 $(3x + 2y) - [x - (6y - 3x)]$

3. $(3R - 2S) - [5R - (R - S)]$

$= 3R - 2S - [5R - R + S]$ Remove both sets of parentheses

$= 3R - 2S - [4R + S]$ Combine like terms within brackets

$= 3R - 2S - 4R - S$ Remove brackets

$= -R - 3S$ Combine like terms

Note

There were two separate groups in this problem, so we removed grouping symbols in each group at the same time.

You are now ready to do C_3. ■

Answers to section 3–2 margin exercises

A_1 $2x$ A_2 $3a + 3b$ A_3 $a^2b + 2ab^2$ B_1 $3a^2 + 2a + 3$ B_2 $2x^2 + 6x - 4$ B_3 $y^2z + yz + 11$ B_4 $4a - 8$ C_1 $-2a - b + c$ C_2 $6a - 5b$ C_3 $-x + 8y$

Mastery points

Can you

- Identify like terms?
- Perform addition and subtraction of algebraic expressions?
- Remove grouping symbols?

Exercise 3–2

Directions Perform the indicated addition and subtraction. See examples 3–2 A.

Example A_2 $7a - 2b - 4a + 5b$

Solution

$= (7a - 4a) + (-2b + 5b)$ Commutative and associative properties

$= (7 - 4)a + (-2 + 5)b$ Distributive property

$= 3a + 3b$ Combine numerical coefficients

1. $2x + x + 6x$
2. $8y - y + 2y$
3. $4a - 2b + 9a + 4b$
4. $a + 4b + 6a - 8b$
5. $4x^2 - y^2 - x^2 + 12y^2$
6. $5a + 4a^2 - 2a - a^2$
7. $x^2 + 5x - 8x + 2x^2$
8. $8ab + 7a^2b + 6a^2b^2 - 4a^2b$
9. $x^2y^2 + 9xy - 2x^2y - 4xy$
10. $a^2b + 8ab + 3a^2b - 4a^2b^2$
11. $x^2 + 5x - 6 + 7x^2 - 3x + 7$
12. $6a^2 - 5a + 3 - 2a^2 - 4a + 8$

Directions Remove all grouping symbols and combine like terms. See examples 3–2 B and C.

Example $\boxed{B_2}$ $(5x^2 + 2x - 1) - (3x^2 - 4x + 3)$

Solution

$= 5x^2 + 2x - 1 - 3x^2 + 4x - 3$ Change the sign of each term in the second parentheses

$= (5x^2 - 3x^2) + (2x + 4x) + (-1 - 3)$ Commutative and associative properties

$= 2x^2 + 6x - 4$ Combine like terms

Example $\boxed{C_2}$ $5a - \{2a + [5b - 3a]\}$

Solution

$= 5a - \{2a + 5b - 3a\}$ Remove brackets first

$= 5a - \{-a + 5b\}$ Combine like terms within braces

$= 5a + a - 5b$ Remove braces

$= 6a - 5b$ Combine like terms

13. $(2x^2y - xy^2 + 7xy) + (xy^2 - 5x^2y + 8xy)$

14. $(5x^2 - y^2) - (6x^2 - 3y^2) - (8x^2 + 2y^2)$

15. $(8a^3 - 2a^2b + 4ab^2 - 6b^3) - (4a^3 - 3a^2b - 2ab^2 - b^3)$

16. $(13a - 24bc) + (46bc - 16a - 26d)$

17. $(48a + 3b) - (-22a - 6b)$

18. $(3x^2y - 6xy + 32z) + (7xy - 3x^2y)$

[19.] $(8xy + 9y^2z) - (13xy - 14yz)$

20. $(18a + 31bc) - (23a - 14bc)$

21. $(a - 3b + 2) - (a + 5b - 8)$

22. $(2x + 6z - 10y) - (8y + 3z - 6x + 4)$

23. $(3a - 2b) - (a + 4b) - (-a + 3b)$

24. $(5xy - y) - (3yz + 2xy) + (3y - 4xy)$

25. $(7x^2 - 2y) + (3z - 4y) - (4x^2 - 6y)$

26. $2x - [3x - (5x - 3)]$

27. $x - 1 + [2x - (x - 1)]$

28. $3a + [2a - (a - b)]$

29. $5x - [4a + 3b + (x - 2y)]$

30. $2a - [a - b - (3a + 2b)]$

31. $5a - (a + b) - [2a - b - (3a + 5b)]$

32. $x - [y + (2x - 3y)] + [2x - y]$

33. $-[4a + 7b - (3a + 5b)]$

34. $6x - \{5a + y + (4x - 7y)\}$

35. $2a + [a - (b - c)] - [2a - (b - c)]$

36. $3x - [6x - (4x - 3y)] - [4y - 3x]$

Review exercises

Directions Perform the indicated multiplication. See sections 1–4 and 1–6.

1. $3 \cdot (-5)$ **2.** $(-7)(-4)$ **3.** $(-8) \cdot 5$ **4.** $(-4)(-3)(-2)$

5. $6 \cdot 0 \cdot (-7)$ **6.** $(-7)^2$ **7.** -4^2 **8.** $5 \cdot (-4) \cdot 2$

3–3 Products of algebraic expressions

Polynomials

In section 1–7, an algebraic expression was defined. We will now define a special type of algebraic expression called a **polynomial.** The following are characteristics of a polynomial.

1. It has real number coefficients.
2. All variables in a polynomial are raised only to natural number powers.
3. The operations performed by the variables are limited to addition, subtraction, and multiplication.

A polynomial that contains just one term is called a **monomial;** a polynomial that contains two terms is called a **binomial;** and a polynomial that contains three terms is called a **trinomial.** Any polynomial that contains more than one term is called a **multinomial,** but no special names are given to polynomials that contain more than three terms.

Example 3–3 A

Determine if each of the following algebraic expressions is a polynomial. If it is a polynomial, what name best describes it? If it is not a polynomial, state why it is not.

1. x, $4x$, 3, and $5x^2y$ are monomials.
2. $3x + 1$, $x + y$, and $81W^2 - 9T^2$ are binomials.
3. $5x^3 + 2y - 1$ and $z^2 + 9z - 10$ are trinomials.
4. $6x^3 - 2x^2 + 4x + 1$ is a polynomial of 4 terms.
5. $\frac{4}{x + 2}$ is not a polynomial since it contains a variable in the denominator.

Note
We should simplify any expression before identifying it. Also in an expression, the combining of all of the constant terms is understood to be a single term. For example, $x + 3 + \pi$ is thought of as $x + (3 + \pi)$ and is a binomial.

You are now ready to do **A_1, A_2, A_3, A_4, and A_5.** ■

A_1 $5x^2y + 2z$

A_2 $6ab^2$

A_3 $3x^2 - 2x + 7$

A_4 $5x^2y + \frac{2}{z}$

A_5 $6x^3 - 2x^2 + 3x - 4$

B₁ $5a \cdot 2ab$

Another way that we identify different types of polynomials is by the **degree** of the polynomial. **The degree of a polynomial in one variable is the greatest exponent of that variable in any one term.**

1. $5x^3$ — Third degree because the exponent of x is 3

2. $x^4 - 2x^3 + 3x - 5$ — Fourth degree because the greatest exponent of x in any one term is 4

> **Note**
> In example 2, the polynomial has been arranged in *descending powers* of the variable. This is the form that we will use when we write polynomials in one variable.

3. $4y^5 - 7y^2 + 3$ — Fifth degree because the greatest exponent of y in any one term is 5

B₂ $3x^2 \cdot 2x^3y$

Products of monomials

In section 3–1, we multiplied two groups of factors by first multiplying their numerical coefficients and then multiplying the like bases. The following examples review those problems.

Example 3–3 B

Perform the indicated multiplication.

1. $4x \cdot 3xy = (4 \cdot 3) \cdot (x \cdot x) \cdot y$
$= 12x^2y$

You are now ready to do **B₁**.

B₃ $(3a^2)(-4ab^2)$

2. $8a^3 \cdot 4a^3 \cdot 3a = (8 \cdot 4 \cdot 3) \cdot (a^3 \cdot a^3 \cdot a)$
$= 96a^7$

You are now ready to do **B₂**.

3. $(-2a^2) \cdot (3ab) = (-2 \cdot 3) \cdot (a^2 \cdot a) \cdot b$
$= -6a^3b$

You are now ready to do **B₃**.

4. $(5x^2y^3z)(4x^3yz^4) = (5 \cdot 4)(x^2x^3)(y^3y)(zz^4)$
$= 20x^5y^4z^5$

Commutative and associative properties allow us to rearrange and group the factors. We then multiply the numerical coefficients and the like bases.

You are now ready to do **B₄**. ■

B₄ $(3a^2bc^4)(5a^5bc^3)$

> **Note**
> It is a good procedure to write the variable parts of any term in alphabetical order. This makes identifying like terms much simpler. For example, $3a^2c^3b$ and $4bc^3a^2$ are like terms, but recognizing that fact would have been easier if they had been written as $3a^2bc^3$ and $4a^2bc^3$.

Product of a monomial and a multinomial

To multiply a monomial times a multinomial (a polynomial of more than one term), we use the distributive property. For example, to multiply

$$3x^2y(x^2 + xy + y^2),$$

we multiply the monomial $3x^2y$ times each term in the trinomial to get

$$(3x^2y \cdot x^2) + (3x^2y \cdot xy) + (3x^2y \cdot y^2),$$

which yields

$$3x^2y(x^2 + xy + y^2) = 3x^4y + 3x^3y^2 + 3x^2y^3.$$

In each indicated product, note that we multiplied like bases by using the product property of exponents. For example, in the first term,

$$3x^2y \cdot x^2 = 3 \cdot (x^2 \cdot x^2) \cdot y = 3 \cdot x^{2+2} \cdot y = 3x^4y.$$

C₁ $2a(a + 3)$

Example 3–3 C

Perform the indicated multiplication.

1. $5y(2y + 3) = 5y \cdot 2y + 5y \cdot 3$ — Multiply $5y$ times each term in the parentheses

$= 10y^2 + 15y$ — Multiply monomials

You are now ready to do **C₁**.

2. $x^3(x^2 + xy - y^2) = x^3 \cdot x^2 + x^3 \cdot xy - x^3 \cdot y^2$ — Distribute the x^3

$= x^5 + x^4y - x^3y^2$ — Multiply monomials

C₂ $a^5(a^2 + ab^2 - b^2)$

> **Note**
> In example 2, when we multiplied x^3 times the third term of the trinomial, y^2, the subtraction sign remained, giving $-x^3y^2$.

You are now ready to do **C₂**.

3. $-5a^3(a^2 + 2ab - b^3) = -5a^3 \cdot a^2 - 5a^3 \cdot 2ab + 5a^3 \cdot b^3$ — Distribute the $-5a^3$

$= -5a^5 - 10a^4b + 5a^3b^3$ — Multiply monomials

You are now ready to do **C₃**.

4. $4x^2y(2x^3 - 3x^2y^2 + y^4) = 4x^2y \cdot 2x^3 - 4x^2y \cdot 3x^2y^2 + 4x^2y \cdot y^4$ — Distribute the $4x^2y$

$= 8x^5y - 12x^4y^3 + 4x^2y^5$ — Multiply monomials

C₃ $4x^2(2x^2 - xy - y^2)$

You are now ready to do **C₄**. ■

Product of two multinomials

The product of two multinomials requires the use of the distributive property several times. That is, in the product

$$(x + 2y)(x + y),$$

we consider $(x + 2y)$ a single number and apply the distributive property.

$$(x + 2y)(x + y) = (x + 2y) \cdot x + (x + 2y) \cdot y$$

We now apply the distributive property again.

$$(x + 2y) \cdot x + (x + 2y) \cdot y = x \cdot x + 2y \cdot x + x \cdot y + 2y \cdot y$$
$$= x^2 + 2xy + xy + 2y^2$$

C₄ $3ab^2(2a - 3b)$

The last step in the problem is to combine like terms, if there are any.

$$x^2 + (2xy + xy) + 2y^2 = x^2 + 3xy + 2y^2$$

Notice that in this product, each term of the first factor is multiplied by each term of the second factor. We can generalize our procedure as follows:

> **Multiplying two multinomials**
>
> When we are multiplying two multinomials, we multiply each of the terms in the first multinomial by each of the terms in the second multinomial. We then combine like terms.

D₁ $(x - 1)(x + 6)$

Example 3–3 D

Perform the indicated multiplication and simplify.

1. $(a + 3)(a - 4) = a \cdot a - a \cdot 4 + 3 \cdot a - 3 \cdot 4$ — Distribute multiplication
$= a^2 - 4a + 3a - 12$ — Multiply monomials
$= a^2 - a - 12$ — Combine like terms

Note
We have drawn arrows to indicate the multiplication that is being carried out. This should be a convenient way for us to indicate the multiplication to be performed.

You are now ready to do **D₁**.

D₂ $(2a + 1)(a + 3)$

2. $(2x + 3)(5x - 2) = 10x^2 - 4x + 15x - 6$ — Distribute and multiply
$= 10x^2 + 11x - 6$ — Combine like terms

(F O I L)

Note
A word that is useful for remembering the multiplication to be performed when multiplying two binomials is **FOIL.** Foil is an abbreviation signifying **F**irst times first, **O**uter times outer, **I**nner times inner, and **L**ast times last.

You are now ready to do **D₂**.

3. $(a + b)(a + 2b) = a^2 + 2ab + ab + 2b^2$ — Distribute and multiply
$= a^2 + 3ab + 2b^2$ — Combine like terms

You are now ready to do **D₃**. ■

D₃ $(2x + y)(x - 3y)$

Special products

Three special products appear so often that we should be able to write the polynomial form of the product without computation. Consider the product

$$(x + 6)^2 = (x + 6)(x + 6),$$

which becomes

$$x^2 + 6x + 6x + 36.$$

When we combine the second and third terms, we get

$$x^2 + 12x + 36.$$

This is called the **square of a binomial** or a **perfect square trinomial.**

The square of a binomial

1. The first term of the product is the **square of the first term** of the binomial $[(x)^2 = x^2]$.
2. The second term of the product is **two times the product of the two terms of the binomial** $[2(x \cdot 6) = 12x]$.
3. The third term of the product is the **square of the second term** of the binomial $[(6)^2 = 36]$.

In general, for real numbers a and b,

$$(a + b)^2 = a^2 + 2ab + b^2$$

and if we replace b with $-b$, we obtain

$$(a - b)^2 = a^2 - 2ab + b^2.$$

$\mathbf{E_1}$ $(a + 4)^2$

Note
$(a + b)^2 = a^2 + 2ab + b^2$, not $a^2 + b^2$. This is a common error.
The square of a binomial is always a trinomial.

Example 3–3 E

Perform the indicated multiplication and simplify.

1. $(2x + 3)^2 = (2x)^2 + (2 \cdot 2x \cdot 3) + (3)^2$ — Apply special products
$= 4x^2 + 12x + 9$ — Multiply monomials

You are now ready to do $\mathbf{E_1}$.

2. $(5a - 4b)^2 = (5a)^2 + [2 \cdot 5a \cdot (-4b)] + (-4b)^2$ — Special products
$= 25a^2 + [-40ab] + 16b^2$ — Multiply monomials
$= 25a^2 - 40ab + 16b^2$ — Standard form

$\mathbf{E_2}$ $(x - 3y)^2$

You are now ready to do $\mathbf{E_2}$. ■

A third special product comes from multiplying the sum and the difference of the same two terms. Consider the product

$$(x + 6)(x - 6),$$

which becomes

$$x^2 - 6x + 6x - 36.$$

The second and third terms are additive inverses, and the expression becomes

$$x^2 - 36.$$

This special product is called the **difference of two squares.**

The difference of two squares

1. The product is obtained by first squaring the first term of the factors, and then
2. subtracting the square of the second term of the factors.

In general, for real numbers a and b,

$$(a + b)(a - b) = a^2 - b^2.$$

F_1 $(a + 2)(a - 2)$

Example 3–3 F

Perform the indicated multiplication and simplify.

1. $(x + 7)(x - 7) = (x)^2 - (7)^2$ Special products
$= x^2 - 49$ Standard form

You are now ready to do F_1.

2. $(a + 2b)(a - 2b) = (a)^2 - (2b)^2$ Special products
$= a^2 - 4b^2$ Standard form

F_2 $(x - 3y)(x + 3y)$

You are now ready to do F_2.

3. $(3x - 2y)(3x + 2y) = (3x)^2 - (2y)^2$ Special products
$= 9x^2 - 4y^2$ Standard form

You are now ready to do F_3. ■

In all the examples that we have looked at, whether they were special products or not, a single property is sufficient.

F_3 $(3a - 4b)(3a + 4b)$

Multiplying two multinomials

When multiplying two multinomials together, **we multiply each of the terms in the first multinomial by each of the terms in the second multinomial and then combine like terms.**

Example 3–3 G

G_1 $(a + b)(2a - 3b)$

Perform the indicated multiplication and simplify.

1. $(3x - y)(2x + 3y) = 6x^2 + 9xy - 2xy - 3y^2$ Distribute multiplication
$= 6x^2 + 7xy - 3y^2$ Combine like terms

You are now ready to do G_1.

2. $(a - 2)(2a^2 + 3a + 2) = 2a^3 + 3a^2 + 2a - 4a^2 - 6a - 4$ Distribute multiplication
$= 2a^3 - a^2 - 4a - 4$ Combine like terms

G_2 $(x - y)(x^2 + 2xy - y^2)$

Note
Although there are three terms in the second parentheses, we still follow the procedure of each term in the first parentheses times each term in the second parentheses.

You are now ready to do G_2.

G_3 $(2a - b)(a^2 + 3ab + 2b^2)$

3. $(x - y)(x^2 + 3xy - y^2) = x^3 + 3x^2y - xy^2 - x^2y - 3xy^2 + y^3$ Distribute multiplication
$= x^3 + 2x^2y - 4xy^2 + y^3$ Combine like terms

You are now ready to do G_3. ■

Answers to section 3–3 margin exercises

A_1 binomial A_2 monomial A_3 trinomial A_4 not a polynomial because a variable is used as a divisor (appears in the denominator) A_5 polynomial of 4 terms B_1 $10a^2b$ B_2 $6x^5y$ B_3 $-12a^3b^2$ B_4 $15a^7b^2c^7$ C_1 $2a^2 + 6a$ C_2 $a^7 + a^6b^2 - a^5b^2$ C_3 $8x^4 - 4x^3y - 4x^2y^2$ C_4 $6a^2b^2 - 9ab^3$ D_1 $x^2 + 5x - 6$ D_2 $2a^2 + 7a + 3$ D_3 $2x^2 - 5xy - 3y^2$ E_1 $a^2 + 8a + 16$ E_2 $x^2 - 6xy + 9y^2$ F_1 $a^2 - 4$ F_2 $x^2 - 9y^2$ F_3 $9a^2 - 16b^2$ G_1 $2a^2 - ab - 3b^2$ G_2 $x^3 + x^2y - 3xy^2 + y^3$ G_3 $2a^3 + 5a^2b + ab^2 - 2b^3$

Mastery points

Can you

- Multiply monomials?
- Multiply a monomial with a multinomial?
- Multiply multinomials?
- Use the special products of the square of a binomial or the difference of two squares?

Exercise 3–3

Directions Determine if each of the following algebraic expressions is a polynomial. If it is a polynomial, what name best describes it? If it is not a polynomial, state why it is not. See example 3–3 A.

Examples $\boxed{A_1}$ $5x^2y + 2z$

Solutions polynomial, since there are two terms, it is a binomial

$\boxed{A_4}$ $5x^2y + \dfrac{2}{z}$

not a polynomial because a variable is used as a divisor (appears in the denominator)

1. $ax^2 + bx + c$
2. $mx + b$
3. $5x^2 + 2x$
4. $y + \dfrac{1}{x}$
5. $\dfrac{a+b}{5} - c$
6. $\dfrac{a+b}{c} + d$
7. $4x^5 - 7x^3 + 3x - 2$
8. $9x^6 + 2x^2 + 4$

Directions Perform the indicated multiplication and simplify. See examples 3–3 B, C, D, E, F, and G.

Examples $\boxed{C_4}$ $3ab^2(2a - 3b)$

Solutions
$= 3ab^2 \cdot 2a - 3ab^2 \cdot 3b$ Distributive property
$= 6a^2b^2 - 9ab^3$ Multiply monomials

$\boxed{D_3}$ $(2x + y)(x - 3y)$

$= 2x \cdot x - 2x \cdot 3y + y \cdot x - y \cdot 3y$ Distribute
$= 2x^2 - 6xy + xy - 3y^2$ Multiply
$= 2x^2 - 5xy - 3y^2$ Combine like terms

9. $(6x^3)(5x^2)$
10. $(4a)(3a^4)$
11. $(7ab)(2ab)$
12. $(5xy)(xy)$
13. $(3a^2b)(4a^3b^2)$
14. $(a^3b^4)(5a^2b^5)$

15. $(-2a^2b)(3ab^4)$

16. $(-5x^2y^5)(-2x^2y)$

17. $2ab(a^2 - bc + c^2)$

18. $6x(4y + 7z)$

19. $3a(5b^2 - 7c^2)$

20. $-ab(a^4 - a^2b^2 - b^4)$

21. $-5ab^2(3a^2 - ab + 4b^2)$

22. $6x^2(4x^2 - 2x + 3)$

23. $3ab(a^2 - 2ab - b^2)$

24. $(3a)(2a - b)(2b^2)$

25. $(2x)(x - y + 5)(5y)$

26. $(x^2y)(x^2 + y^2)(xy^2)$

27. $(x + 3)(x + 4)$

28. $(a + 5)(a - 3)$

29. $(y - 9)(y - 4)$

30. $(z + 7)(z - 11)$

31. $(a + 1)(a + 1)$

32. $(b - 1)(b - 1)$

33. $(R - 3)^2$

34. $(R + 2)(R - 2)$

35. $(a + 3)(a - 3)$

36. $(3x + 2)(x - 4)$

37. $(3a - 5)(2a - 7)$

38. $(3 - 2y)(2 - y)$

39. $(7 + 2x)(2x - 7)$

40. $(4r + 3)(r - 12)$

41. $(3k + w)(k - 6w)$

42. $(a - 6bc)(5a + 4bc)$

43. $(a + 6b)^2$

44. $(2a + 3b)^2$

45. $(2a + 3b)(2a - 3b)$

46. $(4x - y)(4x + y)$

47. $(a + 4b)(a^2 - 2ab + b^2)$

48. $(x - 2y)(2x^2 - 3xy + y^2)$

49. $(x + 4)(6x^2 - 3x + 7)$

50. $(x - y)(x^2 - 2xy + y^2)$

51. $(a + b)(a^2 - ab + b^2)$

52. $(x - y)(x^2 + xy + y^2)$

53. $(2x - y)(x^2 + 3xy + 2y^2)$

54. $(a + 3b)(2a^2 - 3ab - b^2)$

55. The area of the shaded region between the two circles is $\pi(R + r)(R - r)$. Perform the indicated multiplication.

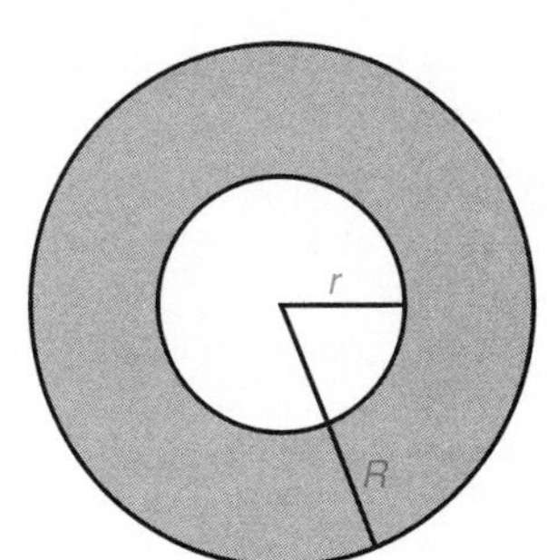

56. When squares of c units on a side are cut from the corners of a square sheet of metal x units on a side, and the metal sheet is then folded up into a tray, the volume is $c(x - 2c)(x - 2c)$. Perform the indicated multiplication.

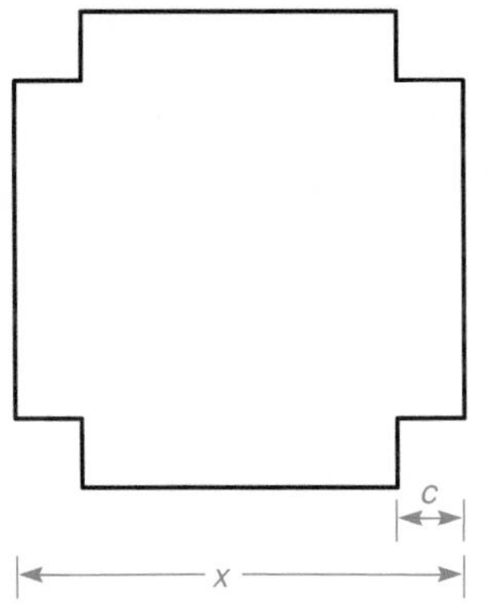

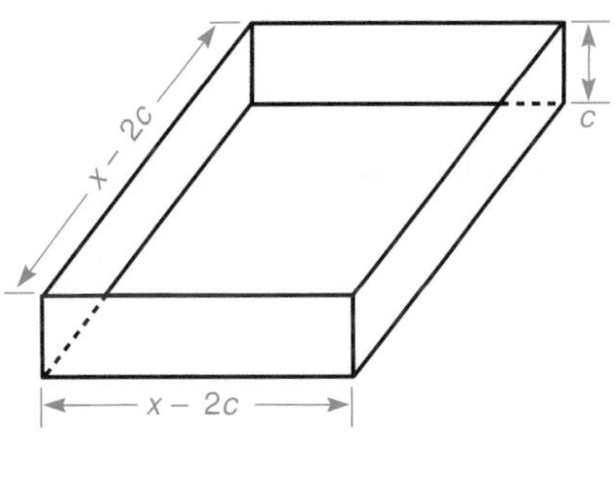

Review exercises

Directions Perform the indicated addition or subtraction. See sections 1–2 and 1–3.

1. $(-3) + (-2)$
2. $8 - (-4)$
3. $(-7) - (-10)$
4. $2 + (-5) + (-6)$

Directions Simplify by using the properties of exponents. See section 3–1.

5. $x^4 \cdot x^8$
6. $(a^3)^5$
7. $(3a^2b)^3$
8. $\left(\dfrac{2x}{y^2}\right)^3$

$\mathbf{A_1}$ $\dfrac{y^9}{y^4}$

3–4 Exponents—II

Division of like bases

Another useful property of exponents can be observed from the following example. Consider the expression

$$\frac{x^6}{x^2}, \text{ where } x \neq 0.$$

We can use the definition of exponents to write the fraction as

$$\frac{x^6}{x^2} = \frac{x \cdot x \cdot x \cdot x \cdot x \cdot x}{x \cdot x}.$$

We reduce the fraction as follows:

$$\frac{x \cdot x \cdot x \cdot x \cdot x \cdot x}{x \cdot x} = \frac{x \cdot x \cdot x \cdot x}{1} = \frac{x^4}{1} = x^4.$$

In our example, we reduced by two factors of x, leaving $6 - 2 = 4$ factors of x in the numerator. Therefore

$$\frac{x^6}{x^2} = x^{6-2} = x^4.$$

Thus we have the following property of exponents.

Quotient property of exponents

$$a^m \div a^n = \frac{a^m}{a^n} = a^{m-n}, \; a \neq 0.$$

Concept

To divide quantities having *like* bases, subtract the exponent of the denominator from the exponent of the numerator to get the exponent of the given base in the quotient.

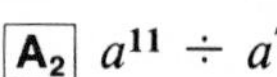

$\mathbf{A_2}$ $a^{11} \div a^7$

Note

If the base a is zero, $a = 0$, we have an expression that has no meaning. Therefore $a \neq 0$ indicates that we want our variables to assume no values that would cause the denominator to be zero.

Example 3–4 A

Simplify. Assume no variable is equal to zero.

1. $\dfrac{x^7}{x^5} = x^{7-5}$ — Division of like bases

$= x^2$ — Subtract exponents

You are now ready to do $\mathbf{A_1}$.

2. $a^{11} \div a^4 = a^{11-4}$ — Division of like bases

$= a^7$ — Subtract exponents

You are now ready to do $\mathbf{A_2}$.

3. $\frac{5^4}{5} = 5^{4-1}$ Division of like bases

$= 5^3$ Subtract exponents

$= 125$ Standard form

You are now ready to do **A₃**.

Note
Remember that when we are dividing like bases, their exponents are subtracted, but **the base is not changed.**

4. $\frac{a^5 \cdot a^2}{a^4} = \frac{a^{5+2}}{a^4}$ Multiply like bases in numerator

$= \frac{a^7}{a^4}$ Add exponents in numerator

$= a^{7-4}$ Division of like bases

$= a^3$ Subtract exponents

You are now ready to do **A₄**.

5. $\frac{a^5b^{12}}{a^2b^8} = a^{5-2}b^{12-8}$ Division of like bases

$= a^3b^4$ Subtract exponents

Note
The division is carried out between *like* bases.

You are now ready to do **A₅**. ■

A₃ $\frac{4^5}{4}$

A₄ $\frac{x \cdot x^6}{x^3}$

A₅ $\frac{x^5y^{10}}{x^4y^2}$

Negative exponents

To this point, we have considered only those problems where the exponent of the numerator is greater than the exponent of the denominator. Consider the following example,

$$\frac{x^2}{x^6}, \text{ where } x \neq 0.$$

By the definition of exponents, this becomes

$$\frac{x^2}{x^6} = \frac{x \cdot x}{x \cdot x \cdot x \cdot x \cdot x \cdot x},$$

and reducing the fraction,

$$\frac{x \cdot x}{x \cdot x \cdot x \cdot x \cdot x \cdot x} = \frac{1}{x \cdot x \cdot x \cdot x} = \frac{1}{x^4}.$$

Again, we reduced by two factors of x, leaving $6 - 2 = 4$ factors of x in the denominator. Hence

$$\frac{x^2}{x^6} = \frac{1}{x^4}.$$

However using the division property of exponents to carry out the division, we would have

$$\frac{x^2}{x^6} = x^{2-6} = x^{-4}.$$

Since we should arrive at the same answer regardless of which procedure we use, then x^{-4} must be $\frac{1}{x^4}$. Thus $x^{-4} = \frac{1}{x^4}$. This leads us to the definition of a negative exponent.

B₁ b^{-2}

> **Definition of a negative exponent**
>
> $$a^{-n} = \frac{1}{a^n},\ a \neq 0.$$
>
> **Concept**
>
> A negative exponent on any base (except zero) can be written as 1 over that base with a positive exponent.

Example 3–4 B

Simplify. Leave the answer with only positive exponents. Assume that no variable is equal to zero.

B₂ 5^{-2}

1. $x^{-3} = \dfrac{1}{x^3}$ — Rewritten as 1 over x to the positive 3rd

You are now ready to do **B₁**.

2. $a^{-9} = \dfrac{1}{a^9}$ — Rewritten as 1 over a to the positive 9th

Note

From the definition of a negative exponent, if a **factor** is moved from either the numerator to the denominator or from the denominator to the numerator, the sign of its exponent will change. The sign of the base will not be affected by this change.

B₃ $\dfrac{1}{y^{-2}}$

2. *Alternative procedure*

$a^{-9} = \dfrac{a^{-9}}{1}$ — Rewrite as a fraction

$= \dfrac{1}{a^9}$ — Sign of the exponent is changed as the **factor** is moved from numerator to denominator

You are now ready to do **B₂**.

3. $\dfrac{1}{b^{-4}} = \dfrac{b^4}{1}$ — Sign of the exponent is changed as the **factor** is moved from denominator to numerator

$= b^4$ — Standard form is to leave only positive exponents

You are now ready to do **B₃**.

4. $(-3)^{-3} = \dfrac{1}{(-3)^3}$ — Sign of the exponent is changed as the factor is moved from numerator to denominator

B₄ $-z^{-3}$

$= \dfrac{1}{-27}$ or $-\dfrac{1}{27}$ — Standard form

You are now ready to do **B₄**.

Note

In example 4, only the sign of the exponent changed, not the sign of the base. ■

Zero as an exponent

C_1 c^0

Now consider the situation involving the division of like bases that are raised to the same power.

$$\frac{x^3}{x^3}, \text{ where } x \neq 0.$$

By the definition of exponents, we have

$$\frac{x^3}{x^3} = \frac{x \cdot x \cdot x}{x \cdot x \cdot x} = \frac{1}{1} = 1.$$

By the division property of exponents,

C_2 10^0

$$\frac{x^3}{x^3} = x^{3-3} = x^0.$$

Since $\frac{x^3}{x^3} = 1$ and $\frac{x^3}{x^3} = x^0$, then x^0 must be equal to 1.

This leads us to the definition of zero as an exponent.

> **Definition of zero as an exponent**
>
> $$a^0 = 1, a \neq 0.$$
>
> **Concept**
>
> *Any* number other than zero raised to the zero power is equal to 1.

C_3 $(5a)^0$

Example 3–4 C

Simplify. Assume that no variable is equal to zero.

1. $r^0 = 1$

You are now ready to do **C_1**.

C_4 $5a^0$

2. $5^0 = 1$

You are now ready to do **C_2**.

3. $(-2)^0 = 1$

You are now ready to do **C_3**.

4. $3x^0 = 3 \cdot 1 = 3$

> **Note**
>
> The exponent acts only on the symbol immediately to its left. In this example, only x is raised to the zero power. The exponent of 3 is understood to be 1.

D_1 $\frac{b^4}{b^{10}}$

You are now ready to do **C_4**. ■

Example 3–4 D

Simplify. Leave the answer with only positive exponents. Assume that no variable is equal to zero.

1. $\frac{x^5}{x^{11}} = x^{5-11}$ Division of like bases

$= x^{-6}$ Subtract exponents

$= \frac{1}{x^6}$ Standard form

You are now ready to do **D_1**.

D_2 $x^8 \cdot x^{-12}$

2. $a^{-7} \cdot a^5 = a^{-7+5}$ — Multiplication of like bases

$= a^{-2}$ — Add exponents

$= \dfrac{1}{a^2}$ — Standard form

You are now ready to do **D_2**.

3. $(b^{-2})^{-4} = b^{(-2)\cdot(-4)}$ — Power of a power

$= b^8$ — Multiply exponents

D_3 $(a^{-3})^{-2}$

You are now ready to do **D_3**.

4. $\dfrac{a^3b^5}{a^7b^2} = a^{3-7}b^{5-2}$ — Division of like bases

$= a^{-4}b^3$ — Subtract exponents

$= \dfrac{b^3}{a^4}$ — Standard form

D_4 $\dfrac{x^7y^3}{x^2y^9}$

You are now ready to do **D_4**.

5. $\dfrac{a^3b^2c^4}{ab^5c^4} = a^{3-1}b^{2-5}c^{4-4}$ — Division of like bases

$= a^2b^{-3}c^0$ — Subtract the exponents

$= \dfrac{a^2 \cdot 1}{b^3}$ — The a's remain in the numerator, the b's drop to the denominator, and c^0 is 1

$= \dfrac{a^2}{b^3}$ — Standard form

D_5 $\dfrac{xy^5z^4}{xyz^8}$

You are now ready to do **D_5**.

6. $(3a^{-2}b^3)^{-3} = 3^{-3}(a^{-2})^{-3}(b^3)^{-3}$ — Each factor is raised to the power

$= 3^{-3}a^6b^{-9}$ — Power of a power

$= \dfrac{a^6}{3^3b^9}$ — The 3s and the b's drop to the denominator

$= \dfrac{a^6}{27b^9}$ — Standard form

D_6 $(2x^{-4}y^2)^{-2}$

You are now ready to do **D_6**.

7. $\dfrac{a^{-2}b^4}{a^{-5}b^6} = a^{-2-(-5)}b^{4-6}$ — Division of like bases

$= a^3b^{-2}$ — Subtract exponents

$= \dfrac{a^3}{b^2}$ — Standard form

D_7 $\dfrac{x^5y^{-2}}{x^4y^{-6}}$

You are now ready to do **D_7**.

8. $\left(\dfrac{a^{-2}b}{c^3}\right)^{-2} = \dfrac{(a^{-2}b)^{-2}}{(c^3)^{-2}}$ — Numerator and denominator are raised to the power

$= \dfrac{(a^{-2})^{-2}b^{-2}}{(c^3)^{-2}}$ — Numerator has a group of factors to a power

$= \dfrac{a^{(-2)(-2)}b^{-2}}{c^{(3)(-2)}}$ — Power of a power

$= \dfrac{a^4b^{-2}}{c^{-6}}$ — Multiply exponents

$= \dfrac{a^4c^6}{b^2}$ — Standard form, factors raised to a negative power are moved to the other side of the fraction bar

D_8 $\left(\dfrac{x^2y^{-4}}{z^{-3}}\right)^{-2}$

You are now ready to do **D_8**. ■

Answers to section 3–4 margin exercises

A_1 y^5 **A_2** a^4 **A_3** $4^4 = 256$ **A_4** x^4 **A_5** xy^8 **B_1** $\frac{1}{b^2}$ **B_2** $\frac{1}{5^2} = \frac{1}{25}$ **B_3** y^2

B_4 $-\frac{1}{z^3}$ **C_1** 1 **C_2** 1 **C_3** 1 **C_4** 5 **D_1** $\frac{1}{b^6}$ **D_2** $\frac{1}{x^4}$

D_3 a^6 **D_4** $\frac{x^5}{y^6}$ **D_5** $\frac{y^4}{z^4}$ **D_6** $\frac{x^8}{4y^4}$ **D_7** xy^4 **D_8** $\frac{y^8}{x^4z^6}$

Mastery points

Can you

- Perform division involving exponents?
- Perform operations involving negative exponents?
- Perform operations involving zero as an exponent?

Exercise 3–4

Directions Write each expression with only positive exponents. Assume that no variable is equal to zero. See examples 3–4 B and C.

Examples **C_1** c^0

Solutions $= 1$ By definition is equal to 1

B_1 b^{-2}

$= \frac{1}{b^2}$ Rewritten as 1 over *b* to the positive 2nd

1. x^0 **2.** $(2y)^0$ **3.** $5a^0$ **4.** $7x^0$ **5.** S^{-2}

6. R^{-5} **7.** $(2x)^{-3}$ **8.** $(3P)^{-2}$ **9.** $4z^{-2}$ **10.** $9C^{-4}$

11. $\frac{1}{x^{-5}}$ **12.** $\frac{5}{x^{-4}}$ **13.** $\frac{1}{2y^{-3}}$ **14.** $\frac{1}{3x^{-2}}$ **15.** $2x^{-4}y^2$

16. $x^{-2}y^4$ **17.** $p^0r^{-2}t^5$ **18.** $x^{-3}y^2z^{-4}$

Directions Perform all indicated operations and leave your answer with only positive exponents. Assume that no variable is equal to zero. See examples 3–4 A, B, and D.

Examples **A₂** $a^{11} \div a^7$

Solutions $= a^{11-7}$ Division of like bases

$= a^4$ Subtract exponents

D₁ $\frac{b^4}{b^{10}}$

$= b^{4-10}$ Division of like bases

$= b^{-6}$ Subtract exponents

$= \frac{1}{b^6}$ Standard form

19. $x^{12} \div x^6$

20. $\frac{a^5}{a^3}$

21. $\frac{b^9}{b^7}$

22. $C^6 \div C^9$

23. $\frac{3^4}{3^2}$

24. $\frac{2^5}{2^3}$

25. $\frac{4^2}{4^5}$

26. $\frac{x^4x^3}{x^2}$

27. $\frac{y^5y}{y^2}$

28. $\frac{x^7}{x^2x^3}$

29. $\frac{y^3}{y^4y^5}$

30. $\frac{b^2}{bb^4}$

31. $\frac{a^7b^5}{a^4b^2}$

32. $\frac{2^3x^3y^7}{2xy^5}$

33. $\frac{3a^2b^5}{3^4a^5b^5}$

34. $\frac{5^2a^3b}{5^3a^7b^3}$

35. $x^{-4}x^7$

36. $y^{-2}y^{10}$

37. a^5a^{-11}

38. $R^{-2}R^{-5}$

39. $(-5)^{-3}$

40. $(-2)^{-4}$

41. $\frac{3^{-2}}{3^{-5}}$

42. $\frac{2^{-6}}{2^{-3}}$

43. $(2a^2)^{-2}$

44. $(x^{-4})^{-3}$

45. $(b^2)^{-3}$

46. $(a^{-3})^{-2}$

47. $(a^{-2}b^3)^{-2}$

48. $(x^4y^{-2})^{-3}$

49. $(2a^{-3}b)^{-2}$ **50.** $(3x^4y^{-2})^{-3}$ **51.** $\dfrac{a^{-2}b^3}{a^3b^{-5}}$ **52.** $\dfrac{R^2S^{-4}}{R^{-3}S^5}$ **53.** $\dfrac{4y^{-3}}{4^{-1}y^2}$

54. $\dfrac{4^{-1}a^{-2}b^3c^0}{2a^{-3}b^{-1}c^{-2}}$ 55. $\dfrac{2a^{-1}b^0c^2}{5a^3b^{-1}c^{-3}}$ **56.** $\dfrac{8a^{-2}b^{-5}}{2a^{-1}b^4}$ **57.** $\dfrac{2x^{-1}y^{-2}}{3x^{-2}y^2}$ **58.** $\left(\dfrac{xy^{-2}}{z^{-4}}\right)^{-1}$

59. $\left(\dfrac{x^{-3}y}{z^5}\right)^{-2}$ **60.** $\left(\dfrac{2a^{-3}}{b^5}\right)^{-2}$ **61.** $\left(\dfrac{4^{-1}a^{-2}}{b^{-5}}\right)^{-2}$

Review exercises

Directions Perform the indicated multiplication. See section R–2.

1. $(6.2) \cdot (5.7)$ **2.** $(2.8) \cdot (3.7)$ **3.** $(1.9) \cdot (8.8)$

4. $(4.2) \cdot (6.9)$ **5.** $(9.9) \cdot (1.9)$ **6.** $(7.5) \cdot (6.6)$

3–5 Scientific notation

Scientific notation

An important use of integer exponents is in scientific, engineering, and technical fields where we deal with very large or very small numbers. For example, the mass of a hydrogen atom is 0.000 000 000 000 000 000 000 001 67 gram; the mass of an electron is 0.000 000 000 000 000 000 000 000 000 91 gram; the half-life of lead-204 is 14,000,000,000,000,000,000 years. To work with such numbers on the calculator, they must often be entered in scientific notation form. We define the scientific notation form of a positive number X to be the product

$$X = a \times 10^n,$$

where $1 \leq a < 10$ and n is an integer. To achieve this form of the decimal number X, use the following steps.

A_1 4,380

Scientific notation

Step 1 Move the decimal point to a position immediately following the first nonzero digit in *X*.
Step 2 Count the number of places the decimal point has been moved. This is the power, *n*, to which 10 is raised.
Step 3 If
a. the decimal point is moved to the *left*, *n* is *positive*.
b. the decimal point is moved to the *right*, *n* is *negative*.
c. the decimal point already follows the first nonzero digit, *n* is *zero*.

A_2 188,000

Example 3–5 A

Express the following numbers in scientific notation.

1. $250 = 2.50. \times 10^2$ — Decimal point is moved 2 places to the left, exponent is positive 2
   $= 2.5 \times 10^2$ — Scientific notation form

You are now ready to do **A_1**.

2. $45{,}000{,}000 = 4.5000000. \times 10^7$ — Decimal point is moved 7 places to the left, exponent is positive 7
   $= 4.5 \times 10^7$ — Scientific notation form

A_3 9

You are now ready to do **A_2**.

3. $5 = 5 \times 10^0$ — Decimal point already follows the first nonzero digit, exponent is 0

You are now ready to do **A_3**.

4. $0.000152 = 0.0001.52 \times 10^{-4}$ — Decimal point is moved 4 places to the right, exponent is negative 4
   $= 1.52 \times 10^{-4}$ — Scientific notation form

You are now ready to do **A_4**.

A_4 0.00316

Note
To write a negative number in scientific notation, we use the same procedure as for a positive number except that a negative sign, −, is placed in front of *a*.

5. $-0.0234 = -0.02.34 \times 10^{-2}$ — Decimal point is moved 2 places to the right, the exponent is negative 2
   $= -2.34 \times 10^{-2}$ — Scientific notation form

You are now ready to do **A_5**. ■

A_5 −0.00592

Standard form

Sometimes it is necessary to convert a number in scientific notation to its standard form. To do this, we apply the rules in reverse.

Standard form

When the power of 10 is
1. *positive*, the decimal point is moved to the *right n* places.
2. *negative*, the decimal point is moved to the *left n* places.
3. *zero*, the decimal point is not moved.

Example 3–5 B

Express the following numbers in standard form.

1. $1.45 \times 10^4 = 1.4500.$ — The exponent of 10 is positive 4. Move decimal point 4 places to the *right*

$= 14{,}500.$ — Standard form

You are now ready to do **B₁**.

2. $5.23 \times 10^{-3} = 0.005.23$ — The exponent of 10 is -3, move decimal point 3 places to the left

$= 0.00523$ — Standard form

Note
In each example, it was necessary to insert zeros to properly locate the decimal point.

You are now ready to do **B₂**.

3. $-4.07 \times 10^{-2} = -0.04.07$ — The exponent of 10 is -2, move the decimal point 2 places to the left

$= -0.0407$ — Standard form

Note
The negative sign preceding the number is carried along into the standard form.

You are now ready to do **B₃**. ■

B_1 6.23×10^3

B_2 9.98×10^{-4}

B_3 -5.63×10^4

Computation using scientific notation

Scientific notation can be used to simplify numerical calculations when the numbers are very large or very small. We first change the numbers to scientific notation and use the properties of exponents to help perform the indicated operations.

Example 3–5 C

Perform the indicated operations using scientific notation.

1. $(349{,}000{,}000)(0.0816)$

$= (3.49 \times 10^8)(8.16 \times 10^{-2})$	Scientific notation
$= (3.49 \cdot 8.16) \times (10^8 \cdot 10^{-2})$	Commutative and associative properties
$= 28.4784 \times 10^6$	Multiply
$= 28{,}478{,}400$	Standard form

You are now ready to do **C₁**.

2. $\dfrac{(102{,}000{,}000)(0.00105)}{(1{,}190)(0.012)}$

$= \dfrac{(1.02 \times 10^8)(1.05 \times 10^{-3})}{(1.19 \times 10^3)(1.2 \times 10^{-2})}$	Scientific notation
$= \dfrac{(1.02)(1.05)10^8 \cdot 10^{-3}}{(1.19)(1.2)10^3 \cdot 10^{-2}}$	Commutative and associative properties
$= \dfrac{(1.02)(1.05)}{(1.19)(1.2)} \times \dfrac{10^5}{10^1}$	Properties of exponents
$= 0.75 \times 10^4$	Multiplication and division
$= 7{,}500$	Standard form

You are now ready to do **C₂**. ■

C_1 $(7.98 \times 10^6) \cdot (6.43 \times 10^{-12})$

C_2 $(1{,}071{,}000) \div (63{,}000)$

Answers to section 3–5 margin exercises

A_1 4.38×10^3 A_2 1.88×10^5 A_3 9×10^0 A_4 3.16×10^{-3} A_5 -5.92×10^{-3}
B_1 6,230 B_2 0.000998 B_3 −56,300 C_1 0.0000513114 C_2 17

Mastery points

Can you

- Express a number in scientific notation?
- Convert a number from scientific notation to standard form?
- Do computations using scientific notation?

Exercise 3–5

Directions Express the following numbers in scientific notation. See example 3–5 A.

Examples [A_1] 4,380

Solutions $= 4.38 \times 10^3$ Move the decimal point three places to the left, exponent is 3

[A_5] −0.00592

$= -5.92 \times 10^{-3}$ Move the decimal point three places to the right, exponent is −3

1. 255 **2.** 65,000,000 **3.** 12,345 **4.** 14,800 **5.** 155,000

6. 14.36 **7.** 855.076 **8.** 1,570.7 **9.** 1,007,600 **10.** 6,000,736

11. 0.00012 **12.** 0.0863 **13.** 0.0000081 **14.** 0.0000147 **15.** 0.0007

16. 0.12079 **17.** 0.000000000094 **18.** −456 **19.** −4,500 **20.** −0.00087

21. −5,850,000 **22.** −0.0567 **23.** −45.78 **24.** −34,000,000 **25.** −0.00000002985

Directions Convert the following numbers in scientific notation to their standard form. See example 3–5 B.

Examples [B_2] 9.98×10^{-4}

Solutions = 0.000998 Exponent is −4, move 4 places to the left

[B_3] -5.63×10^4

= −56,300 Exponent is 4, move 4 places to the right

26. 2.07×10^3 **27.** 4.99×10^7 **28.** 5.061×10^5 **29.** 7.23×10^0

30. 1.073×10^4 **31.** 4.2×10^{-3} **32.** 7.611×10^{-7} **33.** 1.47×10^{-6}

34. 5.0×10^{-2}

35. 7.89×10^{-4}

36. -2.3×10^{5}

37. -4.82×10^{-9}

38. -2.61×10^{2}

39. -4.92×10^{-6}

40. -9.3×10^{8}

Directions Express the following numbers in scientific notation or in standard form. See examples 3–5 A and B.

41. A nanometer equals 0.000000001 of a meter. Write this number in scientific notation.

42. The speed of light is approximately 30,000,000,000 centimeters per second. Write this in scientific notation.

43. The average human body manufactures approximately 2,000,000,000,000 red blood cells each day. Write this in scientific notation.

44. A person working for 30 years earning at least $13 per hour will earn in excess of 7.6×10^{5} dollars. Write this in standard form.

45. A person with a heartbeat of 72 beats per minute will experience more than 3.56×10^{7} heartbeats in one year. Write this in standard form.

46. Light travels approximately 9,500,000,000,000 kilometers in one year. Write this number in scientific notation.

47. One atom of iron has a mass of 9.3×10^{-23}. Write this in standard form.

48. The planet Pluto is about 4,250 million miles from the Earth. Write this in scientific notation.

49. One gallon of oil releases 1.4×10^{5} BTU of heat energy when burned. Write this in standard form.

50. There are 3.3×10^{22} molecules in one cubic centimeter of water. Write this in standard form.

Directions Perform the indicated operations using scientific notation. Leave the answer in scientific notation. See example 3–5 C.

51. $(6{,}370{,}000) \cdot (19{,}200{,}000)$

52. $(18{,}700{,}000) \cdot (52{,}600{,}000)$

53. $(9.41 \times 10^{12}) \cdot (3.86 \times 10^{-14})$

54. $(4.49 \times 10^{-18}) \cdot (5.89 \times 10^{27})$

55. $(0.00341) \cdot (0.0000519)$

56. $(0.00827) \cdot (0.0196)$

57. $(5.93 \times 10^{-4}) \cdot (8.17 \times 10^{11})$

58. $(177{,}000) \div (0.15)$

59. $(1.344 \times 10^{-8}) \div (9.6 \times 10^{-12})$

60. $(1.036 \times 10^{15}) \div (3.7 \times 10^{-4})$

61. $\dfrac{(92{,}000{,}000) \cdot (0.0036)}{(0.018) \cdot (4{,}000)}$

62. $\dfrac{(39{,}600) \cdot (0.00264)}{(0.00000132) \cdot (66{,}000{,}000)}$

Review exercises

Directions Perform the indicated addition and subtraction. See section 3–2.

1. $3x + 2x$

2. $6a^2 - 3a^2$

3. $5ab + 7ab$

Directions Perform the indicated multiplication. See section 3–3.

4. $x^2(x + 2)$

5. $3a(2a - 5)$

6. $x^2y(3x + 2y - 7)$

Chapter 3 lead-in problem

If Diane makes $13 per hour and works 40 hours per week, she will earn more than one million dollars over the next 40 years. How much money will Diane earn? Perform the computations using scientific notation.

Solution

hourly rate		hours worked per week		weeks per year		number of years worked	
13	·	40	·	52	·	40	Original problem

$= (1.3 \times 10)(4.0 \times 10)(5.2 \times 10)(4.0 \times 10)$ Scientific notation

$= (1.3)(4.0)(5.2)(4.0) \times (10 \cdot 10 \cdot 10 \cdot 10)$ Associative and commutative properties

$= 108.16 \times 10^4$ Multiply

$= 1{,}081{,}600$ Standard form

Diane will earn $1,081,600 over the next 40 years.

Chapter 3 summary

1. In the expression x^6, x is called the **base** and 6 the **exponent.**

2. $a^n = \overbrace{a \cdot a \cdot a \cdots a}^{n \text{ factors}}$, where n is a positive integer.

3. Properties and definitions of exponents

$a^m \cdot a^n = a^{m+n}$

$(ab)^n = a^nb^n$

$(a^m)^n = a^{n \cdot m}$

$\left(\dfrac{a}{b}\right)^n = \dfrac{a^n}{b^n}, b \neq 0$

$a^m \div a^n = \dfrac{a^m}{a^n} = a^{m-n}, a \neq 0$

$a^{-n} = \dfrac{1}{a^n}, a \neq 0$

$a^0 = 1, a \neq 0$

4. A **polynomial** is a special kind of algebraic expression. A **monomial** is a polynomial that contains one term; a **binomial** contains two terms; a **trinomial** contains three terms; a **multinomial** contains more than one term.
5. **Like terms** or **similar terms** are terms whose variable factors are the same.
6. We can *add* or *subtract* only like, or similar, terms.
7. When *multiplying* two multinomials, we multiply each of the terms in the first multinomial by each of the terms in the second multinomial. We then combine like terms.
8. Three **special products** are:
   $(a + b)^2 = a^2 + 2ab + b^2$
   $(a - b)^2 = a^2 - 2ab + b^2$
   $(a + b)(a - b) = a^2 - b^2$
9. The scientific notation form of a positive number X is $X = a \times 10^n$, where $1 \leq a < 10$ and n is an integer.

Chapter 3 review

[3–1]

Directions Simplify and leave the answers with only positive exponents. Assume that no variable is equal to zero.

1. $a^5 \cdot a^7$
2. $a \cdot a^4 \cdot a^9$
3. $4^3 \cdot 4^2$
4. $(xy)^4$
5. $(a^3)^5$
6. $(2a^2b^3)^3$
7. $(3^3x^4y^5)^4$
8. $(3x^2y^3)(2xy^4)$
9. $(5ab^3)(4a^3b^2)$
10. $(x^5y^4)^4(2x^2y^3)^3$
11. $(2a^2b)^3(3a^4)^2$
12. $\left(\frac{a}{b}\right)^5$
13. $\left(\frac{2yz}{x}\right)^2$
14. $\left(\frac{a^3b}{c^4}\right)^3$
15. $\left(\frac{3a^3b^2}{c^5}\right)^2$
16. $\left(\frac{2xy^4}{z^6}\right)^5$

Directions Write an algebraic expression for each of the following.

17. 5 times x
18. 7 less than y
19. 4 more than z
20. 2 times a number, plus 6

[3–2]

Directions Remove all grouping symbols and combine like terms.

21. $(3x^2 + 2x - 1) + (x^2 - 5x + 4)$

22. $(a^2 - 3a + 4) - (2a^2 - 4a - 7)$

23. $(4a^2 - b^2) - (3a^2 + 2b^2) - (7a^2 - 3b^2)$

24. $(5x^3 - 2xy^2 + 3x^2y - 4y^3)$
$- (4x^2 + 3x^2y - 2y^3 + 5xy^2)$

25. $(4ab + 7b^2c) - (15ab - 11bc)$

26. $(x - 2y + 7) - (x + 4b + 6)$

27. $(4ab - 2ac) - (6bc - 5ac) + (ab + 2bc)$

28. $3a - [4a - (a - 5)]$

29. $5x + [3x - (x - y)]$

30. $4x - (x - y) - [3x - y - (2x + 3y)]$

31. $5a - \{6b + a - (5a - 4b)\}$

[3–3]

Directions Determine which of the following algebraic expressions are polynomials. If it is a polynomial, what name best describes it? If it is not a polynomial, state why not.

32. $\frac{x+y}{3} + z$ **33.** $x^3 - x^2$ **34.** $4a^2b^3c$ **35.** $\frac{a+b}{c}$

Directions Perform the indicated multiplication and simplify.

36. $(5x^2y)(2x^3y^4)$ **37.** $(-3a^2b^3)(2a^4b^7)$ **38.** $5x(3x - 2y)$

39. $-3a^2b(2a^2 - 3ab + 4b^2)$ **40.** $(5x)(3x - y)(2y^2)$ **41.** $(x + 3)(x - 4)$

42. $(x + 5)^2$ **43.** $(a - 7)(a + 7)$ **44.** $(5x - y)(3x + 2y)$

45. $(x - 2y)(x^2 + 3xy + y^2)$

[3–4]

Directions Simplify and leave the answers with only positive exponents. Assume that no variable is equal to zero.

46. $\frac{b^5}{b^7}$ **47.** $5a^{-2}$ **48.** $a^{-5} \cdot a^9$ **49.** $\frac{x^3x^2}{x^8}$ **50.** $(3a^2b)^0$

51. $5x^{-3}y^{-2}$ **52.** $\frac{a^{-4}}{a^{-7}}$ **53.** $(2xy^{-3})^{-2}$ **54.** $\frac{2x^{-1}y^0z^3}{4x^{-2}y^{-3}}$ **55.** $\frac{8a^{-5}b^{-4}c^0}{4a^{-7}b^2c^{-3}}$

[3–5]

Directions Express the following numbers in scientific notation.

56. 1,840

57. 0.00157

58. 107,000,000

59. 849,000,000,000

60. -37.5

61. -0.00543

Directions Express the following numbers in standard form.

62. 5.04×10^5

63. 6.39×10^{-3}

64. -5.96×10^2

65. -8.86×10^{-3}

66. 7.35×10^{-7}

67. 8.12×10^8

Directions Perform the indicated operations using scientific notation. Leave the answer in scientific notation.

68. $(456{,}000{,}000) \cdot (0.000587)$

69. $(0.0000183) \cdot (0.000846)$

70. $(756{,}000) \div (105{,}000{,}000)$

71. $(0.00525) \div (42{,}000)$

NAME

Chapter 3 cumulative test

CLASS/SECTION DATE

Directions Perform the indicated operations, if possible, and simplify.

[1–2] **1.** $(-8) + (-4)$

[3–1] **2.** $x^2 \cdot x \cdot x^3$

[1–6] **3.** $14 + 2 \cdot 15 \div 6 - 3 + 4$

[3–2] **4.** $(2a - b) - (a - 4b)$

[1–3] **5.** $(-10) - (-14)$

[3–3] **6.** $(2x - y)^2$

[1–5] **7.** $\frac{-24}{-8}$

[3–1] **8.** $(2a^2bc^3)^3$

[1–6] **9.** $5(-4 + 7) - 3(8 - 5)$

[3–2] **10.** $(3x^2y - 2xy^2) - (5xy^2 - x^2y)$

[3–3] **11.** $(3a - 2b)(3a + 2b)$

[1–6] **12.** -5^2

[3–1] **13.** $\left(\frac{2a^2}{b}\right)^3$

[1–5] **14.** $\frac{8}{0}$

[3–1] **15.** $(2x^2y)(3xy^3)$

[3–2] **16.** $5a + 3a^2 - 4a - a^2 + 5 + a^3 - 6$

[3–3] **17.** $(2x + 3)(x - 4)$

[3–2] **18.** $x - [3x - (y + x) + (2x - 3y)]$

Directions Two numbers are listed. Find two integers so that their product is the first number and their sum is the second number.

[1–4] **19.** $-30, 1$

[1–4] **20.** $24, -10$

[1–4] **21.** $30, -17$

[1–4] **22.** $48, 19$

Directions Find the solution.

[2–3] **23.** $10x - 7 = 4x + 3$

[2–7] **24.** $3x + (x - 1) > 7 - x$

[2–3] **25.** $16 - 2(4x - 1) = 3x - 12$

[2–7] **26.** $-1 < 2x + 3 < 11$

[2–4] **27.** Phil has $10,000, part of which he invests at 6% and the rest at 5%. If his total income from the two investments was $560, how much did he invest at each rate?

[2–4] **28.** The sum of three consecutive even integers is 48. Find the integers.

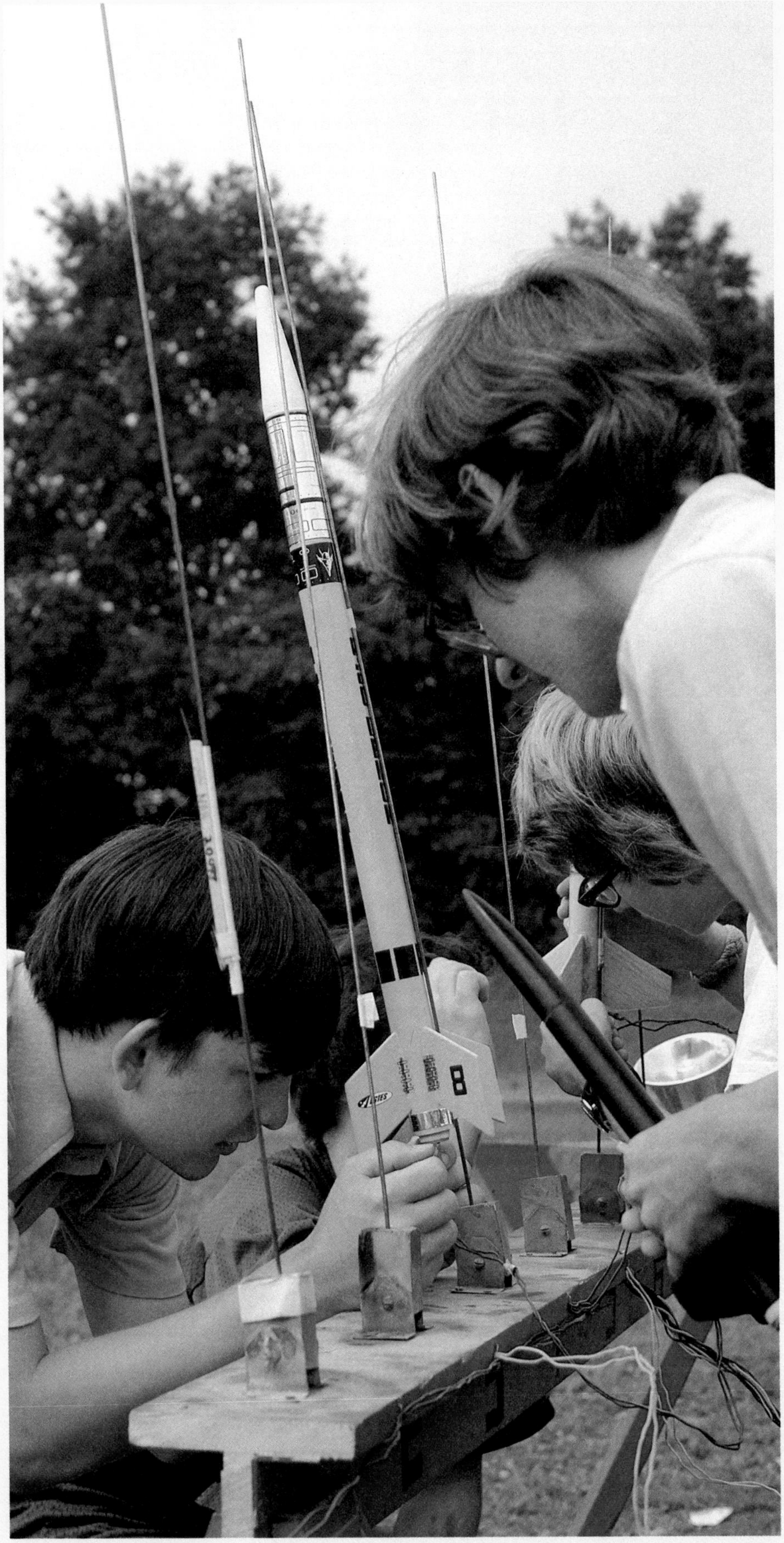

CHAPTER

4

Factoring and Solution of Quadratic Equations by Factoring

The formula $s = vt - 16t^2$ gives the height s in feet that an object will travel in t seconds if it is propelled directly upward at an initial velocity of v feet per second. If an object is thrown upward at 96 feet per second, how long will it take the object to reach a height of 144 feet?

Proficiency check

[3–3] **1.** $(a - 2b)^2$

[3–1] **2.** $(a^3)^2$

[3–3] **3.** $(x - 2y)(x + 2y)$

[3–3] **4.** $2x(3y - z)$

[3–3] **5.** $(3a - b)(a - 2b)$

[3–3] **6.** $5a^2b(3a + 2a^2b^2 - 4b^5)$

[3–3] **7.** $(x + 3y)^2$

[3–3] **8.** $(3x + 2y)(x - y)$

[3–3] **9.** $(2x - y)(4x^2 + 2xy + y^2)$

[3–3] **10.** $(a^2 - 5bc)(a^2 + 5bc)$

4–1 Common factors

Greatest common factor

To find the solution of certain equations that are not linear, we will need to study a technique called **factoring a polynomial.** Factoring polynomials will also be useful in dealing with algebraic fractions since, as we have seen with arithmetic fractions, we must have the numerator and the denominator of the fractions in a factored form to reduce or to find a common denominator.

The first type of factoring that we will do involves finding the **greatest common factor** (GCF) of the polynomial. Recall the statement of the distributive property:

$$a(b + c) = ab + ac.$$

$a(b + c)$ is called the **factored form** of $ab + ac$.

When a polynomial is factored, we "factor out" the greatest common factor, GCF. The greatest common factor consists of the following:

Greatest common factor

1. The greatest integer that is a common factor of all the numerical coefficients, and
2. The variable factor(s) raised to the least power to which they were raised in any of the terms

Factoring →

Polynomial (*terms*)	**Distributive Property** (*determine the GCF*)	**Factored Form** (*factors*)
$3x + 6$	$\mathbf{3} \cdot x + \mathbf{3} \cdot 2$	$3(x + 2)$
$10x^2 + 15y$	$\mathbf{5} \cdot 2x^2 + \mathbf{5} \cdot 3y$	$5(2x^2 + 3y)$
$12a - 42b$	$\mathbf{6} \cdot 2a - \mathbf{6} \cdot 7b$	$6(2a - 7b)$
$18xy + 12xz$	$\mathbf{6x} \cdot 3y + \mathbf{6x} \cdot 2z$	$6x(3y + 2z)$

← *Multiplying*

In the previous examples, we determined the greatest common factor by inspection. In some problems, this may not be possible, and the following procedure will be necessary. Factor the polynomial $12x^3y + 30x^2y^3$.

Factoring the greatest common factor

Step 1 Factor each term such that it is the product of primes* and variables to powers.

$$12x^3y \qquad\qquad 30x^2y^3$$
$$2^2 \cdot 3 \cdot x^3 \cdot y \qquad\qquad 2 \cdot 3 \cdot 5 \cdot x^2 \cdot y^3$$

Step 2 Write down all the numbers and variables that are common to *every* term.

$$2 \cdot 3 \cdot x \cdot y$$

Note
We do not have 5 as part of our greatest common factor since it does not appear as a factor in *all* of the terms.

Step 3 Take the numbers and variables in step 2. Raise them to the *least* power to which they were raised in any of the terms.

$$2^1 \cdot 3^1 \cdot x^2 \cdot y^1 = 6x^2y$$

This is the greatest common factor.

Step 4 Find the multinomial factor (the polynomial within the parentheses) by dividing each term of the polynomial being factored by the GCF.

$$\frac{12x^3y}{6x^2y} = 2x \quad \text{and} \quad \frac{30x^2y^3}{6x^2y} = 5y^2$$

The multinomial factor is $(2x + 5y^2)$.

Step 5 We can now write the polynomial in its factored form.

$$12x^3y + 30x^2y^3$$
$$= 6x^2y \cdot 2x + 6x^2y \cdot 5y^2$$
$$= 6x^2y(2x + 5y^2)$$

Completely factored form

In the previous example of $12x^3y + 30x^2y^3$, the polynomial could also be factored to $3xy(4x^2 + 10xy^2)$ or $12y\left(x^3 + \frac{5}{2}x^2y^2\right)$. This allows room for a given polynomial to be factored in many ways, unless some restrictions are placed on the procedure. We wish to factor each polynomial in a unique manner that will not permit such variations in the results. Thus it is customary to adopt the following criteria for a completely factored polynomial.

*Primes and prime factorization are covered in section R–1.

A₁ $9x + 6y + 3$

> **Completely factored form**
>
> A polynomial with integer coefficients will be considered to be in **completely factored form** when it satisfies the following criteria:
>
> 1. The polynomial is written as a product of polynomials with integer coefficients.
> 2. None of the polynomial factors other than the monomial factor can be factored further.

We see that $6x^2y(2x + 5y^2)$ is the completely factored form of the expression $12x^3y + 30x^2y^3$ since all of the coefficients are integers and, except for the monomial factor $6x^2y$, the remaining factor contains no other factor with integer coefficients.

In general, whenever we factor a monomial out of a polynomial, we factor the monomial so that it has a positive coefficient. Realize that we could also factor out the opposite, or negative, of this common factor. We could have factored out $-6x^2y$ from our example. The completely factored form would have been

A₂ $2a^3 - 4a^2 + 12a$

$$-6x^2y(-2x - 5y^2).$$

Observe that the only change in our answer when we factor out the opposite of the common factor is that this changes the signs of all terms inside the parentheses.

Example 4–1 A

Write in completely factored form.

1. $7a^3 + 14a$

$= 7a(\quad + \quad)$ ← Multinomial factor will have as many terms as the original expression; GCF is $7a$

$= 7a(a^2 + 2)$ Completely factored form ($a^2 = \frac{7a^3}{7a}$, $2 = \frac{14a}{7a}$)

If we want to check the answer, we apply the distributive property and perform the multiplication as follows:

A₃ $20a^4b^3 - 30a^2b^5 - 5a^2b^3$

$7a(a^2 + 2) = 7a \cdot a^2 + 7a \cdot 2$ Distributive property

$= 7a^3 + 14a.$ Carry out the multiplication

You are now ready to do **A₁**.

2. $9x^5 + 6x^3 - 18x^2$

$= 3^2x^5 + 2 \cdot 3x^3 - 2 \cdot 3^2x^2$ Factor each term

$= 3x^2(\quad + \quad - \quad)$ Determine the GCF

$= 3x^2(3x^3 + 2x - 6)$ Completely factored form

You are now ready to do **A₂**.

3. $72a^2b - 84a^3b^4 + 48a^4b^2$

$= 2^3 \cdot 3^2 \cdot a^2 \cdot b - 2^2 \cdot 3 \cdot 7 \cdot a^3 \cdot b^4 + 2^4 \cdot 3 \cdot a^4 \cdot b^2$ Factor each term

$= 12a^2b(\quad - \quad + \quad)$ Determine the GCF

$= 12a^2b(6 - 7ab^3 + 4a^2b)$ Completely factored form

You are now ready to do **A₃**.

4. $3x^3y^2 + 15x^2y^4 + 3xy^2$
$= 3 \cdot x^3 \cdot y^2 + 3 \cdot 5 \cdot x^2 \cdot y^4 + 3 \cdot x \cdot y^2$ Factor each term
$= 3xy^2(\quad + \quad + \quad)$ Determine the GCF
$= 3xy^2(x^2 + 5xy^2 + 1)$ Completely factored form

Note
In example 4, the last term in the factored form is 1. This situation occurs when a term and the GCF are the same, that is, whenever we are able to factor all of the numbers and variables out of a given term. For example, $\frac{3xy^2}{3xy^2} = 1$. The number of terms inside the parentheses must be equal to the number of terms in the original polynomial.

You are now ready to do **A₄**. ■

A₄ $9x^3y^2 - 18x^2y^3$

Remember the fact that when something is within a grouping symbol, we treat the quantity as just one number. Therefore if we have a quantity common to all of the terms, it can be factored out of the polynomial.

B₁ $x(y + 5) - z(y + 5)$

Example 4–1 B

Factor completely.

1. $x(a - 2b) + y(a - 2b)$
The quantity $(a - 2b)$ is common to both terms. We can then factor the common quantity out of each term and place the remaining factors from each term in the second parentheses.

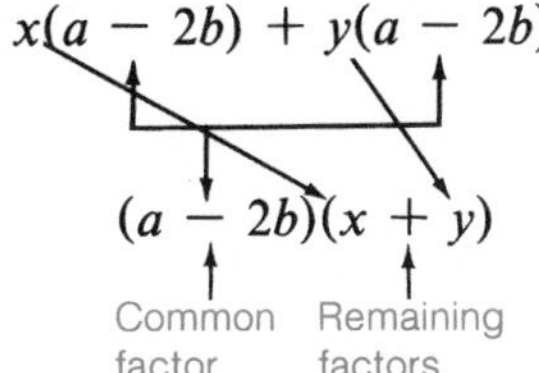

You are now ready to do **B₁**.

2. $x^2(a + b) + (a + b)$
$= (a + b)(\quad + \quad)$ Determine the GCF
$= (a + b)(x^2 + 1)$ Completely factored form

B₂ $a^2(x - y) + (x - y)$

You are now ready to do **B₂**.

3. $3x^2(2a - b) - 9x(2a - b)$
$= 3x^2(2a - b) - 3^2x(2a - b)$ Factor each term
$= 3x(2a - b)(\quad - \quad)$ Determine the GCF
$= 3x(2a - b)(x - 3)$ Completely factored form

B₃ $2x^2(a - 3b) - 4y^2(a - 3b)$

You are now ready to do **B₃**. ■

Factoring by grouping

Consider the expression $ax + ay + bx + by$. We observe that this is a four-term polynomial and we will *try* to factor it by grouping.

$$ax + ay + bx + by = (ax + ay) + (bx + by)$$

There is a common factor of a in the first two terms and a common factor of b in the last two terms.

$$(ax + ay) + (bx + by) = a(x + y) + b(x + y)$$

C_1 $ax + ay + 3bx + 3by$

The quantity $(x + y)$ is common to both terms, and factoring it out, we have

$$a(x + y) + b(x + y) = (x + y)(a + b).$$

Therefore we have factored the polynomial by grouping.

Factoring a four-term polynomial by grouping

1. Arrange the four terms so that the first two terms have a common factor and the last two terms have a common factor.
2. Determine the GCF of each pair of terms and factor it out.
3. If step 2 produces a common binomial factor in each term, factor it out.
4. If step 2 does not produce a common binomial factor in each term, try grouping the terms of the original polynomial in a different way.
5. If step 4 does not produce a common binomial factor in each term, the polynomial will not factor by this procedure.

C_2 $3ax + 6bx + 2ay + 4by$

Example 4–1 C

Factor completely.

1. $ax + 2ay + bx + 2by$

$= (ax + 2ay) + (bx + 2by)$ Group in pairs
$= a(x + 2y) + b(x + 2y)$ Factor out the GCF
$= (x + 2y)(a + b)$ Factor out the common binomial

You are now ready to do **C_1**.

C_3 $ax + 2ay - 2bx - 4by$

2. $3ac + 6ad + 2bc + 4bd$

$= (3ac + 6ad) + (2bc + 4bd)$ Group in pairs
$= 3a(c + 2d) + 2b(c + 2d)$ Factor out the GCF
$= (c + 2d)(3a + 2b)$ Factor out the common binomial

You are now ready to do **C_2**.

3. $2ax - 2ay + bx - by$

$= (2ax - 2ay) + (bx - by)$ Group in pairs
$= 2a(x - y) + b(x - y)$ Factor out the GCF
$= (x - y)(2a + b)$ Factor out the common binomial

You are now ready to do **C_3**.

4. $6ax + by + 3ay + 2bx$

$= 6ax + 3ay + 2bx + by$ Rearrange the terms
$= (6ax + 3ay) + (2bx + by)$ Group in pairs
$= 3a(2x + y) + b(2x + y)$ Factor out the GCF
$= (2x + y)(3a + b)$ Factor out the common binomial

C_4 $2ax + 4ay + bx + 2by$

Note
As in example 4, sometimes the terms must be rearranged so that the pairs will have a common factor.

You are now ready to do **C_4**. ■

It is important to remember to look for the greatest common factor first *when we attempt to determine the completely factored form of any polynomial. If we fail to do this, the answer may not be in a completely factored form or we may not see how to factor the problem by an appropriate procedure.*

Answers to section 4–1 margin exercises

A_1 $3(3x + 2y + 1)$ A_2 $2a(a^2 - 2a + 6)$ A_3 $5a^2b^3(4a^2 - 6b^2 - 1)$
A_4 $9x^2y^2(x - 2y)$ B_1 $(y + 5)(x - z)$ B_2 $(x - y)(a^2 + 1)$ B_3 $2(a - 3b)(x^2 - 2y^2)$
C_1 $(x + y)(a + 3b)$ C_2 $(a + 2b)(3x + 2y)$ C_3 $(x + 2y)(a - 2b)$
C_4 $(x + 2y)(2a + b)$

Mastery points

Can you

- Determine the greatest common factor?
- Factor a four-term polynomial by grouping?

Exercise 4–1

Directions Write in completely factored form. See example 4–1 A.

Examples $\boxed{A_1}$ $9x + 6y + 3$

Solutions
$= 3 \cdot 3x + 3 \cdot 2y + 3 \cdot 1$ Factor each term
$= 3(\quad + \quad + \quad)$ Determine the GCF
$= 3(3x + 2y + 1)$ Completely factored form

$\boxed{A_4}$ $9x^3y^2 - 18x^2y^3$

$= 9x^2y^2 \cdot x - 9x^2y^2 \cdot 2y$ Factor each term
$= 9x^2y^2(\quad - \quad)$ Determine the GCF
$= 9x^2y^2(x - 2y)$ Completely factored form

1. $2y + 6$

2. $3a - 12$

3. $4x^2 + 8y$

4. $8y^2 + 10x^2$

5. $3x^2y + 15z$

6. $5r^2 + 10rs - 20s$

7. $7a - 14b + 21c$

8. $8x - 12y + 16z$

9. $15xy - 18z + 3x^2$

10. $18ab - 27a + 3ac$

11. $42xy - 21y^2 + 7$

12. $3a^2 - 27b^2 + 12ab$

13. $8x - 10y + 12z - 18w$

14. $15L^2 - 21W^2 + 36H$

15. $5a^2 - 60ab + 45b^2$

16. $4x^2 + 8x$

17. $3x^2y + 6xy$

18. $8x^3 + 4x^2$

19. $3x^2 - 3xy + 3x$

20. $2x^3 - x^2 + x$

21. $24a^2 + 12a - 6a^3$

22. $2x^4 - 6x^2 + 8x$

23. $xy^2 + xyz + xy$

24. $18x^3y - 24x^2y^2 + 30x^4y^3$

25. $14a^2b - 21ac^2 + 42abc$

26. $5p^2 + 10p - 15p^3$

27. $16x^3y - 3x^2y^2 + 24x^2y^3$

Directions Supply the missing factor.

Example **a.** $-3a - 6b = -3(\quad)$

Solution **a.** Since $-3a - 6b = (-3) \cdot a + (-3) \cdot 2b$, then $-3a - 6b = -3(a + 2b)$, the missing factor is $(a + 2b)$.

Example **b.** $-a^2b^3 + a^2b^2 = -a^2b^2(\quad)$

Solution **b.** $-a^2b^3 + a^2b^2 = (-a^2b^2)(b) + (-a^2b^2)(-1)$ Divide each term by $-a^2b^2$ to find the missing factor
$= -a^2b^2(b - 1)$, the missing factor is $(b - 1)$.

28. $-2a + 2 = -2(\quad)$

29. $-6x - 9 = -3(\quad)$

30. $-5a + 10b = 5(\quad)$

31. $6x - 8z - 12w = 2(\quad)$

32. $5 - 10r^2 + 15s - 25r = 5(\quad)$

33. $-4a^3 - 36ab + 16ab^2 - 24b^3 = -4(\quad)$

34. $-ab - a^2b = ab(\quad)$

35. $-3a + a^3b = -a(\quad)$

36. $-x + 2xy + xy^2 = x(\quad)$

37. $-x + x^2 - x^3 = -x(\quad)$

38. $-4x^2 + 8x - 12x^3 = -4x(\quad)$

39. $-xyz + x^2yz - xy^2z + xyz^2 = -xyz(\quad)$

Directions Write in completely factored form. See example 4–1 B.

Example **B₁** $x(y + 5) - z(y + 5)$

Solution $= (y + 5)(\quad - \quad)$ Determine the GCF

$= (y + 5)(x - z)$ Completely factored form

40. $3a(x - y) + b(x - y)$

41. $x(a + b) + y(a + b)$

42. $21R(L + 2N) - 35S(L + 2N)$

43. $15x(2a + b) + 10y(2a + b)$

44. $4RS(2P + q) - 8RT(2P + q)$

45. $3xy(a + 4b) + 6xy(a + 4b)$

46. $2x(y + 32) - (y + 32)$

47. $8a(b + 6) - (b + 6)$

48. $15a^3b^2(x + y) + 30a^2b^5(x + y)$

49. $12x^2y(a - 2b) + 8xy^2(a - 2b)$

Directions Write the following in completely factored form. See example 4–1 C.

Example C_2 $3ax + 6bx + 2ay + 4by$

Solution

$= (3ax + 6bx) + (2ay + 4by)$ Group in pairs

$= 3x(a + 2b) + 2y(a + 2b)$ Factor out the GCF

$= (a + 2b)(3x + 2y)$ Factor out the common binomial

50. $rt + ru + st + su$

51. $ac + ad + bc + bd$

52. $5ax - 3by + 15bx - ay$

53. $6ax - 2by + 3bx - 4ay$

54. $2ax^2 - bx^2 + 6a - 3b$

55. $20x^2 + 5xz - 12xy - 3yz$

56. $ac + ad - 2bc - 2bd$

57. $2ac + 6bc - ay - 3by$

58. $2ac + bc - 4ay - 2by$

59. $2ac + 3bc + 8ay + 12by$

60. $5ac - 3by + 15bc - ay$

61. $6ax + by + 2ay + 3bx$

62. $2ax - ad + 4bx - 2bd$

63. $3ax - 2bd - 6ad + bx$

64. $6ax + 3bd - 2ad - 9bx$

65. $2a^3 + 15 + 10a^2 + 3a$

66. $3a^3 - 6a^2 + 5a - 10$

67. $8a^3 - 4a^2 + 6a - 3$

Directions Write in completely factored form. See example 4–1 A.

68. The area of the surface of a cylinder is determined by $A = 2\pi rh + 2\pi r^2$. Factor the right member. (π is the Greek letter pi.)

69. The equation for distance traveled by a rocket fired vertically upward into the air is given by $S = 560t - 16t^2$, where the rocket is S feet from the ground after t seconds. Factor the right member.

70. The total surface area of a right circular cone is given by $A = \pi rs + \pi r^2$. Factor the right member.

71. In engineering, the equation for deflection of a beam is given by

$$Y = \frac{2wx^4}{48EI} - \frac{3\ell wx^3}{48EI} - \frac{\ell^3 wx}{48EI}.$$

Factor the right member.

Review exercises

Directions Two numbers are listed. Find two integers such that their product is the first number and their sum is the second number. See section 1–4.

1. 20, 9

2. 12, 7

3. $-16, -6$

4. $-16, 6$

5. 16, 10

6. $16, -10$

7. 36, 12

8. 11, 12

4–2 Factoring trinomials of the form $x^2 + bx + c$

Determining when a trinomial will factor

In section 3–3, we learned how to multiply two binomials as follows:

Factors Terms

$$(x + 2)(x + 6) = x^2 + 6x + 2x + 12 = x^2 + 8x + 12$$

Multiplying ⟶

In this section, we are going to reverse the procedure and factor the trinomial.

Terms Factors

$$x^2 + 8x + 12 = (x + 2)(x + 6)$$

Factoring ⟶

The following group of trinomials will enable us to see how a trinomial factors.

$$12 = 2 \cdot 6$$
1. $x^2 + 8x + 12 = (x + 2)(x + 6)$
$$8 = 2 + 6$$

$$12 = (-2) \cdot (-6)$$
2. $x^2 - 8x + 12 = (x - 2)(x - 6)$
$$-8 = (-2) + (-6)$$

$$-12 = (-2) \cdot 6$$
3. $x^2 + 4x - 12 = (x - 2)(x + 6)$
$$4 = (-2) + 6$$

$$-12 = 2 \cdot (-6)$$
4. $x^2 - 4x - 12 = (x + 2)(x - 6)$
$$-4 = 2 + (-6)$$

In general,

$$(x + m)(x + n) = x^2 + (m + n)x + m \cdot n$$

The trinomial $x^2 + bx + c$ will factor with integer coefficients only if there are two integers, which we will call m and n, such that $m + n = b$ and $m \cdot n = c$.

$$m + n \qquad m \cdot n$$
$$x^2 + bx + c = (x + m)(x + n)$$

The signs (+ or −) for m and n

1. If c is positive, then m and n have the same sign as b.
2. If c is negative, then m and n have different signs and the one with the greater absolute value has the same sign as b.

Example 4–2 A

Factor completely each trinomial.

1. $a^2 + 11a + 18 \qquad m + n = 11$ and $m \cdot n = 18$
Since $b = 11$ and $c = 18$ are both positive, then m and n are both positive.

List the factorizations of 18	Sum of the factors of 18	
$1 \cdot 18$	$1 + 18 = 19$	
$2 \cdot 9$	$2 + 9 = 11$	← Correct sum
$3 \cdot 6$	$3 + 6 = 9$	

The m and n values are 2 and 9. The factorization is

$a^2 + 11a + 18 = (a + 2)(a + 9)$.

A_1 $x^2 + 10x + 21$

The answer can be checked by performing the indicated multiplication.

$$(a + 2)(a + 9) = a^2 + 9a + 2a + 18 = a^2 + 11a + 18$$

Note
The commutative property allows us to write the factors in any order. That is, $(a + 2)(a + 9) = (a + 9)(a + 2)$.

You are now ready to do **A_1**.

A_2 $y^2 - 6y - 16$

2. $b^2 - 2b - 15$ $\quad m + n = -2$ and $m \cdot n = -15$
Since $b = -2$ and $c = -15$ are both negative, then m and n have different signs and the one with the greater absolute value is negative.

Factorizations of -15, where the negative sign goes with the factor with the greater absolute value	Sum of the factors of -15
$1 \cdot (-15)$	$1 + (-15) = -14$
$3 \cdot (-5)$	$3 + (-5) = -2 \leftarrow$ Correct sum

The m and n values are 3 and -5. The factorization is

$$b^2 - 2b - 15 = (b + 3)(b - 5).$$

You are now ready to do **A_2**.

A_3 $z^2 + 8z - 20$

3. $5x - 24 + x^2$
It is easier to identify b and c if we write the trinomial in descending powers of the variable, which is called **standard form.**

$x^2 + 5x - 24$ $\quad m + n = 5$ and $m \cdot n = -24$

Since $b = 5$ is positive and $c = -24$ is negative, m and n have different signs and the one with the greater absolute value is positive.

Factorizations of -24, where the positive factor is the one with the greater absolute value	Sum of the factors of -24
$(-1) \cdot 24$	$(-1) + 24 = 23$
$(-2) \cdot 12$	$(-2) + 12 = 10$
$(-3) \cdot 8$	$(-3) + 8 = 5 \leftarrow$ Correct sum
$(-4) \cdot 6$	$(-4) + 6 = 2$

The m and n values are -3 and 8. The factorization is

$$x^2 + 5x - 24 = (x - 3)(x + 8).$$

You are now ready to do **A_3**.

A_4 $x^2 - 8x + 15$

4. $c^2 - 9c + 14$ $\quad m + n = -9$ and $m \cdot n = 14$
Since $b = -9$ is negative and $c = 14$ is positive, m and n are both negative.

List the factorizations of 14	Sum of the factors of 14
$(-1)(-14)$	$(-1) + (-14) = -15$
$(-2)(-7)$	$(-2) + (-7) = -9 \leftarrow$ Correct sum

The m and n values are -2 and -7. The factorization is

$$c^2 - 9c + 14 = (c - 2)(c - 7).$$

You are now ready to do **A_4**.

5. $x^2 + 5x + 12 \qquad m + n = 5 \quad \text{and} \quad m \cdot n = 12$
Since $b = 5$ and $c = 12$ are both positive, m and n are both positive.

Factorizations of 12	Sum of the factors of 12
$1 \cdot 12$	$1 + 12 = 13$
$2 \cdot 6$	$2 + 6 = 8$
$3 \cdot 4$	$3 + 4 = 7$

No sum equals 5

Since none of the factorizations of 12 add to 5, there is no pair of integers (m and n) and the trinomial will not factor using integer coefficients. We call this a **prime polynomial.**

You are now ready to do **A₅**.

A₅ $x^2 + 7x + 16$

6. $x^4 - 4x^3 - 21x^2 = x^2(x^2 - 4x - 21)$ Common factor of x^2
To complete the factorization, we see if the trinomial $x^2 - 4x - 21$ will factor. We need to find m and n that add to -4 and multiply to -21. The values are 3 and -7. The completely factored form is

$$x^4 - 4x^3 - 21x^2 = x^2(x + 3)(x - 7).$$

Note
A common error when the polynomial has a common factor is to factor it out but to forget to include it as one of the factors in the completely factored form.

You are now ready to do **A₆**.

A₆ $a^4 - 5a^3 - 24a^2$

7. $x^2y^2 + 9xy + 20$
Rewriting the polynomial as $(xy)^2 + 9xy + 20$, we want to find values for m and n that add to 9 and multiply to 20. The numbers are 4 and 5. The factorization is

$$x^2y^2 + 9xy + 20 = (xy + 4)(xy + 5).$$

You are now ready to do **A₇**.

A₇ $a^2b^2 + 10ab + 16$

8. $x^2 - 5ax + 6a^2 \qquad m + n = -5a \quad \text{and} \quad m \cdot n = 6a^2$
We need to find m and n that add to $-5a$ and multiply to $6a^2$. The values are $-2a$ and $-3a$. The factorization is

$$x^2 - 5ax + 6a^2 = (x - 2a)(x - 3a).$$

You are now ready to do **A₈**. ■

A₈ $x^2 - 7ax + 10a^2$

Factoring a trinomial of the form $x^2 + bx + c$

1. Factor out the GCF. If there is a common factor, make sure to include it as part of the final factorization.
2. Determine if the trinomial is factorable by finding m and n such that $m + n = b$ and $m \cdot n = c$. If m and n do not exist, we conclude that the trinomial will not factor.
3. Using the m and n values from step 2, write the trinomial in factored form.

Answers to section 4–2 margin exercises
A₁ $(x + 7)(x + 3)$ **A₂** $(y - 8)(y + 2)$ **A₃** $(z - 2)(z + 10)$ **A₄** $(x - 3)(x - 5)$
A₅ will not factor, prime polynomial **A₆** $a^2(a + 3)(a - 8)$ **A₇** $(ab + 2)(ab + 8)$
A₈ $(x - 2a)(x - 5a)$

Mastery points

Can you

- Determine two integers whose product is one number and whose sum is another number?
- Recognize when the trinomial $x^2 + bx + c$ will factor and when it will not?
- Factor trinomials of the form $x^2 + bx + c$?
- Always remember to look for the greatest common factor before applying any of the factoring rules?

Exercise 4–2

Directions Factor completely each trinomial. If a trinomial will not factor, so state. See example 4–2 A.

Example $\boxed{A_3}$ $z^2 + 8z - 20$

Solution Since $b = 8$ is positive and $c = -20$ is negative, m and n have different signs and the one with the greater absolute value is positive.

Factorizations of −20, where the positive factor is the one with the greater absolute value	Sum of the factors of −20
$(-1) \cdot 20$	$(-1) + 20 = 19$
$(-2) \cdot 10$	$(-2) + 10 = 8$ ← Correct sum
$(-4) \cdot 5$	$(-4) + 5 = 1$

The m and n values are -2 and 10. The factorization is

$z^2 + 8z - 20 = (z - 2)(z + 10)$.

1. $a^2 + 9a + 18$

2. $c^2 + 9c + 20$

3. $x^2 + 11x - 12$

4. $x^2 + 13x + 12$

5. $y^2 + 13y - 30$

6. $a^2 + 9a + 14$

7. $x^2 - 14x + 24$

8. $b^2 - 10b + 21$

9. $a^2 + 5a - 24$

10. $y^2 + 9y - 36$

11. $x^2 + 8x + 12$

12. $c^2 + 8c + 15$

13. $a^2 - 2a - 24$

14. $z^2 - 5z - 36$

15. $2x^2 + 6x - 20$

16. $2a^2 + 26a + 24$

17. $3x^2 - 18x - 48$

18. $a^2 - 9a + 4$

19. $x^2 + 5x + 7$

20. $x^2 - 4x + 6$

21. $y^2 + 17y + 30$

22. $b^2 + 13b + 40$

23. $4x^2 - 4x - 24$

24. $5y^2 + 5y - 30$

25. $5a^2 - 15a - 50$

26. $x^2y^2 - 4xy - 21$

27. $x^2y^2 - 3xy - 18$

28. $x^2y^2 - xy - 30$

29. $x^2y^2 + 13xy + 12$

30. $4a^2b^2 - 32ab + 28$

31. $3x^2y^2 - 3xy - 36$

32. $3x^2y^2 + 21xy + 36$

33. $x^2 + 3xy + 2y^2$

34. $a^2 - ab - 2b^2$

35. $a^2 - 2ab - 3b^2$

36. $a^2 - 7ab + 10b^2$

37. $a^2 - ab - 6b^2$

38. $x^2 + 2xy - 8y^2$

39. $x^2 - 2xy - 15y^2$

40. $a^2 + 7ab + 12b^2$

Review exercises

Directions Factor completely. See section 4–1.

1. $ax^2 + bx^2 + cx^2$
2. $3x^3 + 12x^2 - 6x$
3. $3x(2x + 1) + 5(2x + 1)$
4. $2x(3x - 2) + 3(3x - 2)$
5. $4x(5x + 1) + (5x + 1)$
6. $6x(2x + 3) - (2x + 3)$
7. $x(3x - 5) - 2(3x - 5)$
8. $7x(x - 9) - 3(x - 9)$

4–3 Factoring trinomials of the form $ax^2 + bx + c$

How to factor trinomials

In this section, we are going to factor trinomials of the form $ax^2 + bx + c$. This is called the **standard form** of a trinomial, where we have a single variable and the terms of the polynomial are arranged in descending powers of that variable. The a, b, and c in our standard form represent integer constants. a is called the *leading coefficient*. For example,

$$2x^2 + 9x + 9$$

is a trinomial in standard form, where $a = 2$, $b = 9$, and $c = 9$.

Consider the product

$$(2x + 3)(x + 3).$$

By multiplying these two quantities together, we get a trinomial.

$$\begin{aligned}(2x + 3)(x + 3) &= 2x^2 + 6x + 3x + 9\\ &= 2x^2 + 9x + 9\end{aligned}$$

To completely factor the trinomial $2x^2 + 9x + 9$ entails reversing this procedure to get

$$(2x + 3)(x + 3).$$

The trinomial will factor with integer coefficients if we can find a pair of integers (m and n) whose sum is equal to b, and whose product is equal to $a \cdot c$. In the trinomial $2x^2 + 9x + 9$, b is equal to 9, and $a \cdot c$ is $2 \cdot 9 = 18$. Therefore we want $m + n = 9$ and $m \cdot n = 18$. The values for m and n are 3 and 6.

If we observe the multiplication process in our example, we see that m and n appear as the coefficients of the middle terms that are to be combined for our final answer.

$$\begin{aligned}(2x + 3)(x + 3) &= 2x^2 + 6x + 3x + 9\\ &= 2x^2 + 9x + 9\end{aligned}$$

This is precisely what we do with the m and n values. We replace the coefficient of the middle term in the trinomial with these values. In our example, m and n are 6 and 3 and we replace the 9 with them.

$$2x^2 + 9x + 9 = 2x^2 + \overbrace{6x + 3x}^{9x} + 9$$

Our next step is to group the first two terms and the last two terms.

$$(2x^2 + 6x) + (3x + 9)$$

Now we factor out what is common in each pair. We see that the first two terms contain the common factor $2x$ and the last two terms contain the common factor 3.

$$2x(x + 3) + 3(x + 3)$$

When we reach this point, what is inside the parentheses in each term will be the same. Since the quantity $(x + 3)$ is common to both terms, we can factor it out.

$$2x\underbrace{(x + 3)} + 3\underbrace{(x + 3)}$$

Common to both terms

Having factored out what is common, what is left in each term is placed in a second parentheses.

$$2x(x + 3) + 3(x + 3)$$
$$(x + 3)(2x + 3)$$

Common factor   Remaining factors

The trinomial is factored.

A summary of the steps follows:

Factoring a trinomial of the form $ax^2 + bx + c$

Step 1 Determine if the trinomial $ax^2 + bx + c$ is factorable by finding m and n such that $m \cdot n = a \cdot c$ and $m + n = b$. If m and n do not exist, we conclude that the trinomial will not factor.

Step 2 Replace the middle term, bx, by the sum of mx and nx.

Step 3 Place parentheses around the first and second terms and around the third and fourth terms. Factor out what is common to each pair.

Step 4 Factor out the common quantity of each term and place the remaining factors from each term in the second parentheses.

We determine the signs (+ or −) for m and n in a fashion similar to that of section 4–2.

The signs (+ or −) for m and n

1. If $a \cdot c$ is positive, then m and n have the same sign as b.
2. If $a \cdot c$ is negative, then m and n have different signs and the one with the greater absolute value has the same sign as b.

A₁ $6x^2 + 23x + 15$

Example 4–3 A

Factor completely the following trinomials. If a trinomial will not factor, so state.

1. $6x^2 + 13x + 6$

Step 1 $m \cdot n = 6 \cdot 6 = 36$ and $m + n = 13$
We determine by inspection that m and n are 9 and 4.

Step 2 $= 6x^2 + \overbrace{9x + 4x}^{13x} + 6$ — Replace bx with mx and nx
Step 3 $= (6x^2 + 9x) + (4x + 6)$ — Group the first two terms and the last two terms
$= 3x(2x + 3) + 2(2x + 3)$ — Factor out what is common to each pair
Step 4 $= (2x + 3)(3x + 2)$ — Factor out the common quantity

Note
The order in which we place m and n into the problem will not change the answer.

(Alternate)

Step 2 $= 6x^2 + \overbrace{4x + 9x}^{13x} + 6$ — Replace bx with mx and nx
Step 3 $= (6x^2 + 4x) + (9x + 6)$ — Group the first two terms and the last two terms
$= 2x(3x + 2) + 3(3x + 2)$ — Factor out what is common to each pair
Step 4 $= (3x + 2)(2x + 3)$ — Factor out the common quantity

We see that the outcome in step 4 is the same regardless of the order of m and n in the problem.

A₂ $3x^2 + 7x + 2$

Note
The order in which the two factors are written in the answer does not matter. That is, $(2x + 3)(3x + 2) = (3x + 2)(2x + 3)$.

You are now ready to do **A₁**.

2. $3x^2 + 5x + 2$

Step 1 $m \cdot n = 3 \cdot 2 = 6$ and $m + n = 5$
m and n are 2 and 3.

Step 2 $= 3x^2 + \overbrace{2x + 3x}^{5x} + 2$ — Replace bx with mx and nx
Step 3 $= (3x^2 + 2x) + (3x + 2)$ — Group the first two terms and the last two terms
$= x(3x + 2) + 1(3x + 2)$ — Factor out what is common to each pair

We observe in the last two terms that the greatest common factor is only 1 or -1. We factor out 1 so that we have the same quantity inside the parentheses.

Step 4 $= (3x + 2)(x + 1)$ — Factor out the common quantity

You are now ready to do **A₂**.

A₃ $2x^2 - x - 28$

3. $4x^2 - 11x + 6$

Step 1 $m \cdot n = 4 \cdot 6 = 24$ and $m + n = -11$

m and n are -3 and -8.

$$\overbrace{}^{-11x}$$

Step 2	$= 4x^2 - 3x - 8x + 6$	Replace bx with mx and nx
Step 3	$= (4x^2 - 3x) + (-8x + 6)$	Group the first two terms and the last two terms
	$= x(4x - 3) - 2(4x - 3)$	Factor out what is common to each pair

We have 2 or -2 as the greatest common factor in the last two terms. We factor out -2 so that we will have the same quantity inside the parentheses.

Step 4	$= (4x - 3)(x - 2)$	Factor out the common quantity

Note
If the third term in step 2 is preceded by a minus sign, we will usually factor out the negative factor.

You are now ready to do **A₃**.

4. $12x^2 - 4x - 5$

Step 1 $m \cdot n = 12(-5) = -60$ and $m + n = -4$

m and n are 6 and -10.

$$\overbrace{}^{-4x}$$

Step 2	$= 12x^2 + 6x - 10x - 5$	Replace bx with mx and nx
Step 3	$= (12x^2 + 6x) + (-10x - 5)$	Group the first two terms and the last two terms
	$= 6x(2x + 1) - 5(2x + 1)$	Factor out what is common to each pair
Step 4	$= (2x + 1)(6x - 5)$	Factor out the common quantity

A₄ $5a^2 - 7a - 6$

You are now ready to do **A₄**.

5. $6x^2 - 9x - 4$

$m \cdot n = 6 \cdot (-4) = -24$ and $m + n = -9$

Our m and n values are not obvious by inspection.

Note
If you cannot determine the m and n values by inspection, then you should use the following systematic procedure to list all the possible factorizations of $a \cdot c$. This way you will either find m and n or verify that the trinomial will not factor using integers.

1. Take the natural numbers 1,2,3,4, . . . and divide them into the $a \cdot c$ product. Those that divide into evenly we write as a factorization using the correct m and n signs.

Factorization of -24, where the negative sign goes with the factor with the greater absolute value

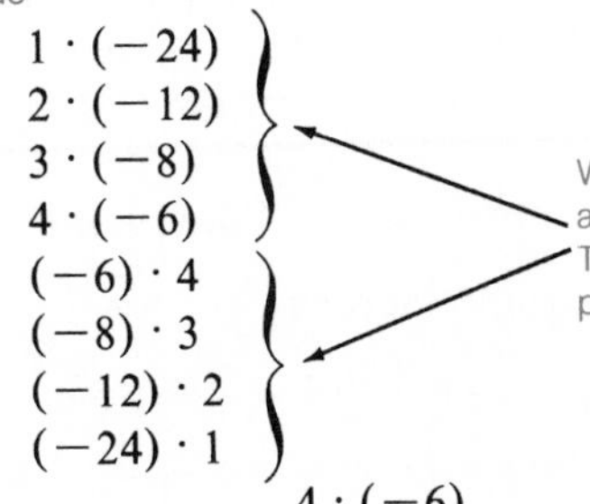

We note that the top four factorizations are the same as the bottom four. Therefore we need only perform this procedure until the factors repeat

$4 \cdot (-6)$

$(-6) \cdot 4$

Factors repeat

A_5 $4a^2 - 5a + 7$

2. Find the sum of the factorizations of $a \cdot c$. If there is a sum equal to b, the trinomial will factor. If there is no sum equal to b, then the trinomial will not factor with integer coefficients.

Factorizations of -24	Sum of the factors of -24	
$1 \cdot (-24)$	$1 + (-24) = -23$	
$2 \cdot (-12)$	$2 + (-12) = -10$	
$3 \cdot (-8)$	$3 + (-8) = -5$	← Passed -9
$4 \cdot (-6)$	$4 + (-6) = -2$	

No sum equals -9

Since none of the factorizations of -24 add to -9, there is no pair of integers (m and n) and the trinomial will not factor.

Note
Regardless of the signs of m and n, the column of values of the sum of the factors will either be increasing or decreasing. Therefore once the desired value has been passed, the process can be stopped and the trinomial will not factor.

You are now ready to do **A_5**.

6. $24x^2 - 39x - 18$
Before we attempt to apply any factoring rule, recall that we must always factor out what is common to each term. Therefore we have

$24x^2 - 39x - 18 = 3(8x^2 - 13x - 6).$ Common factor of 3

Now we are ready to factor the trinomial.

A_6 $12x^2 + 12x - 9$

Step 1 $m \cdot n = 8(-6) = -48$ and $m + n = -13$
m and n are 3 and -16.

Step 2 $= 3(8x^2 + \overbrace{3x - 16x}^{-13x} - 6)$ Replace bx with mx and nx
Step 3 $= 3[(8x^2 + 3x) + (-16x - 6)]$ Group the first two terms and the last two terms
$= 3[x(8x + 3) - 2(8x + 3)]$ Factor out what is common to each pair
Step 4 $= 3(8x + 3)(x - 2)$ Factor out the common quantity

Note
In example 6, we factored out 3 that was common to all the original terms. A common error is to forget to include it as one of the factors in the answer.

You are now ready to do **A_6**. ■

Factoring by inspection—an alternative approach

In the beginning of this section, we studied a systematic procedure for determining if a trinomial will factor and how to factor it. In many instances, we can determine how the trinomial will factor by inspecting the problem rather than by applying this procedure.

Factoring by inspection is accomplished as follows: Factor $7x + 2x^2 + 3$.

Step 1 Write the trinomial in standard form.

$2x^2 + 7x + 3$ Arrange terms in descending powers of x

Step 2 Determine the possible combinations of first-degree factors of the first term.

$(2x \quad)(x \quad)$ The only factorization of $2x^2$ is $2x \cdot x$

Step 3 Combine with the factors of step 2 all the possible factors of the third term.

$(2x \quad 3)(x \quad 1)$ The only factorization of 3 is $3 \cdot 1$

$(2x \quad 1)(x \quad 3)$

Step 4 Determine the possible symbol (+ or −) between the terms in each binomial.

$(2x + 3)(x + 1)$

$(2x + 1)(x + 3)$

The rules of real numbers given in chapter 1 provide the answer to step 4.

1. If the third term is preceded by a + sign and the middle term is preceded by a + sign, then the symbols will be

$(\quad + \quad)(\quad + \quad)$.

2. If the third term is preceded by a + sign and the middle term is preceded by a − sign, then the symbols will be

$(\quad - \quad)(\quad - \quad)$.

3. If the third term is preceded by a − sign, then the symbols will be

$(\quad + \quad)(\quad - \quad)$

or

$(\quad - \quad)(\quad + \quad)$.

Note

It is assumed that the first term is preceded by a + sign or no sign. If it is preceded by a − sign, these rules could still be used if (−1) is first factored out of all the terms.

Step 5 Determine which factors, if any, yield the correct middle term.

$(2x + 3)(x + 1)$

inner: $+3x$; outer: $+2x$

$(+3x) + (+2x) = +5x$

$(2x + 1)(x + 3)$

inner: $+x$; outer: $+6x$

$(+x) + (+6x) = +7x$ Correct middle term

The second set of factors gives us the correct middle term. Therefore $(2x + 1)(x + 3)$ is the factorization of $2x^2 + 7x + 3$.

B₁ $4x^2 + 13x + 3$

Example 4–3 B

Factor completely the following trinomials by inspection.

1. $6x^2 + 17x + 5$

Step 1 $6x^2 + 17x + 5$ — Standard form

Step 2 $(6x \quad)(x \quad)$ — $6x^2 = 3x \cdot 2x$ or $6x \cdot x$
$(3x \quad)(2x \quad)$

Step 3 $(6x \quad 5)(x \quad 1)$
$(6x \quad 1)(x \quad 5)$ — The only factorization of 5 is $5 \cdot 1$
$(3x \quad 5)(2x \quad 1)$
$(3x \quad 1)(2x \quad 5)$

Step 4 $(6x + 5)(x + 1)$
$(6x + 1)(x + 5)$ — Using the rules of signed numbers, determine the possible signs between the terms
$(3x + 5)(2x + 1)$
$(3x + 1)(2x + 5)$

Step 5 $(6x + 5)(x + 1)$
inner: $+5x$, outer: $+6x$ — $(+5x) + (+6x) = +11x$

$(6x + 1)(x + 5)$
inner: $+x$, outer: $+30x$ — $(+x) + (+30x) = +31x$

$(3x + 5)(2x + 1)$
inner: $+10x$, outer: $+3x$ — $(+10x) + (+3x) = +13x$

$(3x + 1)(2x + 5)$
inner: $+2x$, outer: $+15x$ — $(+2x) + (+15x) = +17x$
Correct middle term

The last set of factors gives us the correct middle term. Hence $(3x + 1)(2x + 5)$ is the factorization of $6x^2 + 17x + 5$.

You are now ready to do **B₁**.

2. $4x^2 - 5x + 1$

Step 1 $4x^2 - 5x + 1$ — Standard form

Step 2 $(4x \quad)(x \quad)$ — $4x^2 = 2x \cdot 2x$ or $4x \cdot x$
$(2x \quad)(2x \quad)$

Step 3 $(4x \quad 1)(x \quad 1)$ — The only factorization of 1 is $1 \cdot 1$
$(2x \quad 1)(2x \quad 1)$

Step 4 $(4x - 1)(x - 1)$ — Determine the possible signs between the terms
$(2x - 1)(2x - 1)$

Step 5 $(4x - 1)(x - 1)$

inner: $-x$, outer: $-4x$

$(-x) + (-4x) = -5x$ Correct middle term

$(2x - 1)(2x - 1)$

inner: $-2x$, outer: $-2x$

$(-2x) + (-2x) = -4x$

The first set of factors gives us the correct factorization.

$4x^2 - 5x + 1 = (4x - 1)(x - 1)$

You are now ready to do **B_2**.

B_2 $6x^2 + 11x - 2$

3. $13x - 5 + 6x^2$

Step 1 $6x^2 + 13x - 5$ Write in standard form

Step 2 $(6x \quad)(x \quad)$ $6x^2 = 6x \cdot x$ or $2x \cdot 3x$
$(2x \quad)(3x \quad)$

Step 3 $(6x \quad 5)(x \quad 1)$
$(6x \quad 1)(x \quad 5)$ The only factorization of 5 is $5 \cdot 1$
$(2x \quad 5)(3x \quad 1)$
$(2x \quad 1)(3x \quad 5)$

Step 4 $(6x + 5)(x - 1)$ or $(6x - 5)(x + 1)$ Determine the possible signs between the terms
$(6x + 1)(x - 5)$ or $(6x - 1)(x + 5)$
$(2x + 5)(3x - 1)$ or $(2x - 5)(3x + 1)$
$(2x + 1)(3x - 5)$ or $(2x - 1)(3x + 5)$

B_3 $4x^2 + 4x - 15$

Step 5 $(6x + 5)(x - 1)$ or $(6x - 5)(x + 1)$.

inner: $+5x$, outer: $-6x$; inner: $-5x$, outer: $+6x$

$(+5x) + (-6x) = -x$ or $(-5x) + (+6x) = +x$

$(6x + 1)(x - 5)$ or $(6x - 1)(x + 5)$

inner: $+x$, outer: $-30x$; inner: $-x$, outer: $+30x$

$(+x) + (-30x) = -29x$ or $(-x) + (+30x) = +29x$

$(2x + 5)(3x - 1)$ or $(2x - 5)(3x + 1)$

inner: $+15x$, outer: $-2x$; inner: $-15x$, outer: $+2x$

$(+15x) + (-2x) = +13x$ or $(-15x) + (+2x) = -13x$

Correct middle term

$(2x + 1)(3x - 5)$ or $(2x - 1)(3x + 5)$

inner: $+3x$, outer: $-10x$; inner: $-3x$, outer: $+10x$

$(+3x) + (-10x) = -7x$ or $(-3x) + (+10x) = +7x$

The factorization of $6x^2 + 13x - 5$ is $(2x + 5)(3x - 1)$.

You are now ready to do **B_3**. ■

Answers to section 4–3 margin exercises

A_1 $(6x + 5)(x + 3)$ **A_2** $(3x + 1)(x + 2)$ **A_3** $(2x + 7)(x - 4)$ **A_4** $(5a + 3)(a - 2)$
A_5 will not factor, prime polynomial **A_6** $3(2x + 3)(2x - 1)$ **B_1** $(4x + 1)(x + 3)$
B_2 $(6x - 1)(x + 2)$ **B_3** $(2x - 3)(2x + 5)$

Mastery points

Can you

- Determine two integers whose product is one number and whose sum is another number?
- Recognize when the trinomial $ax^2 + bx + c$ will factor and when it will not?
- Factor trinomials of the form $ax^2 + bx + c$?
- Always remember to look for the greatest common factor before applying any of the factoring rules?

Exercise 4–3

Directions Factor completely each trinomial. If a trinomial will not factor, so state. See examples 4–3 A and B.

Example **A_1** $6x^2 + 23x + 15$

Solution

$m \cdot n = 6 \cdot 15 = 90$ — Determine m and n
$m + n = 23$
m and n are 5 and 18.

$6x^2 + \overbrace{5x + 18x}^{23x} + 15$ — Replace bx with mx and nx
$(6x^2 + 5x) + (18x + 15)$ — Group first two terms and last two terms
$x(6x + 5) + 3(6x + 5)$ — Factor out what is common to each pair
$(6x + 5)(x + 3)$ — Factor out the common quantity

Example **A_6** $12x^2 + 12x - 9$

Solution

$3(4x^2 + 4x - 3)$ — Common factor of 3
$m \cdot n = 4(-3) = -12$
$m + n = 4$
m and n are -2 and 6. — Determine m and n

$3[4x^2 \overbrace{- 2x + 6x}^{4x} - 3]$ — Replace bx with mx and nx
$3[2x(2x - 1) + 3(2x - 1)]$ — Group first two terms and last two terms, factor out what is common
$3(2x - 1)(2x + 3)$ — Factor out the common quantity

1. $2x^2 + x - 6$ **2.** $3x^2 + 7x - 6$ **3.** $2x^2 + 3x + 1$ **4.** $4x^2 - 5x + 1$

5. $2R^2 - 7R + 6$ **6.** $R^2 - 4R + 6$ 7. $5x^2 - 7x - 6$ **8.** $2x^2 - x - 1$

9. $9x^2 - 6x + 1$
10. $8x^2 - 17x + 2$
11. $5x^2 + 4x + 6$
12. $2x^2 - 11x + 12$
13. $6x^2 + 13x + 6$
14. $2r^2 + 13r + 18$
15. $4x^2 + 20x + 21$
16. $7R^2 + 20R - 3$
17. $4x^2 - 2x + 5$
18. $4x^2 - 4x - 3$
19. $9y^2 - 21y - 8$
20. $6x^2 - 23x - 4$
21. $10x^2 + 7x - 6$
22. $10x^2 + 9x + 2$
23. $2x^2 - 9x + 10$
24. $7x^2 - 3x + 6$
25. $4x^2 + 14x + 12$
26. $5R^2 - 9R - 2$
27. $4x^2 + 10x + 6$
28. $6x^2 - 17x + 12$
29. $6x^2 + 7x - 3$
30. $3x^2 + 12x + 12$
31. $2x^2 + 6x - 20$
32. $3a^2 + 8a - 4$
33. $6x^2 + 5x - 6$
34. $3x^2 - 19x + 20$
35. $4x^2 + 12x + 9$
36. $9z^2 - 30z + 25$
37. $7x^2 - 36x + 5$
38. $3x^2 + 2x + 4$
39. $15P^2 + 2P - 1$
40. $12x^2 + 13x - 4$
41. $2x^3 - 6x^2 - 20x$
42. $4x^2 + 10x + 4$
43. $2a^3 + 15a^2 + 7a$
44. $9x^2 + 27x + 8$
45. $8x^2 - 14x - 15$
46. $8x^2 - 18x + 9$

47. When a stone is thrown vertically into the air, the height S of the stone at any instant in time t is given by $S = -16t^2 + 32t - 16$. Factor the right member.

Review exercises

Directions Use the special product rules to carry out the indicated multiplication. See section 3–3.

1. $(x - y)(x + y)$
2. $(3a - 2b)(3a + 2b)$
3. $(x - y)^2$
4. $(5a + 4b)(5a - 4b)$
5. $(2a + b)^2$
6. $(4x - y)^2$
7. $(x^2 + 1)(x^2 - 1)$
8. $(a^2 - 4)(a^2 + 4)$

4–4 The difference of two squares and perfect square trinomials

In section 3–3, we saw that the product of $(a + b)(a - b)$ was $a^2 - b^2$. We refer to the indicated product $(a + b)(a - b)$ as the *product* of the *sum* and *difference* of the same two terms. Notice that in one factor we *add* the terms and in the other we find the *difference* between these same terms. The product will *always* be the *difference of the squares* of the two terms. To factor the **difference of two squares,** we reverse the formula from section 3–3.

Factoring the difference of two squares

$$a^2 - b^2 = (a + b)(a - b).$$

Concept

(first term)² − (second term)² factors into
(first term + second term)(first term − second term)

To use this factoring technique, we must be able to recognize **perfect squares.** A perfect square is the product when a number is written as a factor twice.

Example 4–4 A

Write the following as perfect squares, if possible.

1. $16 = 4 \cdot 4$ — 16 is a perfect square
$= (4)^2$ — 16 can be written as 4 squared

You are now ready to do **A_1**.

2. $x^2 = x \cdot x$ — x is written as a factor twice
$= (x)^2$ — Writing x^2 as $(x)^2$ shows this is a perfect square

You are now ready to do **A_2**.

A_1 64

A_2 y^2

3. $25a^2 = 5a \cdot 5a$ — 25 is 5 · 5 and a^2 is $a \cdot a$
$= (5a)^2$ — It is now rewritten as a square

You are now ready to do **A₃**.

A₃ $36b^2$

4. $9y^4 = 3y^2 \cdot 3y^2$ — 9 is 3 · 3 and y^4 could be written as $y^2 \cdot y^2$
$= (3y^2)^2$ — It is now rewritten as a square

You are now ready to do **A₄**. ■

This is the procedure we use for factoring the difference of two squares.

A₄ $9x^4$

Factoring the difference of two squares

Step 1 Identify that we have a perfect square *minus* another perfect square.
Step 2 Rewrite the problem as a first term squared minus a second term squared.

(first term)² − (second term)²

Step 3 Factor the problem into the first term plus the second term times the first term minus the second term.

(first term + second term)(first term − second term)

B₁ $t^2 - 64$

Example 4–4 B

Write the following in completely factored form.

	Step 1 Identify		*Step 2* Rewrite		*Step 3* Factor
	$a^2 - b^2$	=	$(a)^2 - (b)^2$	=	$(a + b)(a - b)$
1.	$x^2 - 9$	=	$(x)^2 - (3)^2$	=	$(x + 3)(x - 3)$

B₂ $x^2 - 25y^2$

You are now ready to do **B₁**.

2. $4a^2 - b^2 = (2a)^2 - (b)^2 = (2a + b)(2a - b)$

B₃ $4a^2 - b^2c^2$

You are now ready to do **B₂**.

3. $4p^2 - 25v^2 = (2p)^2 - (5v)^2 = (2p + 5v)(2p - 5v)$

You are now ready to do **B₃**.

4. $r^4 - 49 = (r^2)^2 - (7)^2 = (r^2 + 7)(r^2 - 7)$

You are now ready to do **B₄**. ■

B₄ $x^4 - y^2$

Our first step in any factoring problem is to look for any common factors. Often an expression that does not appear to be factorable becomes so by taking out the common factor. When we have applied a factoring rule to a problem, *we must inspect all parts of our answer to make sure that nothing will factor further.*

Example 4–4 C

Write the following in completely factored form.

C₁ $3a^2 - 27b^2$

1. $2x^2 - 18y^2 = 2(x^2 - 9y^2)$ — Factor out what is common, 2
$= 2[(x)^2 - (3y)^2]$ — Identify and rewrite as squares
$= 2(x + 3y)(x - 3y)$ — Factor and inspect the factors

You are now ready to do **C₁**.

C_2 $ab^2 - ac^2$

2. $3w^2 - 48 = 3(w^2 - 16)$ Common factor of 3
$= 3[(w)^2 - (4)^2]$ Identify and rewrite
$= 3(w + 4)(w - 4)$ Factor and inspect the factors

You are now ready to do C_2.

3. $5a^4 - 45a^2b^2 = 5a^2(a^2 - 9b^2)$ Common factor of $5a^2$
$= 5a^2[(a)^2 - (3b)^2]$ Identify and rewrite
$= 5a^2(a + 3b)(a - 3b)$ Factor and inspect the factors

You are now ready to do C_3.

4. $a^4 - 16 = (a^2)^2 - (4)^2$ Identify and rewrite
$= (a^2 + 4)(a^2 - 4)$ Factor and inspect the factors
$= (a^2 + 4)[(a)^2 - (2)^2]$ Identify and rewrite
$= (a^2 + 4)(a + 2)(a - 2)$ Factor and inspect

C_3 $x^2y^4 - y^2z^2$

Note
In example 4, $a^2 + 4$ is called the *sum of two squares.* This will *not* factor using integers.

You are now ready to do C_4.

5. $2x^4 - 162 = 2(x^4 - 81)$ Common factor of 2
$= 2[(x^2)^2 - (9)^2]$ Identify and rewrite
$= 2(x^2 + 9)(x^2 - 9)$ Factor and inspect
$= 2(x^2 + 9)[(x)^2 - (3)^2]$ Identify and rewrite
$= 2(x^2 + 9)(x + 3)(x - 3)$ Factor and inspect

You are now ready to do C_5.

C_4 $a^4 - b^4$

Note
A common error in examples 1, 2, 3, and 5 is to factor out something that is common but forget to include it as a factor in the final answer. ■

Perfect square trinomials

In section 3–3, two of the special products that we studied were the squares of a binomial. We will now restate those special products:

$$a^2 + 2ab + b^2 = (a + b)^2$$

and

$$a^2 - 2ab + b^2 = (a - b)^2.$$

C_5 $3a^4 - 48$

The right members of the equations are called the squares of binomials, and the left members are called perfect square trinomials. Perfect square trinomials can always be factored by our factoring procedure. However if we observe that the first and last terms of a trinomial are perfect squares, we should see if the trinomial will factor as the square of a binomial. To factor a trinomial as a perfect square trinomial, the following three conditions need to be met.

Necessary conditions for a perfect square trinomial

1. The first term must have a positive coefficient and be a perfect square, a^2.
2. The last term must have a positive coefficient and be a perfect square, b^2.
3. The middle term must be twice the product of the bases of the first and last terms, $2ab$ or $-2ab$.

We observe that

$$9x^2 + 12x + 4$$
$$= (3x)^2 + 2(3x)(2) + (2)^2.$$

Condition 1 Condition 3 Condition 2

Therefore it is a perfect square trinomial and factors into

$$(3x + 2)^2.$$

Example 4–4 D

The following examples show the factoring of some other perfect square trinomials.

	Condition 1		*Condition 3*		*Condition 2*		*Square of a binomial*
1. $4x^2 + 20x + 25 =$	$(2x)^2$	$+$	$2(2x)(5)$	$+$	$(5)^2$	$=$	$(2x + 5)^2$
2. $9x^2 - 6x + 1 =$	$(3x)^2$	$-$	$2(3x)(1)$	$+$	$(1)^2$	$=$	$(3x - 1)^2$
3. $16x^2 + 24x + 9 =$	$(4x)^2$	$+$	$2(4x)(3)$	$+$	$(3)^2$	$=$	$(4x + 3)^2$
4. $9y^2 - 30y + 25 =$	$(3y)^2$	$-$	$2(3y)(5)$	$+$	$(5)^2$	$=$	$(3y - 5)^2$

You are now ready to do **D_1, D_2, D_3,** and **D_4**. ■

D_1 $4a^2 + 20a + 25$

D_2 $9b^2 - 24b + 16$

D_3 $36b^2 + 12b + 1$

D_4 $49x^2 - 28x + 4$

Answers to section 4–4 margin exercises

A_1 $(8)^2$ **A_2** $(y)^2$ **A_3** $(6b)^2$ **A_4** $(3x^2)^2$ **B_1** $(t + 8)(t - 8)$
B_2 $(x + 5y)(x - 5y)$ **B_3** $(2a + bc)(2a - bc)$ **B_4** $(x^2 + y)(x^2 - y)$
C_1 $3(a + 3b)(a - 3b)$ **C_2** $a(b + c)(b - c)$ **C_3** $y^2(xy + z)(xy - z)$
C_4 $(a^2 + b^2)(a + b)(a - b)$ **C_5** $3(a^2 + 4)(a + 2)(a - 2)$ **D_1** $(2a + 5)^2$
D_2 $(3b - 4)^2$ **D_3** $(6b + 1)^2$ **D_4** $(7x - 2)^2$

Mastery points

Can you

- Identify and rewrite a perfect square?
- Factor the difference of two squares?
- Remember that $a^2 + b^2$ will not factor?
- Factor out any greatest common factor before applying other factoring rules?
- Inspect all factors to make sure the problem is completely factored?
- Factor perfect square trinomials?

Exercise 4–4

Directions Write the following as a perfect square, if possible. See example 4–4 A.

Examples A_1 64

Solutions
$= 8 \cdot 8$ Identify
$= (8)^2$ Rewrite

A_4 $9x^4$
$= 3x^2 \cdot 3x^2$ Identify
$= (3x^2)^2$ Rewrite

1. 36 **2.** 25 **3.** c^2 **4.** e^2

5. $16x^2$ **6.** $49b^2$ **7.** $4z^4$ **8.** $25b^2$

Directions Write in completely factored form. See examples 4–4 B, C, and D.

Examples [B₁] $t^2 - 64$ Identify

Solutions $= (t)^2 - (8)^2$ Rewrite
$= (t + 8)(t - 8)$ Factor

[B₃] $4a^2 - b^2c^2$ Identify
$= (2a)^2 - (bc)^2$ Rewrite
$= (2a + bc)(2a - bc)$ Factor

9. $x^2 - 1$ **10.** $x^2 - 25$ **11.** $a^2 - 4$ **12.** $r^2 - s^2$

13. $9 - E^2$ **14.** $49 - R^2$ 15. $1 - k^2$ **16.** $4y^2 - 9$

[**17.**] $9b^2 - 16$ **18.** $x^2 - 16z^2$ 19. $b^2 - 36c^2$ **20.** $16x^2 - y^2$

21. $4a^2 - 25b^2$ **22.** $a^2 - 16b^2$ **23.** $25p^2 - 81$ **24.** $r^2 - 4s^2$

[**25.**] $8x^2 - 32y^2$ **26.** $3a^2 - 27b^2$ 27. $5r^2 - 125s^2$ **28.** $20 - 5b^2$

29. $50 - 2x^2$ **30.** $x^2y^2 - 4z^2$ **31.** $r^2s^2 - 25t^2$ **32.** $a^4 - 25$

33. $x^4 - 9$ [**34.**] $x^4 - 1$ 35. $r^4 - 81$ **36.** $16t^4 - 1$

37. $49x^2 - 64y^4$ **38.** $125p^2 - 20v^2$ **39.** $98x^2y^2 - 50p^2c^2$ **40.** $a^2 + 10a + 25$

[**41.**] $c^2 - 14c + 49$ **42.** $b^2 + 8b + 16$ 43. $a^2 + 6a + 9$ **44.** $x^2 - 12x + 36$

45. $y^2 - 6y + 9$

46. $a^2 + 6ab + 9b^2$

47. $4a^2 - 12ab + 9b^2$

48. $x^2 - 16xy + 64y^2$

49. $9c^2 - 12cd + 4d^2$

50. $9a^2 - 30ab + 25b^2$

51. In engineering, the equation of transverse shearing stress in a rectangular beam is given by $T = \frac{V}{8I}(h^2 - 4v_1^2)$. Factor the right member.

Review exercises

Directions Factor completely. See sections 4–1, 4–2, 4–3, and 4–4.

1. $x^2 + 8x + 12$

2. $49a^2 - 81$

3. $3ax + bx - 12ay - 4by$

4. $2x^3 + 14x^2 + 24x$

5. $10a^2 + 21a + 9$

6. $4a^2 - 20a + 25$

7. $x^2y^2 + 8xy + 15$

8. $x^2 + 4xy + 4y^2$

■ 4–5 Factoring: A general strategy

In this section, we will review the different methods of factoring that we have studied in the previous sections. The following outline gives a general strategy for factoring polynomials.

I. Factor out any common factors.
   Examples
   1. $5a^3 - 25a^2 = 5a^2(a - 5)$ — Common monomial factor
   2. $c(a - 2b) + 2d(a - 2b) = (a - 2b)(c + 2d)$ — Common binomial factor

II. Count the number of terms.
   A. Two terms: Check to see if the polynomial is the difference of two squares.
      Example
      $a^2 - 16b^2 = (a - 4b)(a + 4b)$ — Difference of two squares
   B. Three terms: Check to see if the polynomial is a perfect square trinomial. If it is not, use one of the general methods for factoring a trinomial.
      Examples
      1. $a^2 + 6a + 9 = (a + 3)^2$ — Perfect square trinomial
      2. $a^2 + 5a - 14 = (a + 7)(a - 2)$ — General trinomial, leading coefficient of 1
      3. $6a^2 + 7a - 20 = (2a + 5)(3a - 4)$ — General trinomial, leading coefficient other than 1

A_1 $9a^2 - 36b^2$

C. Four terms: Check to see if we can factor by grouping.

Examples

1. $ac + 3a - 2bc - 6b = (a - 2b)(c + 3)$ Group in pairs
2. $a^3 + 2a^2 - 3a - 6 = (a^2 - 3)(a + 2)$ Group in pairs

III. Check to see if any of the factors we have written can be factored further. Any common factors that were missed in part I can still be factored out here.

Examples

1. $c^4 - 11c^2 + 28 = (c^2 - 4)(c^2 - 7)$ General trinomial, leading coefficient of 1

   $= (c - 2)(c + 2)(c^2 - 7)$ Difference of two squares

2. $4a^2 - 36b^2 = (2a - 6b)(2a + 6b)$ Difference of two squares

   $= 2(a - 3b)2(a + 3b)$ Overlooked common factor

   $= 4(a - 3b)(a + 3b)$ Completely factored

The following examples illustrate our strategy for factoring polynomials.

Examples 4–5 A

A_2 $6ax + 3ay + 2bx + by$

Completely factor the following polynomials.

1. $3x^3 - 3xy^2$

I. First we look for any common factors.

$3x^3 - 3xy^2 = 3x(x^2 - y^2)$ Common factor of $3x$

II. The factor $x^2 - y^2$ has two terms and is the difference of two squares.

$x^2 - y^2 = (x - y)(x + y)$ Factoring the binomial

III. After checking to see if any of the factors will factor further, we conclude that $3x(x - y)(x + y)$ is the completely factored form. Therefore

$3x^3 - 3xy^2 = 3x(x - y)(x + y).$

You are now ready to do **A_1**.

2. $3ax + bx + 6ay + 2by$

I. There is no common factor (other than 1 or -1).

II. The polynomial has four terms and we factor it by grouping.

$(3ax + bx) + (6ay + 2by)$ Group in pairs

$= x(3a + b) + 2y(3a + b)$ Factor out what is common to each pair

$= (3a + b)(x + 2y)$ Factor out the common quantity

A_3 $4a^2 - 4a - 15$

III. None of the factors will factor further.

$3ax + bx + 6ay + 2by = (3a + b)(x + 2y)$

You are now ready to do **A_2**.

3. $3a^2 - 2a - 8$

I. There is no common factor (other than 1 or -1).

II. The polynomial has three terms and the coefficient of a^2 is not 1. Therefore we must find m and n and factor the trinomial. $m \cdot n = -24$ and $m + n = -2$, the values for m and n are -6 and 4.

$= 3a^2 - 6a + 4a - 8$ Replace $-2a$ with $-6a + 4a$

$= (3a^2 - 6a) + (4a - 8)$ Group the first 2 terms and the last 2 terms

$= 3a(a - 2) + 4(a - 2)$ Factor out what is common to each pair

$= (a - 2)(3a + 4)$ Factor out the common quantity

III. None of the factors will factor further.

$3a^2 - 2a - 8 = (a - 2)(3a + 4)$

You are now ready to do **A_3**. ■

Answers to section 4–5 margin exercises

A_1 $9(a - 2b)(a + 2b)$ **A_2** $(2x + y)(3a + b)$ **A_3** $(2a + 3)(2a - 5)$

Mastery points
Can you • Factor out the greatest common factor? • Factor the difference of two squares? • Factor trinomials? • Factor a four-term polynomial? • Use the general strategy for factoring polynomials?

Exercise 4–5

Directions Completely factor the following polynomials. If a polynomial will not factor, so state. See the outline of the general strategy for factoring polynomials and example 4–5 A.

1. $n^2 - 49$

2. $a^2 + 6a + 5$

3. $7b^2 + 36b + 5$

4. $2x^2 + 15x + 18$

5. $x^2y^2 + 2xy - 8$

6. $y^2 + 11y + 10$

7. $36 - y^2$

8. $25a^2(3b + c) + 5a(3b + c)$

9. $10a^2 - 20ab + 10b^2$

10. $a^2b^2 - 5ab - 14$

11. $4a^2 - 16b^2$

12. $12x^3y^2 - 18x^2y^2 + 16xy^4$

13. $3ax + 6ay - bx - 2by$

14. $5x^2 + 18x - 60$

15. $6x^2 + 7x - 5$

16. $9x^5y - 6x^3y^3 + 3x^2y^2$

17. $6am + 4bm - 3an - 2bn$

18. $5x^2 - 32x - 21$

19. $7b^2 + 16b - 15$

20. $3a^2 + 13a + 4$

21. $4x^2 + 17x - 15$

22. $5y^2 + 16y + 12$

23. $6x^2 - 24xy - 48y^2$

24. $4ab(x + 3y) - 8a^2b^2(x + 3y)$

25. $3x^2y(m - 4n) + 15xy^2(m - 4n)$

26. $4x^2 - 20xy + 25y^2$

27. $9a^2 - 30ab + 25b^2$

28. $80y^4 - 5y$

29. $3a^5 - 48a$

30. $3a^5b - 18a^3b^3 + 27ab^5$

31. $3a^3b^3 + 6a^2b^4 + 3ab^5$

32. $3b^2 + 8b - 91$

33. $3b^2 - 32b - 91$

34. $b^4 - 81$

35. $3ax + 6bx + 2ay + 4by$

36. $12ax + 4bx - 3ay - by$

37. $6x^2 + 11x - 2$

38. $6x^2 - 17x - 3$

39. $3x^4 - 48x^2$

40. $3x^3 + 3x^2 - 18x$

Review exercises

Directions Find the solution of the following equations. See section 2–3.

1. $2x + 6 = 0$

2. $4x - 12 = 0$

3. $3x - 18 = 0$

4. $5x + 3 = 0$

5. $6x + 4 = 0$

6. $3x + 1 = 0$

7. $4x - 1 = 0$

8. $3x = 0$

4–6 Solving quadratic equations by factoring

The standard form of a quadratic equation

In chapter 2, we studied linear equations, also called first-degree equations. Recall that the **degree** of an equation in one variable is the greatest exponent of that variable in any one term. In this section, we will find the solutions to an equation that contains the second, but no higher, power of that variable. Such an equation is a **second-degree equation,** also called a **quadratic equation.**

Quadratic equations can be written in the form

$$ax^2 + bx + c = 0,$$

where a, b, and c are constants, $a \neq 0$.

> **Note**
> It is necessary that $a \neq 0$. If $a = 0$ and $b \neq 0$, then $0 \cdot x^2 + bx + c$ becomes $bx + c = 0$, which is a linear equation.

We call $ax^2 + bx + c = 0$ the **standard quadratic form** of a quadratic equation. Notice that in standard form the terms of the quadratic expression are written in descending powers of the variable. The other member contains *only zero.* In most of our work with quadratic equations, it will be necessary to write the equation in standard quadratic form.

Solution of quadratic equations in factored form

Suppose we have the equation $x^2 - x - 6 = 0$ stated in the factored form, $(x - 3)(x + 2) = 0$. This equation states that the product of two factors, $x - 3$ and $x + 2$, is 0. To find the necessary numbers, we use the algebraic property called the **zero product property.**

> **Zero product property**
> Given real numbers a and b, if $ab = 0$, then $a = 0$ or $b = 0$.
>
> **Concept**
> If the product of two factors is zero, then at least one of the factors is zero.

Extending this property, if $(x + c)(x + d) = 0$, then $x + c = 0$ or $x + d = 0$. Therefore by this property, $(x - 3)(x + 2) = 0$ only if $x - 3 = 0$ or $x + 2 = 0$. Since each of these equations is linear, we use the methods for solving linear equations. We find $x = 3$ when $x - 3 = 0$ and $x = -2$ when $x + 2 = 0$. Then 3 and -2 are solutions of the equation $(x - 3)(x + 2) = 0$.

From this discussion, we can see that to solve any equation in *factored form* whose product is 0, we do the following:

> **Solving an equation of the form $ab = 0$**
>
> 1. Set *each* factor equal to 0.
> 2. Solve the resulting equations for the variable.

A₁ $(x + 6)(x - 2) = 0$

Solution set

A set is any collection of things. This may be a collection of books, people, coins, golf clubs, and so on. In mathematics, we use the idea of a set primarily to denote a group of numbers. Any one of the things that belongs to the set is called a **member,** or an **element,** of the set. One way we write a set is by listing the elements, separating them by commas, and including this listing within a pair of braces, $\{\ \}$. In chapter 2, we stated that a replacement value for the variable that forms a true statement is called a **root,** or a **solution,** of the equation. We say that a root of the given equation *satisfies* that equation. The **solution set** is the set of all values for the variable that cause the equation to be a true statement.

In the example $x^2 - x - 6 = 0$, we saw that the solutions of the equation, $(x - 3)(x + 2) = 0$, were 3 and -2. To express this as a solution set, we would write the solutions in any order, separated by a comma and enclosed within a pair of braces. The solution set for the equation is $\{-2,3\}$.

Example 4–6 A

Find the solution set of the following equations.

A₂ $(2x + 3)(x + 1) = 0$

1. $(x + 5)(x - 4) = 0$ — The equation is in factored form

$x + 5 = 0$ or $x - 4 = 0$ — Set each factor equal to 0 and solve

$x = -5$ $\quad x = 4$ — The solutions

$\{-5,4\}$ — The solution set

Check for $x = -5$ — Check for $x = 4$

$(-5 + 5)(-5 - 4) = 0$ — $(4 + 5)(4 - 4) = 0$ — Substitute the solution for x

$0 \cdot (-9) = 0$ — $9 \cdot 0 = 0$ — Order of operations

$0 = 0$ — $0 = 0$ — True, both solutions check

Note
In future examples, we will not always show a check of the solutions, but checking your solutions is always an important part of the problem.

You are now ready to do **A₁**.

2. $(x - 3)(3x + 1) = 0$ — The equation is in factored form

$x - 3 = 0$ or $3x + 1 = 0$ — Set each factor equal to 0 and solve

$x = 3$ $\quad 3x = -1$ — Add 3, subtract 1

A₃ $2x(x - 9) = 0$

$x = -\frac{1}{3}$ — Divide by 3

$x = 3$ or $x = -\frac{1}{3}$ — The solutions

$\left\{-\frac{1}{3},3\right\}$ — The solution set

You are now ready to do **A₂**.

3. $3x(x - 7) = 0$ — The equation is in factored form

$3x = 0$ or $x - 7 = 0$ — Set each factor equal to 0 and solve

$x = 0$ $\quad x = 7$ — Dividing by 3, adding 7 gives the solutions

$\{0,7\}$ — The solution set

Note
A common error is to find only the solution to the binomial factor $x - 7$ and forget to find the solution for the other factor, $3x$, when it is equal to zero.

You are now ready to do **A₃**. ■

Solving quadratic equations by factoring

In general, to find the solution set of a quadratic equation by factoring, we use the following procedure:

Solving a quadratic equation by factoring

Step 1 Write the equation in standard quadratic form.
Step 2 Completely factor the quadratic expression.
Step 3 Set each of the factors containing the variable equal to 0 and solve the resulting equations.
Step 4 Write the solutions in a solution set.
Step 5 Check your solutions by substituting into the original equation.

B₁ $x^2 - 7x + 12 = 0$

Examples 4–6 B

Find the solution set of the following equations.

1. $x^2 + 5x = -6$

$x^2 + 5x + 6 = 0$ — Write the equation in standard form

$(x + 2)(x + 3) = 0$ — Factor $x^2 + 5x + 6 = (x + 2)(x + 3)$

$x + 2 = 0$ or $x + 3 = 0$ — Set each factor equal to 0

$x = -2$ $\quad x = -3$ — Solve each equation, giving the solutions

$\{-3,-2\}$ — The solution set

Check:

(1) Let $x = -2$.

$x^2 + 5x = -6$

$(-2)^2 + 5(-2) = -6$

$4 - 10 = -6$

$-6 = -6$ True

(2) Let $x = -3$.

$x^2 + 5x = -6$

$(-3)^2 + 5(-3) = -6$

$9 - 15 = -6$

$-6 = -6$ True

You are now ready to do **B₁**.

B₂ $2a^2 = 5a$

2. $x^2 = 2x$

$x^2 - 2x = 0$ — Write the equation in standard form

$x(x - 2) = 0$ — Factor completely

$x = 0$ or $x - 2 = 0$ — Set each factor equal to 0

$x = 0$ $\quad x = 2$ — Solve each equation, giving the solutions

$\{0,2\}$ — The solution set

Check your solutions by substituting 0 and 2 for x in the original equation.

You are now ready to do **B₂**.

B₃ $4y^2 = 9$

3. $x^2 = 16$

$x^2 - 16 = 0$ — Write the equation in standard form.

$(x - 4)(x + 4) = 0$ — Factor $x^2 - 16 = (x - 4)(x + 4)$

$x - 4 = 0$ or $x + 4 = 0$ — Set each factor equal to 0

$x = 4$ $\quad x = -4$ — Solve each equation, giving the solutions

$\{-4,4\}$ — The solution set

Check your solutions by substituting 4 and -4 for x in the original equation.

You are now ready to do **B₃**.

B4 $3x^2 = 7x + 6$

4. $4x^2 = 20x - 25$

$4x^2 - 20x + 25 = 0$ Write the equation in standard form

$(2x - 5)^2 = 0$ $4x^2 - 20x + 25 = (2x - 5)^2$

$2x - 5 = 0$ Set the repeated factor equal to 0

$x = \frac{5}{2}$ Solve the equation for x, giving the solution

$\left\{\frac{5}{2}\right\}$ The solution set

Check your solution by substituting $\frac{5}{2}$ for x in the original equation.

Note
In example 4, we have *two* factors, $(2x - 5)$ and $(2x - 5)$, but since they are the same, the equation has only *one* distinct solution.

You are now ready to do **B4**.

5. $3x^2 + 3 = -6x$

$3x^2 + 6x + 3 = 0$ Write the equation in standard form

$3(x^2 + 2x + 1) = 0$ Factor $3x^2 + 6x + 3 = 3(x + 1)^2$

$3(x + 1)^2 = 0$ Set the only distinct factor with a variable equal to 0

$x + 1 = 0$

$x = -1$ Solve the equation, giving the solution

$\{-1\}$ The solution set

Check your answer by substituting -1 for x in $3x^2 + 3 = -6x$.

You are now ready to do **B5**. ■

B5 $12(x^2 - 2x) = -9$

In conclusion, let us compare the quadratic equation with the linear equation.

1. A **linear equation** is an equation of the form $ax + b = 0$, where $a \neq 0$. A **quadratic equation** is an equation of the form $ax^2 + bx + c = 0$, where a, b, and c are constants, $a \neq 0$.
2. A linear equation is solved by isolating the variable. Some quadratic equations are solved by factoring and setting the linear factors equal to zero.
3. A conditional linear equation has at most *one solution*. A quadratic equation has at most *two real solutions*, which may or may not be distinct.

Answers to section 4–6 margin exercises

A1 $\{-6,2\}$ **A2** $\left\{-\frac{3}{2},-1\right\}$ **A3** $\{0,9\}$ **B1** $\{3,4\}$ **B2** $\left\{0,\frac{5}{2}\right\}$ **B3** $\left\{-\frac{3}{2},\frac{3}{2}\right\}$ **B4** $\left\{-\frac{2}{3},3\right\}$ **B5** $\left\{\frac{1}{2},\frac{3}{2}\right\}$

Mastery points

Can you

- Find the solution set of an equation in factored form whose product is equal to zero?
- Find the solution set of a quadratic equation by factoring?

Exercise 4–6

Directions Find the solution set of the following equations. See example 4–6 A.

Example A₂ $(2x + 3)(x + 1) = 0$ — The equation is in factored form

Solution Set each factor equal to 0 and solve the equations.

$$2x + 3 = 0 \quad \text{or} \quad x + 1 = 0$$ The factors are set equal to 0

$$2x = -3$$ Solve each equation

$$x = -\frac{3}{2} \qquad x = -1$$ The solutions

$$\left\{-\frac{3}{2}, -1\right\}$$ The solution set

1. $(x + 5)(x - 5) = 0$

2. $(x - 1)(x + 1) = 0$

3. $x(x + 6) = 0$

4. $x(x - 8) = 0$

5. $3a(a - 7) = 0$

6. $5p(p + 9) = 0$

7. $(3x - 9)(2x + 3) = 0$

8. $(2x + 1)(3x - 2) = 0$

9. $(4y - 3)(5y + 2) = 0$

10. $(5x - 1)(5x + 1) = 0$

11. $(4 - 3u)(8 - 5u) = 0$

12. $(7 + 3y)(2 - 3y) = 0$

13. $(5 - x)(5 + x) = 0$

14. $(8 - x)(8 + x) = 0$

15. $x(2x - 3)(x + 1) = 0$

16. $3x(x - 12)(3x + 1) = 0$

17. $(5x + 3)(x - 10)(4x - 1) = 0$

18. $(8x - 1)(2x + 7)(x - 3) = 0$

Directions Find the solution set of the following quadratic equations by factoring. Check the solutions. See example 4–6 B.

Example **B₂** $2a^2 = 5a$

Solution

$2a^2 - 5a = 0$ — Write the equation in standard form

$a(2a - 5) = 0$ — Factor $2a^2 - 5a = a(2a - 5)$

$a = 0$ or $2a - 5 = 0$ — Set each factor equal to 0

$2a = 5$ — Solve each equation

$a = 0$ $\quad a = \frac{5}{2}$ — The solutions

$\left\{0, \frac{5}{2}\right\}$ — The solution set

Check

(1) Let $a = 0$.

$$2a^2 = 5a$$
$$2(0)^2 = 5(0)$$
$$0 = 0 \quad \text{True}$$

(2) Let $a = \frac{5}{2}$.

$$2\left(\frac{5}{2}\right)^2 = 5\left(\frac{5}{2}\right)$$
$$2\left(\frac{25}{4}\right) = \frac{25}{2}$$
$$\frac{25}{2} = \frac{25}{2} \quad \text{True}$$

Example **B₃** $4y^2 = 9$

Solution

$4y^2 - 9 = 0$ — Write the equation in standard form

$(2y + 3)(2y - 3) = 0$ — Factor $4y^2 - 9 = (2y + 3)(2y - 3)$

$2y + 3 = 0$ or $2y - 3 = 0$ — Set each factor equal to 0

$2y = -3$ $\quad 2y = 3$ — Solve each equation

$y = -\frac{3}{2}$ $\quad y = \frac{3}{2}$ — The solutions

$\left\{-\frac{3}{2}, \frac{3}{2}\right\}$ — The solution set

Check by replacing y with $-\frac{3}{2}$ and $\frac{3}{2}$ in the original equation.

19. $x^2 + 4x = 0$ **20.** $y^2 - 4y = 0$ **21.** $3a^2 - 5a = 0$ **22.** $4x^2 + 7x = 0$

23. $2x^2 + 6x = 0$ **24.** $3b^2 = 9b$ **25.** $10a^2 = -15a$ **26.** $4y^2 = -6y$

27. $a^2 = 25$ **28.** $y^2 = 49$ **29.** $7x^2 - 28 = 0$ **30.** $5y^2 - 45 = 0$

31. $8x^2 - 18 = 0$

32. $7x^2 - 7 = 0$

Directions Find the solution set of the following quadratic equations by factoring. Check the solutions. See example 4–6 B.

Example $\boxed{B_1}$ $x^2 - 7x + 12 = 0$

Solution

$x^2 - 7x + 12 = 0$ — The equation is in standard form

$(x - 3)(x - 4) = 0$ — Factor $x^2 - 7x + 12 = (x - 3)(x - 4)$

$x - 3 = 0$ or $x - 4 = 0$ — Set each factor equal to 0

$x = 3$ $\quad x = 4$ — Solve each equation, giving the solutions

$\{3,4\}$ — The solution set

Check

(1) Let $x = 3$.

$$x^2 - 7x + 12 = 0$$
$$(3)^2 - 7(3) + 12 = 0$$
$$9 - 21 + 12 = 0$$
$$-12 + 12 = 0$$
$$0 = 0 \quad \text{True}$$

(2) Let $x = 4$.

$$x^2 - 7x + 12 = 0$$
$$(4)^2 - 7(4) + 12 = 0$$
$$16 - 28 + 12 = 0$$
$$-12 + 12 = 0$$
$$0 = 0 \quad \text{True}$$

33. $y^2 + 6y - 16 = 0$

34. $x^2 - 3x - 4 = 0$

35. $a^2 + 14a + 49 = 0$

36. $x^2 - 16x + 64 = 0$

$\boxed{37.}$ $b^2 + 5b - 14 = 0$

38. $x^2 + x - 42 = 0$

39. $x^2 + 3x + 2 = 0$

40. $y^2 = -11y - 10$

41. $a^2 - 11a = 12$

$\boxed{42.}$ $x^2 - 14x = 15$

43. $y^2 - 32 = 4y$

44. $x^2 = 27 - 6x$

Example **B4** $3x^2 = 7x + 6$

Solution

$3x^2 - 7x - 6 = 0$	Write in standard form
$(3x + 2)(x - 3) = 0$	Factor $3x^2 - 7x - 6 = (3x + 2)(x - 3)$
$3x + 2 = 0$ or $x - 3 = 0$	Set each factor equal to 0
$3x = -2$ $x = 3$	Solve the equations
$x = -\frac{2}{3}$ $x = 3$	The solutions
$\left\{-\frac{2}{3}, 3\right\}$	The solution set

Check by replacing x with $-\frac{2}{3}$ and 3 in the original equation.

45. $2x^2 - 7x - 9 = 0$

46. $2y^2 - y - 3 = 0$

47. $6a^2 - 5a + 1 = 0$

48. $3p^2 + 10p - 8 = 0$

49. $6x^2 + x - 12 = 0$

50. $4y^2 = 4y + 3$

51. $6a^2 + 3 = 11a$

52. $9x^2 = 8x + 1$

53. $6p^2 - 7p = 20$

54. $9y^2 + 20 = -27y$

55. $3x^2 + 6x = -3$

56. $9x^2 + 30x = -25$

Example **B5** $12(x^2 - 2x) = -9$

Solution

$12x^2 - 24x = -9$	Multiply in the left member
$12x^2 - 24x + 9 = 0$	Write the equation in standard form
$3(4x^2 - 8x + 3) = 0$	Factor common factor 3
$3(2x - 1)(2x - 3) = 0$	Factor $4x^2 - 8x + 3 = (2x - 1)(2x - 3)$
$2x - 1 = 0$ or $2x - 3 = 0$	Set each factor containing the variable equal to 0
$2x = 1$ $2x = 3$	Solve each equation
$x = \frac{1}{2}$ $x = \frac{3}{2}$	The solutions
$\left\{\frac{1}{2}, \frac{3}{2}\right\}$	The solution set

Check by replacing x by $\frac{1}{2}$ and $\frac{3}{2}$ in the original equation.

Note
The constant factor 3 cannot be zero, so we disregard it when finding the solutions.

57. $x(x + 3) = -2$

58. $3x(3x + 2) = 24$

59. $2x(2x + 6) = -8$

60. $2(x^2 - 6) = -5x$

61. $x(x - 6) = 18 + x$

62. $x(x + 1) - 6 = 0$

63. $4 = 3x(4 - 3x)$

64. $2x(3 - x) = 4$

65. $5(x^2 - 5) = 20x$

66. $x(x + 7) = 36 - 2x$

Review exercises

Directions Write an algebraic expression for each of the following. See section 1–7.

1. 7 more than a number

2. A number decreased by 11

3. 6 times the sum of x^2 and x

4. The sum of x^2 and $2x$, divided by 8

Directions Solve the following word problems. See section 2–4.

5. Three times a number is increased by 12 and the result is 51. Find the number.

6. One number is two more than five times another number. If their sum is 38, find the numbers.

7. The sum of three consecutive even integers is 72. Find the integers.

A_1 The product of two consecutive even integers is 224. Find the integers.

4–7 Applications of the quadratic equation

Many formulas used in the physical world are quadratic in nature since they become second-degree equations when solving for one of the variables. Likewise, many verbal problems require the use of quadratic equations for their solutions. We now consider some of these common uses of the quadratic equation.

Be aware that a check of the solutions by merely substituting them into the equation set up to solve the problem *will not* guarantee the correct answer. We should check the results to ensure that the physical conditions of the verbal problem are satisfied.

Example 4–7 A

1. The product of two consecutive even integers is 168. Find the integers.

   Let x = the lesser even integer. Then $x + 2$ = the next consecutive even integer.

   Note
   Consecutive even or odd integers are given by $x, x + 2, x + 4, \cdots$.

   two consecutive even integers (product of) is 168

   $$x \cdot (x + 2) = 168$$

$x^2 + 2x = 168$	Original equation
$x^2 + 2x - 168 = 0$	Write in standard form
$(x + 14)(x - 12) = 0$	Factor the left member
$x + 14 = 0$ or $x - 12 = 0$	Set each factor equal to zero
$x = -14$ $x = 12$	Solve each equation

   When $x = -14$, then $x + 2 = -14 + 2 = -12$.
   When $x = 12$, then $x + 2 = 12 + 2 = 14$.
   Then the two consecutive even integers are -14 and -12 or 12 and 14.
   Check: Since $(-14)(-12) = 168$ and $(12)(14) = 168$, and both sets are consecutive even integers, the conditions of the problem are met.

You are now ready to do **A_1**.

2. The area of a rectangle is $A = \ell w$, where ℓ is the length and w is the width of the rectangle. The length of a rectangle is 2 inches more than three times the width. If the area is 33 square inches, find the length and width of the rectangle.

   Let w = the width of the rectangle. Then the length $\ell = 3w + 2$.

area of a rectangle	is	length	times	width
A	$=$	ℓ	$\cdot$	w
33	$=$	$(3w + 2)$	$\cdot$	w

$w(3w + 2) = 33$	Original equation
$3w^2 + 2w = 33$	Distribute multiplication
$3w^2 + 2w - 33 = 0$	Write in standard form
$(3w + 11)(w - 3) = 0$	Factor the left member
$3w + 11 = 0$ or $w - 3 = 0$	Set each factor equal to zero
$3w = -11$ $w = 3$	Solve each equation
$w = -\frac{11}{3}$ $w = 3$	Solutions of the equation

The solution set of the equation we wrote is $\left\{-\frac{11}{3}, 3\right\}$. Since the width cannot be negative, $w = -\frac{11}{3}$ is not a solution of the problem, even though it *is* in the solution of the equation. So $w = 3$ is the only physical solution and
$\ell = 3w + 2 = 3(3) + 2 = 9 + 2 = 11.$
The rectangle is 3 inches wide and 11 inches long.
Check: Since 11 is two more than 3 times 3 and $(3)(11) = 33$, the conditions of the problem are met.

You are now ready to do **A_2**.

A_2 The area of a rectangle is 42 square meters. If the length, ℓ, is two meters longer than 4 times the width, w, what are the dimensions of the rectangle?

3. Current in a circuit flows according to the equation $i = 16 - 16t^2$, where i is the current in amperes and t is the time in seconds. Find the time t when $i = 0$ amperes (no current).

Replacing i by 0, we have the equation

$0 = 16 - 16t^2$	Substitute 0 for i
$0 = 16(1 - t^2)$	Factor the common factor 16
$0 = 16(1 - t)(1 + t)$	Factor $1 - t^2 = (1 - t)(1 + t)$
$1 - t = 0$ or $1 + t = 0$	Set each factor containing the variable equal to 0
$t = 1$ $\quad t = -1$	Solutions of the equation

Since time cannot be negative, $t = 1$ second.

You are now ready to do **A_3**. ■

A_3 Using $i = 16 - 16t^2$, find t when $i = 7$ amperes.

Answers to section 4–7 margin exercises

A_1 14, 16 or −16, −14 **A_2** $w = 3$ m, $\ell = 14$ m **A_3** $\frac{3}{4}$ sec

Exercise 4–7

Directions Solve the following verbal problems by using a quadratic equation. See example 4–7 A–1.

1. The product of two consecutive odd integers is 143. Find the integers.

2. The product of two consecutive integers is 132. Find the integers.

3. The product of two consecutive even integers is 224. Find the integers.

4. The product of two consecutive integers is 306. Find the integers.

5. One integer is six more than a second integer. The product of the two integers is 91. Find the integers.

6. One integer is eight less than a second integer. The product of the two integers is 153. Find the integers.

7. The product of two consecutive even integers is four more than two times their sum. Find the integers.

8. The product of two consecutive odd integers is five more than six times the lesser integer. Find the integers.

9. The sum of two integers is -13 and their product is 36. Find the integers.

10. The sum of two integers is -3 and their product is -70. Find the integers.

11. One number is one more than three times the other. Their product is 14. Find the numbers.

12. One number is two more than the other and their product is -1. Find the numbers.

See example 4–7 A–2.

13. The length of a rectangle is 2 meters less than twice the width. If the area is 24 square meters, what are the dimensions of the rectangle?

14. The area of a rectangle is 21 square feet. What are its dimensions if the length is 5 feet less than four times the width?

15. The area of a rectangle is numerically equal to twice the length. If the length is 3 feet more than the width, what are the dimensions of the rectangle?

16. The length of a rectangle is three less than twice the width. If the area is numerically five times the length, find the dimensions of the rectangle.

17. The height of a page of a book is 3 inches more than the width. If the area of the page is twelve less than ten times the width, find the dimensions of the page.

18. The height of a page of a book is 4 inches more than the width. If there is a margin of 1 inch all around the printed matter of the page and the area of the printed matter is 32 square inches, what are the dimensions of the page?

See example 4–7 A–3.

19. An object with initial velocity v undergoes an acceleration a for time t. The displacement s of the object for this time is given by the equation

$s = vt + \frac{1}{2}at^2$.

a. Find t when $s = 8$, $v = 2$, $a = 2$.

b. Find t when $s = 6$, $v = 3$, $a = 6$.

20. The current in a circuit flows according to the equation $i = 12 - 12t^2$, where i is the current in amperes and t is the time in seconds.

a. Find t when i is 0 amperes.

b. Find t when i is 9 amperes.

21. The power output of a generator armature is given by $P = EI - rI^2$.

a. Find I when $P = 120$, $E = 22$, $r = 1$.

b. Find I when $P = 120$, $E = 16$, $r = \frac{1}{2}$.

22. The output power P of a 100-volt electric generator is defined by $P = 100I - 5I^2$, where I is amperes.

a. Find I when $P = 480$.

b. Find I when $P = 375$.

23. A ball rolls down a slope and travels a distance $d = 6t + \frac{t^2}{2}$ feet in t seconds.

a. Find t when $d = 14$ feet.

b. Find t when $d = 32$ feet.

24. Because of gravity, an object falls a distance s feet according to the formula $s = 16t^2$, where t seconds is the time it falls.

a. How long will it take the object to fall 256 feet?

b. How long will it take the object to fall 49 feet?

c. How long will it take the object to fall $2\frac{1}{4}$ feet?

d. How long will it take the object to fall 1,024 feet?

Directions The formula $s = vt - 16t^2$ gives the height s in feet that an object will travel in t seconds if it is propelled directly upward at an *initial* velocity of v feet per second. (Use this formula in exercises 25 through 28.)

25. If an object is thrown upward at 96 feet per second, when will the object be at a height of 80 feet?

26. How long will it take before the object of exercise 25 hits the ground? (*Hint:* $s = 0$ when this happens.)

27. A projectile is fired upward with an initial velocity of 144 feet per second. How long will it take before the projectile strikes an object 288 feet directly overhead?

28. How long will it take before the projectile in exercise 27 falls back to the ground?

29. The formula for the area A of a trapezoid is $A = \frac{1}{2}h(b + c)$, where h is the altitude (height) of the trapezoid and the parallel bases are b and c (see diagram). If the area of the trapezoid is 63 square inches, base b is 10 inches long, and the altitude h is 1 inch less than the length of c, find the length of h and c.

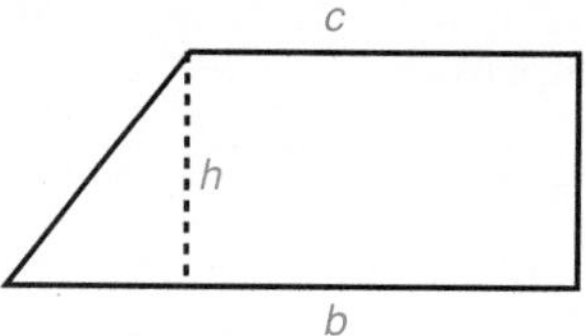

30. If the area of a trapezoid is 21 square feet, base c is 5 feet long, and base b is 6 feet longer than the altitude h, find the altitude of the trapezoid. See exercise 29.

31. The altitude and base c of a trapezoid have the same length. If the area of the trapezoid is 24 square meters and base b is twice as long as base c, find the dimensions of the trapezoid. See exercise 29.

32. One base of a trapezoid is three times the length of the other base. If the altitude is twice as long as the shorter base and the area is 36 square centimeters, find the dimensions of the trapezoid. See exercise 29.

33. The volume of a box (rectangular solid) is given by $V = \ell wh$, where ℓ is the length, w is the width, and h is the height of the box (see diagram). If the box is 4 feet tall, the length is 1 foot longer than the width, and the volume is 224 cubic feet, find the length and width of the box.

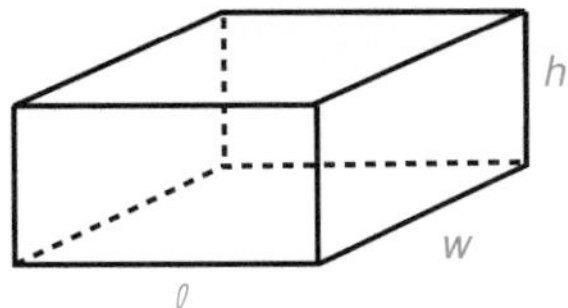

34. A box is 9 inches long and has a volume of 162 cubic inches. If the width of the box is twice the height, find the width and the height of the box. See exercise 33.

35. A storage room is three times as long as it is wide. If the room contains 756 cubic feet of space and has a ceiling 7 feet high, find the length and width of the room. See exercise 33.

36. A cardboard box has a volume of 108 cubic inches. If the length of the box is 1 inch more than two times its width and the box has a height of 3 inches, find the length and width of the box. See exercise 33.

Review exercises

Directions Find the solution(s). Write the solutions of the quadratic equations as a solution set. See sections 2–3 and 4–6.

1. $3x - 2 = 0$

2. $4a - 5 = 0$

3. $x^2 - 9 = 0$

4. $x^2 + 6x + 8 = 0$

Directions Evaluate the following expressions if $a = 4$, $b = -3$, $c = -6$, and $d = 5$. See section 1–8.

5. $ab - cd$

6. $b^2 - c^2$

7. $\dfrac{c - 2b}{d - a}$

8. $\dfrac{c + d}{3a + 4b}$

Chapter 4 lead-in problem

The formula $s = vt - 16t^2$ gives the height s in feet that an object will travel in t seconds if it is propelled directly upward at an initial velocity of v feet per second. If an object is thrown upward at 96 feet per second, how long will it take the object to reach a height of 144 feet?

Solution

$s = vt - 16t^2$	Original equation
$(144) = (96)t - 16t^2$	Substitute 144 for s and 96 for v
$16t^2 - 96t + 144 = 0$	Standard form
$16(t^2 - 6t + 9) = 0$	Common factor
$16(t - 3)(t - 3) = 0$	Factor the trinomial
$t - 3 = 0$	Set the repeated factor equal to zero
$t = 3$	Solve

The object will reach a height of 144 feet in 3 seconds.

Chapter 4 summary

1. **Common factors** are factors that appear in all the original terms.
2. A polynomial with integer coefficients is in **completely factored form** when
   a. the polynomial is written as a product of polynomials with integer coefficients;
   b. none of the polynomial factors, other than the monomial factor, can be factored further.
3. The trinomial $x^2 + bx + c$ will factor only if we can find a pair of integers, m and n, whose product is c and whose sum is b.
4. The **trinomial** $ax^2 + bx + c$ will factor only if we can find a pair of integers, m and n, whose product is $a \cdot c$ and whose sum is b.
5. The **difference of two squares** factors as
$$a^2 - b^2 = (a + b)(a - b).$$
6. **Perfect square trinomials** factor as
$$a^2 + 2ab + b^2 = (a + b)^2$$
and
$$a^2 - 2ab + b^2 = (a - b)^2.$$
7. We try to factor **four-term polynomials** by grouping.
8. A **quadratic equation** is an equation that contains the second, but no higher, power of the variable.
9. The product of two factors $(x + a)(x + b) = 0$ only if $x + a = 0$ or $x + b = 0$.

Chapter 4 review

[4–1]

Directions Supply the missing factors.

1. $3x + 9 = 3(\quad)$
2. $9x^2 - 18x = 9x(\quad)$
3. $-4y^3 + 8y^2 = -4y^2(\quad)$
4. $7a + 14b - 28c = 7(\quad)$
5. $-5a^2 - 15a + 30a^3$
$= -5a(\quad)$

Directions Write in completely factored form.

6. $3a^2 - 3ab + 3b$
7. $x^2y + xyz + xy^2z$
8. $a^3b + a^3b^2$
9. $3R^3 - 2R^2 + 6R^4$
10. $4y^2 + 8y + 12y^3$
11. $x^4 + 3x^3 + 9x^2$

12. $16R^3S^2 - 12R^4S^3 + 24R^2S^2$

13. $10a^4b^3 + 15a^2b^2 - 20a^3b^2$

14. $2(a + b) + x(a + b)$

15. $y(x - 3z) + 4(x - 3z)$

16. $a(3R + 1) + b(3R + 1)$

17. $2a(x - 3y) - 3b(x - 3y)$

18. $6ax - 3ay - 2bx + by$

19. $4ax + 6by + 8ay + 3bx$

20. $ax + 3bx - 4a - 12b$

21. $ax^2 - 2bx^2 + 4a - 8b$

[4–2]

Directions Write in completely factored form.

22. $x^2 - 9x + 14$

23. $2a^3 - 8a^2 - 10a$

24. $a^2 + 14a + 24$

25. $x^2 - 4x - 32$

26. $a^2 - 16a - 36$

27. $3x^2 - 9x - 30$

28. $x^3 - x^2 - 6x$

29. $x^3 - 4x^2 - 21x$

30. $a^2b^2 + ab - 6$

31. $a^2b^2 + 10ab + 24$

32. $a^2b^2 - 9ab + 18$

33. $a^2b^2 - 8ab - 20$

[4–3]

Directions Write in completely factored form.

34. $4x^2 + 4x + 1$

35. $9r^2 - 36r + 36$

36. $4x^2 - 5x + 1$

37. $9a^2 + 9a - 10$

38. $8a^2 - 2a - 3$

39. $24x^2 + 22x + 3$

40. $8a^2 - 18a + 9$

41. $2a^2 + 15a + 18$

[4–4]

Directions Write in completely factored form.

42. $4a^2 - 9$

43. $36b^2 - c^2$

44. $25 - a^2$

45. $16x^2 - 4y^2$

46. $9x^2 - y^4$

47. $x^4 - 16$

48. $y^4 - 81$

49. $b^2 + 12b + 36$

50. $c^2 - 10c + 25$

51. $4x^2 - 12x + 9$

52. $9x^2 - 12x + 4$

[4–5]

Directions Write in completely factored form.

53. $12x^4 - 3x^3$

54. $a^2 - 3a - 10$

55. $4a^2 - 21a + 5$

56. $9y^2 - 4$

57. $6ax + 9bx - 4a - 6b$

58. $b^2 - b - 20$

59. $9x^2 + 21x + 10$

60. $a^2 + 14a + 49$

61. $12x^5 - 3x^3$

62. $c^3 + 9c^2 + 20c$

63. $16a^2 - 8a + 1$

64. $b^4 - 1$

[4–6]

Directions Determine the solution set for the following equations.

65. $(x - 1)(x + 3) = 0$

66. $3x(x - 8) = 0$

67. $(5x + 1)(3x - 7) = 0$

68. $(7x - 1)(5x - 8) = 0$

69. $(4 - 3x)(9 - x) = 0$

70. $5x(x + 9)(3x + 12) = 0$

71. $(5x - 4)(5x + 4) = 0$

72. $(4x + 4)(5x - 15)(7x + 14) = 0$

Directions Find the solution set of the following quadratic equations by factoring.

73. $4x^2 - 9x = 0$

74. $y^2 = 1$

75. $2a^2 = 128a$

76. $3x^2 - 75 = 0$

77. $x^2 - x - 30 = 0$

78. $2y = y^2 + 1$

79. $4a^2 + 13a + 3 = 0$

80. $5x^2 - 4 = 8x$

81. $x(x - 8) = -16$

82. $3(x^2 + 3) = 12x$

83. $8y^2 + y - 6 = -y$

84. $4a - 12 = 2a - 2a^2$

[4–7]

Directions Solve the following verbal problems.

85. If the product of two consecutive integers is ten less than the square of the greater integer, determine the integers.

86. The length of a rectangular flower garden is 5 feet more than its width. If the area of the garden is 104 square feet, find the dimensions of the flower garden.

87. A farmer has some cattle to sell to a slaughterhouse. When the manager of the slaughterhouse asked how many cattle he had to sell, the farmer replied, "If you triple the square of the number of cattle you get 1,200." How many cattle did the farmer have to sell?

88. The height h in feet of a projectile launched vertically upward from the top of a 96-foot tall tower when time $t = 0$ is given by $h = 96 + 80t - 16t^2$. How long will it take the projectile to strike the ground?

NAME

Chapter 4 cumulative test

CLASS/SECTION DATE

Directions Perform the indicated operations and simplify.

[1–6] **1.** $40 - 2 \cdot 8 \div 4 - 6 + 3$

[3–1] **2.** $(2a^2b)^3$

[3–3] **3.** $(a + 2b)^2$

[3–1] **4.** $a^3 \cdot a^2 \cdot a$

[1–6] **5.** $3[6 - 4(5 - 2) + 10]$

[3–1] **6.** $(x^2y^3)(x^3y)$

[3–2] **7.** $(3x - y) - (4y - 3x) - (x + 2y)$

[3–3] **8.** $(3x - 2y)(3x + 2y)$

[3–1] **9.** $\left(\frac{2a^2}{b}\right)^3$

[3–2] **10.** $3x - [x - y - (2x + 3y)]$

[3–4] **11.** $x^6 \cdot x^{-4}$

Directions Find the solution(s). Write the solutions of the quadratic equations as a solution set.

[2–3] **12.** $3(3x - 2) = 4x + 3$

[2–7] **13.** $2x + 7 \geq 13$

[2–3] **14.** $2(2x - 1) = 6(x - 2) - 4$

[4–6] **15.** $x^2 - 7x + 10 = 0$

[4–6] **16.** $x^2 - 9 = 0$

[2–7] **17.** $3(2x + 1) < 4x + 8$

Directions Solve for the specified variable.

[2–5] **18.** $3x - y = x + 5y$ for x

[2–5] **19.** $2x + 5 - 3y = 5x + 3 - 8y$ for x

Directions Write in completely factored form.

[4–1] **20.** $2ab - 4a^2b^2 - 8a^3b^5$

[4–4] **21.** $4a^2 + 12a + 9$

[4–4] **22.** $25c^2 - 9d^2$

[4–3] **23.** $4a^2 - 4a - 15$

[4–2] **24.** $x^2 + 9x + 18$

Directions Set up an equation and solve for the unknown(s).

[2–4] **25.** One number is eleven more than twice a second number. If their sum is 53, what are the numbers?

[4–7] **26.** The product of two consecutive positive odd integers is 143. Find the integers.

[2–4] **27.** Terry has $15,000. He invests part of this money at 8% and the rest at 6%, and his income for one year from these investments totals $1,100. How much was invested at each rate?

[4–7] **28.** The area of a rectangle is six more than ten times the width. If the length is 5 meters longer than the width, what are the dimensions of the rectangle?

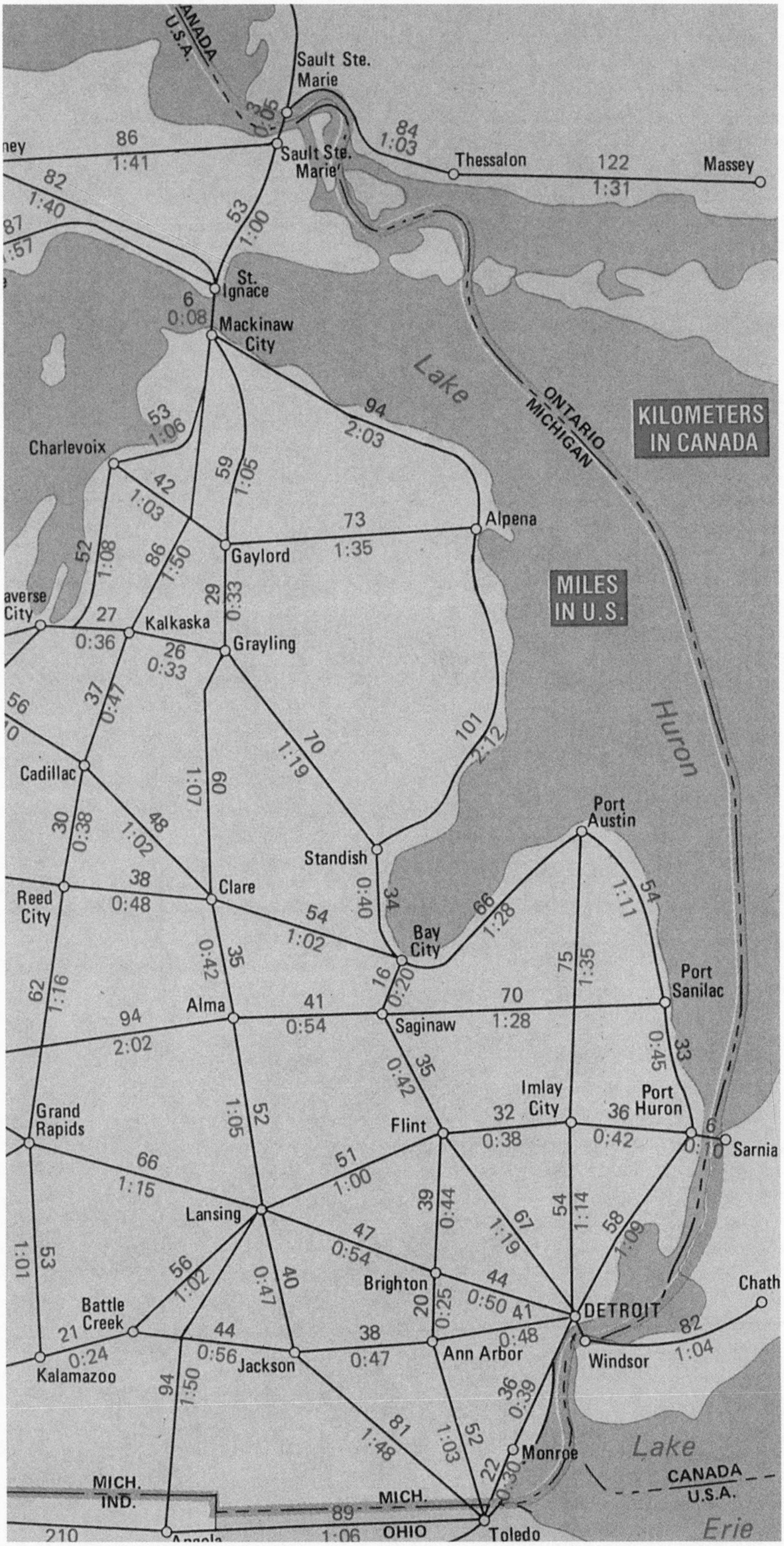

CHAPTER

5

Rational Expressions, Ratio and Proportion

On a road map, 3 inches represents a distance of 45 miles. If the distance between Detroit and Sault Ste. Marie is 23 inches on the map, how far is it from Detroit to Sault Ste. Marie?

Proficiency check

[R–1] **1.** Write in prime factor form.
a. 28

b. 90

[R–1] **2.** Find the least common denominator, LCD, of the following fractions.
a. $\frac{2}{9}, \frac{7}{8}$

b. $\frac{3}{4}, \frac{5}{6}, \frac{1}{8}$

[R–1] **3.** Reduce the fraction $\frac{36}{42}$ to lowest terms.

[R–1] **4.** Perform the indicated operations.
a. $\frac{1}{6} \cdot \frac{9}{2}$

b. $\frac{3}{4} \div \frac{6}{7}$

c. $\frac{2}{3} + \frac{5}{6}$

d. $\frac{13}{5} - \frac{7}{8}$

[4–1, 4–2, 4–3] **5.** Factor the following expressions.
a. $x^2 - 9$

b. $y^2 - 2y + 1$

c. $3x^2 + 12x - 15$

[4–6] **6.** Find the solution set of the following equations.
a. $x^2 - 5x - 6 = 0$

b. $2y^2 + 13y - 7 = 0$

▣ 5–1 Rational expressions

A rational expression

In chapter 1, we defined a rational number.

> **Rational numbers**
> A rational number is any number that can be written as the quotient of two integers with the divisor (denominator) not zero.

Examples of rational numbers are

$$\frac{6}{1},\quad \frac{3}{4},\quad \frac{-5}{6},\quad \text{and } \frac{8}{7}.$$

We extend this definition to involve the quotient of two polynomials and define a **rational expression.**

> **Rational expressions**
> A **rational expression** is any expression that can be written as the quotient of two polynomials with the denominator not zero.

For example,

$$\frac{2x}{x+1},\quad \frac{x^2-2}{x^2-x-6},\quad \text{and}\quad \frac{x^2+x}{5}$$

are all rational expressions.

Just as a rational number has a numerator and a denominator, so does a rational expression. In the rational expression

$$\frac{x^2-2}{x^2-x-6},$$

the polynomial on the top, $x^2 - 2$, is called the **numerator** and the polynomial on the bottom, $x^2 - x - 6$, is called the **denominator.**

Evaluating rational expressions

In chapter 2, we evaluated algebraic expressions by substituting given values for the variables and performing the indicated operations. We follow the same procedure when evaluating rational expressions.

Example 5–1 A

Evaluate the following rational expressions for the given value of the variable.

1. $\dfrac{5x-2}{4x+3}$, $x = 2$

$$\frac{5x-2}{4x+3} = \frac{5(2)-2}{4(2)+3} \qquad \text{Replace } x \text{ with 2}$$

$$= \frac{10-2}{8+3} \qquad \text{Perform indicated operations}$$

$$= \frac{8}{11}$$

A₁ $\frac{6x - 1}{3x + 2}, x = 3$

Note
We always work such problems using the order of operations. That is, we multiply in the numerator and the denominator before we add or subtract.

You are now ready to do **A_1**.

2. $\frac{x + 2}{x^2 - 3x - 10}, x = 5$

$$\frac{x + 2}{x^2 - 3x - 10} = \frac{5 + 2}{(5)^2 - 3(5) - 10}$$ Replace x with 5

$$= \frac{7}{25 - 15 - 10}$$ Perform indicated operations

$$= \frac{7}{10 - 10}$$

$$= \frac{7}{0} \quad \text{(undefined)}$$

Therefore, for the rational expression to be defined, x cannot be 5.

A_2 $\frac{x + 5}{x^2 - 4x - 12}, x = 6$

You are now ready to do **A_2**.

3. $\frac{x - 5}{2x^2 + x - 1}, x = -\frac{1}{2}$

$$\frac{x - 5}{2x^2 + x - 1} = \frac{\left(-\frac{1}{2}\right) - 5}{2\left(-\frac{1}{2}\right)^2 + \left(-\frac{1}{2}\right) - 1}$$ Replace x with $-\frac{1}{2}$

$$= \frac{-\frac{1}{2} - \frac{10}{2}}{\frac{1}{2} - \frac{1}{2} - 1}$$ Perform indicated operations

$$= \frac{-\frac{11}{2}}{-1}$$ Subtract in numerator and denominator

$$= \frac{11}{2}$$ Divide by -1

A_3 $\frac{z - 3}{3z^2 + z - 3}, z = \frac{1}{3}$

You are now ready to do **A_3**. ■

Domain of a rational expression

Notice in example 2, the answer was undefined since division by zero is not defined. The rational expression becomes *meaningless* for those values of the variable for which the denominator equals zero, as with $x = 5$ in example 2. Finding the value(s) of the variable that will make the denominator zero is called *finding the restrictions on the variable(s).*

Note
The restrictions on the variables are found by setting all factors of the denominator *containing variables* equal to zero and solving for the variables.

All other values of the variable for which the expression is defined make up the **domain** of the rational expression.

Domain of a rational expression

All replacement values of the variable for which a rational expression is defined defines the **domain** of the rational expression.

B_1 $\dfrac{x-6}{x-7}$

Example 5–1 B

Determine the domain of each of the following rational expressions.

1. $\dfrac{a-3}{a-4}$

$a - 4 = 0$ — Set denominator equal to 0

$a = 4$ — Solve equation for a

The restriction is that $a \neq 4$.
Domain is all real numbers except 4.

B_2 $\dfrac{5y}{y^2 + 7y - 18}$

You are now ready to do **B_1**.

Note
We look *only* at the denominator. The value(s) of the variable for which the numerator is zero is of no concern to us.

2. $\dfrac{3x^2}{x^2 - x - 6}$

$x^2 - x - 6 = (x - 3)(x + 2)$ — Factor denominator

$x - 3 = 0$ or $x + 2 = 0$ — Set each factor equal to 0

$x = 3$ $\quad$ $x = -2$ — Solve each equation for x

The restrictions are $x \neq 3$ or $x \neq -2$.
Domain is all real numbers except 3 or -2.

B_3 $\dfrac{x-7}{2x^2 + 3}$

You are now ready to do **B_2**.

3. $\dfrac{x+3}{x^2 + 5}$

$x^2 + 5$ does not factor. If there is a restriction, it will occur when x^2 is -5. Since x^2 is never negative, there are no restrictions on the variable. Domain is all real numbers.

You are now ready to do **B_3**.

4. $\dfrac{x-3}{x^2 - x}$

B_4 $\dfrac{x+7}{x^2 + 5x}$

$x^2 - x = x(x - 1)$ — Factor denominator

$x = 0$ or $x - 1 = 0$ — Set each factor equal to 0

$x = 0$ $\quad$ $x = 1$ — Solve each equation for x

The restrictions are $x \neq 0$ or $x \neq 1$. Domain is all real numbers except 0 or 1.

Note
In example 4, a common error is to forget to place restrictions on the factor x.

You are now ready to do **B_4**. ■

Answers to section 5–1 margin exercises

A_1 $\frac{17}{11}$ **A_2** undefined **A_3** $\frac{8}{7}$ **B_1** $x \neq 7$, domain is all real numbers except 7. **B_2** $y \neq -9$, $y \neq 2$, domain is all real numbers except -9 or 2 **B_3** no restrictions, domain is all real numbers **B_4** $x \neq 0$, $x \neq -5$, domain is all real numbers except 0 or -5

Mastery points

Can you

- Evaluate a rational expression for a given value of the variable?
- Determine the restrictions on the variable in a rational expression?
- Determine the domain of a rational expression?

Exercise 5–1

Directions Evaluate each given rational expression using the given value of the variable. If the given value is not in the domain of the rational expression, so state. See example 5–1 A.

Example **A_1** $\frac{6x - 1}{3x + 2}$, $x = 3$

Solution

$$\frac{6x - 1}{3x + 2} = \frac{6(3) - 1}{3(3) + 2}$$ Replace x with 3

$$= \frac{18 - 1}{9 + 2}$$ Perform indicated operations

$$= \frac{17}{11}$$

1. $\frac{x}{3x}$, $x = 2$

2. $\frac{2x + 1}{5x - 3}$, $x = 3$

3. $\frac{5a^2 + 2}{3a - 1}$, $a = -1$

4. $\frac{x^2 - 1}{x}$, $x = -4$

5. $\frac{-4p^2}{2p - 3}$, $p = 1$

6. $\frac{-5b^3}{5 - 2b}$, $b = -2$

7. $\frac{x + 9}{x^2 + 2x - 1}$, $x = -9$

8. $\frac{n + 3}{3n^2 + n - 1}$, $n = -3$

9. $\frac{(-2x)^2}{x^2 + 3x + 7}$, $x = 0$

10. $\frac{x + 3}{x^2 + 2x - 1}$, $x = 0$

11. $\frac{3 - 4x}{x^2 - x}$, $x = 0$

12. $\frac{x + 5}{x - 2}$, $x = 2$

13. $\dfrac{3x + 1}{x^2 - 1}, x = \dfrac{1}{2}$

14. $\dfrac{x + 4}{x^2 + 5x + 6}, x = -\dfrac{1}{3}$

Directions Determine the domain of the given rational expression. See example 5–1 B.

Example [B₂] $\dfrac{5y}{y^2 + 7y - 18}$

Solution

$y^2 + 7y - 18 = (y + 9)(y - 2)$	Factor denominator
$y + 9 = 0$ or $y - 2 = 0$	Set each factor equal to 0
$y = -9$ $\quad$ $y = 2$	Solve each equation for y

The restrictions are $y \neq -9$ or $y \neq 2$.
Domain is all real numbers except -9 or 2.

15. $\dfrac{4}{3x}$

16. $\dfrac{5}{4x}$

17. $\dfrac{8}{x - 2}$

18. $\dfrac{10}{x - 5}$

19. $\dfrac{x}{x + 7}$

20. $\dfrac{3x^2}{x + 3}$

[21.] $\dfrac{x + 1}{2x - 1}$

22. $\dfrac{a + 9}{4a - 3}$

[23.] $\dfrac{p - 3}{5 - 2p}$

24. $\dfrac{y + 4}{8 - 3y}$

25. $\dfrac{7x}{3x + 15}$

26. $\dfrac{5b - 1}{9b + 21}$

27. $\dfrac{x + 7}{x^2 + 3x - 18}$

28. $\dfrac{8b + 1}{b^2 - 7b + 6}$

[29.] $\dfrac{2x^2}{x^2 + 9}$

30. $\dfrac{5x - 3}{2x^2 + 1}$

[31.] $\dfrac{5s^2 + 7}{2s^2 - s - 3}$

32. $\dfrac{8z}{3z^2 + 2z - 8}$

33. $\dfrac{4}{x^2 - 16}$

34. $\dfrac{5x}{9x^2 - 4}$

35. $\dfrac{x - 5}{x^2 - 25}$

36. $\dfrac{3x - 1}{3x^2 - 5x - 2}$

37. $\dfrac{3x + 1}{x^2 + 4x + 3}$

38. $\dfrac{y + 2}{y^2 - 4}$

39. $\dfrac{z - 8}{z^2 - 64}$

40. $\dfrac{2y + 3}{2y^2 + 7y + 3}$

Review exercises

1. The statement $4(5 + 6) = 4 \cdot 5 + 4 \cdot 6$ demonstrates what property of real numbers? See section 1–6.

2. Simplify the expression $2[3 - 4(1 + 6)]$ by performing the indicated operations. See section 1–6.

3. Evaluate the expression $a[b + (c - d)]$ when $a = 1$, $b = -2$, $c = 3$, and $d = -4$. See section 1–8.

4. Reduce the fraction $\dfrac{35}{63}$ to lowest terms. See section R–1.

5. Subtract $\dfrac{3}{5} - \dfrac{2}{3}$. See section R–3.

Factor the following polynomials. See section 4–3.

6. $2x^2 - 9x - 5$

7. $4y^2 - 40y + 100$

5–2 Simplifying rational expressions

A_1 $\dfrac{64}{72}$

The fundamental principle of rational expressions

One of the most important procedures we can use when we work with rational expressions is the simplification of the rational expression. To do this, we use a principle called the **fundamental principle of rational expressions.**

Fundamental principle of rational expressions

If P is any polynomial and Q and R are nonzero polynomials, then

$$\frac{PR}{QR} = \frac{P}{Q} \text{ and } \frac{P}{Q} = \frac{PR}{QR}.$$

Concept

To change the appearance of a rational expression without changing its value, we may multiply or divide both the numerator and the denominator by the same nonzero polynomial.

This property is based on 1 being the identity element for multiplication. That is,

$$\frac{PR}{QR} = \frac{P}{Q} \cdot \frac{R}{R} = \frac{P}{Q} \cdot 1 = \frac{P}{Q}.$$

This property permits us to **reduce** rational expressions to *lowest terms.* A rational expression is *completely reduced* if the greatest factor common to both the numerator and the denominator is 1. We can see that the key to reducing rational expressions is *finding* and dividing out *factors* that are common to both the numerator and the denominator. Reducing rational expressions to lowest terms is called *simplifying* the rational expression.

To reduce a rational expression

1. Write the numerator and the denominator in factored form.
2. Divide the numerator and the denominator by all common factors.

Example 5–2 A

Simplify the following rational expressions by reducing to lowest terms. Assume that no denominator equals zero.

1. $\dfrac{45}{60} = \dfrac{3 \cdot 3 \cdot 5}{2 \cdot 2 \cdot 3 \cdot 5}$ Factor numerator and denominator to prime numbers

$= \dfrac{3 \cdot (3 \cdot 5)}{2 \cdot 2 \cdot (3 \cdot 5)}$ Group common factors $(3 \cdot 5)$

$= \dfrac{3}{2 \cdot 2}$ Divide numerator and denominator by $(3 \cdot 5)$

$= \dfrac{3}{4}$ Multiply remaining factors

You are now ready to do **A_1**.

A₂ $\frac{25z^4}{15z^5}$

2. $\frac{14x^2}{10x^3} = \frac{7 \cdot 2 \cdot x \cdot x}{5 \cdot 2 \cdot x \cdot x \cdot x}$ Factor numerator and denominator

$= \frac{7 \cdot (2 \cdot x \cdot x)}{5 \cdot x \cdot (2 \cdot x \cdot x)}$ Group common factors $(2 \cdot x \cdot x)$

$= \frac{7}{5x}$ Divide numerator and denominator by common factor $(2 \cdot x \cdot x)$

You are now ready to do **A₂**.

3. $\frac{5a - 15}{4a - 12} = \frac{5(a - 3)}{4(a - 3)}$ Factor numerator and denominator

$= \frac{5}{4}$ Divide numerator and denominator by common factor $(a - 3)$

You are now ready to do **A₃**.

A₃ $\frac{12b + 36}{15b + 45}$

4. $\frac{x^2 - 4}{x^2 - 2x - 8} = \frac{(x - 2)(x + 2)}{(x - 4)(x + 2)}$ Factor numerator and denominator

$= \frac{x - 2}{x - 4}$ Divide numerator and denominator by common factor $x + 2$

You are now ready to do **A₄**.

5. $\frac{y - 7}{y^2 - 49} = \frac{y - 7}{(y + 7)(y - 7)}$ Factor denominator

$= \frac{1}{y + 7}$ Divide numerator and denominator by common factor $y - 7$

A₄ $\frac{a^2 - 36}{a^2 - a - 30}$

Note

The fundamental principle allows us to divide by common *factors only.* A common error in example 5 is to divide the numerator and the denominator by y and 7.

$$\frac{y - 7}{y^2 - 49} \neq \frac{\overset{1}{\cancel{y}} - \overset{1}{\cancel{7}}}{\underset{y}{\cancel{y^2}} - \underset{7}{\cancel{49}}}$$ Divide first terms by y and second terms by 7

This error can be avoided by always remembering that the fundamental principle of rational expressions allows us to divide the numerator and the denominator by common factors. y and 7 are *terms* and *not factors.*

You are now ready to do **A₅**. ■

A₅ $\frac{z + 9}{z^2 - 81}$

Reducing $\frac{a - b}{b - a}$

Consider the rational expression $\frac{x - 5}{5 - x}$, which does not appear to be reducible by a common factor. However,

$5 - x = -1(-5 + x)$ Factor out -1

$= -1(x - 5)$ Rearrange terms

Thus,

$\frac{x - 5}{5 - x} = \frac{x - 5}{-1(x - 5)}$

$= \frac{1}{-1}$ Reduce by common factor $x - 5$

$= -1$

> **Reducing additive inverses**
> For all real numbers a and b, $a \neq b$,
> $$\frac{a-b}{b-a} = -1,$$
> where $a - b$ and $b - a$ are *additive inverses.*

B₁ $\dfrac{5-p}{p^2-25}$

Example 5–2 B

Simplify the following rational expressions by reducing to lowest terms. Assume that no denominator equals zero.

1. $\dfrac{4-x}{x^2-16}$

$= \dfrac{4-x}{(x-4)(x+4)}$ Completely factor denominator

$= \dfrac{4-x}{x-4} \cdot \dfrac{1}{x+4}$ $4 - x$ and $x - 4$ are additive inverses

$= -1 \cdot \dfrac{1}{x+4}$ $\dfrac{4-x}{x-4} = -1$

$= \dfrac{-1}{x+4}$ Multiply numerator by -1

You are now ready to do **B₁**.

2. $\dfrac{1-x^2}{2x^2+x-3}$

$= \dfrac{(1-x)(1+x)}{(x-1)(2x+3)}$ Completely factor numerator and denominator

$= \dfrac{1-x}{x-1} \cdot \dfrac{1+x}{2x+3}$ $1 - x$ and $x - 1$ are additive inverses

$= -1 \cdot \dfrac{1+x}{2x+3}$ $\dfrac{1-x}{x-1} = -1$

$= \dfrac{-1(1+x)}{2x+3}$ Multiply numerator by -1

$= \dfrac{-1-x}{2x+3}$ or $\dfrac{-x-1}{2x+3}$ Alternative forms of answer

You are now ready to do **B₂**. ■

B₂ $\dfrac{16-y^2}{3y^2-11y-4}$

Answers to section 5-2 margin exercises

A₁ $\dfrac{8}{9}$ **A₂** $\dfrac{5}{3z}$ **A₃** $\dfrac{4}{5}$ **A₄** $\dfrac{a+6}{a+5}$ **A₅** $\dfrac{1}{z-9}$ **B₁** $\dfrac{-1}{p+5}$
B₂ $\dfrac{-(4+y)}{3y+1}$ or $\dfrac{-4-y}{3y+1}$

> **Mastery points**
>
> ***Can you***
> - Reduce a rational expression to lowest terms using the fundamental principle of rational expressions?
> - Recognize factors $a - b$ and $b - a$ and use $\dfrac{a-b}{b-a} = -1$?

Exercise 5–2

Directions Simplify the following rational expressions by reducing to lowest terms. Assume that no denominator equals zero. See example 5–2 A.

Examples $\boxed{A_2}$ $\frac{25z^4}{15z^5}$

Solutions

$= \frac{5 \cdot 5 \cdot z \cdot z \cdot z \cdot z}{5 \cdot 3 \cdot z \cdot z \cdot z \cdot z \cdot z}$ Factor numerator and denominator

$= \frac{5 \cdot (5 \cdot z \cdot z \cdot z \cdot z)}{3 \cdot z \cdot (5 \cdot z \cdot z \cdot z \cdot z)}$ Group common factors $(5 \cdot z \cdot z \cdot z \cdot z)$

$= \frac{5}{3z}$ Divide numerator and denominator by $5 \cdot z \cdot z \cdot z \cdot z$

$\boxed{A_4}$ $\frac{a^2 - 36}{a^2 - a - 30}$

$= \frac{(a + 6)(a - 6)}{(a + 5)(a - 6)}$ Factor numerator and denominator

$= \frac{a + 6}{a + 5}$ Divide numerator and denominator by $(a - 6)$

1. $\frac{54}{72}$
2. $\frac{75}{145}$
3. $\frac{6x}{15}$
4. $\frac{8a}{10}$
5. $\frac{16x^2}{12x}$
6. $\frac{15b^3}{20b}$
7. $\frac{-8x^2}{6x^4}$
8. $\frac{3a^6}{-9a^3}$
9. $\frac{16a^2b}{20ab^2}$
10. $\frac{15a^2x^3}{35ax^2}$
11. $\frac{10(x + 5)}{8(x + 5)}$
12. $\frac{24(x - 3)}{15(x - 3)}$
13. $\frac{6(x - 2)}{(x + 3)(x - 2)}$
14. $\frac{-8(x + 1)}{4(x + 1)(x - 6)}$
15. $\frac{3m - 6}{5m - 10}$
16. $\frac{8b + 12}{10b + 15}$
17. $\frac{3x - 3}{6x - 6}$
18. $\frac{4 - 8x}{6 - 12x}$
19. $\frac{a + b}{a^2 - b^2}$
20. $\frac{x^2 - y^2}{x - y}$
21. $\frac{6y - 6}{8y^2 - 8}$
22. $\frac{2y^2 - 2x^2}{x - y}$
23. $\frac{n^2 - m^2}{(m + n)^2}$
24. $\frac{a^2 - 10a + 25}{a^2 - 25}$
25. $\frac{x^2 - 9}{x^2 + 6x + 9}$
26. $\frac{y^2 - y - 42}{y^2 + 12y + 36}$
27. $\frac{x^2 - 3x - 10}{x^2 - x - 6}$
28. $\frac{4m^2 + 15m - 4}{8m^2 - 22m + 5}$

29. $\dfrac{2y^2 - 3y - 9}{4y^2 - 13y + 3}$ 30. $\dfrac{3x^2 + 14x - 5}{x^2 + 10x + 25}$ 31. $\dfrac{6x^2 - x - 2}{4x^2 + 4x + 1}$

Directions Simplify by reducing to lowest terms. Assume that no denominator equals zero. See example 5–2 B.

Example B2 $\dfrac{16 - y^2}{3y^2 - 11y - 4}$

Solution

$$= \frac{(4 - y)(4 + y)}{(y - 4)(3y + 1)} \quad \text{Factor numerator and denominator}$$

$$= \frac{4 - y}{y - 4} \cdot \frac{4 + y}{3y + 1} \quad 4 - y \text{ and } y - 4 \text{ are opposites}$$

$$= -1 \cdot \frac{4 + y}{3y + 1} \quad \frac{4 - y}{y - 4} = -1$$

$$= \frac{-1(4 + y)}{3y + 1} \quad \text{Multiply } -1 \text{ times the numerator}$$

$$= \frac{-4 - y}{3y + 1} \text{ or } \frac{-y - 4}{3y + 1} \quad \text{Alternative forms of answer}$$

32. $\dfrac{a - b}{b^2 - a^2}$ 33. $\dfrac{(x - y)^2}{y^2 - x^2}$ 34. $\dfrac{2x - 8}{12 - 3x}$

35. $\dfrac{8b - 8a}{a - b}$ 36. $\dfrac{4x - 4y}{y^2 - x^2}$ 37. $\dfrac{x - 3}{12 - x - x^2}$

38. $\dfrac{4 - y}{2y^2 - 7y - 4}$ 39. $\dfrac{p^2 - q^2}{q^2 - p^2}$ 40. $\dfrac{3p - 3q}{6q^2 - 6p^2}$

Review exercises

1. Write the decimal number 0.000314 in scientific notation. See section 3–5.

2. Given $x = 2$, $y = -3$ and $z = -1$, evaluate the expression $\dfrac{4x - y}{2y + z}$. See sections 1–8 and 5–1.

3. Divide $53.25 \div 2.13$. See section R–2.

4. A piece of lumber 16 feet long is to be divided into two pieces so that one piece is 1 foot longer than twice the length of the other piece. Find the lengths of the two pieces of lumber. See sections 2–6 and 2–7.

Simplify the following expressions. See section 3–4.

5. $(5x^{-2}y^3)^0$ **6.** $\frac{3xy^2}{3^{-2}xy^{-1}}$ **7.** $(-2x^3y^2)^3$

A₁ $a^{10} \div a^5$

5–3 The quotient of two polynomials

In section 3–4, we observed the process of dividing a monomial by a monomial. We shall first review this process before we deal with other types of polynomial division. Recall the property for division of like bases, $a^m \div a^n = a^{m-n}$.

Example 5–3 A

Find the indicated quotients. Assume that no denominator equals zero.

1. $x^7 \div x^4 = x^{7-4}$ Subtract exponents when dividing
$= x^3$

You are now ready to do **A₁**.

A₂ $\frac{5^3x^4}{5x}$

2. $\frac{2^2a^5}{2a^3} = 2^{2-1}a^{5-3}$ Divide like bases by subtracting exponents
$= 2^1a^2$ Perform subtractions
$= 2a^2$ $2^1 = 2$

You are now ready to do **A₂**. ■

Division of a polynomial by a monomial

To perform this division, we use a principle of fractions.

$$\frac{a}{c} + \frac{b}{c} = \frac{a+b}{c}$$

By reversing this equation, the principle can be used to divide a polynomial by a monomial.

B₁ $\frac{12a^7 - 18a^9}{3a}$

> **Division of a polynomial by a monomial**
>
> $$\frac{a+b}{c} = \frac{a}{c} + \frac{b}{c}\ (c \neq 0).$$
>
> **Concept**
>
> To divide a polynomial by a monomial, divide each term of the polynomial by the monomial.

Note

We will assume that no divisor or denominator is equal to zero.

Example 5–3 B

Find the indicated quotients.

1. $\frac{6x^4 - 6x^3 + 12x^2}{6x} = \frac{6x^4}{6x} - \frac{6x^3}{6x} + \frac{12x^2}{6x}$ Divide polynomial by monomial
$= x^3 - x^2 + 2x$ Use properties of exponents

You are now ready to do **B₁**.

2. $\dfrac{8a^4 + 4a^2 - 12a}{4a} = \dfrac{8a^4}{4a} + \dfrac{4a^2}{4a} - \dfrac{12a}{4a}$ Divide polynomial by monomial

$= 2a^3 + a - 3$ Use properties of exponents

B₂ $\dfrac{16x^5 + 20x^3 - 4x^2}{4x^2}$

You are now ready to do **B₂**. ■

Recall that we can check our division by

quotient · divisor = dividend.

In example 2,

$(2a^3 + a - 3) \cdot 4a = 2a^3 \cdot 4a + a \cdot 4a - 3 \cdot 4a$ Distributive property

$= 8a^4 + 4a^2 - 12a.$ Dividend

Note

A common error in this type of problem is demonstrated in the following example:

$$\frac{x^3 + x^2}{x^2} \neq \frac{x^3 + 1}{1}.$$

It is tempting to simply "cancel" the x^2 in the numerator with the x^2 in the denominator, but the correct procedure would be

$$\frac{x^3 + x^2}{x^2} = \frac{x^3}{x^2} + \frac{x^2}{x^2} = x + 1.$$

Division of a polynomial by a polynomial

Consider a quotient in which the divisor is not a monomial. For example,

$$\frac{y^2 - y - 2}{y - 2},$$

which involves the division of a trinomial by a binomial. We handle this just like long division with numbers. Set it up in the form

$$y - 2\overline{)y^2 - y - 2}.$$

Note

The divisor and dividend must be arranged in descending powers of one variable with zeros inserted to hold the position of any missing term.

The following table demonstrates writing a polynomial in descending powers of the variable and inserting zeros to hold the position of missing terms.

Dividend	Dividend arranged in descending powers	
$x^3 + 2x + 3x^4 + 4x^2 - 1$	$3x^4 + x^3 + 4x^2 + 2x - 1$	
$x^3 + x - 9$	$x^3 + 0x^2 + x - 9$	Insert zero placeholders
$x^4 - 1$	$x^4 + 0x^3 + 0x^2 + 0x - 1$	Insert zero placeholders

The method for dividing polynomials is similar to the long division used in dividing whole numbers. To demonstrate this, we divide 972 by 36 step-by-step as we divide $(y^2 - y - 2)$ by $(y - 2)$.

$36\overline{)972}$ $\qquad$ $y - 2\overline{)y^2 - y - 2}$

Step 1 Divide 36 into 97, which goes 2 times. Place 2 over 7 in the dividend.

$$\begin{array}{r} 2 \\ 36\overline{)972} \end{array}$$

Divide y into y^2, which goes y times. Place y over y in the dividend.

$$\begin{array}{r} y\phantom{{}-y-2} \\ y - 2\overline{)y^2 - y - 2} \end{array}$$

Step 2 Multiply 2 times 36, place 72 below 97 in the dividend.

$$\begin{array}{r} 2 \\ 36\overline{)972} \\ \underline{72} \end{array}$$

Multiply y times $y - 2$, place $y^2 - 2y$ below $y^2 - y$ in the dividend.

$$\begin{array}{r} y \\ y - 2\overline{)y^2 - y - 2} \\ \underline{y^2 - 2y} \end{array}$$

Step 3 Subtract 72 from 97. The difference is 25.

$$\begin{array}{r} 2 \\ 36\overline{)972} \\ (-)\underline{72} \\ 25 \end{array}$$

Subtract $y^2 - 2y$ from $y^2 - y$. $(y^2 - y) - (y^2 - 2y) = y^2 - y - y^2 + 2y = y$

$$\begin{array}{r} y \\ y - 2\overline{)y^2 - y - 2} \\ (-)\underline{y^2 - 2y} \\ y \end{array} \leftarrow \text{Change signs and add}$$

Step 4 Bring down the next digit of the dividend, 2.

$$\begin{array}{r} 2 \\ 36\overline{)972} \\ \underline{72} \\ 252 \end{array}$$

Bring down the next term of the dividend, -2.

$$\begin{array}{r} y \\ y - 2\overline{)y^2 - y - 2} \\ \underline{y^2 - 2y} \\ y - 2 \end{array}$$

Step 5 Divide 36 into 252, which goes 7 times. Place 7 over 2 in the dividend.

$$\begin{array}{r} 27 \\ 36\overline{)972} \\ \underline{72} \\ 252 \end{array}$$

Divide y into y, which goes 1 time. Place 1 over 2 in the dividend with a plus sign between y and 1.

$$\begin{array}{r} y + 1 \\ y - 2\overline{)y^2 - y - 2} \\ \underline{y^2 - 2y} \\ y - 2 \end{array}$$

Step 6 Multiply 7 times 36, which is 252. Place this product below 252 at the bottom.

$$\begin{array}{r} 27 \\ 36\overline{)972} \\ \underline{72} \\ 252 \\ (-)\underline{252} \\ 0 \end{array}$$

Multiply 1 times $y - 2$, which is $y - 2$. Place this below $y - 2$ at the bottom.

$$\begin{array}{r} y + 1 \\ y - 2\overline{)y^2 - y - 2} \\ \underline{y^2 - 2y} \\ y - 2 \\ (-)\underline{y - 2} \\ 0 \end{array} \leftarrow \text{Change signs and add}$$

Step 7 Subtract $252 - 252 = 0$. There is no remainder.

$972 \div 36 = 27$

Subtract $(y - 2) - (y - 2) = 0$.

$(y^2 - y - 2) \div (y - 2) = y + 1$

Step 8 Check your division by multiplying the quotient by the divisor to see if you get the original dividend.

$27 \cdot 36 = 972$ $\quad (y + 1)(y - 2) = y^2 - y - 2$

Note

A common error is committed when we subtract polynomials as we did in step 3. Remember, to subtract two polynomials, *change the signs of the second polynomial and then add.*

$$\begin{array}{rcr} y^2 - y & \rightarrow & y^2 - y \\ (-)\ \underline{y^2 - 2y} & \rightarrow & \underline{-y^2 + 2y} \\ & & 0 + y = y \end{array}$$

The large majority of errors in this type of problem occur when polynomials are subtracted. Be very careful!

Example 5–3 C

Find the indicated quotient and check the answer.

1. $\dfrac{x^2 + 3x - 4}{x + 4}$

$$\begin{array}{r} x - 1 \\ x + 4\overline{)x^2 + 3x - 4} \\ \underline{x^2 + 4x} \\ -x - 4 \\ \underline{-x - 4} \\ 0 \end{array}$$

$x(x + 4) = x^2 + 4x$
Subtract to get $-x$ and bring down -4
$-1(x + 4) = -x - 4$
Subtract to get 0

Therefore, $\dfrac{x^2 + 3x - 4}{x + 4} = x - 1.$

Check: $(x - 1)(x + 4) = x^2 + 4x - x - 4$
$= x^2 + 3x - 4$

You are now ready to do **C₁**.

C₁ $\dfrac{a^2 + 7a + 10}{a + 5}$

2. $\dfrac{2x^2 + x - 3}{x - 1}$

$$\begin{array}{r} 2x + 3 \\ x - 1\overline{)2x^2 + x - 3} \\ \underline{2x^2 - 2x} \\ 3x - 3 \\ \underline{3x - 3} \\ 0 \end{array}$$

$2x(x - 1) = 2x^2 - 2x$
Subtract to get $3x$ and bring down -3
$3(x - 1) = 3x - 3$
Subtract to get 0

Hence, $\dfrac{2x^2 + x - 3}{x - 1} = 2x + 3.$

Check: $(2x + 3)(x - 1) = 2x^2 - 2x + 3x - 3$
$= 2x^2 + x - 3$

You are now ready to do **C₂**.

C₂ $\dfrac{6x^2 - 7x - 3}{2x - 3}$

If we still have a remainder after "bringing down" all of the terms of the dividend, handle it as follows:

3. $\dfrac{a^2 + 5a + 6}{a - 2}$

$$\begin{array}{r} a + 7 \\ a - 2\overline{)a^2 + 5a + 6} \\ \underline{a^2 - 2a} \\ 7a + 6 \\ \underline{7a - 14} \\ 20 \end{array}$$

$a(a - 2) = a^2 - 2a$
Subtract to get $7a$. Bring down 6
$7(a - 2) = 7a - 14$
$(7a + 6) - (7a - 14) = 7a + 6 - 7a + 14 = 20$

$\dfrac{a^2 + 5a + 6}{a - 2} = a + 7 + \dfrac{20}{a - 2}$, where the remainder 20 is placed over the divisor $a - 2$.

To check our answer, we add the remainder of 20 to the product of $(a + 7)$ and $(a - 2)$.

$(a + 7)(a - 2) + 20 = a^2 - 2a + 7a - 14 + 20$
$= a^2 + 5a + 6$

You are now ready to do **C₃**.

C₃ $\dfrac{a^2 + 2a - 13}{a - 3}$

C_4 $\dfrac{x^3 - 3x - 4}{x + 5}$

4. $\dfrac{x^3 - x + 2}{x - 3}$

Note that there is no term in the dividend that contains x^2. The division will be easier to perform if the term $0x^2$ is inserted as a placeholder so that all powers of the variable x are present in descending order. Thus, we have

$$\frac{x^3 + 0x^2 - x + 2}{x - 3},$$

and the value of the dividend has not been changed since we have added $0x^2$, which is 0. Therefore, to perform the division, we get

$$\begin{array}{rll} & x^2 + 3x + 8 & \\ x - 3\,\big) & x^3 + 0x^2 - x + 2 & \\ & x^3 - 3x^2 & x^2(x - 3) = x^3 - 3x^2 \\ & 3x^2 - x & \text{Subtract to get } 3x^2\text{. Bring down } -x \\ & 3x^2 - 9x & 3x(x - 3) = 3x^2 - 9x \\ & 8x + 2 & \text{Subtract to get } 8x\text{. Bring down 2} \\ & 8x - 24 & 8(x - 3) = 8x - 24 \\ & 26 & \end{array}$$

$$\frac{x^3 - x + 2}{x - 3} = x^2 + 3x + 8 + \frac{26}{x - 3}.$$

Check: $(x^2 + 3x + 8)(x - 3) + 26$
$= x^3 - 3x^2 + 3x^2 - 9x + 8x - 24 + 26$
$= x^3 - x + 2$

You are now ready to do **C_4**. ■

Answers to section 5-3 margin exercises

A_1 a^5 **A_2** $25x^3$ **B_1** $4a^6 - 6a^8$ **B_2** $4x^3 + 5x - 1$ **C_1** $a + 2$ **C_2** $3x + 1$
C_3 $a + 5 + \dfrac{2}{a - 3}$ **C_4** $x^2 - 5x + 22 - \dfrac{114}{x + 5}$

Mastery points

Can you

- Divide a monomial by a monomial?
- Divide a polynomial by a monomial?
- Divide a polynomial by a polynomial?
- Check the answer?

Exercise 5–3

Directions Perform the indicated divisions and check the answers. Assume that no denominator equals zero. See example 5–3 A.

Example [A_2] $\dfrac{5^3x^4}{5x}$

Solution

$= 5^{3-1}x^{4-1}$	Divide like bases by subtracting exponents
$= 5^2x^3$	Perform subtractions
$= 25x^3$	$5^2 = 25$

1. $\dfrac{8x^3}{2x}$ 2. $\dfrac{-15x^5}{3x^2}$ [3.] $\dfrac{-65x^4y^2z}{13xy}$ 4. $\dfrac{-28a^3b}{-7ab}$ 5. $\dfrac{3(a-b)^2}{a-b}$

See example 5–3 B.

Example B$_2$ $\dfrac{16x^5 + 20x^3 - 4x^2}{4x^2}$

Solution $= \dfrac{16x^5}{4x^2} + \dfrac{20x^3}{4x^2} - \dfrac{4x^2}{4x^2}$ Divide denominator into each term of numerator

$= 4x^3 + 5x - 1$ Divide constants and apply properties of exponents

6. $\dfrac{6x - 9}{3}$

7. $\dfrac{bx^2 - bx}{bx}$

8. $\dfrac{a^3 - 3a^2 + 2a}{a}$

9. $\dfrac{12x^3 - 8x^2 + 3x}{4x}$

10. $\dfrac{15a^3 - 9a^2 + 12a - 6}{3a}$

11. $\dfrac{24a^2 - 12a}{-6}$

12. $\dfrac{13a - a^2b^2 + a^2b}{a^2b}$

13. $\dfrac{x^2y - xy^2 - 2xy^3}{-xy}$

14. $\dfrac{14a^2b^3 - 21a^2b^2 - 28ab}{7ab}$

15. $\dfrac{30x^3y^4 + 21x^2y^2 - 18x^2y^4}{3x^2y^2}$

16. $\dfrac{-21m^2n^5 + 35m^3n^2 - 14m^2n^2}{-7m^2n^2}$

17. $\dfrac{a(b - 1) - c(b - 1)}{b - 1}$

18. $\dfrac{a(x - y) - b(x - y)}{x - y}$

See example 5–3 C.

Example C$_2$ $\dfrac{6x^2 - 7x - 3}{2x - 3}$

Solution

$$\begin{array}{r} 3x + 1 \\ 2x - 3\,\overline{)\,6x^2 - 7x - 3} \\ (-)\underline{6x^2 - 9x} \\ 2x - 3 \\ (-)\underline{2x - 3} \\ 0 \end{array}$$

$3x(2x - 3) = 6x^2 - 9x$

Subtract to get $2x$. Bring down -3

$1(2x - 3) = 2x - 3$

$(2x - 3) - (2x - 3) = 2x - 3 - 2x + 3 = 0$

$$\frac{6x^2 - 7x - 3}{2x - 3} = 3x + 1$$

The check is left to the student.

19. $\dfrac{x^2 + 7x + 10}{x - 2}$

20. $\dfrac{x^2 + 8x + 15}{x + 5}$

21. $\dfrac{y^2 + 5y + 10}{y + 3}$

22. $\dfrac{x^2 - 72 - x}{x + 8}$

23. $(y^2 - 11y + 34) \div (y - 5)$

24. $(z^2 + 6z + 10) \div (z + 3)$

25. $(4a^2 + 1 + 4a) \div (2a + 1)$

26. $(9a^2 - 24a + 12) \div (3a - 4)$

27. $(27a^3 - 1) \div (3a - 1)$

28. $(x^3 - 8) \div (x - 2)$

29. $(x^4 - 14) \div (x - 2)$

30. $\dfrac{x^3 + 4x^2 + 7x + 6}{x + 2}$

31. $\dfrac{2a^3 - 3a^2 - 13a + 12}{a - 5}$

32. $\dfrac{b^3 + 6b^2 + 7b - 8}{b - 1}$

33. $\dfrac{6x^4 - x^3 - 2x^2 - 7x - 19}{2x - 3}$

34. $(15a^2 + 28a - 32) \div (-5a + 4)$

35. $(x^4 - 2x^3 + 4x^2 - x + 3) \div (x^2 - x + 4)$

36. $(x^4 + 3x^3 - 6x^2 + 3x - 8) \div (x^2 + 3x - 5)$

37. $(y^4 + 2y^3 - 4y + 2) \div (y^2 - y + 1)$

38. $(y^4 + 2y - 3) \div (y^2 + 2y - 5)$

39. A contractor uses the expression $x^2 + 6x + 8$ to represent the square footage of a room. If she decides that the length of the room will be represented by $x + 4$, what will the width of the room be in terms of x?

40. An electrician uses the expression $4x^2 + 11x + 6$ to determine the amount of wire to order when wiring a house. If the formula comes from multiplying the number of rooms times the number of outlets and he knows the number of rooms to be $x + 2$, find the number of outlets in terms of x.

41. What polynomial when divided by $3x - 2$ yields a quotient $2x^2 + 3x - 5$?

42. What polynomial when divided by $-2x + 5$ yields a quotient $3x^3 - 2x + 6$?

Review exercises

1. Find the solution set of the quadratic equation $4y^2 + 9y + 2 = 0$. See section 4–6.

2. The area of a rectangle is 42 square feet. If the length is 1 foot longer than the width, what are the dimensions of the rectangle? See section 4–6.

Directions Find the following products. See section 3–3.

3. $(4x - 3)^2$

4. $(x + 2)(x^2 + x - 1)$

5. $(5y - 1)(5y + 1)$

Directions Reduce to lowest terms. See section 5–2.

6. $\dfrac{3y^2 - 5y - 2}{2y^2 - y - 6}$

5–4 Ratio and proportion

A ratio

We learned the fraction $\frac{a}{b}$ represents the indicated quotient of a divided by b. A **ratio** compares two numbers, or quantities, in the same way.

> **Ratio**
> A ratio is the comparison of two numbers (or quantities) by division.

A_1 The ratio of 9 to 10

The ratio of the number a to the number b is written

$$a \text{ to } b, \quad \frac{a}{b}, \quad \text{or} \quad a : b.$$

We read $a : b$ as "the ratio of a to b," where a and b are called the *terms* of the ratio. The first number given is always the numerator and the second number is the denominator of the fraction representing the ratio.

Example 5–4 A

Write each ratio statement in the forms $a : b$ and $\frac{a}{b}$ reduced to lowest terms.

A_2 The ratio of 18 to 21

1. The ratio of 3 to 4

$3:4$ — Form $a : b$

$\frac{3}{4}$ — Written as a fraction

You are now ready to do **A_1**.

2. The ratio of 15 to 9

$15 : 9$ or $5 : 3$ — Form $a : b$ (divide 15 and 9 by common factor 3)

$\frac{15}{9} = \frac{5}{3}$ — Written as a fraction reduced to lowest terms

You are now ready to do **A_2**.

If the quantities have the same unit of measure, the ratio will be expressed by a fraction without any unit designation required.

A_3 63 hours to 42 hours

3. 45 minutes to 60 minutes

$$45 \text{ min} : 60 \text{ min} = \frac{45 \text{ min}}{60 \text{ min}}$$ Write as fraction $\frac{a}{b}$

$$= \frac{3}{4} \text{ or } 3 : 4$$ Reduce by dividing each term by 15

You are now ready to do **A_3**.

When the compared quantities are not of the same unit of measure but *can be stated* in the same unit, it may be desirable to do so. The ratio again becomes only a fraction, as in example 3.

4. 3 feet to 4 inches

Since 3 ft = 36 in., we have

A_4 16 minutes to 2 hours

$$36 \text{ in.} : 4 \text{ in.} = \frac{36 \text{ in.}}{4 \text{ in.}}$$ Write as fraction $\frac{a}{b}$

$$= \frac{9}{1} \text{ or } 9 : 1.$$ Reduce by dividing each term by 4

Note

We reduced to $\frac{9}{1}$ to demonstrate the comparison that is present. That is, do not write $\frac{9}{1}$ as 9.

You are now ready to do **A_4**.

Note
When we change to a common unit of measure, it is easiest to change to the *smaller* unit of measure, as we did in the previous examples. Changing to the larger unit of measure usually produces fractions that are more difficult to reduce. ■

B_1 240 pounds to 16 feet

Ratios are used to indicate relationships in many areas of the physical world.

1. The geographer makes maps and prints to scale, 20 miles to 1 inch.
2. The physicist measures air pressure and uses force per unit of area, $14.7 \text{ lb/in.}^2 = \dfrac{14.7 \text{ lb}}{1 \text{ in.}^2}$.
3. The auto mechanic interprets engine specifications by compression ratio, 9 to 1 or 9 : 1.
4. The machinist is concerned with gear ratio, 2 to 1 or 2 : 1.

When you compare two measurable quantities by ratio, it is not necessary for them to have the same unit of measure. If the units are not the same, you *must include the units* when you are expressing the ratio. These ratios represent rates of change.

Example 5–4 B

Express the following as a ratio in lowest terms.

1. 50 miles to 1 inch

$$50 \text{ mi} : 1 \text{ in.} = \frac{50 \text{ mi}}{1 \text{ in.}}$$
$$= 50 \text{ miles per inch}$$

You are now ready to do **B_1**.

B_2 64 pounds to 8 square inches

2. 350 miles to 7 hours

$$350 \text{ mi} : 7 \text{ hr} = \frac{350 \text{ mi}}{7 \text{ hr}} \quad \text{Write as a fraction}$$
$$= \frac{50 \text{ mi}}{1 \text{ hr}} \quad \text{Reduce by dividing by 7}$$
$$= 50 \text{ miles per hour}$$

You are now ready to do **B_2**. ■

A proportion

Definition of a proportion
A **proportion** is a statement of equality of two ratios.

Given the ratios a to b and c to d,

$$\frac{a}{b} = \frac{c}{d} \quad \text{or} \quad a : b = c : d$$

is a proportion. We read the statement $a : b = c : d$ "a is to b as c is to d." The numbers a, b, c, and d are called the *terms* of the proportion.

Referring again to the proportion $\dfrac{a}{b} = \dfrac{c}{d}$,

$$bd \cdot \frac{a}{b} = bd \cdot \frac{c}{d} \quad \text{Multiply each member by } bd$$
$$ad = bc. \quad \text{Reduce by } b \text{ on the left and by } d \text{ on the right}$$

Property of proportions

If $\frac{a}{b} = \frac{c}{d}$, then $ad = bc$.

Note

This process is frequently called "cross-multiplying." That is,

If $\frac{a}{b} \times \frac{c}{d}$,

then $ad = bc$.

Example 5–4 C

Determine if the following statements form a proportion.

1. $\frac{3}{5} = \frac{12}{20}$

   Using the property of proportions, we obtain

   $5 \cdot 12 = 60$ and $3 \cdot 20 = 60$.

   The cross products are both 60 so we have a proportion.

You are now ready to do **C_1**.

2. $\frac{5}{6} = \frac{16}{18}$

   Using the property of proportions, we obtain

   $6 \cdot 16 = 96$ and $5 \cdot 18 = 90$.

   The cross products are not the same so we do not have a proportion.

You are now ready to do **C_2**. ■

We use this property of proportions to solve a proportion if three of the four terms are known.

Example 5–4 D

Find the unknown term of the given proportion. Check your solution.

1. $\frac{x}{8} = \frac{16}{64}$

$64 \cdot x = 8 \cdot 16$ — Property of proportions

$64x = 128$ — Multiply as indicated

$x = 2$ — Divide each member by 64

Check: $\frac{2}{8} = \frac{16}{64}$

$2 \cdot 64 = 8 \cdot 16$

$128 = 128.$

You are now ready to do **D_1**.

C_1 $\frac{6}{5} = \frac{42}{35}$

C_2 $\frac{7}{8} = \frac{21}{22}$

D_1 Find the unknown term of the proportion $\frac{x}{7} = \frac{25}{35}$

2. $\frac{49}{y} = \frac{35}{5}$

$49 \cdot 5 = 35 \cdot y$ Property of proportions

$35y = 245$ Multiply as indicated

$y = 7$ Divide each member by 35

Check: $\frac{49}{7} = \frac{35}{5}$

$5 \cdot 49 = 7 \cdot 35$

$245 = 245.$

You are now ready to do **D₂**. ■

D₂ Find the unknown term of the proportion $\frac{72}{z} = \frac{24}{5}$.

Proportions are used in solving many applied problems. Consider the following examples.

Example 5–4 E

Set up a proportion for each problem and solve.

1. Two gears are in the ratio of 4 : 5. If the smaller gear has 32 teeth, how many teeth are there in the larger gear?

Let $x =$ the number of teeth in the larger gear. Now, 4 is to 5 as 32 is to x.

$\frac{4}{5} = \frac{32}{x}$ Set up a proportion

$4 \cdot x = 5 \cdot 32$ Property of proportions

$4x = 160$ Multiply as indicated

$x = \frac{160}{4} = 40$ Divide each member by 4

Thus, there are 40 teeth in the larger gear.

You are now ready to do **E₁**.

E₁ Two gears are in the ratio of 3:8. If the smaller gear has 18 teeth, how many teeth are there in the larger gear?

2. On a map, 1 inch represents 6 miles. How many inches are needed to represent 28 miles?

Let $x =$ the number of inches representing 28 miles. Now, 1 inch is to 6 miles as x inches is to 28 miles.

$\frac{1 \text{ in.}}{6 \text{ mi}} = \frac{x \text{ in.}}{28 \text{ mi}}$ Set up a proportion

$6 \cdot x = 1 \cdot 28$ Property of proportions

$6x = 28$ Multiply as indicated

$x = \frac{28}{6} = \frac{14}{3} = 4\frac{2}{3}$ Divide each member by 6

Therefore, 28 miles are represented by $4\frac{2}{3}$ inches on the map.

Note

In example 2, **the same units of measure are in the numerator of the ratios and the same units of measure are in the denominators.** That is, we placed inches in the numerator and miles in the denominator of each ratio. This step is important in setting up the proportion you will use to solve for the unknown.

You are now ready to do **E₂**.

E₂ On a map, 1 inch represents 9 miles. How many inches are needed to represent 48 miles?

E_3 John was able to save \$120 each month when he was earning \$1,000 per month. His salary has been increased to \$1,200 per month. How much should he save now for his monthly savings to be proportional to what he saved before?

3. Cheryl set aside \$20 per week for her savings program when her salary was \$200 per week. If her salary is now \$250 per week, how much should she set aside for her weekly savings to be proportional to what she saved before?

Let x = the amount to be set aside when Cheryl earns \$250 per week. Then, \$20 is to \$200 as x is to \$250.

$$\frac{20}{200} = \frac{x}{250}$$ Set up a proportion

$$200 \cdot x = 20 \cdot 250$$ Property of proportions

$$200x = 5{,}000$$ Multiply as indicated

$$x = 25$$ Divide each member by 200

Cheryl should set aside \$25 when making \$250 per week.

You are now ready to do $\mathbf{E_3}$. ■

Answers to section 5–4 margin exercises

A_1 9 : 10 or $\frac{9}{10}$ A_2 6 : 7 or $\frac{6}{7}$ A_3 3 : 2 or $\frac{3}{2}$ A_4 2 : 15 or $\frac{2}{15}$

B_1 $\frac{15 \text{ lb}}{1 \text{ ft}}$ or 15 lb per ft B_2 $\frac{8 \text{ lb}}{1 \text{ in.}^2}$ or 8 lb per square in. C_1 210 = 210, proportion

C_2 $154 \neq 168$, not a proportion D_1 $x = 5$ D_2 $z = 15$ E_1 48 teeth E_2 $5\frac{1}{3}$ in.

E_3 \$144

Mastery points

Can you

- Write ratios?
- Reduce ratios?
- Write proportions?
- Solve proportions for the unknowns?
- Set up proportions to solve problems?

Exercise 5–4

Directions Express the given ratios in two ways, $\frac{a}{b}$ and $a : b$, reduced to lowest terms. See example 5–4 A, 1 and 2.

Example $\boxed{A_2}$ The ratio of 18 to 21

Solution 18 : 21 or 6 : 7 — Form $a : b$ (reduce by dividing by 3)

$\frac{18}{21}$ or $\frac{6}{7}$ — Write as a fraction reduced to lowest terms

1. 12 to 7

2. 8 to 19

3. 24 to 9

4. 7 to 42

$\boxed{\textbf{5.}}$ 32 to 60

6. 90 to 40

7. 15 to 6

8. 8 to $\frac{3}{4}$

9. $2\frac{1}{2}$ to 10

Directions Find the indicated ratios reduced to lowest terms. See examples 5–4 A 3 and 4.

Example A_4 16 minutes to 2 hours

Solution Since 2 hours = 120 minutes (1 hour = 60 minutes),

$$\begin{aligned} 16 \text{ min} : 2 \text{ hr} &= 16 \text{ min} : 120 \text{ min} && \text{Replace 2 hr by 120 min} \\ &= 16 : 120 && \text{Eliminate unit of measure} \\ &= 2 : 15 \text{ or } \frac{2}{15}. && \text{Reduce to lowest terms; Divide by 8} \end{aligned}$$

The ratio of 16 min to 2 hr is 2 : 15 or $\frac{2}{15}$.

10. 6 in. to 14 in.

11. 35 lb to 5 lb

12. 25 cm to 10 cm

13. 36 km to 24 km

14. 15 in. to 3 ft

15. 5 days to 15 weeks

16. \$3 to 35¢

17. 16 lb to 8 oz

18. 30 min to 13 hr

19. 50 cm to 5 in.^{3}

20. 300 mi to 10 gal

21. 105 kg to 35 m^3

22. 1,020 mi to 17 hr

See example 5–4 B.

Example B_2 64 pounds to 8 square inches

Solution

$$\begin{aligned} 64 \text{ lb to 8 sq in.} &= \frac{64 \text{ lb}}{8 \text{ sq in.}} && \text{Write ratio as a fraction} \\ &= \frac{8 \text{ lb}}{1 \text{ sq in.}} && \text{Reduce to lowest terms; Divide by 8} \\ &= 8 \text{ lb/sq in.} && \text{Write as a rate} \end{aligned}$$

23. The *pitch* of a roof is the ratio of the *rise* of a rafter to the *span* of the roof.

$$\text{pitch} = \frac{\text{rise of rafter}}{\text{span of roof}}$$

Find the pitch if the roof rises 7 feet in a span of 21 feet.

24. The mechanical advantage of a hydraulic press can be given by the ratio

$$\text{mechanical advantage} = \frac{\text{area of the large piston}}{\text{area of the small piston}}.$$

If the large piston has area 32 square centimeters and the small piston has area 12 square centimeters, find the mechanical advantage of the press.

25. The *output* in horsepower is the useful energy delivered by an engine and the *input* in horsepower is the amount of energy delivered to an engine. The *mechanical efficiency* of the engine is given by the ratio

$$\text{mechanical efficiency} = \frac{\text{output}}{\text{input}}.$$

Find the mechanical efficiency of an engine rated to deliver 425 horsepower (input) when it delivers only 375 horsepower (output).

26. An automobile engine is rated at 350 horsepower. When the engine is tested, it produces only 325 horsepower. What is the mechanical efficiency of the engine? (Refer to exercise 25.)

27. The smaller of two belted pulleys makes 240 revolutions per minute and the larger one makes 100 revolutions per minute.

What is the ratio of (a) the speed of the larger pulley to the smaller pulley? (b) the smaller pulley to the larger pulley?

28. Tool steel may be worked at a cutting speed of 20 feet per minute and cast iron may be worked at a cutting speed of 45 feet per minute. What is the ratio of the cutting speed of tool steel to cast iron?

29. A mathematics class contains 22 male students and 10 female students. What is the ratio of the male students to the female students?

30. A particular stock costing $63 paid an earnings of $6. What is the cost : earnings ratio?

31. A doctor having earnings of $60,000 in a given year paid income taxes of $8,400. What is the ratio of taxes to income?

32. The stress caused by a heavy load is defined by the ratio

$$\text{stress} = \frac{\text{distorting force } (F)}{\text{area } (A)}$$

measured in lb/in.² Find the stress of a force of a 4,400-pound load on an area of 1,200 square inches.

33. The magnification (M) of an object by a lens is given by the ratio $M = \frac{q}{p}$, where $q =$ the image distance and $p =$ the object distance from the lens. Find the magnification of an object whose image distance is 27 feet and object distance is 12 feet.

Directions Find the value of the unknown that makes the statement a proportion. See example 5–4 D.

Example D₂ Find the unknown term of the proportion $\frac{72}{z} = \frac{24}{5}$.

Solution

$$\frac{72}{z} = \frac{24}{5}$$

$24 \cdot z = 72 \cdot 5$ — Property of proportions

$24z = 360$ — Multiply as indicated

$z = \frac{360}{24} = 15$ — Divide each member by 24

Thus, $z = 15$ makes the equation a proportion.

34. $\frac{36}{x} = \frac{9}{5}$

35. $\frac{3}{10} = \frac{p}{20}$

36. $\frac{6}{15} = \frac{x}{8}$

37. $R : 12 = 15 : 100$

38. $1.2 : x = 3.6 : 9$

39. $1\frac{1}{2} : a = 4\frac{3}{4} : 2$

Directions Solve the following problems by first choosing a letter to represent the unknown and then setting up the proper proportion. See example 5–4 E.

Example **E₂** On a map, 1 inch represents 9 miles. How many inches are needed to represent 48 miles?

Solution Let x = the number of inches representing 48 miles. Then, 1 inch is to 9 miles as x inches is to 48 miles.

$$\frac{1 \text{ inch}}{9 \text{ miles}} = \frac{x \text{ inches}}{48 \text{ miles}} \quad \text{Set up a proportion}$$

$$9 \cdot x = 1 \cdot 48 \quad \text{Property of proportions}$$

$$9x = 48 \quad \text{Multiply as indicated}$$

$$x = \frac{48}{9} = \frac{16}{3} = 5\frac{1}{3} \quad \text{Divide each member by 9}$$

Thus, $5\frac{1}{3}$ inches represents 48 miles on the map.

40. An automobile uses 8 liters of gasoline to travel 84 kilometers. How many liters are needed to travel 1,428 kilometers?

41. A man earns $180 per week. How many weeks must he work to earn $1,260?

42. If 24 grams of water will yield 4 grams of hydrogen, how many grams of hydrogen will there be in 216 grams of water?

43. The power-to-weight ratio of a given engine is 5 : 3. What is the weight of the engine if it produces 650 horsepower?

44. If a 20-pound casting costs $1.50, at this same rate, how much would a 42-pound casting cost?

45. A copper wire 300 feet long has a resistance of 1,024 ohms. What is the resistance of 2,000 feet of copper wire?

46. Sarah is operating a machine that can produce 14 parts in 20 minutes. How long will it take for her to produce 224 parts?

47. A rectangular picture that is 10 inches long and 8 inches wide is to be enlarged so that the enlargement is to be 36 inches wide. What should be the length of the enlargement?

48. A punch machine can make 72 holes in 4 minutes. How many holes can the machine make in 3 hours?

49. On a draftsman scale, $\frac{1}{8}$ inch represents 1 foot. What length will a measurement of $2\frac{5}{8}$ inches on the scale represent?

50. Nat can type 3 pages of an English paper in 15 minutes. How long would it take him to type 54 pages? (State your answer in hours and minutes.)

Review exercises

Directions Perform the indicated operations. See section R–2.

1. $\frac{3}{5} + \frac{2}{3}$
2. $\frac{3}{4} - \frac{1}{2}$
3. $\frac{2}{3} \cdot \frac{6}{7}$
4. $\frac{6}{5} \div \frac{3}{10}$

Directions Solve the following equations. See sections 2–3 and 2–4.

5. $6y + 5 = y - 4$
6. $P = 2\ell + 2w$ for w

7. The product of two consecutive odd integers is 143. Find the integers. See section 4–5.

Chapter 5 lead-in problem

On a road map, 3 inches represents a distance of 45 miles. If the distance between Detroit and Sault Ste. Marie is 23 inches on the map, how far is it from Detroit to Sault Ste. Marie?

Solution

Let $x =$ the distance from Detroit to Sault Ste. Marie. Then, since 3 inches represents 45 miles on the map, we use the relationship

3 in. is to 45 mi as 23 in. is to x mi,

which we write as the proportion

$$\frac{3}{45} = \frac{23}{x}$$

$$3 \cdot x = 45 \cdot 23 \quad \text{Property of proportions}$$

$$x = \frac{45 \cdot 23}{3} \quad \text{Divide each member by 3}$$

$$x = 15 \cdot 23 \quad \text{Reduce by 3}$$

$$x = 345. \quad \text{Multiply in the right member}$$

The distance from Detroit to Sault Ste. Marie is 345 miles.

Chapter 5 summary

1. A **rational expression** can be written in the form $\frac{P}{Q}$, where P and Q are polynomials, $Q \neq 0$.
2. The **domain** of a rational expression in one variable is the set of all replacement values of the variable for which the rational expression is defined.
3. The **fundamental principle of rational expressions** is used to *reduce* rational expressions *to lowest terms* and to attain equivalent expressions having the same denominator for addition and subtraction. It states, $\frac{PR}{QR} = \frac{P}{Q}$ or $\frac{P}{Q} = \frac{PR}{QR}$, where P, Q, and R are polynomials, Q and R are not equal to zero.
4. To **reduce** a rational expression to lowest terms, we divide the numerator and the denominator by any common factors.
5. To divide a polynomial by a monomial, divide each term of the polynomial by the monomial.
6. To divide a polynomial by a polynomial, the dividend and the divisor must be arranged in descending powers of the same variable with zeros inserted for missing variables.
7. A **ratio** is the comparison of two numbers by division.
8. A **proportion** is a statement of equality of two ratios.
9. If $\frac{a}{b} = \frac{c}{d}$, then $ad = bc$.

Chapter 5 review

[5–1]

Directions Evaluate the following expressions for the given value of the variable.

1. $\frac{3x}{x-2}, x = 3$
2. $\frac{-4y}{y^2-4}, y = -2$
3. $\frac{z+6}{z^2-2z+1}, z = 0$
4. $\frac{x-5}{x^2-3x-10}, x = -\frac{1}{2}$
5. $\frac{2y-1}{y^2-y-12}, y = -2$

Directions Determine the domain of the given rational expression.

6. $\frac{x+1}{x}$
7. $\frac{y-3}{y+7}$
8. $\frac{3x+1}{x-9}$
9. $\frac{2z-5}{3z+2}$
10. $\frac{x}{5x-3}$
11. $\frac{x^2-x+4}{x^2+x-12}$
12. $\frac{x^2+3x+2}{x^2-1}$

[5–2]

Directions Reduce the following rational expressions to lowest terms. Assume no denominator is equal to zero.

13. $\dfrac{18ab^2}{6a^2b}$

14. $\dfrac{45x^2yz^3}{30xy^3z^2}$

15. $\dfrac{x^2 - 49}{x^2 + 14x + 49}$

16. $\dfrac{x^2 - 3x - 18}{x^2 + x - 42}$

17. $\dfrac{18a - 6b}{15a - 5b}$

18. $\dfrac{x^2 - y^2}{y - x}$

19. $\dfrac{3p^2 - 8p + 4}{5p^2 - 9p - 2}$

20. $\dfrac{2R^2 - 32}{6R^2 + 22R - 8}$

21. $\dfrac{20 - 9n + n^2}{8 + 2n - n^2}$

[5–3]

Directions Find the indicated quotients.

22. $\dfrac{24x^3}{-3x}$

23. $\dfrac{2a^2 - 3a + 5a^3}{a}$

24. $\dfrac{5x^2y - 3xy^4 + x^2y^2}{xy}$

25. $\dfrac{8a^3b + 12a^2b^2 - 24a^3b^7}{4a^2b}$

26. $\dfrac{8a^2 - 2a - 3}{2a - 1}$

27. $\dfrac{3a^2 - 17a + 11}{a - 5}$

28. $\dfrac{x^2 - 49}{x + 7}$

29. $\dfrac{20x^3 - 19x^2 - 13x + 12}{4x - 3}$

[5–4]

Directions Find the indicated ratios reduced to lowest terms.

30. 15 meters to 35 meters

31. 36 pounds to 16 pounds

32. 12 inches to $2\frac{1}{2}$ feet

33. 450 miles to 15 gallons

34. In business, the current ratio compares current assets to current liabilities and represents the measure of the firm's ability to pay off the liabilities over a time period. What is the current ratio, reduced to lowest terms, if the firm's total current assets are $4,386 and total current liabilities are $1,762?

35. The May company has 42 sales representatives who are meeting their sales quota. If another 18 sales representatives have fallen short of their quota, what is the ratio of success to failure?

Directions Find the value of the unknown that makes the statement a proportion.

36. $\frac{8}{x} = \frac{9}{36}$

37. $\frac{5.4}{3.6} = \frac{a}{2.4}$

38. $y : 18 = 15{:}25$

39. $\frac{5}{6} : \frac{1}{2} = \frac{2}{3} : p$

40. If a blueprint is drawn to the scale $\frac{1}{8}$ inch = 1 foot, what is the size of the corresponding part of a final product if the blueprint measurement is $4\frac{3}{8}$ inches?

41. An automobile has a 16-quart cooling system. If the ratio of antifreeze to water is 3 to 1, how much of each does the system have? (*Hint:* Let x be the amount of antifreeze. Then $16 - x$ is the amount of water.)

NAME

Chapter 5 cumulative test

CLASS/SECTION DATE

Directions Perform the indicated operations.

[1–6] **1.** $-4[7(12 - 2) - 8^3 + 3]$

[1–6] **2.** $\dfrac{(-6)(-8)}{(-2)(0)}$

[3–1] **3.** -6^2

Directions Perform the indicated operations and simplify.

[3–2] **4.** $(5a - b) - [3a - (4b + 3a)]$

[3–3] **5.** $(3x - 2)^2$

[3–3] **6.** $(5y - 2)(5y + 2)$

[3–3] **7.** $(4a + 3b)(a - 6b)$

[3–3] **8.** $(x - y)^3$

[1–8] **9.** Given $a = -5$, $b = 3$, $c = 4$, and $d = -6$, evaluate the expression $(2a - 3b) - (5c + d)$.

Directions Find the solution.

[2–3] **10.** $3(x + 2) - 2(x - 4) = 12$

[2–3] **11.** $\dfrac{3x}{4} - 5 = 1$

[2–3] **12.** $3(7 - 2x) = 30 - 7(x + 1)$

[2–5] **13.** $\ell = a + (n - 1)d$, for n

Directions Write in completely factored form.

[4–5] **14.** $x(m + n) - y(m + n)$

[4–3] **15.** $3a^2 + 7a + 4$

[4–3] **16.** $4x^2 - 20x + 25$

[4–4] **17.** $4z^2 - 9$

[4–4] **18.** $36 - y^2$

[4–2] **19.** $x^2 - 12x - 45$

[4–3] **20.** $6x^2 - 3x - 9$

Directions Find the solution set.

[4–6] **21.** $x^2 - 5x - 14 = 0$

[4–6] **22.** $2y^2 + 3y - 9 = 0$

Directions Simplify and leave answers with only positive exponents.

[3–4] **23.** $(4yz^{-1})^{-3}$

[3–4] **24.** $\dfrac{a^{-7}}{a^{-10}}$

[3–4] **25.** $(4ab^2)(-2a^3b)(-a^{-1}b^{-3})$

[5–4] **26.** Find x when $36{:}x = 21{:}14$.

[5–4] **27.** What is the ratio of 52 pounds to 24 pounds?

[5–3] **28.** Divide $(x^2 - 8x + 13) \div (x - 2)$.

Directions Reduce the following expressions to lowest terms. Assume that no denominator is equal to zero.

[R–2] **29.** $\dfrac{56}{42}$

[5–2] **30.** $\dfrac{36ab^3}{28a^3b^2}$

[5–2] **31.** $\dfrac{a^2 - 36}{a^2 - a - 42}$

[5–2] **32.** $\dfrac{8x - 8y}{5x^2 - 5y^2}$

[5–2] **33.** $\dfrac{y^2 - y - 20}{y^2 - 25}$

[5–2] **34.** $\dfrac{2x^2 - 5xy - 3y^2}{6x^2 + 7xy + 2y^2}$

[5–4] **35.** A photograph that is 8 inches by 12 inches is to be enlarged. If the enlargement calls for the longest side to be 32 inches, how many inches should the other side be?

[5–4] **36.** Two lots are proportional in their lengths and widths. If the larger lot is 15 feet wide and 28 feet long and the length of the smaller lot is 24 feet, how wide is the smaller lot?

CHAPTER

6

Operations with Rational Expressions

Marc owns $\frac{5}{8}$ interest in a print shop and his uncle owns $\frac{1}{4}$ interest in the shop. In a given year, they shared earnings of \$140,000. How much did the shop earn that year?

Proficiency check

[R–1] **1.** Perform the indicated operations.

a. $\frac{5}{6} + \frac{7}{8}$

b. $\frac{8}{3} - \frac{3}{4}$

c. $\frac{5}{6} \cdot \frac{9}{10}$

d. $\frac{9}{4} \div \frac{3}{8}$

[5–2] **2.** Reduce the following to lowest terms.

a. $\frac{24}{45}$

b. $\frac{8y - 4}{4y^2 - 4y + 1}$

[2–3] **3.** Solve the following equations.

a. $5x - 3 = 2x + 5$

b. $\frac{1}{2}y - \frac{1}{3} = \frac{5}{6}$

▣ 6–1 Multiplication and division of rational expressions

Multiplication of rational expressions

Recall that to multiply two real number fractions, we multiply the numerators and multiply the denominators.

> **Multiplication property of fractions**
>
> If a, b, c, and d are real numbers, then
>
> $$\frac{a}{b} \cdot \frac{c}{d} = \frac{a \cdot c}{b \cdot d} \quad (b, d \neq 0).$$

Note

Any possible reduction is performed *before* the multiplication takes place.

Example 6–1 A

Multiply the fractions $\frac{3}{7}$ and $\frac{14}{27}$ and simplify the product.

$$\frac{3}{7} \cdot \frac{14}{27} = \frac{3 \cdot 14}{7 \cdot 27}$$ Multiply numerators / Multiply denominators

$$= \frac{3 \cdot 2 \cdot 7}{7 \cdot 3 \cdot 3 \cdot 3}$$ Factor numerator and denominator

$$= \frac{2 \cdot (3 \cdot 7)}{3 \cdot 3 \cdot (3 \cdot 7)}$$ Group common factors $(3 \cdot 7)$

$$= \frac{2}{3 \cdot 3}$$ Divide numerator and denominator by $(3 \cdot 7)$

$$= \frac{2}{9}$$ Multiply remaining factors

You are now ready to do **A₁**. ■

A₁ $\frac{7}{9} \cdot \frac{27}{35}$

This same procedure is followed when we multiply two rational expressions.

> **Multiplication property of rational expressions**
>
> Given rational expressions $\frac{P}{Q}$ and $\frac{R}{S}$, then
>
> $$\frac{P}{Q} \cdot \frac{R}{S} = \frac{P \cdot R}{Q \cdot S} \quad (Q, S, \neq 0).$$

Since we want the resulting product to be stated in lowest terms, we then apply the *fundamental principle of rational expressions* and divide both the numerator and the denominator by their common factors.

B₁ $\frac{7a}{5} \cdot \frac{6}{11b}$

> **To multiply rational expressions**
>
> 1. Multiply the numerators and the denominators.
> 2. Factor the numerator and the denominator.
> 3. Divide the numerators and the denominators by the factors that are common.
> 4. Multiply the remaining factors in the numerator and place this product over the product of the remaining factors in the denominator.

Example 6–1 B

Perform the indicated multiplication and simplify your answer. Assume that no denominator equals zero.

1. $\frac{3x}{4} \cdot \frac{5}{2y}$

$$= \frac{3x \cdot 5}{4 \cdot 2y}$$ Multiply numerators and denominators

$$= \frac{15x}{8y}$$ Will not reduce

You are now ready to do **B₁**.

B₂ $\frac{y-3}{2y+1} \cdot \frac{3}{y+1}$

2. $\frac{x+1}{x-3} \cdot \frac{4}{x+2}$

$= \frac{(x+1) \cdot 4}{(x-3)(x+2)}$ Multiply numerators and denominators

$= \frac{4x+4}{x^2-x-6}$

You are now ready to do **B₂**.

B₃ $\frac{12}{5y} \cdot \frac{15y^2}{4}$

3. $\frac{4}{9x} \cdot \frac{3x^2}{2}$

$= \frac{4 \cdot 3x^2}{9x \cdot 2}$ Multiply numerators; Multiply denominators

$= \frac{2 \cdot 2 \cdot 3 \cdot x \cdot x}{3 \cdot 3 \cdot 2 \cdot x}$ Factor numerator and denominator

$= \frac{2 \cdot x \cdot (2 \cdot 3 \cdot x)}{3 \cdot (2 \cdot 3 \cdot x)}$ Identify common factors

$= \frac{2x}{3} \; (x \neq 0)$ Divide numerator and denominator by $(2 \cdot 3 \cdot x)$

You are now ready to do **B₃**.

B₄ $\frac{z+3}{2-z} \cdot \frac{(z-2)^2}{z+1}$

4. $\frac{x+1}{3-x} \cdot \frac{(x-3)^2}{x-2}$

$= \frac{(x+1) \cdot (x-3)^2}{(3-x) \cdot (x-2)}$ Multiply numerators; Multiply denominators

$= \frac{(x+1)(x-3)(x-3)}{-(x-3)(x-2)}$ $3 - x = -(x-3)$

$= \frac{(x+1)(x-3)(x-3)}{-(x-2)(x-3)}$ Commutative property

$= \frac{(x+1)(x-3)}{-(x-2)}$ Divide numerator and denominator by $x-3$

$= \frac{x^2-2x-3}{2-x}$ Multiply in numerator and denominator

You are now ready to do **B₄**.

B₅ $\frac{x+4}{x-2} \cdot \frac{x^2-x-2}{x^2-16}$

5. $\frac{x+1}{x-3} \cdot \frac{x^2-x-6}{x^2-1}$

$= \frac{(x+1)(x^2-x-6)}{(x-3)(x^2-1)}$ Multiply numerators and denominators

$= \frac{(x+1)(x-3)(x+2)}{(x-3)(x+1)(x-1)}$ Factor numerator and denominator

$= \frac{x+2}{x-1}$ Divide numerator and denominator by common factors $(x+1)$ and $(x-3)$

You are now ready to do **B₅**.

B₆ $\frac{x^2-6x+9}{x^2+4x-12} \cdot \frac{x^2-7x+10}{x^2-2x-3}$

6. $\frac{x^2-8x+16}{x^2+3x-10} \cdot \frac{x^2-4}{x^2-5x+4}$

$= \frac{(x^2-8x+16)(x^2-4)}{(x^2+3x-10)(x^2-5x+4)}$ Multiply numerators and denominators

$= \frac{(x-4)(x-2)}{(x-4)(x-2)} \frac{(x-4)(x+2)}{(x+5)(x-1)}$ Factor numerator and denominator

$= \frac{(x-4)(x+2)}{(x+5)(x-1)}$ Divide numerator and denominator by common factors $(x-4)$ and $(x-2)$

$= \frac{x^2-2x-8}{x^2+4x-5}$ Multiply remaining factors

You are now ready to do **B₆**. ■

Division of rational expressions

C₁ $\frac{24}{15} \div \frac{18}{5}$

Recall that to divide two fractions $\frac{a}{b}$ and $\frac{c}{d}$, we multiply $\frac{a}{b}$ by the *reciprocal* of $\frac{c}{d}$, which is $\frac{d}{c}$.

Division property of fractions

$$\frac{a}{b} \div \frac{c}{d} = \frac{a}{b} \cdot \frac{d}{c} = \frac{a \cdot d}{b \cdot c} \quad (b, c, d \neq 0).$$

Example 6–1 C

Find the indicated quotient. Reduce answer to lowest terms.

$\frac{18}{25} \div \frac{9}{5}$

$= \frac{18}{25} \cdot \frac{5}{9}$ — Multiply by the reciprocal of $\frac{9}{5}$

$= \frac{2 \cdot 3 \cdot 3 \cdot 5}{5 \cdot 5 \cdot 3 \cdot 3}$ — Factor in numerator and denominator

$= \frac{2 \cdot (3 \cdot 3 \cdot 5)}{5 \cdot (3 \cdot 3 \cdot 5)}$ — Identify common factors

$= \frac{2}{5}$ — Divide numerator and denominator by common factor $(3 \cdot 3 \cdot 5)$

You are now ready to do **C₁**. ■

Division of rational expressions is done in the same way.

Division property of rational expressions

If $\frac{P}{Q}$ and $\frac{R}{S}$ are rational expressions, then

$$\frac{P}{Q} \div \frac{R}{S} = \frac{P}{Q} \cdot \frac{S}{R} = \frac{P \cdot S}{Q \cdot R} \quad (Q, R, S \neq 0).$$

Notice that once the operation of division has been changed to multiplication, we proceed exactly as we did with the multiplication of rational expressions.

To divide rational expressions

1. Multiply the first rational expression by the reciprocal of the second.
2. Proceed as in the multiplication of rational expressions.

D₁ $\frac{6xy}{7} \div \frac{9xyz}{21}$

D₂ $\frac{a^2 - 25}{6} \div \frac{a + 5}{18}$

D₃ $\frac{6y - 3}{y - 4} \div \frac{2y - 1}{8 - 2y}$

D₄ $\frac{x^2 - 4}{4x - 1} \div \frac{2 - x}{4x^2 + 3x - 1}$

Example 6–1 D

Find the indicated quotients. Leave the answer in simplest form. Assume all denominators are nonzero.

1. $\frac{3ab}{5} \div \frac{9abc}{10}$

$= \frac{3ab}{5} \cdot \frac{10}{9abc}$ Multiply by the reciprocal of $\frac{9abc}{10}$

$= \frac{3ab \cdot 2 \cdot 5}{5 \cdot 3 \cdot 3 \cdot abc}$ Factor numerator and denominator

$= \frac{2 \cdot (3 \cdot 5 \cdot ab)}{3 \cdot c \cdot (3 \cdot 5 \cdot ab)}$ Identify common factors $(3 \cdot 5 \cdot ab)$

$= \frac{2}{3c}$ Divide numerator and denominator by common factors $(3 \cdot 5 \cdot ab)$

You are now ready to do **D₁**.

2. $\frac{x^2 - 4}{5} \div \frac{x - 2}{15}$

$= \frac{x^2 - 4}{5} \cdot \frac{15}{x - 2}$ Multiply by the reciprocal of $\frac{x - 2}{15}$

$= \frac{(x - 2)(x + 2) \cdot 3 \cdot 5}{5 \cdot (x - 2)}$ Factor in numerator and denominator

$= \frac{3 \cdot (x + 2) \cdot 5(x - 2)}{5(x - 2)}$ Identify common factors $5(x - 2)$

$= \frac{3(x + 2)}{1} = 3x + 6$ Divide by common factors $5(x - 2)$

You are now ready to do **D₂**.

3. $\frac{4x + 2}{x - 1} \div \frac{2x + 1}{4 - 4x}$

$= \frac{4x + 2}{x - 1} \cdot \frac{4 - 4x}{2x + 1}$ Multiply by the reciprocal of $\frac{2x + 1}{4 - 4x}$

$= \frac{2(2x + 1) \cdot -4(x - 1)}{(x - 1)(2x + 1)}$ Factor numerator and denominator

$= \frac{2 \cdot -4(2x + 1)(x - 1)}{(2x + 1)(x - 1)}$ Divide by common factors $(x - 1)$ and $(2x + 1)$

$= 2 \cdot -4$

$= -8$

You are now ready to do **D₃**.

4. $\frac{x^2 - 9}{2x + 1} \div \frac{3 - x}{2x^2 + 7x + 3}$

$= \frac{x^2 - 9}{2x + 1} \cdot \frac{2x^2 + 7x + 3}{3 - x}$ Multiply by the reciprocal of $\frac{3 - x}{2x^2 + 7x + 3}$

$= \frac{(x - 3)(x + 3) \cdot (2x + 1)(x + 3)}{(2x + 1)(3 - x)}$ Factor numerator and denominator

$= \frac{(x - 3)(2x + 1)(x + 3)(x + 3)}{-(x - 3)(2x + 1)}$ $3 - x = -1(x - 3)$

$= \frac{1(x + 3)(x + 3)}{-1}$ Divide by common factors $(x - 3)$ and $(2x + 1)$

$= -1(x + 3)^2$ Divide by -1

$= -1(x^2 + 6x + 9)$ $(x + 3)^2 = x^2 + 6x + 9$

$= -x^2 - 6x - 9$ Multiply by -1

You are now ready to do **D₄**. ■

Answers to section 6–1 margin exercises

A_1 $\frac{3}{5}$ **B_1** $\frac{42a}{55b}$ **B_2** $\frac{3y-9}{2y^2+3y+1}$ **B_3** $9y$ **B_4** $\frac{-z^2-z+6}{z+1}$ **B_5** $\frac{x+1}{x-4}$

B_6 $\frac{x^2-8x+15}{x^2+7x+6}$ **C_1** $\frac{4}{9}$ **D_1** $\frac{2}{z}$ **D_2** $3a-15$ **D_3** -6 **D_4** $-x^2-3x-2$

Mastery points

Can you

- Multiply rational expressions?
- Divide rational expressions?

Exercise 6–1

Directions Find the indicated product or quotient. Write your answer in simplest form. See examples 6–1 A–D.

Example **B3** $\frac{12}{5y}\cdot\frac{15y^2}{4}$

Solution

$$=\frac{12\cdot 15y^2}{5y\cdot 4}$$ Multiply numerator and denominator

$$=\frac{3\cdot 2\cdot 2\cdot 3\cdot 5\cdot y\cdot y}{5\cdot y\cdot 2\cdot 2}$$ Factor numerator and denominator

$$=\frac{3\cdot 3\cdot y(5\cdot y\cdot 2\cdot 2)}{1(5\cdot y\cdot 2\cdot 2)}$$ Group common factors $(5\cdot y\cdot 2\cdot 2)$

$$=\frac{9y}{1}=9y$$ Divide by common factors $(5\cdot y\cdot 2\cdot 2)$

Example **D4** $\frac{x^2-4}{4x-1}\div\frac{2-x}{4x^2+3x-1}$

Solution

$$=\frac{x^2-4}{4x-1}\cdot\frac{4x^2+3x-1}{2-x}$$

$$=\frac{(x+2)(x-2)\cdot(4x-1)(x+1)}{(4x-1)(2-x)}$$ Factor numerator and denominator

$$=\frac{(x+2)(x+1)(x-2)(4x-1)}{-(x-2)(4x-1)}$$ $(2-x)=-(x-2)$

$$=\frac{(x+2)(x+1)}{-1}$$ Divide by common factors $(x-2)$ and $(4x-1)$

$$=\frac{x^2+3x+2}{-1}$$ Multiply in numerator

$$=-x^2-3x-2$$ Divide by -1

1. $\frac{24}{35}\cdot\frac{7}{8}$

2. $\frac{3}{8}\cdot\frac{5}{9}\cdot\frac{12}{5}$

3. $\frac{7}{10}\div\frac{21}{25}$

4. $\frac{56}{39}\div\frac{8}{13}$

5. $\frac{5}{6}\cdot\frac{3x}{10y}$

6. $\frac{7a}{12b}\cdot\frac{9b}{28}$

7. $\dfrac{9x^2}{8} \cdot \dfrac{4}{6x}$

8. $\dfrac{36p^2}{7q} \cdot \dfrac{14q^2}{28p^3}$

9. $\dfrac{4a}{5} \div \dfrac{3}{5}$

10. $\dfrac{16b}{7a} \div \dfrac{4}{5}$

11. $\dfrac{14}{3a} \div \dfrac{7}{15a}$

12. $\dfrac{14y}{23x} \div 7y$

13. $6a \div \dfrac{24a}{35x}$

14. $7y \div \dfrac{14y}{23x}$

15. $\dfrac{28m}{15n} \div \dfrac{7m^2}{3n^3}$

16. $\dfrac{5x^2}{9y^3} \div \dfrac{20x}{6y}$

17. $\dfrac{21ab}{16c} \cdot \dfrac{8c^2}{3ab^2}$

18. $\dfrac{18x^2y^2}{5ab} \cdot \dfrac{25a^2b}{12xy}$

19. $\dfrac{3ab}{8x^2} \div \dfrac{15b^3}{16x}$

20. $\dfrac{5(a - b)}{8} \cdot \dfrac{12}{10(a - b)}$

21. $\dfrac{9 - p}{7} \div \dfrac{4(p - 9)}{21}$

22. $\dfrac{4x - 2}{15} \div \dfrac{1 - 2x}{27}$

23. $\dfrac{3b - 6}{4b + 8} \cdot \dfrac{5b + 10}{2 - b}$

24. $\dfrac{8y + 16}{3 - y} \cdot \dfrac{4y - 12}{3y + 6}$

25. $\dfrac{4a + 12}{a - 5} \div (a + 3)$

26. $\dfrac{9 - 3z}{2z + 8} \div (6 - 2z)$

27. $(x^2 - 4x + 4) \cdot \dfrac{18}{x^2 - 4}$

28. $\dfrac{21}{a^2 - 9} \cdot (a^2 + a - 12)$

29. $\dfrac{r^2 - 16}{r + 1} \div \dfrac{r + 4}{r^2 - 1}$

30. $\dfrac{a + 2}{3a} \div \dfrac{a^2 + 2a}{6a - 3}$

31. $\dfrac{6}{3m + 4} \div \dfrac{4m + 4}{9m^2 + 12m}$

32. $\dfrac{b^2 - a^2}{2a + 4b} \cdot \dfrac{a + 2b}{a - b}$

33. $\frac{a^2 - 5a - 14}{a^2 - 9a - 36} \cdot \frac{a^2 + 10a + 21}{a^2 + 4a - 77}$

34. $\frac{a^2 - 5a + 6}{a^2 - 9a + 20} \cdot \frac{a^2 - 5a + 4}{a^2 - 3a + 2}$

35. $\frac{x^2 - 2x - 3}{x^2 + 3x - 4} \div \frac{x^2 - x - 6}{x^2 + x - 12}$

36. $\frac{4x^2 - 4}{3x^2 - 13x - 10} \cdot \frac{x^2 - 6x + 5}{4x + 4}$

37. $\frac{6r^2 - r - 7}{12r^2 + 16r - 35} \div \frac{r^2 - r - 2}{2r^2 + r - 10}$

38. $\frac{4x^2 - 9}{x^2 - 9x + 18} \div \frac{2x^2 - 5x - 12}{x^2 - 10x + 24}$

39. $\frac{6m^2 - 7m + 2}{6m^2 + 5m + 1} \cdot \frac{2m^2 + m}{4m^2 - 1} \cdot \frac{12m^2 - 5m - 3}{12m^2 - 17m + 6}$

40. $\frac{y^2 + 8y + 16}{y + 4} \cdot \frac{y^2 - 25}{y^2 + 9y + 20} \cdot \frac{y^2 + 5y}{y^2 - 5y}$

41. $(3x^2 - 2x - 8) \div \frac{x^2 - 4}{x + 2}$

42. $\frac{m^2 - 3m - 10}{m^2 - 4} \div (2m^2 - 9m - 5)$

Review exercises

Directions Add or subtract the following. See section R–1.

1. $\frac{3}{4} + \frac{5}{6}$

2. $\frac{7}{8} - \frac{5}{12}$

Directions Completely factor the following. See sections 4–2 and 4–4.

3. $2x^2 - 50$

4. $x^2 + 9x - 22$

5. $x^2 + 8x + 16$

Directions Solve the following proportions. See section 5–4.

6. $\frac{3}{x} = \frac{5}{8}$

7. $\frac{5}{9} = \frac{y}{27}$

8. Write the number 0.0000789 in scientific notation. See section 3–5.

6–2 Addition and subtraction of rational expressions

Recall that to add or subtract fractions having the same denominator, you add, or subtract, the numerators and place this sum, or difference, over the same denominator.

Adding and subtracting properties for fractions

If a, b, and c are real numbers, $b \neq 0$, then

$$\frac{a}{b} + \frac{c}{b} = \frac{a + c}{b} \quad \text{and} \quad \frac{a}{b} - \frac{c}{b} = \frac{a - c}{b}.$$

Example 6–2 A

1. $\frac{3}{11} + \frac{4}{11} = \frac{3 + 4}{11}$ Add numerators

$= \frac{7}{11}$ $3 + 4 = 7$

2. $\frac{3}{7} - \frac{1}{7} = \frac{3 - 1}{7}$ Subtract numerators

$= \frac{2}{7}$ $3 - 1 = 2$ ■

We use the following similar procedure to add or subtract rational expressions.

Adding and subtracting properties for rational expressions

If $\frac{P}{R}$ and $\frac{Q}{R}$ are rational expressions, $R \neq 0$, then

$$\frac{P}{R} + \frac{Q}{R} = \frac{P + Q}{R} \quad \text{and} \quad \frac{P}{R} - \frac{Q}{R} = \frac{P - Q}{R}.$$

Note

Rational expressions having common denominators are called *like* rational expressions.

To add or subtract like rational expressions

1. Add or subtract the numerators.
2. Place the sum or difference over the common denominator.
3. Reduce the resulting rational expression to lowest terms.

Example 6–2 B

Find the indicated sum or difference. Assume all denominators are nonzero.

1. $\frac{3}{x-2}+\frac{5}{x-2}=\frac{3+5}{x-2}$ — Add numerators and place over $x-2$

$=\frac{8}{x-2}$ — $3+5=8$

You are now ready to do **B₁**.

2. $\frac{x+3}{x^2-1}+\frac{2x-5}{x^2-1}=\frac{(x+3)+(2x-5)}{x^2-1}$ — Place numerators in parentheses and add

$=\frac{3x-2}{x^2-1}$ — Remove parentheses and combine

You are now ready to do **B₂**.

3. $\frac{5y}{3y+5}-\frac{9y}{3y+5}=\frac{5y-9y}{3y+5}$ — Subtract numerators and place over $3y+5$

$=\frac{-4y}{3y+5}$ — $5y-9y=-4y$

You are now ready to do **B₃**.

4. $\frac{2x-1}{x^2+5x+6}-\frac{4-x}{x^2+5x+6}$

$=\frac{(2x-1)-(4-x)}{x^2+5x+6}$ — Place numerators in parentheses and subtract

$=\frac{2x-1-4+x}{x^2+5x+6}$ — Remove parentheses and subtract

$=\frac{3x-5}{x^2+5x+6}$ — Combine like terms

You are now ready to do **B₄**.

Note
Notice that when we subtracted $2x-1$ and $4-x$, we placed parentheses around each polynomial. This step is *important* to avoid the common mistake of failing to change signs in the second expression when subtraction is involved.

5. $\frac{2x-1}{x^2+5x+6}+\frac{4-x}{x^2+5x+6}$

$=\frac{(2x-1)+(4-x)}{x^2+5x+6}$ — Place numerators in parentheses and add

$=\frac{x+3}{x^2+5x+6}$ — Remove parentheses and combine like terms

$=\frac{x+3}{(x+3)(x+2)}$ — Factor denominator

$=\frac{1}{x+2}$ — Reduce by common factor $x+3$

Note
In the last step, *always* look for a possible reduction to lowest terms as we did in example 5.

You are now ready to do **B₅**. ■

B₁ $\frac{6}{x+6}+\frac{7}{x+6}$

B₂ $\frac{z+9}{z^2-16}+\frac{2z-1}{z^2-16}$

B₃ $\frac{3y}{y+7}-\frac{2}{y+7}$

B₄ $\frac{4m-5}{m^2+9}-\frac{2m-3}{m^2+9}$

B₅ $\frac{4y+3}{y^2-y-20}+\frac{1-3y}{y^2-y-20}$

C₁ $\frac{4y}{2} + \frac{5}{-2}$

When one denominator is the additive inverse of the other, as in the indicated sum

$$\frac{2x}{3} + \frac{5}{-3},$$

we first multiply one of the expressions by $\frac{-1}{-1}$ to obtain equivalent expressions with the same denominator.

Example 6–2 C

Find the indicated sum or difference. Assume all denominators are not zero.

1. $\frac{2x}{3} + \frac{5}{-3} = \frac{2x}{3} + \frac{-1}{-1} \cdot \frac{5}{-3}$ — Multiply $\frac{5}{-3}$ by $\frac{-1}{-1}$

$= \frac{2x}{3} + \frac{-1(5)}{-1(-3)}$ — Multiply numerators and denominators

$= \frac{2x}{3} + \frac{-5}{3}$ — Common denominator of 3

$= \frac{2x + (-5)}{3}$ — Add numerators and place over 3

$= \frac{2x - 5}{3}$ — Definition of subtraction

You are now ready to do **C₁**.

C₂ $\frac{x + 7}{x - 1} + \frac{3x + 1}{1 - x}$

2. $\frac{5y - 1}{y - 4} + \frac{2y + 3}{4 - y}$

$= \frac{5y - 1}{y - 4} + \frac{-1}{-1} \cdot \frac{2y + 3}{4 - y}$ — Multiply $\frac{2y + 3}{4 - y}$ by $\frac{-1}{-1}$

$= \frac{5y - 1}{y - 4} + \frac{-1(2y + 3)}{-1(4 - y)}$

$= \frac{5y - 1}{y - 4} + \frac{-2y - 3}{y - 4}$ — Same denominator: $-1(4 - y) = y - 4$

$= \frac{(5y - 1) + (-2y - 3)}{y - 4}$ — Add numerators in parentheses

$= \frac{5y - 1 - 2y - 3}{y - 4}$ — Remove parentheses

$= \frac{3y - 4}{y - 4}$ — Combine like terms

Note

We could have multiplied $\frac{5y - 1}{y - 4}$ by $\frac{-1}{-1}$. The resulting denominator would then have been $4 - y$ and the numerator would have been $4 - 3y$. We would then multiply this by $\frac{-1}{-1}$ to obtain the same form of the answer.

You are now ready to do **C₂**.

3. $\dfrac{2x+1}{x-5} - \dfrac{x-4}{5-x}$

$= \dfrac{2x+1}{x-5} - \dfrac{-1}{-1} \cdot \dfrac{x-4}{5-x}$ Multiply $\dfrac{x-4}{5-x}$ by $\dfrac{-1}{-1}$

$= \dfrac{2x+1}{x-5} - \dfrac{-1(x-4)}{-1(5-x)}$

$= \dfrac{2x+1}{x-5} - \dfrac{4-x}{x-5}$ Same denominator: $-1(x-4) = 4-x$; $-1(5-x) = x-5$

$= \dfrac{(2x+1)-(4-x)}{x-5}$ Place parentheses around numerators and subtract

$= \dfrac{2x+1-4+x}{x-5}$ Definition of subtraction

$= \dfrac{3x-3}{x-5}$ Combine like terms

You are now ready to do **C_3**. ■

C_3 $\dfrac{8y+1}{y-3} - \dfrac{6-y}{3-y}$

The least common denominator (LCD)

If the fractions to be added or subtracted do not have the same denominator, we must change at least one of the fractions to an equivalent fraction so the fractions have a common denominator. There are many such numbers we could use as a common denominator. However, the most convenient denominator to use is the smallest (least) number that is exactly divisible by each of the denominators—called the **least common denominator,** denoted by LCD. For example, the least common denominator (LCD) of the two fractions

$$\frac{5}{6} \text{ and } \frac{2}{9}$$

is 18, since 18 is the smallest (least) number that is exactly divisible by both 6 and 9.

D_1 12; 8

To find the LCD of two or more rational expressions

1. Factor each denominator completely. Write each factorization using exponential notation.
2. List each *different* factor that appears in any one of the factorizations in step 1.
3. Raise each factor of step 2 to the *greatest* power that factor has in step 1. Form the product of these factors.

Note
The LCD of two or more rational expressions is also called the least common multiple (LCM) of the denominators.

Example 6–2 D

Find the LCD of rational expressions having the following denominators.

1. 6; 9

$6 = 2 \cdot 3 = 2^1 \cdot 3^1$
$9 = 3 \cdot 3 = 3^2$ Factor each denominator

The different factors are 2 and 3. The greatest power of 2 is 2^1 and of 3 is 3^2.

LCD is $2^1 \cdot 3^2 = 2 \cdot 9 = 18$.

You are now ready to do **D_1**.

D₂ $12x;\ 10x^2$

D₃ $24a^4b^3;\ 36a^2b^5$

D₄ $y^2 + 6y - 7;\ y^2 - 10y + 9$

D₅ $y^2 + 10y + 25;\ y^2 - 25$

2. $16a;\ 8a^2$

$$\left.\begin{aligned} 16a &= 2 \cdot 2 \cdot 2 \cdot 2 \cdot a = 2^4 \cdot a^1 \\ 8a^2 &= 2 \cdot 2 \cdot 2 \cdot a^2 = 2^3 \cdot a^2 \end{aligned}\right\} \text{ Factor each denominator}$$

The factors to be considered are 2 and a. The greatest power of 2 is 2^4 and of a is a^2.

The LCD is $2^4 \cdot a^2 = 16a^2$.

You are now ready to do **D₂**.

3. $50x^3y^2;\ 20x^2y^5$

$$\left.\begin{aligned} 50x^3y^2 &= 2 \cdot 5 \cdot 5 \cdot x^3 \cdot y^2 = 2^1 \cdot 5^2 \cdot x^3 \cdot y^2 \\ 20x^2y^5 &= 2 \cdot 2 \cdot 5 \cdot x^2 \cdot y^5 = 2^2 \cdot 5^1 \cdot x^2 \cdot y^5 \end{aligned}\right\} \text{ Factor each denominator}$$

The different factors are 2, 5, x, and y. The greatest power of 2 is 2^2, of 5 is 5^2, of x is x^3, and of y is y^5.

The LCD is $2^2 \cdot 5^2 \cdot x^3 \cdot y^5 = 4 \cdot 25 \cdot x^3 \cdot y^5 = 100x^3y^5$.

You are now ready to do **D₃**.

4. $x^2 + x - 12;\ x^2 + 2x - 8$

$$\left.\begin{aligned} x^2 + x - 12 &= (x + 4)^1(x - 3)^1 \\ x^2 + 2x - 8 &= (x + 4)^1(x - 2)^1 \end{aligned}\right\} \text{ Factor each denominator}$$

The different factors are $(x + 4)$, $(x - 3)$, and $(x - 2)$. Since the highest power of each factor is 1, the LCD is $(x + 4)(x - 3)(x - 2)$.

Note
To multiply these factors would cause unnecessary work and difficulty when finding equivalent fractions later. Therefore, we will *always* leave the least common denominator in factored form.

You are now ready to do **D₄**.

5. $x^2 - 6x + 9;\ x^2 - 9$

$$\left.\begin{aligned} x^2 - 6x + 9 &= (x - 3)^2 \\ x^2 - 9 &= (x + 3)^1(x - 3)^1 \end{aligned}\right\} \text{ Factor each denominator}$$

Since we have $(x - 3)^2$ and $(x + 3)^1$, the LCD is $(x - 3)^2(x + 3)$.

You are now ready to do **D₅**. ■

Answers to section 6–2 margin exercises

B₁ $\dfrac{13}{x + 6}$ **B₂** $\dfrac{3z + 8}{z^2 - 16}$ **B₃** $\dfrac{3y - 2}{y + 7}$ **B₄** $\dfrac{2m - 2}{m^2 + 9}$ **B₅** $\dfrac{1}{y - 5}$ **C₁** $\dfrac{4y - 5}{2}$
C₂ $\dfrac{-2x + 6}{x - 1}$ **C₃** $\dfrac{7y + 7}{y - 3}$ **D₁** 24 **D₂** $60x^2$ **D₃** $72a^4b^5$
D₄ $(y + 7)(y - 1)(y - 9)$ **D₅** $(y + 5)^2(y - 5)$

Mastery points

Can you

- Add and subtract like rational expressions?
- Add and subtract rational expressions having denominators that are additive inverses?
- Find the least common denominator (LCD) of two or more rational expressions?

Exercise 6–2

Directions Combine the given rational expressions and reduce the answer to lowest terms. Assume all denominators are nonzero. See example 6–2 B.

Example B4 $\frac{4m-5}{m^2+9}-\frac{2m-3}{m^2+9}$

Solution $=\frac{(4m-5)-(2m-3)}{m^2+9}$ Place numerators in parentheses and subtract

$=\frac{4m-5-2m+3}{m^2+9}$ Remove parentheses and subtract in numerator

$=\frac{2m-2}{m^2+9}$ Combine like terms in numerator

1. $\frac{5}{x}+\frac{3}{x}$ **2.** $\frac{8}{y^2}+\frac{10}{y^2}$ **3.** $\frac{9}{p}-\frac{2}{p}$ **4.** $\frac{18}{m^2}-\frac{5}{m^2}$

5. $\frac{5x}{x+2}+\frac{9x}{x+2}$ **6.** $\frac{8y}{y-1}+\frac{3y}{y-1}$ **7.** $\frac{x-1}{2x}-\frac{x+3}{2x}$ **8.** $\frac{3y-2}{y^2}-\frac{4y-1}{y^2}$

9. $\frac{3x+5}{x^2-1}+\frac{2x+3}{x^2-1}$ **10.** $\frac{b^2+2}{b+3}-\frac{b^2+2b-3}{b+3}$

See example 6–2 C.

Example C2 $\frac{x+7}{x-1}+\frac{3x+1}{1-x}$

Solution $=\frac{x+7}{x-1}+\frac{-1}{-1}\cdot\frac{3x+1}{1-x}$ Multiply $\frac{3x+1}{1-x}$ by $\frac{-1}{-1}$

$=\frac{x+7}{x-1}+\frac{-1(3x+1)}{-1(1-x)}$

$=\frac{x+7}{x-1}+\frac{-3x-1}{x-1}$ Same denominator: $-1(1-x)=x-1$

$=\frac{x+7-3x-1}{x-1}$ Add numerators

$=\frac{-2x+6}{x-1}$ Combine like terms

11. $\frac{5}{7}+\frac{6}{-7}$ **12.** $\frac{9}{10}-\frac{3}{-10}$ **13.** $\frac{4}{z}-\frac{5}{-z}$

14. $\frac{6}{y} + \frac{9}{-y}$

15. $\frac{5}{x-2} + \frac{12}{2-x}$

16. $\frac{1}{x-7} - \frac{5}{7-x}$

17. $\frac{5y}{y-6} - \frac{4y}{6-y}$

18. $\frac{4z}{z-3} + \frac{z}{3-z}$

19. $\frac{x+1}{x-5} + \frac{2x-3}{5-x}$

20. $\frac{4y+3}{y-9} - \frac{2y-7}{9-y}$

21. $\frac{2y-5}{2y-3} - \frac{y+7}{3-2y}$

22. $\frac{z+5}{4z-3} + \frac{4z-1}{3-4z}$

23. $\frac{2x+5}{5-2x} + \frac{x+9}{2x-5}$

24. $\frac{5-y}{6-5y} - \frac{9y+1}{5y-6}$

Directions Find the least common denominator (LCD) of rational expressions having the following denominators. See example 6–2 D.

Example $\boxed{D_4}$ $y^2 + 6y - 7; y^2 - 10y + 9$

Solution

$$\left.\begin{aligned} y^2 + 6y - 7 &= (y+7)^1(y-1)^1 \\ y^2 - 10y + 9 &= (y-9)^1(y-1)^1 \end{aligned}\right\} \quad \text{Factor each denominator}$$

Since the different factors are $y + 7$, $y - 1$, and $y - 9$ and each is carried to the first power, the LCD is $(y + 7)(y - 1)(y - 9)$.

25. $6x$ and $9x$

26. $8a$ and $12a$

27. $16x^2$ and $24x$

28. $6b^2$ and $14b$

29. $28y^2$ and $35y^3$

30. $9z$ and $7z^4$

31. $32a^2$ and $64a^4$

32. $4x^2$, $3x$, and $8x^3$

33. $10a^2$, $12a^3$, and $9a$

34. $4x - 2$ and $2x - 1$

35. $x - 4$ and $3x - 12$

36. $6x - 12$ and $9x - 18$

37. $18y^3$ and $9y - 36$

38. $32z^2$ and $16z - 32$

39. $a^2 + a$ and $a^2 - 1$

40. $(z - 1)^2$ and $z^2 - 1$

41. $8a + 16$ and $a^2 + 3a + 2$

42. $9p - 18$ and $p^2 - 7p + 10$

43. $a^2 - 5a + 6$ and $a^2 - 4$

44. $y^2 - y - 12$ and $y^2 + 6y + 9$

45. $a^2 - 36$; $a^2 - 5a + 6$; $a^2 - 4a - 12$

46. $p^2 - 9$, $p^2 + p - 6$, and $p^2 - 4p + 4$

47. $x^2 - 49$, $7 - x$, and $2x + 14$

48. $5 - y$, $y^2 - 25$, and $y^2 - 10y + 25$

Review exercises

1. Divide $3.257 \div 2.12$. See section R–2.

2. What percent of 42 is 28? See section R–3.

3. The statement $4(y + 3) = 4(3 + y)$ demonstrates what property of real numbers? See section 1–6.

Directions Factor the following expressions. See sections 4–3 and 4–4.

4. $5y^2 - 20$

5. $x^2 + 20x + 100$

6. $3y^2 - y - 4$

Directions Add or subtract as indicated. See section R–1.

7. $\frac{5}{8} + \frac{3}{4}$

8. $\frac{8}{9} - \frac{5}{6}$

6–3 Addition and subtraction of rational expressions with unlike denominators

Now that we can find the least common denominator (LCD) of a group of rational expressions, let us review the process for building a fraction (or rational expression) to an equivalent fraction with a new denominator (see section R–1).

Example 6–3 A

1. Build $\frac{7}{15}$ to an equivalent fraction having denominator 60.

We want $\frac{7}{15} = \frac{?}{60}$.

Since $60 = 15 \cdot 4$ (factor 4 is found by dividing $60 \div 15 = 4$), we multiply the given fraction by $\frac{4}{4}$ $\left(\frac{4}{4} = 1\right)$.

A₁ Build $\frac{8}{9}$ to an equivalent fraction having denominator 45.

$$\frac{7}{15} = \frac{7}{15} \cdot \frac{4}{4}$$

$$= \frac{7 \cdot 4}{15 \cdot 4} \quad \text{Multiply numerators / Multiply denominators}$$

$$= \frac{28}{60}$$

Thus, $\frac{7}{15} = \frac{28}{60}$.

You are now ready to do **A₁**.

2. Build $\frac{x+1}{x-4}$ to an equivalent rational expression having denominator $x^2 - 2x - 8$.

We want $\frac{x+1}{x-4} = \frac{?}{x^2 - 2x - 8}$.

Since $x^2 - 2x - 8 = (x - 4)(x + 2)$, we multiply the given rational expression by $\frac{x+2}{x+2}$.

$$\frac{x+1}{x-4} = \frac{x+1}{x-4} \cdot \frac{x+2}{x+2}$$

$$= \frac{(x+1)(x+2)}{(x-4)(x+2)} \quad \text{Multiply numerators / Multiply denominators}$$

$$= \frac{x^2 + 3x + 2}{x^2 - 2x - 8} \quad \text{Perform indicated operations}$$

Thus, $\frac{x+1}{x-4} = \frac{x^2 + 3x + 2}{x^2 - 2x - 8}$.

A₂ Build $\frac{y-1}{y+5}$ to an equivalent rational expression with denominator $y^2 - 25$.

You are now ready to do **A₂**. ■

Once equivalent rational expressions are obtained with the LCD as the denominator, we add or subtract as previously learned. Use the following steps to add or subtract rational expressions having different denominators.

To add or subtract rational expressions having different denominators

1. Find the LCD of the rational expressions.
2. Write each rational expression as an equivalent rational expression with the LCD as the denominator.
3. Perform the indicated addition or subtraction as before.
4. Reduce the results to lowest terms.

Example 6–3 B

Add the following rational expressions. Assume the denominators are not equal to zero.

1. $\frac{5x}{8} + \frac{7x}{12}$

$$\left.\begin{aligned} 8 &= 2^3 \\ 12 &= 2^2 \cdot 3 \end{aligned}\right\} \text{LCD} = 2^3 \cdot 3 = 24 \quad \text{Find the LCD}$$

Since $\frac{24}{8} = 3$ and $\frac{24}{12} = 2$,

$$\frac{5x}{8} + \frac{7x}{12} = \frac{5x}{8} \cdot \frac{3}{3} + \frac{7x}{12} \cdot \frac{2}{2}$$ Multiply $\frac{5x}{8}$ by $\frac{3}{3}$ and $\frac{7x}{12}$ by $\frac{2}{2}$

$$= \frac{15x}{24} + \frac{14x}{24}$$ Multiply numerators and denominators

$$= \frac{15x + 14x}{24}$$ Add numerators

$$= \frac{29x}{24}.$$ Combine as indicated

You are now ready to do **B₁**.

B₁ $\frac{5y}{6} + \frac{3y}{15}$

2. $\frac{15}{4x^2} + \frac{25}{18x}$

$$\left.\begin{aligned} 4x^2 &= 2^2 \cdot x^2 \\ 18x &= 2 \cdot 3^2 \cdot x \end{aligned}\right\} \text{LCD} = 2^2 \cdot 3^2 \cdot x^2 = 36x^2$$ Find the LCD

Since $\frac{36x^2}{4x^2} = 9$ and $\frac{36x^2}{18x} = 2x$,

$$\frac{15}{4x^2} + \frac{25}{18x} = \frac{15}{4x^2} \cdot \frac{9}{9} + \frac{25}{18x} \cdot \frac{2x}{2x}$$ Multiply $\frac{15}{4x^2}$ by $\frac{9}{9}$ and $\frac{25}{18x}$ by $\frac{2x}{2x}$

$$= \frac{135}{36x^2} + \frac{50x}{36x^2}$$ Multiply numerators and denominators

$$= \frac{135 + 50x}{36x^2}.$$ Add numerators

You are now ready to do **B₂**.

B₂ $\frac{20}{3y} + \frac{25}{12y^2}$

3. $\frac{3y + 2}{y^2 - 16} + \frac{y - 4}{3y + 12}$

$$\left.\begin{aligned} y^2 - 16 &= (y + 4)(y - 4) \\ 3y + 12 &= 3(y + 4) \end{aligned}\right\} \text{LCD} = 3(y + 4)(y - 4)$$ Find the LCD

Since $\frac{3(y + 4)(y - 4)}{(y + 4)(y - 4)} = 3$ and $\frac{3(y + 4)(y - 4)}{3(y + 4)} = y - 4$, then

$$\frac{3y + 2}{y^2 - 16} + \frac{y - 4}{3y + 12}$$

$$= \frac{3y + 2}{(y + 4)(y - 4)} \cdot \frac{3}{3} + \frac{y - 4}{3(y + 4)} \cdot \frac{y - 4}{y - 4}.$$ Multiply first term by $\frac{3}{3}$ and second term by $\frac{y-4}{y-4}$

$$= \frac{3(3y + 2)}{3(y + 4)(y - 4)} + \frac{(y - 4)(y - 4)}{3(y + 4)(y - 4)}$$ Multiply numerators and denominators

$$= \frac{(9y + 6) + (y^2 - 8y + 16)}{3(y + 4)(y - 4)}$$ Add numerators

$$= \frac{y^2 + y + 22}{3(y + 4)(y - 4)}$$ Remove parentheses and combine

You are now ready to do **B₃**.

B₃ $\frac{x - 3}{x^2 - 4} + \frac{2x + 5}{5x - 10}$

Note
When the numerators have two or more terms as in example 3, we place the quantities in parentheses when we add the numerators. This is a good practice to avoid a *most common* mistake when subtracting. ■

C₁ $\frac{2x}{3x+1} - \frac{2x-3}{x-4}$

Example 6–3 C

Subtract the following rational expressions. Assume the denominators are not equal to zero.

1. $\frac{5y}{2y-1} - \frac{y+1}{y+2}$

The LCD of the rational expressions is $(2y-1)(y+2)$.

$$\frac{5y}{2y-1} - \frac{y+1}{y+2}$$

$$= \frac{5y}{2y-1}\cdot\frac{y+2}{y+2} - \frac{y+1}{y+2}\cdot\frac{2y-1}{2y-1}$$

Multiply first term by $\frac{y+2}{y+2}$ and second term by $\frac{2y-1}{2y-1}$

$$= \frac{5y(y+2)}{(2y-1)(y+2)} - \frac{(y+1)(2y-1)}{(2y-1)(y+2)}$$

Multiply numerators and denominators

$$= \frac{(5y^2+10y)-(2y^2+y-1)}{(2y-1)(y+2)}$$

Subtract numerators

Don't forget the parentheses

$$= \frac{5y^2+10y-2y^2-y+1}{(2y-1)(y+2)}$$

Remove parentheses and change signs when subtracting

$$= \frac{3y^2+9y+1}{(2y-1)(y+2)}$$

Combine like terms

Note

The numerator $3y^2 + 9y + 1$ cannot be factored so we are unable to reduce. We should always check this!

C₂ $\frac{2y}{y+2} - \frac{6}{3y+6}$

You are now ready to do **C₁**.

2. $\frac{9x}{2x-8} - \frac{7}{x-4}$

$$\left.\begin{aligned} 2x-8 &= 2(x-4) \\ x-4 &= (x-4) \end{aligned}\right\}\ \text{LCD is } 2(x-4).$$

Find the LCD

$$\frac{9x}{2x-8} - \frac{7}{x-4} = \frac{9x}{2(x-4)} - \frac{7}{x-4}\cdot\frac{2}{2}$$

Multiply $\frac{7}{x-4}$ by $\frac{2}{2}$

$$= \frac{9x}{2(x-4)} - \frac{14}{2(x-4)}$$

Multiply numerators

$$= \frac{9x-14}{2(x-4)}$$

Subtract numerators

You are now ready to do **C₂**.

3. $\frac{5x-4}{x^2-2x+1} - \frac{3x}{x^2+4x-5}$

$$\left.\begin{aligned} x^2-2x+1 &= (x-1)^2 \\ x^2+4x-5 &= (x+5)(x-1) \end{aligned}\right\}\ \text{LCD} = (x-1)^2(x+5)$$

Find the LCD

$$\frac{5x-4}{x^2-2x+1} - \frac{3x}{x^2+4x-5}$$

Factor denominators

$$= \frac{5x-4}{(x-1)^2} - \frac{3x}{(x+5)(x-1)}$$

$$= \frac{5x-4}{(x-1)^2}\cdot\frac{x+5}{x+5} - \frac{3x}{(x+5)(x-1)}\cdot\frac{x-1}{x-1}$$

Multiply first term by $\frac{x+5}{x+5}$ and second term by $\frac{x-1}{x-1}$

$$= \frac{(5x - 4)(x + 5)}{(x - 1)^2(x + 5)} - \frac{3x(x - 1)}{(x - 1)^2(x + 5)}$$ Multiply numerators and denominators

$$= \frac{(5x^2 + 21x - 20) - (3x^2 - 3x)}{(x - 1)^2(x + 5)}$$ Subtract numerators

$$= \frac{5x^2 + 21x - 20 - 3x^2 + 3x}{(x - 1)^2(x + 5)}$$ Remove parentheses and change signs

$$= \frac{2x^2 + 24x - 20}{(x - 1)^2(x + 5)}$$ Combine like terms

Don't forget the parentheses

You are now ready to do **C_3**. ■

C_3 $\frac{y + 1}{y^2 - y - 12} - \frac{3y + 2}{y^2 - 9y + 20}$

Problem solving

Example 6–3 D

Set up a rational expression for the following verbal statements.

1. If Dick can mow his lawn in h hours, what part of the lawn can he mow in 2 hours?

   We must find what part of the total time, h hours, is 2 hours. Thus, Dick can mow the fractional part

   $$\frac{2}{h}$$

   of the lawn in 2 hours.

You are now ready to do **D_1**.

D_1 If Pam can bake a batch of cookies in h hours, what part of the batch can she bake in 1 hour?

2. If the area (A) of a rectangle is n square inches, what is the expression for the length, ℓ, if the width is 12 inches? ($A = \ell \cdot w$)

   Using $A = \ell \cdot w$, we have $\ell = \frac{A}{w}$ and so the length

   $\ell = \frac{n}{12}$ inches. Replace A with n and w with 12

You are now ready to do **D_2**. ■

D_2 If the area of a rectangle is A square yards, write an expression for the width if the length is 5 yards.

Answers to section 6–3 margin exercises

A_1 $\frac{40}{45}$ **A_2** $\frac{y^2 - 6y + 5}{y^2 - 25}$ **B_1** $\frac{31y}{30}$ **B_2** $\frac{80y + 25}{12y^2}$ **B_3** $\frac{2x^2 + 14x - 5}{5(x + 2)(x - 2)}$
C_1 $\frac{-4x^2 - x + 3}{(3x + 1)(x - 4)}$ **C_2** $\frac{2(y - 1)}{y + 2}$ **C_3** $\frac{-2y^2 - 15y - 11}{(y + 3)(y - 4)(y - 5)}$ **D_1** $\frac{1}{h}$
D_2 width $= \frac{A}{5}$

Mastery points

Can you

- Add or subtract rational expressions having different denominators?

Exercise 6–3

Directions Perform the indicated addition and reduce the answer to lowest terms. Assume all denominators are not equal to zero. See example 6–3 B.

Example $\boxed{B_2}$ $\dfrac{20}{3y} + \dfrac{25}{12y^2}$

Solution $\left.\begin{aligned} 3y &= 3 \cdot y \\ 12y^2 &= 3 \cdot 2^2 \cdot y^2 \end{aligned}\right\}$ LCD $= 3 \cdot 2^2 \cdot y^2 = 12y^2$

$\dfrac{12y^2}{3y} = 4y$ and the denominator of the second expression is the LCD, $12y^2$.

$$\frac{20}{3y} + \frac{25}{12y^2} = \frac{20}{3y} \cdot \frac{4y}{4y} + \frac{25}{12y^2}$$ Multiply numerator and denominator of $\frac{20}{3y}$ by $4y$

$$= \frac{80y}{12y^2} + \frac{25}{12y^2}$$

$$= \frac{80y + 25}{12y^2}$$ Add numerators and place over common denominator

1. $\dfrac{x}{6} + \dfrac{3}{4}$

2. $\dfrac{3z}{10} + \dfrac{2z}{15}$

3. $\dfrac{4}{3x} + \dfrac{5}{2x}$

4. $\dfrac{2x - 1}{16} + \dfrac{x + 2}{24}$

5. $\dfrac{3a + 1}{a} + \dfrac{2a - 3}{3a}$

6. $\dfrac{4}{x - 1} + \dfrac{5}{x + 3}$

7. $\dfrac{8}{y + 4} + \dfrac{7}{y - 5}$

8. $\dfrac{x}{x + 2} + \dfrac{3x}{4x - 1}$

9. $5 + \dfrac{4x}{x + 8}$

10. $9 + \dfrac{y + 9}{y - 1}$

11. $\dfrac{15}{5y - 10} + \dfrac{14}{2y - 4}$

12. $\dfrac{21}{6x + 12} + \dfrac{15}{2x + 4}$

13. $\dfrac{12}{x^2 - 4} + \dfrac{7}{4x - 8}$

14. $\dfrac{16}{2y + 6} + \dfrac{5}{y^2 - 9}$

15. $\dfrac{x}{x - 1} + \dfrac{3x}{x^2 - 1}$

16. $\dfrac{2y}{y^2 - 16} + \dfrac{5y}{2y - 8}$

17. $\dfrac{4}{x^2 - x - 6} + \dfrac{5}{x^2 - 9}$

18. $\dfrac{6}{x^2 - 4x - 12} + \dfrac{5}{x^2 - 36}$

19. $\dfrac{2y}{y^2 - 6y + 9} + \dfrac{5y}{y^2 - 2y - 3}$

20. $\dfrac{4z}{z^2 + z - 20} + \dfrac{z}{z^2 - 8z + 16}$

21. $\dfrac{y - 2}{y^2 - 3y - 10} + \dfrac{y + 1}{y^2 - y - 6}$

22. $\dfrac{2x + 1}{x^2 + 6x + 5} + \dfrac{4x - 3}{x^2 - x - 30}$

Directions Perform the indicated subtraction and reduce to lowest terms. Assume all denominators are not zero. See example 6–3 C.

Example C3 $\dfrac{y + 1}{y^2 - y - 12} - \dfrac{3y + 2}{y^2 - 9y + 20}$

Solution $\left.\begin{array}{l} y^2 - y - 12 = (y - 4)(y + 3) \\ y^2 - 9y + 20 = (y - 4)(y - 5) \end{array}\right\}$ LCD is $(y - 4)(y + 3)(y - 5)$.

$$\frac{y + 1}{y^2 - y - 12} - \frac{3y + 2}{y^2 - 9y + 20}$$

$$= \frac{y + 1}{(y - 4)(y + 3)} \cdot \frac{y - 5}{y - 5} - \frac{3y + 2}{(y - 4)(y - 5)} \cdot \frac{y + 3}{y + 3}$$

Multiply numerator and denominator of $\dfrac{y + 1}{(y - 4)(y + 3)}$ by $y - 5$ and of $\dfrac{3y + 2}{(y - 4)(y - 5)}$ by $y + 3$

$$= \frac{(y + 1)(y - 5)}{(y - 4)(y + 3)(y - 5)} - \frac{(3y + 2)(y + 3)}{(y - 4)(y + 3)(y - 5)}$$

$$= \frac{(y^2 - 4y - 5) - (3y^2 + 11y + 6)}{(y - 4)(y + 3)(y - 5)}$$

Don't forget the parentheses

Multiply in each numerator, place parentheses around each product, and subtract

$$= \frac{y^2 - 4y - 5 - 3y^2 - 11y - 6}{(y - 4)(y + 3)(y - 5)}$$

Remove parentheses, change signs, and subtract

$$= \frac{-2y^2 - 15y - 11}{(y - 4)(y + 3)(y - 5)}$$

Combine like terms in numerator

23. $\dfrac{y}{9} - \dfrac{5}{6}$

24. $\dfrac{5y}{12} - \dfrac{y}{8}$

25. $\dfrac{9}{14y} - \dfrac{1}{21y}$

26. $\dfrac{7}{12z} - \dfrac{10}{9z}$

27. $\dfrac{5a + 3}{12} - \dfrac{a - 4}{10}$

28. $\dfrac{2x + 9}{8} - \dfrac{x - 7}{20}$

29. $\dfrac{2x + 5}{6x} - \dfrac{x - 5}{9x}$

30. $\dfrac{4y - 1}{3y} - \dfrac{2y - 3}{15y}$

31. $\dfrac{7}{2x - 3} - \dfrac{6}{x - 5}$

32. $\frac{7}{4x - 6} - \frac{12}{3x + 9}$

33. $\frac{12}{3y + 6} - \frac{11}{7y + 14}$

34. $\frac{14}{5x - 15} - \frac{8}{2x - 6}$

35. $9 - \frac{6}{x + 8}$

36. $12 - \frac{7}{z - 12}$

37. $\frac{2x}{3x + 1} - 9$

38. $\frac{4y}{5y - 4} - 10$

39. $\frac{-3}{a^2 - 5a + 6} - \frac{3}{a^2 - 4}$

40. $\frac{8}{x^2 - 25} - \frac{7}{x^2 + 3x - 10}$

41. $\frac{20}{y^2 - 2y - 24} - \frac{8}{y^2 + y - 12}$

42. $\frac{2p}{p^2 - 9p + 20} - \frac{5p - 2}{p - 5}$

43. $\frac{2a - 3}{a^2 - 5a + 6} - \frac{3a}{a - 2}$

44. $\frac{5}{z^2 - 4} - \frac{z}{z^2 - 1} + \frac{4}{z^2 + z - 2}$

45. $\frac{4a}{a^2 + 2a - 15} + \frac{3a}{2a^2 + 11a + 5} - \frac{5a}{2a^2 - 5a - 3}$

46. $\frac{y - 1}{y^2 - 25} + \frac{y}{5y - 25} - \frac{y - 2}{10y + 50}$

47. Women A, B, and C can complete a given job in a, b, and c hours, respectively. Working together they can complete in one hour $\frac{1}{a} + \frac{1}{b} + \frac{1}{c}$ of the job. By combining, obtain a single expression for what they can do together in one hour.

48. In electricity, the total resistance of any parallel circuit may be given by

$$\frac{1}{R_t} = \frac{I_1}{E_1} + \frac{I_2}{E_2} + \frac{I_3}{E_3}.$$

Combine the expression in the right member.

See example 6–3 D.

Example D_2 If the area of a rectangle is A square yards, write an expression for the width if the length is 5 yards.

Solution Using $A = \ell \cdot w$, we are given that $\ell = 5$ yards. Substituting, we obtain

$$A = 5 \cdot w,$$

and solving for w, we divide each member by 5. Thus $w = \frac{A}{5}$.

49. A faucet when fully open, can fill the sink in m minutes. What part of the sink can it fill in 3 minutes?

50. An inlet pipe to a swimming pool can fill the pool in h hours. What part of the pool can it fill in 9 hours?

51. An outlet pipe can drain a swimming pool in 36 hours. What part of the pool can it drain in h hours?

52. Jane can paint her house in h hours. What part of the house can she paint in 1 hour?

53. The product of two numbers is 48. If one of the numbers is m, what is the other number?

54. The area of a rectangle is 54 square centimeters. What is the length ℓ if the width is w centimeters?

55. The area of a rectangle is A square feet. What is the width if the length is 23 feet?

56. The area of a triangle is 21 square yards. If the triangle has a base length b, what is the altitude h of the triangle? $\left(A = \frac{1}{2}bh\right)$

57. The area of a triangle is A square rods. If the altitude h is 9 rods, what is the length of the base b?

58. John drives 25 miles in h hours. At what speed, r, did he travel? [*Hint:* Use distance traveled (d) = rate $(r) \times$ time (t).]

59. Mabel travels d miles at a rate of 55 miles per hour. Write an expression for the time t that she traveled.

Review exercises

Directions Completely factor the following expressions. See sections 4–2 and 4–3.

1. $x^2 - 14x + 49$ **2.** $2x^2 - 11x + 5$ **3.** $4x^2 - 16$

Directions Multiply the following expressions. See section 3–3.

4. $(x + 9)(x - 9)$ **5.** $(4x + 3)^2$ **6.** $(2x + 1)(x - 8)$

Directions Find the LCD of expressions having the following denominators. See section 6–2.

7. 16, 12, 6

8. $4x, 2x^2, 6$

9. $x^2 - 9;\ x^2 - 6x + 9;\ x + 3$

Directions Add or subtract the following. See section 6–3.

10. $\dfrac{5}{x} + \dfrac{3}{2x}$

11. $\dfrac{5}{x-2} - \dfrac{3}{x-1}$

6–4 Complex fractions

A complex fraction

A **complex fraction** is a fraction (rational expression) whose numerator, denominator, or both contain fractions (or rational expressions). The fractions

$$\frac{\frac{3}{4}}{\frac{5}{6}},\quad \frac{\frac{1}{3}+2}{1-\frac{1}{2}},\quad \text{and}\quad \frac{\frac{x-1}{x-2}}{\frac{x+3}{x}}$$

are examples of complex fractions. Given a complex fraction, we reduce the fraction by *eliminating the fractions within the numerator and/or the denominator.*

We name the parts of a complex fraction as shown in the following examples.

$$\frac{\frac{3}{x}+\frac{4}{y}}{\frac{1}{x}-\frac{2}{y}}$$

$\frac{3}{x}+\frac{4}{y}$ } Primary numerator

$\frac{1}{x}-\frac{2}{y}$ } Primary denominator

In $\dfrac{\frac{3}{x}+\frac{4}{y}}{\frac{1}{x}-\frac{2}{y}}$: 3, 4 ← Secondary numerators; x, y ← Secondary denominators; 1, 2 ← Secondary numerators; x, y ← Secondary denominators

To simplify a complex fraction, we use one of the following methods.

Simplifying a complex fraction

Method 1 Multiply the primary numerator and the primary denominator by the LCM of the secondary denominators and reduce if possible.

Method 2 Form a single fraction in the numerator and the denominator and divide the primary numerator by the primary denominator.

Example 6–4 A

Simplify the complex fraction. Assume all denominators are nonzero.

1. $\dfrac{\frac{3}{4}}{\frac{5}{6}}$

Method 1

$$\frac{\frac{3}{4}}{\frac{5}{6}} = \frac{\frac{3}{4} \cdot 12}{\frac{5}{6} \cdot 12}$$

Multiply primary numerator and primary denominator by the LCM of 4 and 6, which is 12

$$= \frac{3 \cdot \frac{12}{4}}{5 \cdot \frac{12}{6}}$$

Divide 4 into 12

Divide 6 into 12

$$= \frac{3 \cdot 3}{5 \cdot 2} = \frac{9}{10}$$

Multiply in numerator and denominator

Method 2

$$\frac{\frac{3}{4}}{\frac{5}{6}} = \frac{3}{4} \div \frac{5}{6} = \frac{3}{4} \cdot \frac{6}{5}$$

Multiply by the reciprocal of $\frac{5}{6}$

$$= \frac{3 \cdot 6}{4 \cdot 5}$$

Multiply numerators and denominators

$$= \frac{18}{20} = \frac{9}{10}$$

Multiply and reduce to lowest terms

You are now ready to do **A₁**.

2. $\dfrac{\frac{5a}{6b}}{\frac{10a}{27b}}$

Method 1

$$\frac{\frac{5a}{6b}}{\frac{10a}{27b}} = \frac{\frac{5a}{6b} \cdot 54b}{\frac{10a}{27b} \cdot 54b}$$

Multiply primary numerator and primary denominator by the LCM of $6b$ and $27b$, which is $54b$

$$= \frac{5a \cdot \frac{54b}{6b}}{10a \cdot \frac{54b}{27b}}$$

Divide $54b$ by $6b$

Divide $54b$ by $27b$

$$= \frac{5a \cdot 9}{10a \cdot 2}$$

Reduce in numerator and denominator

$$= \frac{45a}{20a} = \frac{9}{4}$$

Multiply and reduce to lowest terms

A_1 Simplify the complex fraction $\dfrac{\frac{1}{4}}{\frac{3}{10}}$ by either method.

A_2 Simplify the complex fraction by either method. $\dfrac{\frac{4x}{9y}}{\frac{5x}{12y}}$

Method 2

$$\frac{\frac{5a}{6b}}{\frac{10a}{27b}} = \frac{5a}{6b} \div \frac{10a}{27b} = \frac{5a}{6b} \cdot \frac{27b}{10a}$$ Multiply by the reciprocal of $\frac{10a}{27b}$

$$= \frac{5a \cdot 27b}{6b \cdot 10a}$$ Multiply numerators and denominators

$$= \frac{5 \cdot a \cdot 3 \cdot 3 \cdot 3 \cdot b}{2 \cdot 3 \cdot b \cdot 2 \cdot 5 \cdot a}$$ Factor in numerator and denominator

$$= \frac{3 \cdot 3 \cdot (3 \cdot 5 \cdot a \cdot b)}{2 \cdot 2 \cdot (3 \cdot 5 \cdot a \cdot b)}$$ Group common factors

$$= \frac{9}{4}$$ Reduce to lowest terms and multiply

You are now ready to do **A_2**.

3. $\dfrac{\frac{3}{a} - 1}{1 + \frac{4}{b}}$

Method 1

$$\frac{\frac{3}{a} - 1}{1 + \frac{4}{b}} = \frac{\left(\frac{3}{a} - 1\right) \cdot ab}{\left(1 + \frac{4}{b}\right) \cdot ab}$$ Multiply primary numerator and primary denominator by the LCM of *a* and *b*, which is *ab*

$$= \frac{\frac{3}{a} \cdot ab - 1 \cdot ab}{1 \cdot ab + \frac{4}{b} \cdot ab}$$ Apply distributive property by multiplying each term by *ab*

$$= \frac{3b - ab}{ab + 4a} = \frac{b(3 - a)}{a(b + 4)}$$ Reduce and factor

A_3 Simplify the complex fraction by either method. $\dfrac{\frac{5}{x} - 3}{3 + \frac{2}{y}}$

Method 2

$$\frac{\frac{3}{a} - 1}{1 + \frac{4}{b}} = \left(\frac{3}{a} - 1\right) \div \left(1 + \frac{4}{b}\right)$$

$$= \left(\frac{3}{a} - \frac{a}{a}\right) \div \left(\frac{b}{b} + \frac{4}{b}\right)$$ Write each term over common denominator

$$= \left(\frac{3 - a}{a}\right) \div \left(\frac{b + 4}{b}\right)$$ Subtract in primary numerator and add in primary denominator

$$= \frac{3 - a}{a} \cdot \frac{b}{b + 4}$$ Multiply by the reciprocal of the primary denominator

$$= \frac{b(3 - a)}{a(b + 4)}$$ Multiply numerator and denominator

Note
It is *wrong to invert before* forming a single fraction in the numerator and the denominator.

You are now ready to do **A_3**.

4. $\dfrac{\dfrac{4}{x} - \dfrac{3}{y}}{\dfrac{5}{x} + \dfrac{7}{y}}$

Method 1

$$\frac{\dfrac{4}{x} - \dfrac{3}{y}}{\dfrac{5}{x} + \dfrac{7}{y}} = \frac{\left(\dfrac{4}{x} - \dfrac{3}{y}\right) \cdot xy}{\left(\dfrac{5}{x} + \dfrac{7}{y}\right) \cdot xy}$$

Multiply primary numerator and primary denominator by the LCM of secondary denominators x and y, which is xy

$$= \frac{\dfrac{4}{x} \cdot xy - \dfrac{3}{y} \cdot xy}{\dfrac{5}{x} \cdot xy + \dfrac{7}{y} \cdot xy}$$

Apply the distributive property and multiply each term by xy

$$= \frac{4y - 3x}{5y + 7x}$$

Reduce each term

Method 2

$$\frac{\dfrac{4}{x} - \dfrac{3}{y}}{\dfrac{5}{x} + \dfrac{7}{y}} = \left(\frac{4}{x} - \frac{3}{y}\right) \div \left(\frac{5}{x} + \frac{7}{y}\right)$$

$$= \left(\frac{4y}{xy} - \frac{3x}{xy}\right) \div \left(\frac{5y}{xy} + \frac{7x}{xy}\right)$$

Write each term over common denominator xy

$$= \frac{4y - 3x}{xy} \div \frac{5y + 7x}{xy}$$

Add and subtract as indicated

$$= \frac{4y - 3x}{xy} \cdot \frac{xy}{5y + 7x}$$

Multiply by the reciprocal of the primary denominator

$$= \frac{4y - 3x}{5y + 7x}$$

Reduce by xy and multiply

You are now ready to do **A₄**. ■

A₄ Simplify the complex fraction by either method. $\dfrac{\dfrac{6}{a} - \dfrac{3}{b}}{\dfrac{1}{a} + \dfrac{5}{b}}$

Answers to section 6–4 margin exercises

A₁ $\dfrac{5}{6}$ **A₂** $\dfrac{16}{15}$ **A₃** $\dfrac{y(5 - 3x)}{x(3y + 2)}$ **A₄** $\dfrac{3(2b - a)}{b + 5a}$

Mastery points

Can you

- Simplify complex fractions?

Exercise 6–4

Directions Reduce each complex fraction. See example 6–4 A.

Example $\boxed{A_3}$ $\dfrac{\dfrac{5}{x} - 3}{3 + \dfrac{2}{y}}$

Solutions *Method 1*

$$\frac{\dfrac{5}{x} - 3}{3 + \dfrac{2}{y}} = \frac{\left(\dfrac{5}{x} - 3\right) \cdot xy}{\left(3 + \dfrac{2}{y}\right) \cdot xy} = \frac{\dfrac{5}{x} \cdot xy - 3 \cdot xy}{3 \cdot xy + \dfrac{2}{y} \cdot xy}$$

Multiply primary numerator and primary denominator by the LCD of primary denominators, xy

$$= \frac{5y - 3xy}{3xy + 2x}$$

Reduce each term

$$= \frac{y(5 - 3x)}{x(3y + 2)}$$

Factor to check for reducibility

Method 2

$$\frac{\dfrac{5}{x} - 3}{3 + \dfrac{2}{y}} = \left(\frac{5}{x} - 3\right) \div \left(3 + \frac{2}{y}\right)$$

$\dfrac{a}{b}$ can be written $a \div b$

$$= \left(\frac{5}{x} - \frac{3x}{x}\right) \div \left(\frac{3y}{y} + \frac{2}{y}\right)$$

Write each fraction with the common denominator

$$= \frac{5 - 3x}{x} \div \frac{3y + 2}{y}$$

Subtract and add rational expressions

$$= \frac{5 - 3x}{x} \cdot \frac{y}{3y + 2}$$

Multiply by the reciprocal of the primary denominator

$$= \frac{y(5 - 3x)}{x(3y + 2)}$$

Multiply numerators and denominators

1. $\dfrac{\frac{2}{3}}{\frac{4}{5}}$

2. $\dfrac{\frac{7}{8}}{\frac{5}{6}}$

3. $\dfrac{\frac{4}{3}}{\frac{8}{9}}$

4. $\dfrac{\frac{9}{10}}{\frac{7}{6}}$

5. $\dfrac{1 + \dfrac{3}{5}}{2 - \dfrac{1}{5}}$

6. $\dfrac{5 - \dfrac{3}{4}}{1 + \dfrac{5}{8}}$

7. $\dfrac{7}{2 + \dfrac{4}{5}}$

8. $\dfrac{10}{4 - \dfrac{11}{12}}$

9. $\dfrac{4 + \dfrac{3}{5}}{6}$

10. $\dfrac{10 - \dfrac{7}{8}}{3}$

11. $\dfrac{\dfrac{6}{7} - \dfrac{5}{14}}{\dfrac{3}{14} - \dfrac{5}{7}}$

12. $\dfrac{\dfrac{3}{4} + \dfrac{5}{8}}{\dfrac{1}{2} - \dfrac{1}{4}}$

13. $\dfrac{x + \dfrac{1}{4}}{x - \dfrac{3}{4}}$

14. $\dfrac{y - \dfrac{5}{6}}{y + \dfrac{1}{2}}$

15. $\dfrac{\dfrac{1}{a} + 3}{\dfrac{2}{a} - 4}$

16. $\dfrac{5 - \dfrac{3}{b}}{6 + \dfrac{5}{b}}$

17. $\dfrac{\dfrac{3}{a^2} + 4}{5 - \dfrac{3}{a}}$

18. $\dfrac{\dfrac{5}{x} - 5}{6 + \dfrac{4}{x^3}}$

19. $\dfrac{a - \dfrac{3}{b}}{a + \dfrac{4}{b}}$

20. $\dfrac{x + \dfrac{4}{y}}{x - \dfrac{5}{y}}$

21. $\dfrac{\dfrac{1}{x} + \dfrac{1}{y}}{\dfrac{1}{x} - \dfrac{1}{y}}$

22. $\dfrac{\dfrac{3}{x^2} - \dfrac{4}{y}}{\dfrac{5}{x} + \dfrac{2}{y^2}}$

23. $\dfrac{x + y}{\dfrac{1}{x} + \dfrac{1}{y}}$

24. $\dfrac{\dfrac{1}{a} - \dfrac{1}{b}}{\dfrac{1}{a^2} - \dfrac{1}{b^2}}$

25. $\dfrac{\dfrac{1}{x} + \dfrac{1}{y}}{\dfrac{1}{x^2} - \dfrac{1}{y^2}}$

26. $\dfrac{\dfrac{1}{x} - \dfrac{1}{y}}{\dfrac{1}{y^2} - \dfrac{1}{x^2}}$

27. $\dfrac{\dfrac{1}{a} + \dfrac{2}{b}}{\dfrac{4}{b^2} - \dfrac{1}{a^2}}$

28. $\dfrac{\dfrac{1}{a^2} - \dfrac{1}{b}}{a - b}$

29. $\dfrac{\dfrac{1}{x^2} - \dfrac{1}{y^2}}{x + y}$

30. $\dfrac{\dfrac{1}{x + y} - \dfrac{1}{x - y}}{\dfrac{1}{x + y} + \dfrac{1}{x - y}}$
[*Hint:* LCM is $(x + y)(x - y)$.]

31. $\dfrac{\dfrac{b}{a + b} - \dfrac{a}{a - b}}{a^2 - b^2}$

32. $\dfrac{\dfrac{x + y}{x - y} + \dfrac{x - y}{x + y}}{x^2 - y^2}$

33. $\dfrac{\dfrac{5}{x^2y^2} - \dfrac{4}{xy}}{xy}$

34. $\dfrac{\dfrac{2}{ab} + \dfrac{3}{ab^2}}{a^2b^2}$

35. $\dfrac{\dfrac{7}{x - 4} - \dfrac{5}{x + 3}}{\dfrac{5}{x + 3} + \dfrac{9}{x - 4}}$

36. $\dfrac{\dfrac{2}{a + 3} + \dfrac{1}{a - 2}}{\dfrac{3}{a - 2} - \dfrac{4}{a + 3}}$

37. $\dfrac{\dfrac{7}{b-7}+\dfrac{8}{b-5}}{\dfrac{6}{b^2-12b+35}}$

38. $\dfrac{\dfrac{5}{x^2-x-12}}{\dfrac{4}{x+3}-\dfrac{5}{x-4}}$

39. $\dfrac{\dfrac{6}{x-5}+7}{\dfrac{8}{x-5}-\dfrac{9}{x+3}}$

40. $\dfrac{3-\dfrac{4}{a+4}}{\dfrac{5}{a+4}-\dfrac{6}{a-1}}$

41. A refrigeration coefficient-of-performance formula for the ideal refrigerator is given by

$$cp=\frac{1}{\dfrac{T_2}{T_1}-1}.$$

Simplify the right member.

42. In electronics, a formula for coupled inductance in parallel is given by

$$L_t=\frac{1}{\dfrac{1}{L_1-M}+\dfrac{1}{L_2+M}}.$$

Simplify the right member.

Review exercises

Directions Reduce the following national expressions to lowest terms. See section 5–2.

1. $\dfrac{36}{42}$

2. $\dfrac{x^2-5x-14}{x^2+4x+4}$

3. Subtract $(3x^3-2x^2+x-12)-(x^3-5x^2+9)$. See section 3–2.

Directions Solve the following equations. See sections 2–3 and 4–6.

4. $4x+3x=21$

5. $8y-4=5y-10$

6. $x^2+2x-3=0$

Directions Determine the domain of the following rational expressions. See section 5–1.

7. $\dfrac{3}{x+7}$

8. $\dfrac{y-4}{y^2-4}$

A₁ $\dfrac{y+4}{6} = \dfrac{y}{12}$

6–5 Rational equations

A rational equation

An algebraic equation that contains *at least one* rational expression is called a **rational equation.** The basic operations for solving equations that you learned in chapter 2 will apply to rational equations once the denominators in the equation are eliminated. We eliminate the denominator by using the multiplication property of equality. The multiplier is the least common multiple (LCM) of all denominators in the rational expressions of the equation.

To solve a rational equation

1. Eliminate the denominators by multiplying each term of both members of the equation by the LCD of the denominators in the equation.
2. Use the four steps to solve a linear equation from section 2–3.
3. If the resulting equation is quadratic, solve as in section 4–6.

Example 6–5 A

Find the solution(s) of each of the following rational equations.

1. $\dfrac{x-3}{4} = \dfrac{x}{8}$

The LCM of 4 and 8 is 8.

$$\frac{8}{1}\cdot\frac{(x-3)}{4} = \frac{8}{1}\cdot\frac{x}{8}$$ Multiply each member by 8

$$2(x-3) = x$$ Reduce in each member

$$2x-6 = x$$ Multiply in left member

$$x-6 = 0$$ Subtract x from each member

$$x = 6$$ Add 6 to each member

The solution of the equation is 6. To check our answer, we replace x with 6 in the original equation.

$$\frac{(6)-3}{4} = \frac{(6)}{8}$$ Replace x by 6 in the original equation

$$\frac{3}{4} = \frac{3}{4}$$ True

You are now ready to do **A₁**.

2. $\frac{t}{4} - \frac{t-4}{5} = \frac{7}{10}$

The LCM of 4, 5, and 10 is 20.

$$\frac{20}{1} \cdot \frac{t}{4} - \frac{20}{1} \cdot \frac{t-4}{5} = \frac{20}{1} \cdot \frac{7}{10}$$ Multiply each term by 20

$$5t - 4(t-4) = 2 \cdot 7$$ Reduce in each term

$$5t - 4t + 16 = 14$$ Multiply in each term

$$t + 16 = 14$$ Combine like terms

$$t = -2$$ Subtract 16 from each member

The solution is -2. Check your answer by replacing t with -2 in the original equation.

Note
A common error that is made when multiplying $-4(t-4)$ is to get $-4t - 16$. Do not forget that you are using the distributive property to multiply -4 times each term in the group $(t-4)$. The correct result is $-4t + 16$.

You are now ready to do **A_2**.

A_2 $\frac{p}{6} - \frac{p+3}{8} = \frac{7}{24}$

3. $\frac{5}{3a} + \frac{4}{9} = \frac{4}{12a}$

The LCM of $3a$, 9, and $12a$ is $36a$.

$$36a \cdot \frac{5}{3a} + 36a \cdot \frac{4}{9} = 36a \cdot \frac{4}{12a}$$ Multiply each term by $36a$

$$12 \cdot 5 + 4a \cdot 4 = 3 \cdot 4$$ Reduce in each term

$$60 + 16a = 12$$ Multiply in each term

$$16a = -48$$ Subtract 60 from each member

$$a = -3$$ Divide each member by 16

A check would show that the solution is -3. You should do this.

You are now ready to do **A_3**.

A_3 $\frac{6}{4z} + \frac{7}{8} = \frac{10}{16z}$

Note
The domain of the variable is every real number *except* 0 since two of the terms are undefined when $a = 0$. This is an important observation to make as shown in example 4.

4. $\frac{3}{y} = \frac{4}{y^2 - 2y} - \frac{2}{y-2}$

Factor the denominator $y^2 - 2y$ to get $y(y-2)$. We determine that the LCM is $y(y-2)$.

$$y(y-2) \cdot \frac{3}{y} = y(y-2) \cdot \frac{4}{y(y-2)} - y(y-2) \cdot \frac{2}{y-2}$$ Multiply each term by $y(y-2)$

$$(y-2) \cdot 3 = 4 - y \cdot 2$$ Reduce in each term

$$3y - 6 = 4 - 2y$$ Multiply in each term

$$3y + 2y = 4 + 6$$ Add 6 and $2y$ to each member

$$5y = 10$$ Combine in each member

$$y = 2$$ Divide each member by 5

But 2 *is not in the domain* of the variable y, since $y - 2 = 0$ when $y = 2$. So 2 cannot be a solution of the equation. Therefore, the equation has no solution.

You are now ready to do **A_4**.

A_4 $\frac{5}{z-3} - 3 = \frac{z+2}{z-3}$

A_5 $\frac{1}{2}y^2 - \frac{17}{4}y + 2 = 0$

We conclude there is no solution for the equation of example 4. The number 2 in that example is called an *extraneous solution.* An extraneous solution can occur whenever the variable appears in the denominator of one or more of the terms of the equation. Thus, you should *always* check your possible solution(s) of a rational equation.

5. $\frac{1}{3}x^2 - \frac{5}{2}x + 3 = 0$

The LCM of 3 and 2 is 6.

$$6 \cdot \frac{1}{3}x^2 - 6 \cdot \frac{5}{2}x + 6 \cdot 3 = 6 \cdot 0$$ Multiply each term by 6

$$2x^2 - 15x + 18 = 0$$ Write the equation in standard form

$$(2x - 3)(x - 6) = 0$$ Factor $2x^2 - 15x + 18 = (2x - 3)(x - 6)$

$$2x - 3 = 0 \quad \text{or} \quad x - 6 = 0$$ Set each factor equal to 0

$$2x = 3 \qquad x = 6$$ Solve each equation

$$x = \frac{3}{2} \qquad x = 6$$

A check will show that *both* $\frac{3}{2}$ and 6 are solutions of the original equation.

You are now ready to do **A_5**.

Note

We eliminate all the denominators *only* when solving rational equations. This is *never done* when adding or subtracting rational expressions.

To illustrate, given the equation $\frac{6}{x} - \frac{4}{x^2} = 0$, we multiply each term by x^2, whereas given the subtraction problem $\frac{6}{x} - \frac{4}{x^2}$, we do *not* multiply each term by x^2. ■

Rational equations in more than one variable

In scientific fields, equations and formulas involving rational expressions and *more than one variable* are common. It is often desirable to solve such equations for one variable in terms of the other variables in the equation. The procedures for finding such solutions are identical to those used in solving the preceding equations.

To solve a rational equation in more than one variable

1. Remove the fractions by multiplying each member by the LCM.
2. Collect all terms containing the variable you are solving for in one member of the equation and all other terms in the other member.
3. Factor out the variable you are solving for if it appears in more than one term.
4. Divide each member by the coefficient of the variable for which you are solving.

Example 6–5 B

1. Solve $\dfrac{a}{3} + \dfrac{3x}{2} = c$ for x.

The LCM of 2 and 3 is 6.

$6 \cdot \dfrac{a}{3} + 6 \cdot \dfrac{3x}{2} = 6 \cdot c$	Multiply each term by 6
$2 \cdot a + 3 \cdot 3x = 6c$	Reduce where possible
$2a + 9x = 6c$	Multiply in left member
$2a + 9x - 2a = 6c - 2a$	Subtract $2a$ from each member
$9x = 6c - 2a$	Combine like terms
$x = \dfrac{6c - 2a}{9}$	Divide each member by the coefficient 9

You are now ready to do **B_1**.

2. Solve $\dfrac{1}{a} = \dfrac{1}{b} + \dfrac{1}{c}$ for c.

The LCM of a, b, and c is abc.

$abc \cdot \dfrac{1}{a} = abc \cdot \dfrac{1}{b} + abc \cdot \dfrac{1}{c}$	Multiply each term by abc
$bc = ac + ab$	Reduce where possible

Note

Since we are solving for c, we must get all terms containing c in the same member of the equation.

$bc - ac = ac + ab - ac$	Subtract ac from each member
$bc - ac = ab$	Combine like terms
$(b - a)c = ab$	Factor c from each term in the left member
$\dfrac{(b - a)c}{(b - a)} = \dfrac{ab}{(b - a)}$	Divide each member by the coefficient of c, that is, $(b - a)$
$c = \dfrac{ab}{b - a}$ or $\dfrac{-ab}{a - b}$	Reduce in left member

You are now ready to do **B_2**. ■

B_1 $\dfrac{p}{5} + \dfrac{x}{4} = q$ for x

B_2 $\dfrac{1}{x} = \dfrac{1}{y} + \dfrac{1}{z}$ for z

Answers to section 6–5 margin exercises

A_1 $y = -8$ **A_2** $p = 16$ **A_3** $z = -1$ **A_4** no solution since $z \neq 3$

A_5 $y = \dfrac{1}{2}, 8$ **B_1** $\dfrac{20q - 4p}{5}$ **B_2** $\dfrac{xy}{y - x}$ or $\dfrac{-xy}{x - y}$

Mastery points

Can you

- Solve rational equations?
- Solve rational equations for one variable in terms of the other variables?

Exercise 6–5

Directions Find the solution(s) of each rational equation. Indicate any restrictions on the domain of the variables. See example 6–5 A.

Example **A3** $\dfrac{6}{4z} + \dfrac{7}{8} = \dfrac{10}{16z}$

Solution The LCM of the denominators is $16z$.

$16z \cdot \dfrac{6}{4z} + 16z \cdot \dfrac{7}{8} = 16z \cdot \dfrac{10}{16z}$	Multiply each term by 16z
$4 \cdot 6 + 2z \cdot 7 = 10$	Reduce in each term
$24 + 14z = 10$	Multiply in each term
$14z = -14$	Subtract 24 from each member
$z = -1$	Divide each member by 14

1. $\dfrac{y}{6} = \dfrac{2}{3}$

2. $\dfrac{x}{5} = \dfrac{4}{3}$

3. $\dfrac{x}{6} - 5 = \dfrac{5}{6}$

4. $\dfrac{z}{8} + 3 = \dfrac{1}{4}$

5. $\dfrac{3a}{6} + \dfrac{2a}{5} = 1$

6. $\dfrac{5x}{8} - \dfrac{3x}{12} = 3$

7. $\dfrac{2x+1}{7} - \dfrac{3x-1}{14} = 1$

8. $\dfrac{3a+1}{9} - \dfrac{1}{3} = \dfrac{2a-1}{3}$

9. $\dfrac{3}{2x} = \dfrac{4}{5} + \dfrac{2}{x}$

10. $\dfrac{3}{4b} - \dfrac{2}{b} = \dfrac{5}{12}$

11. $\dfrac{4}{6y} + 5 = \dfrac{1}{9y} + 2$

12. $\dfrac{16}{5a} - 1 = 5 + \dfrac{3}{4a}$

13. $\dfrac{5}{3b} - \dfrac{1}{2} = \dfrac{7}{6b}$

14. $3 - \dfrac{5}{9x} = \dfrac{4}{6x}$

15. $\dfrac{a-4}{3a} = \dfrac{2a-1}{4a}$

16. $\dfrac{5 - x}{8x} = \dfrac{2x + 5}{6x}$

17. $\dfrac{4}{x - 4} = \dfrac{5}{x + 4}$

18. $\dfrac{9}{3 - x} = \dfrac{8}{2x + 1}$

19. $\dfrac{5}{x - 3} + 7 = \dfrac{4x - 2}{2x - 6}$

20. $1 + \dfrac{6}{3a - 9} = \dfrac{10}{a - 3}$

21. $\dfrac{b - 1}{b^2 - 4} = \dfrac{6}{b + 2}$

22. $\dfrac{5}{x + 3} = \dfrac{4x + 3}{x^2 - 9}$

23. $\dfrac{5}{a^2 - 25} + \dfrac{3}{a - 5} = \dfrac{4}{a + 5}$

24. $\dfrac{5}{y - 4} - \dfrac{y + 11}{y^2 - 5y + 4} = \dfrac{3}{y - 1}$

25. $\dfrac{5}{x^2 + x - 6} = \dfrac{2}{x^2 + 3x - 10}$

26. $\dfrac{8}{a^2 - 6a + 8} = \dfrac{1}{a^2 - 16}$

See example 6–5 A–5.

27. $3x^2 + 4x + \dfrac{4}{3} = 0$

28. $3x^2 + \dfrac{11}{2}x + \dfrac{3}{2} = 0$

29. $b^2 + \dfrac{3}{2}b = \dfrac{9}{2}$

30. $\dfrac{2}{3}x^2 + x = \dfrac{20}{3}$

31. $x^2 - \dfrac{5}{6}x = \dfrac{2}{3}$

32. $\dfrac{3}{4}z^2 = 2 - \dfrac{5}{2}z$

Directions Solve the following rational equations for the indicated letter. See example 6–5 B.

Example B₂ Solve $\frac{1}{x} = \frac{1}{y} + \frac{1}{z}$ for z.

Solution The LCM of the denominators is xyz.

$$xyz \cdot \frac{1}{x} = xyz \cdot \frac{1}{y} + xyz \cdot \frac{1}{z}$$ Multiply each term by xyz

$$yz = xz + xy$$ Reduce in each term

$$yz - xz = xy$$ Subtract xz from each member

$$z(y - x) = xy$$ Factor z in left member

$$z = \frac{xy}{y - x}$$ Divide each member by $y - x$

33. $\frac{2}{x} + \frac{1}{y} = 3$ for x

34. $\frac{5}{I} - 6 = \frac{8}{E}$ for I

35. $\frac{1}{c} = \frac{1}{c_1} + \frac{1}{c_2}$ for c_1

36. $\frac{1}{x} - \frac{1}{y} - \frac{1}{z} = 6$ for y

37. $\frac{1}{8} = \frac{1}{a} + \frac{1}{b}$ for a

38. $\frac{3}{a} - \frac{4}{b} = \frac{5}{ab}$ for a

39. The principal amount of money P in a savings account paying interest rate r, over a given period of time t, that pays interest I is given by $P = \frac{I}{rt}$. Solve the equation for r.

40. The pressure p per square inch of steam or water in a pipe is given by $p = \frac{P}{LD}$, where $P =$ the total pressure on a diametral plane, $L =$ the length of the pipe in inches, and $D =$ the diameter of the pipe in inches. Solve for D.

41. The safe internal unit pressure p in a given pipe of given thickness is given by $p = \frac{2st}{D}$, where $s =$ unit tensile stress, $t =$ thickness of the pipe, and $D =$ diameter of the pipe. Solve for s.

42. Given F is the force on the large piston and f is the force on the small piston of a hydraulic press, then $\frac{F}{f} = \frac{A}{a}$, where A is the area of the large piston and a is the area of the small piston. Solve for f.

43. The coefficient of linear expansion, k, of a solid when heated is given by $k = \frac{L_t - L_0}{L_0 t}$, where L_0 is the length at 0° C, L_t is the length at t° C, and t is any given temperature in Celsius. Solve for L_t. Solve for L_0.

44. Charles' Law is in regard to the relationship between pressure P, volume V, and the absolute temperature T of a gas as it expands when heated. Charles' Law is represented by $\frac{P_1V_1}{T_1} = \frac{P_2V_2}{T_2}$, where P_1, V_1, and T_1 are the initial conditions of the gas and P_2, V_2, and T_2 are the final conditions. Solve for T_2.

45. A formula for resistors in parallel is given by $R = \frac{R_1R_2}{R_1 + R_2}$. Solve for R_1.

46. Carnot's ideal efficiency of any heat engine operating between the temperature limits T_1 and T_2 is given by $E = \frac{T_1 - T_2}{T_1}$. Solve for T_1.

Review exercises

Directions Evaluate each expression for the given values. See sections 1–8 and 5–1.

1. $5x - 3y + z$ when $x = 1$, $y = -2$, and $z = 3$

2. $\frac{3a - b}{2a + b}$ when $a = 4$ and $b = -5$

3. $\frac{y_1 - y_2}{x_1 - x_2}$ when $x_1 = 3$, $x_2 = 1$, $y_1 = 3$, and $y_2 = -5$

Directions Solve each equation for y. See section 2–4.

4. $5x + y = 4$

5. $2x + 3y = 6$

6. $x - 4y = 8$

Directions Simplify the following expressions. Assume all denominators are nonzero. See section 3–4.

7. $(3y^{-1})(y^2x^{-2})$

8. $\frac{x^{-3}y^3}{x^2y^{-1}}$

A_1 Two pipes feed into a swimming pool. If one pipe can fill the pool in 30 hours and the other pipe can fill the pool in 36 hours, how long will it take to fill the pool if both pipes are open?

6–6 Rational expression applications

Rational expressions occurring in rational equations have many applications in the physical and scientific world. We now wish to discuss some of the more common applications.

Example 6–6 A

Choose a variable, set up an appropriate equation, and solve the following problems.

1. A water holding tank is fed by two pipes. If it takes the smaller pipe 12 hours to fill the tank and the larger pipe 9 hours to fill the tank, how long would it take to fill the tank if both pipes are open? (This is called a *work* problem.)

Let x = the number of hours it takes the two pipes to fill the tank. Now,

a. the smaller pipe can fill $\frac{1}{12}$ of the tank in 1 hour,

b. the larger pipe can fill $\frac{1}{9}$ of the tank in 1 hour,

c. the two pipes together can fill $\frac{1}{x}$ of the tank in 1 hour.

The amount of the tank filled by the smaller pipe in 1 hour plus the amount of the tank filled by the larger pipe in 1 hour must be equal to the amount of the tank filled by the two pipes together in 1 hour. Thus, the equation is

Amount by larger pipe ↓

Amount by smaller pipe → $\frac{1}{12} + \frac{1}{9} = \frac{1}{x}$. ← Amount together

The LCM of 12, 9, and x is $36x$.

$$36x \cdot \frac{1}{12} + 36x \cdot \frac{1}{9} = 36x \cdot \frac{1}{x} \quad (x \neq 0)$$ Multiply each term by $36x$

$$3x + 4x = 36$$ Reduce in each term

$$7x = 36$$ Combine in left member

$$x = \frac{36}{7}$$ Divide each member by 7

Therefore, together the two pipes can fill the tank in $\frac{36}{7}$ hours, or $5\frac{1}{7}$ hours, that is, approximately 5 hours and 9 minutes.

You are now ready to do **A_1**.

2. Jim James drove a distance of 120 miles, part at 50 miles per hour (mph) and part at 60 mph. If he drove the 120 miles in $2\frac{1}{4}$ hours, how many miles did he drive at 50 mph? (This is called a *distance–rate–time* problem.)

Note
In a distance (d)–rate (r)–time (t) problem, we use $d = rt$, $t = \frac{d}{r}$, or $r = \frac{d}{t}$.

Let x = the distance he drove at 50 mph. Then $120 - x$ = the distance he drove at 60 mph.

The time traveled at 50 mph plus the time traveled at 60 mph equals the total time traveled, $2\frac{1}{4}$ hr $\left(\text{or } \frac{9}{4} \text{ hr}\right)$. We use the following table for distance–rate–time problems.

distance (d)	rate (r)	time (t)
x	50	$\frac{x}{50}$
$120 - x$	60	$\frac{120 - x}{60}$

$t = \frac{d}{r}$

The equation is then

$$\frac{x}{50} + \frac{120 - x}{60} = \frac{9}{4}$$

$$300 \cdot \frac{x}{50} + 300 \cdot \frac{120 - x}{60} = 300 \cdot \frac{9}{4}$$ Multiply each term by the LCM of 50, 60, and 4, 300

$$6x + 5(120 - x) = 675$$ Reduce in each term

$$6x + 600 - 5x = 675$$ Distributive property

$$x + 600 = 675$$ Combine in left member

$$x = 75.$$ Subtract 600 from each member

Thus, Jim James drove 75 miles at 50 mph.

Note
He drove $120 - x = 120 - 75 = 45$ miles at 60 mph.

You are now ready to do **A_2**.

A_2 Jennifer Jones drove a distance of 300 miles through mountains in 6 hours. If she drove part at 45 mph and the rest at 60 mph, how many miles did she drive at 60 mph?

3. The denominator of a fraction is 3 more than the numerator. If 4 is added to the numerator and the denominator, the resulting fraction is $\frac{3}{4}$. Find the original fraction.

Let $x =$ the numerator of the original fraction. Then $x + 3 =$ the denominator of the fraction. Adding 4 to the numerator and the denominator, the fraction becomes

$$\frac{x + 4}{(x + 3) + 4}.$$

The equation we get is

$$\frac{x + 4}{(x + 3) + 4} = \frac{3}{4} \quad \text{or} \quad \frac{x + 4}{x + 7} = \frac{3}{4}.$$

The LCM of 4 and $x + 7$ is $4(x + 7)$.

$$4(x + 7) \cdot \frac{x + 4}{x + 7} = 4(x + 7) \cdot \frac{3}{4}$$ Multiply each member by $4(x + 7)$

$$4(x + 4) = (x + 7) \cdot 3$$ Reduce in each term

$$4x + 16 = 3x + 21$$ Distributive property

$x = 5$ is the numerator — Subtract $3x$ and 16 from each member

and $x + 3 = 8$ is the denominator.

The original fraction is $\frac{5}{8}$.

You are now ready to do **A_3**.

A_3 If the same number is added to the numerator and the denominator of $\frac{3}{4}$ we get $\frac{5}{6}$. What is the number?

A_4 Find the total resistance of an electrical circuit connected in parallel if two resistors have resistances of 8 ohms and 10 ohms.

4. In an electrical circuit, when two resistors are connected in parallel, the total resistance R of the circuit in ohms is given by

$$\frac{1}{R} = \frac{1}{R_1} + \frac{1}{R_2},$$

where R_1 and R_2 are the resistances of the two resistors in ohms and the circuit is connected in parallel as shown in the diagram. Find the total resistance R of an electrical circuit having two resistors connected in parallel if their resistances are 4 ohms and 6 ohms.

R_1

R_2

We want R when $R_1 = 4$ ohms and $R_2 = 6$ ohms.

$$\frac{1}{R} = \frac{1}{4} + \frac{1}{6}$$

The LCM of 4, 6, and R is $12R$.

$$12R \cdot \frac{1}{R} = 12R \cdot \frac{1}{4} + 12R \cdot \frac{1}{6}$$ Multiply each member by $12R$

$$12 = 3R + 2R$$ Reduce in each member

$$12 = 5R$$ Combine in right member

$$\frac{12}{5} = R$$ Divide each member by 5

Therefore the total resistance is $\frac{12}{5}$, or $2\frac{2}{5}$, ohms.

You are now ready to do **A_4**. ■

Answers to section 6–6 margin exercises

A_1 $16\frac{4}{11}$ hr **A_2** 120 mi **A_3** 2 **A_4** $4\frac{4}{9}$ ohms

Mastery points

Can you

- Solve work problems?
- Solve distance—rate—time problems?
- Solve number problems?
- Find resistances in electrical circuit problems?

Exercise 6–6

Directions Choose a variable, set up an equation, and solve the following problems. See example 6–6 A–1.

1. Jim can mow his parents' lawn in 50 minutes. His younger brother Kenny can mow the lawn in 70 minutes. How long would it take the boys to mow the lawn if they mow together using two lawnmowers?

2. In a factory, worker A can do a certain job in 6 hours while worker B can do the same job in 5 hours. How long would it take workers A and B to do the same job working together?

3. Three different sized pipes feed water into a swimming pool. If the pipes can fill the same pool individually in 6 hours, 8 hours, and 9 hours, respectively, how long would it take to fill the same pool if all three pipes were open?

4. During "clean-up week" in Podunk Junction, Jane, Joan, and Ruth work to clean up a vacant lot. The girls can do the job individually in 2 hours, 3 hours, and 4 hours, respectively. How long will it take them, working together, to clean the lot?

5. It takes two men—Harry and Dick—working together 4 hours to paint the exterior of a house. If Harry could do the job in 6 hours working alone, how long would it take Dick to paint the house alone?

6. A water tank has two drain pipes. If the larger pipe could empty the tank in 45 minutes and the two pipes together could drain the tank in 30 minutes, how long would it take the smaller pipe to drain the tank?

7. Three machines—*A*, *B*, and *C*—working together can harvest a field of oats in $1\frac{1}{2}$ hours. If *A* could do the job alone in 5 hours and *B* could do it alone in 6 hours, how long would it take for machine *C* to do the same job alone?

8. In a pizzeria, three women are at work making pizzas. The three could make 50 pizzas in $1\frac{1}{3}$ hours working together. If two of the women could make the same number of pizzas in 4 hours and 5 hours, respectively, working alone, how long would it take the third woman to make the 50 pizzas working alone?

9. A tank has one inlet pipe and one outlet pipe. If the inlet pipe can fill the tank in $3\frac{1}{3}$ hours and the outlet pipe can empty the tank in 5 hours, how long would it take to fill the tank if both pipes are left open? (*Hint:* Subtract the drainage.)

10. A sink drain, when left open, can empty a sink full of water in 4 minutes. If the cold water and hot water faucets can, when fully open, fill the sink in $2\frac{1}{2}$ minutes and 3 minutes, respectively, how long would it take to fill the sink if all three are open simultaneously?

See example 6–6 A–2.

11. Jack drove 320 miles in $5\frac{1}{2}$ hours. If he drove part of the trip averaging 55 mph and the rest averaging 60 mph, how many miles did he drive at each speed?

12. A. J. Foyt, when driving the Indianapolis 500 Race, averaged 210 mph over part of the race. Due to an accident on the track, he averaged 160 mph over the rest. If the race took 2 hours and 40 minutes to run, how many miles did he drive at an average of 210 mph?

13. Car A travels 120 miles in the same time that car B travels 150 miles. If car B averages 10 mph faster than car A, how fast is each car traveling?

14. A freight train travels 260 kilometers in the same time a passenger train travels 320 kilometers. If the passenger train averages 15 kilometers per hour faster than the freight train, what is the average speed of the freight train?

15. Sheila can row a boat 2 mph in still water. How fast is the current of a river if she takes the same length of time to row 4 miles upstream as she does to row 10 miles downstream? (*Hint:* Subtract current upstream and add downstream.)

16. An airplane flew 1,000 miles with the wind in the same length of time it took to fly 850 miles against the wind. If the wind was blowing at 25 miles/hour, what was the average air speed of the plane?

17. On a trip from Detroit, Michigan, to Columbus, Ohio, Mrs. Smith drove at an average speed of 60 mph. Returning, her average speed was 55 mph. If it took her $\frac{1}{3}$ hour longer on the return trip, how far is it from Detroit to Columbus?

18. A jet plane flew at an average speed of 240 miles per hour going from city A to city B and averaged 300 miles/hour on the return flight. Its return flight took 1 hour and 40 minutes less time. How far is it from city A to city B? (Disregard any wind.)

See example 6–6 A–3.

19. The numerator of a given fraction is 4 less than the denominator. If 5 is added to both the numerator and the denominator, the resulting fraction is $\frac{5}{7}$. What is the original fraction?

20. The denominator of a fraction exceeds the numerator by 7. If 3 is added to the numerator and 1 is subtracted from the denominator, the resulting fraction is $\frac{4}{5}$. Find the original fraction.

21. One number is four times another number. The sum of their reciprocals is $\frac{5}{12}$. What are the numbers?

22. One number is four times another number. The sum of their reciprocals is $\frac{1}{4}$. What are the numbers?

23. If $\frac{1}{2}$ is added to three times the reciprocal of a number, the result is 1. Find the number.

24. If $\frac{1}{2}$ is subtracted from four times the reciprocal of a number, the result is 0. Find the number.

25. When a certain number is added to the numerator and subtracted from the denominator of the fraction $\frac{2}{5}$, the result is 6. What is the number?

26. When a certain number is added to the numerator and subtracted from the denominator of the fraction $\frac{5}{9}$, the result is $\frac{4}{7}$. What is the number?

Directions Use the formula $\frac{1}{R} = \frac{1}{R_1} + \frac{1}{R_2}$ to solve the following exercises. See example 6–6 A–4.

27. Two resistors in an electric circuit have resistances of 6 ohms and 8 ohms and are connected in parallel. Find the total resistance of the circuit.

28. Two resistors of an electric circuit are connected in parallel. If one has a resistance of 5 ohms and the other has a resistance of 12 ohms, what is the total resistance in the circuit?

29. Three resistors connected in parallel have resistances of 4 ohms, 6 ohms, and 10 ohms. What is the total resistance in the electric circuit? $\left(\textit{Hint:}\text{ Use } \frac{1}{R} = \frac{1}{R_1} + \frac{1}{R_2} + \frac{1}{R_3}.\right)$

30. The total resistance in a parallel wiring circuit is 12 ohms. If the resistance in one branch is 30 ohms, what is the resistance in the other branch?

31. The resistance in one branch of a two-resistor parallel wiring circuit is 10 ohms. If the total resistance in the circuit is 6 ohms, what is the resistance in the other branch?

32. A three-resistor parallel wiring circuit has a total resistance of 10 ohms. If two of the branches of the circuit have resistances of 20 ohms and 30 ohms, what is the resistance in the third branch? (See hint in exercise 29.)

Review exercises

Directions Solve the following equations. See sections 2–3 and 2–4.

1. $2y + 3 = 4y - 1$
2. $2y - 3x = 6$ for y

Directions Factor the following expressions. See sections 4–3 and 4–4.

3. $8y^2 - 32$
4. $x^2 + 20x + 100$
5. $3y^2 - 4y - 4$

Directions Combine the following rational polynomial. See section 6–3.

6. $\dfrac{3x}{x-1} + \dfrac{2x}{x+3}$
7. $\dfrac{4y}{2y+1} - \dfrac{3y}{y-5}$

Chapter 6 lead-in problem

Marc owns $\frac{5}{8}$ interest in a print shop and his uncle owns $\frac{1}{4}$ interest in the shop. In a given year, they shared earnings of $140,000. How much did the shop earn that year?

Solution

Let $x =$ the total earnings of the print shop.

	Interest	Shop earnings	Income
Marc	$\frac{5}{8}$	x	$\frac{5}{8}x$
Rolfe	$\frac{1}{4}$	x	$\frac{1}{4}x$

Then $\frac{5}{8}x + \frac{1}{4}x = 140{,}000$ — Together they earned $140,000

$8 \cdot \frac{5}{8}x + 8 \cdot \frac{1}{4}x = 8 \cdot 140{,}000$ — Multiply each term by the LCM of 4 and 8, 8

$5x + 2x = 1{,}120{,}000$ — Perform indicated multiplications

$7x = 1{,}120{,}000$ — Combine like terms

$x = 160{,}000$ — Divide each member by 7

The print shop earned $160,000 in the given year.

Chapter 6 summary

1. To *multiply* two rational expressions, multiply the numerators and place the product over the product of the denominators.
2. To *divide* two rational expressions, $\frac{P}{Q} \div \frac{R}{S}$, multiply $\frac{P}{Q}$ by the reciprocal of $\frac{R}{S}$, which is $\frac{S}{R}$.
3. To find the **least common denominator** (LCD) of two or more rational expressions
   a. Write each denominator in completely factored form.
   b. Take each different factor that appears in the factorizations and write it as a product.
   c. Raise each factor to the greatest power it has in step a.
4. To obtain an *equivalent rational expression,* multiply, or divide, the numerator and the denominator of the given rational expression by the same nonzero polynomial.
5. **To add or subtract rational expressions**
   a. Write each rational expression as an equivalent rational expression with the same denominator, preferably the LCD.
   b. Add, or subtract, numerators and place this sum, or difference, over the common denominator.
6. A **complex fraction** is a fraction whose numerator or denominator, or both, contains at least one fraction.
7. In the *complex fraction*

$$\frac{\frac{a}{b}}{\frac{c}{d}},$$

we call $\frac{a}{b}$ the *primary numerator,* $\frac{c}{d}$ the *primary denominator,* and b and d the *secondary denominators.*

8. **To simplify a complex fraction**
   a. Divide the primary numerator by the primary denominator after making a single fraction of each. OR
   b. Multiply the primary numerator and the primary denominator by the LCM of the secondary denominators and reduce the result, where possible.
9. A **rational equation** is an equation in which one or more terms involves a rational expression.
10. **To solve a rational equation**
    a. Multiply each term of the equation by the LCD to eliminate the fractions.
    b. Use the basic procedures for solving equations.
    c. Check for extraneous solutions.

Chapter 6 review

[6–1]

Directions Perform the indicated multiplication and reduce the product to lowest terms. Assume all denominators are nonzero.

1. $\frac{24b}{7a} \cdot \frac{21a^2}{8b^2}$
2. $\frac{5x - 10}{x + 3} \cdot \frac{3x + 9}{15}$
3. $\frac{y}{y^2 - 1} \cdot \frac{y + 1}{y^2 - y}$
4. $\frac{5 - x}{6a - 3} \cdot \frac{2a - 1}{x^2 - 25}$

Directions Find the indicated quotients and state the answer reduced to lowest terms. Assume all denominators are nonzero.

5. $\frac{14a}{9} \div \frac{7}{3}$
6. $\frac{24ab}{7} \div \frac{16a^2b^2}{21}$
7. $\frac{x + 6}{x^2 - 4} \div \frac{(x + 6)^2}{x + 2}$
8. $\frac{x^2 + 16x + 64}{x^2 + 9x + 8} \div \frac{x^2 - 64}{x + 1}$
9. $\frac{9a^2 + 15a + 6}{a^2 + 3a - 4} \div \frac{36a^2 - 16}{3a^2 + 10a - 8}$

[6–2]

Directions Find the least common denominator of the given rational expressions and convert them to equivalent rational expressions with the common denominator as the LCD.

10. $\frac{5}{14ab}; \frac{8}{21a^2b^2}$

11. $\frac{4y}{y^2 - 2y - 15}; \frac{9y}{y^2 - 25}$

12. $\frac{2x - 1}{x^2 + x}; \frac{x + 3}{x^2 + 2x + 1}; \frac{x}{3x^2 - 2x - 5}$

[6–3]

Directions Add or subtract as indicated and reduce your answer to lowest terms.

13. $\frac{25}{16a} - \frac{13}{12a}$

14. $\frac{5}{3x + 1} + \frac{9}{4x - 3}$

15. $\frac{4}{ab^2} + \frac{12}{5a^2b} - \frac{3}{4ab}$

16. $\frac{7}{x^2 + 1} - 10$

17. $\frac{4y}{y^2 - 7y - 18} + \frac{9y}{y^2 - 4}$

18. $\frac{9}{x} - \frac{4}{x - 5} + \frac{3}{x + 4}$

[6–4]

Directions Simplify the given complex fractions and reduce to lowest terms.

19. $\frac{\frac{4}{7}}{\frac{9}{4}}$

20. $\frac{\frac{4}{5} + 1}{2 - \frac{1}{5}}$

21. $\frac{\frac{4}{x^2} + \frac{3}{x}}{\frac{2}{x^2} - \frac{5}{x}}$

22. $\frac{\frac{1}{x} - \frac{1}{y}}{\frac{1}{xy}}$

23. $\frac{\frac{a^2}{b^2} - 2a - 3}{\frac{a - 3b}{ab}}$

[6–5]

Directions Find the solution(s) of the following rational equations.

24. $\frac{x}{8} - 3 = \frac{2x}{12} + 1$

25. $\frac{12}{4a} - \frac{5}{6a} = 4$

26. $\frac{1}{y+3} - \frac{6}{y} = \frac{7}{y} + \frac{2}{y+3}$

27. $\frac{x^2}{4} - 3x = 0$

28. $\frac{x^2}{2} - \frac{15}{2} = -x$

Directions Solve for the indicated variable.

29. $\frac{a}{x} + \frac{b}{x} = 3$ for x

30. $\frac{3}{4-y} = \frac{a}{b}$ for y

31. The efficiency of a screw jack is calculated by the formula $E = \frac{Wp}{2 + LF}$. Solve for L.

32. The total reaction force F of air against a plane at the bottom of a vertical loop in centripetal force is given by $F = \frac{mv^2}{r} + mg$. Solve for m.

[6–6]

33. With different equipment, one painter can paint a house three times faster than a second painter. Working together they can do it in 4 hours. How long would it take each of them to paint the house working together?

34. Paul can row his boat at a rate of 4 miles per hour in still water. It takes him as long to row 20 miles downstream as it takes him to row 8 miles upstream. What is the rate of the current?

35. The sum of three times a number and twice its reciprocal is 5. Find the number.

NAME

Chapter 6 cumulative test

CLASS/SECTION DATE

Directions Compute and simplify.

[1–6] **1.** $-\frac{1}{3}+\frac{1}{4}+(-6)+\frac{1}{6}$

[1–4] **2.** $-\frac{4}{5}\left(-\frac{15}{16}\right)$

[1–3] **3.** $\frac{5}{6}-\left(-\frac{3}{5}\right)$

[1–6] **4.** $-\frac{24}{35}\div\left(-\frac{3}{7}\right)$

Directions Simplify the following expressions with only positive exponents.

[3–1] **5.** $x^8 \cdot x^3 \cdot x^0$

[3–4] **6.** $\frac{y^{-5}}{y^4}$

[3–4] **7.** $(-5x^2y^{-3})^2$

[3–2] **8.** $(9x^3 - 3x^2 + 4x - 8) - (-x^3 + x^2 - 7x + 1)$

Directions Find the solution(s) of the following equations.

[2–3] **9.** $-5(2x + 5) = -3x + 1$

[2–3] **10.** $\frac{1}{3}x - \frac{3}{4} = 6$

[4–6] **11.** $2y^2 - y = 6$

Directions Completely factor each expression.

[4–4] **12.** $2x^2 - 18$

[4–1] **13.** $6x^5 - 36x^3 + 9x^2$

[4–3] **14.** $4x^2 + 16x + 15$

[4–4] **15.** $3 - 12x^6$

Directions Perform the indicated operations.

[3–3] **16.** $(7x - 6)^2$

[3–3] **17.** $\left(5 - \frac{1}{2}x\right)\left(5 + \frac{1}{2}x\right)$

[3–3] **18.** $(2x - 3)(3x^2 - 5x + 11)$

[3–3] **19.** $(3 - 2x^2)(5 - 4x^2)$

[5–4] **20.** Find x when $\frac{x}{24} = \frac{5}{6}$.

[1–8] **21.** Power (in foot-pounds per minute) is given by the ratio of work, w, and time, t. Find the power exerted by pushing an 80-pound load 180 feet in 6 minutes. (*Hint:* w = weight × length.)

Directions Perform the indicated operations and reduce the answers to lowest terms.

[6–1] **22.** $\frac{4a}{5b} \cdot \frac{a}{b}$

[6–1] **23.** $\frac{y + 3}{y - 6} \cdot \frac{y + 7}{y - 2}$

[6–1] **24.** $\frac{y^2 - 4}{y + 3} \cdot \frac{y^2 - 9}{y + 2}$

[6–1] **25.** $\frac{x^2 - y^2}{9} \div \frac{y^2 + xy}{9x - 9}$

[6–3] **26.** $\frac{2}{x^2y} + \frac{4}{xy^2}$

[6–3] **27.** $\frac{6}{x - y} - \frac{3}{x + y}$

[6–3] **28.** $\frac{a + 1}{a - 2} + \frac{a - 8}{2 - a}$

[6–3] **29.** $\frac{7}{x^2 - 49} + \frac{6}{x^2 - 5x - 14}$

[6–3] **30.** $\frac{2x}{x^2 + x - 6} - \frac{3x}{x^2 - 3x - 18}$

Directions Simplify the following complex rational expressions.

[6–4] **31.** $\dfrac{3 - \frac{1}{y}}{4 + \frac{5}{y}}$

[6–4] **32.** $\dfrac{\frac{1}{x} + \frac{1}{y}}{\frac{3}{y} - \frac{4}{x}}$

[6–4] **33.** $\dfrac{\frac{x - 4}{x + 7}}{\frac{x + 5}{x^2 - 49}}$

Directions Find the solution(s) of the following equations.

[6–5] **34.** $\frac{4}{x} = \frac{6}{2x - 1}$

[6–5] **35.** $x^2 - 2 = \frac{17x}{3}$

[6–5] **36.** Solve the equation $\frac{1}{f} = \frac{1}{p} + \frac{1}{q}$ for q.

Directions Choose a variable, set an appropriate equation, and solve the following problems.

[6–6] **37.** John can build a fence in 6 days and Harry can build the same fence in 4 days. How long would it take them to build the fence working together?

[6–6] **38.** The denominator of a fraction is one more than two times the numerator. If 2 is added to the numerator and 3 is subtracted from the denominator, the resulting fraction is $\frac{5}{7}$. Find the original fraction.

CHAPTER

7

Linear Equations in Two Variables

Tickets to a football game at Podunk High School cost $1.25 for students and $3.00 for adults. The total receipts for a game with University High School were $1,020. Write an equation using x for the number of students and y for the number of adults attending the game.

Proficiency check

[2–4] **1.** Solve the following equations for y.

a. $4x + y = 5$

b. $2y - 3x = 4$

c. $x + 3y = -9$

[1–8] **2.** Evaluate y when $y = 3x + 4$ and

a. $x = 2$

b. $x = -4$

c. $x = 0$

[2–2] **3.** Find the value of y when $3x + 2y = 1$ and $x = 7$.

[2–2] **4.** Find the value of x when $2x - 5y = 3$ and $y = -1$.

7–1 Ordered pairs and the rectangular coordinate system

Linear equations in two variables

In chapter 2, we developed methods for solving linear equations (first-degree equations) in one variable. All such equations could be stated in the form

$$ax + b = 0,$$

where a and b are real number constants and $a \neq 0$. In this chapter, we expand our work to linear equations in *two variables*. The equations

$$3x + 4y = 8 \quad \text{and} \quad 4y - x = 0$$

are examples of linear equations in two variables.

> **Definition**
>
> A **linear equation in two variables** x and y is any equation that can be written in the form
>
> $$ax + by = c,$$
>
> where a, b, and c are real numbers and a and b are not both zero.

Our primary concern with all equations is finding their **solution(s).** These are the replacement values for the variable(s) that satisfy the equation. In an equation in two variables, x and y, any *pair* of values for x and y that satisfies the equation is a solution of the equation.

Example 7–1 A

Given the linear equation $3x + 2y = 6$, determine if the given values of x and y are solutions of the equation.

1. Let $x = 2$ and $y = 0$.

$$
\begin{aligned}
3x + 2y &= 6 \\
3(2) + 2(0) &= 6 && \text{Replace } x \text{ with 2 and } y \text{ with 0 in the equation} \\
6 + 0 &= 6 && \text{Multiply as indicated} \\
6 &= 6 && \text{(True)}
\end{aligned}
$$

We see that the given values satisfy the equation, so $x = 2$ and $y = 0$ is a solution.

You are now ready to do $\mathbf{A_1}$.

2. Let $x = 1$ and $y = \frac{3}{2}$.

$$
\begin{aligned}
3x + 2y &= 6 \\
3(1) + 2\left(\frac{3}{2}\right) &= 6 && \text{Replace } x \text{ with 1 and } y \text{ with } \frac{3}{2} \text{ in the equation} \\
3 + 3 &= 6 && \text{Multiply as indicated} \\
6 &= 6 && \text{(True)}
\end{aligned}
$$

Again we see that the values $x = 1$ and $y = \frac{3}{2}$ satisfy the equation and thereby form a solution.

You are now ready to do $\mathbf{A_2}$.

3. Let $x = 3$ and $y = 1$.

$$
\begin{aligned}
3x + 2y &= 6 \\
3(3) + 2(1) &= 6 && \text{Replace } x \text{ with 3 and } y \text{ with 1 in the equation} \\
9 + 2 &= 6 && \text{Multiply as indicated} \\
11 &= 6 && \text{(False)}
\end{aligned}
$$

We conclude that $x = 3$ and $y = 1$ *do not* satisfy the equation and hence *do not form a solution.*

You are now ready to do $\mathbf{A_3}$. ■

$\mathbf{A_1}$ Determine if $x = -2$ and $y = 6$ satisfy the equation $3x + 2y = 6$.

$\mathbf{A_2}$ Show that $x = 0$ and $y = 3$ satisfy the equation $3x + 2y = 6$.

$\mathbf{A_3}$ Show that $x = 4$ and $y = -2$ *do not* satisfy the equation $3x + 2y = 6$.

Ordered pairs of numbers

The pairs of values for x and y used in example 7–1 A may be written as a pair of numbers. We separate them by a comma and place them inside the parentheses. The value of x is *always* given first. That is, the pair of numbers is written (x,y). In the examples we used the pairs

$$(2,0),\ \left(1,\frac{3}{2}\right),\ \text{and } (3,1).$$

Pairs of numbers written in this special *order* (with the x value always first) are called **ordered pairs of numbers.** The *first number* of the ordered pair (the value of x) is called the *first component* of the ordered pair. The *second number* (the value of y) is called the *second component* of the ordered pair.

To determine ordered pairs that are solutions of an equation in two variables, we use the following procedure:

To find ordered pair solutions

1. Choose a value for one of the variables.
2. Replace the variable with this known value and solve the resulting equation for the other variable.

Example 7–1 B

Find the missing variable and write the ordered pair solution of the equation.

1. Given $y = 2x + 1$:

a. Let $x = 3$.

$y = 2(3) + 1$ Replace x with 3 in the equation
$y = 6 + 1$ Multiply as indicated
$y = 7$ Add in right member

The ordered pair (3,7) is a solution.

You are now ready to do **B₁**.

B₁ Let $x = 5$. Find y when $y = 2x + 1$.

b. Let $x = -2$.

$y = 2(-2) + 1$ Replace x with -2 in the equation
$y = -4 + 1$ Multiply as indicated
$y = -3$ Add in right member

The ordered pair $(-2,-3)$ is a solution.

You are now ready to do **B₂**.

B₂ Let $x = -4$. Find y when $y = 2x + 1$.

c. Let $y = 5$.

$5 = 2x + 1$ Replace y with 5 in the equation
$4 = 2x$ Subtract 1 from each member
$2 = x$ Divide each member by 2

The ordered pair (2,5) is a solution.

You are now ready to do **B₃**.

B₃ Let $y = -7$. Find x when $y = 2x + 1$.

Note
We can choose *infinitely many* values for x and get a corresponding value of y for each choice of x and thus have infinitely many solutions.

2. Given $3x - 2y = 4$:

a. Let $x = 2$.

$3(2) - 2y = 4$ Replace x with 2 in the equation
$6 - 2y = 4$ Multiply as indicated
$-2y = -2$ Subtract 6 from each member
$y = 1$ Divide each member by -2

The ordered pair (2,1) is a solution.

You are now ready to do **B₄**.

B₄ Let $x = 3$ and $x = -2$. Given $3x - 2y = 4$, find y.

b. Let $y = 7$.

$3x - 2(7) = 4$ Replace y with 7 in the equation
$3x - 14 = 4$ Multiply as indicated
$3x = 18$ Add 14 to each member
$x = 6$ Divide each member by 3

The ordered pair (6,7) is a solution.

You are now ready to do **B₅**.

B₅ Let $y = -2$. Find x when $3x - 2y = 4$.

3. Given $y = 6$, we can rewrite this equation as

$y + 0 \cdot x = 6$.

a. Let $x = 3$.

$$\begin{aligned} y + 0(3) &= 6 && \text{Replace } x \text{ with } 3 \\ y + 0 &= 6 && \text{Multiply as indicated} \\ y &= 6 && y + 0 = y \end{aligned}$$

The ordered pair (3,6) is a solution.

You are now ready to do **B_6**.

B_6 Let $x = 4$. Find y when $y = 6$.

b. Let $x = -7$.

$$\begin{aligned} y + 0(-7) &= 6 && \text{Replace } x \text{ with } -7 \\ y + 0 &= 6 && \text{Multiply as indicated} \\ y &= 6 && y + 0 = y \end{aligned}$$

The ordered pair $(-7,6)$ is a solution.

You are now ready to do **B_7**.

B_7 Let $x = -9$. Find y when $y = 6$.

Note
No matter what *value* we choose for *x*, *y* will *always* be 6. Then *every* ordered pair will have a 6 in the second position, the "*y*-spot."

4. Given $x + 3 = 0$, we can rewrite this equation as $x = -3$ and then as

$x + 0 \cdot y = -3$.

a. Let $y = 1$.

$$\begin{aligned} x + 0(1) &= -3 && \text{Replace } y \text{ with } 1 \\ x + 0 &= -3 && \text{Multiply as indicated} \\ x &= -3 && x + 0 = x \end{aligned}$$

The ordered pair $(-3,1)$ is a solution.

You are now ready to do **B_8**.

B_8 Let $y = 6$. Find x when $x + 3 = 0$.

b. Let $y = -4$.

$$\begin{aligned} x + 0(-4) &= -3 && \text{Replace } y \text{ with } -4 \\ x + 0 &= -3 && \text{Multiply as indicated} \\ x &= -3 && x + 0 = x \end{aligned}$$

The ordered pair $(-3,-4)$ is a solution.

You are now ready to do **B_9**.

B_9 Let $y = -1$. Find x when $x + 3 = 0$.

Note
No matter what *value* we choose for *y*, *x* will *always* be -3. Then every ordered pair will have a -3 in the first position, the "*x*-spot." ■

From examples 3 and 4, we can see that solutions of linear equations in two variables that can be written in the form

$$y = b \quad \text{or} \quad x = a,$$

where *a* and *b* are constants, have very special characteristics. Given

1. $x = a$, the *first component* in every ordered pair is always the number *a*.
2. $y = b$, the *second component* in every ordered pair is always the number *b*.

The rectangular coordinate plane

In chapter 1, we associated the set of real numbers with points on a straight line and called this the number line. This number line was then used to draw the graph of the solution of an equation or inequality in one variable. Now we associate the solutions of a linear equation *in two variables* with *points* on a surface, called a *plane*.

We draw two number lines on the plane that are perpendicular to each other, called *axes*. These two number lines are represented in figure 7–1. One line (x-axis) is associated with values of x, and the other line (y-axis) is associated with values of y. The horizontal number line is called the x-*axis*, and the vertical number line is called the y-*axis*. Together, the x- and y-axes form the **rectangular coordinate plane** (or Cartesian coordinate plane).

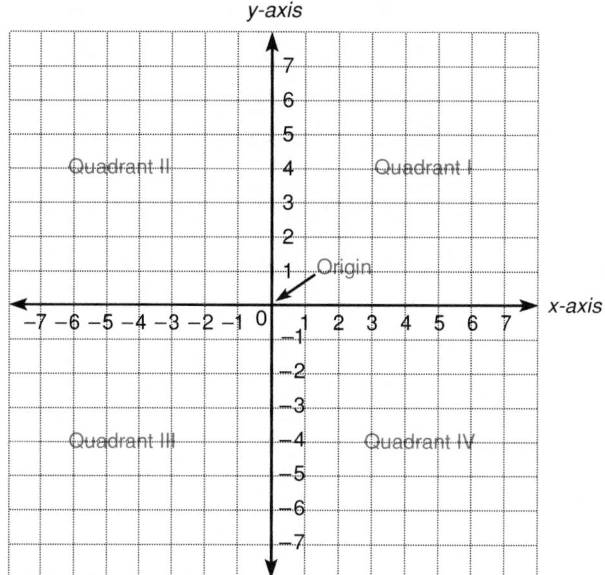

Figure 7–1

The point at which the two axes intersect is their common zero point and is called the *origin*. The origin corresponds to the ordered pair (0,0). The two axes separate the coordinate plane into four regions called *quadrants*. These quadrants are named as shown in figure 7–1. Points that lie on the x-axis or y-axis *do not* lie in any of the quadrants.

On the x-axis, numbers to the right of the origin are positive and those to the left of the origin are negative. On the y-axis, the positive numbers are above the origin, and the negative numbers are below the origin. For each point on the x-axis, $y = 0$, and for each point on the y-axis, $x = 0$.

Note
We have chosen to make each unit on the axes equal to 1. Other choices are possible and, in fact, may be necessary in some instances.

Each ordered pair (x,y) corresponds to *exactly* one point, called the *graph* of the ordered pair. To find the location of such a point is called *plotting* the point. We can plot any ordered pair, (x,y), on our coordinate plane if we consider the ordered pair as two instructions to direct us from the origin to the proper location of the point. To plot the point that corresponds to the ordered pair (4,3), we start at the origin. Since the x-value, also called the **abscissa** of the point, is 4, we move four units *to the right* (the positive direction) along the x-axis. From this position, the y-value, also called the **ordinate** of the point, instructs us to move *up* (the positive direction) three units parallel to the y-axis. The abscissa and ordinate are usually called the *coordinates* of a point. We have plotted the point that is the graph of the ordered pair (4,3) as shown in figure 7–2.

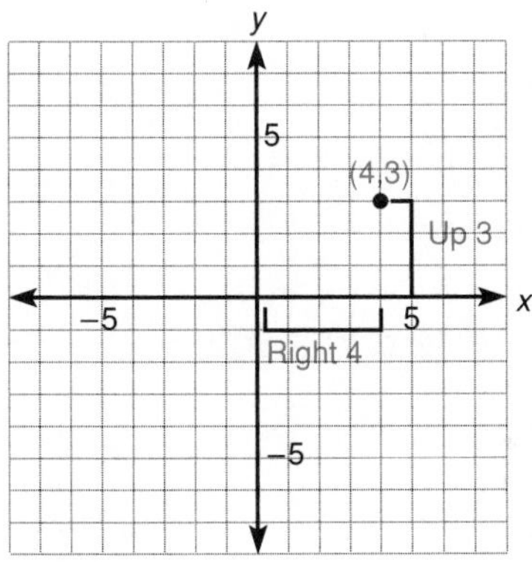

Figure 7–2

Similarly, to plot the graph of $(-3,-5)$, we start at the origin. Since $x = -3$, we move three units *to the left* (the negative direction).

Next, $y = -5$ instructs us to move *down* (the negative direction) five units parallel to the y-axis. We have plotted the graph of the ordered pair $(-3,-5)$ as shown in figure 7–3.

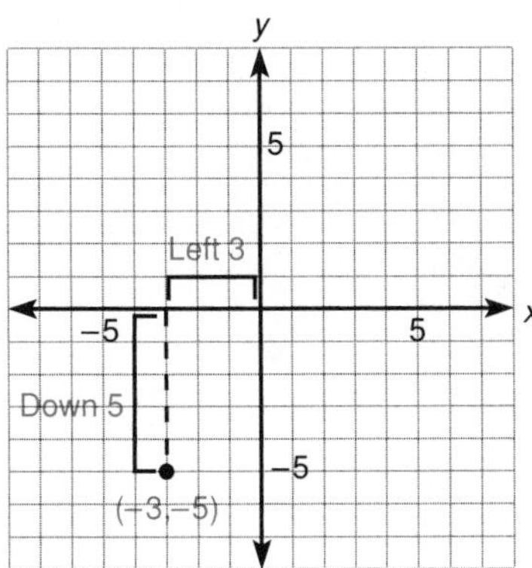

Figure 7–3

Points are often named by capital letters. The notation $A(x,y)$ indicates that the *name* of the point is A and the *coordinates* of the point are (x,y).

Example 7–1 C

Plot the following points as shown in the figure.

a. $A(2,4)$
b. $B(-1,-3)$
c. $C(-4,3)$
d. $D(5,0)$
e. $E(2,-3)$
f. $F(0,4)$
g. $G(-3,0)$
h. $H\left(2,\frac{3}{2}\right)$

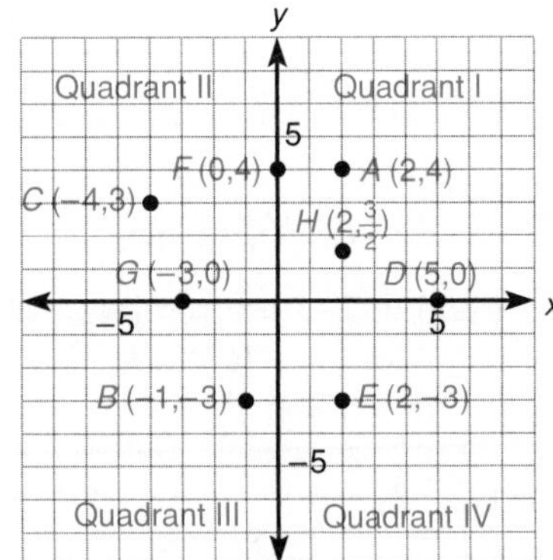

You are now ready to do $\mathbf{C_1}$.

Note
Whenever either one of the coordinates of the point is zero, the point is located on an axis. If the abscissa is zero, the point is on the y-axis. If the ordinate is zero, the point is on the x-axis.

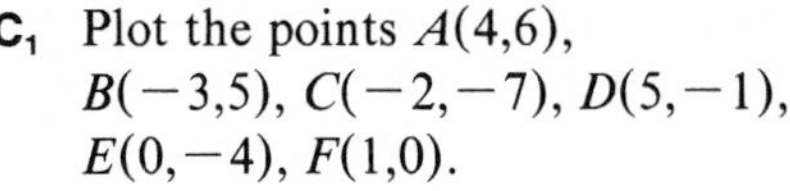
$\mathbf{C_1}$ Plot the points $A(4,6)$, $B(-3,5)$, $C(-2,-7)$, $D(5,-1)$, $E(0,-4)$, $F(1,0)$.

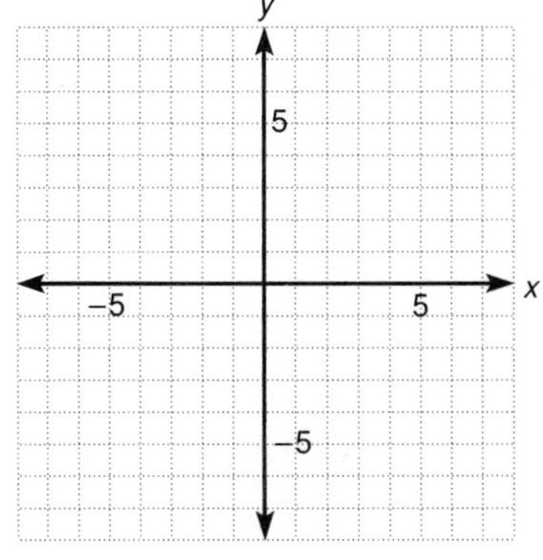

D₁ Given $y = x + 5$, let $x = -1$, $x = -5$, $x = 0$, and $x = 2$. Plot the ordered pairs that are solutions of the equation.

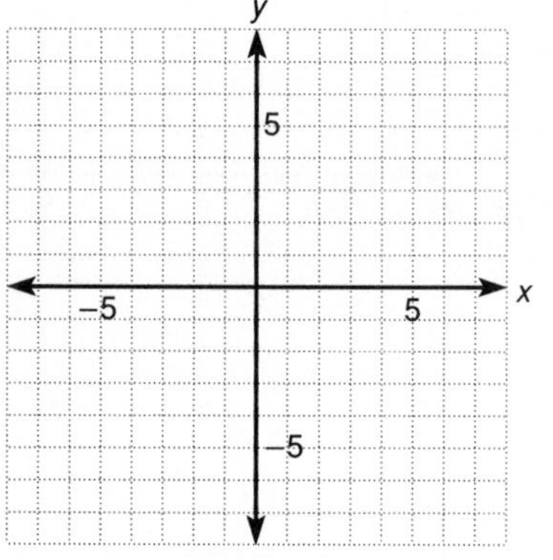

We can see in the diagram that a point is in

1. quadrant I when x and y are both positive,
2. quadrant II when x is negative and y is positive,
3. quadrant III when x and y are both negative,
4. quadrant IV when x is positive and y is negative. ■

Graphs of solutions—linear equations in two variables

Example 7–1 D

Now consider the graphs of some of the ordered pairs that are solutions of the linear equation in two variables $y = 2x + 1$. Suppose we let $x = -3$, $x = 0$, $x = 2$, and $x = 3$. Then

when $x = -3$, $y = 2(-3) + 1 = -6 + 1 = -5$;
when $x = 0$, $y = 2(0) + 1 = 0 + 1 = 1$;
when $x = 2$, $y = 2(2) + 1 = 4 + 1 = 5$; and
when $x = 3$, $y = 2(3) + 1 = 6 + 1 = 7$.

The ordered pairs $(-3,-5)$, $(0,1)$, $(2,5)$, and $(3,7)$ are solutions of the equation $y = 2x + 1$. These ordered pairs are often shown in an x/y table

x	$y = 2x + 1$	Ordered pair
−3	$2(-3) + 1 = -5$	$(-3,-5)$
0	$2(0) + 1 = 1$	$(0,1)$
2	$2(2) + 1 = 5$	$(2,5)$
3	$2(3) + 1 = 7$	$(3,7)$

We now plot these points.

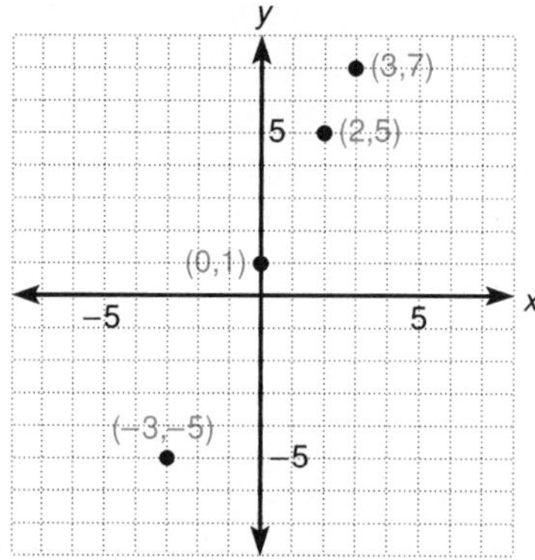

You are now ready to do **D₁**. ■

Answers to section 7–1 margin exercises

A₁ yes **A₂** $3(0) + 2(3) = 6$
$0 + 6 = 6$
$6 = 6$
A₃ $3(4) + 2(-2) = 6$
$12 + (-4) = 6$
$8 \neq 6$

B₁ $y = 11$; $(5,11)$ **B₂** $y = -7$; $(-4,-7)$ **B₃** $x = -4$; $(-4,-7)$

B₄ $y = \frac{5}{2}$; $\left(3,\frac{5}{2}\right)$ $y = -5$; $(-2,-5)$ **B₅** $x = 0$; $(0,-2)$ **B₆** $y = 6$; $(4,6)$

B₇ $y = 6$; $(-9,6)$ **B₈** $x = -3$; $(-3,6)$ **B₉** $x = -3$; $(-3,-1)$

C_1

D_1

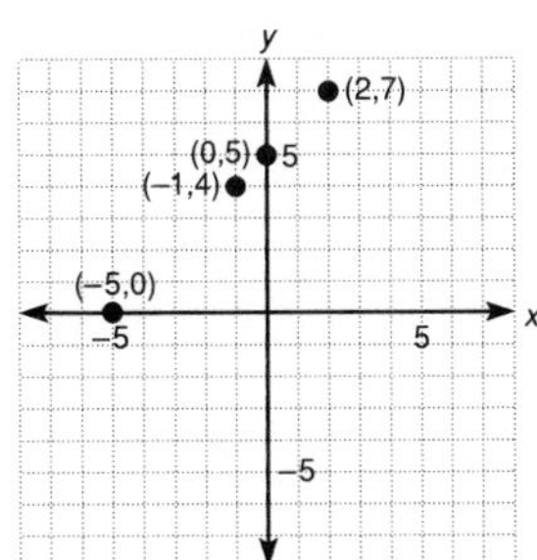

Mastery points
Can you • Determine whether or not an ordered pair is a solution of a given equation? • Find the value of one variable, given the value of the other variable? • Plot ordered pairs in the rectangular coordinate plane? • Plot ordered pair solutions of linear equations?

Exercise 7–1

Directions Determine whether or not the given ordered pairs are solutions of the given equation. See example 7–1 A.

Example $\boxed{A_1}$ Determine if $x = -2$ and $y = 6$ satisfy the equation $3x + 2y = 6$.

Solution

$3(-2) + 2(6) = 6$ — Replace x with -2 and y with 6

$-6 + 12 = 6$ — Multiply as indicated

$6 = 6$ — (True)

$x = -2$ and $y = 6$ satisfy the equation $3x + 2y = 6$.

1. $y = 3x - 1$; $(1,2)$, $(-1,-4)$, $(2,3)$

2. $y = 2x + 4$; $(-1,3)$, $(0,4)$, $(2,8)$

3. $x + 2y = 3$; $(1,2)$, $(-1,2)$, $(3,0)$

4. $3x - y = 4$; $(1,-1)$, $\left(\frac{1}{3},2\right)$, $(0,-4)$

5. $3y - 4x = 2$; $(1,2)$, $(-2,1)$, $\left(\frac{1}{2},1\right)$

6. $5x - 2y = 6$; $(2,2)$, $(0,-3)$, $(4,-2)$

7. $3x = 2y$; $(2,3)$, $(3,2)$, $(0,0)$

8. $3y = -4x$; $(4,-3)$, $(-4,3)$, $(-6,8)$

9. $x = -4$; $(-4,1)$, $(4,2)$, $(-4,-4)$

10. $y = 3$; $(2,3)$, $(-5,2)$, $\left(\frac{3}{4},3\right)$

11. $x + 5 = 0$; $(3,-5)$, $(-5,3)$, $(-5,8)$

12. $y - 2 = 0$; $(-2,2)$, $\left(\frac{2}{3},-2\right)$, $(5,2)$

Directions Find the value for y corresponding to the given values for x in each equation. Express your answer as an ordered pair. See example 7–1 B.

Example $\boxed{B_4}$ Let $x = 3$ and $x = -2$. Given $3x - 2y = 4$, find y.

Solution

$3x - 2y = 4$	$3x - 2y = 4$	
$3(3) - 2y = 4$	$3(-2) - 2y = 4$	Replace values of x
$9 - 2y = 4$	$-6 - 2y = 4$	Multiply and solve for y
$-2y = -5$	$-2y = 10$	
$y = \frac{5}{2}$	$y = -5$	

The ordered pair $\left(3,\frac{5}{2}\right)$ is a solution.

The ordered pair $(-2,-5)$ is a solution.

13. $y = 3x + 2$; $x = 1$, $x = -2$, $x = 0$

14. $y = 4x - 3$; $x = -1$, $x = 2$, $x = 0$

15. $3x + y = 4$; $x = 3$, $x = -2$, $x = 0$

16. $x - 5y = 3$; $x = -2$, $x = 3$, $x = 0$

17. $5x + 2y = -3$; $x = 1$, $x = -1$, $x = 0$

18. $2x - 3y = 1$; $x = \frac{1}{4}$, $x = -4$, $x = 0$

19. $y = 5$; $x = 1$, $x = -6$, $x = 0$

20. $y + 1 = 0$; $x = 7$, $x = -\frac{3}{5}$, $x = 0$

Directions Find the value for x corresponding to the given values for y in each equation. Express your answer as an ordered pair. See example 7–1 B.

21. $x = -3y + 1$; $y = -1$, $y = 2$, $y = 0$

22. $3y - 2x = 0$; $y = 2$, $y = -4$, $y = 0$

23. $x + 7 = 0$; $y = -1$, $y = 3$, $y = 0$

24. $3x - 4y = 1$; $y = 2$, $y = -3$, $y = 0$

25. $5x + 2y = -4$; $y = 3$, $y = -7$, $y = 0$

Directions Solve the following verbal problems.

Example The total cost c in dollars of producing x units of a certain commodity is given by the equation $c = 2x + 20$. Find the cost of producing (a) 75 units; (b) 300 units; (c) 1,000 units of the commodity. Write the answers as ordered pairs.
We are given the number of units of the commodity, x, and want the total cost, c.

Solutions a. When $x = 75$,

$c = 2x + 20$
$= 2(75) + 20$ Replace x with 75
$= 150 + 20$ Multiply
$= 170.$

We have the ordered pair (75,170).

b. When $x = 300$,

$c = 2x + 20$
$= 2(300) + 20$ Replace x with 300
$= 600 + 20$ Multiply
$= 620.$

We have the ordered pair (300,620).

c. When $x = 1{,}000$,

$c = 2x + 20$
$= 2(1{,}000) + 20$ Replace x with 1,000
$= 2{,}000 + 20$ Multiply
$= 2{,}020.$

We have the ordered pair (1,000;2,020).

26. In the example, find the number of units produced when the total cost is (a) \$430; (b) \$700; (c) \$1,400. Write the answers as ordered pairs.

27. The cholesterol level in the blood, y, is related to the dosage of a new anticholesterol drug in grams, x, by the equation $y = 240 - 2x$. Find the cholesterol level in the blood when the dosage is (a) 2 grams, (b) 12 grams, (c) 0 grams. Write the answers as ordered pairs.

28. In exercise 27, determine the number of grams in the dosage when the cholesterol level in the blood is (a) 200, (b) 0, (c) 210. Write the answers as ordered pairs.

29. Suppose the equation $y = 3x + 20$ represents the number of students present in a mathematics class, where x represents the number of hours of study required and y represents the number of students present. Find the number of hours of study required when there are (a) 26 students present, (b) 23 students present, (c) 32 students present. Write the answers as ordered pairs.

30. In exercise 29, find the number of students present when the class requires (a) 0 hours of study, (b) 5 hours of study, (c) 3 hours of study. Write the answers as ordered pairs.

31. If the distance, y, that Mary Jane travels in x hours of driving is given by the equation $y = 55x$, how far does Mary Jane travel in (a) 3 hours, (b) 8 hours, (c) 5 hours and 12 minutes $\left(5\frac{1}{5} \text{ hours}\right)$? Write the answers as ordered pairs.

Directions Plot the following ordered pairs on a rectangular coordinate plane. See example 7–1 C.

32. a. (2,4) i. (5,1)
b. (−1,3) j. (−4,4)
c. (−4,−1) k. (−2,−3)
d. (0,4) l. (0,2)
e. (5,0) m. (−4,0)
f. (−5,0) n. (0,0)
g. $\left(\frac{1}{2},3\right)$ o. $\left(\frac{2}{3},-2\right)$
h. $\left(\frac{3}{2},0\right)$

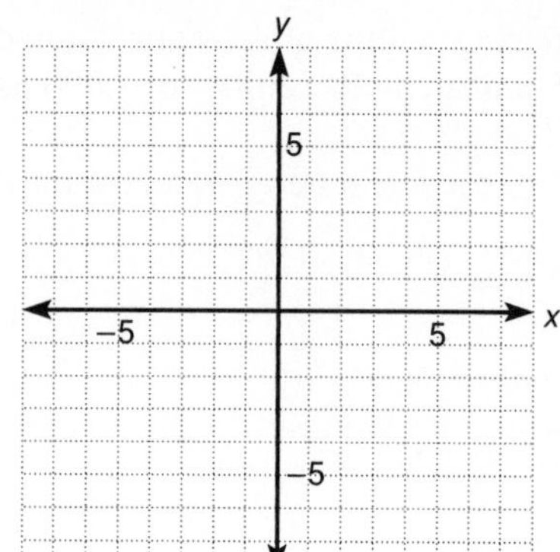

Directions State the quadrant in which each point lies.

Example (−1,3) lies in the second quadrant because the x-component is negative and the y-component is positive.

33. (−2,−5) **34.** (4,−1) **35.** (5,3)

36. (−7,−9) **37.** $\left(-\frac{2}{3},7\right)$ **38.** $\left(\frac{1}{2},-4\right)$

39. $\left(-\frac{5}{2},-\frac{3}{4}\right)$ **40.** $\left(\frac{7}{8},-\frac{7}{8}\right)$

Directions Find the missing component in each ordered pair using the given equation. Then plot the ordered pairs using separate coordinate axes for each problem. See example 7–1 D.

Example $\boxed{D_1}$ Given $y = x + 5$, let $x = -1$, $x = -5$, $x = 0$, and $x = 2$. Plot the ordered pairs that are solutions of the equation.

Solution When $x = -1$, then $y = -1 + 5 = 4$; the ordered pair is $(-1,4)$.
When $x = -5$, then $y = -5 + 5 = 0$; the ordered pair is $(-5,0)$.
When $x = 0$, then $y = 0 + 5 = 5$; the ordered pair is $(0,5)$.
When $x = 2$, then $y = 2 + 5 = 7$; the ordered pair is $(2,7)$.

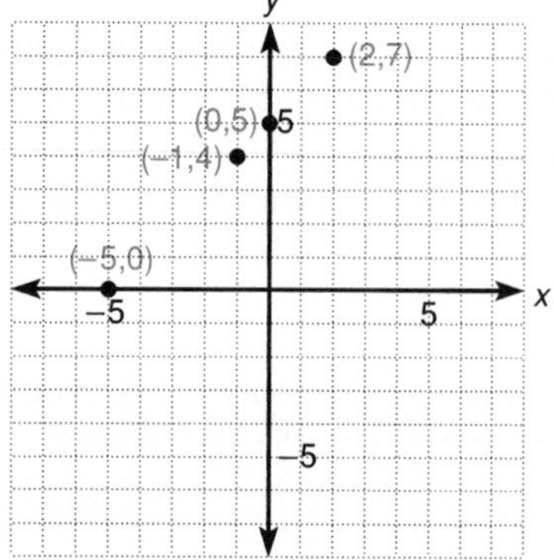

41. $y = x + 4$ $(0, \ ), (-4, \ ), (-2, \ ), (2, \ )$

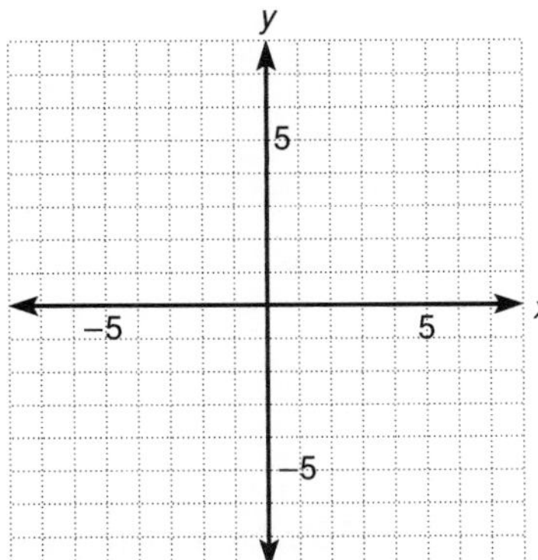

42. $y = 2x + 1$ $(0, \ ), \left(-\frac{1}{2}, \ \right), (2, \ ), (-1, \ )$

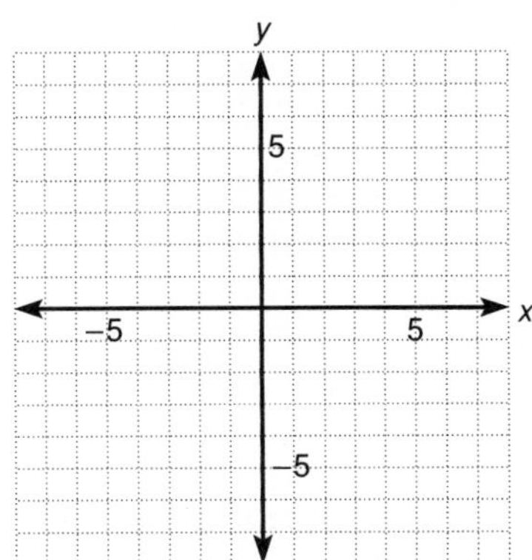

43. $y = 3x - 4$ $(0, \ ), (-1, \ ), \left(-\frac{1}{3}, \ \right), (2, \ )$

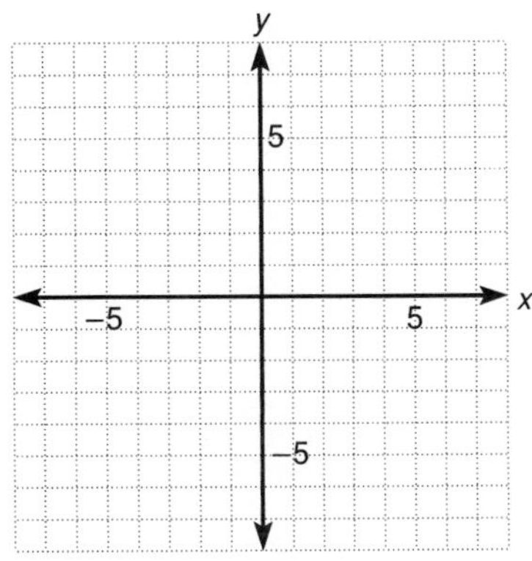

44. $y = 2x$ $(0, \ ), \left(\frac{1}{2}, \ \right), (2, \ ), (-1, \ )$

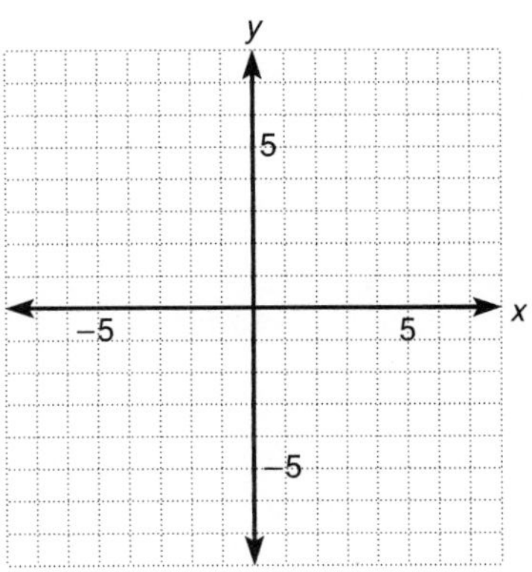

45. $y = -x + 3$ $(0, \ ), (-3, \ ), (3, \ ), \left(\frac{5}{2}, \ \right)$

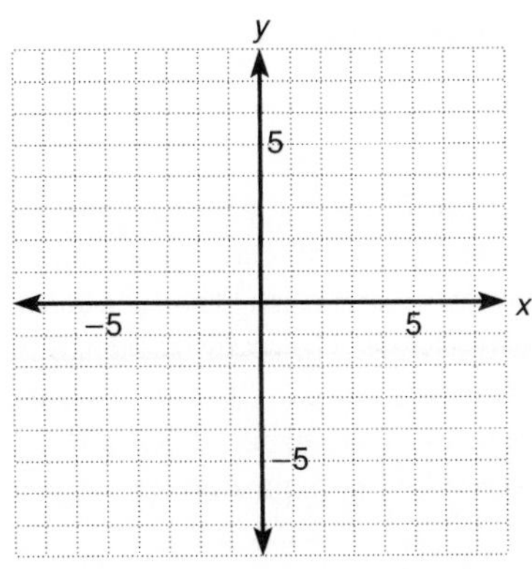

46. $y = -2x + 3$ $(0, \ ), (3, \ ), (-2, \ ), \left(\frac{3}{2}, \ \right)$

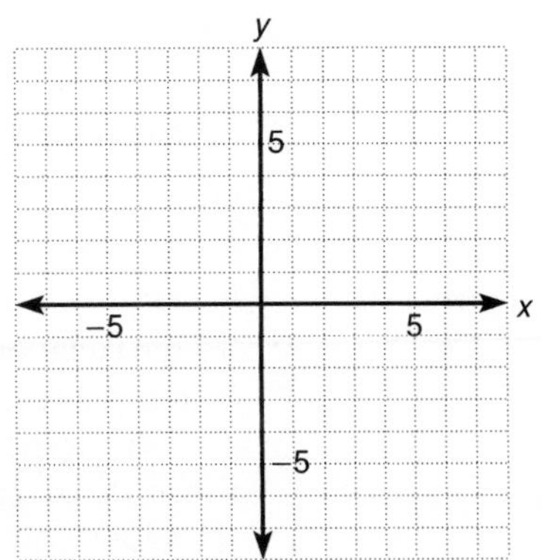

47. $y = 4 - x$ (0,), (−3,), (2,), (3,)

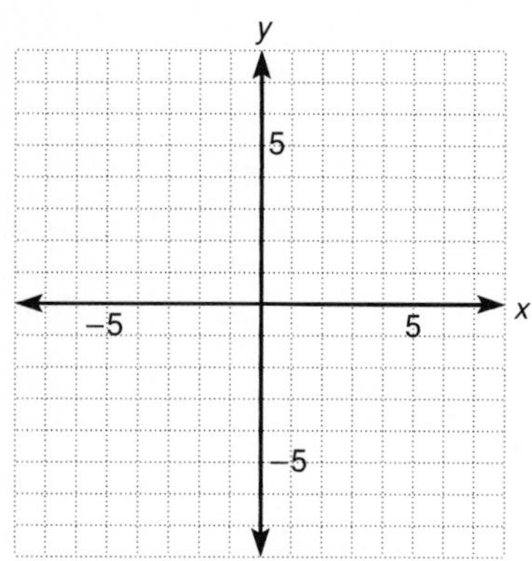

48. What is the value of x and y at the origin?

49. What is the value of x for any point on the y-axis?

50. In what quadrant will all points having negative values of x and positive values of y lie?

51. What is the value of y for any point on the x-axis?

52. On what axis does each of the following points lie?
a. (0,−5) b. (2,0)
c. (−8,0) d. (0,5)

Review exercises

Directions Perform the indicated operations. See sections 6–1 and 6–3.

1. $\dfrac{x^2 - 4}{3x} \cdot \dfrac{6x^2}{x - 2}$

2. $\dfrac{2x - 1}{x + 3} \div \dfrac{4x^2 - 1}{x^2 + 6x + 9}$

3. $\dfrac{4}{x - 2} - \dfrac{3}{x + 1}$

4. Find $-|-8|$. See section 1–1.

5. Multiply $x^2 \cdot x \cdot x^0$. See section 3–1.

6. Multiply $(-2)(-3)(4)(0)$. See section 1–4.

▣ 7–2 Graphs of linear equations

Graph of a linear equation

In section 7–1, we learned that there are infinitely many ordered pairs that will satisfy an equation in two variables. That is, given the linear equation $3x + y = 4$, we can find many ordered pairs (as many as we wish) that are solutions of the equation. To list all of these solutions is impossible. However, these solutions can be represented geometrically by a graph of the ordered pairs that are solutions.

In section 7–1, we plotted the graphs of several of the ordered pairs that satisfied the given equations. To illustrate again, consider the equation $3x + y = 4$. In figure 7–4, we plot the ordered pairs

$$(0,4),\ (1,1),\ (-1,7),\ \text{and}\ (3,-5)$$

that are solutions of the equation.

Connecting the points, we find they all lie on the same straight line. We have drawn arrowheads in each direction at each end of the line to indicate that the line goes on indefinitely in each direction. *Any point whose coordinates satisfy the equation* $3x + y = 4$ *will lie on this line,* and *the coordinates of any point on this line will satisfy the equation.* We have a graphical representation of a portion of all solutions of the equation. Then, the straight line in figure 7–4 is called the *graph of the equation* $3x + y = 4$.

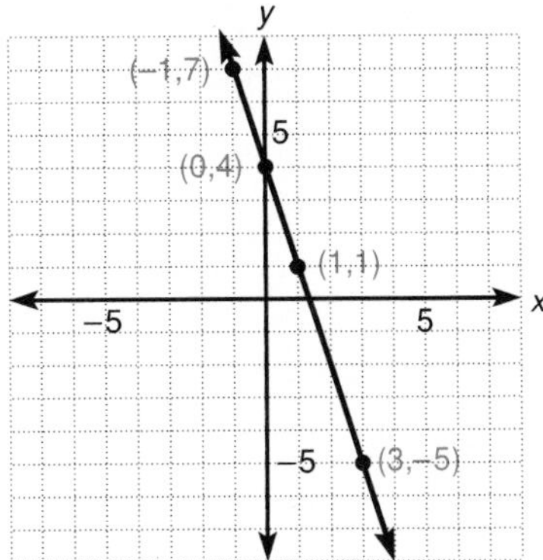

Figure 7–4

Straight line

In general, the graph of *any* linear equation in two variables is a *straight line.* A geometric fact we now use is that *through any two given points in the plane we can draw one and only one straight line.* Thus, since we know the graph of a linear equation in two variables is a straight line, we can determine the graph of the equation using only two points. However, it is a good idea to find a third point as a check on our work. (Remember, the word *line* appears in the name *line*ar equation.)

Example 7–2 A

Graph the equation $y = 2x + 4$.

We choose *three* arbitrary values of x and find corresponding values for y. Let $x = 0$ and $x = -2$.

When $x = 0$,

$y = 2x + 4$
$y = 2(0) + 4$ Replace x with 0
$y = 0 + 4$
$y = 4.$

When $x = -2$,

$y = 2x + 4$
$y = 2(-2) + 4$ Replace x with -2
$y = -4 + 4$
$y = 0.$

We now have the points (0,4) and (−2,0). They would be sufficient, but we obtain a third point as a check. All three points must lie on a straight line when you draw a line through them. Let $x = 2$. (Any other number replacement for x or y could be used.)

When $x = 2$,

$y = 2x + 4$
$y = 2(2) + 4$ Replace x with 2
$y = 4 + 4$
$y = 8.$

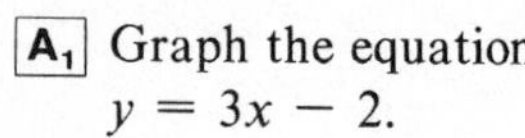

A_1 Graph the equation $y = 3x - 2$.

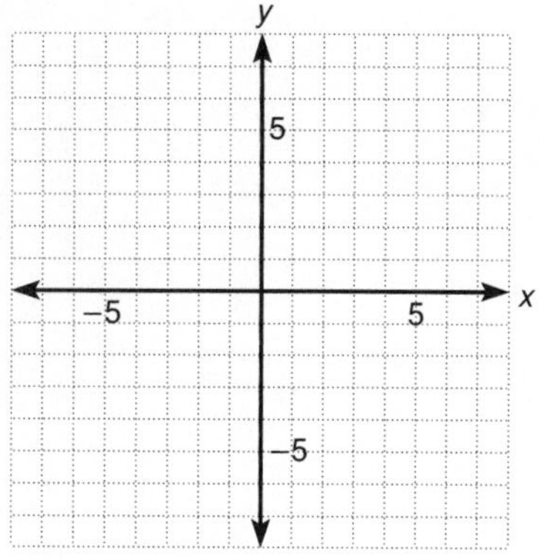

We now have the third point, (2,8). Plot these points and draw a straight line through them.

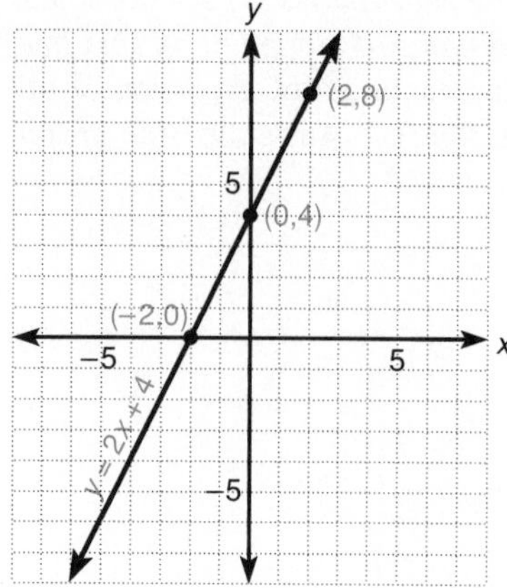

You are now ready to do $\mathbf{A_1}$. ■

The *x*- and *y*-intercepts

Notice the graph of $y = 2x + 4$ crosses the y-axis at (0,4) and the x-axis at $(-2,0)$. The points (0,4) and $(-2,0)$ are called the *y-intercept* and the *x-intercept,* respectively. Since we need only two points to sketch the graph of a linear equation in two variables, in many cases we use the x- and y-intercepts. Observe from the example that when the line crosses the x-axis, the value of y is zero. When the line crosses the y-axis, the value of x is zero.

x- and y-intercepts

1. To find the x-intercept, we let $y = 0$ and find the corresponding value of x. This is the point $(x,0)$.
2. To find the y-intercept, we let $x = 0$ and find the corresponding value for y. This is the point $(0,y)$.

Example 7–2 B

Plot the graphs of the following linear equations using x- and y-intercepts.

1. $y = -2x + 3$

Let $x = 0$ to find the y-intercept; let $y = 0$ to find the x-intercept.

$y = -2x + 3$		$y = -2x + 3$	
$y = -2(0) + 3$	Replace x with 0	$0 = -2x + 3$	Replace y with 0
$y = 0 + 3$	Multiply as indicated	$2x = 3$	Add $2x$ to each member
$y = 3$		$x = \frac{3}{2}$	
The point (0,3) is the y-intercept.		The point $\left(\frac{3}{2},0\right)$ is the x-intercept.	

To find another point, choose $x = 2$.

$y = -2x + 3$
$y = -2(2) + 3$ Replace x with 2
$y = -4 + 3$ Multiply as indicated
$y = -1$

The third point is $(2,-1)$.

We now plot the three points (0,3), $\left(\frac{3}{2},0\right)$ and (2,−1) and draw a straight line through them.

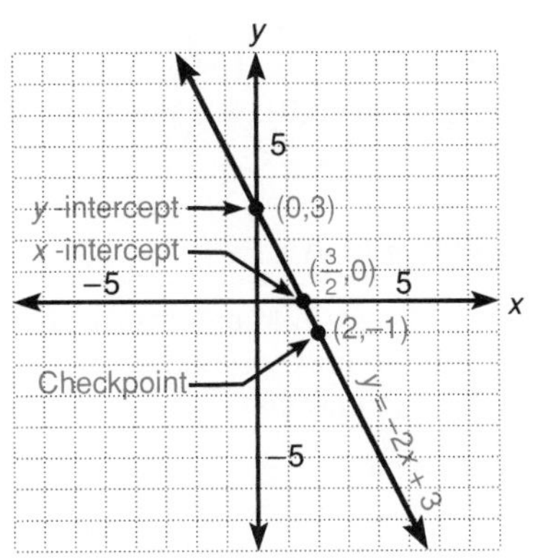

You are now ready to do **B₁**.

B₁ $y = -x + 5$

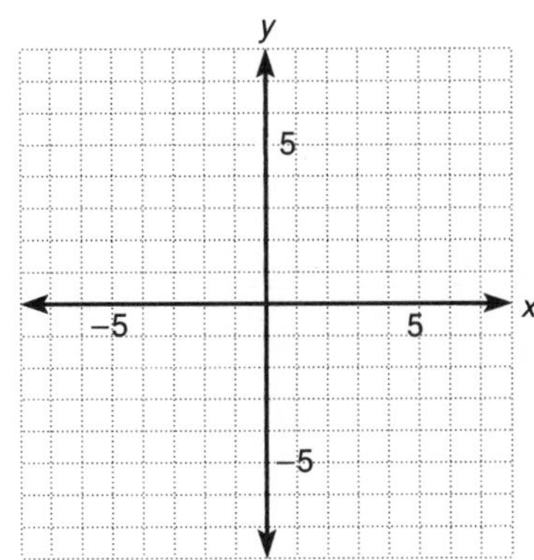

2. $3y - 2x = 9$

Let $x = 0$ to find the y-intercept; let $y = 0$ to find the x-intercept.

When $x = 0$,

$$\begin{aligned} 3y - 2x &= 9 \\ 3y - 2(0) &= 9 \quad \text{Replace } x \text{ with } 0 \\ 3y - 0 &= 9 \\ 3y &= 9 \\ y &= 3. \end{aligned}$$

The point (0,3) is the y-intercept.

When $y = 0$,

$$\begin{aligned} 3y - 2x &= 9 \\ 3(0) - 2x &= 9 \quad \text{Replace } y \text{ with } 0 \\ 0 - 2x &= 9 \\ -2x &= 9 \\ x &= -\frac{9}{2}. \end{aligned}$$

The point $\left(-\frac{9}{2},0\right)$ is the x-intercept.

For the checkpoint, let $x = 3$.

$$\begin{aligned} 3y - 2x &= 9 \\ 3y - 2(3) &= 9 \quad \text{Replace } x \text{ with } 3 \\ 3y - 6 &= 9 \\ 3y &= 15 \\ y &= 5 \end{aligned}$$

The checkpoint is (3,5).

Plot the points (0,3), $\left(-\frac{9}{2},0\right)$, and (3,5) and draw a straight line through them.

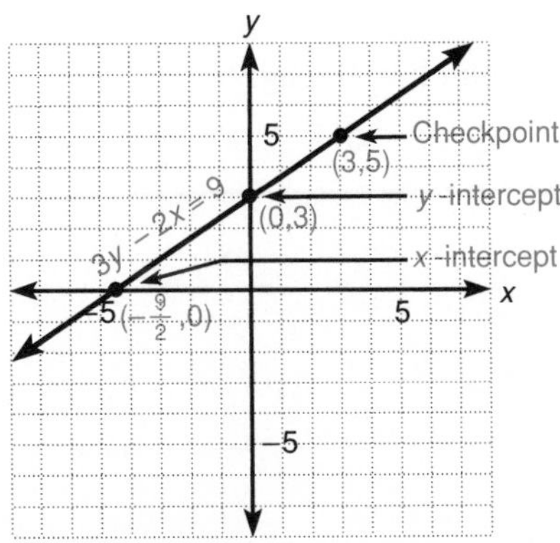

You are now ready to do **B₂**.

B₂ $2y - 3x = 12$

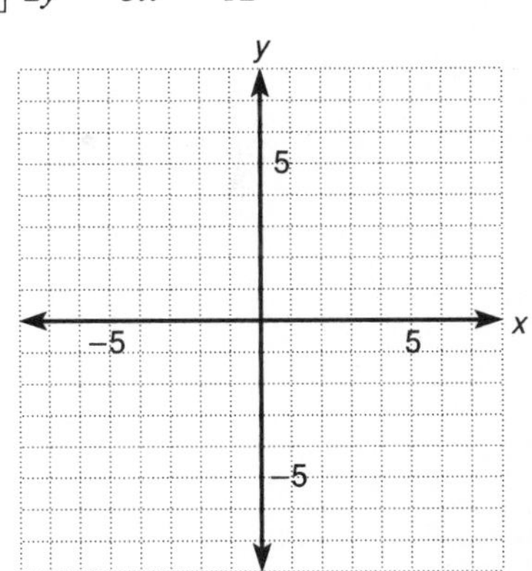

B_3 $y = 2x$

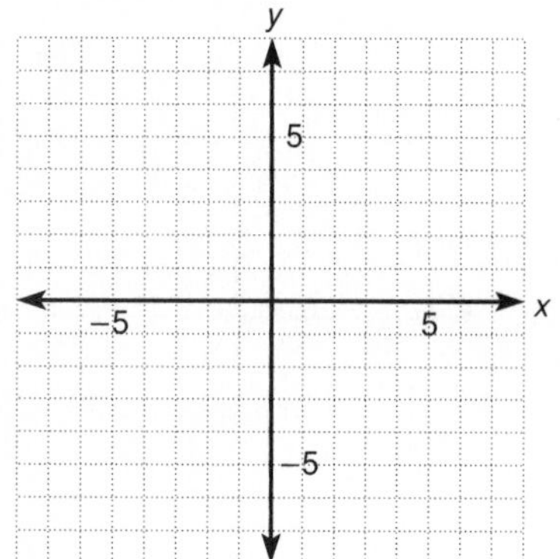

In the previous examples, the x- and y-intercepts were different points. For some equations, the x- and y-intercepts are the same point, as demonstrated in example 3.

3. $y = 3x$

If we let $x = 0$, then $y = 3(0) = 0$, giving the ordered pair (0,0). When $y = 0$, then $0 = 3x$ and $x = 0$, giving the same point (0,0). We must choose two additional values for x or y. Let $x = 1$ and $x = -1$.

x	$y = 3x$	Ordered pair (x,y)	
0	$3(0) = 0$	(0,0)	x- and y-intercepts
1	$3(1) = 3$	(1,3)	Arbitrary second point
−1	$3(-1) = -3$	(−1,−3)	Checkpoint

Plot the points (0,0), (1,3), and (−1,−3) and draw a straight line through them.

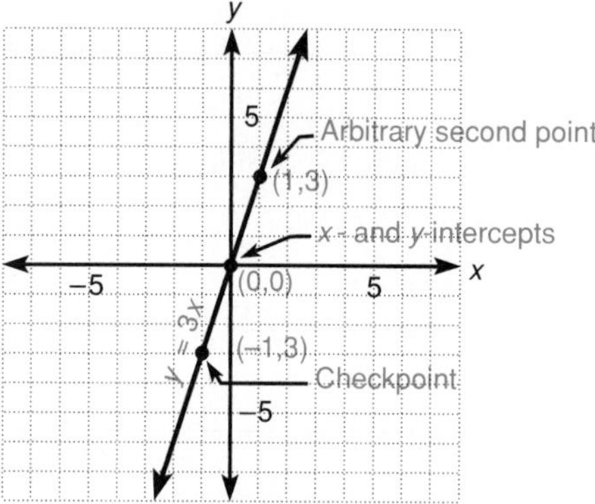

You are now ready to do **B_3**.

To generalize,

> Any linear equation that can be written in the form
>
> $$y = kx \quad \text{or} \quad x = ky,$$
>
> where k is a real number, will pass through the origin (0,0).

The next two examples show what happens when one of the variables is missing.

4. $y = -3$

Recall that this equation could be written $y = 0 \cdot x - 3$ and that for *any* value of x we might choose, y is *always* equal to -3. Therefore, we choose any three values for x and obtain $y = -3$. We choose $x = -2$, $x = 0$, and $x = 2$. The ordered pairs thus obtained are $(-2,-3)$, $(0,-3)$, and $(2,-3)$. We plot these three points and draw a horizontal line through them.

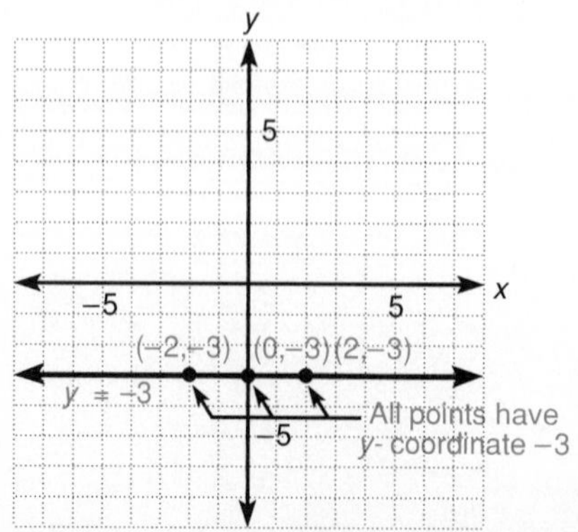

Note
The graph has a y-intercept, -3, but no x-intercept. The graph is a horizontal straight line. In fact, the graph of any equation of the form $y = b$ will be a horizontal line passing through the point with coordinates $(0,b)$, the y-intercept.

You are now ready to do **B_4**.

5. $x - 4 = 0$
We first add 4 to each member to get the equation $x = 4$. Recall we discussed in section 7–1 that this equation can be written $x + 0 \cdot y = 4$ and that the value of x will be 4 for *any* value of y. If we let $y = -2$, $y = 0$, and $y = 2$, we obtain the ordered pairs $(4,-2)$, $(4,0)$, and $(4,2)$. We plot these three points and draw a vertical line through them.

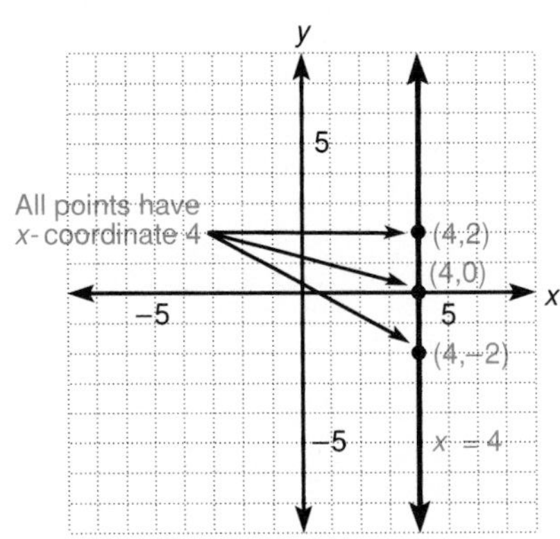

Note
The graph has an x-intercept, 4, but no y-intercept. The graph is a *vertical* line (parallel to the y-axis) passing through the point with coordinates $(4,0)$. In fact, the graph of any equation of the form $x = a$ will be a vertical line passing through the point with coordinates $(a,0)$, the x-intercept.

You are now ready to do **B_5**. ■

We now summarize the different forms that linear equations might take.

1. $ax + by = c$ Graph by finding the x-intercept (let $y = 0$), the y-intercept (let $x = 0$), and a third checkpoint by choosing any value for x or y not yet used.

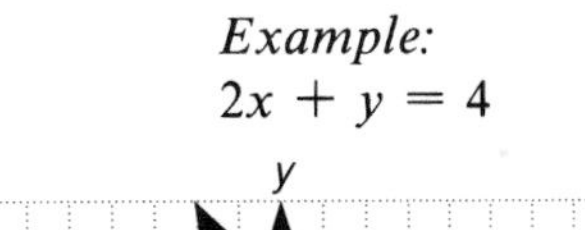

Example:
$2x + y = 4$

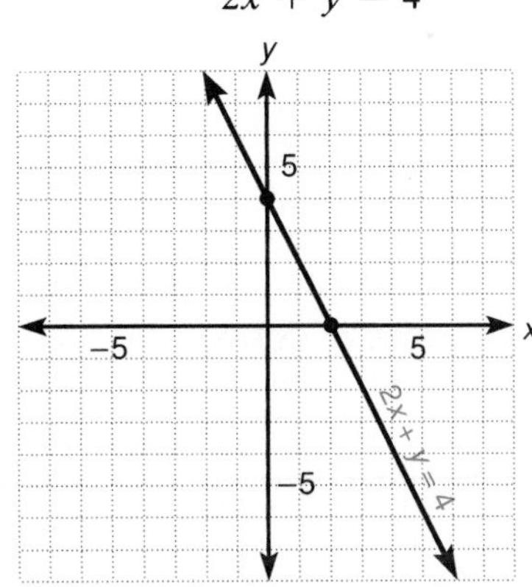

B_4 $y = 4$

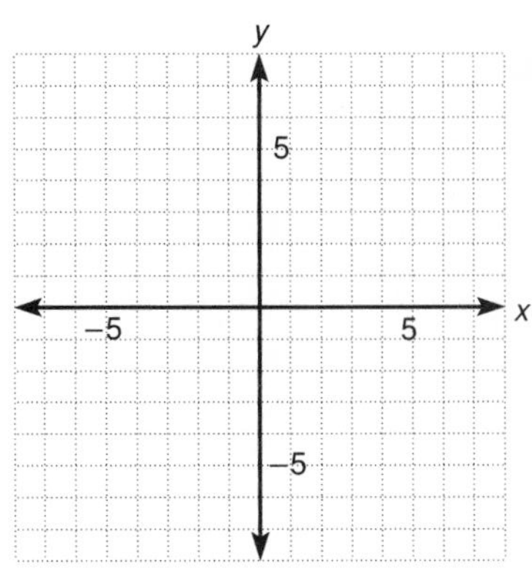

B_5 $x + 3 = 0$

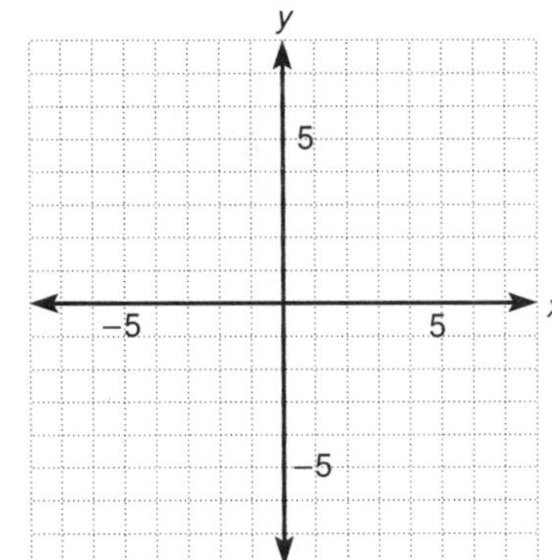

2. $y = kx$ or $x = hy$	Graph goes through the origin (0,0). Find two other points by choosing values for x or y other than 0.	*Examples:* $y = 2x$ and $x = -3y$
3. $x = a$	Graph is a vertical line through $(a,0)$.	*Example:* $x = 1$
4. $y = b$	Graph is a horizontal line through $(0,b)$.	*Example:* $y = -6$

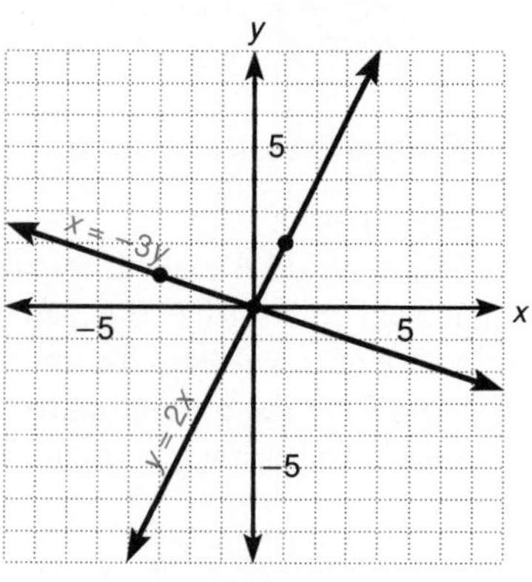

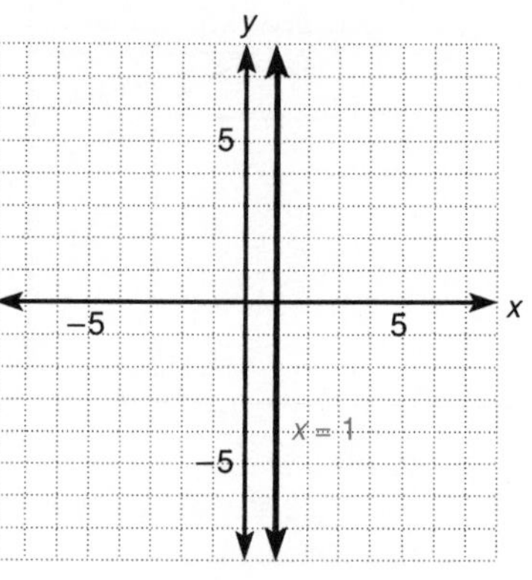

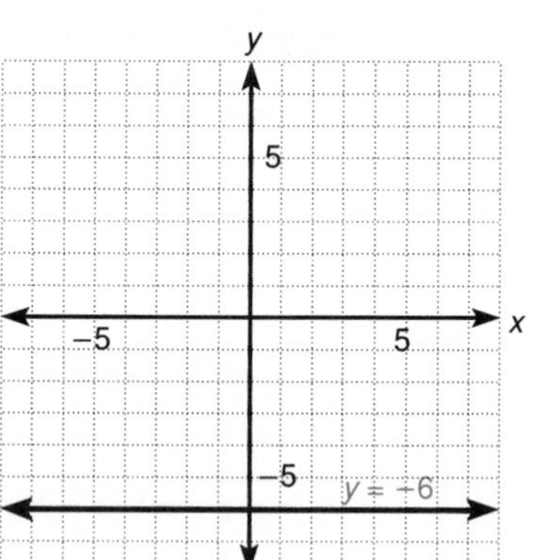

Answers to section 7–2 margin exercises

A_1

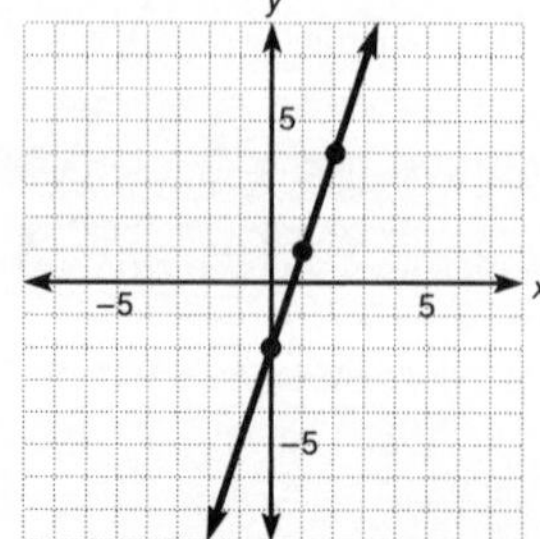

B_1

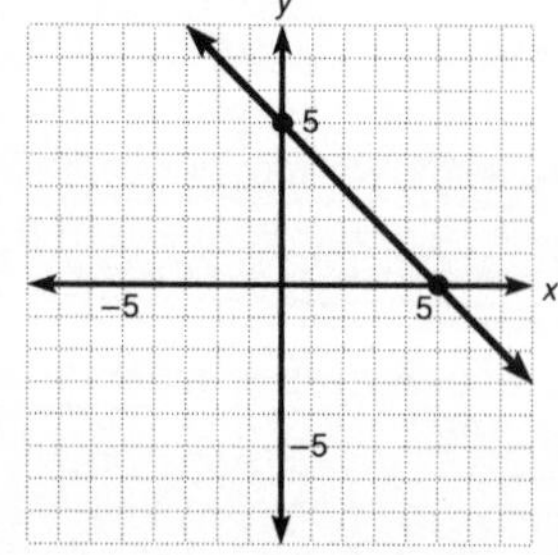

B_2

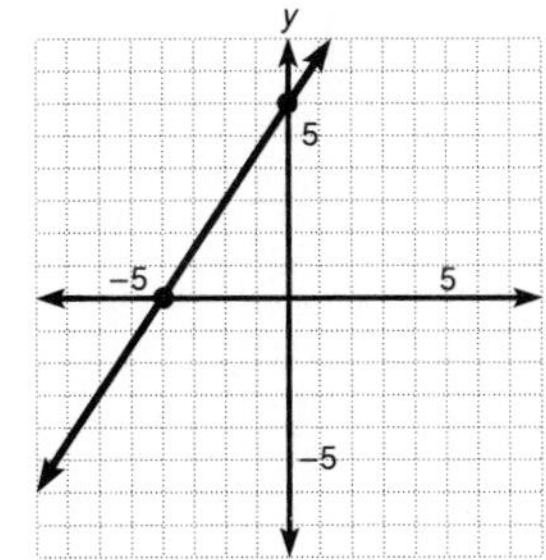

B_3

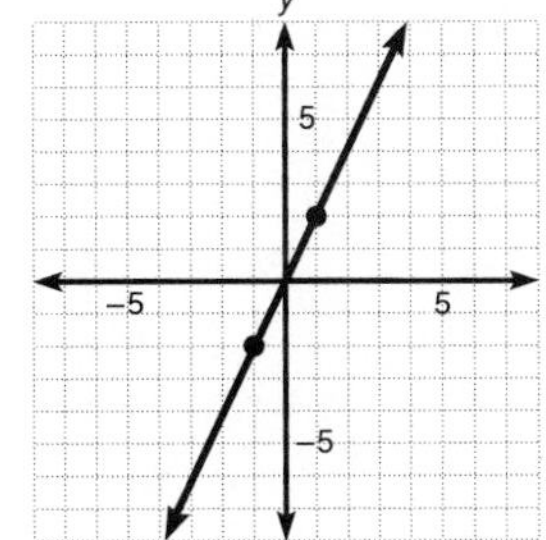

B_4

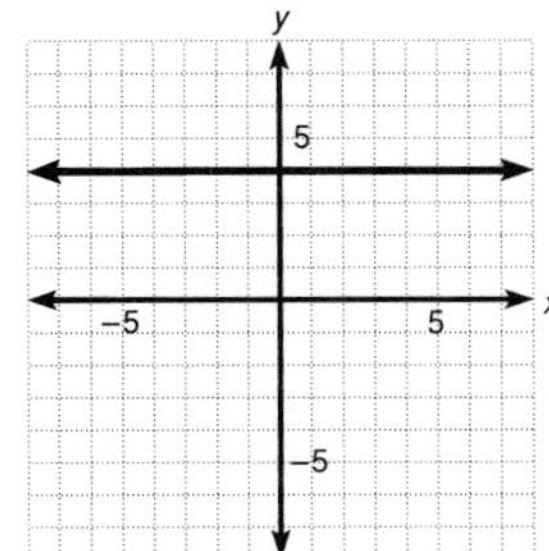

B_5

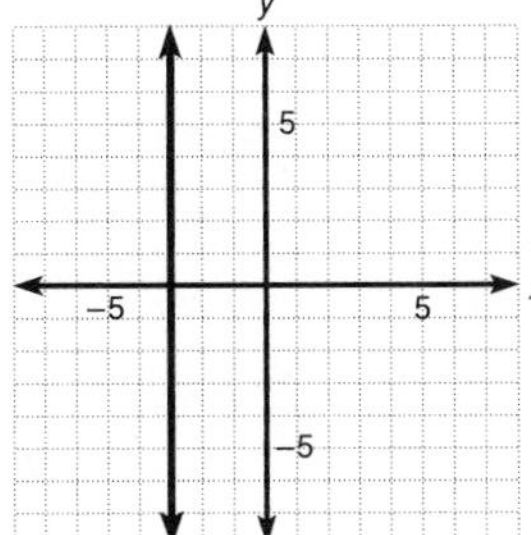

Mastery points

Can you

- Plot the graph of linear equations using ordered pairs?
- Find the *x*- and *y*-intercepts of a linear equation?
- Plot the graph of linear equations using the *x*- and *y*-intercepts?
- Plot graphs of the equations $y = b$ and $x = a$, where a and b are constants?

Exercise 7–2

Directions Find the solutions of the given equation using the given values of x and y. Graph the equation by plotting the points and drawing a straight line through them. See example 7–2 A.

Example A_1 $y = 3x - 2$; $x = 1$, $x = 0$, $y = 4$

Solution

When $x = 1$,

$y = 3x - 2$

$y = 3(1) - 2$ Replace x with 1

$y = 3 - 2$

$y = 1$.

When $x = 0$,

$y = 3x - 2$

$y = 3(0) - 2$ Replace x with 0

$y = 0 - 2$

$y = -2$.

When $y = 4$,

$y = 3x - 2$

$4 = 3x - 2$ Replace y with 4

$6 = 3x$ Add 2 to each member

$x = 2$. Divide each member by 3

The ordered pairs thus obtained are (1,1), (0,−2), and (2,4).

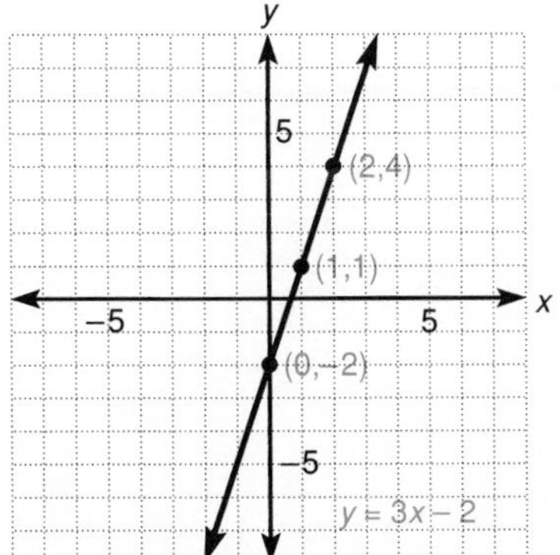

1. $y = 2x + 1$; $x = -1$, $x = -2$, $y = 3$

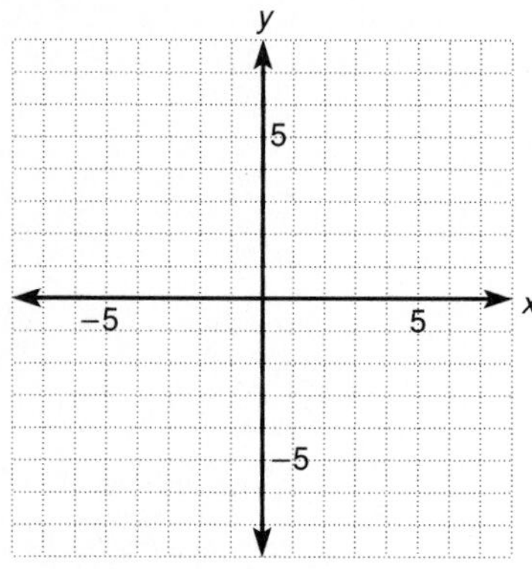

2. $y = x + 3$; $x = 0$, $y = 2$, $y = -1$

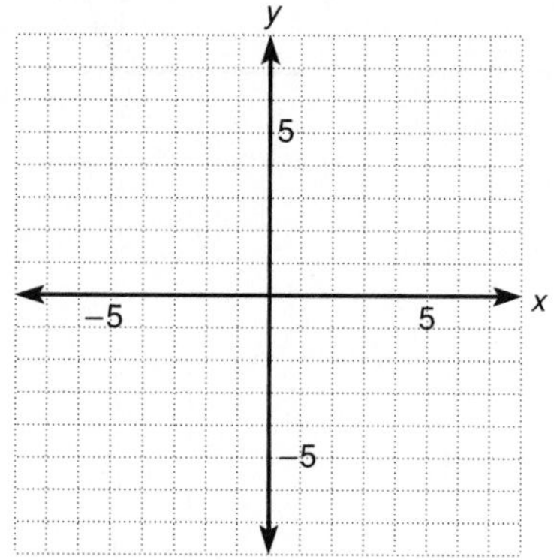

3. $2x + 3y = 6$; $x = 3$, $y = 2$, $x = -3$

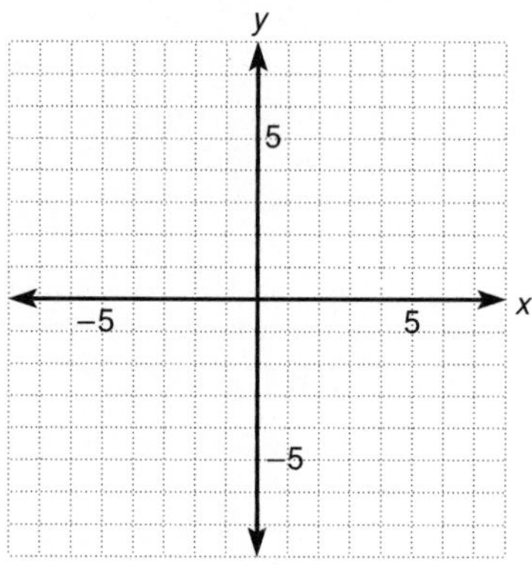

4. $x - 4y = 0$; $x = 0$, $y = 1$, $x = -4$

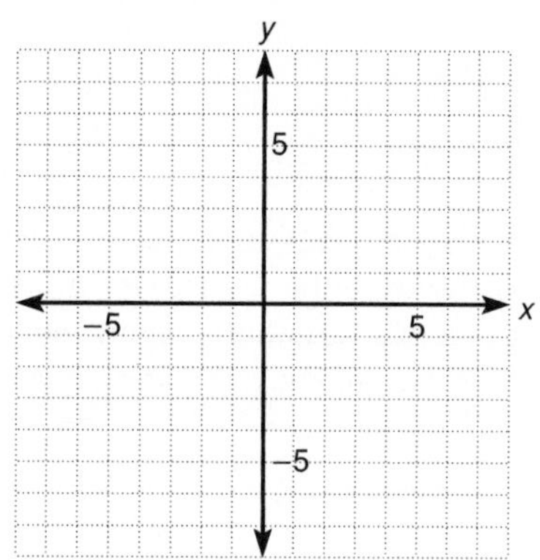

Directions Plot the graphs of the given linear equations using the x- and y-intercepts and a checkpoint. See example 7–2 B.

Example **B₂** $2y - 3x = 12$

Solution

When $x = 0$,

$$\begin{aligned} 2y - 3x &= 12 \\ 2y - 3(0) &= 12 \\ 2y - 0 &= 12 \\ 2y &= 12 \\ y &= 6. \end{aligned}$$

The point (0,6) is the y-intercept.

When $y = 0$,

$$\begin{aligned} 2y - 3x &= 12 \\ 2(0) - 3x &= 12 \\ 0 - 3x &= 12 \\ -3x &= 12 \\ x &= -4. \end{aligned}$$

The point $(-4,0)$ is the x-intercept.

When $x = -2$,

$$\begin{aligned} 2y - 3x &= 12 \\ 2y - 3(-2) &= 12 \\ 2y - (-6) &= 12 \\ 2y + 6 &= 12 \\ 2y &= 6 \\ y &= 3. \end{aligned}$$

The check point is $(-2,3)$.

We now plot the points (0,6), $(-4,0)$, and $(-2,3)$ and draw a line through them.

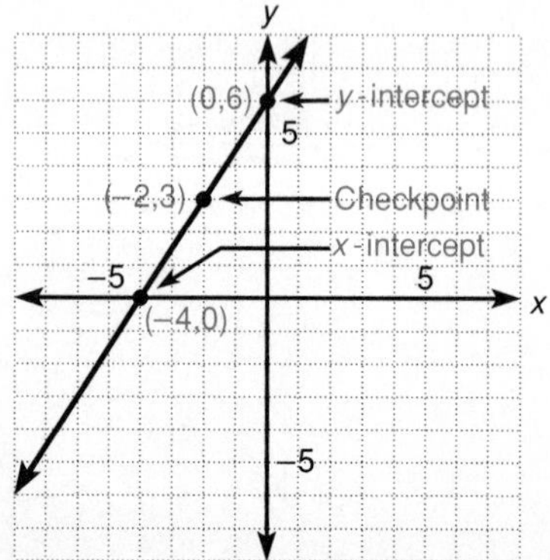

5. $y = x - 2$

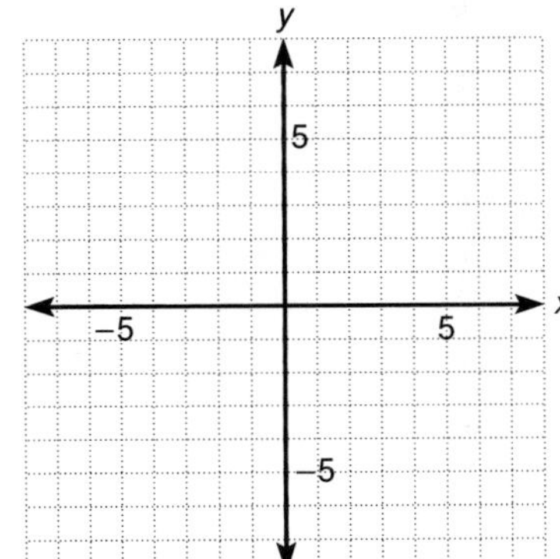

6. $y = 3x + 6$

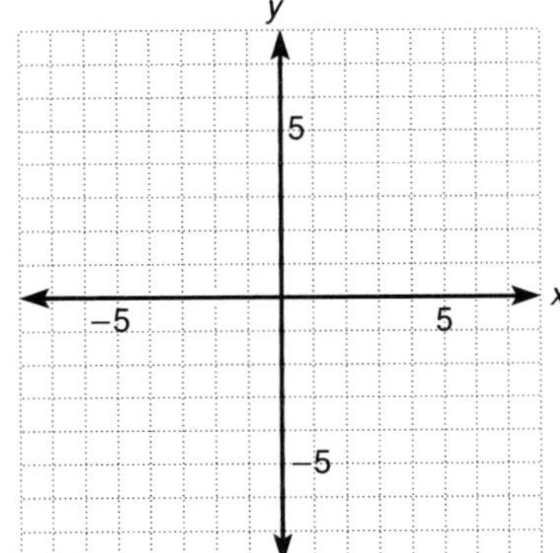

7. $y = 2x - 8$

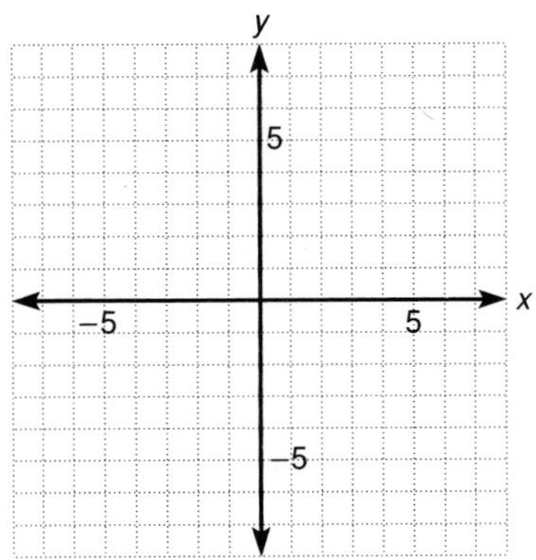

8. $2y + 5x = 10$

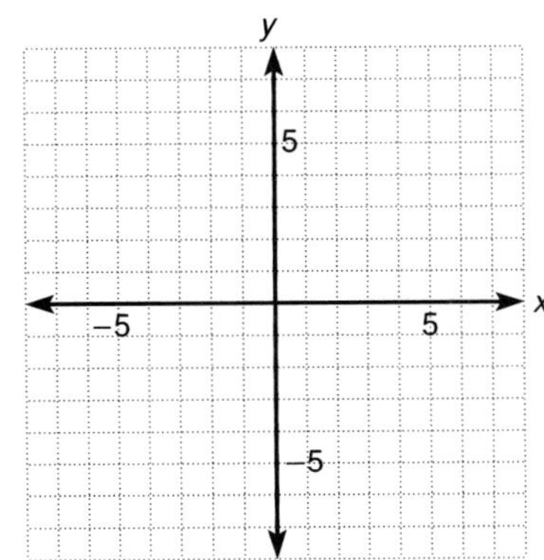

9. $4x - 3y = 12$

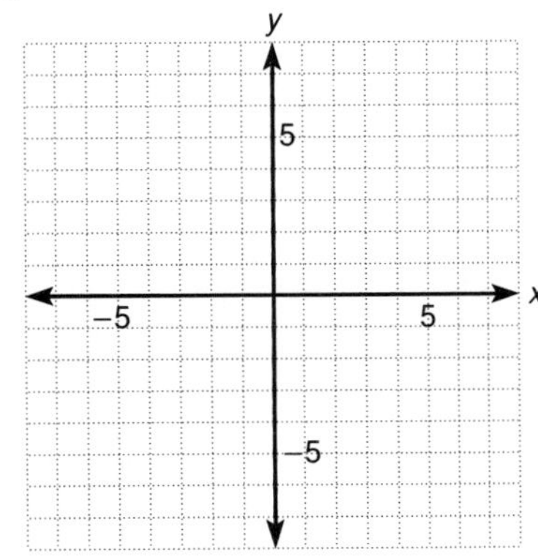

10. $3y - 5x = 15$

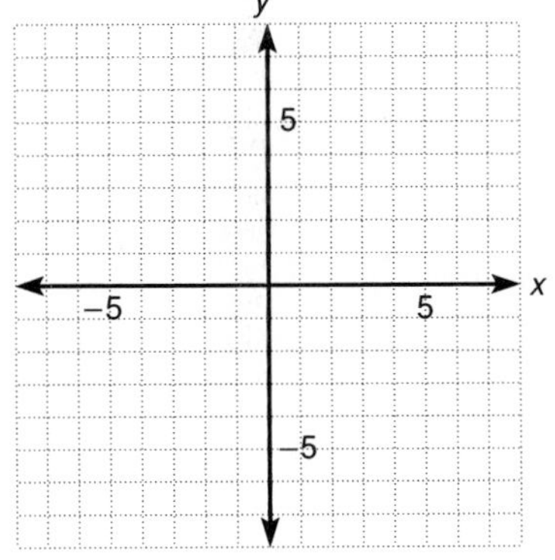

11. $5x - 6y = 30$

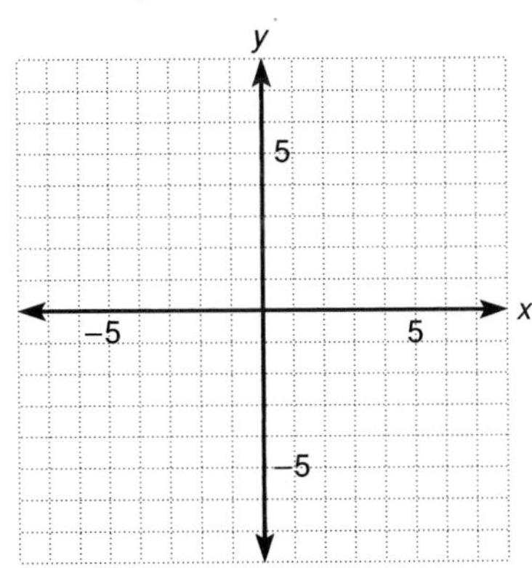

12. $5x = 2y - 10$

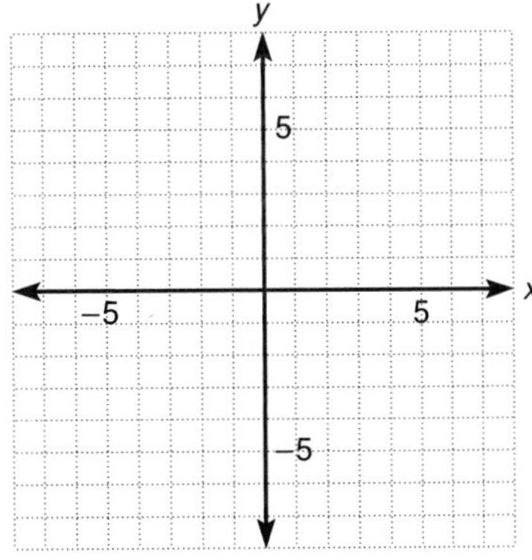

13. $2y = 6 - 3x$

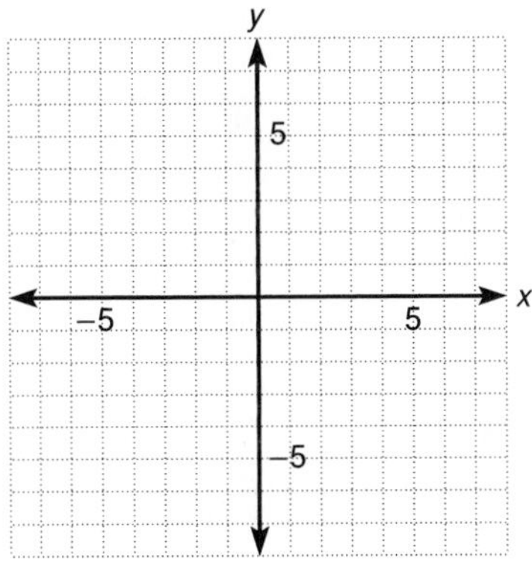

14. $y = 4x$

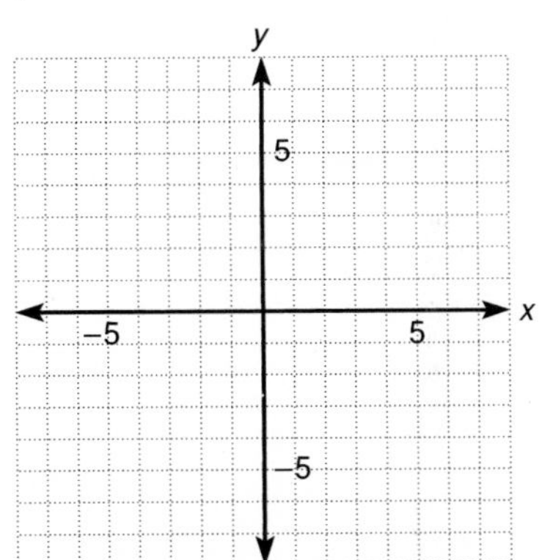

15. $y = -2x$

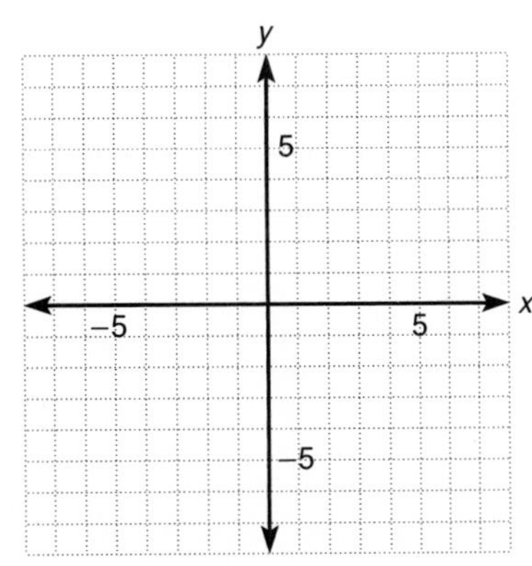

16. $y = x$

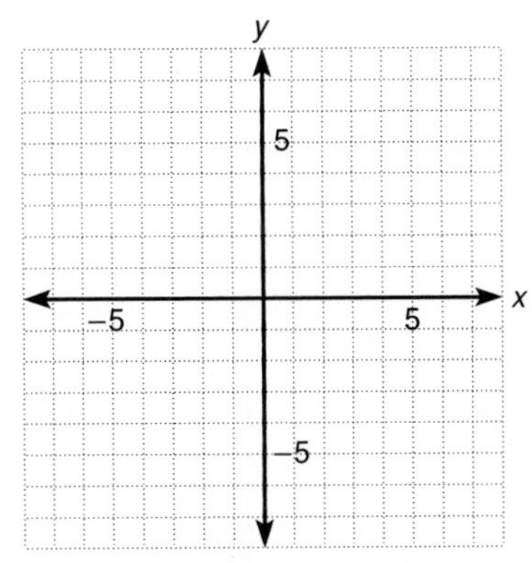

17. $x + y = 0$

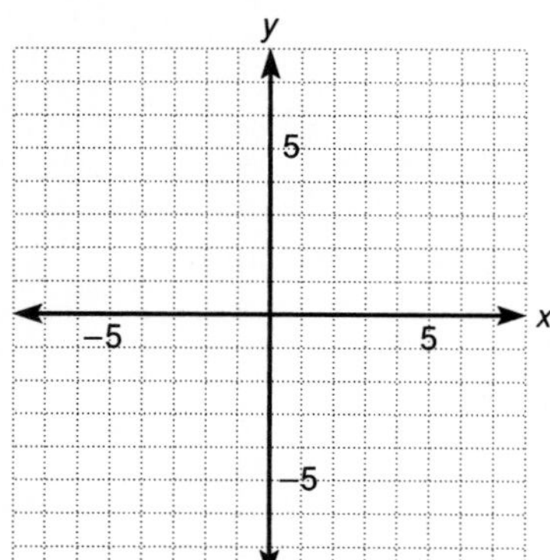

18. $v - 2x = 0$

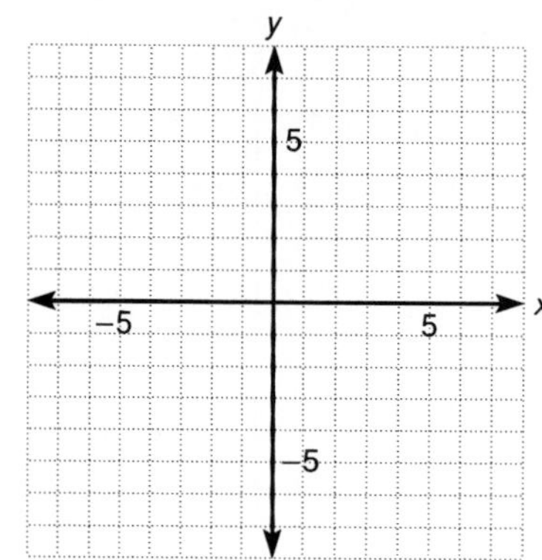

19. $3y + 2x = 0$

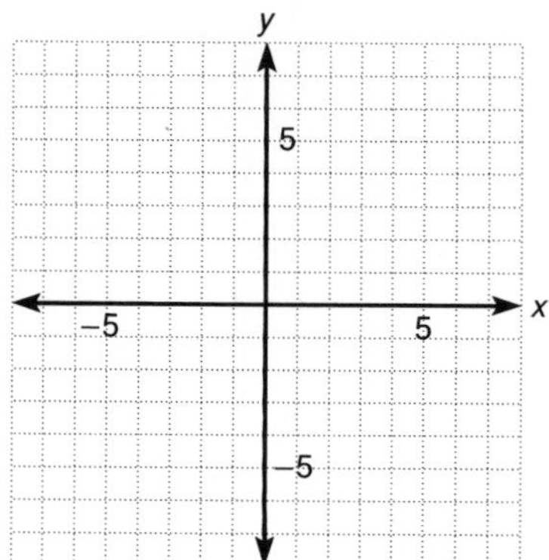

20. $y = 6$

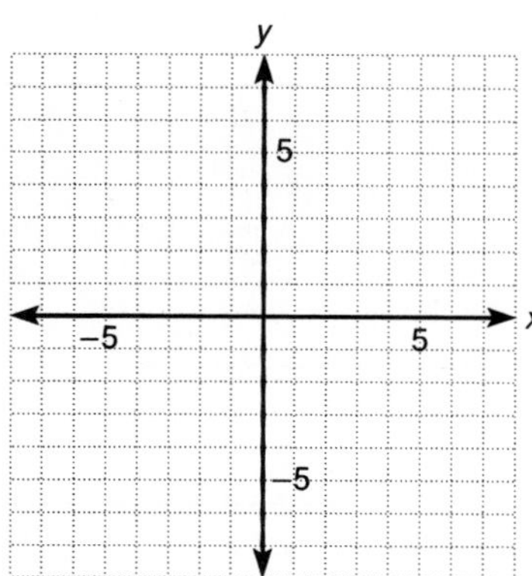

21. $x = 5$

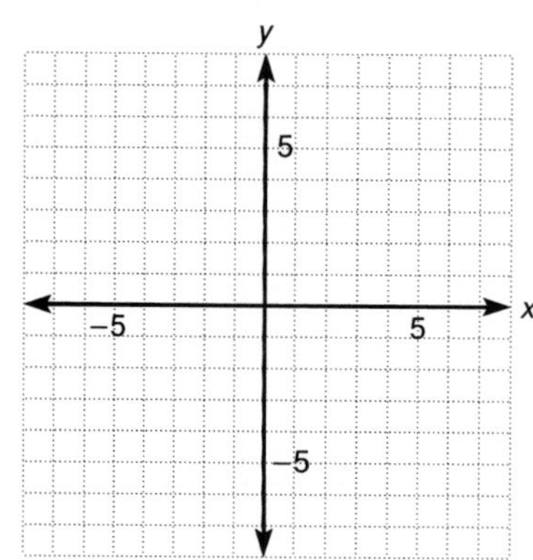

22.

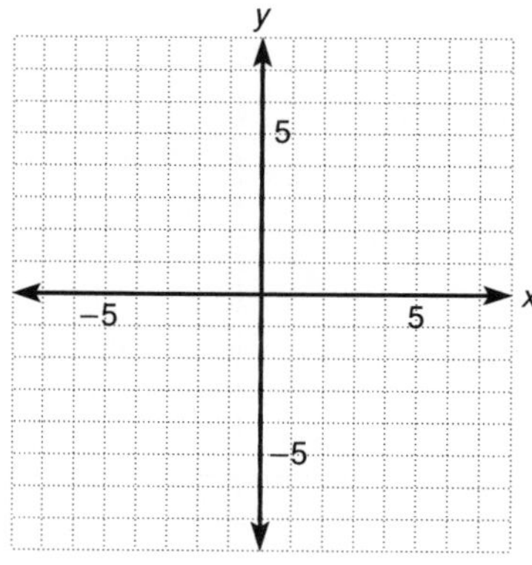

23. $x = 0$

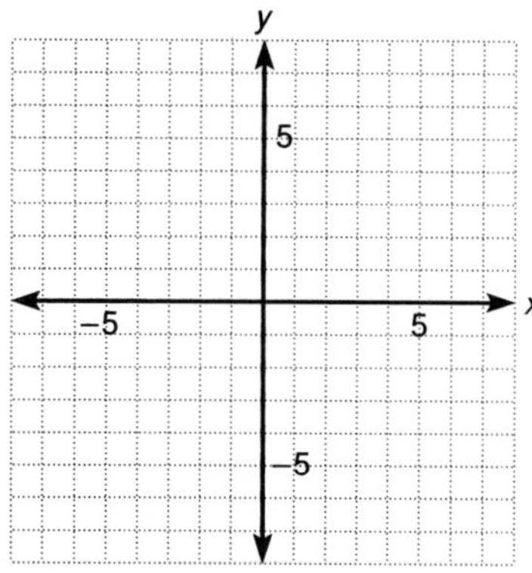

24. $y = 0$

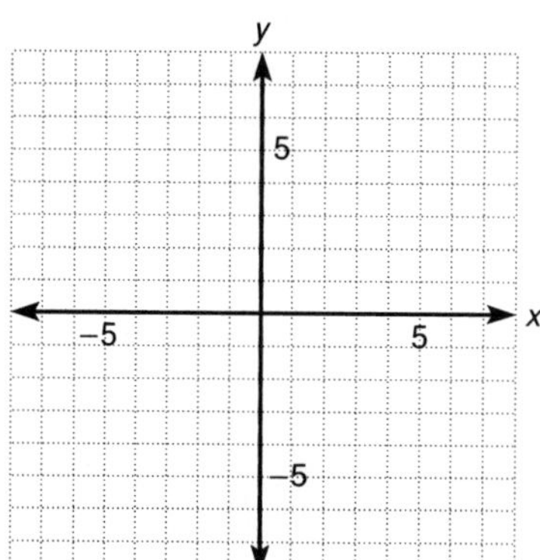

25. $y + 4 = 0$

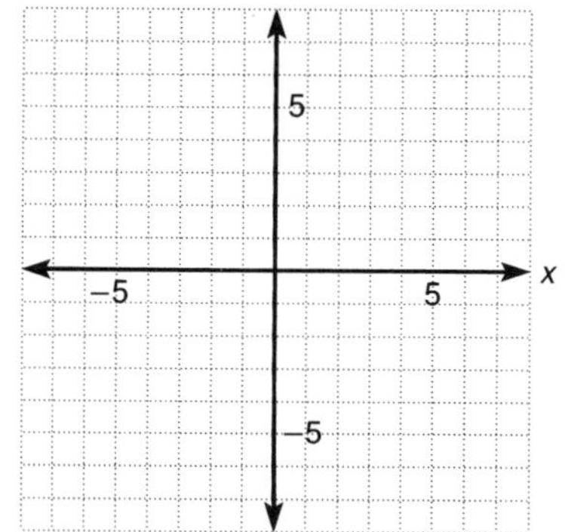

26. Plot the graph of the equation $y = 2x + b$ for (a) $b = 5$, (b) $b = 0$, and (c) $b = -3$ all on the same coordinate system.

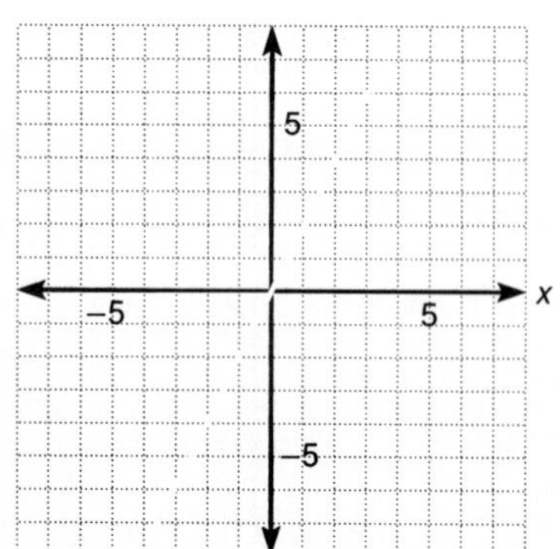

27. Plot the graph of the equation $y = mx + 1$ for (a) $m = 1$, (b) $m = \frac{1}{2}$, and (c) $m = -2$ all on the same coordinate system.

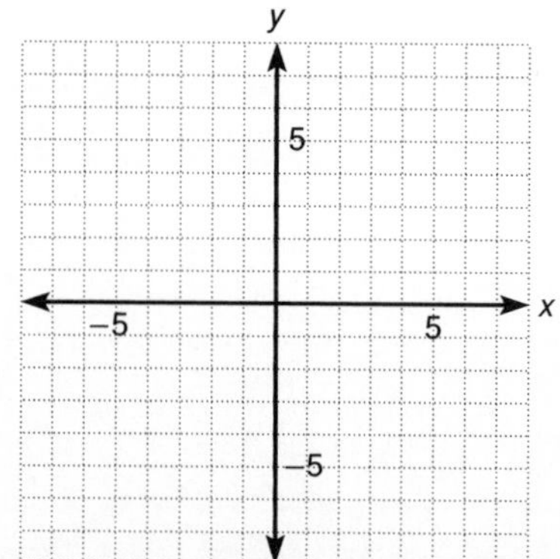

Directions Write an equation for each statement and plot the graph of the equation.

Example The value of y is 6 more than twice the value of x.

Solution The equation is $y = 2x + 6$.

x	y	
0	6	y-intercept
−3	0	x-intercept
−2	2	Checkpoint

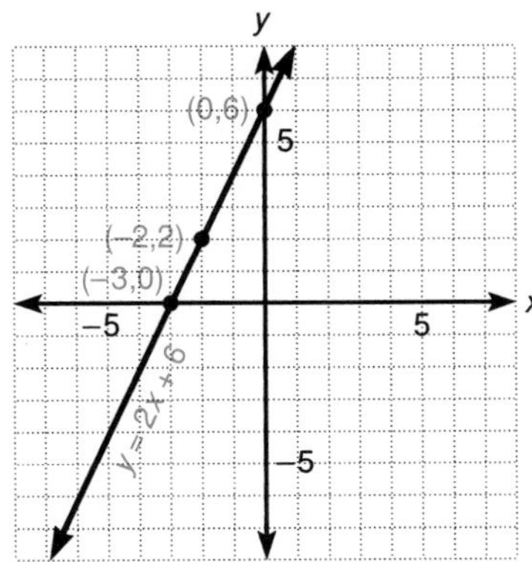

28. The value of y is 3 less than two times the value of x.

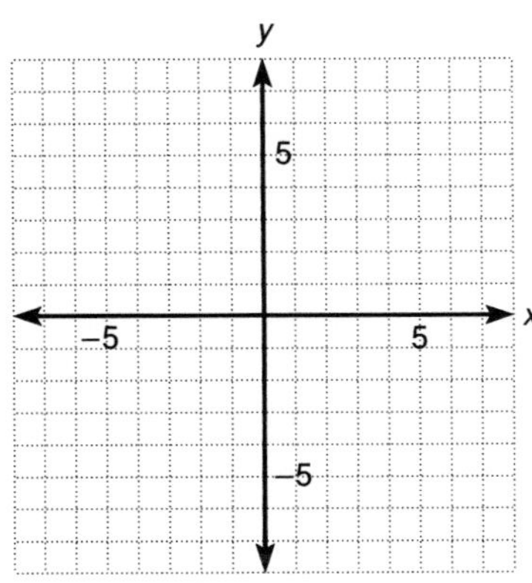

29. The value of x is 4 more than the value of y.

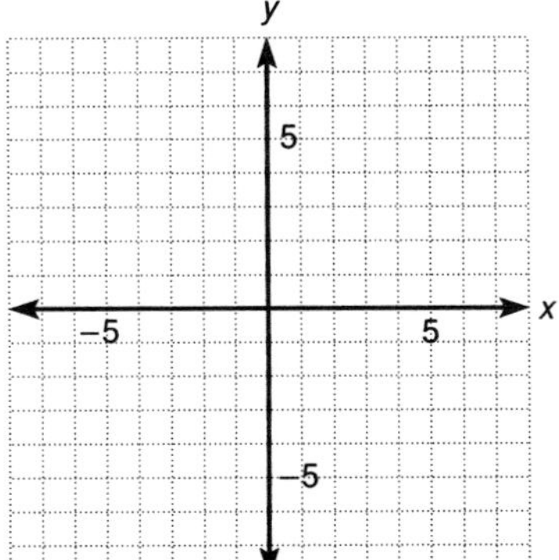

30. Two times x taken away from three times y is 6.

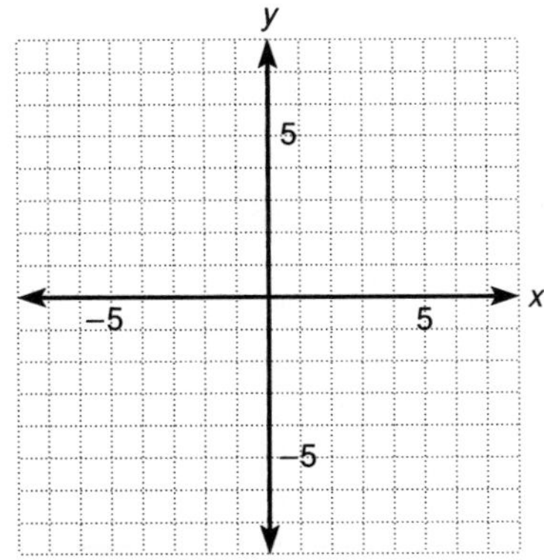

31. Five times x less the product of 2 and y gives 10.

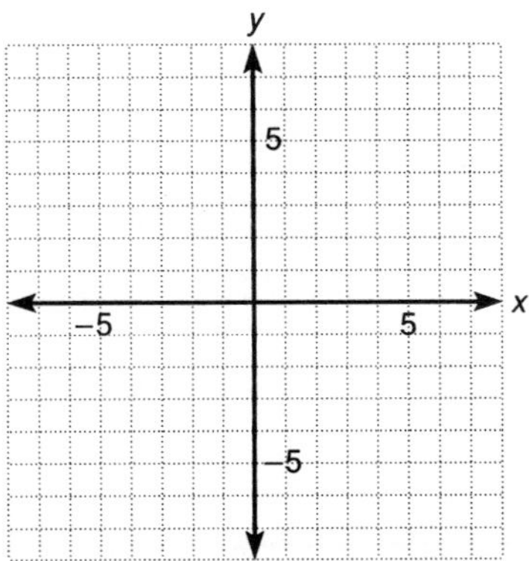

Directions Graph the two given equations on the same axes and determine (to the nearest integer) the coordinates of the point at which they intersect.

Example $x + y = 2$
$2x - y = 4$

Solution Graph each equation using the x- and y-intercepts and a checkpoint for each equation as we have done before.

$x + y = 2$

x	y
0	2
2	0
1	1

$2x - y = 4$

x	y	
0	-4	x-intercept
2	0	y-intercept
3	2	Checkpoint

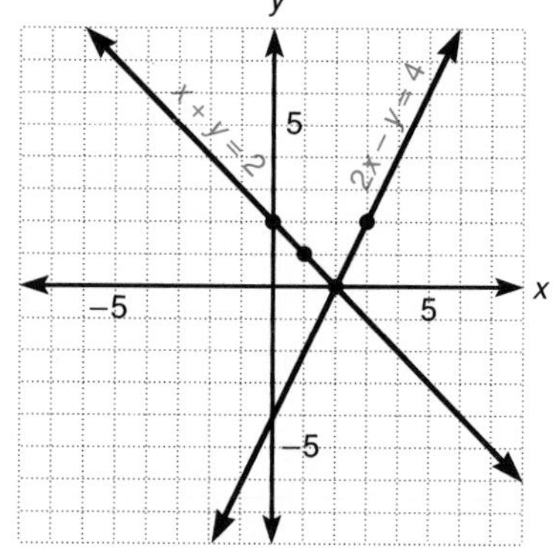

The point of intersection is the point (2,0).

32. $x + y = 3$
$2x - y = 0$

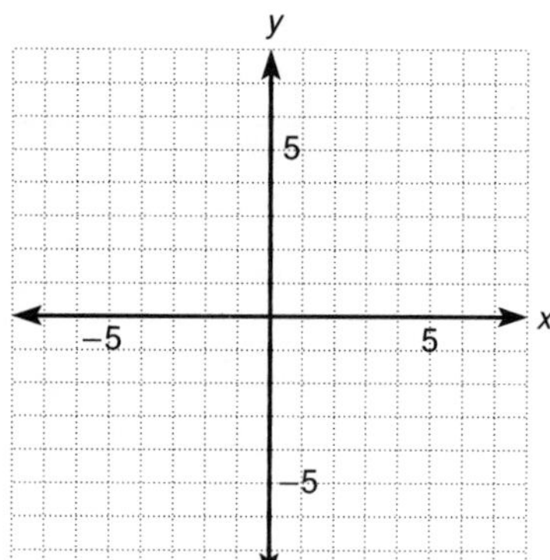

33. $y = 2x - 3$
$y = x + 1$

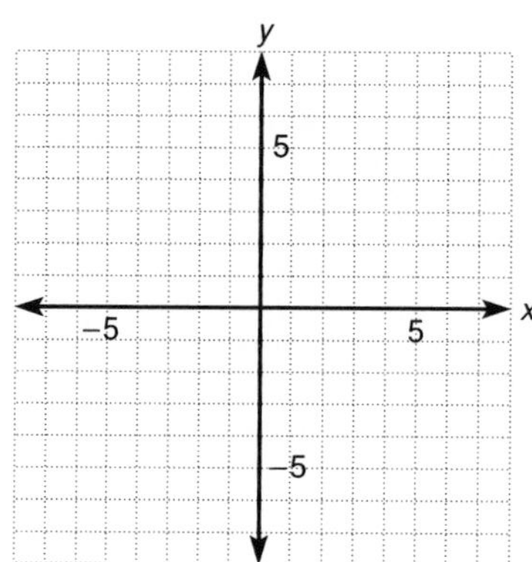

34. $x = 2y$
$2x + y = 5$

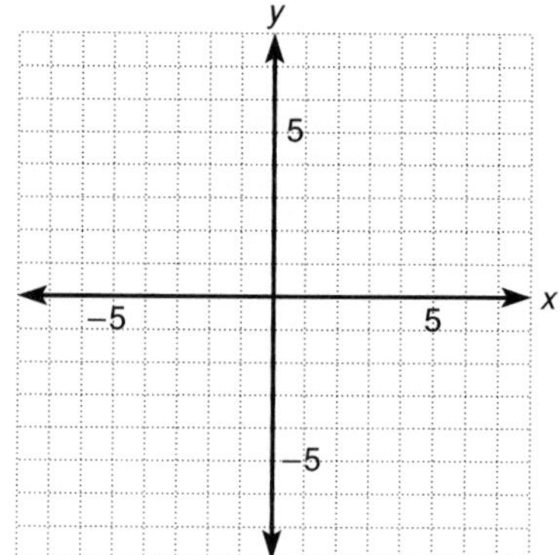

Review exercises

Directions Reduce the following expressions to lowest terms. See sections R–1 and 5–2. Assume all denominators are nonzero.

1. $\dfrac{18}{15}$

2. $\dfrac{x - 3}{x^2 + x - 12}$

3. $\dfrac{x^2 - 8x + 16}{x^2 + x - 20}$

4. Given $\dfrac{a - b}{c - d}$, evaluate the expression when $a = 2$, $b = 1$, $c = -3$, and $d = 2$. See section 5–1.

5. Given $y = mx + b$, find y when $m = -3$ and $b = 6$. See section 1–8.

6. If the product of a number and three times that number is 48, find the number. See section 4–6.

▣ 7–3 The slope of a line

Subscripts

In some formulas, two or more measurements of the same unit may be given. It is customary to label these by using **subscripts.** To illustrate, given two different measurements of pressure P in a science experiment, we might label them

$$P_1 \text{ and } P_2.$$

The 1 and 2 are the subscripts. Subscripts are always written to the lower right of the letter. The symbols above are read "P sub-one" and "P sub-two."

Note
Do not confuse a subscript, such as P_2, which helps distinguish between different measurements, and an exponent, such as P^2, which indicates the number of times a given base is used as a factor in an indicated product. Subscripts are written to the lower right of the symbol. Exponents are written to the upper right of the symbol.

The slope

Consider the portions of the two roadways denoted by R_1 and R_2 (read "R sub-one" and "R sub-two") shown in figure 7–5.

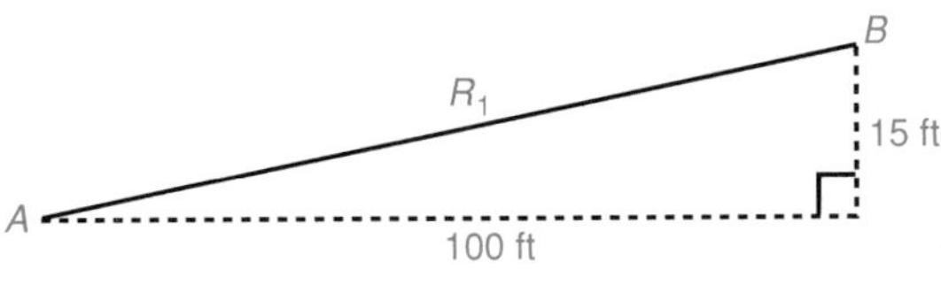

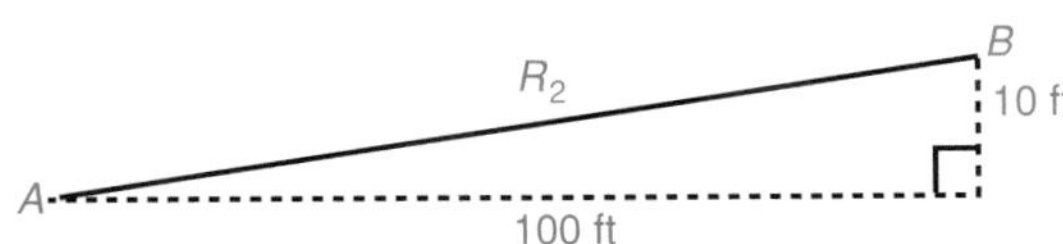

Figure 7–5

We would say roadway R_1 is "steeper" than roadway R_2. In moving from point A to point B on each roadway, a horizontal change in position of 100 feet, the vertical change in position is

$$15 \text{ feet on roadway } R_1$$

and

$$10 \text{ feet on roadway } R_2.$$

If we measure this "steepness" by the ratio

$$\frac{\text{vertical change}}{\text{horizontal change}},$$

the roadway

$$R_1 \text{ has "steepness"} = \frac{15 \text{ ft}}{100 \text{ ft}} = \frac{3}{20}$$

and

$$R_2 \text{ has "steepness"} = \frac{10 \text{ ft}}{100 \text{ ft}} = \frac{1}{10}.$$

Note

$\frac{3}{20}$ is greater than $\frac{1}{10}$, so R_1 is "steeper" than R_2.

When applying this concept to any straight line, "steepness" is called the **slope** of the line. Thus, the slope of any line L is given by

$$\text{slope} = \frac{\text{vertical change}}{\text{horizontal change}}.$$

Observe that *slope is a ratio.* (See figure 7–6.)

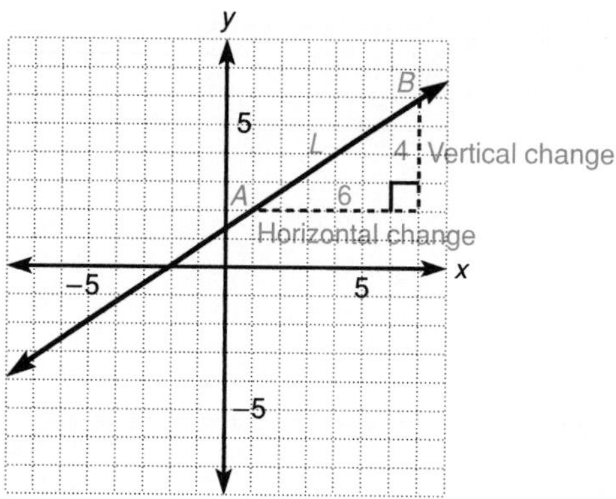

Figure 7–6

In figure 7–6, line L has from point A to point B

$$\text{a vertical change} = 4 \text{ units}$$

and

$$\text{a horizontal change} = 6 \text{ units}.$$

Thus, the

$$\text{slope of } L = \frac{\text{vertical change}}{\text{horizontal change}} = \frac{4}{6} = \frac{2}{3}$$

To obtain the slope of a nonvertical straight line, given points P_1 and P_2 (read "P sub-one" and "P sub-two") which have coordinates (x_1,y_1) and (x_2,y_2), respectively, we use the following definition.

Definition

The slope m of the line through the points P_1 and P_2 is given by

$$m = \frac{y_2 - y_1}{x_2 - x_1} \quad (x_1 \neq x_2).$$

Concept

The slope of a line is determined by dividing the change in y-values by the change in x-values of any two points on the line.

See figure 7–7.

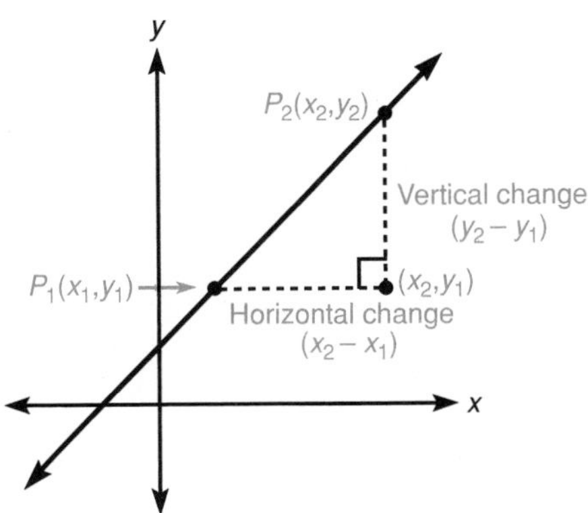

Figure 7–7

A₁ Find the slope of the line through the points $P_1(4,3)$ and $P_2(6,5)$.

Note
The vertical change is sometimes called the *rise* and the horizontal change is called the *run*. Thus, slope m can be defined

$$m = \frac{\text{rise}}{\text{run}}.$$

Example 7–3 A

1. Find the slope of the line through the points $P_1(2,3)$ and $P_2(5,9)$.

$$\begin{aligned} \text{slope } m &= \frac{y_2 - y_1}{x_2 - x_1} \\ &= \frac{(9) - (3)}{(5) - (2)} && \text{Replace } y_2 \text{ with 9, } y_1 \text{ with 3, } x_2 \text{ with 5, } x_1 \text{ with 2} \\ &= \frac{6}{3} && \text{Subtract as indicated} \\ &= 2 \end{aligned}$$

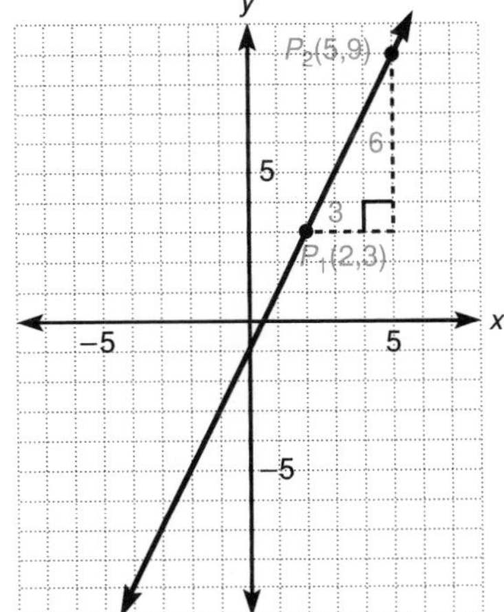

Note
The x- and y-values may be subtracted in any order as long as the coordinates of one point are in the same position in the numerator and the denominator. Thus,

$$m = \frac{(3) - (9)}{(2) - (5)} = \frac{-6}{-3} = 2,$$

in which we used

$$m = \frac{y_1 - y_2}{x_1 - x_2}.$$

You are now ready to do **A₁**.

A₂ Find the slope of the line through the points $P_1(-4,3)$ and $P_2(2,-5)$.

2. Find the slope of the line through points $P_1(-3,2)$ and $P_2(5,-4)$.

$$\text{slope } m = \frac{y_2 - y_1}{x_2 - x_1}$$
$$= \frac{(-4) - (2)}{(5) - (-3)} \qquad \text{Replace } y_2 \text{ with } -4,\ y_1 \text{ with } 2,\ x_2 \text{ with } 5,\ x_1 \text{ with } -3$$
$$= \frac{-6}{8}$$
$$= \frac{-3}{4} = -\frac{3}{4}$$

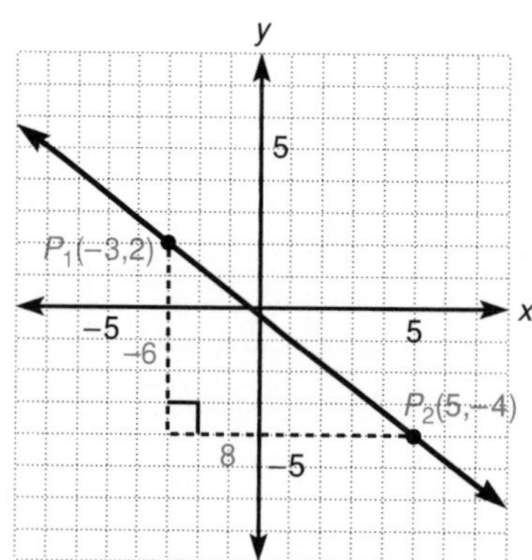

Note

$$m = \frac{y_1 - y_2}{x_1 - x_2} = \frac{(2) - (-4)}{(-3) - (5)} = \frac{6}{-8} = \frac{-3}{4} = -\frac{3}{4}$$

You are now ready to do **A₂**.

A₃ Find the slope of the line through the points $P_1(-5,1)$ and $P_2(6,1)$.

3. Find the slope of the horizontal line through $P_1(-3,4)$ and $P_2(2,4)$.

$$\text{slope } m = \frac{y_2 - y_1}{x_2 - x_1}$$
$$= \frac{(4) - (4)}{(2) - (-3)} \qquad \text{Replace } y_2 \text{ with } 4,\ y_1 \text{ with } 4,\ x_2 \text{ with } 2,\ x_1 \text{ with } -3$$
$$= \frac{0}{5}$$
$$= 0$$

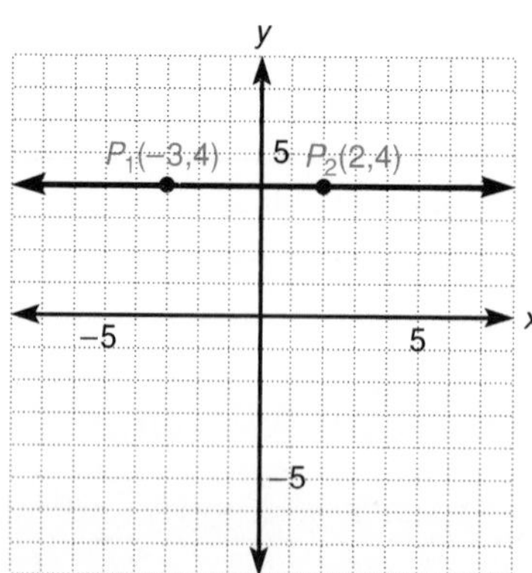

The slope $m = 0$ and the line is a horizontal line. Recall, the equation of any horizontal line is of the form $y = b$, or $y - b = 0$, where b is the y-intercept. In this case, the equation of the line is $y = 4$.

> The slope m of any horizontal line having equation $y = b$ is $m = 0$.

You are now ready to do **A₃**.

4. Find the slope of the vertical line through $P_1(-4,1)$ and $P_2(-4,-3)$.

$$\text{slope } m = \frac{y_2 - y_1}{x_2 - x_1}$$

$$= \frac{(-3) - 1}{(-4) - (-4)} \quad \text{Replace } y_2 \text{ with } -3,\ y_1 \text{ with } 1,\ x_2 \text{ with } -4,\ x_1 \text{ with } -4$$

$$= \frac{-4}{0} \quad \text{(Undefined)}$$

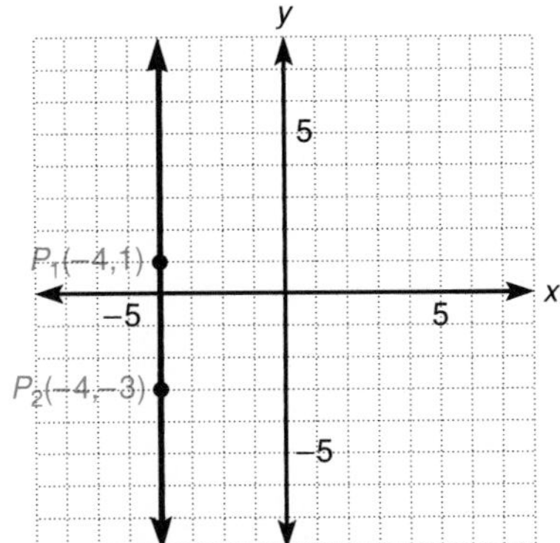

The line is a vertical line and the slope is undefined. Recall, the equation of any vertical line is of the form $x = a$, or $x - a = 0$, where a is the x-intercept. In this case, the equation of the line is $x = -4$.

> Any vertical line having equation $x = a$ *has an undefined slope.*

You are now ready to do **A_4**.

A_4 Find the slope of the line through the points $P_1(2,-5)$ and $P_2(2,1)$.

It is important to realize that the *slope of a nonvertical line is the same no matter what two points on the line are used to compute the slope.* Consider figure 7–8.

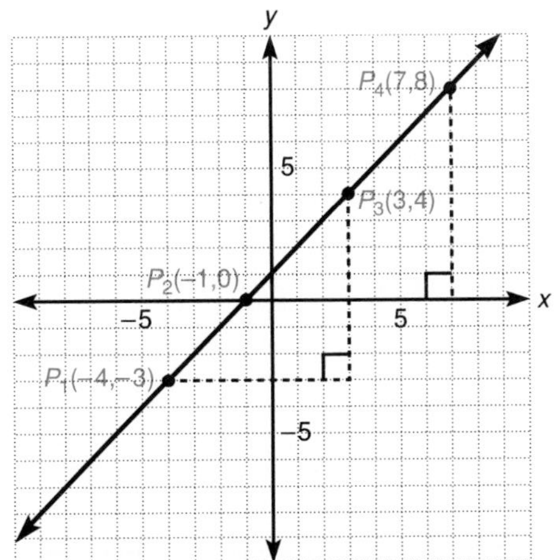

Figure 7–8

Using P_1 and P_3, $m = \frac{(4) - (-3)}{(3) - (-4)} = \frac{7}{7} = 1$, and

using P_2 and P_4, $m = \frac{(8) - (0)}{(7) - (-1)} = \frac{8}{8} = 1$.

We obtain the same slope, $m = 1$.

Answers to section 7–3 margin exercises

A₁ $m = 1$ **A₂** $m = -\frac{4}{3}$ **A₃** $m = 0$ **A₄** slope is undefined

Mastery points

Can you

- Find the slope of a line given two points on the line?
- Determine the slope of a horizontal line and of a vertical line?

Exercise 7–3

Directions Find the slope of the line passing through each of the following pairs of points. Draw the graph of the line in exercises 1–8. See example 7–3 A.

Examples **A₂** $P_1(-4,3)$ and $P_2(2,-5)$

Solutions

$$m = \frac{y_1 - y_2}{x_1 - x_2}$$

$$= \frac{(-5) - (3)}{(2) - (-4)}$$ Replace y_2 with -5, y_1 with 3, x_2 with 2, and x_1 with -4

$$= \frac{-8}{2 + 4}$$ Subtract in numerator and denominator

$$= \frac{-8}{6}$$ Add in denominator

$$= -\frac{4}{3}$$ Reduce to lowest terms

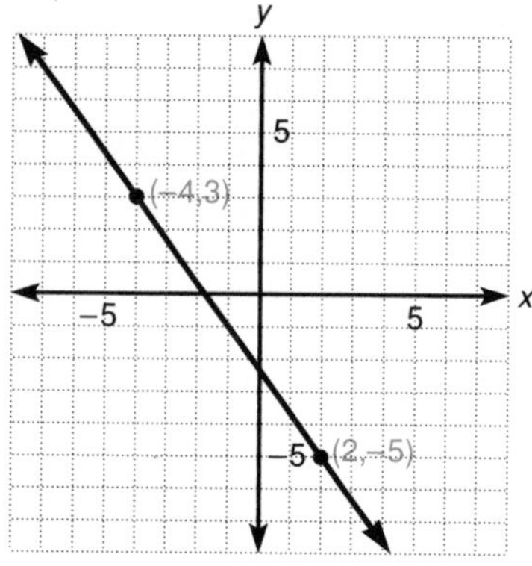

A₄ $P_1(2,-5)$ and $P_2(2,1)$

$$m = \frac{(1) - (-5)}{(2) - (2)}$$ Replace y_1 with -5, y_2 with 1, x_1 with 2, and x_2 with 2

$$= \frac{1 + 5}{0}$$

$$= \frac{6}{0}$$ Undefined

The slope is undefined (does not exist).

1. (5,2), (3,3)

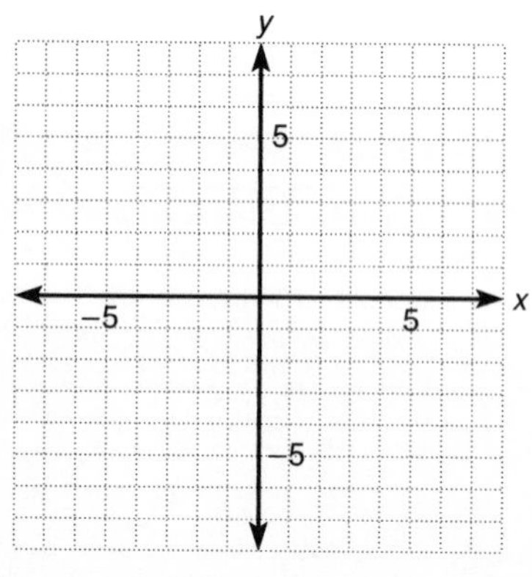

2. (4,3), (−2,2)

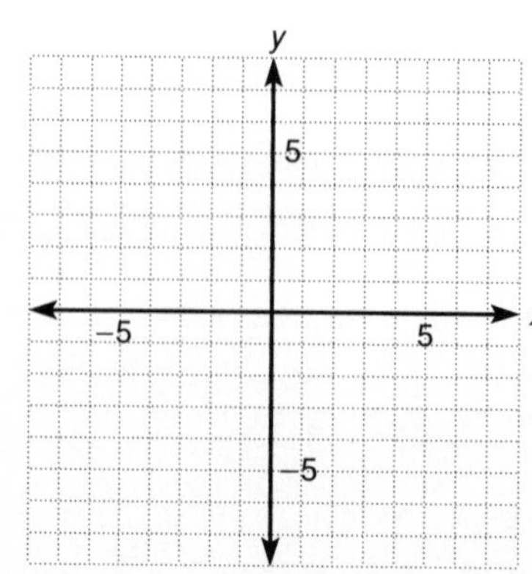

3. (−4,−1), (2,3)

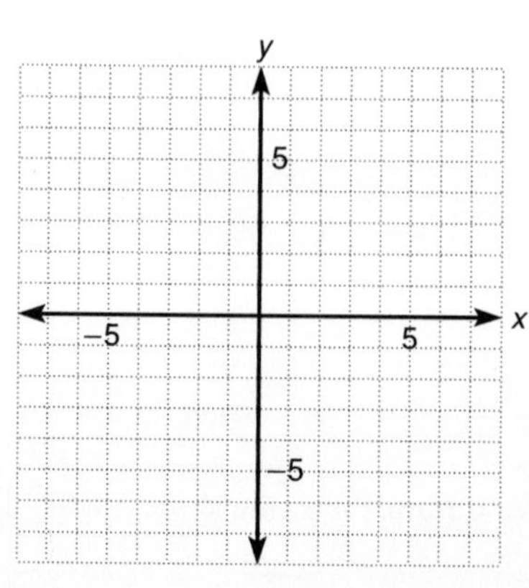

4. $(-2,3)$, $(5,-3)$

5. $(-4,3)$, $(2,3)$

6. $(4,-4)$, $(2,-4)$

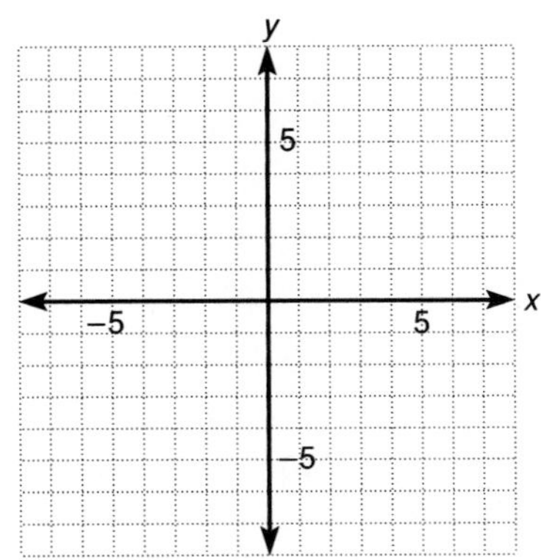

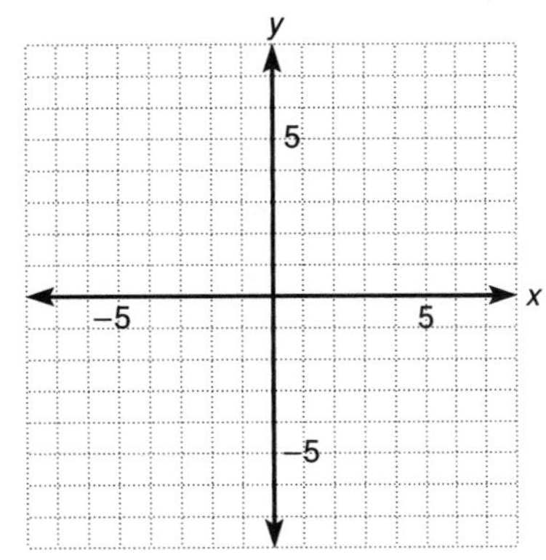

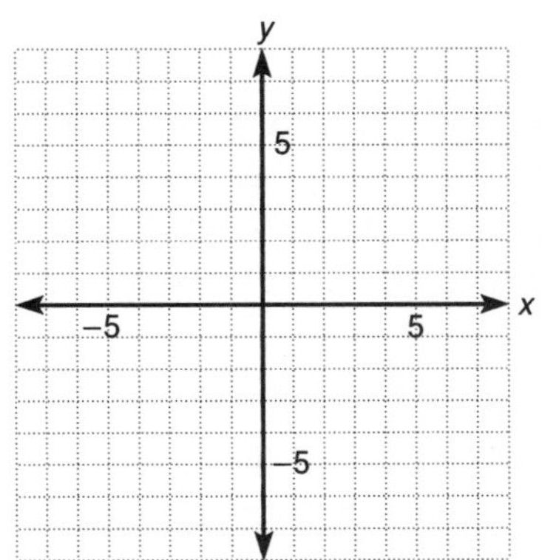

7. $(6,-7)$, $(6,1)$

8. $(-1,4)$, $(-1,-3)$

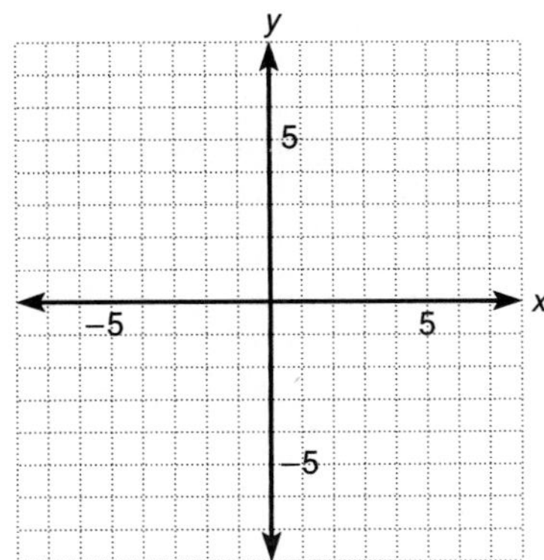

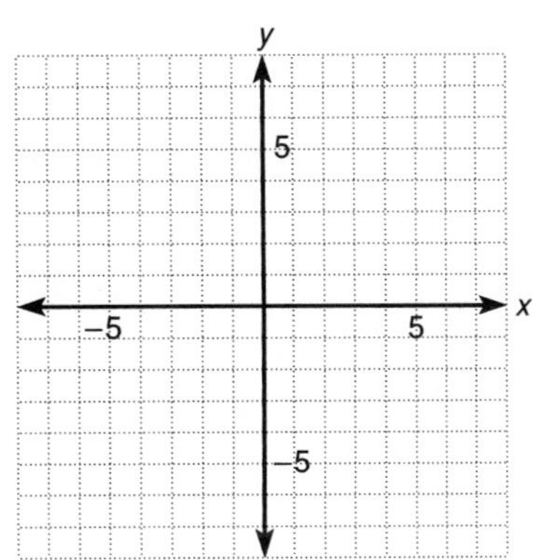

9. $(-3,1)$, $(0,3)$

10. $(4,0)$, $(-2,8)$

11. $(-3,9)$, $(-3,-5)$

12. $(5,0)$, $(-3,0)$

13. $(5,6)$, $(0,0)$

14. $(0,0)$, $(-4,3)$

15. $(0,7)$, $(0,-8)$

16. $(-1,3)$, $(-4,2)$

17. $(-8,-3)$, $(-1,-2)$

18. $(-6,-5)$, $(-4,-3)$

19. $(-10,4)$, $(2,4)$

20. $(7,-3)$, $(8,-7)$

21. $(5,7)$, $(-6,-3)$

22. $(9,4)$, $(1,-1)$

Example A boy is flying his kite. The kite is 35 feet above the ground, and the distance from the boy to a point directly below the kite is 40 feet. If the string from the boy to the kite is a straight line, what is the slope of the string?

Solution Using $m = \dfrac{\text{vertical change}}{\text{horizontal change}}$, the vertical change is 35 feet and the horizontal change is 40 feet.

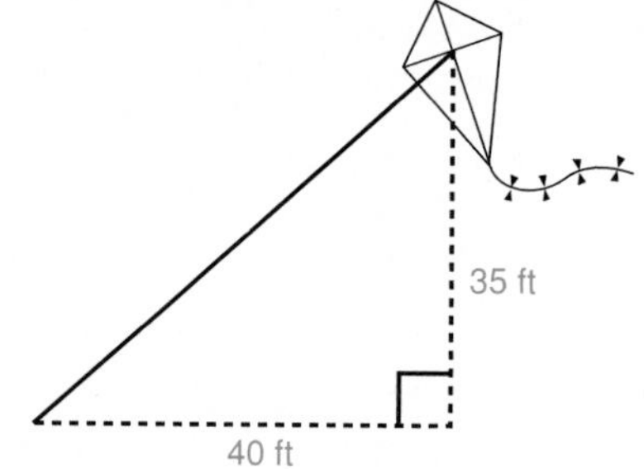

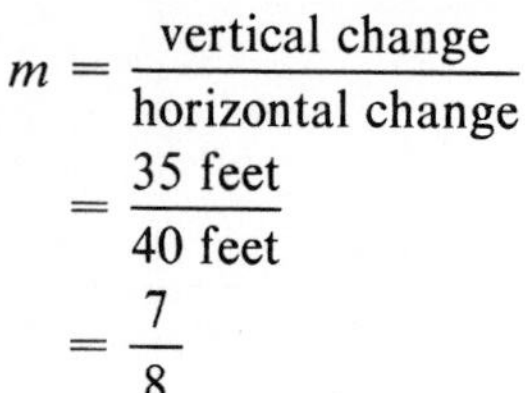

$$m = \frac{\text{vertical change}}{\text{horizontal change}} = \frac{35 \text{ feet}}{40 \text{ feet}} = \frac{7}{8}$$

23. The roof of a home rises vertically a distance of 8 feet through a horizontal distance of 12 feet. Find the pitch (slope) of the roof.

24. The roof of a factory rises vertically 6 feet through a horizontal run of 27 feet. What is the pitch of the roof?

25. A ladder leaning against the side of a building touches the building at a point 12 meters from the ground. If the foot of the ladder is 18 meters from the base of the building, what is the slope of the ladder?

26. A guy wire is attached to a telephone pole. If the wire is attached to the ground at a point 15 feet from the base of the pole and to the pole at a point 12 feet up on the pole, what is the slope of the wire?

27. A company's profits (P) are related to the number of items produced (x) by a linear equation. If profits rise by $1,000 for every 250 items produced, what is the slope of the graph of the equation?

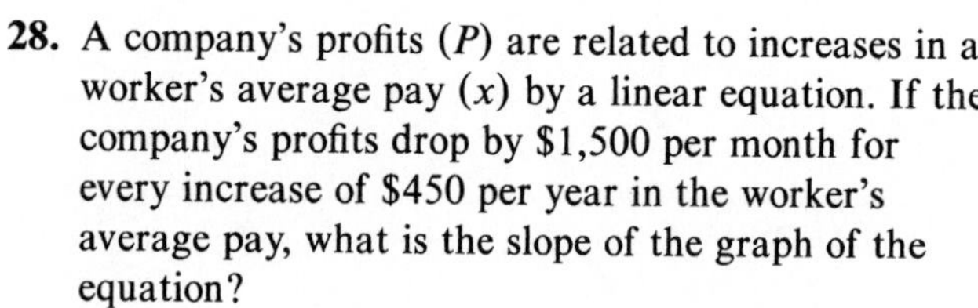

28. A company's profits (P) are related to increases in a worker's average pay (x) by a linear equation. If the company's profits drop by $1,500 per month for every increase of $450 per year in the worker's average pay, what is the slope of the graph of the equation?

29. The diagram shows a linear representation of a jogger's heartbeat in beats per minute as his speed is increased (in feet per second). What is the slope of the line?

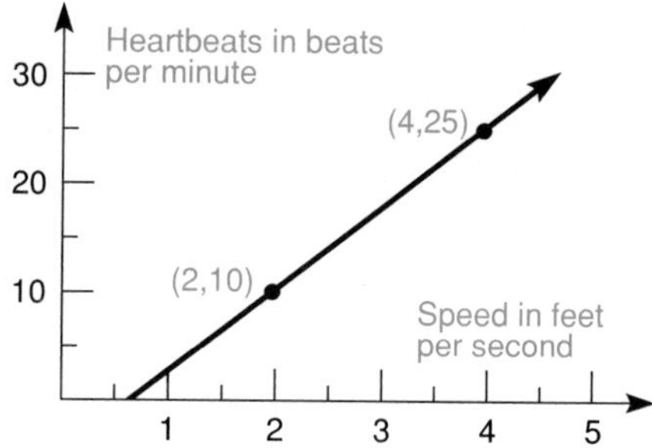

30. The diagram shows a linear representation of the bacteria count in a culture as related to the hours it exists. What is the slope of the line?

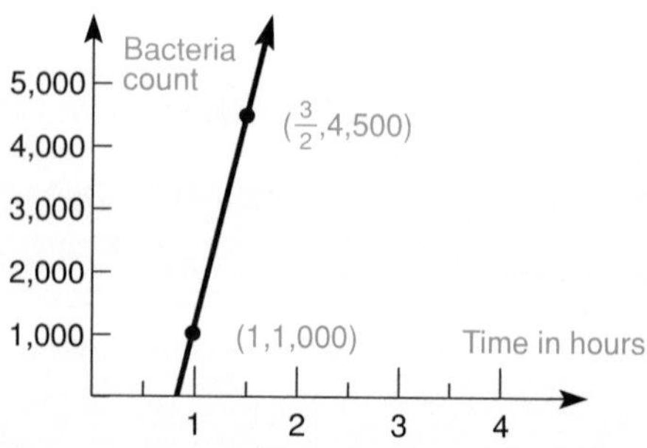

Directions Graph and determine the slope of each of the following equations.

Example $y = x + 3$

Solution The slope requires two different points on the line. Get these by choosing two different values of x and obtaining the corresponding values of y.

When $x = -1$,

$$\begin{aligned} y &= x + 3 \\ &= -1 + 3 \\ &= 2. \end{aligned}$$

When $x = 2$,

$$\begin{aligned} y &= x + 3 \\ &= 2 + 3 \\ &= 5. \end{aligned}$$

The ordered pairs are $(-1,2)$ and $(2,5)$.

$$m = \frac{(5) - (2)}{(2) - (-1)} = \frac{5 - 2}{2 + 1} = \frac{3}{3} = 1$$

The slope of the line is 1.

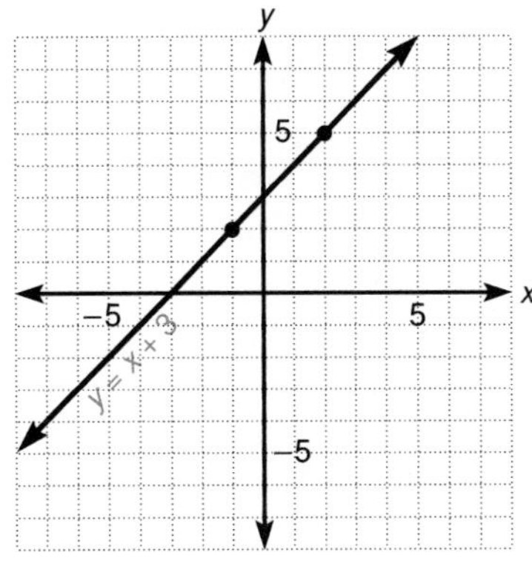

31. $y = 2x - 2$

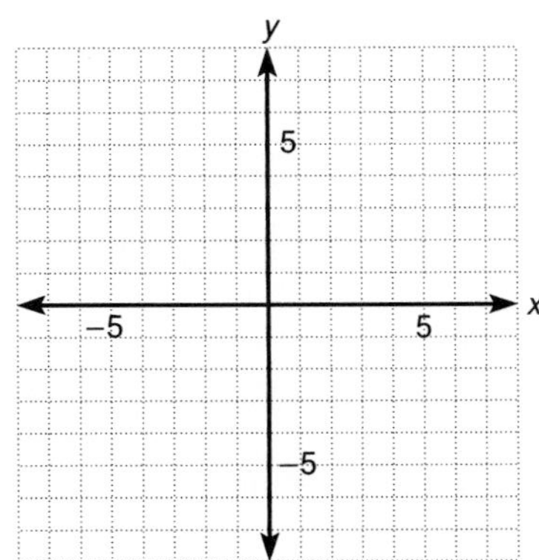

32. $y = -3x + 2$

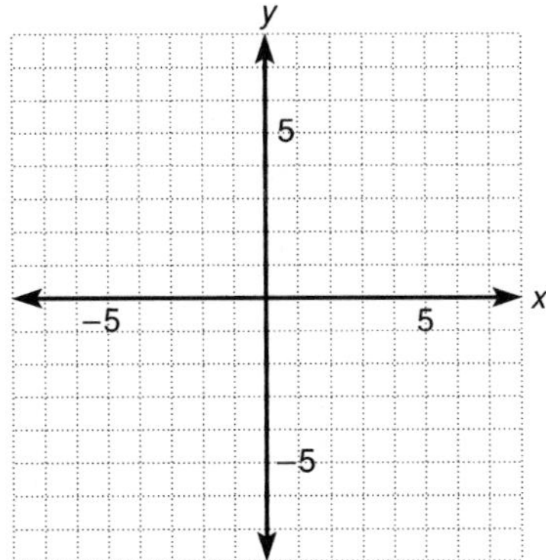

33. $y = 4x$

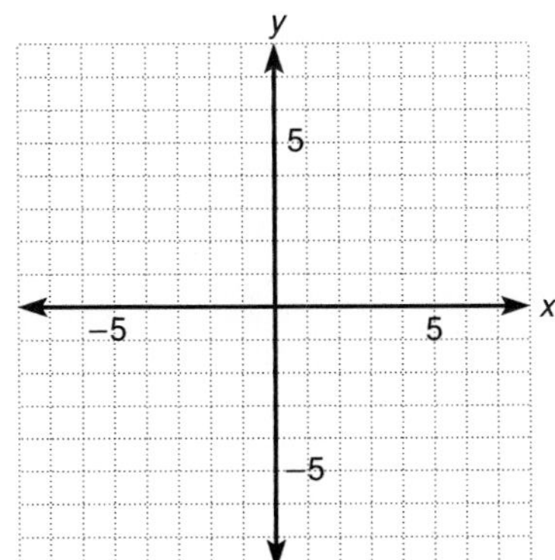

34. $y = -2x$

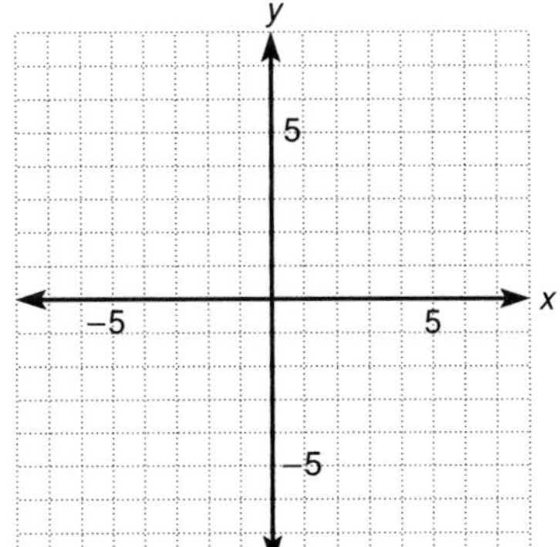

Review exercises

1. Simplify the expression $3 - 4(5 - 2)$. See section 1–6.

2. $4^2 - 2^3 - 3 \cdot 5 - 2 \cdot 3$ See section 1–6.

Directions Simplify the following. Use only positive exponents. See section 3–4.

3. $(-2)^{-3}$

4. $\dfrac{a^{-2}b^3}{a^3b^{-2}}$

5. $x^{-2} \cdot x^3 \cdot x^0$

6. When four times a number is increased by 12, the result is 64. What is the number? See section 2–4.

Directions Solve the following equations for y. See section 2–5.

7. $3x + y = -1$

8. $3x - 3y = 6$

▣ 7–4 The equation of a line

In section 7–2, we discussed the straight line graph of a linear equation in two variables. In this section, we discuss how to determine the equation of a straight line when we know certain facts about the line. There are three forms of the equation of a straight line that are of use to us: the *standard* form, the *point-slope* form, and the *slope-intercept* form,

The standard form

The **standard form** of the equation of a straight line is stated here.

> **Standard form of the equation of a line**
>
> $$ax + by = c,$$
>
> where a, b, and c are integers, $a \geq 0$, a and b not both zero.

To illustrate, the equations

$$2x + 3y = 6,\ 4x - 2y = 0, \text{ and } x - 6y = -2$$

are written in standard form. In most situations, the equations will be written in this form.

The point-slope form

Consider again the formula for the slope of a line,

$$m = \frac{y_2 - y_1}{x_2 - x_1} \qquad (x_1 \neq x_2),$$

where (x_1,y_1) and (x_2,y_2) are coordinates of two *known* points on the line. Suppose we replace the known point (x_2,y_2) with *any other arbitrary point* (x,y) on the line.

Then the slope is given by

$$m = \frac{y - y_1}{x - x_1} \qquad (x \neq x_1).$$

Multiply both members of the equation by $x - x_1$ to get

$$m(x - x_1) = y - y_1,$$

which we write

$$y - y_1 = m(x - x_1).$$

We call this the **point-slope form** of the equation of a line, where (x_1,y_1) is a known point on the line, m is the slope, and (x,y) is *any* other unknown point on the line.

Point-slope equation of a line

$$y - y_1 = m(x - x_1),$$

where m is the slope and (x_1,y_1) is a known point on the line.

We can use this form to find the equation of a line if we know the slope of the line and the coordinates of at least one point on the line.

Example 7–4 A

1. Find the equation of a line having slope $m = 2$ and passing through the point $(4,-3)$.

   Using the point-slope form, we know $m = 2$ and $(x_1,y_1) = (4,-3)$.

$$y - y_1 = m(x - x_1)$$

$$y - (-3) = 2(x - 4) \qquad \text{Replace } y_1 \text{ with } -3 \text{ and } x_1 \text{ with } 4$$

$$y + 3 = 2x - 8 \qquad \text{Multiply and subtract as indicated}$$

$$y = 2x - 11 \qquad \text{Add } -3 \text{ to both members}$$

$$-2x + y = -11 \qquad \text{Add } -2x \text{ to both members}$$

$$2x - y = 11 \qquad \text{Multiply each member by } -1$$

   Note

   We wrote our final answer in *standard form, $ax + by = c$.*

You are now ready to do **A_1**.

2. Find the equation of the line passing through the points $(-3,2)$ and $(5,1)$.

   We use the two points to find the slope.

$$m = \frac{y_2 - y_1}{x_2 - x_1}$$

$$= \frac{(1) - (2)}{(5) - (-3)} \qquad \text{Replace } y_2 \text{ with } 1,\ y_1 \text{ with } 2,\ x_2 \text{ with } 5, \text{ and } x_1 \text{ with } -3$$

$$= \frac{-1}{8} = -\frac{1}{8} \qquad \text{Subtract as indicated}$$

A_1 Find the equation of the line having slope $m = 3$ and passing through the point $(1,-5)$.

A_2 Find the equation of the line passing through the points $(-2,3)$ and $(6,2)$.

Choosing *either* of the points $(-3,2)$ or $(5,1)$ together with the slope, we use the point-slope form.

$$
\begin{aligned}
y - y_1 &= m(x - x_1) \\
y - 2 &= -\frac{1}{8}[x - (-3)] && \text{Use point } (-3,2)\text{. Replace } y_1 \text{ with 2 and } x_1 \text{ with } -3 \\
y - 2 &= -\frac{1}{8}(x + 3) \\
8(y - 2) &= -1(x + 3) && \text{Multiply each member by 8} \\
8y - 16 &= -x - 3 && \text{Perform indicated multiplications} \\
8y &= -x + 13 && \text{Add 16 to both members} \\
x + 8y &= 13 && \text{Add } x \text{ to each member}
\end{aligned}
$$

Note

If we had used the point $(5,1)$, then

$$
\begin{aligned}
y - y_1 &= m(x - x_1) \\
y - 1 &= -\frac{1}{8}(x - 5) \\
8(y - 1) &= -1(x - 5) \\
8y - 8 &= -x + 5 \\
8y &= -x + 13 \\
x + 8y &= 13. && \text{(Produces the same equation.)}
\end{aligned}
$$

You are now ready to do **A_2**. ■

The slope-intercept form

Suppose a given line L, having slope m, passes through the point $(0,b)$, the y-intercept of the line. Using the point-slope form of the equation of a line,

$$
\begin{aligned}
& y - b = m(x - 0). && \text{Replace } y_1 \text{ with } b \text{ and } x_1 \text{ with } 0 \\
\text{Then} \quad & y - b = mx && x - 0 = x \\
\text{and} \quad & y = mx + b. && \text{Add } b \text{ to each member } y\text{-intercept}
\end{aligned}
$$

Slope (m) — y-intercept (b)

We call $y = mr + b$ the **slope-intercept** form of the equation of a line.

> **Slope-intercept form of the equation of a line**
>
> $$y = mx + b,$$
>
> where m and b are real numbers. The slope of the line is m and the y-intercept is $(0,b)$.

We can use the slope-intercept form of the equation of a line to find the slope and the y-intercept of a line and to graph a linear equation in two variables.

Example 7–4 B

1. Find the slope and the y-intercept of the line defined by the equation $3y - 5x = 9$.

$$
\begin{aligned}
3y - 5x &= 9 && \text{Solve for } y \\
3y &= 5x + 9 && \text{Add } 5x \text{ to each member} \\
y &= \frac{5x + 9}{3} && \text{Divide each member by 3} \\
y &= \frac{5}{3}x + 3 && \text{Write in slope-intercept form by dividing 3 into 5 and into 9}
\end{aligned}
$$

Then slope $m = \frac{5}{3}$ and y-intercept is the point (0,3).

You are now ready to do **B₁**.

2. Sketch the graph of the equation $3y - 5x = 9$ using slope and y-intercept.

From example 1, we determined the slope $m = \frac{5}{3}$ and since $b = 3$, the y-intercept is (0,3). We use the slope $\frac{5}{3}$ to find another point on the graph. To do this, we plot the y-intercept (0,3). Using the slope $\frac{5}{3}$, from the point (0,3) move three units to the *right* (the run, denominator) and from this new point move five units *up* (the rise, numerator) to find a second point. Draw the line through this new point and the y-intercept to obtain the graph.

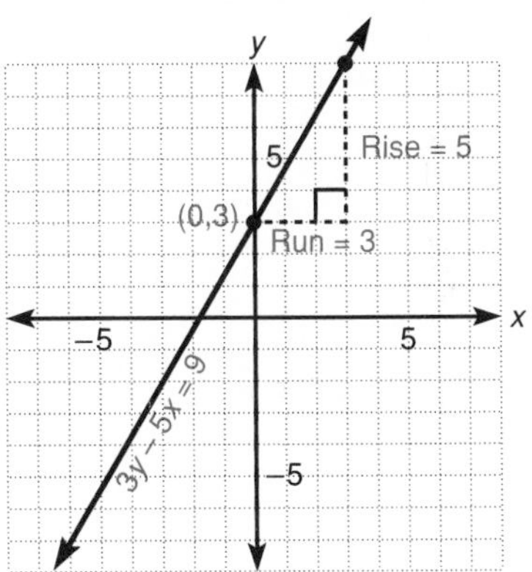

You are now ready to do **B₂**.

3. Graph the line through the point (0, −2) and having slope $-\frac{3}{2}$.

We plot the point (0, −2). From this point, move two units to the right (denominator). From this new point, move three units *down* (numerator, −3) to find the second point. Draw the line through this second point and the y-intercept to obtain the graph.

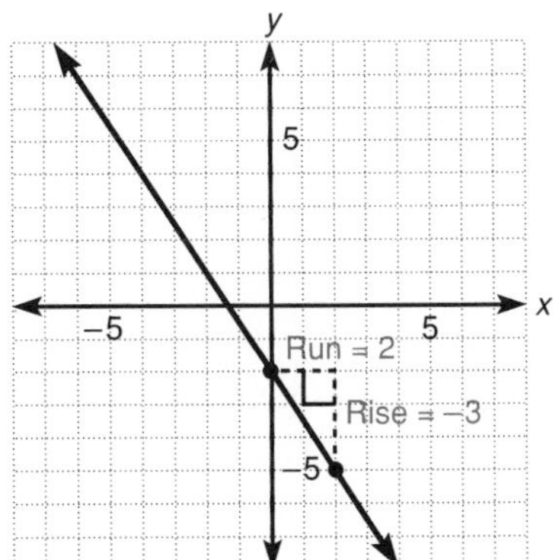

Note

$$m = -\frac{3}{2} = \frac{-3}{2} = \frac{\text{negative rise (fall)}}{\text{run}}$$

You are now ready to do **B₃**. ■

B₁ Find the slope and y-intercept of the line defined by the equation $2y - 5x = 6$.

B₂ Sketch the graph of the equation $3x - 2y = 4$ using slope m and y-intercept $(0,b)$.

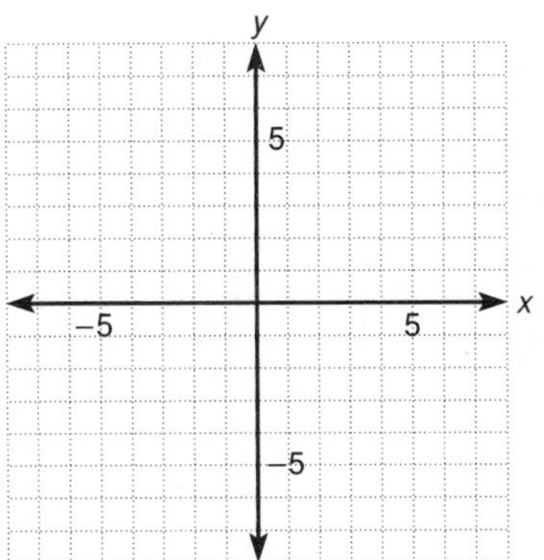

B₃ Graph the line through (0,3) and having slope $-\frac{2}{3}$.

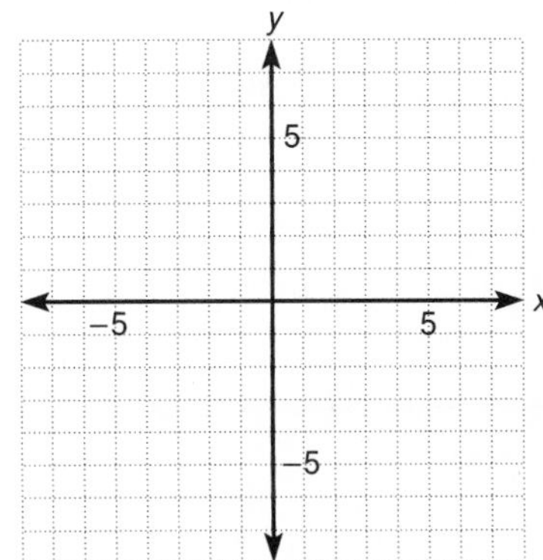

C_1 Find the equation of the line having slope $m = -2$ and y-intercept (0,4).

Given the slope of a line and its y-intercept, it is then possible to determine the equation of the line.

Example 7–4 C

1. Find the equation of the line having slope $m = -3$ and y-intercept (0,2).
   Using $y = mx + b$, $m = -3$ and $b = 2$, we obtain

   $y = -3x + 2.$ Replace m with -3 and b with 2

You are now ready to do **C_1**.

2. Find the equation of the line having slope $m = \frac{2}{3}$ and passing through point (0,−4).
   Since the point (0,−4) is on the y-axis, it is the y-intercept, so $b = -4$.

   $y = mx + b$

   $y = \frac{2}{3}x + (-4)$ Replace m with $\frac{2}{3}$ and b with -4

   $y = \frac{2}{3}x - 4$ Definition of subtraction

C_2 Find the equation of the line having slope $m = \frac{3}{4}$ and passing through the point (0,3).

You are now ready to do **C_2**.

3. Find the equation of the line with slope $m = 0$ and having y-intercept 3.

   $y = mx + b$
   $y = (0)x + 3$ Replace m with 0 and b with 3
   $y = 0 + 3$ $0 \cdot x = 0$
   $y = 3$

   Note
   The equation is of the form $y = b$ and the graph is a horizontal line.

You are now ready to do **C_3**. ■

Parallel and perpendicular lines

C_3 Find the equation of the line having y-intercept (0,−6) and slope $m = 0$.

Given two distinct straight lines in a plane, they will either be parallel (never meet no matter how far they are extended) or intersect in one point.

For two nonvertical lines to be parallel, they must *have the same slope and different y-intercepts.*

> **Slopes of parallel lines**
> Two distinct nonvertical lines having slopes m_1 and m_2 are parallel if and only if $m_1 = m_2$ and $b_1 \neq b_2$.

Note
All vertical lines (whose slopes are undefined) are parallel to one another.

Example 7–4 D

Show that distinct lines $x - 2y = 2$ and $2x - 4y = -8$ are parallel lines.

We solve each equation for y to write them in slope-intercept form $y = mx + b$.

$x - 2y = 2$		$2x - 4y = -8$	
$-2y = -x + 2$	Subtract x from each member	$-4y = -2x - 8$	Subtract $2x$ from each member
$y = \dfrac{-x + 2}{-2}$	Divide each member by -2	$y = \dfrac{-2x - 8}{-4}$	Divide each member by -4
$y = \dfrac{1}{2}x - 1$	Write in slope-intercept form	$y = \dfrac{1}{2}x + 2$	Write in slope-intercept form
$m_1 = \dfrac{1}{2}$		$m_2 = \dfrac{1}{2}$	

Since $m_1 = \dfrac{1}{2} = m_2$, the lines are parallel.

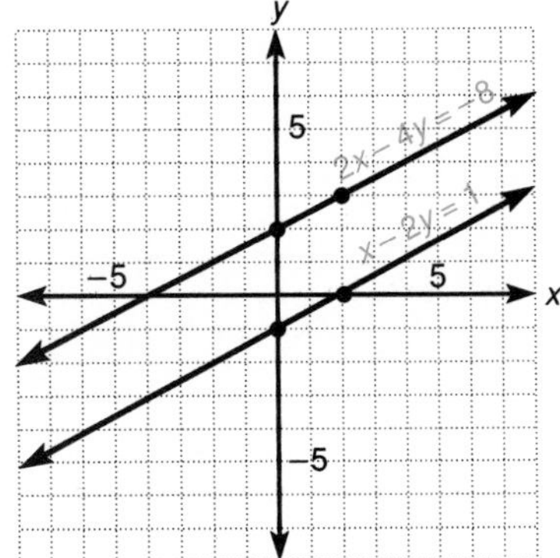

You are now ready to do $\mathbf{D_1}$. ■

Two lines that intersect in a single point can be *perpendicular.* Perpendicular lines make *right angles* with one another. Nonvertical lines having slopes m_1 and m_2, respectively, are perpendicular if the *product* of their slopes is -1.

> **Slopes of perpendicular lines**
>
> Two distinct nonvertical lines having slopes m_1 and m_2 are perpendicular if and only if $m_1m_2 = -1$.

To illustrate, lines having slopes $\dfrac{3}{4}$ and $-\dfrac{4}{3}$ are perpendicular since

$$\left(\frac{3}{4}\right)\left(-\frac{4}{3}\right) = -1.$$

Note

The slopes $\dfrac{3}{4}$ and $-\dfrac{4}{3}$ are *negative reciprocals* of each other.

From this, we can conclude that the slopes of perpendicular lines will be negative reciprocals.

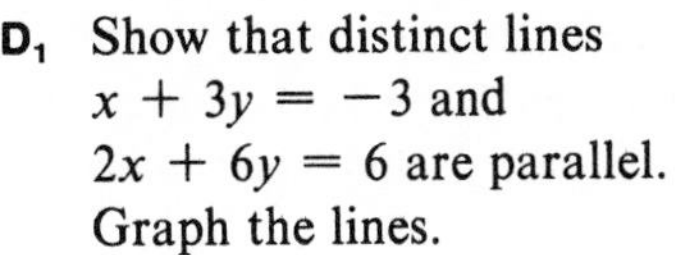

D₁ Show that distinct lines $x + 3y = -3$ and $2x + 6y = 6$ are parallel. Graph the lines.

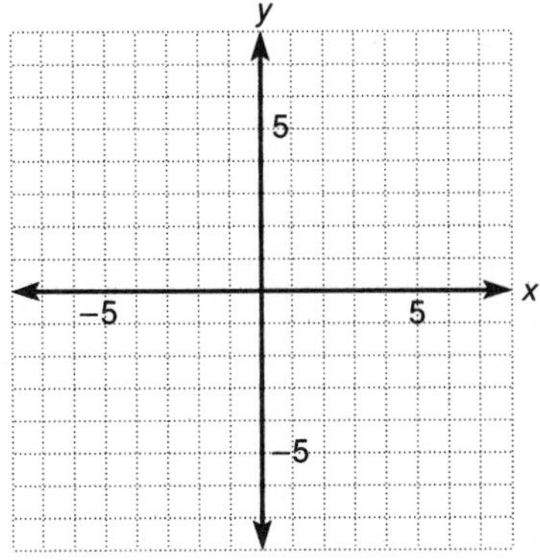

E₁ Show that the lines $2x + 3y = 0$ and $3x - 2y = 4$ are perpendicular. Graph the lines.

Example 7–4 E

Show that the lines $x - 3y = 4$ and $3x + y = -1$ are perpendicular lines.

We solve for y to write each equation in slope-intercept form $y = mx + b$.

$$x - 3y = 4$$

$$-3y = -x + 4 \quad \text{Subtract } x \text{ from each member}$$

$$y = \frac{1}{3}x - \frac{4}{3} \quad \text{Divide each term by } -3$$

$$m_1 = \frac{1}{3}$$

$$3x + y = -1$$

$$y = -3x - 1 \quad \text{Subtract } 3x \text{ from each member}$$

$$m_2 = -3$$

Since $m_1 m_2 = \frac{1}{3} \cdot (-3) = -1$, the lines are perpendicular.

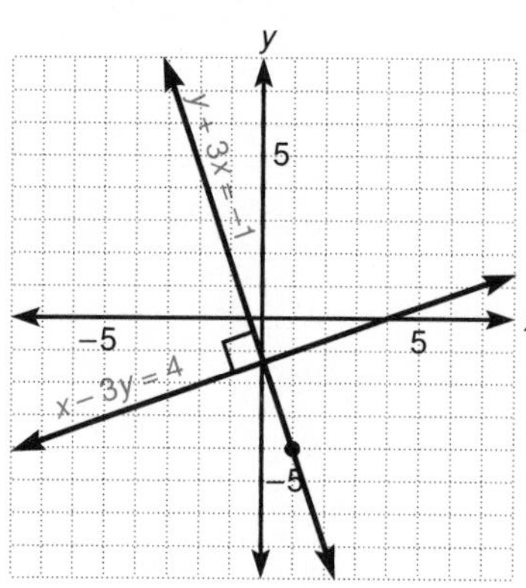

Note

$\frac{1}{3}$ and -3 are *negative reciprocals* of each other.

You are now ready to do **E₁**. ■

All vertical lines are perpendicular to all horizontal lines even though the product of their slopes does not exist. For example, the lines $x = -2$ and $y = 4$ are perpendicular.

Answers to section 7–4 margin exercises

A₁ $3x - y = 8$ **A₂** $x + 8y = 22$ **B₁** $m = \frac{5}{2}$, $b = 3$, y-intercept is (0,3)

B₂

B₃

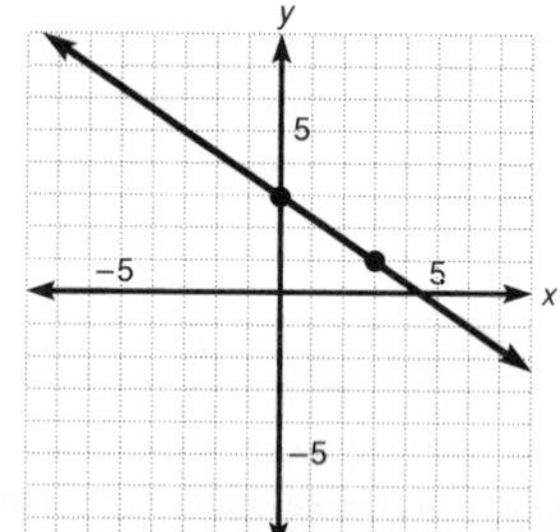

C₁ $y = -2x + 4$ **C₂** $y = \frac{3}{4}x + 3$ **C₃** $y = -6$

D_1 both have $m = -\dfrac{1}{3}$

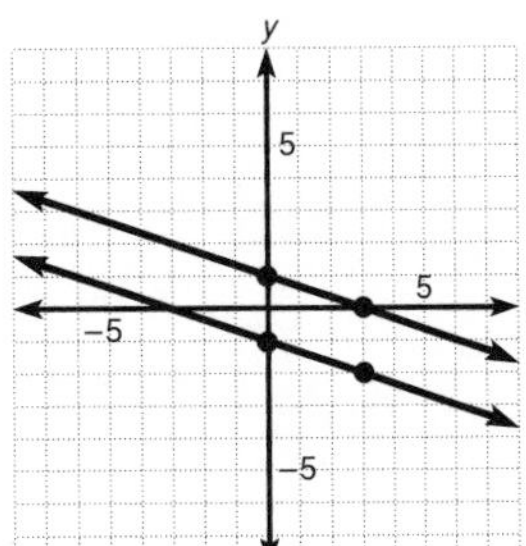

E_1 $2x + 3y = 0$; $m_1 = -\dfrac{2}{3}$

$3x - 2y = 4$; $m_2 = \dfrac{3}{2}$

$\left(-\dfrac{2}{3}\right)\left(\dfrac{3}{2}\right) = -1$

lines are perpendicular

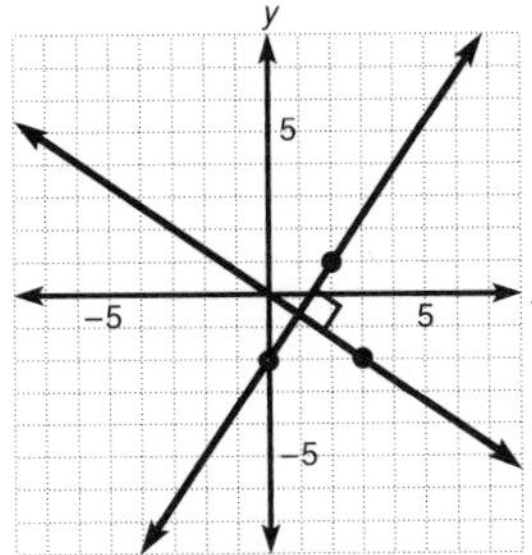

Mastery points

Can you

- Write the equation of a line in standard form?
- Find the equation of a line knowing the slope and a point or two points on the line?
- Find the slope and *y*-intercept of a line knowing the equation of the line?
- Graph a linear equation in two variables using the slope and *y*-intercept?
- Graph a linear equation in two variables using the slope and a point of the line?
- Find the equation of a line given the slope and the *y*-intercept?
- Determine whether two lines are parallel or perpendicular?

Exercise 7–4

Directions Write the following equations in standard form. $ax + by = c$, a and b are integers, $a \geq 0$.

Example $y = \dfrac{3}{4}x - 7$

Solution

$4y = 4\left(\dfrac{3}{4}x - 7\right)$ Multiply each member by 4

$4y = 3x - 28$ Apply distributive property

$-3x + 4y = -28$ Subtract $3x$ from each member

$3x - 4y = 28$ Multiply each member by -1

1. $x = 3y + 4$

2. $3x = y + 4$

3. $y - 2x = 5$

4. $4y = 3 - 5x$

5. $y = \dfrac{2}{3}x + 3$

6. $y = -\dfrac{1}{2}x - 6$

7. $4(2x + 1) = 5y$

Directions Write the equation of the line passing through the given point and having the given slope, using the point-slope form $y - y_1 = m(x - x_1)$. Write your answer in standard form $ax + by = c$, $a \geq 0$. See example 7–4 A.

Example **A₁** $(1,-5)$; $m = 3$

Solution

$$y - y_1 = m(x - x_1)$$
$$y - (-5) = 3(x - (1)) \quad \text{Replace } y_1 \text{ with } -5,\ m \text{ with } 3, \text{ and } x_1 \text{ with } 1$$
$$y + 5 = 3x - 3 \quad \text{Perform indicated operations}$$
$$-3x + y = -8 \quad \text{Subtract } 3x \text{ and } 5 \text{ from each member}$$
$$3x - y = 8 \quad \text{Multiply each member by } -1$$

8. $(1,3)$; $m = 4$

9. $(-3,1)$; $m = 2$

10. $(-1,5)$; $m = \frac{4}{7}$

11. $(-3,0)$; $m = -\frac{5}{8}$

12. $(-3,-7)$; $m = \frac{5}{4}$

13. $(-7,3)$; $m = 0$

14. $(1,-8)$; slope is undefined.

Directions Find the equation of the line passing through each pair of given points. Write the equation in standard form $ax + by = c$, where a, b, and c are integers, $a \geq 0$. See example 7–4 A.

Example **A₂** $(-2,3)$ and $(6,2)$

Solution We first must find the slope.

$$m = \frac{y_2 - y_1}{x_2 - x_1}$$
$$= \frac{(3) - (2)}{(-2) - (6)} \quad \text{Replace } y_2 \text{ with } 3,\ y_1 \text{ with } 2,\ x_2 \text{ with } -2, \text{ and } x_1 \text{ with } 6$$
$$= \frac{1}{-8} = -\frac{1}{8}$$

Using the point-slope form $y - y_1 = m(x - x_1)$ and the point $(6,2)$,

$$y - y_1 = m(x - x_1)$$
$$y - (2) = \left(-\frac{1}{8}\right)(x - (6)) \quad \text{Replace } y_1 \text{ with } 2,\ m \text{ with } -\frac{1}{8}, \text{ and } x_1 \text{ with } 2$$
$$8(y - 2) = -1(x - 6) \quad \text{Multiply each member by } 8$$
$$8y - 16 = -x + 6 \quad \text{Perform indicated operations}$$
$$x + 8y = 22. \quad \text{Add } x \text{ and } 16 \text{ to each member}$$

15. $(3,2)$ and $(5,1)$

16. $(2,1)$ and $(6,3)$

17. $(-6,2)$ and $(4,-3)$

18. $(1,-5)$ and $(-2,2)$

19. $(5,6)$ and $(5,0)$

20. $(0,8)$ and $(-3,8)$

21. $(7,-1)$ and $(0,0)$

22. $(-2,-3)$ and $(-1,-5)$

Directions Write the following equations in slope-intercept form $y = mx + b$ and determine the slope and the y-intercept of each line. See example 7–4 B.

Example $\boxed{B_1}$ $2y - 5x = 6$

Solution

$$2y - 5x = 6$$
$$2y = 5x + 6 \quad \text{Add } 5x \text{ to each member}$$
$$y = \frac{5x + 6}{2} \quad \text{Divide each member by 2}$$
$$y = \frac{5}{2}x + 3 \quad \text{Divide 2 into 5 and 6}$$

The slope is $\frac{5}{2}$ and the y-intercept is the point (0,3).

23. $x + y = 2$

24. $y - x = 3$

25. $3x + y = -2$

26. $y - 4x = 5$

$\boxed{27.}$ $2x + 5y = 10$

28. $3x + 2y = 8$

29. $8x - 9y = 1$

30. $-7x + 4y = -5$

Directions Use the slope m and the y-intercept b to graph the following equations. See example 7–4 B.

Example $\boxed{B_2}$ $3x - 2y = 4$

Solution We first write the equation in slope-intercept form $y = mx + b$.

$$3x - 2y = 4$$
$$-2y = -3x + 4$$
$$y = \frac{3}{2}x - 2$$

The slope is $\frac{3}{2}$ and the y-intercept is the point $(0,-2)$.

From the point $(0,-2)$, move two units to the *right* and then three units *up* to find a second point. Draw a line through $(0,-2)$ and the second point.

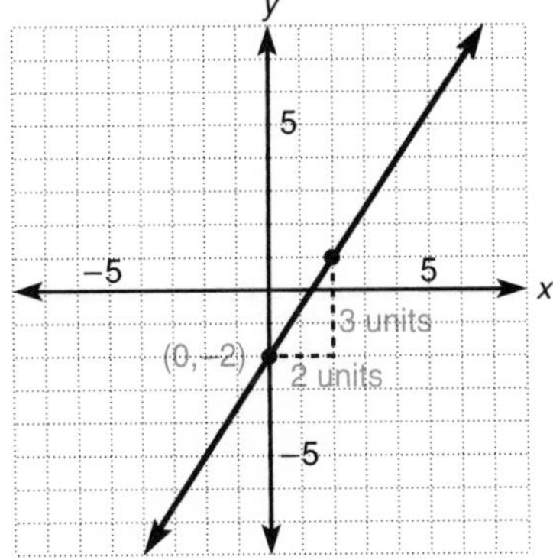

31. $y = 2x - 4$

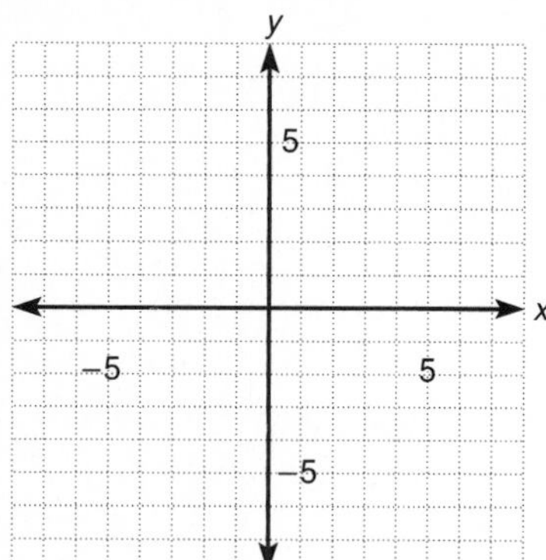

32. $y = 3x + 1$

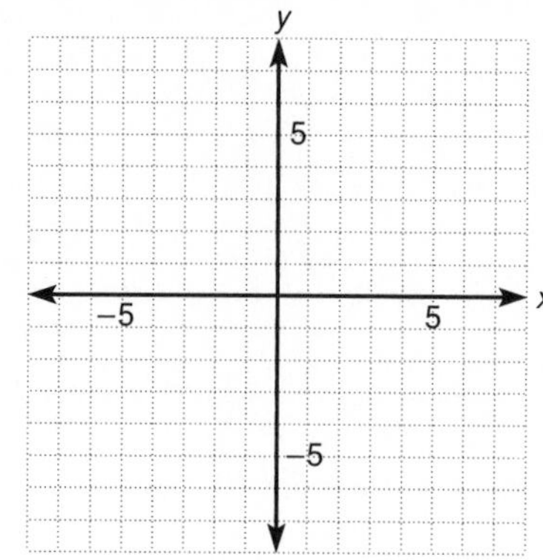

33. $y = -5x + 2$

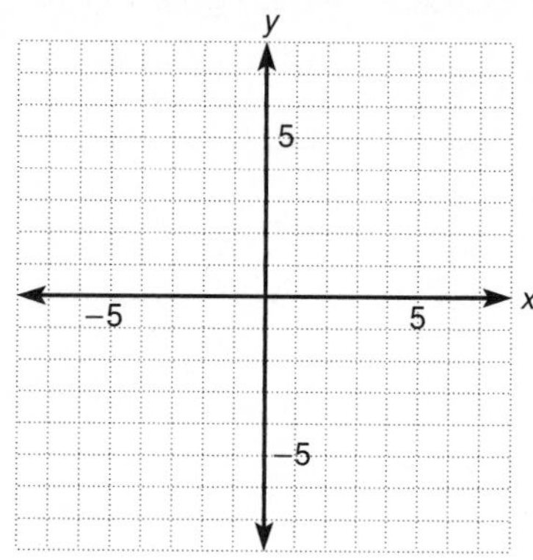

34. $y = -2x - 3$

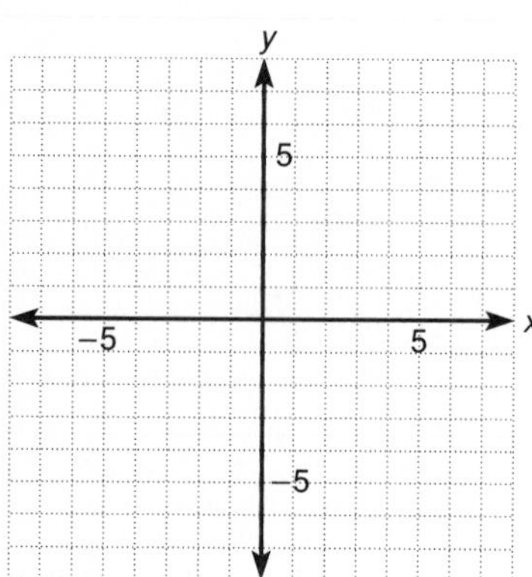

35. $y = \frac{2}{3}x - 1$

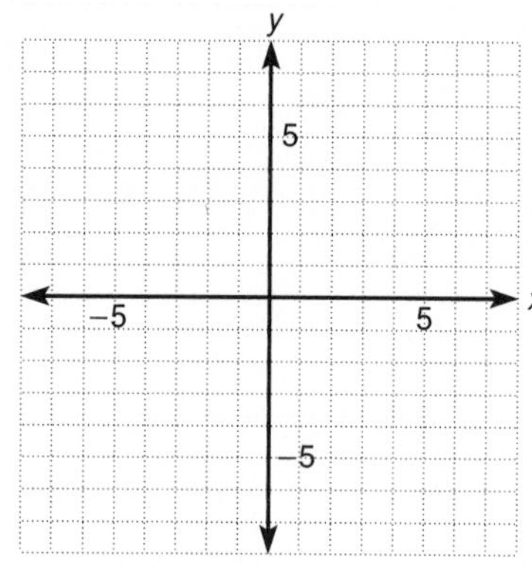

36. $y = \frac{-4}{3}x + 3$

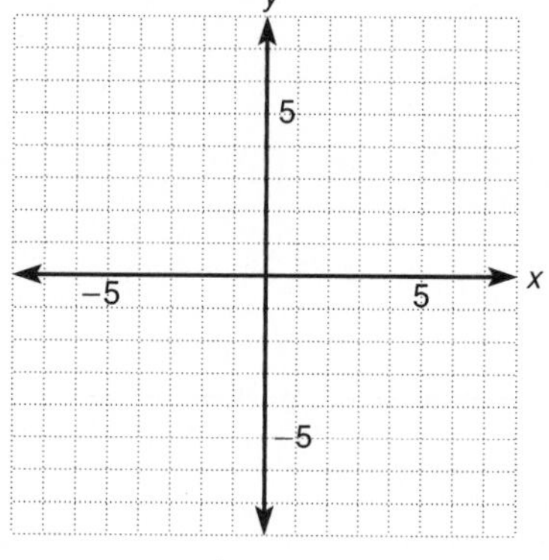

37. $3x + 4y = 8$

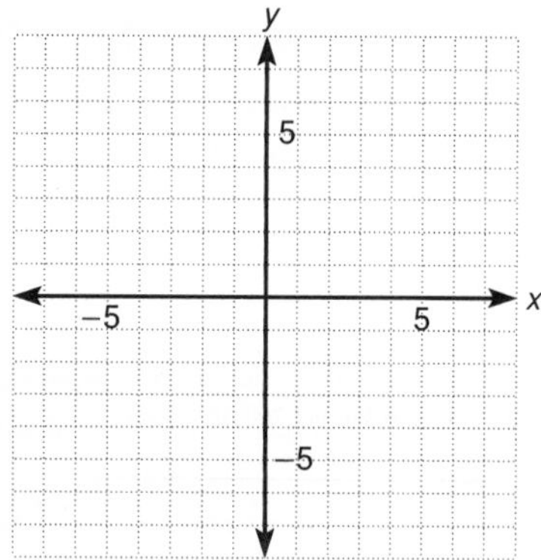

38. $5x - 2y = 6$

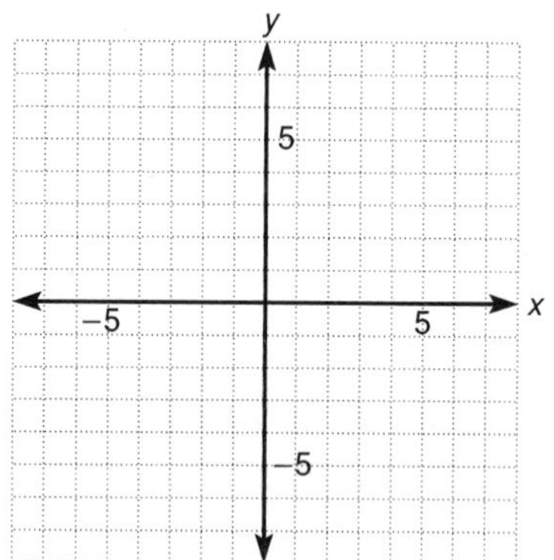

39. $3x - 5y = -15$

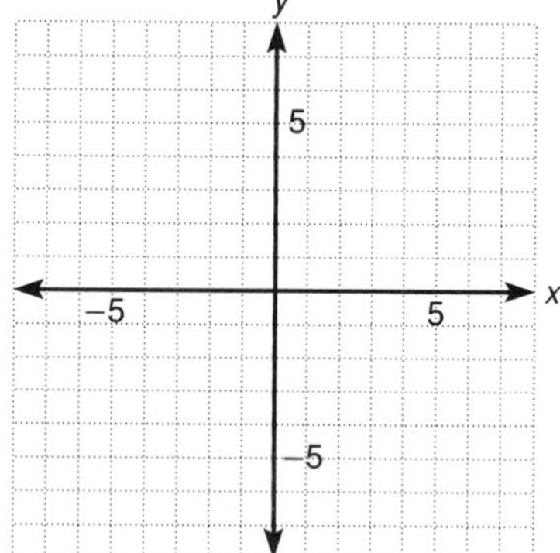

40. $4x + 3y = -9$

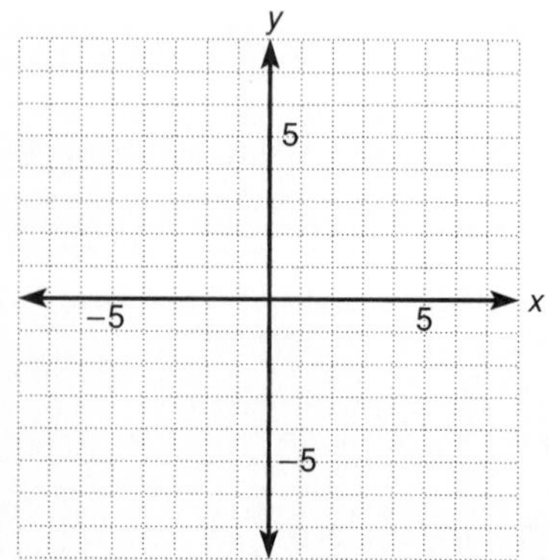

Directions Find the equation of the line having the given slope and y-intercept. See example 7–4 C.

Example C₂ $m = \frac{3}{4}$ and through (0,3)

Solution Using the slope-intercept form $y = mx + b$,

$y = mx + b$

$y = \frac{3}{4}x + 3.$ Replace m with $\frac{3}{4}$ and b with 3

41. $m = 3; b = 5$

42. $m = -4; b = -6$

43. $m = \frac{5}{4}$; point (0,2)

44. $m = -\frac{6}{7}$; point (0,−9)

45. $m = 0$; point (0,−3)

46. m is undefined; point (6,0)

Directions Find the slope of each line and determine if each pair of lines is parallel, perpendicular, or neither. Graph the equations. See example 7–4 E.

Example E₁ $2x + 3y = 0$
$3x - 2y = 4$

Solution We must write each equation in slope-intercept form $y = mx + b$.

$2x + 3y = 0$

$3y = -2x + 0$ Subtract $2x$ from each member

$y = -\frac{2}{3}x + \frac{0}{3}$ Divide each member by 3

$y = -\frac{2}{3}x + 0$ $\frac{0}{3} = 0$

$m_1 = -\frac{2}{3}$

$3x - 2y = 4$

$-2y = -3x + 4$ Subtract $3x$ from each member

$y = \frac{3}{2}x + 2$ Divide each member by -2

$m_2 = \frac{3}{2}$

Since the product of the slopes $\left(-\frac{2}{3}\right)\left(\frac{3}{2}\right) = -1$ (the slopes are negative reciprocals), the lines are perpendicular.

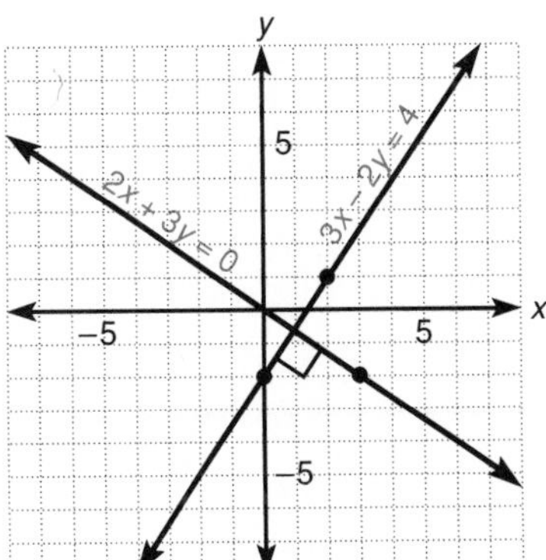

47. $x + y = 4$
$x + y = -7$

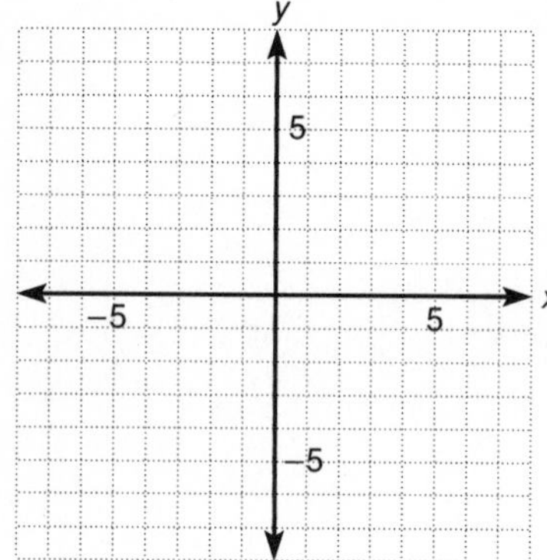

48. $x + y = 5$
$-x + y = -1$

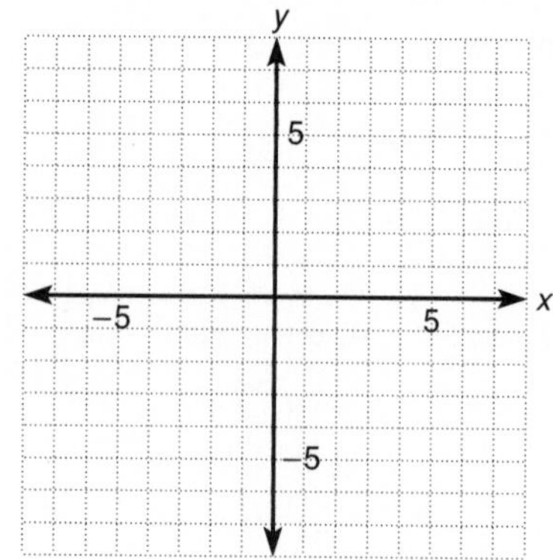

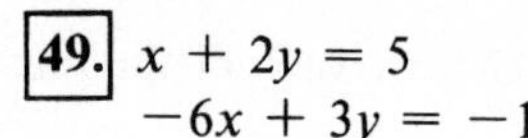

49. $x + 2y = 5$
$-6x + 3y = -1$

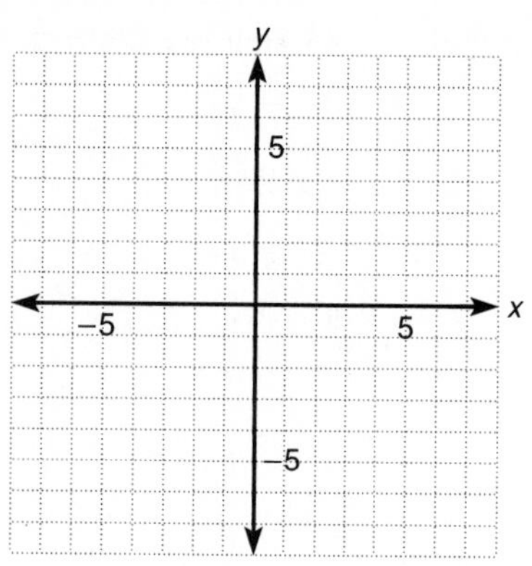

50. $3x - y = 2$
$6x + 2y = -5$

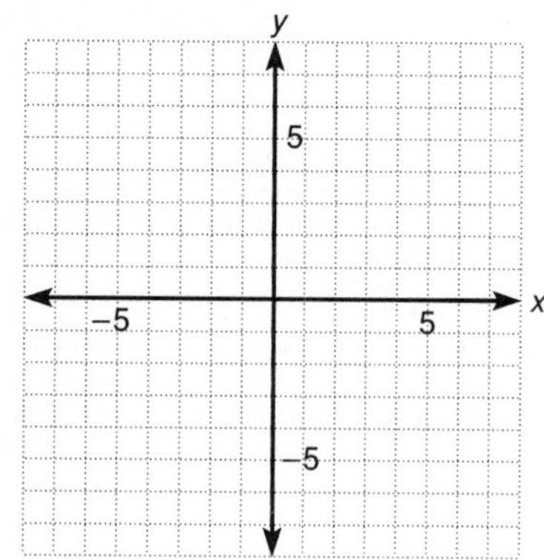

51. $4x - y = 5$
$12x - 3y = 1$

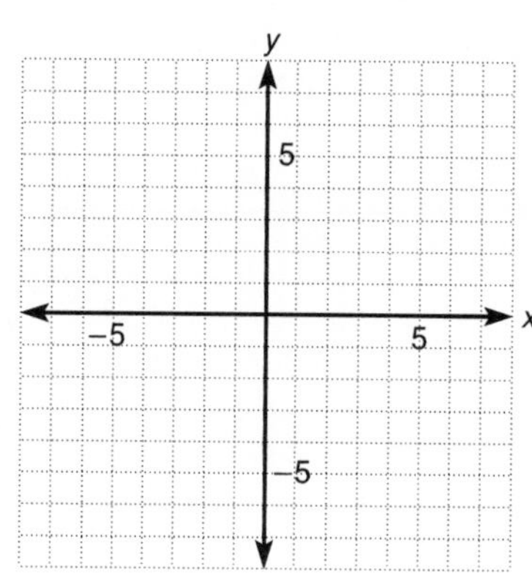

52. $y = 5$
$x = 2$

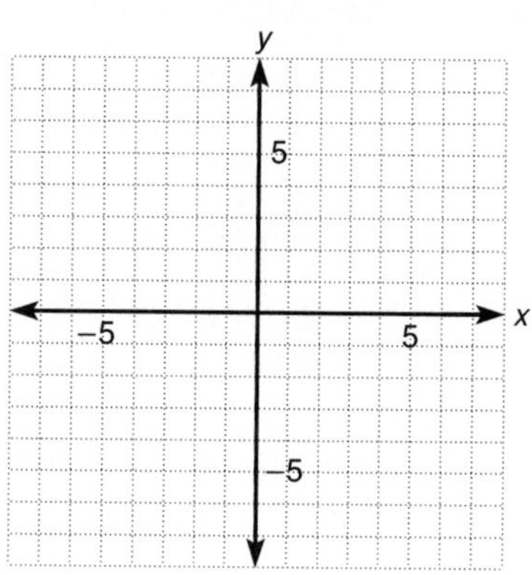

53. $5x + y = 1$
$10x + 3y = 2$

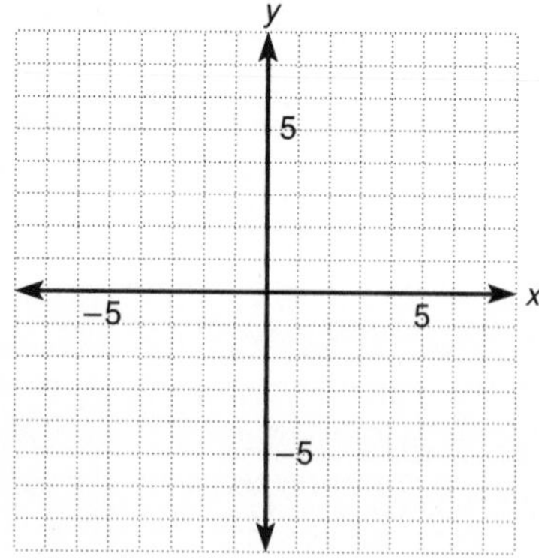

54. $4x + 6y = -3$
$6x + 9y = 4$

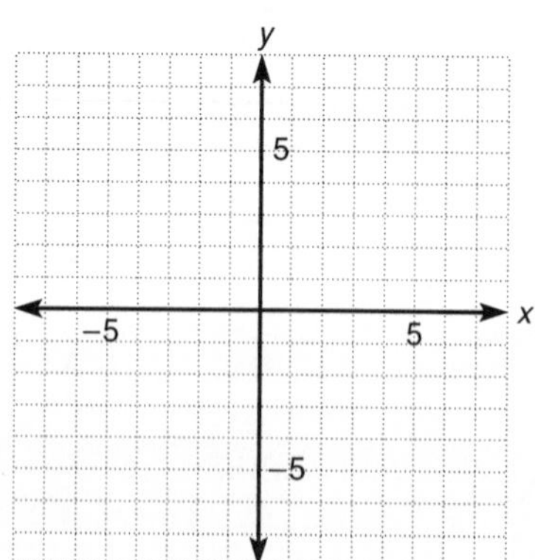

Review exercises

1. A 100-foot extension cord is to be cut into two pieces so that one piece is 17 feet longer than the other. What is the length of each piece? See section 2–6.

2. From the numbers $0, -3, \frac{3}{4}, 9, -\frac{7}{8}, \frac{9}{3}$, and $\frac{0}{4}$, choose the integers. See section 1–1.

Directions Solve the following equations. See sections 2–3 and 6–4.

3. $4y + 1 = 2y - 5$

4. $3(2y - 1) = -1(y + 2)$

5. $\frac{3x}{5} - \frac{x}{2} = 1$

Directions Factor the following polynomials. See sections 4–2, 4–3, and 4–4. If the polynomial does not factor, so state.

6. $3x^2 + 4x - 4$

7. $x^2 + 5x + 7$

8. $8y^2 - 32x^2$

▣ 7–5 Graphing linear inequalities in two variables

In section 7–2, we graphed linear equations in two variables such as $2x + y = 6$. In this section, we consider the graphs of *linear inequalities* in two variables such as

$$2x + y < 6 \quad \text{and} \quad 2x + y \geq 6,$$

where the equals sign has been replaced by one of the order (inequality) symbols,

$$<, \leq, >, \text{ or } \geq.$$

We learned that the graph of the equation $2x + y = 6$ is a straight line in the plane. This line divides the plane into two regions called *half-planes* and serves as the *boundary line* for each half-plane. See figure 7–9.

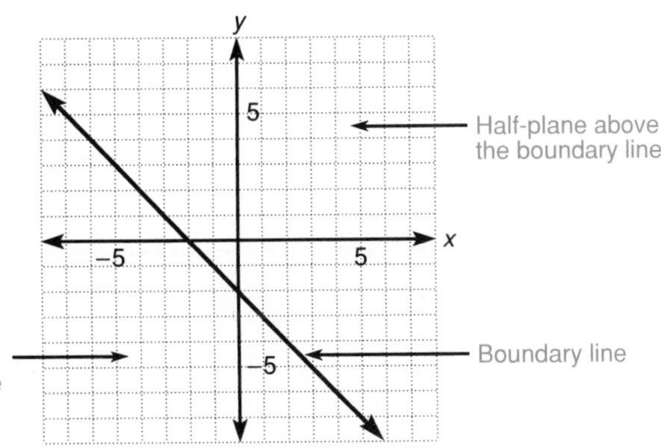

Figure 7–9

Graph of a linear inequality

The graph of any linear inequality in two variables is a half-plane.

The inequality $2x + y \geq 6$ is read "$2x + y$ is greater than or equal to 6" so

$$2x + y > 6 \quad \text{or} \quad 2x + y = 6.$$

The graph *will include the boundary line* together with the proper half-plane. The inequality $2x + y > 6$ is read "$2x + y$ is greater than 6" so the boundary line *is not* a part of the graph of the inequality. To indicate this:

1. For $2x + y \geq 6$, the boundary line $2x + y = 6$ is a *solid* line, to show the points on the line are included.
2. For $2x + y > 6$, the boundary line $2x + y = 6$ is a *dashed* line to show the points on the line are *not* included.

See figure 7–10.

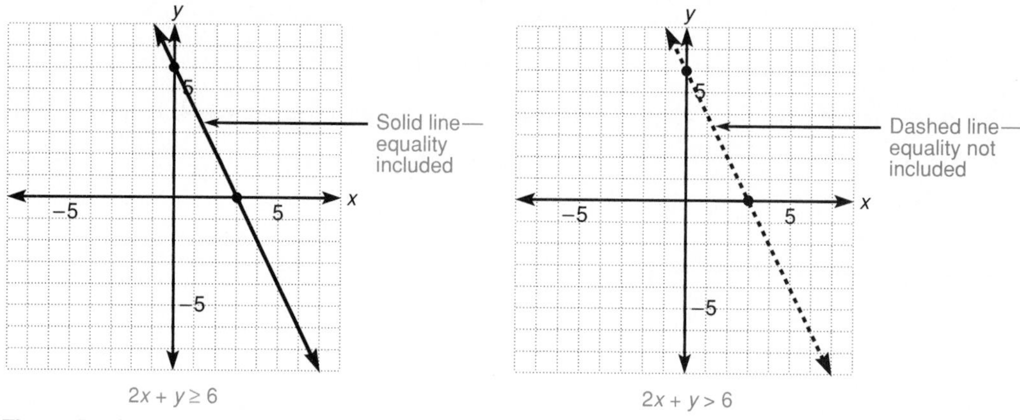

Figure 7–10

To determine the proper half-plane to shade, we choose a *test point* in one of the half-planes [usually the origin, (0,0)] and substitute into the inequality.

1. If the point satisfies the inequality, shade the half-plane containing that point,
2. If the point *does not satisfy* the inequality, shade the half-plane that does not contain the point.

To illustrate, consider the inequality $2x + y > 6$ and the test point (0,0).

$$2x + y > 6$$
$$2(0) + 0 > 6 \qquad \text{Replace } x \text{ with 0 and } y \text{ with 0}$$
$$0 + 0 > 6$$
$$0 > 6 \qquad \text{(False statement)}$$

Shade the half-plane that *does not* contain the origin (0,0). See figure 7–11.

Note

We will use the origin (0,0) as the test point in all cases except when the boundary line passes through the origin.

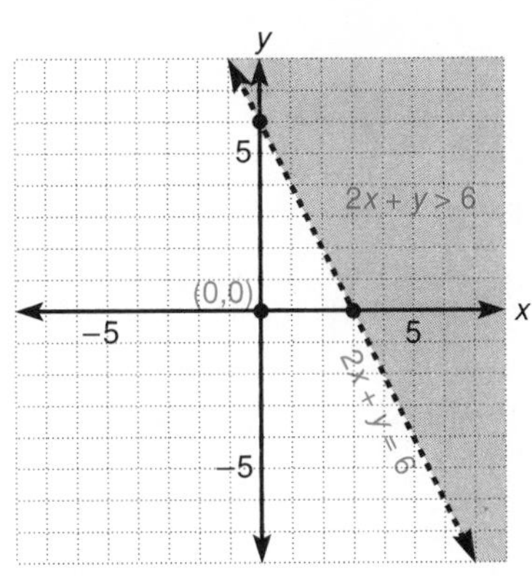

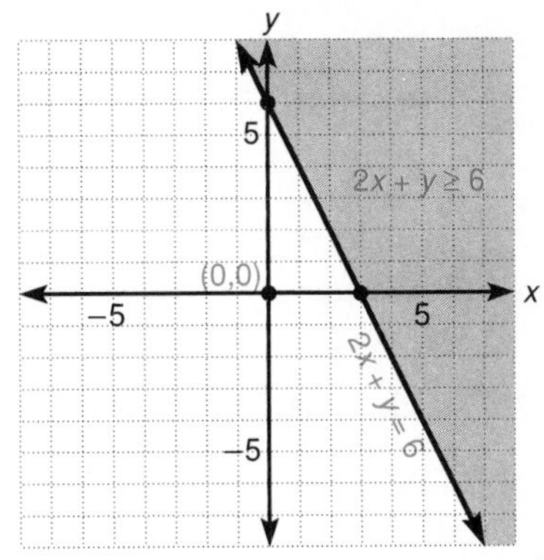

Figure 7–11

A₁ Graph the inequality $x + 2y < 2$.

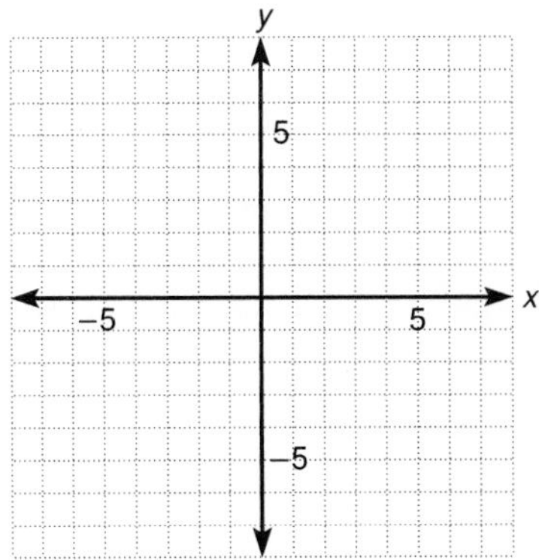

To graph a linear inequality

Step 1 Replace the inequality symbol by the equality symbol.
Step 2 Graph this boundary line as a
a. *solid line* if the inequality symbol is $\leq$ or $\geq$,
b. *dashed line* if the inequality symbol is $<$ or $>$.
Step 3 Choose some test point that is *not* on the line [usually the origin (0,0) since the arithmetic is easiest for this point] and substitute the coordinates of the point into the inequality.
Step 4 If the resulting statement is
a. *true,* shade the half-plane containing the test point,
b. *false,* shade the half-plane that *does not* contain the test point.

Example 7–5 A

Graph the following inequalities.

1. $x + y < 2$

Step 1 Replace $<$ with $=$ to get the equation $x + y = 2$.

Step 2 Graph $x + y = 2$ as a *dashed* line since we have $<$.

Step 3 Since the boundary line does not go through the origin, choose test point (0,0).

$x + y < 2$
$0 + 0 < 2$ Replace x with 0 and y with 0
$0 < 2$ (True statement)

Step 4 Shade the half-plane containing the origin (0,0).

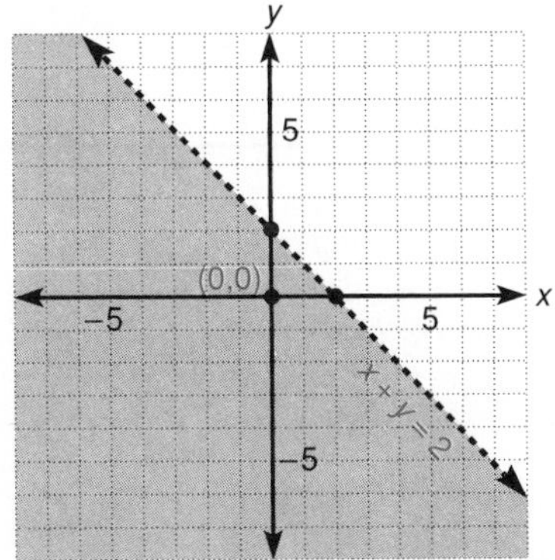

You are now ready to do **A₁**.

A₂ Graph the inequality $5x - 3y \geq 15$.

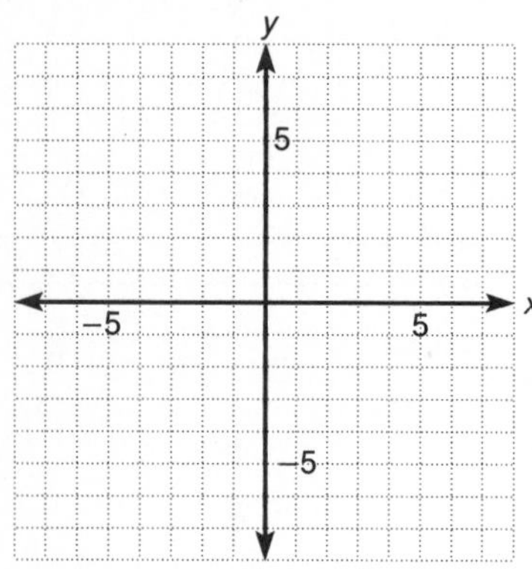

2. $3x - 4y \geq 12$

Step 1 Replace $\geq$ with $=$ to get the equation $3x - 4y = 12$.

Step 2 Graph $3x - 4y = 12$ in a *solid* line since we have $\geq$.

Step 3 The boundary line does not go through the origin, so use (0,0) as the test point.

$$
\begin{aligned}
3x - 4y &\geq 12 \\
3(0) - 4(0) &\geq 12 && \text{Replace } x \text{ with 0 and } y \text{ with 0} \\
0 - 0 &\geq 12 && \text{Multiply as indicated} \\
0 &\geq 12 && \text{(False statement)}
\end{aligned}
$$

Step 4 Shade the half-plane that *does not* contain the origin (0,0).

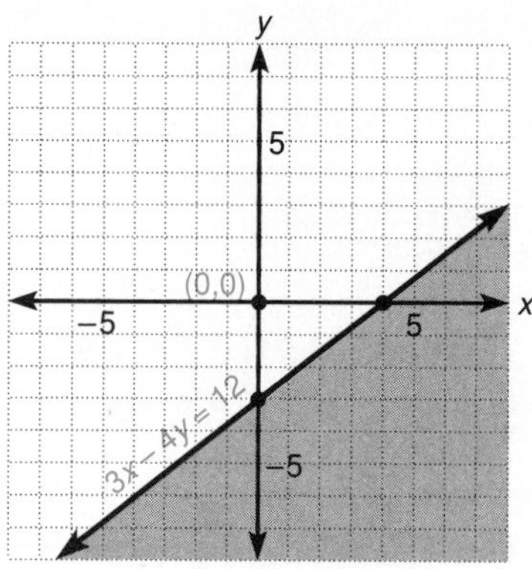

You are now ready to do **A₂**.

A₃ Graph the inequality $4y + x > 0$.

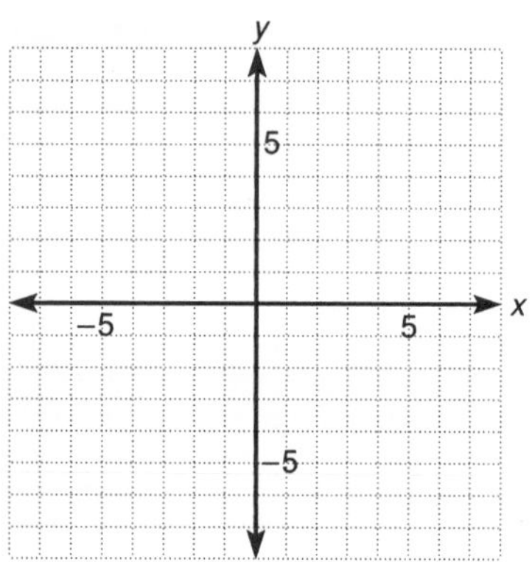

3. $3y - 2x > 0$

Step 1 Replace $>$ with $=$ to get the equation $3y - 2x = 0$.

Step 2 Graph the equation $3y - 2x = 0$ as a *dashed* line since we have $>$.

Step 3 The boundary line goes through the origin, so we choose another test point (2,4).

$$
\begin{aligned}
3y - 2x &> 0 \\
3(4) - 2(2) &> 0 && \text{Replace } x \text{ with 2 and } y \text{ with 4} \\
12 - 4 &> 0 && \text{Multiply as indicated} \\
8 &> 0 && \text{(True statement)}
\end{aligned}
$$

Step 4 Shade the half-plane that contains the test point (2,4).

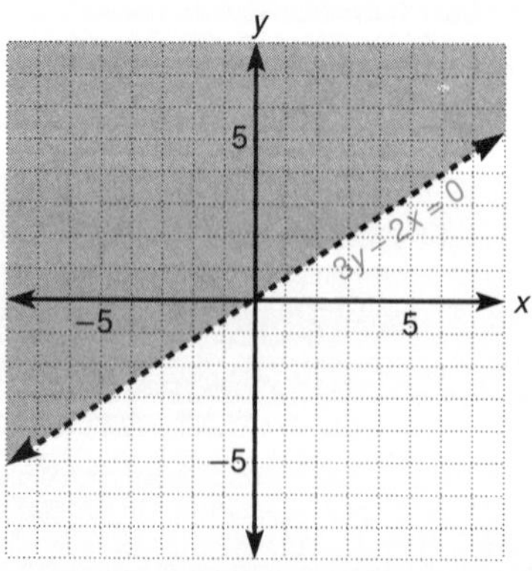

You are now ready to do **A₃**.

4. $y \leq -2$

Step 1 Replace the $\leq$ with $=$ to get the equation $y = -2$.

Step 2 Graph the equation $y = -2$ as a *solid* line since we have $\leq$. The line is a horizontal line through the point $(0,-2)$, as we learned earlier.

Step 3 The boundary line does not go through the origin, so we use (0,0) as the test point.

$y \leq -2$
$0 \leq -2$ (False statement)

Step 4 Shade the half-plane that *does not* contain the origin.

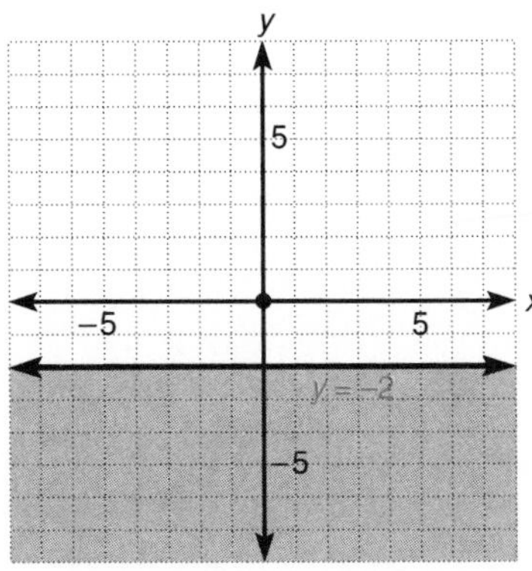

You are now ready to do **A₄**.

A₄ Graph the inequality $x \leq 3$.

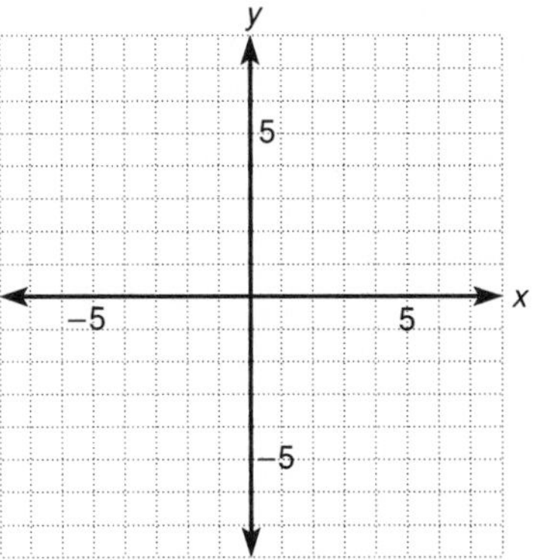

Answers to section 7–5 margin exercises

A₁

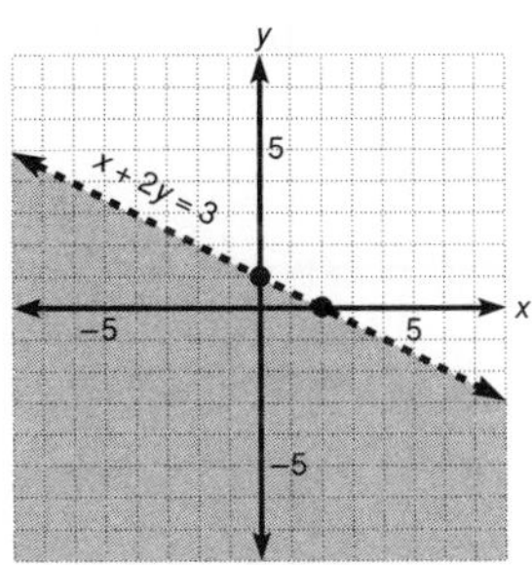

A₂

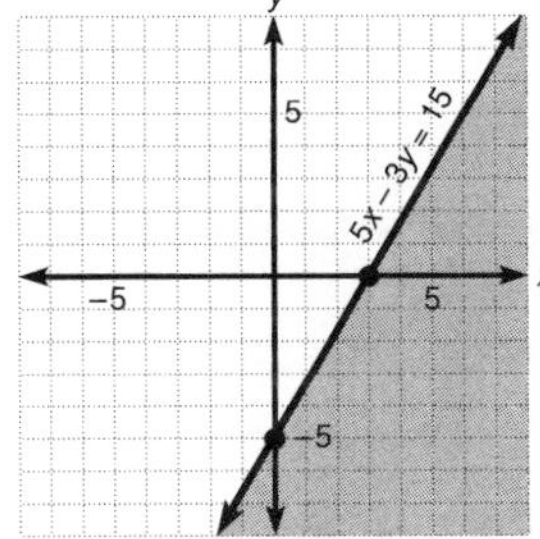

A₃

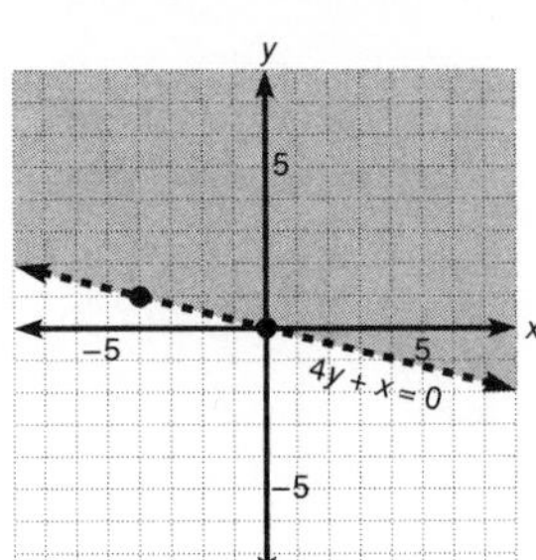

A₄

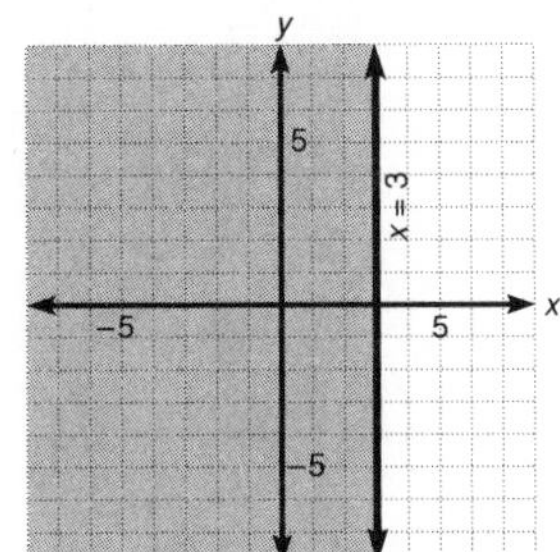

Mastery points
Can you   • Graph a linear inequality in two variables?   • Distinguish when the boundary line is solid and when it is dashed?

Exercise 7–5

Directions Complete the graph of each inequality by shading the correct half-plane. The correct boundary line has been drawn. See example 7–5 A.

Example **A₁** $x + 2y < 2$

Solution The line $x + 2y = 2$ does not pass through the origin, so we use the test point (0,0).

$$x + 2y < 2$$

$$0 + 2(0) < 2 \quad \text{Replace } x \text{ with 0 and } y \text{ with 0}$$

$$0 < 2 \quad \text{True statement}$$

Shade the plane containing the origin (0,0).

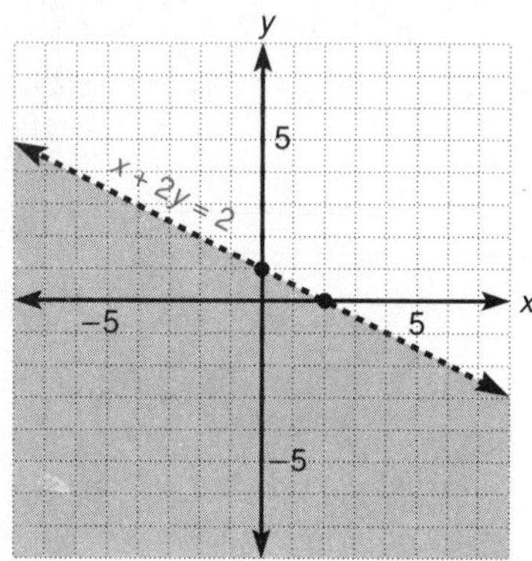

1. $x + y \geq 4$

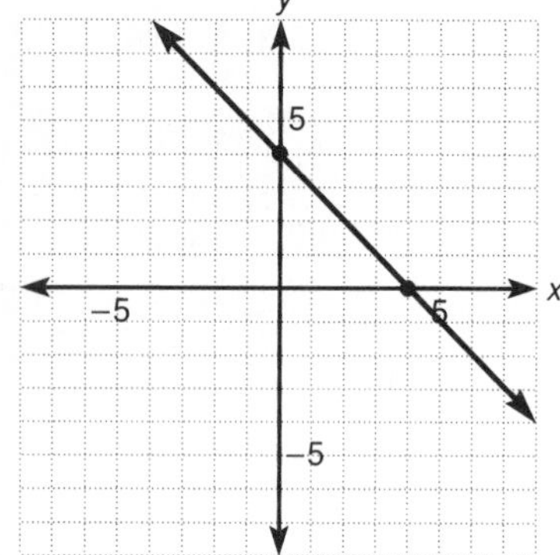

2. $x - y < 1$

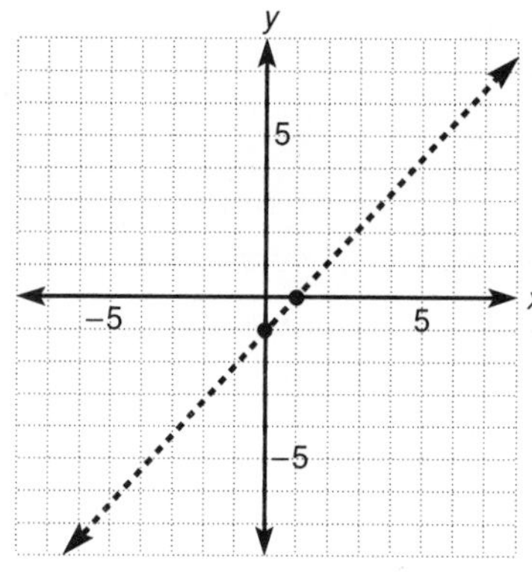

3. $3x - y \leq 4$

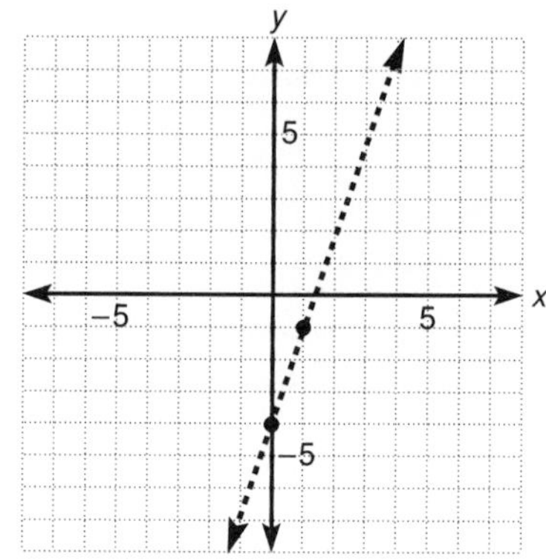

4. $2x - 4y > 8$

5. $3x + 5y \geq 0$

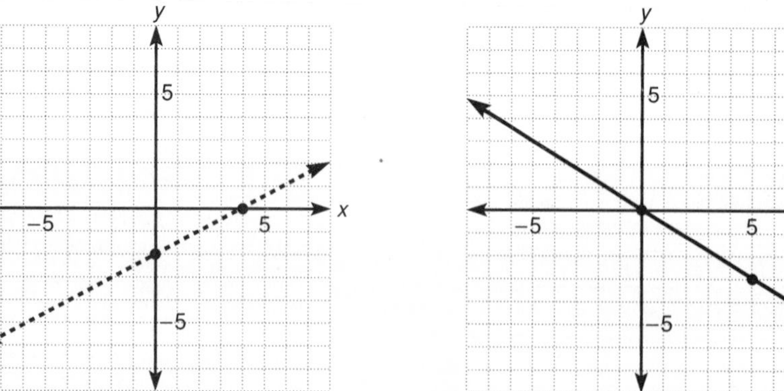

6. $y - 2x < 0$

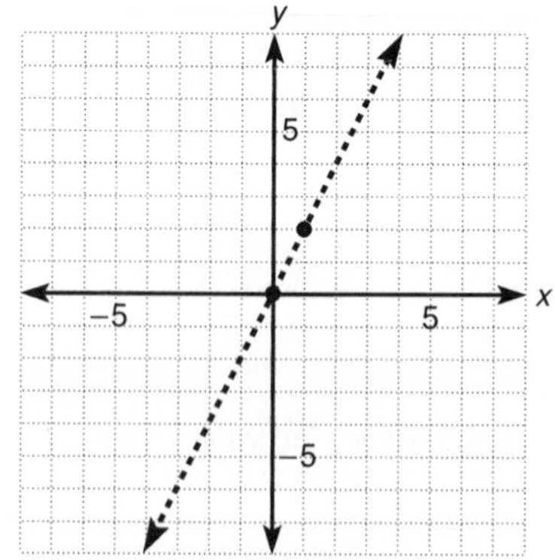

7. $2y \leq 3x$

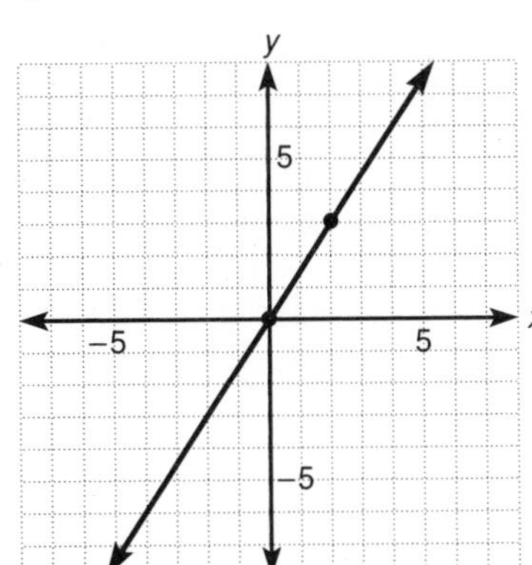

8. $-4x \geq y$

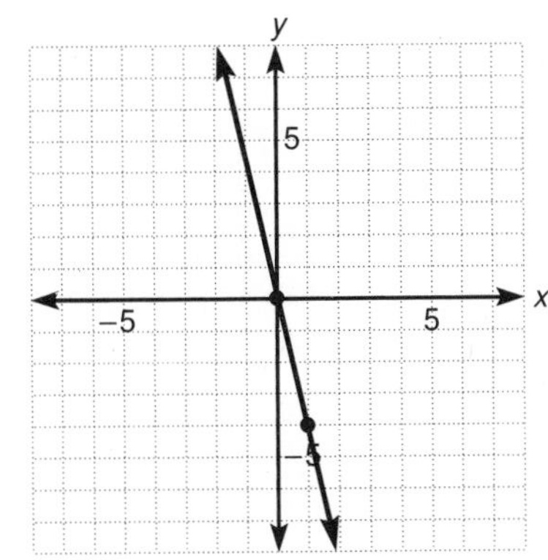

9. $x < 4$

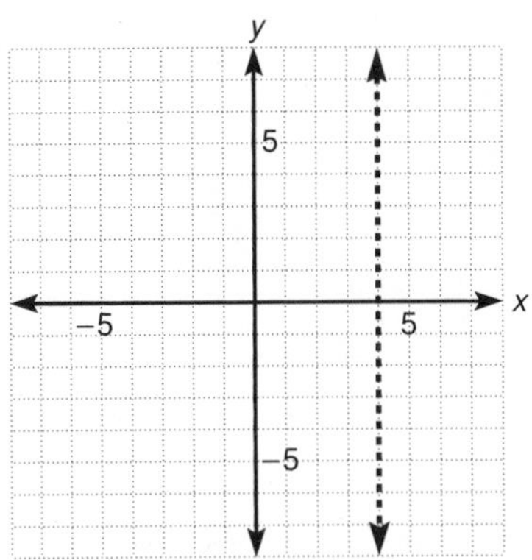

10. $y \geq -5$

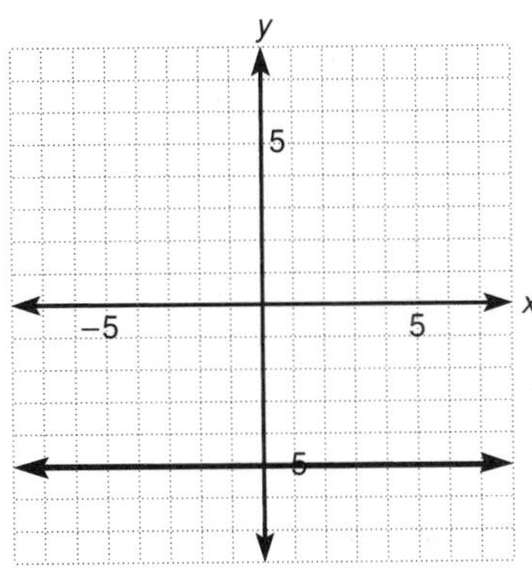

Directions Graph the given linear inequality. See example 7–5 A.

Example A₂ $5x - 3y \geq 15$

Solution ***Step 1*** Replace $\geq$ with $=$ to get the equation $5x - 3y = 15$.
Step 2 Graph $5x - 3y = 15$ as a *solid* line using the x-intercept (3,0) and the y-intercept (0,−5).
Step 3 Use the origin (0,0) as a test point.

$5x - 3y \geq 15$	
$5(0) - 3(0) \geq 15$	Replace x with 0 and y with 0
$0 - 0 \geq 15$	Multiply as indicated
$0 \geq 15$	(False statement)

Step 4 Shade the half-plane that does not contain (0,0).

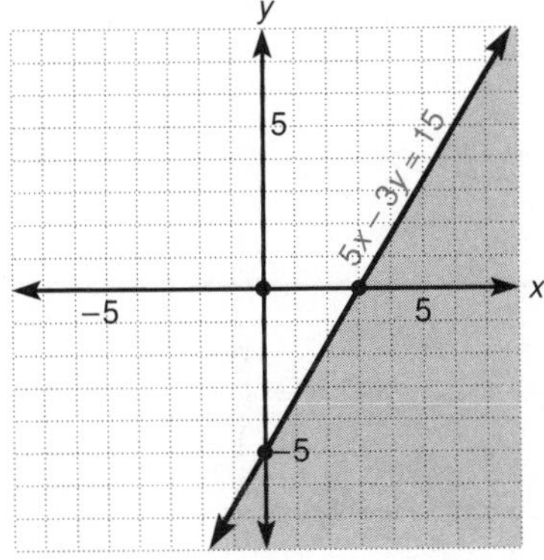

11. $x + y \geq 2$

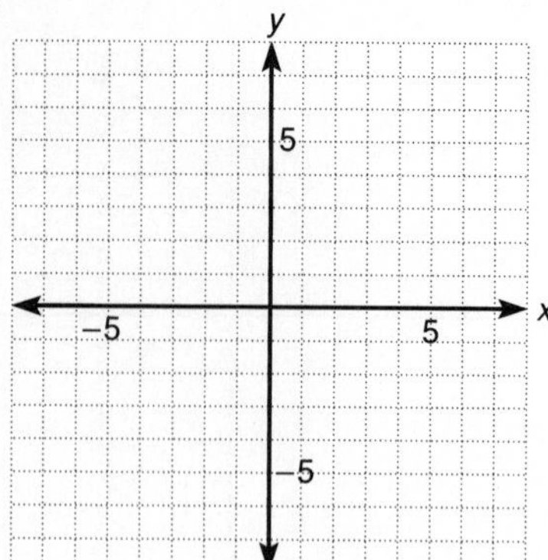

12. $y - x > -3$

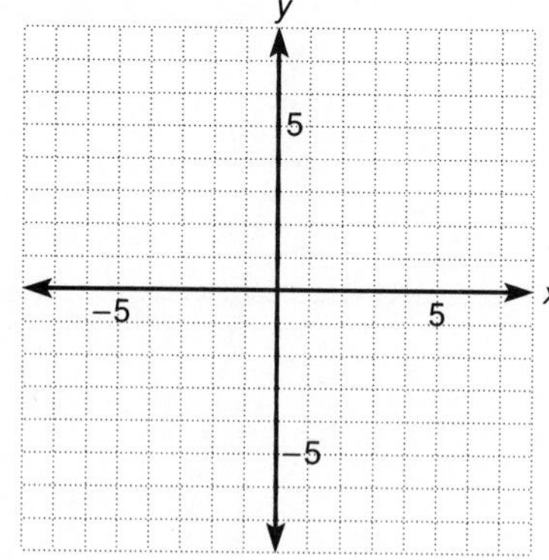

13. $x + y \leq -2$

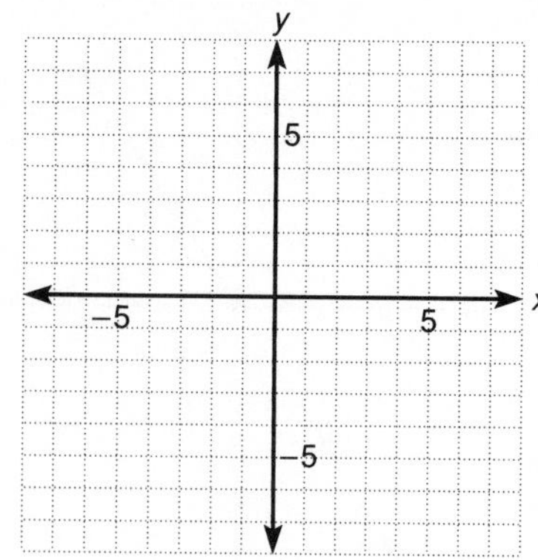

14. $x - y < 6$

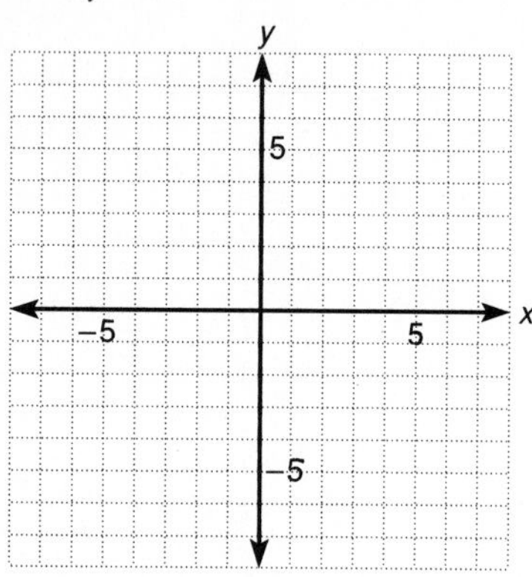

15. $x + 3y > 1$

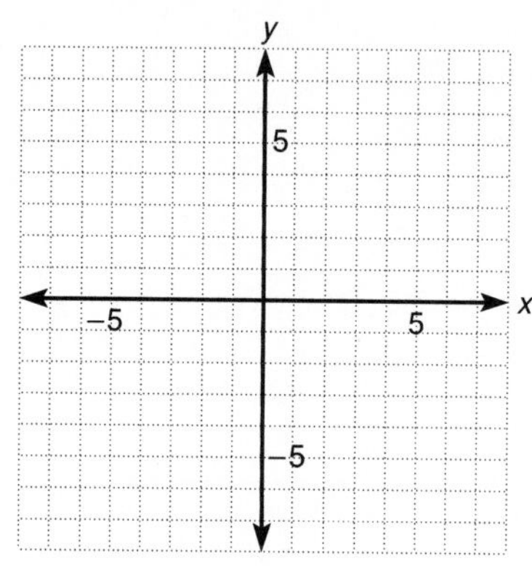

16. $x + 2y \leq -2$

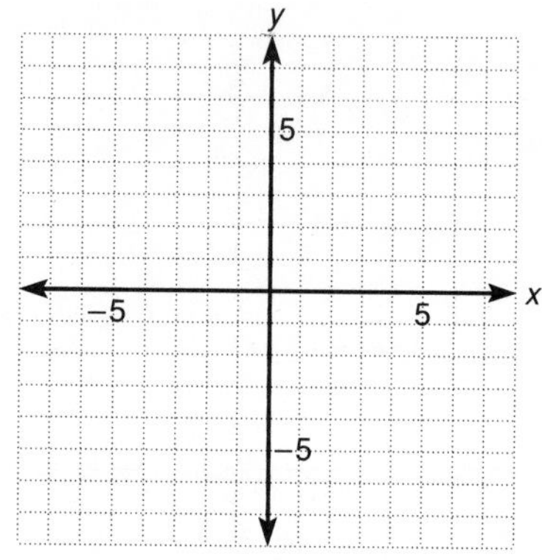

17. $y \geq 4x + 1$

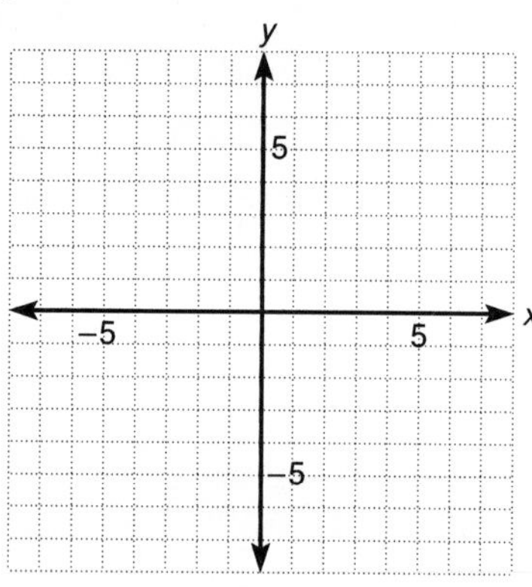

18. $y < 2x - 3$

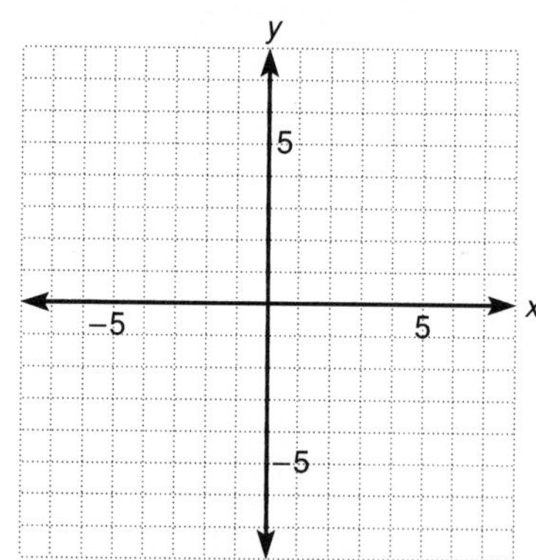

19. $5x + 2y \geq -10$

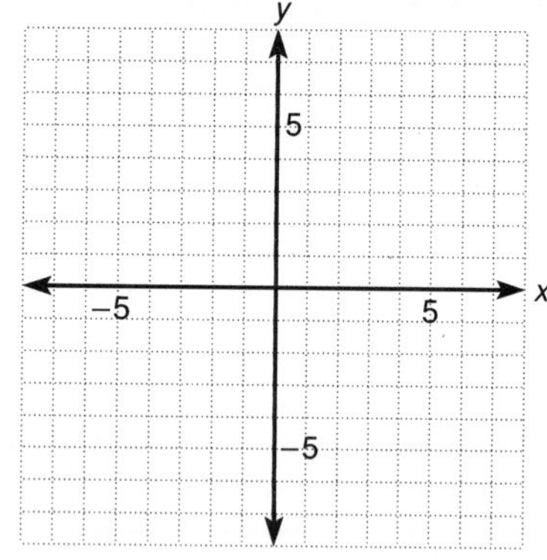

20. $5x - 4y \leq 20$

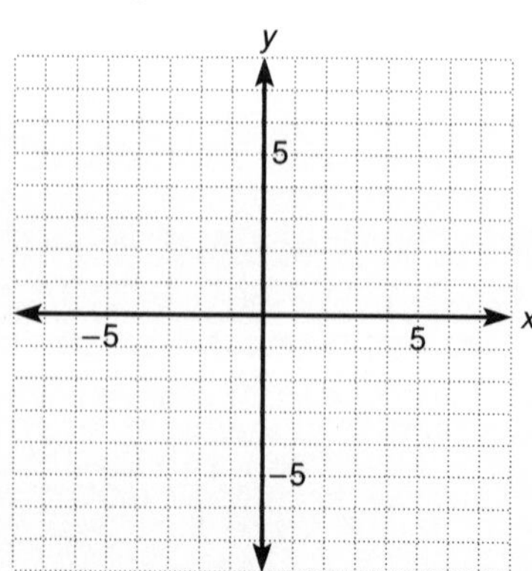

21. $3x - 5y < -15$

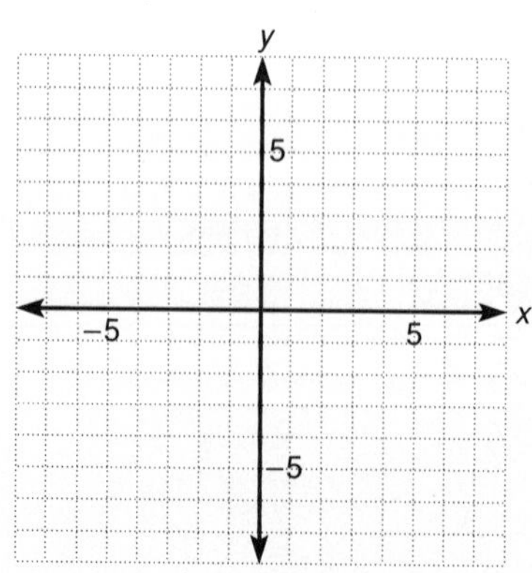

22. $2x - 7y > 14$

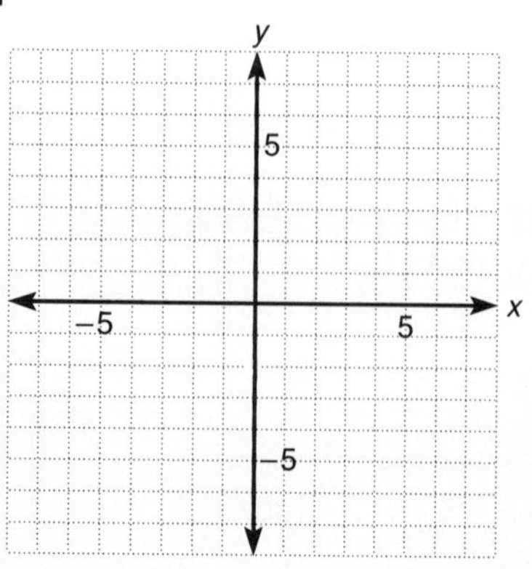

23. $x \geq 3y$

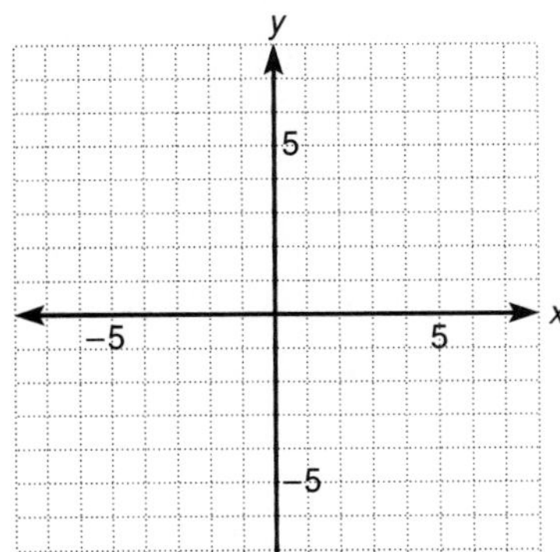

24. $x < -y$

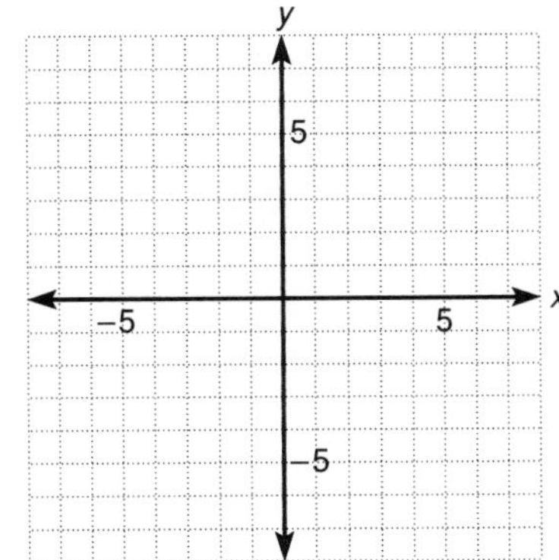

25. $y \leq 4x$

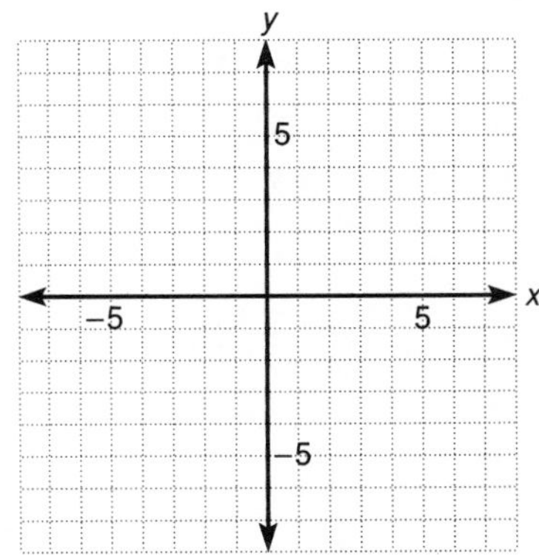

26. $x + 5 > -2$

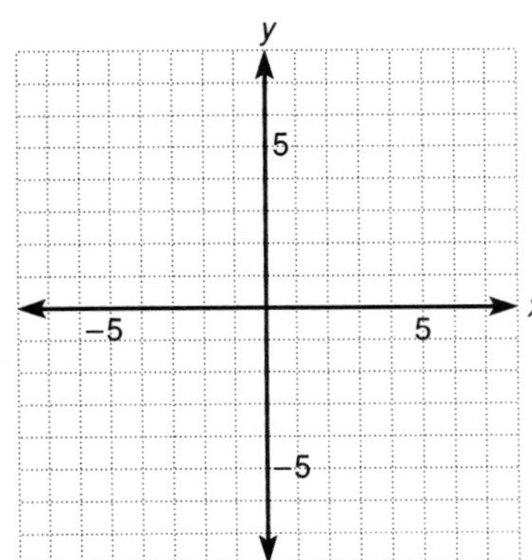

27. $y + 3 \leq 5$

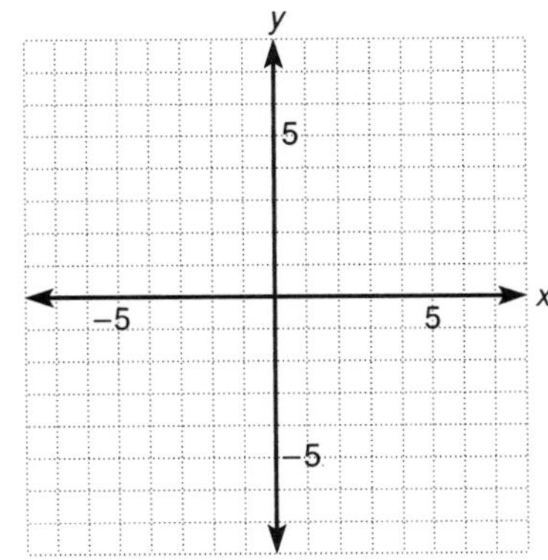

28. $x > 3$

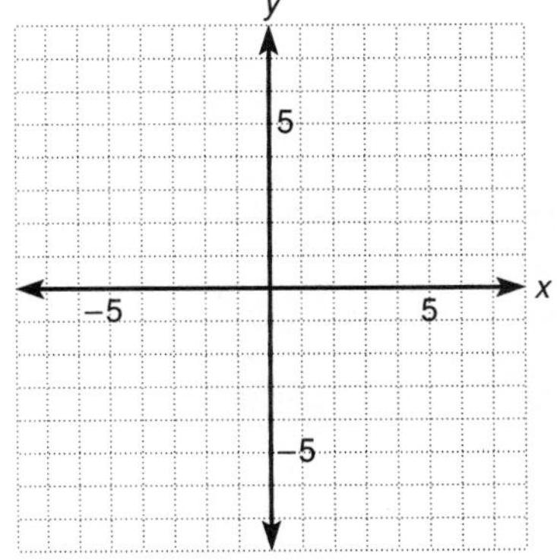

29. $x \leq -2$

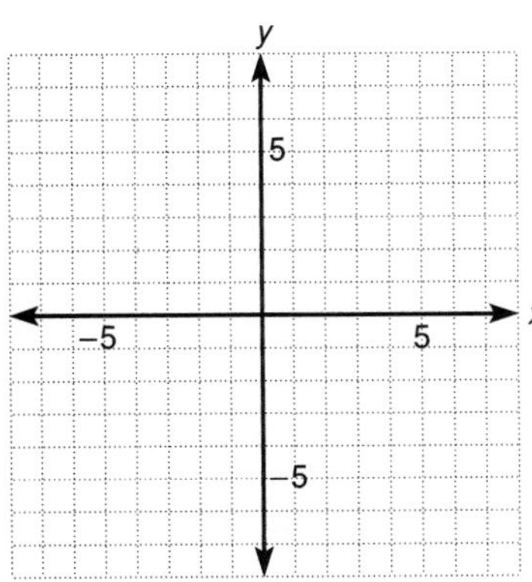

30. $x > -4$

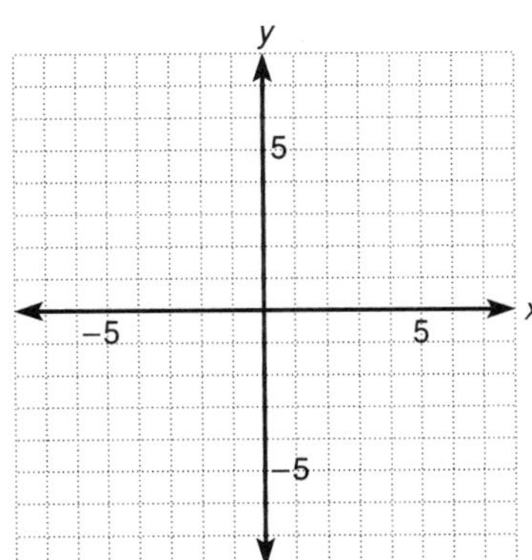

31. $8x - 3y \geq 0$

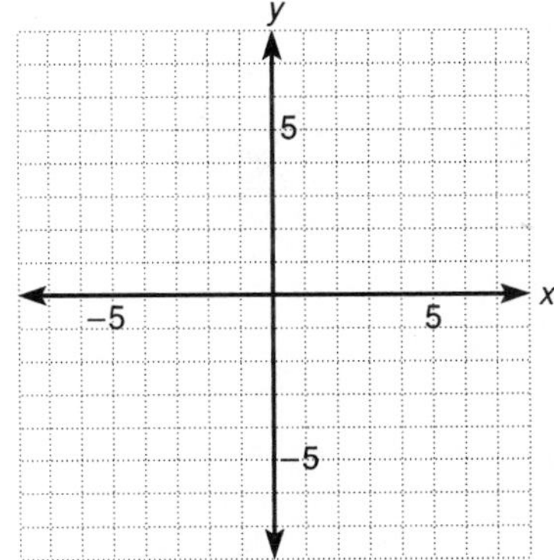

32. $3y + 2x < 0$

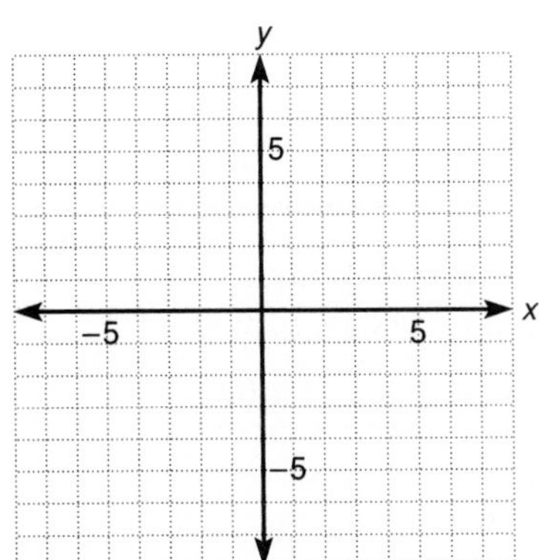

Review exercises

Directions Graph the given pairs of equations on the same set of axes. Find the coordinates of the point where the two lines cross. See section 7–2.

1. $2x - y = 3$
   $x + y = 0$

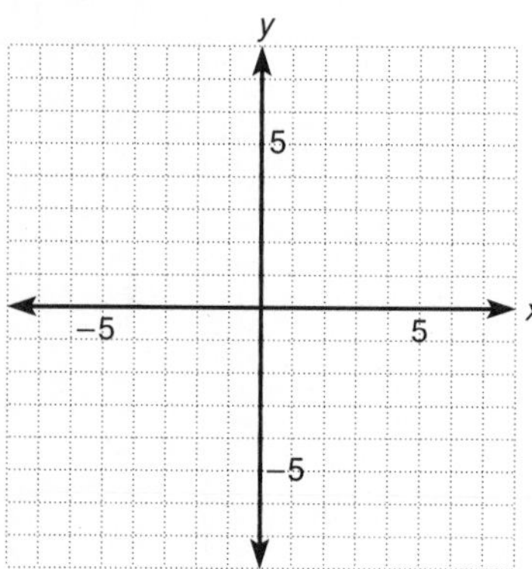

2. $x = -4$
   $3y - x = 7$

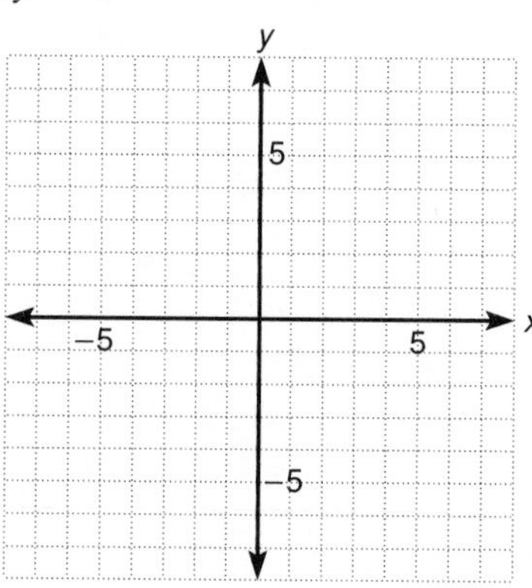

Directions Find the value of the unknown variable given the value of the other variable. See section 7–1.

3. $4x - 2y = 3; x = 2$

4. $4y + x = 1; y = -3$

Directions Find the equation of the straight line having the following characteristics. See section 7–4.

5. Through points $(-2,3)$ and $(4,1)$

6. Having slope $\frac{3}{4}$ and y-intercept -2. Write the equation in standard form.

7. Vertical line through $(-3,6)$

8. Horizontal line through $(8,-3)$

Chapter 7 lead-in problem

Tickets to a football game at Podunk High School cost \$1.25 for students and \$3.00 for adults. The total receipts for a game with University High School were \$1,020. Write an equation using x for the number of students and y for the number of adults attending the game.

Solution

Given x = the number of students at the game
y = the number of adults at the game.

	Cost per ticket	**Number of students**	**Receipts**
Students	1.25	x	$1.25x$
Adults	3.00	y	$3.00y$

We add the individual receipts from the students and the adults to obtain the total receipts, \$1,020.

$$1.25x + 3.00y = 1{,}020$$

Chapter 7 summary

1. A **linear equation in two variables** is an equation that can be written in the form $ax + by = c$, where a, b, and c are constants, and a and b are not both zero.
2. The **solutions** of a linear equation in two variables are the ordered pairs of numbers of the form (x,y) that satisfies the equation.
3. Solutions of linear equations in two variables are found by choosing a value for one variable and evaluating to find the value of the other variable.
4. **Ordered pairs of numbers** may be graphed as points in the **rectangular coordinate plane.**
5. In the ordered pair (x,y), we call x the **abscissa** and y the **ordinate** of the point in the plane that is its graph.
6. Graphs of linear equations in two variables are *straight lines.*
7. To find the *x-intercept,* the abscissa of the point where the graph crosses the x-axis, let $y = 0$ and solve for x.
8. To find the *y-intercept,* the ordinate of the point where the graph crosses the y-axis, let $x = 0$ and solve for y.
9. The graph of the equation $y = b$ is a *horizontal line* passing through the point $(0,b)$.
10. The graph of the equation $x = a$ is a *vertical line* passing through the point $(a,0)$.
11. The **slope** m of a line is the "steepness" of the line and is defined by $m = \dfrac{y_2 - y_1}{x_2 - x_1} = \dfrac{y_1 - y_2}{x_1 - x_2}$, where $P_1(x_1,y_1)$ and $P_2(x_2,y_2)$ are any two points lying on the line.
12. The **standard form** of the equation of a line is $ax + by = c$, where a, b, and c are integers, $a \geq 0$, and a and b not both 0.
13. The **point-slope** form of the equation of a line is given by $y - y_1 = m(x - x_1)$, where m is the slope and the point $P_1(x_1,y_1)$ lies on the line.
14. The **slope-intercept** form of the equation of a line is $y = mx + b$, where m is the slope and $(0,b)$ is the y-intercept.
15. Two distinct nonvertical lines having slopes m_1 and m_2 are **parallel** if and only if $m_1 = m_2$. (The slopes are the same.)
16. Two distinct nonvertical lines having slopes m_1 and m_2 are **perpendicular** if and only if $m_1m_2 = -1$. (The slopes are negative reciprocals of each other.)
17. Vertical lines and horizontal lines are perpendicular to one another.
18. A **linear inequality in two variables** is an inequality of the form $ax + by < c$, $ax + by \leq c$, $ax + by > c$, or $ax + by \geq c$.
19. The graph of a linear inequality is a **half-plane** that
    a. includes the boundary line when the symbols $\leq$ or $\geq$ are used. The line is solid.
    b. excludes the boundary line when the symbols $<$ or $>$ are used. The line is dashed.

Chapter 7 review

[7–1]

Directions Find the value of y corresponding to the given values for x. Express your answer as an ordered pair.

1. $y = 3x + 4$; $x = -1$, $x = 0$, $x = 4$
2. $2x - 3y = -1$; $x = -2$, $x = 0$, $x = 1$
3. $y + 3 = 0$; $x = -7$, $x = 0$, $x = 5$
4. $5x + y = 0$; $x = -3$, $x = 0$, $x = 3$

Directions Find the value of x corresponding to the given values of y. Express your answer as an ordered pair.

5. $x = -3y + 1$; $y = -2$, $y = 0$, $y = 5$
6. $4x + 2y = 7$; $y = -1$, $y = 0$, $y = 3$
7. $x - 1 = 0$; $y = -8$, $y = 0$, $y = 2$
8. $3x - 2y = 0$; $y = -3$, $y = 0$, $y = 1$

[7–2]

Directions Plot the following ordered pairs on a rectangular coordinate system.

9. (1,5) **10.** (4,−4) **11.** (−1,−6)

12. (0,−4) **13.** $\left(2,\frac{1}{2}\right)$ **14.** $\left(5,-\frac{2}{3}\right)$

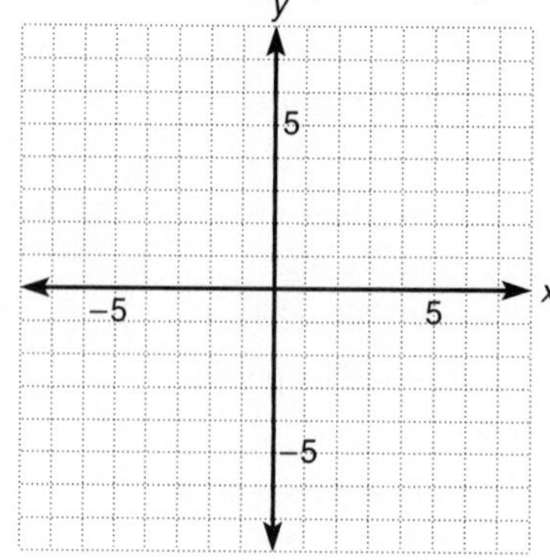

Directions Determine to the nearest integer the coordinates, (x,y), of the given points.

15. A **16.** B **17.** C

18. D **19.** E **20.** F

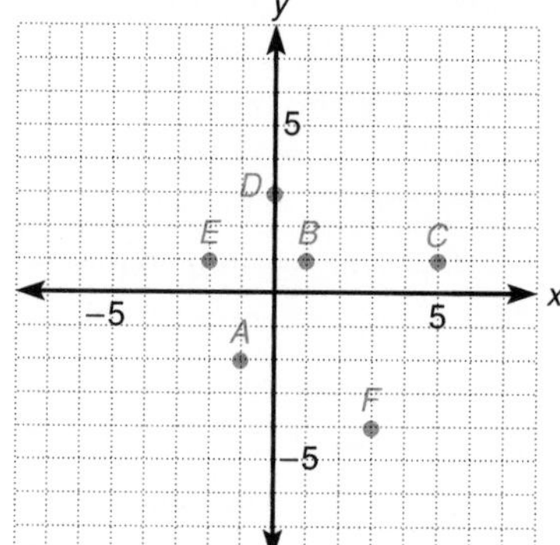

Directions Find the missing component in each ordered pair using the given equation. Then plot the ordered pairs using a separate coordinate system for each problem.

21. $y = x + 4$ (2,), (0,), (−1,), (−2,) **22.** $y = -2x + 5$ (−1,), $\left(\frac{5}{2},\ \right)$, (0,), (3,)

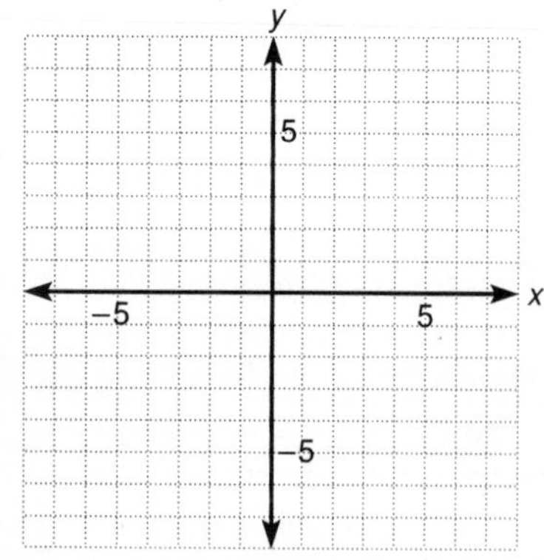

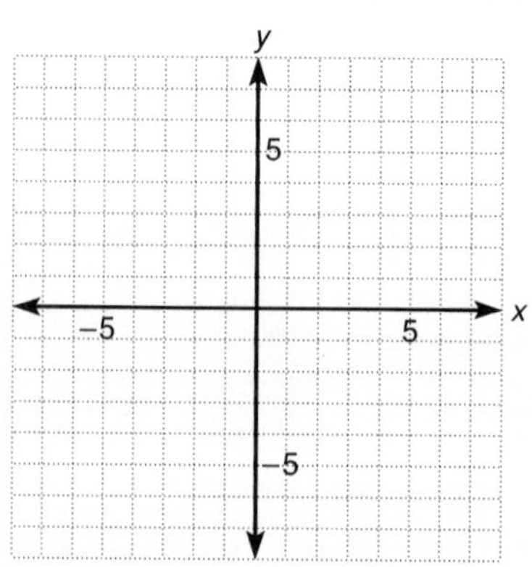

[7–3]

Directions Find the x- and y-intercepts. State your answer as an ordered pair.

23. $y = 3x + 5$

24. $y = -4x$

25. $y + 2 = 3x$

26. $4y - x = -8$

Directions Graph the following linear equations using the x- and y-intercepts, where possible.

27. $y = -x + 7$

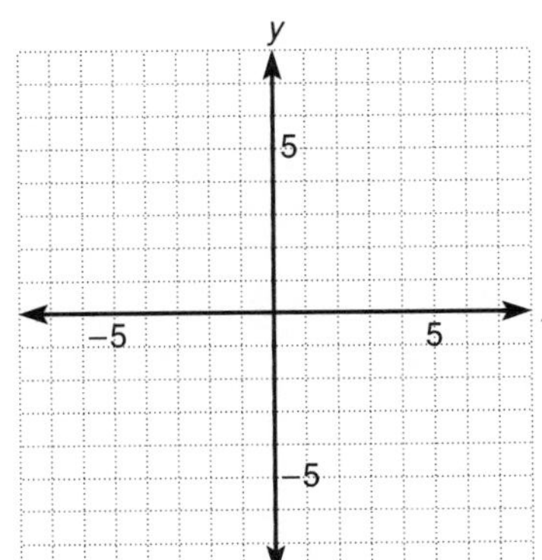

28. $y = \frac{1}{2}x - 1$

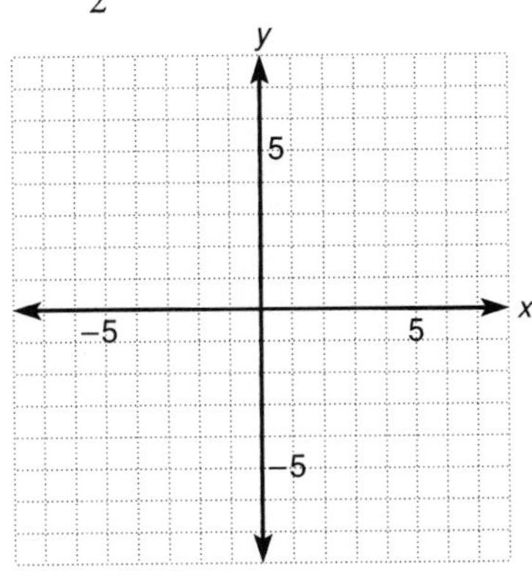

29. $y = -x$

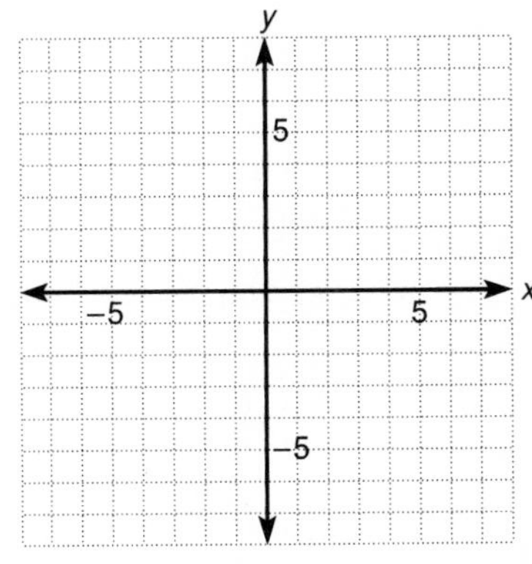

30. $y = 7$

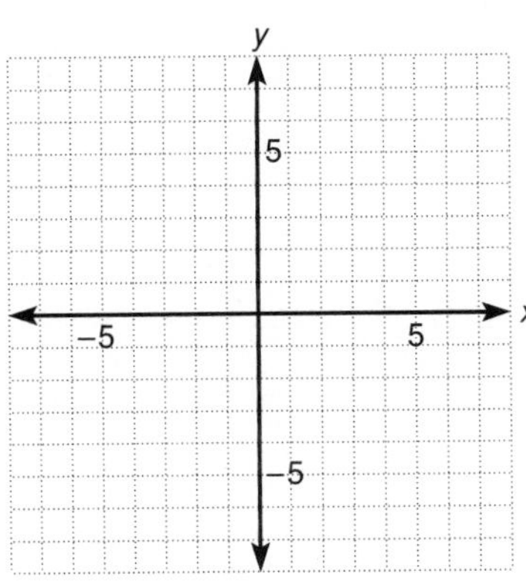

31. $x = -4$

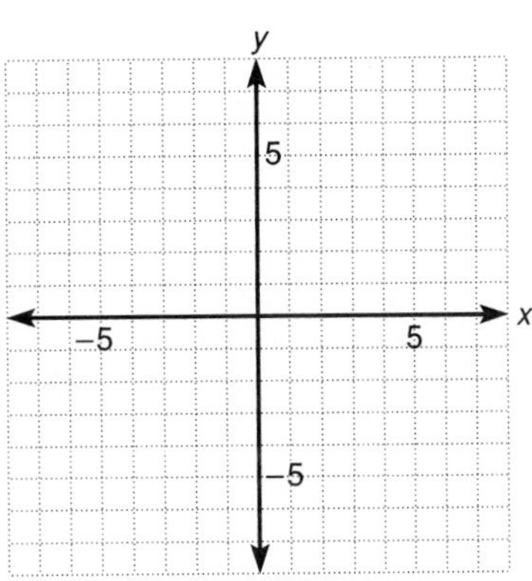

32. $2x - 3y = -6$

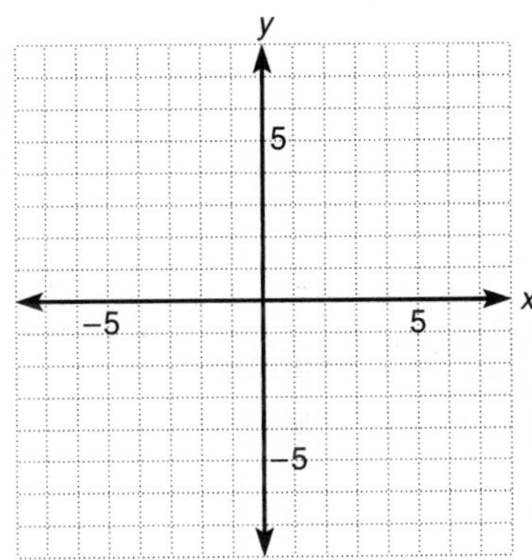

33. $5x - 3y = 15$

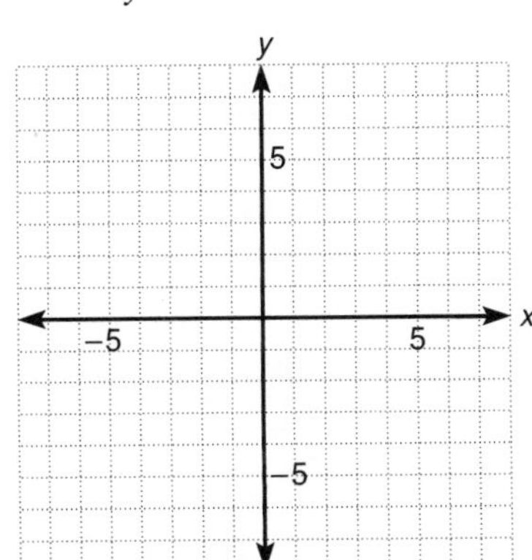

Directions Find the slope of the line passing through the given pairs of points.

34. $(-4,3)$ and $(1,0)$

35. $(-5,3)$ and $(-5,-1)$

[7–4]

Directions Express the following equations in *slope-intercept* form $y = mx + b$ and determine the slope m and y-intercept b.

36. $3x - 4y = 8$

37. $4x + 3y = 2$

38. If the value of y is 3 less than the product of 4 and x, write an equation and graph the equation.

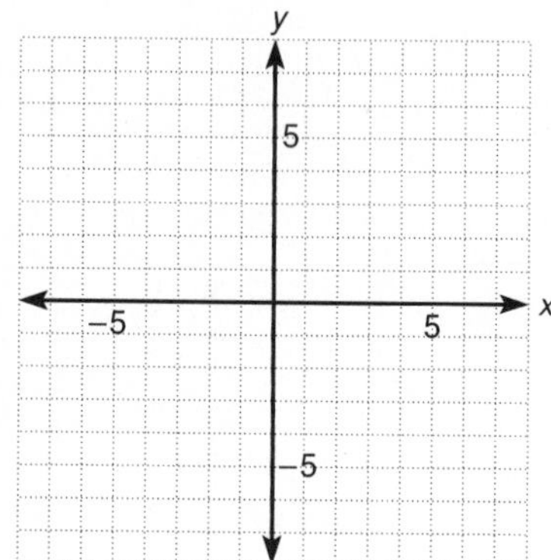

Directions Find the equation of the lines having the given conditions. Write your answer in standard form. $ax + by = c$, a and b are integers, $a \geq 0$.

39. Passing through $(4,5)$ having slope $m = -4$.

40. Having slope $m = \frac{1}{3}$ and y-intercept 4.

41. Passing through points $(5,2)$ and $(-3,1)$.

42. Passing through points $(0,4)$ and $(-3,0)$.

Directions Graph the following equations using the slope m and y-intercept b.

43. $y = 3x + 4$

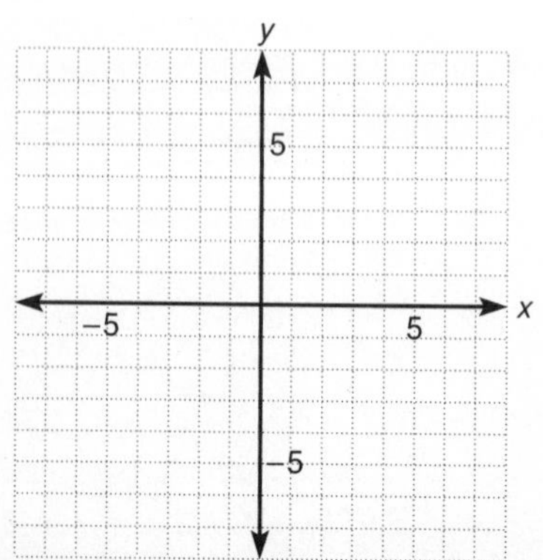

44. $2x - y = 5$

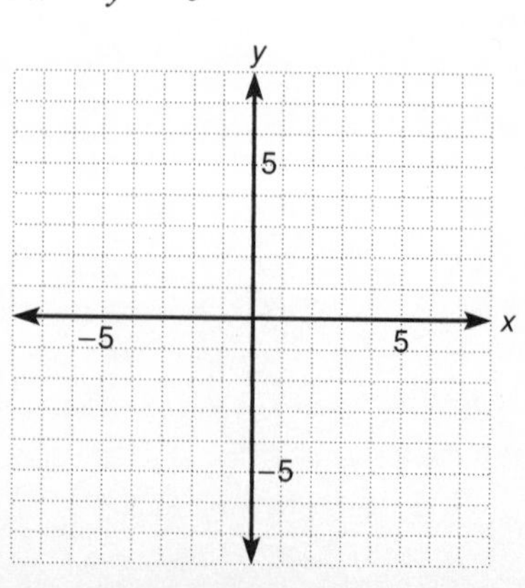

Directions Determine if the given equations are parallel, perpendicular, or neither.

45. $x - 4y = 3$
$4x + y = -2$

46. $3x - 2y = 1$
$9x - 6y = 0$

47. $x + y = 4$
$2x - y = 8$

[7–5]

Directions Graph the following inequalities.

48. $x \leq 2y + 1$

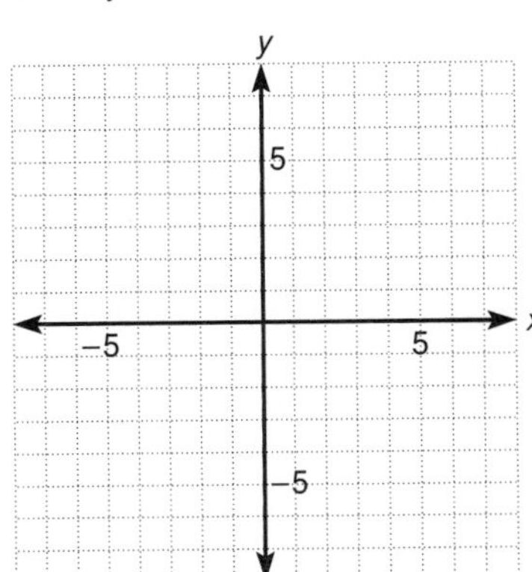

49. $y > 3x - 2$

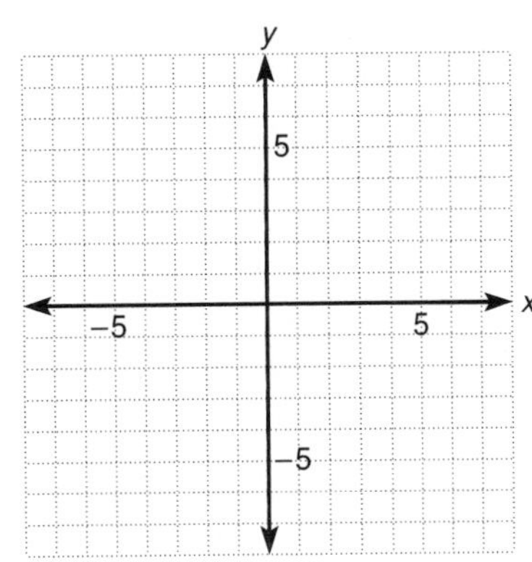

50. $2x - y \geq 4$

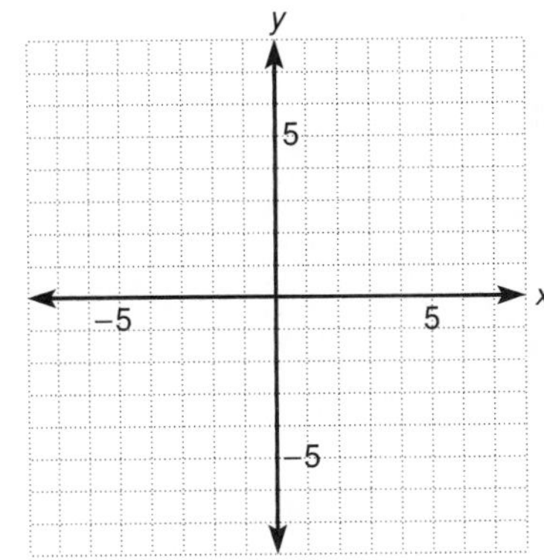

51. $3x + 2y \geq 9$

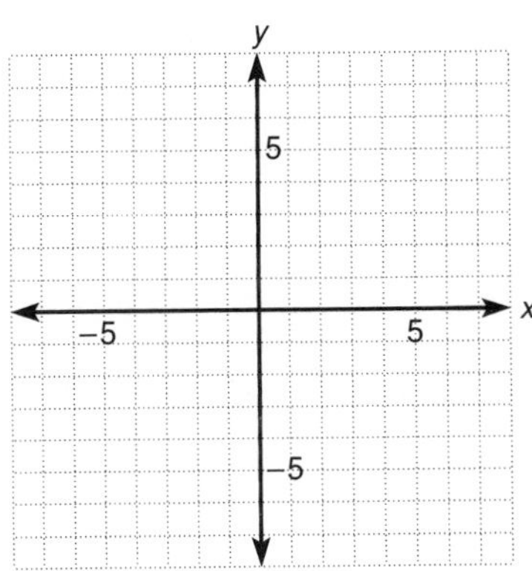

52. $5x - 2y < 10$

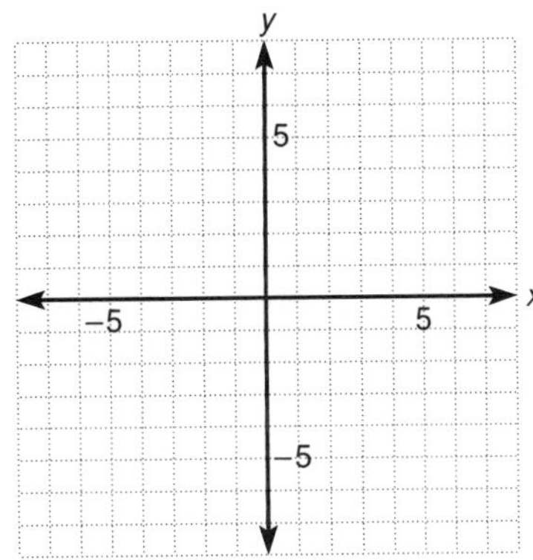

53. $x < -1$

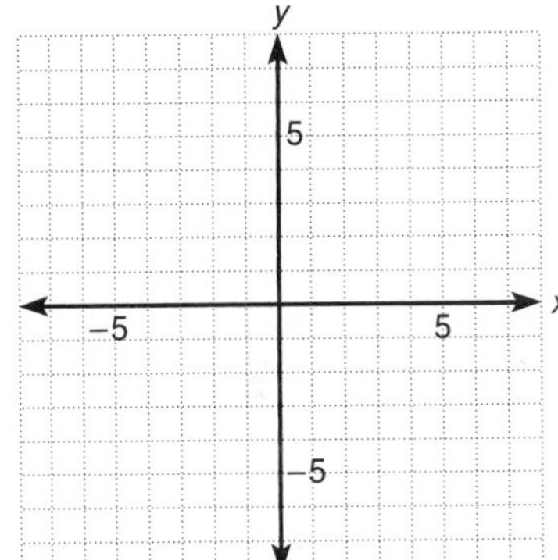

54. $y \leq 5$

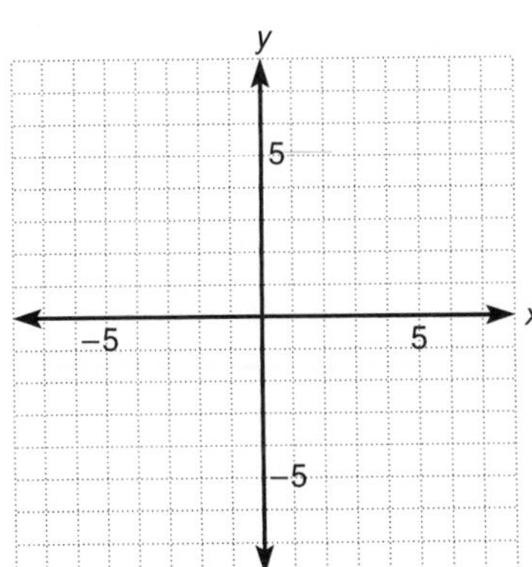

55. $2y - 5x > 0$

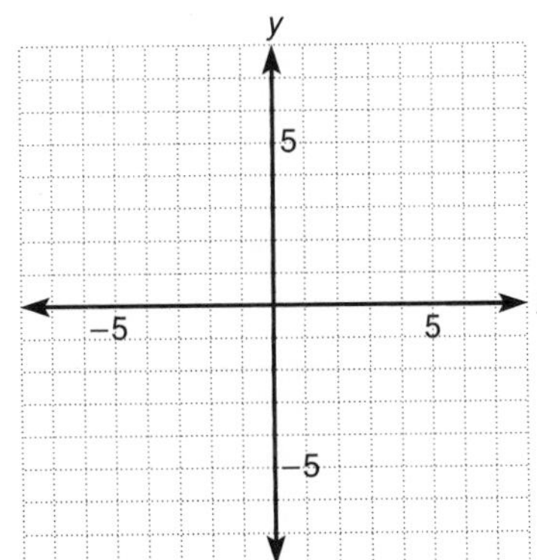

NAME

Chapter 7 cumulative test

CLASS/SECTION DATE

[1–8] **1.** Evaluate the expression $xy + (-xy)^2 - x + y$ when $x = 3$ and $y = -2$.

[1–6] **2.** Remove the grouping symbols and simplify the expression $3 - [5(6x - 8) - (12x - 7) + 9x]$.

Directions Find the solution(s) of the following equations.

[2–3] **3.** $6(x + 2) = 9x + 4$

[2–3] **4.** $\frac{3}{4} = \frac{5}{x} - \frac{2}{3}$

[2–3] **5.** $-4(y + 1) - 8 = -10 - (-3 + y)$

[4–6] **6.** $3 - \frac{4}{x^2} = \frac{4}{x}$

Directions Completely factor the following polynomials.

[4–3] **7.** $7x^2 - 6x - 1$

[4–1] **8.** $y^8 + y^7 - y^6$

[4–4] **9.** $16a^2 - 16b^2$

[4–2] **10.** $t^3 - 8t^2 + 7t$

[4–5] **11.** $-35y - 28z$

Directions Perform the indicated operations.

[3–3] **12.** $(4y - 3x)^2$

[3–3] **13.** $(4x - 7)(5x + 8)$

[3–3] **14.** $\left(5 - \frac{3}{4}y\right)\left(5 + \frac{3}{4}y\right)$

[3–3] **15.** $(x - y)^3$

[3–3] **16.** $(3y^2 + 7)(5y^3 + 6y^2 - y + 8)$

[6–3] **17.** $\frac{2x}{x^2 - x - 42} + \frac{3x}{x^2 - 49}$

[6–3] **18.** $\frac{a + 1}{a + 5} - \frac{a - 3}{a^2 + 3a - 10}$

[6–1] **19.** $\frac{2y - 6}{y + 8} \cdot \frac{3y + 24}{y^2 - 9}$

Directions Simplify the following. Express the answer with positive exponents.

[3–4] **20.** $\frac{x^{-6}}{x^3}$

[3–4] **21.** $8^{-5} \cdot 8^{-3}$

[3–4] **22.** $(-5a^{-3})^3$

[3–5] **23.** Write the number 0.00000776 in scientific notation.

[5–3] **24.** Divide $(3x^3 - 2x^2 + 4x - 5) \div (x + 2)$.

[6–3] **25.** Simplify the complex fraction $\dfrac{\dfrac{2x}{x-3} - \dfrac{3}{x+1}}{\dfrac{3x+4}{x^2 - 2x - 3}}$.

Directions Graph the following equations using the x- and y-intercepts if possible.

[7–2] **26.** $2x - y = 4$

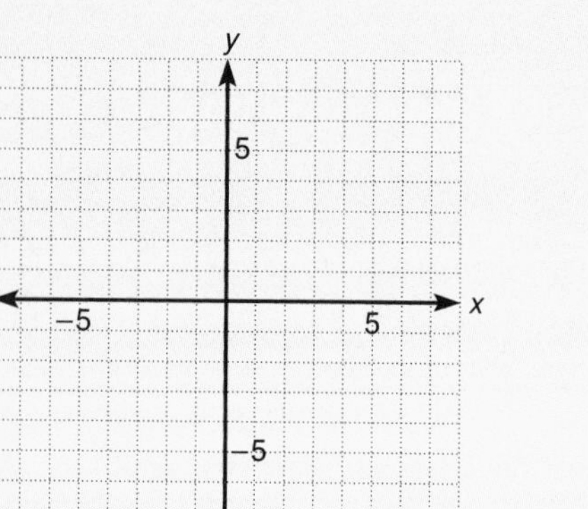

[7–2] **27.** $x - 7 = 0$

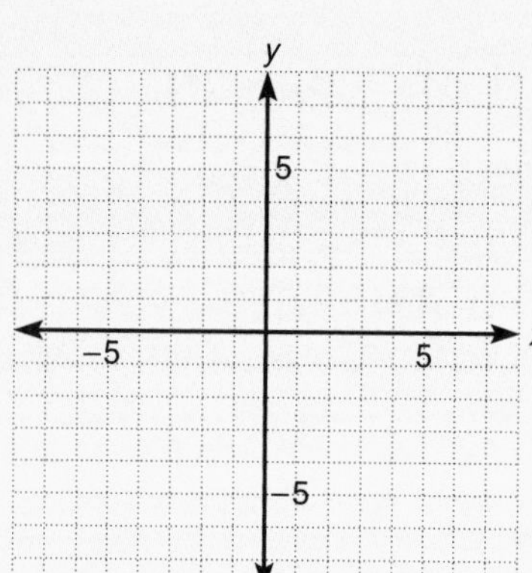

[7–3] **28.** Find the slope of the line through the points (2,3) and (−1,−4).

Directions Find the equation of the line.

[7–4] **29.** Passing through the points (1,4) and (−3,1)

[7–4] **30.** Having slope $-\frac{3}{5}$ and passing through the point (4,3)

Directions Determine if the following lines are parallel, perpendicular, or neither.

[7–4] **31.** $2x - 3y = 4$ and $4x - 6y = -1$

[7–4] **32.** $x + 2y = 6$ and $3x - 6y = 1$

Directions Solve the following verbal problems.

[2–4] **33.** Three-fourths of what number is 102?

[2–4] **34.** The product of a whole number times the next consecutive even whole number is 168. What is the number?

[2–4] **35.** Erica invests $3,000, part at 5% interest and part at 6% interest. Her income from the investments for one year is $169. How much did she invest at each rate?

[7–5] **36.** Graph the linear inequality $3x - 5y > 15$.

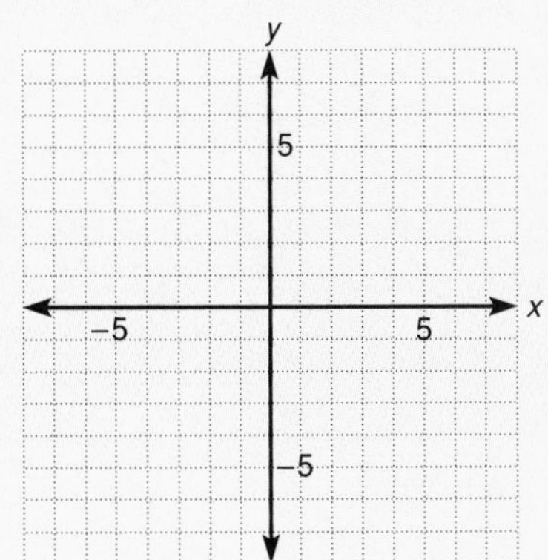

[7–5] **37.** Graph the linear inequality $4x + y \leq 4$.

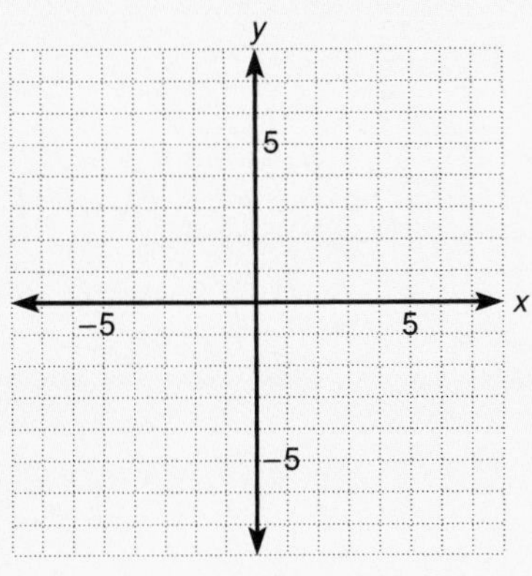

C H A P T E R

8

Systems of Linear Equations

A keypunch operator at a local firm works for $9 per hour while an entry-level typist works for $6.50 per hour. The total pay for an 8-hour day is $476. If there are two more typists than keypunch operators, how many keypunch operators does the firm employ?

Proficiency check

[2–3] **1.** Solve the following linear equations.
a. $4x + 1 = 5$

b. $3y - 2 = 10$

[7–2] **2.** Graph the following linear equations.
a. $3y - x = 2$

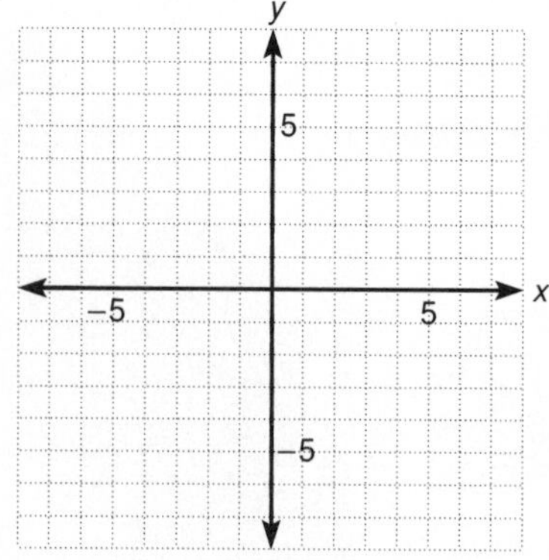

b. $4x + 2y = 1$

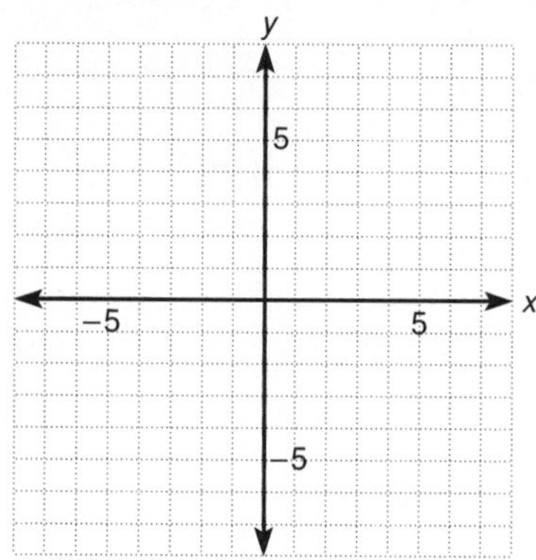

[2–3] **3.** Obtain equivalent equations of the following equations by
a. Multiplying each term of the equation $3x - 2y = 1$ by 3.

b. Multiplying each term of the equation $y - 5x = -2$ by -2.

[1–8] **4.** Substitute $2x - 1$ for y in the equation $3x - 2y = 6$ and solve for x.

[1–8] **5.** Substitute $4 - 3y$ for x in the equation $5x + 3y = -1$ and solve for y.

▣ 8–1 Solutions of systems of linear equations by graphing

Simultaneous solution

In chapter 7, we showed by graphs the relationship between the variables in a linear equation in two variables. We now consider the relationship that exists when *two* linear equations in two variables are graphed on the same coordinate plane. Two or more linear equations involving the same variables form a **system of linear equations.**

Here are examples of systems of linear equations.

I	II	III	IV
$4x - y = 1$	$3x - 7y = 5$	$x = 3y + 1$	$x = 4$
$x + y = 4$	$5x + 2y = 11$	$x + 3y = 4$	$3x - 2y = 5$

A **simultaneous solution** of a system of linear equations is an ordered pair of numbers that satisfies (makes true) all equations in the system.

A₁ Determine if the ordered pair is a solution of the system of equations.
$3x - y = 2$
$x + y = 2$

$(x,y) = (1,1)$

Example 8–1 A

Determine whether the given ordered pair is a solution of the system of linear equations.

1. $4x - y = 1$
$x + y = 4$ $\quad (x,y) = (1,3)$

$$4x - y = 1$$
$$4(1) - (3) = 1 \quad \text{Replace } x \text{ with 1 and } y \text{ with 3}$$
$$4 - 3 = 1$$
$$1 = 1 \quad \text{(True)}$$

$$x + y = 4$$
$$(1) + (3) = 4$$
$$4 = 4 \quad \text{(True)}$$

Both resulting statements are true. Therefore, the ordered pair (1,3) satisfies both equations simultaneously.

You are now ready to do **A₁**.

A₂ Determine if the ordered pair is a solution of the system of equations.
$4x - 3y = 1$
$2x - y = -3$

$(x,y) = (-5,-7)$

2. $3x - 7y = 5$
$5x - 2y = -11$ $\quad (x,y) = (-3,-2)$

$$3x - 7y = 5$$
$$3(-3) - 7(-2) = 5 \quad \text{Replace } x \text{ with } -3 \text{ and } y \text{ with } -2$$
$$-9 - (-14) = 5$$
$$-9 + 14 = 5$$
$$5 = 5 \quad \text{(True)}$$

$$5x - 2y = -11$$
$$5(-3) - 2(-2) = -11$$
$$-15 - (-4) = -11$$
$$-15 + 4 = -11$$
$$-11 = -11 \quad \text{(True)}$$

Therefore, $(-3,-2)$ is a simultaneous solution of the system.

You are now ready to do **A₂**.

3. $5x + 3y = -20$
$7x + 2y = -17$ $\quad (x,y) = (-4,0)$

$$5x + 3y = -20$$
$$5(-4) + 3(0) = -20 \quad \text{Replace } x \text{ with } -4 \text{ and } y \text{ with } 0$$
$$-20 + 0 = -20$$
$$-20 = -20 \quad \text{(True)}$$

$$7x + 2y = -17$$
$$7(-4) + 2(0) = -17$$
$$-28 + 0 = -17$$
$$-28 = -17 \quad \text{(False)}$$

Therefore, $(-4,0)$ is *not* a simultaneous solution of the system.

You are now ready to do **A₃**. ■

A₃ Determine if the ordered pair is a solution of the system of equations.
$3x + 4y = -15$
$5x + 3y = -10$

$(x,y) = (-6,0)$

Graphical solutions

The first method that we shall examine is finding the solution of a system of linear equations by **graphing.** We are looking for the coordinates of any point where the graphs intersect. This point of intersection will give the simultaneous solution of the system. Using the methods for graphing that we learned in chapter 7, we graph each equation on the same coordinate plane, finding the x- and y-intercepts and a checkpoint.

B_1 Find the simultaneous solution by graphing.

$4x - y = 2$
$x + y = 3$

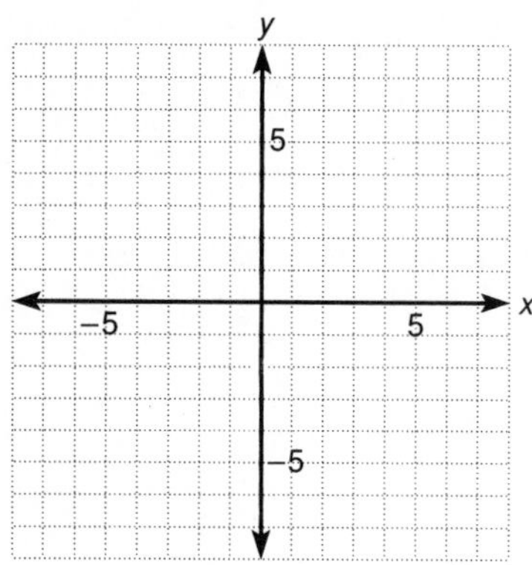

Example 8–1 B

Find the simultaneous solution of each system by graphing.

1. $4x - y = 1$
$x + y = 4$

$4x - y = 1$

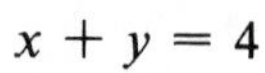
$x + y = 4$

x	y		x	y
0	−1	y-intercept; $x = 0$	0	4
$\frac{1}{4}$	0	x-intercept; $y = 0$	4	0
−1	−5	Checkpoint	2	2

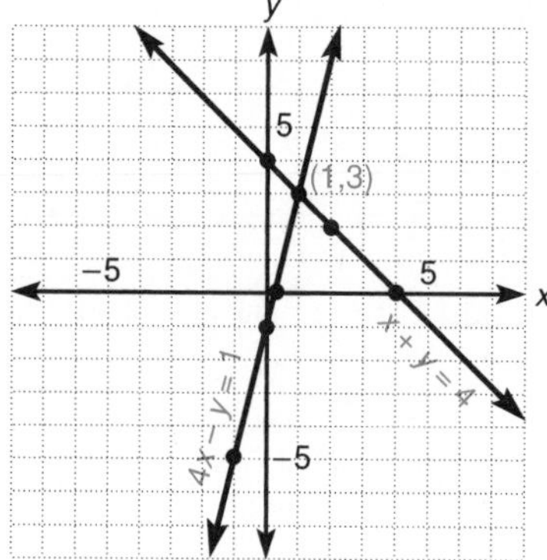

It looks like the point of intersection of the two graphs is the point (1,3). We must check this as the possible simultaneous solution.

$4x - y = 1$
$4(1) - 3 = 1$ Replace x by 1 and y by 3
$4 - 3 = 1$
$1 = 1$ (True)

$x + y = 4$
$1 + 3 = 4$
$4 = 4$ (True)

The simultaneous solution is the ordered pair (1,3).

You are now ready to do **B_1**.

2. $3x + y = 5$
$x - 2y = 4$

$3x + y = 5$ and $x - 2y = 4$

x	y		x	y
0	5	y-intercept; $x = 0$	0	−2
$\frac{5}{3}$	0	x-intercept; $y = 0$	4	0
1	2	Checkpoint	2	−1

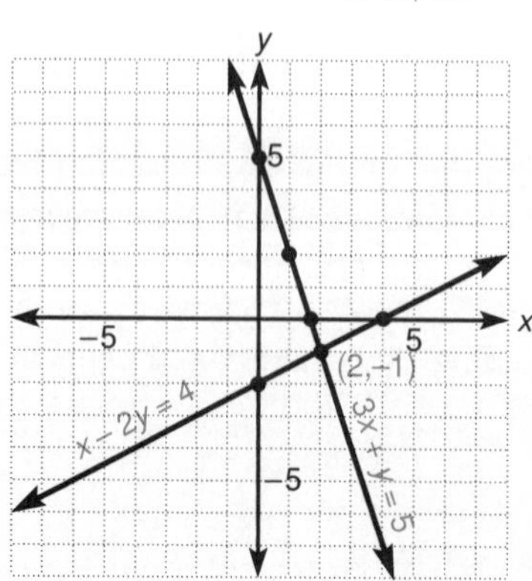

It appears that the point of intersection is $(2,-1)$.

Check:

$$\begin{aligned} 3x + y &= 5 \\ 3(2) + (-1) &= 5 \\ 6 + -1 &= 5 \\ 5 &= 5 \quad \text{(True)} \end{aligned} \qquad \begin{aligned} x - 2y &= 4 \\ 2 - 2(-1) &= 4 \\ 2 + 2 &= 4 \\ 4 &= 4 \quad \text{(True)} \end{aligned}$$

The simultaneous solution of the system is $(2,-1)$.

You are now ready to do **B₂**.

3. $5x - y = 5$
$x + y = 2$

$5x - y = 5$

x	y	
0	-5	y-intercept; $x = 0$
1	0	x-intercept; $y = 0$
$\frac{1}{2}$	$-\frac{5}{2}$	Checkpoint

$x + y = 2$

x	y
0	2
2	0
1	1

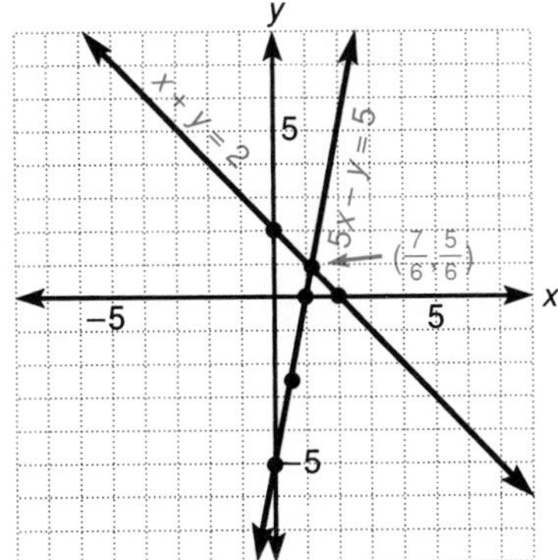

An estimate of the point of intersection might be $(1,1)$. A check shows this is not a correct solution.

$$\begin{aligned} 5x - y &= 5 \\ 5(1) - 1 &= 5 \\ 4 &= 5 \quad \text{(False)} \end{aligned} \qquad \begin{aligned} x + y &= 2 \\ 1 + 1 &= 2 \\ 2 &= 2 \quad \text{(True)} \end{aligned}$$

We will see in section 8–2 that the actual point of intersection is $\left(\frac{7}{6}, \frac{5}{6}\right)$.

You are now ready to do **B₃**. ■

It should be obvious that our graphical method of finding the solution may not be exact because the drawing of the graph depends on measuring devices. Inaccuracies are thereby often produced in the graphing process.

When the graph of a system consists of intersecting lines and thus has a simultaneous solution, the system is said to be **consistent** and **independent.**

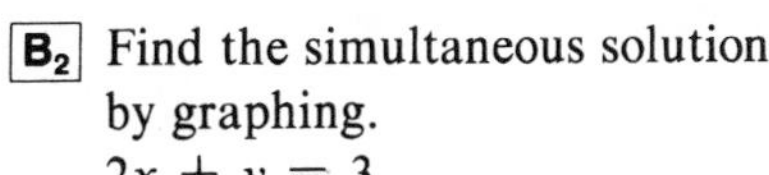

B₂ Find the simultaneous solution by graphing.
$2x + y = 3$
$x - 3y = 5$

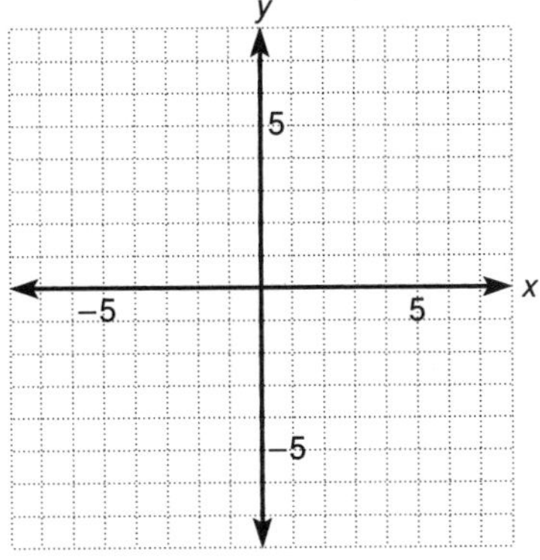

B₃ Find the simultaneous solution by graphing.
$2x + y = 3$
$x - y = 4$

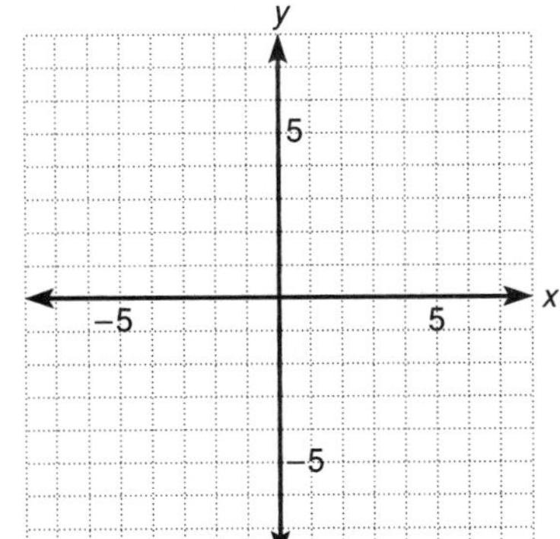

C_1 $2x - 3y = 6$
$4x - 6y = 24$

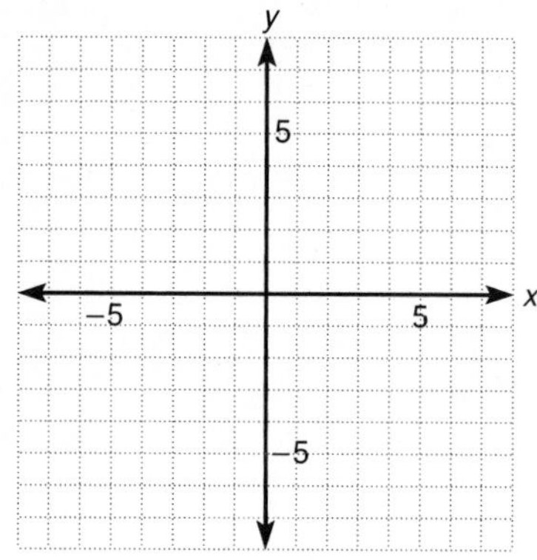

Inconsistent and dependent systems

Sometimes the graphs of the two equations in the system do not intersect at all (are parallel lines) or are one and the same line.

Example 8–1 C

1. $3x - 4y = 12$
   $6x - 8y = -24$

$3x - 4y = 12$

x	y	
0	-3	y-intercept; $x = 0$
4	0	x-intercept; $y = 0$
2	$-\frac{3}{2}$	Checkpoint

$6x - 8y = -24$

x	y
0	3
-4	0
-2	$\frac{3}{2}$

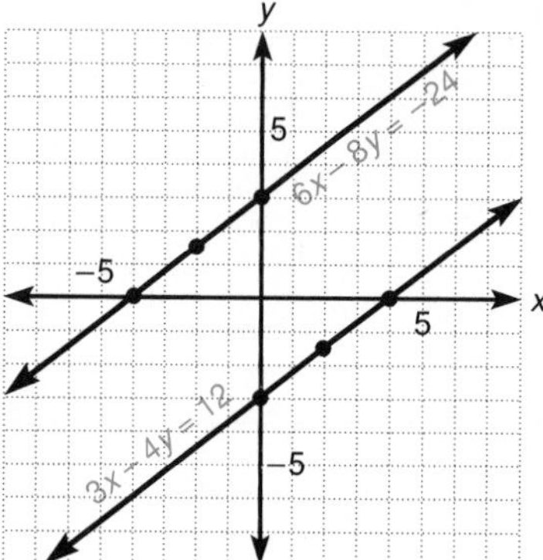

The lines appear to be parallel (they are) and will not intersect. When this condition exists, the system is said to be *inconsistent* and there are no solutions (no points of intersection). We will show later how you can determine by algebra if the lines are or are not parallel.

You are now ready to do **C_1**.

2. $4x - 2y = 6$
   $2x - y = 3$

$4x - 2y = 6$

x	y	
0	-3	y-intercept; $x = 0$
$\frac{3}{2}$	0	x-intercept; $y = 0$
1	-1	Checkpoint

$2x - y = 3$

x	y
0	-3
$\frac{3}{2}$	0
1	-1

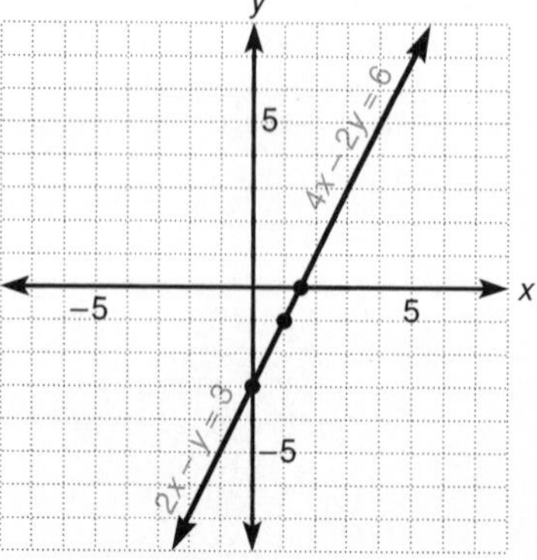

We observe that the intercepts and checkpoint $(1,-1)$, are the same for both lines. Therefore, the two lines coincide and the graph is a single line. Such a system is called a **dependent** system of equations. In a dependent system of equations, there are an unlimited number of simultaneous solutions because each ordered pair that satisfies the first equation will also satisfy the second.

You are now ready to do **C₂**.

C₂ $x + 3y = 6$
$3x + 9y = 18$

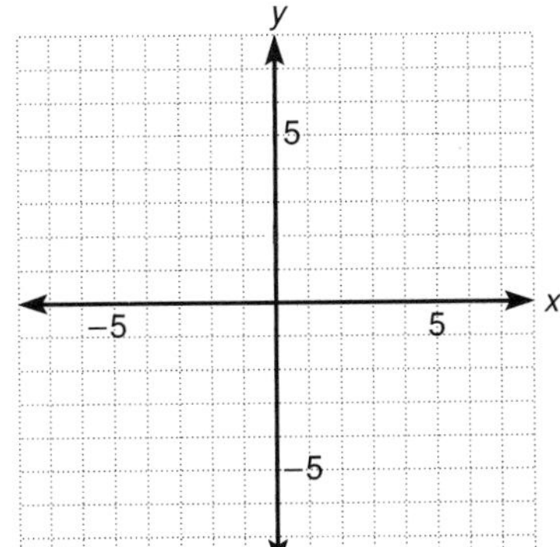

To solve a system of linear equations by graphing

1. Graph each equation on the same set of axes.
2. Their graphs may intersect in
   a. one point—one simultaneous solution (the system is *consistent* and *independent*).
   b. no points—the lines are parallel and there are no simultaneous solutions (the system is *inconsistent*).
   c. all points—the lines are one and the same (the system is *dependent*).
3. If the graphs intersect in one point, check the coordinates of the point in each equation.

Answers to section 8–1 margin exercises

A₁ (1,1) is a solution **A₂** (−5,−7) is a solution **A₃** (−6,0) is not a solution

B₁

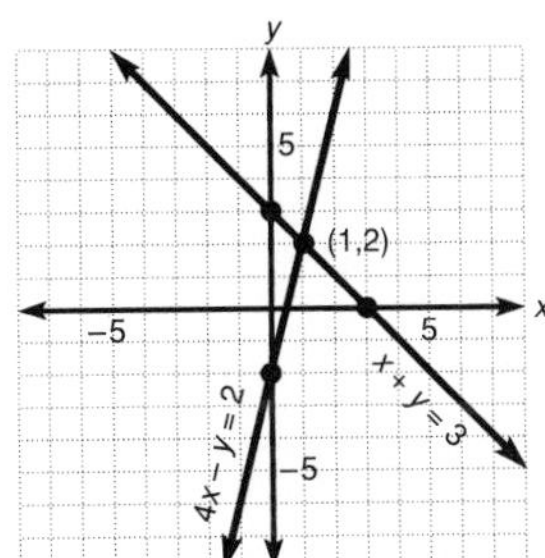

B₂

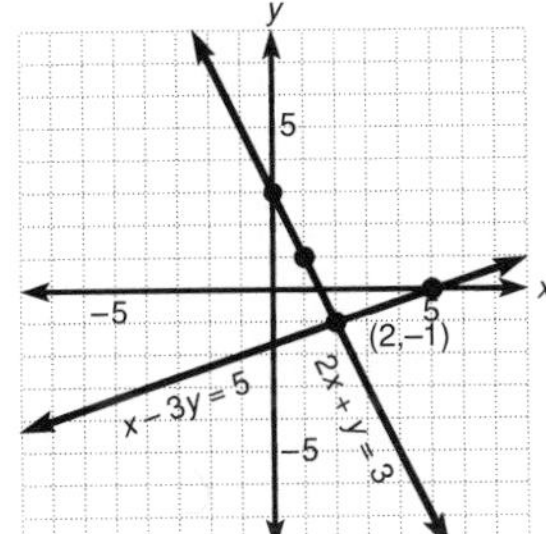

B₃

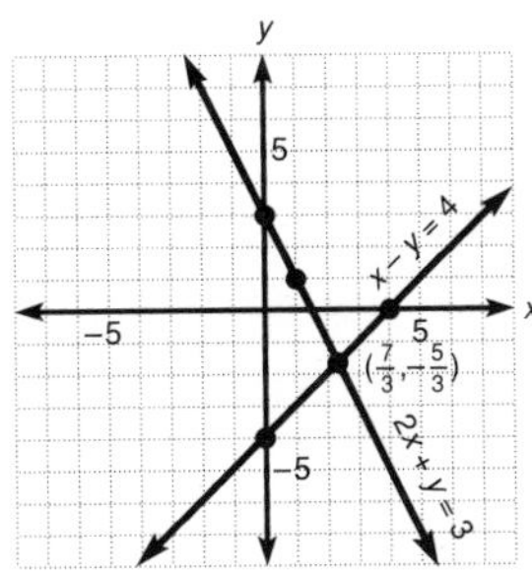

C₁ parallel, no solution, inconsistent

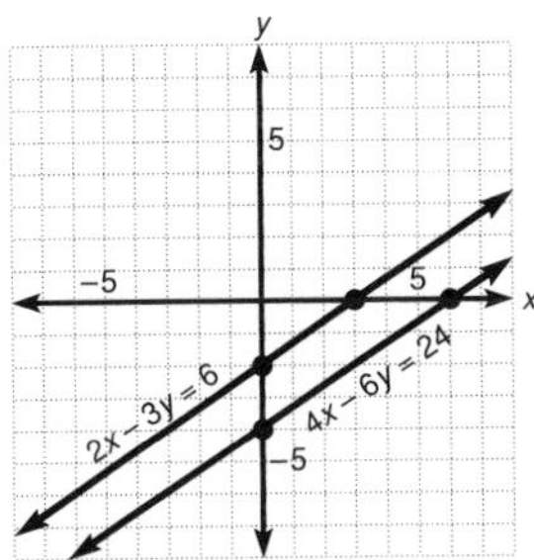

C₂ dependent, infinitely many solutions

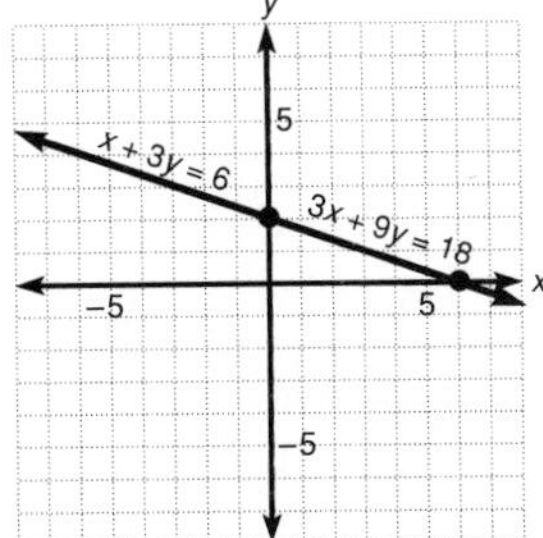

Mastery points

Can you

- Determine if an ordered pair is a simultaneous solution of a system of linear equations?
- Solve a system of linear equations by graphing?
- Recognize an inconsistent and a dependent system of linear equations?

Exercise 8–1

Directions Determine if the given ordered pair is a simultaneous solution to the system of linear equations. See example 8–1 A.

Example A₂ $\begin{aligned} 4x - 3y &= 1 \\ 2x - y &= -3 \end{aligned}$ $(x,y) = (-5,-7)$

Solution

$$\begin{aligned} 4x - 3y &= 1 \\ 4(-5) - 3(-7) &= 1 \quad \text{Replace } x \text{ with } -5 \text{ and } y \text{ with } -7 \\ -20 + 21 &= 1 \\ 1 &= 1 \quad \text{(True)} \end{aligned}$$

$$\begin{aligned} 2x - y &= -3 \\ 2(-5) - (-7) &= -3 \\ -10 + 7 &= -3 \\ -3 &= -3 \quad \text{(True)} \end{aligned}$$

The ordered pair $(-5,-7)$ satisfies each equation so it is a simultaneous solution.

1. $\begin{aligned} x + y &= 2 \\ 3x - y &= 10 \end{aligned}$ $(x,y) = (3,-1)$

2. $\begin{aligned} x + 2y &= 4 \\ x + 4y &= 10 \end{aligned}$ $(x,y) = (-2,3)$

3. $\begin{aligned} x - y &= 1 \\ x + y &= 5 \end{aligned}$ $(x,y) = (3,2)$

4. $\begin{aligned} 3x - y &= -10 \\ 3x + y &= 4 \end{aligned}$ $(x,y) = (-1,7)$

5. $\begin{aligned} 2x + y &= 2 \\ 6x - y &= 22 \end{aligned}$ $(x,y) = (3,-4)$

6. $\begin{aligned} x - 3y &= -1 \\ 3x + y &= -2 \end{aligned}$ $(x,y) = (-1,0)$

7. $\begin{aligned} 3x + 4y &= 14 \\ 2x + y &= 6 \end{aligned}$ $(x,y) = (1,4)$

8. $\begin{aligned} 3x + y &= 12 \\ 2x + 3y &= 15 \end{aligned}$ $(x,y) = (2,6)$

9. $\begin{aligned} x &= 6 \\ 2x - y &= 3 \end{aligned}$ $(x,y) = (6,9)$

10. $\begin{aligned} y &= 4x - 3 \\ y &= -1 \end{aligned}$ $(x,y) = (-1,-1)$

11. $\begin{aligned} 3x - 2y &= 4 \\ y &= x + 3 \end{aligned}$ $(x,y) = (10,2)$

12. $\begin{aligned} y &= 2 - 5x \\ x - y &= 6 \end{aligned}$ $(x,y) = (-1,5)$

Directions Estimate the solution of each system by graphing. All answers in the back of the book will be given exactly. If the system is inconsistent or dependent, so state. See examples 8–1 B and C.

Example **B₂** $2x + y = 3$
$x - 3y = 5$

Solution We find the x- and y-intercepts and another checkpoint to graph each equation.

$2x + y = 3$

x	y	
0	3	y-intercept; let $x = 0$
$\frac{3}{2}$	0	x-intercept; let $y = 0$
1	1	Checkpoint

$x - 3y = 5$

x	y
0	$-\frac{5}{3}$
5	0
2	-1

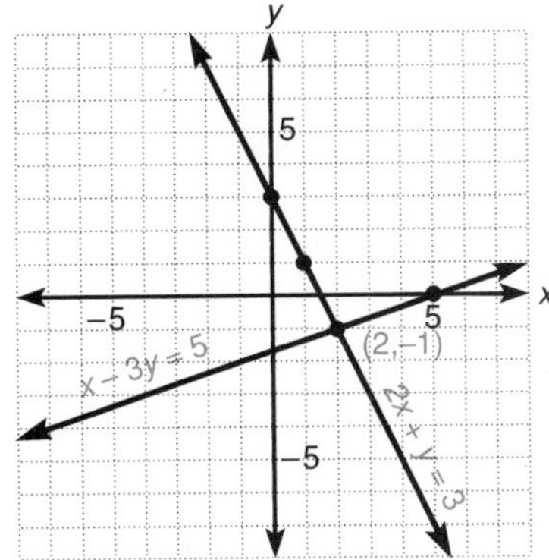

The simultaneous solution appears to be the ordered pair $(2, -1)$. A check of this would prove this to be the correct solution.

13. $x - y = 1$
$x + y = 5$

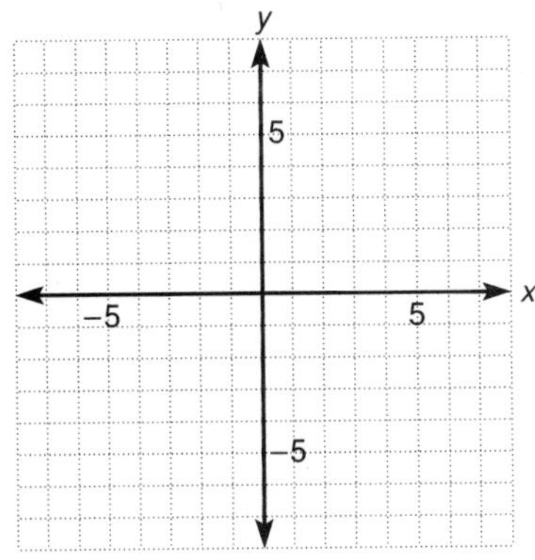

14. $x + 2y = 4$
$x + 4y = 4$

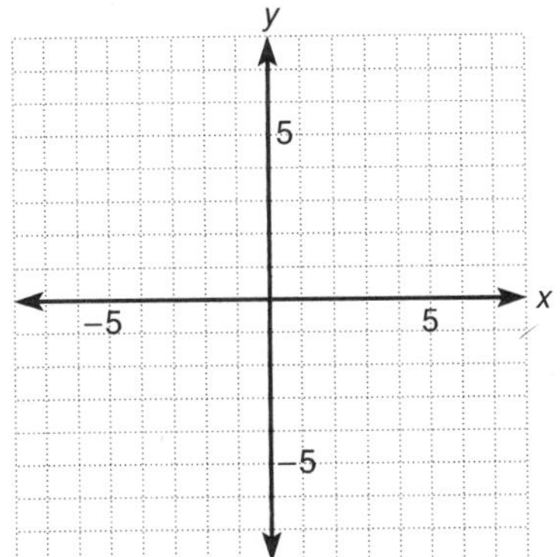

15. $3x - y = 10$
$x + y = 2$

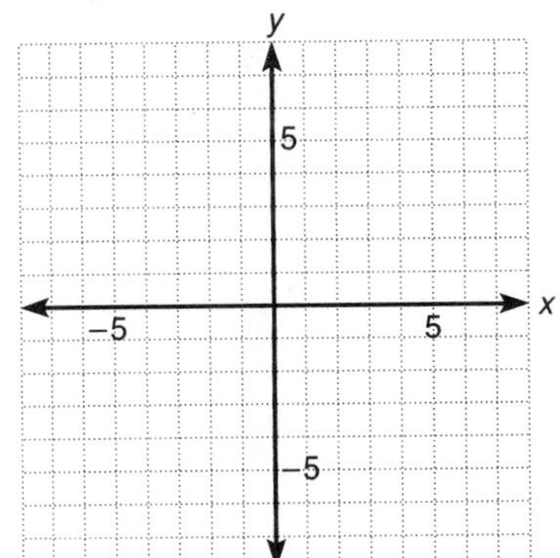

16. $x - y = 3$
$2x + 3y = 11$

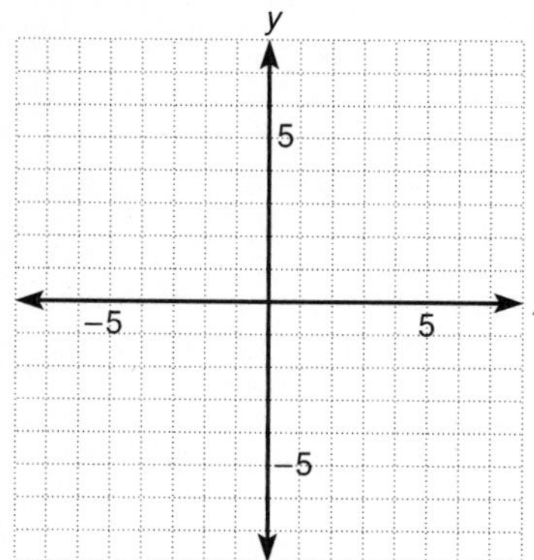

17. $2x - y = 3$
$2x + y = -7$

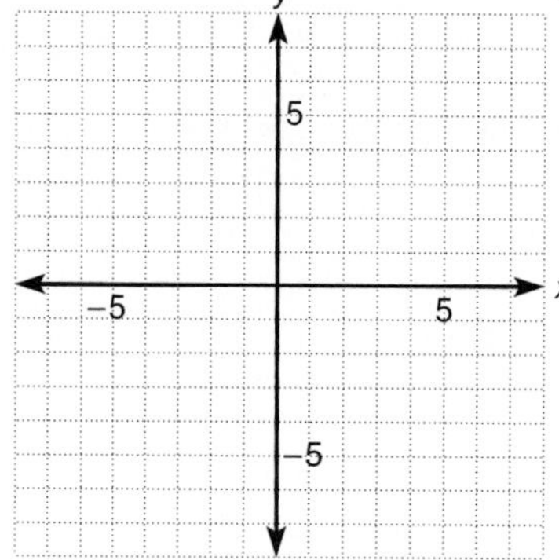

18. $2x + 3y = 13$
$3x - 2y = 0$

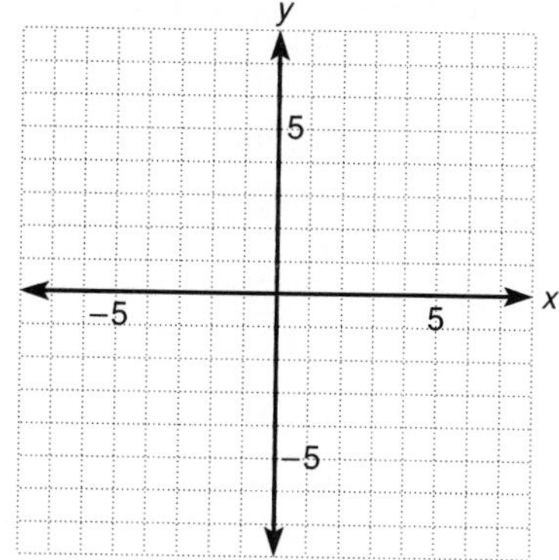

19. $3x + y = 3$
$6x + 2y = 3$

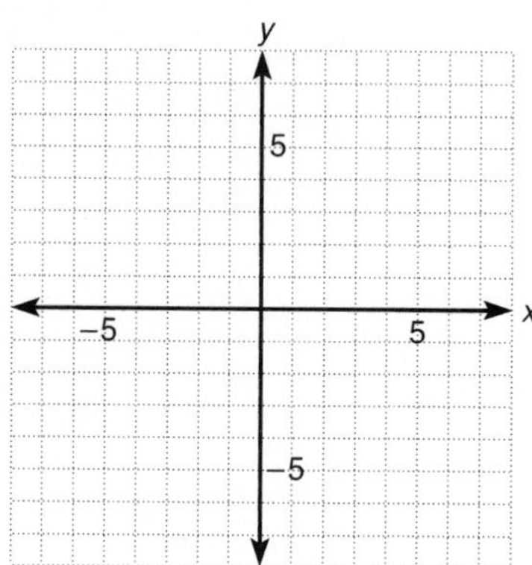

20. $2x + y = 2$
$-6x - 3y = 6$

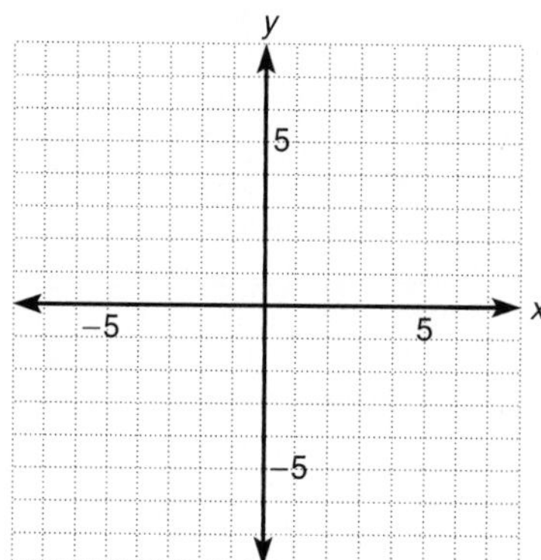

21. $y + 2x = 6$
$4y + 3x = 12$

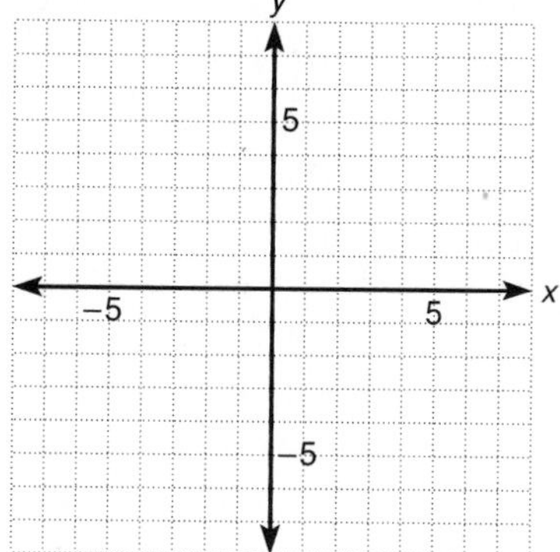

22. $-3x - y = 0$
$x + 3y = 6$

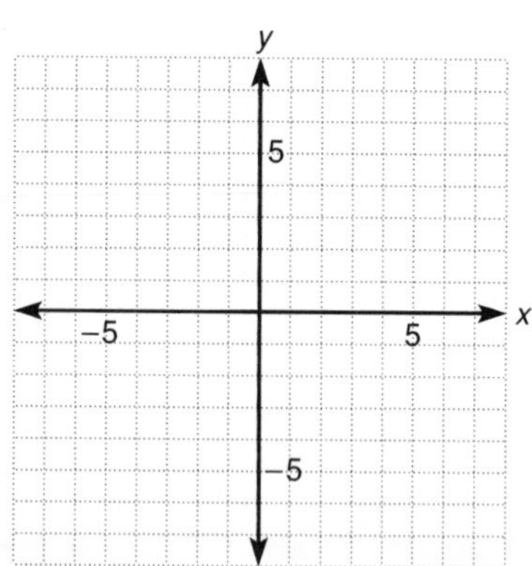

23. $-x + 4y = -4$
$-2x + 8y = -8$

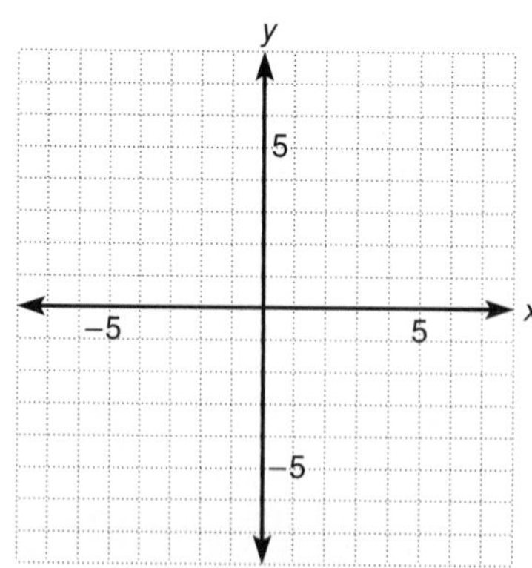

24. $5x + y = -5$
$-10x - 2y = 10$

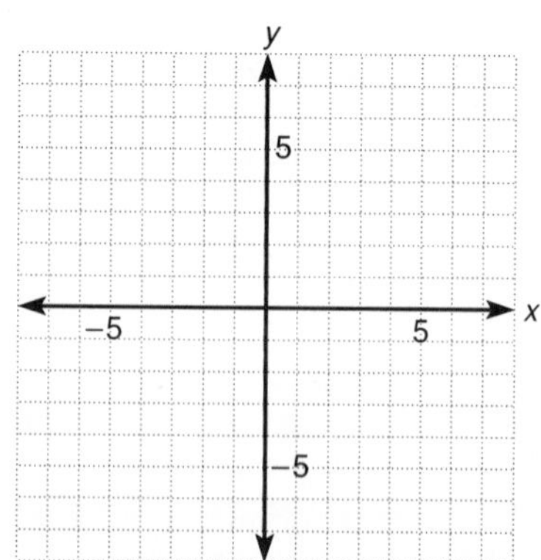

25. $x = 4$
$x + 2y = 4$

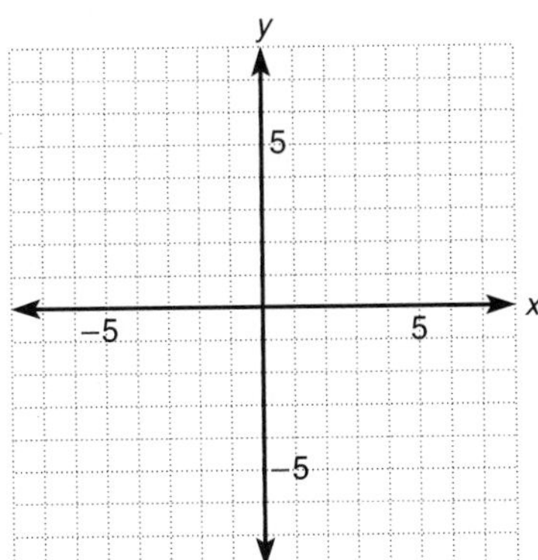

26. $3x + y = -3$
$x = -1$

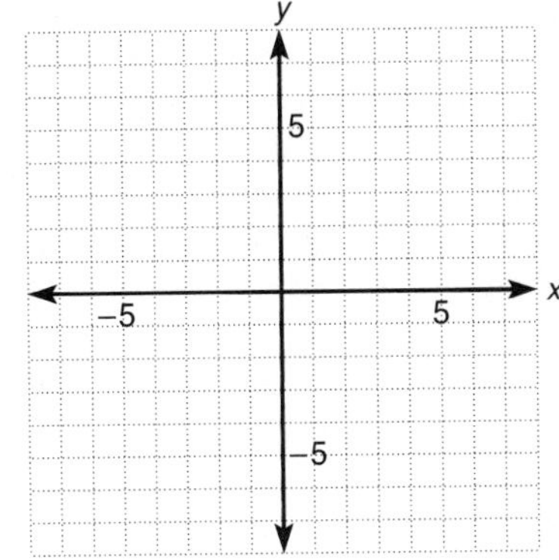

27. $y = 1$
$3x - 2y = -6$

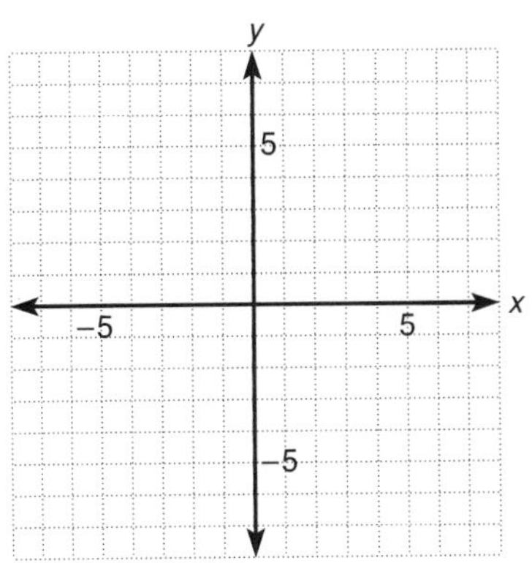

28. $5x - y = 5$
$y = 4$

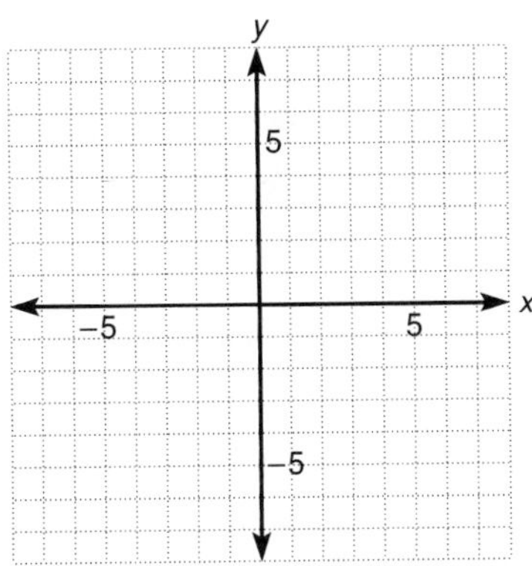

29. $3x - 6y = 12$
$x - 2y = 6$

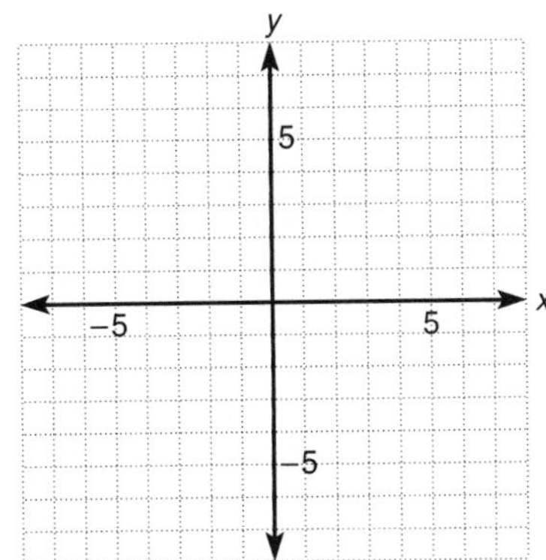

30. $3x + y = 10$
$2x - y = 5$

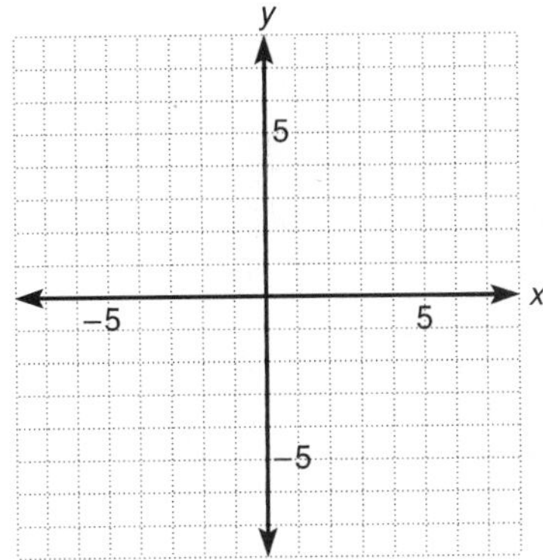

Review exercises

1. Solve the equation $\frac{3x}{2} - \frac{x}{4} = 1$. See section 6–5.

2. Divide as indicated. $(3x^3 - x^2 + 1) \div (x + 3)$ See section 5–3.

Directions Find the solution and graph on the real number line. See section 2–7.

3. $4y - 3 \leq 2y + 7$

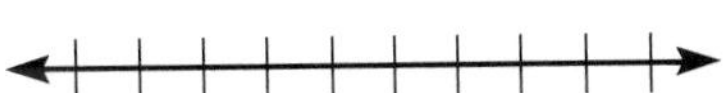

4. $-5 < 2x + 1 \leq 7$

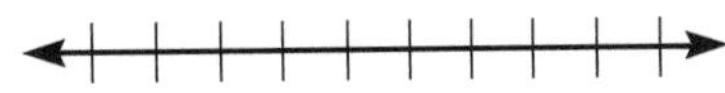

Directions Perform the indicated operations. See sections 3–3 and 3–4.

5. $x^{-3} \cdot x^5 \cdot x^2$

6. $x^3(x^2 - 2x + 1)$

7. $(2x - y)^2$

A_1 Solve the following system by adding.
$3x + y = 5$
$2x - y = 0$

8–2 Solutions of systems of linear equations by addition

In section 8–1, we found solutions to systems of linear equations by graphing the equations and by observing the coordinates of the point of intersection of the two lines. This technique will often produce an approximate solution.

An algebraic method for obtaining an *exact* simultaneous solution to a system involves the operation of *addition,* together with the following property of real numbers.

Property of real numbers

Given a, b, c, and d are real numbers, if $a = b$ and $c = d$, then

$$a + c = b + d.$$

Concept

Equal quantities may be added to equal quantities and the sums will be equal.

This property of real numbers is used to *eliminate* one of the variables in the system. The resulting single equation has only one unknown that we solve to obtain one of the components of the simultaneous solution. We illustrate this property's use in the following examples.

Example 8–2 A

Solve the following systems of linear equations by addition.

1. $2x - y = 4$
$x + y = 2$

Adding the left members and the right members, we obtain

$(2x - y) + (x + y) = 4 + 2$
$2x - y + x + y = 4 + 2$ Remove parentheses
$3x = 6$ Add in each member
$x = 2.$ Divide each member by 3

We have found the value of x to be 2. To find y, we replace x with 2 in *either* of the equations and solve for y.

$x + y = 2$ Choose either equation
$(2) + y = 2$ Replace x with 2
$y = 0$ Subtract 2 from each member

The simultaneous solution of our system is (2,0).

Check:

$2x - y = 4$
$2(2) - 0 = 4$
$4 - 0 = 4$
$4 = 4$ (True)

$x + y = 2$
$2 + 0 = 2$
$2 = 2$ (True)

You are now ready to do **A_1**.

2. $2x + 3y = 5$
$-2x + y = 3$

To add the left members and the right members, we simply draw a line under the second equation and add vertically with the like terms in a column.

$$\begin{aligned} 2x + 3y &= 5 \\ -2x + y &= 3 \\ \hline 4y &= 8 && \text{Add left and right members} \\ y &= 2 && \text{Divide each member by 4} \end{aligned}$$

Replace y with 2 in either equation and solve for x.

$$\begin{aligned} 2x + 3y &= 5 && \text{Choose either equation} \\ 2x + 3(2) &= 5 && \text{Replace } y \text{ with 2} \\ 2x + 6 &= 5 && \text{Multiply in left member} \\ 2x &= -1 && \text{Subtract 6 from each member} \\ x &= -\frac{1}{2} && \text{Divide each member by 2} \end{aligned}$$

The simultaneous solution is the ordered pair $\left(-\frac{1}{2}, 2\right)$.

Check:

$$\begin{aligned} 2x + 3y &= 5 \\ 2\left(-\frac{1}{2}\right) + 3(2) &= 5 \\ -1 + 6 &= 5 \\ 5 &= 5 \quad \text{(True)} \end{aligned} \qquad \begin{aligned} -2x + y &= 3 \\ -2\left(-\frac{1}{2}\right) + 2 &= 3 \\ 1 + 2 &= 3 \\ 3 &= 3 \quad \text{(True)} \end{aligned}$$

We will not show a check in future examples but you should always do this.

You are now ready to do A_2.

A_2 Solve the following system by adding.
$3x + 2y = 4$
$-3x + y = 5$

3. $x = 4 - 3y$
$2x - 3y = 2$
To solve the system by addition, like terms must be in a column.

$$\begin{aligned} x + 3y &= 4 && \text{Add } 3y \text{ to each member of first equation} \\ 2x - 3y &= 2 \\ \hline 3x \qquad &= 6 && \text{Add left and right members} \\ x &= 2 && \text{Divide each member by 3} \end{aligned}$$

Replace x with 2 in either equation and solve for y.

$$\begin{aligned} x + 3y &= 4 && \text{Choose either equation} \\ (2) + 3y &= 4 && \text{Replace } x \text{ with 2} \\ 3y &= 2 && \text{Subtract 2 from each member} \\ y &= \frac{2}{3} && \text{Divide each member by 3} \end{aligned}$$

The simultaneous solution of the system is the ordered pair $\left(2, \frac{2}{3}\right)$. Check the solution.

You are now ready to do A_3. ■

A_3 Solve the following system by adding.
$2x = 2 - 5y$
$3x - 5y = 3$

In the previous examples, we observe that one of the variables was easily eliminated by addition because in the original equations one of the two variables had coefficients that are additive inverses (opposites). When this condition is not present, we must first use the following procedure to obtain the necessary additive inverses.

> Multiply one or both equations by some constant so that equivalent equations are formed where one of the variables has coefficients that are additive inverses (opposites).

B_1 $3x + 2y = 4$
$2x + y = 3$

Example 8–2 B

Solve the following systems of linear equations by addition.

1. $3x + 4y = 14$
$2x + y = 6$
To eliminate the variable y, we can multiply each member of the second equation by -4.

$$\begin{array}{ll} 3x + 4y = 14 & \\ 2x + y = 6 & \text{Multiply by } -4 \end{array} \qquad \begin{array}{rl} 3x + 4y = 14 & \\ -8x - 4y = -24 & \\ \hline -5x = -10 & \text{Add members} \\ x = 2 & \text{Divide by } -5 \end{array}$$

Using one of the *original* equations, $2x + y = 6$, solve for y.

$$\begin{array}{rl} 2x + y = 6 & \text{Choose either equation} \\ 2(2) + y = 6 & \text{Replace } y \text{ with } 2 \\ 4 + y = 6 & \text{Multiply in left member} \\ y = 2 & \text{Subtract 4 from each member} \end{array}$$

The simultaneous solution of the system is (2,2).

> **Note**
> We could have eliminated x by multiplying the first equation by -2 and the second equation by 3 and then adding.

You are now ready to do **B_1**.

B_2 $8x - 3y = 4$
$3x + 2y = -1$

2. $7x + 5y = -9$
$3x - 2y = -8$
To eliminate the y in this system, we must multiply the members of the first equation by 2 and the second equation by 5.

$$\begin{array}{ll} 7x + 5y = -9 & \text{Multiply by 2} \\ 3x - 2y = -8 & \text{Multiply by 5} \end{array} \qquad \begin{array}{rl} 14x + 10y = -18 & \\ 15x - 10y = -40 & \\ \hline 29x = -58 & \text{Add members} \\ x = -2 & \text{Divide by 29} \end{array}$$

Using one of the *original* equations, solve for y.

$$\begin{array}{rl} 3x - 2y = -8 & \text{Choose either equation} \\ 3(-2) - 2y = -8 & \text{Replace } x \text{ with } -2 \\ -6 - 2y = -8 & \text{Multiply in left member} \\ -2y = -2 & \text{Add 6 to each member} \\ y = 1 & \text{Divide each member by } -2 \end{array}$$

The simultaneous solution is the ordered pair $(-2,1)$.

You are now ready to do **B_2**.

> **Note**
> In the previous example, both equations had to be multiplied by a constant to form opposite coefficients of y. We could have eliminated x by multiplying the first equation by 3 and the second equation by -7, forming additive inverse coefficients of 21 and -21.

3. $3x - 4y = 12$
$6x - 8y = -24$
Multiply each member of the first equation by -2.

$$\begin{aligned} 3x - 4y &= 12 \quad \text{Multiply by } -2 \\ \underline{6x - 8y} &\underline{= -24} \end{aligned} \qquad \begin{aligned} -6x + 8y &= -24 \\ \underline{6x - 8y} &\underline{= -24} \\ 0 + 0 &= -48 \quad \text{Add members} \\ 0 &= -48 \quad \text{(False)} \end{aligned}$$

The variables have been eliminated and a *false* statement is obtained. This indicates that there is *no simultaneous* solution and the system is *inconsistent.* The lines are parallel.

You are now ready to do **B₃**.

B₃ $4x + 6y = 3$
$2x + 3y = -2$

4. $4x - 2y = 6$
$2x - y = 3$
Multiply each member of the second equation by -2.

$$\begin{aligned} 4x - 2y &= 6 \\ \underline{2x - y} &\underline{= 3} \quad \text{Multiply by } -2 \end{aligned} \qquad \begin{aligned} 4x - 2y &= 6 \\ \underline{-4x + 2y} &\underline{= -6} \\ 0 + 0 &= 0 \quad \text{Add members} \\ 0 &= 0 \quad \text{(True)} \end{aligned}$$

All variables have again been eliminated and a true statement, $0 = 0$, is obtained. This indicates that any ordered pair that satisfies one equation will also satisfy the other. The system is *dependent*. The lines are one and the same. The system has infinitely many solutions.

You are now ready to do **B₄**. ■

B₄ $x - 6y = 1$
$3x - 18y = 3$

To solve a system of linear equations by addition

1. Multiply the members of one or both equations by a constant that will make the coefficients of one of the variables additive inverses (opposites) of each other.
2. Add the corresponding members of the equations.
3. Solve this new equation for the remaining variable.
4. Substitute the value found in step 3 into either of the original equations and solve this equation for the other variable. The simultaneous solution is the ordered pair of numbers obtained in step 3 and this step.
5. If, when adding in step 2,
   a. both variables are eliminated and a *false statement* is obtained, there are *no solutions* and the system is *inconsistent* (parallel lines).
   b. both variables are eliminated and a *true statement* such as $0 = 0$ is obtained, there are infinitely *many* solutions and the system is *dependent* (same line).
6. If the system has a solution found in step 4, check the solution in both equations.

Answers to section 8-2 margin exercises

A₁ (1,2) **A₂** $\left(-\frac{2}{3}, 3\right)$ **A₃** (1,0) **B₁** (2,−1) **B₂** $\left(\frac{1}{5}, -\frac{4}{5}\right)$ **B₃** parallel lines, no solution, inconsistent **B₄** same line, dependent, infinitely many solutions

Mastery points

Can you

- Solve a system of linear equations by addition?
- Recognize a dependent or an inconsistent system of linear equations while solving by addition?

Exercise 8–2

Directions Solve each system of linear equations by addition. If the system is inconsistent or dependent, so state. See example 8–2 A.

Example $\boxed{A_3}$ $2x = 2 - 5y$
$3x - 5y = 3$

Solution We first must write the equations in form $ax + by = c$ to get like terms in a column.

$$\begin{aligned} 2x + 5y &= 2 && \text{Add 5 to each member} \\ \underline{3x - 5y} &\underline{= 3} && \\ 5x \qquad &= 5 && \text{Add both members} \\ x &= 1 && \text{Divide each member by 5} \end{aligned}$$

Using one of the original equations, solve for y.

$$\begin{aligned} 2x &= 2 - 5y && \text{Choose either equation} \\ 2(1) &= 2 - 5y && \text{Replace } x \text{ with 1} \\ 2 &= 2 - 5y && \text{Multiply in left member} \\ 0 &= -5y && \text{Subtract 2 from each member} \\ y &= 0 && \text{Divide each member by } -5 \end{aligned}$$

The simultaneous solution of the system is (1,0). Check the solution in both equations.

1. $x - y = 1$
$x + y = 5$

2. $x + y = 2$
$3x - y = 10$

3. $3x - 2y = 0$
$x + 2y = 8$

4. $5x - y = -1$
$-5x + 4y = 4$

$\boxed{\textbf{5.}}$ $x = 8 - 4y$
$x - 4y = -2$

6. $x = 2 - y$
$x - y = 6$

7. $3y = 2x - 6$
$-2x = 3y - 2$

8. $4x - 1 = 3y$
$3y + 2 = 3x$

See example 8–2 B.

Example **B₂**

$$8x - 3y = 4$$
$$3x + 2y = -1$$

Solution

$$8x - 3y = 4 \quad \text{Multiply by 2} \qquad 16x - 6y = 8$$
$$3x + 2y = -1 \quad \text{Multiply by 3} \qquad 9x + 6y = -3$$
$$25x = 5 \quad \text{Add members}$$
$$x = \frac{5}{25} = \frac{1}{5} \quad \text{Divide by 25 and reduce}$$

Using one of the original equations, we solve for y.

$$3x + 2y = -1 \quad \text{Choose either equation}$$
$$3\left(\frac{1}{5}\right) + 2y = -1 \quad \text{Replace } x \text{ with } \frac{1}{5}$$
$$\frac{3}{5} + 2y = -1 \quad \text{Multiply in left member}$$
$$2y = -\frac{8}{5} \quad \text{Subtract } \frac{3}{5} \text{ from each member}$$
$$y = -\frac{4}{5} \quad \text{Divide each member by 2}$$

The simultaneous solution of the system is the ordered pair $\left(\frac{1}{5}, -\frac{4}{5}\right)$.

9. $x - y = 3$
$2x + 3y = 6$

10. $3x - 2y = -9$
$2x + y = 1$

11. $5x - y = 4$
$x + 3y = 4$

12. $5x + 2y = 3$
$3x - y = 4$

13. $4x + 7y = 11$
$8x - 3y = -12$

14. $3x - 4y = 31$
$6x + y = -1$

15. $5x - 2y = 4$
$3x + 3y = -6$

16. $x - 2y = 4$
$-x + 2y = -4$

17. $x + 2y = 4$
$x + 4y = 10$

18. $-3x + y = -3$
$3x - y = -1$

19. $2x - 2y = 0$
$4x - 3y = 0$

20. $4x + y = 11$
$2x + 3y = 4$

21. $8x - 4y = 12$
$2x - y = -3$

22. $x - 2y = 1$
$3x - 6y = 3$

23. $\frac{1}{2}x + \frac{1}{3}y = 1$
$\frac{2}{3}x - \frac{1}{4}y = \frac{1}{12}$
(*Hint:* Clear the fractions first.)

24. $\frac{2}{3}x - \frac{1}{4}y = 4$
$\frac{1}{3}x + y = 2$

25. $\frac{1}{2}x + \frac{2}{5}y = \frac{7}{10}$
$\frac{3}{2}x + \frac{6}{5}y = \frac{3}{10}$

26. $\frac{6}{7}x - \frac{3}{5}y = \frac{9}{10}$
$\frac{2}{7}x - \frac{1}{5}y = \frac{5}{10}$

27. $-6x + 3y = 9$
$2x - y = -3$

28. $10x - 5y = 7$
$2x - y = 4$

29. $x + (0.4)y = 3.4$
$(0.6)x - (1.4)y = 0.4$

30. $(0.4)x - (0.7)y = 0.7$
$(0.6)x - (0.5)y = 2.7$

31. Let x represent the width of a rectangle and y represent the length of the rectangle. Write an equation stating that the length is five times the width.

32. The perimeter of the rectangle in exercise 31 is 60 inches. If the perimeter of a rectangle equals twice the width plus twice the length, write an equation for the perimeter of the rectangle.

33. Let x represent the speed of automobile A and y represent the speed of automobile B. Write an equation stating that automobile B travels 20 mph faster than automobile A.

34. If the two automobiles in exercise 33 travel in opposite directions, write an equation that states the two automobiles are 500 miles apart after 3 hours. (*Note:* distance = speed times the time traveled)

35. Let x represent the amount of money Jane invests at 8% and y represent the amount she invests at 7%. Write an equation stating that Jane invests a total of $14,000.

36. In exercise 35, Jane receives a total of $1,000 from her investments. If income equals the amount invested times the rate of interest, write an equation relating Jane's total income to her two investments.

Review exercises

1. Given $2x + y = 3$, solve for x when $y = x + 2$. See sections 1–8 and 2–5.

2. What percent of 40 is 25? See section R–3.

3. 40% of what number is 60? See section R–3.

Directions Factor the following expressions. See sections 4–3 and 4–4.

4. $16x^2 - 4y^2$

5. $9x^2 - 12x + 4$

6. $5y^2 - 6y - 8$

7. Solve the equation $4(3x - 2) + 2x = 6$. See section 2–3.

▣ 8–3 Solutions of systems of linear equations by substitution

A basic property of equality is that if two expressions are equal (represent the same quantity), one expression may replace the other expression in any equation to form an equivalent equation. We use this property to solve systems of equations by a third method, called the **substitution** method. This method is useful when

1. one of the equations is solved for one variable in terms of the other, or
2. one of the equations can *easily* be solved for one variable in terms of the other (usually when the coefficient of the variable is 1).

The following examples demonstrate the method of solving systems of linear equations by substitution.

Example 8–3 A

Solve the following systems of linear equations by substitution.

1. $3x - y = 5$
   $y = 8x$
   Since $y = 8x$ means that y and $8x$ are symbols for the same thing, we replace y with $8x$ (substitute) in the equation $3x - y = 5$ and solve for x.

$$3x - y = 5$$
$$3x - (8x) = 5 \quad \text{Replace } y \text{ with } 8x$$
$$-5x = 5 \quad \text{Subtract in left member}$$
$$x = -1 \quad \text{Divide each member by } -5$$

To find y, replace x with -1 in either of the original equations and solve for y.

$$y = 8x \quad \text{Choose either equation}$$
$$y = 8(-1) \quad \text{Replace } x \text{ with } -1$$
$$y = -8$$

The simultaneous solution of the system of equations is the ordered pair $(-1,-8)$.

A_1 $4x + y = -1$
$y = -3x$

Check:

$3x - y = 5$
$3(-1) - (-8) = 5$ Replace x with -1 and y with -8
$-3 + 8 = 5$
$5 = 5$ (True)

$y = 8x$
$(-8) = 8(-1)$
$-8 = -8$ (True)

You are now ready to do **A_1**.

2. $3x + 2y = 14$
$y = 2x - 7$
Since y and $2x - 7$ are names for the same quantity, replace y with $2x - 7$ in $3x + 2y = 14$ and solve for x.

$3x + 2y = 14$
$3x + 2(2x - 7) = 14$ Replace y with $2x - 7$
$3x + 4x - 14 = 14$ Multiply in left member
$7x - 14 = 14$ Combine like terms
$7x = 28$ Add 14 to each member
$x = 4$ Divide each member by 7

A_2 $2x + 4y = 10$
$y = 3x - 1$

Using the equation $y = 2x - 7$, find y.

$y = 2x - 7$
$y = 2(4) - 7$ Replace x with 4
$y = 8 - 7$ Multiply in left member
$y = 1$ Subtract in right member

The simultaneous solution is the ordered pair (4,1). We will not show a check but you should do this.

You are now ready to do **A_2**.

3. $3x + y = 12$
$2x + 5y = 8$
To use substitution, we must first solve the first equation for y in terms of x.

$3x + y = 12$
$y = 12 - 3x$ Subtract $3x$ from each member

Using $2x + 5y = 8$, we replace y with $12 - 3x$ and solve for x.

$2x + 5y = 8$
$2x + 5(12 - 3x) = 8$ Replace y with $12 - 3x$
$2x + 60 - 15x = 8$ Multiply in left member
$60 - 13x = 8$ Combine like terms
$-13x = -52$ Subtract 60 from each member
$x = 4$ Divide each member by -13

$\boxed{A_3}$ $5x - y = 3$
$4x + 3y = 10$

Replace x with 4 in the equation $y = 12 - 3x$.

$y = 12 - 3x$
$y = 12 - 3(4)$ Replace x with 4
$y = 12 - 12$ Multiply in right member
$y = 0$

The simultaneous solution is the ordered pair (4,0).

You are now ready to do **A_3**.

4. $8x + 2y = 6$
$4x + y = 3$
Solve the second equation for y and substitute.

$4x + y = 3$
$y = 3 - 4x$ Subtract $4x$ from each member

Using $8x + 2y = 6$, we replace y with $3 - 4x$ and solve.

$$\begin{aligned} 8x + 2y &= 6 \\ 8x + 2(3 - 4x) &= 6 && \text{Replace } y \text{ with } 3 - 4x \\ 8x + 6 - 8x &= 6 && \text{Multiply in left member} \\ 6 &= 6 && \text{Combine in left member} \end{aligned}$$

Since $6 = 6$ is a true statement, the system is dependent and there are infinitely many simultaneous solutions (one line).

You are now ready to do **A₄**.

A₄ $x = 4y - 1$
$2x - 8y = -2$

5. $-4x + 2y = 7$
$y = 2x + 9$
Since we have $y = 2x + 9$, we substitute $2x + 9$ for y in the equation $-4x + 2y = 7$ and solve for x.

$$\begin{aligned} -4x + 2y &= 7 \\ -4x + 2(2x + 9) &= 7 && \text{Replace } y \text{ with } 2x + 9 \\ -4x + 4x + 18 &= 7 && \text{Multiply in left member} \\ 18 &= 7 && \text{Combine in left member} \end{aligned}$$

We obtained the *false* statement $18 = 7$. There is no simultaneous solution and the system is inconsistent (parallel lines).

You are now ready to do **A₅**. ■

A₅ $x + 3y = 0$
$3x + 9y = 3$

To solve a system of linear equations by substitution

1. Solve one of the equations for one of the variables in terms of the other (if this is not already done).
2. Substitute the expression obtained in step 1 into the other equation and solve.
3. Substitute the value obtained in step 2 into either equation and solve for the other variable.
4. The simultaneous solution is the ordered pair obtained from steps 2 and 3.
5. If step 2 results in
   a. the variables being eliminated and a true statement is obtained, the system is dependent and there are infinitely many solutions (same line).
   b. the variables being eliminated and a false statement is obtained, the system is inconsistent and there are no simultaneous solutions (parallel lines).

As a final note, when the method of solution for a system of equations is not specified, the following criteria are useful to select a method.

1. The process of addition is generally the easiest.
2. Substitution is most useful when the coefficient of one of the variables is 1 or -1 or one equation is solved for one variable in terms of the other.
3. Graphical solutions are approximations and can be used when exact answers are not necessary or to verify the results that we find algebraically.

Answers to section 8-3 margin exercises

A₁ $(-1,3)$ **A₂** $(1,2)$ **A₃** $(1,2)$ **A₄** dependent, same line, all points in common
A₅ inconsistent, no solution

Mastery points

Can you

- Solve a system of linear equations by substitution?
- Choose an appropriate method for solving a system of linear equations?

Exercise 8–3

Directions Solve each system of linear equations by substitution. If this system is inconsistent or dependent, so state. See example 8–3 A.

Example [A₃] $5x - y = 3$
$4x + 3y = 10$

Solution We solve the first equation for y in terms of x.

$5x - y = 3$
$-y = 3 - 5x$ — Subtract $5x$ from each member
$y = 5x - 3$ — Multiply each member by -1

Replace y with $5x - 3$ in the other equation and solve for x.

$4x + 3y = 10$
$4x + 3(5x - 3) = 10$ — Replace y with $5x - 3$
$4x + 15x - 9 = 10$ — Multiply in left member
$19x - 9 = 10$ — Combine in left member
$19x = 19$ — Add 9 to each member
$x = 1$ — Divide each member by 19

Using $5x - y = 3$, substitute 1 for x and solve for y.

$5x - y = 3$
$5(1) - y = 3$ — Replace x with 1
$5 - y = 3$
$-y = -2$ — Subtract 5 from each member
$y = 2$ — Multiply each member by -1

The simultaneous solution is the ordered pair (1,2).

1. $2x - y = 3$
   $y = 3x$

2. $5x + 2y = 1$
   $y = -3x$

3. $4x - 3y = -5$
   $x = 2y$

4. $3x + y = -11$
   $x = -4y$

[5.] $3x - y = 10$
   $y = x + 2$

6. $2x + 3y = 6$
   $y = x - 3$

[7.] $5x + y = 10$
   $x = 2 - 3y$

8. $2y - x = 3$
   $x = 4y - 1$

9. $-2x + 5y = 17$
   $y = 2x + 5$

10. $3x + y = 10$
$2x + y = 5$

11. $2x + y = 13$
$3x + y = 17$

12. $3y + x = -10$
$3y - x = 4$

13. $2x - y = 2$
$6x - y = 22$

14. $x - y = 3$
$2x + 3y = 11$

15. $2x + y = 3$
$3x - y = -6$

16. $x + 5y = 7$
$2x + 3y = 5$

17. $-3x - y = 6$
$6x + 2y = -12$

18. $3x + y = -3$
$x - 3y = -1$

19. $x - 2y = 6$
$2x + 4y = 4$

20. $5x - 5y = -10$
$x - y = -2$

21. $3x - 7y = 14$
$y = 2$

22. $-5x + 2y = 11$
$x = -3$

23. $2x + y = -3$
$5x - 4y = -1$

24. $5x + 2y = 11$
$7x - y = 4$

25. $x + y = 5$
$3x + 3y = 3$

26. $x + y = 4$
$3x - 5y = 12$

27. $2x + 3y = 5$
$6x - y = 5$

28. $x - 2y = 4$
$3x + 2y = 4$

Directions Solve each system of linear equations by either addition or substitution. Try to choose the most suitable method.

Example $2x - 3y = 2$
$3x + 2y = 3$

Solution Since no variable has a coefficient of 1, we use the addition method of solving the system.

$2x - 3y = 2$	Multiply by 2	$4x - 6y = 4$
$3x + 2y = 3$	Multiply by 3	$9x + 6y = 9$
		$13x = 13$ — Add members
		$x = 1$ — Divide by 13

Replace x with 1 in either equation and solve for y.

$2x - 3y = 2$ — Choose either equation
$2(1) - 3y = 2$ — Replace x with 1
$2 - 3y = 2$
$-3y = 0$ — Subtract 2 from each member
$\frac{-3y}{-3} = \frac{0}{-3}$ — Divide each member by -3
$y = 0$

The simultaneous solution is (1,0). Check the solution.

29. $3x - 2y = -1$
$2x + 2y = 1$

30. $x - y = 2$
$-5x + 2y = -7$

31. $y + 2x = 24$
$x = -6y + 1$

32. $\frac{1}{2}x - y = \frac{7}{2}$
$2x + \frac{1}{3}y = 1$

33. $\frac{y}{3} - \frac{x}{4} = 3$
$\frac{x}{2} + \frac{y}{5} = -2$

34. $y = -3x + 5$
$y = 3x - 5$

35. $x = 2y + 1$
$x = 5y - 11$

36. $2y - 5x = 1$
$6y - 10x = 0$

37. $4x - 3y = 4$
$2x + 2y = 3$

38. $5x + 2y = -5$
$3x - 4y = -16$

39. Let x represent one current in an electrical circuit and y represent a second current. If the first current has twice as many amperes as the second, write an equation stating this.

40. If the sum of the two currents in exercise 39 is 56 amperes, write an equation stating this.

41. A clothier has two kinds of suits. Let x represent the number of suits selling for one price and y represent the number of suits selling for another price. If he has a total of 80 suits, write an equation stating this.

42. In exercise 41, if the cost of the first kind of suit (x) is \$190 per suit and the cost per suit of the second kind (y) is \$250, write an equation stating that the total income from the suits was \$8,400.

Review exercises

1. A 42-foot piece of wood is cut into two pieces. If one piece is 6 feet less than twice the length of the other piece, how long are the pieces of wood? See section 2–4.

2. The length of a rectangle is 1 yard longer than twice its width. If the area of the rectangle is 36 square yards, find the length and width of the rectangle. See section 4–7. (*Hint:* Area = length × width.)

3. Solve the equation $A = \frac{1}{2}h(b + c)$ for b. See section 2–4.

4. Find the slope of the line through the points $(-4,4)$ and $(5,6)$. See section 7–3.

5. Solve the rational equation $\frac{4}{x} - \frac{3}{2x} = 4$. See section 6–4.

6. Solve the inequality $-4 \leq 1 - 5x < 6$. See section 2–7.

8–4 Applications of systems of linear equations

In chapter 2, you learned how to take a verbal statement and translate it into an algebraic equation in one unknown. Many practical problems that can be solved using single equations in one unknown can more easily be solved by translating into *two* equations involving *two* unknowns.

While there is no standard procedure *for solving applied problems,* the following guidelines should be useful.

To solve a word problem using systems of linear equations

1. Read the problem carefully, noting the information given and what you are asked to find.
2. Determine any prior knowledge that may be useful in setting up the equations: formulas, distance-rate-time, interest, and so on. Draw a sketch, if appropriate.
3. Choose two variables, usually x and y, to represent the unknown quantities.
4. Translate separate statements from the verbal statement of the problem into individual equations.
5. Solve the resulting system of equations by one of the methods we have studied.
6. Write the answer—usually a sentence containing the numbers from the simultaneous solution—using the correct units of measure. Check your results in the original statement of the problem.

Example 8–4 A

1. The length of a rectangle is 3 times as long as its width. The perimeter of the rectangle is 40 inches. What are the dimensions of the rectangle?

Note
We need the prior knowledge that the perimeter, P, of a rectangle is given by the formula $P = 2\ell + 2w$, where ℓ is the length and w is the width of the rectangle.

Let ℓ represent the length of the rectangle and w represent the width of the rectangle.

length	is	3 times the width
ℓ	$=$	$3w$

We use the formula for the perimeter, $P = 2\ell + 2w$, and since the perimeter is 40 inches, we have $40 = 2\ell + 2w$. Therefore, we have the system of equations

$$\ell = 3w$$
$$40 = 2\ell + 2w.$$

w

$\ell = 3w$

Using substitution, replace ℓ with $3w$ in the second equation.

$40 = 2(3w) + 2w$ Replace ℓ with $3w$
$40 = 8w$ Combine like terms
$5 = w$ Divide by 8

Substituting 5 for w in the equation $\ell = 3w$, we get

$\ell = 3(5) = 15.$

The rectangle is 15 inches long and 5 inches wide.

Check:

a. The perimeter is 40 inches.

$$2(15) + 2(5) = 40$$
$$30 + 10 = 40$$
$$40 = 40 \quad \text{(True)}$$

b. The length is 3 times the width.

$$15 = 3(5)$$
$$15 = 15 \quad \text{(True)}$$

You are now ready to do **A₁**.

A₁ The length of a rectangle is four times as long as its width. If the perimeter of the rectangle is 50 centimeters, what are the dimensions of the rectangle?

2. A woman has \$10,000, part of which she invests at 11% and the rest at 8% annual interest. If her total yearly income from the two investments is \$980, how much does she invest at each rate?

> **Note**
> The prior knowlege needed for this problem is that Simple interest = Principal × Rate × Time. Time in this example is 1 year. When using this formula, time should be stated in years.

Let x = amount invested at 11% and y = amount invested at 8%.
Then, $(0.11)x$ = interest from the 11% investment for one year,
$(0.08)y$ = interest from the 8% investment for one year.

11% investment	plus	8% investment	is	\$980
$(0.11)x$	$+$	$(0.08)y$	$=$	980

From "A woman has \$10,000 . . . ,"

$x + y = 10{,}000.$

The system of equations is

$$x + y = 10{,}000$$
$$(0.11)x + (0.08)y = 980.$$

Multiply the second equation by 100 to clear the decimal fractions.

$$100(0.11)x + 100(0.08)y = 100(980)$$
$$11x + 8y = 98{,}000$$

We then have the system

$$x + y = 10{,}000 \quad \text{Multiply each term by } (-8) \quad -8x - 8y = -80{,}000$$
$$11x + 8y = 98{,}000. \qquad\qquad\qquad \underline{11x + 8y = 98{,}000}$$
$$3x = 18{,}000 \quad \text{Add equations}$$
$$x = 6{,}000 \quad \text{Divide by 3}$$

Substitute 6,000 for x in $x + y = 10{,}000$.

$$6{,}000 + y = 10{,}000 \quad \text{Replace } x \text{ with } 6{,}000$$
$$y = 4{,}000 \quad \text{Subtract 6,000 from each member}$$

The woman invested \$6,000 at 11% and \$4,000 at 8% interest.

Check:

1. The total yearly income is \$980.

$$(0.11)(6{,}000) + (0.08)(4{,}000) = 980$$
$$660 + 320 = 980$$
$$980 = 980 \quad \text{(True)}$$

A2 Jane Jones invests \$24,000, part at 6% and the rest at 7% annual interest. If her total yearly income is \$1,580, how much did she invest at each rate?

2. The woman has \$10,000.

$$6{,}000 + 4{,}000 = 10{,}000$$
$$10{,}000 = 10{,}000 \quad \text{(True)}$$

You are now ready to do **A2**.

3. The sum of two lengths of wire is 11 meters. If four times the first length is added to the second length, the result is 25 meters. Find the two lengths of wire.

Let $x =$ the first length of wire and $y =$ the second length of wire.

the sum of the two lengths	is	11 meters
$x + y$	$=$	11

four times the first length	added to	the second length	is	25 meters
$4x$	$+$	y	$=$	25

Therefore, we have the system

$$x + y = 11 \quad \text{Multiply each term by } (-1) \qquad -x - y = -11$$
$$4x + y = 25. \qquad\qquad 4x + y = 25$$
$$3x = 14 \quad \text{Add equations}$$
$$x = \frac{14}{3} \quad \text{Divide by 3}$$

Using the first equation $x + y = 11$, substitute $\frac{14}{3}$ for x and solve for y.

$$x + y = 11$$
$$\left(\frac{14}{3}\right) + y = 11 \quad \text{Replace } x \text{ with } \frac{14}{3}$$
$$y = 11 - \frac{14}{3} \quad \text{Subtract } \frac{14}{3} \text{ from each member}$$
$$y = \frac{33}{3} - \frac{14}{3} = \frac{19}{3} \quad \text{Change to common denominator 3 and subtract}$$

A3 The sum of two lengths of a string is 14 feet. If 3 times the length of the shorter piece is added to the longer piece, the result is 20 feet. Find the two lengths of the string.

Thus the two wires have length $\frac{14}{3}$ meters and $\frac{19}{3}$ meters.

Check:

a. The sum of the two lengths is 11.

$$\frac{14}{3} + \frac{19}{3} = 11$$
$$\frac{33}{3} = 11$$
$$11 = 11 \quad \text{(True)}$$

b. Four times the first length added to the second length is 25.

$$4\left(\frac{14}{3}\right) + \frac{19}{3} = 25$$
$$\frac{56}{3} + \frac{19}{3} = 25$$
$$\frac{75}{3} = 25$$
$$25 = 25 \quad \text{(True)}$$

You are now ready to do **A3**.

4. What quantities of silver that are 65% pure and 45% pure must be mixed together to get 100 grams of silver that is 50% pure?

Note
65% pure silver means the metal is 65% silver and 35% of some other metal(s).

Let x = the number of grams of 65% silver and y = the number of grams of 45% silver.

mixed together	to get	100 grams
$x + y$	$=$	100

65% pure silver	mixed together	45% pure silver	to get	100 grams of 50% silver
$(0.65)x$	$+$	$(0.45)y$	$=$	$(0.50)100$

We must now solve the system of equations

$$x + y = 100$$
$$0.65x + 0.45y = 0.50(100).$$

We then have the system of equations

$$x + y = 100$$
$$0.65x + 0.45y = 50.$$

Multiply the second equation by 100 and the first equation by -65 and add.

$$\begin{aligned} x + y &= 100 & &\text{Multiply by } -65 & -65x - 65y &= -6{,}500 \\ 0.65x + 0.45y &= 50 & &\text{Multiply by } 100 & 65x + 45y &= 5{,}000 \\ & & & & -20y &= -1{,}500 \quad \text{Add equations} \\ & & & & y &= 75 \quad \text{Divide by } -20 \end{aligned}$$

Substitute 75 for y in the equation $x + y = 100$ and solve for x.

$$\begin{aligned} x + y &= 100 & & \\ x + (75) &= 100 & &\text{Replace } y \text{ with } 75 \\ x &= 25 & &\text{Subtract 75 from each member} \end{aligned}$$

Then 25 grams of 65% silver must be mixed with 75 grams of 45% silver to get 100 grams of 50% silver.

Check:

a. Mixed together to get 100 grams of silver:

$$\begin{aligned} (75) + (25) &= 100 \\ 100 &= 100 \quad \text{(True)} \end{aligned}$$

b. Quantities of silver 65% and 45% pure mixed together to get 100 grams 50% pure:

$$\begin{aligned} 0.65(25) + 0.45(75) &= 0.50(100) \\ 16.25 + 33.75 &= 50 \\ 50 &= 50 \quad \text{(True)} \end{aligned}$$

You are now ready to do **A_4**.

5. A line whose equation is of the form $y = mx + b$ passes through a point (x,y) if and only if the coordinates of the point satisfy the equation. Find the equation of the line containing the points $(-1,-7)$ and $(2,5)$.

Note
Ordered pairs (x,y) are values of x and y that when substituted into the equation $y = mx + b$ satisfy the equation.

A_4 Two quantities of salt solution that are 45% salt and 70% salt are mixed together to obtain 200 ounces of 60% salt solution. How much of each solution must be mixed together?

A_5 Using a system of equations, find the equation of the line containing the points $(4,-3)$ and $(-2,1)$.

Using $y = mx + b$. When

a. the point is $(-1,-7)$,

$y = mx + b$
$-7 = m(-1) + b$ — Replace y with -7 and x with -1
$-7 = -m + b$
$-m + b = -7$ — Write in form $ax + by = c$

b. the point is $(2,5)$,

$y = mx + b$
$5 = m(2) + b$ — Replace y with 5 and x with 2
$5 = 2m + b$
$2m + b = 5.$ — Write in form $ax + by = c$

Then we have the system of equations

$-m + b = -7$ — Multiply each term by 2 — $-2m + 2b = -14$
$2m + b = 5.$ — $2m + b = 5$ — Add equations
$3b = -9$ — Divide by 3
$b = -3$

Substitute -3 for b in $2m + b = 5$.

$2m + (-3) = 5$ — Replace b with -3
$2m = 8$ — Add 3 to each member
$m = 4$ — Divide each member by 2

The solution of the system is $(m,b) = (4,-3)$. The equation of the line is then

$y = mx + b$
$y = (4)x + (-3)$ — Replace m with 4 and b with -3
$y = 4x - 3.$

Check:

a. Using $(-1,-7)$,

$y = 4x - 3$
$(-7) = 4(-1) - 3$ — Replace y with -7 and x with -1
$-7 = -4 - 3$
$-7 = -7.$ — (True)

b. Using $(2,5)$,

$y = 4x - 3$
$5 = 4(2) - 3$ — Replace y with 5 and x with 2
$5 = 8 - 3$
$5 = 5.$ — (True)

You are now ready to do **A_5**.

6. Two automobiles start at town A and go in opposite directions. After traveling for three hours, they are 351 miles apart. If one automobile is averaging 13 miles per hour faster than the other, what is the average speed of each automobile in miles per hour?

Note
The prior knowledge needed is that distance = rate · time ($d = rt$).

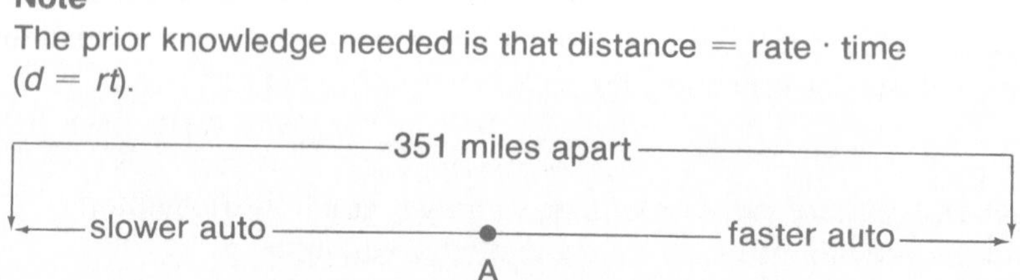

We represent the information given in the following chart. If we let x = the speed of the slower auto and y = the speed of the faster auto,

	r	t	d
Faster auto	y	3	$3y$
Slower auto	x	3	$3x$

$d = r \cdot t$

The two autos traveled a total of 351 miles.

$3x + 3y = 351$
$x + y = 117$ Divide each member by 3

The faster auto traveled 13 mph faster than the slower auto.

$y = x + 13$

The system of equations is

$x + y = 117$
$y = x + 13.$

Using substitution, replace y of equation $x + y = 117$ with $x + 13$.

$x + (x + 13) = 117$
$2x + 13 = 117$ Combine like terms
$2x = 104$ Subtract 13 from each member
$x = 52$ Divide each member by 2

Substitute 52 for x in equation $y = x + 13$.

$y = (52) + 13$ Replace x with 52
$= 65$ Combine in right member

The faster automobile travels 65 mph and the slower automobile travels 52 mph.

Check:

a. One automobile travels 13 mph faster.

$13 + (52) = 65$
$65 = 65$ (True)

b. After 3 hours, they are 351 miles apart.

$3(52) + 3(65) = 351$
$156 + 195 = 351$
$351 = 351$ (True)

You are now ready to do $\mathbf{A_6}$. ■

A_6 Two automobiles start at Greektown in Detroit traveling in opposite directions. After traveling for two hours, the automobiles are 230 miles apart. If one auto averages 11 miles per hour faster than the other, what is the average speed of each auto?

Answers to section 8–4 margin exercises

$\mathbf{A_1}$ $\ell = 20$ cm, $w = 5$ cm $\mathbf{A_2}$ \$10,000 at 6%; \$14,000 at 7% $\mathbf{A_3}$ 3 ft, 11 ft
$\mathbf{A_4}$ 45%, 80 ounces; 70%, 120 ounces $\mathbf{A_5}$ $2x + 3y = -1$ $\mathbf{A_6}$ 52 mph, 63 mph

Mastery points

Can you

- Set up a system of two linear equations in two unknowns for verbal statements?
- Solve the resulting system of equations by a suitable method?
- Check your solution in the word problem?

Exercise 8–4

Directions Solve the following word problems by setting up two linear equations with two unknowns. Check your solutions. See example 8–4 A.

Example $\boxed{A_2}$ Jane Jones invests \$24,000, part at 6% and the rest at 7% annual interest. If her total yearly income is \$1,580, how much did she invest at each rate?

Solution Let x = the amount invested at 6% and y = the amount invested at 7%.
Then, $0.06x$ = income from the 6% investment for 1 year.
$0.07y$ = income from the 7% investment for 1 year.

$0.06x + 0.07y = 1{,}580$ (Total yearly income is \$1,580.)
$x + y = 24{,}000$ (Jane Jones invests \$24,000.)

To clear the decimals, we multiply each member of $0.06x + 0.07y = 1{,}580$ by 100. The system is

$$\begin{aligned} 6x + 7y &= 158{,}000 \\ x + y &= 24{,}000 \quad \text{Multiply by } -6 \end{aligned} \qquad \begin{aligned} 6x + 7y &= 158{,}000 \\ -6x - 6y &= -144{,}000 \\ \hline y &= 14{,}000 \quad \text{Add the members} \end{aligned}$$

Using the equation $x + y = 24{,}000$, we solve for y.

$$\begin{aligned} x + y &= 24{,}000 \\ x + 14{,}000 &= 24{,}000 \quad \text{Replace } y \text{ with } 14{,}000 \\ x &= 10{,}000 \quad \text{Subtract } 14{,}000 \text{ from each member} \end{aligned}$$

Jane Jones invested \$10,000 at 6% and \$14,000 at 7%.

Check a. Total yearly income is \$1,580.

$$\begin{aligned} 0.06x + 0.07y &= 1{,}580 \\ 0.06(10{,}000) + 0.07(14{,}000) &= 1{,}580 \\ 600 + 980 &= 1{,}580 \\ 1{,}580 &= 1{,}580 \quad \text{(True)} \end{aligned}$$

b. Jane Jones invests \$24,000.

$$\begin{aligned} x + y &= 24{,}000 \\ 10{,}000 + 14{,}000 &= 24{,}000 \\ 24{,}000 &= 24{,}000 \quad \text{(True)} \end{aligned}$$

1. The perimeter of a rectangle is 36 meters and the length is 2 meters more than 3 times the width. Find the dimensions.

2. The perimeter of a room is 40 feet, and twice the length increased by three times the width is 48 feet. What are the dimensions?

3. The perimeter of a rectangle is 100 meters. The rectangle is 22 meters longer than it is wide. Find the dimensions in meters.

4. A rectangular field has a length that is 21 yards more than twice the width. The perimeter is 620 yards. What are the dimensions of the field?

5. The length of a room is 2 feet less than twice its width. If its perimeter is 62 feet, what are the dimensions?

See example 8–4 A–2.

6. Phil had $20,000, part of which he invested at 8% interest and the rest at 6%. If his total income from the two investments for one year was $1,460, how much did he invest at each rate?

7. Nancy had $18,000. She invested part of her money at $7\frac{1}{2}$% interest and the rest at 9%. If her income from the two investments was $1,560, how much did she invest at each rate?

8. Rich has $18,000, part of which he invests at 10% interest and the rest at 8%. If his income from each investment was the same, what must he have invested at each rate?

9. Dick has $30,000, part of which he invests at 9% interest and the rest at 7%. If his income from the 7% investment was $820 more than that from the 9% investment, how much was invested at each rate?

10. Lynne made two investments totaling $25,000. On one investment, she made an 18% profit, but on the other investment, she took an 11% loss. If her net gain was $2,470, how much was each investment?

11. Anne made two investments totaling $21,000. One investment made her a 13% profit, but on the other investment, she took a 9% loss. If her net loss was $196, how much was in each investment?

See example 8–4 A–3.

12. A 12-foot board is cut into two pieces so that one piece is 4 feet longer than the other. How long is each piece?

13. A piece of pipe is 19 feet long. The pipe must be cut so that one piece is 5 feet longer than the other piece. What are the lengths of the two pieces of pipe?

14. A 24-foot rope is cut into two pieces so that one piece is twice as long as the other. How long is each piece?

15. The sum of two currents is 80 amperes. If the greater current is 24 amperes more than the lesser current, find their values.

16. A 50-foot extension cord is cut into two pieces so that one piece is 12 feet longer than the other piece. How long is each piece?

17. The sum of the number of teeth on two gears is 64, and their difference is 12. How many teeth are on each gear?

18. Two gears have a total of 83 teeth. One gear has 15 less teeth than the other. How many teeth are on each gear?

19. Two electrical voltages have a total of 126 volts. If one voltage is 32 volts more than the other, find the voltages.

20. The sum of two voltages is 85 and their difference is 32. Find the voltages.

21. The sum of the resistances of two resistors is 24 ohms and their difference is 14 ohms. How many ohms are in each resistor?

22. The resistance of one resistor exceeds that of another resistor by 25 ohms, and their sum is 67 ohms. How many ohms are in each resistor?

23. A clothing store sells suits at $125 and $185 each. The store owners observe that they sold 40 suits for a total of $5,720. How many suits of each type did they sell?

See example 8–4 A–4.

24. A metallurgist wishes to form 2,000 kilograms (kg) of an alloy that is 80% copper. This alloy is to be obtained by fusing some alloy that is 68% copper and some that is 83% copper. How many kilograms of each alloy must be used?

25. An auto mechanic has two bottles of battery acid. One contains a 10% solution and the other a 4% solution. How many cubic centimeters (cc) of each solution must be used to make 120 cubic centimeters of a solution that is 6% acid?

26. A chemist wishes to make 1,000 liters of a 3.5% acid solution by mixing a 2.5% solution with a 4% solution. How many liters of each solution are necessary?

27. If a jeweler wishes to form 12 ounces of 75% pure gold from sources that are 60% and 80% pure gold, how much of each substance must be mixed together to produce this?

28. A pharmacist is able to fill 200 3-grain and 2-grain capsules using 500 grains of a certain drug. How many capsules of each kind does he fill?

29. A drum contains a mixture of antifreeze and water. If 6 liters of antifreeze are added, the mixture will be 90% antifreeze, but if 6 liters of water are added, the mixture will be 70% antifreeze. What is the percentage of antifreeze in the mixture presently in the drum?

30. A druggist has two solutions, one 60% hydrogen peroxide and the other 30% hydrogen peroxide. How many liters of each should be mixed to obtain 30 liters of a solution that is 40% hydrogen peroxide?

31. A solution that is 38% silver nitrate is to be mixed with a solution that is 3% silver nitrate to obtain 100 centiliters (cl) of solution that is 5% silver nitrate. How many centiliters of each solution should be used in the mixture?

See example 8–4 A–5.

32. The line with equation $y = mx + b$ passes through a point (x,y) if and only if the coordinates of the point satisfy the equation. Find the values of m and b so that the line will contain the points $(1,-1)$ and $(2,2)$. Write the equation of the line.

33. Find the values of m and b for the line that passes through the points $(2,1)$ and $(-1,7)$. (Refer to problem 32.) Write the equation of the line.

34. Find the equation of the line that passes through the points $(-1,7)$ and $(2,-2)$.

35. Find the equation of the line that passes through the points $(-2,3)$ and $(3,-7)$.

See example 8–4 A–6.

36. A cyclist and a pedestrian are 20 miles apart. If they travel toward each other, they will meet in 75 minutes, but if they travel in the same direction, the cyclist will overtake the pedestrian in 150 minutes. What are their speeds?

37. Two cars are 100 miles apart. If they drive toward each other, they will meet in 1 hour. If they drive in the same direction, they will meet in 2 hours. Find their speeds.

38. A boat can travel 24 miles downstream in 2 hours and 16 miles upstream in the same length of time. What is the speed of the boat in still water and what is the speed of the current?

39. Jane and Jim leave from a drugstore at the same time, walking in opposite directions. After 1 hour they are 9,680 yards apart. If Jim walked at a rate of 0.5 mph faster than Jane, how fast was each walking in miles per hour? (*Hint:* One mile = 1,760 yards.)

Review exercises

Directions Perform the indicated operations. All exponents are positive. See sections 3–1 and 3–4.

1. $(-4x^2y^3)^3$

2. $\dfrac{x^{-2}y^3}{xy^2}$

3. $4^{-1} + 3^{-1}$

See sections 3–2 and 3–3.

4. $(2x^2 - x + 3) - (x^2 + 4x - 1)$

5. $4x^2(3x^2 + 2x - 3)$

6. $(3y + 2)(3y - 2)$

7. $(4x - 5y)^2$

8. Solve the equation $5(x - 2) = -3(2 - 3x)$. See section 2–3.

9. Solve the quadratic equation $x^2 - 3x - 10 = 0$. See section 4–6.

Chapter 8 lead-in problem

A keypunch operator at a local firm works for \$9 per hour while an entry-level typist works for \$6.50 per hour. The total pay for an 8-hour day is \$476. If there are two more typists than keypunch operators, how many keypunch operators does the firm employ?

Solution

Let x = the number of keypunch operators and y = the number of entry-level typists.
From "there are two more typists than keypunch operators,"

$$y = x + 2.$$

In an 8-hour day, the pay for each

keypunch operator is $8 \cdot 9 = \$72$
typist is $8 \cdot \$6.50 = \$52$.

The table shows the pay for all the workers.

	Number	Pay per worker	Total pay
Keypunch operators	x	72	$72x$
Typists	y	52	$52y$

From "The total pay for an 8-hour day is \$476,"

$$72x + 52y = 476.$$

We must solve the system of equations

$$y = x + 2$$
$$72x + 52y = 476.$$

Using substitution, substitute $x + 2$ for y in the second equation.

$$72x + 52y = 476$$
$$72x + 52(x + 2) = 476 \quad \text{Replace } y \text{ with } x + 2$$
$$72x + 52x + 104 = 476 \quad \text{Distribute in left member}$$
$$124x + 104 = 476 \quad \text{Combine in left member}$$
$$124x = 372 \quad \text{Subtract 104 from each member}$$
$$x = 3 \quad \text{Divide each member by 124}$$

There are 3 keypunch operators working for the firm.

Chapter 8 summary

1. A **system of linear equations** consists of two or more linear equations in the same variables. We have limited the number of variables to two.
2. A **simultaneous solution** of a system of two linear equations is the ordered pair (x,y) that is a solution of both equations.
3. A **graphical solution** to a system of two linear equations is found by estimating the coordinates of the point of intersection.
4. A **consistent** and **independent** system of two linear equations in two variables has one solution.
5. An **inconsistent** system of equations has no solution. (parallel lines)
6. A **dependent** system of equations has an unlimited number of solutions. (same line)
7. A system of equations can be solved by addition or substitution when an exact answer is required.

Chapter 8 review

[8–1]

Directions Solve the following systems by graphing. State your answer to the tenth's position. All answers in the back of the book will be given exactly. If the system is inconsistent or dependent, so state.

1. $x + y = 4$
$x - y = 2$

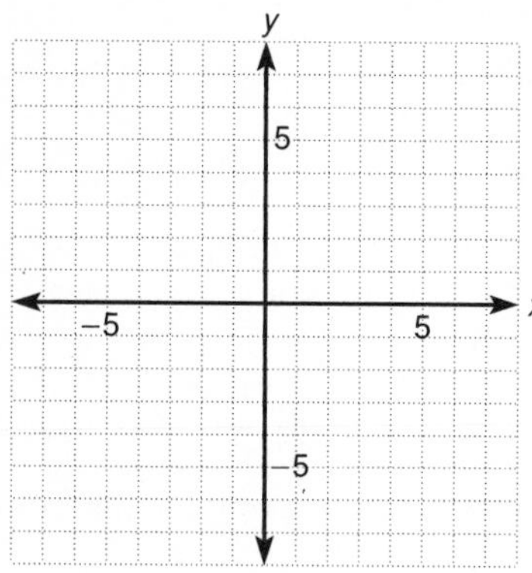

2. $x - 2y = 0$
$2x - y = 6$

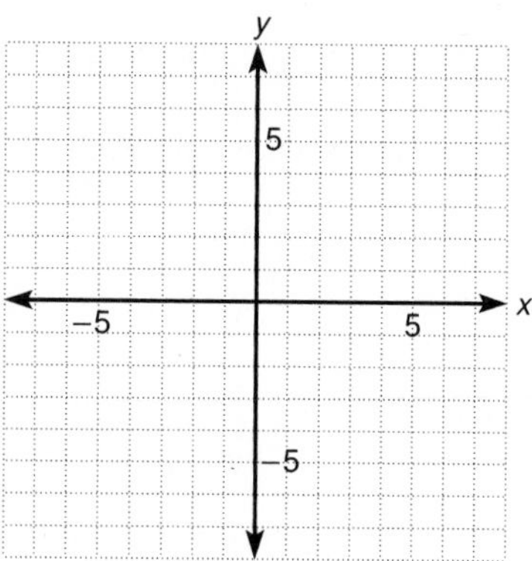

3. $3x - y = 3$
$6x - 2y = -6$

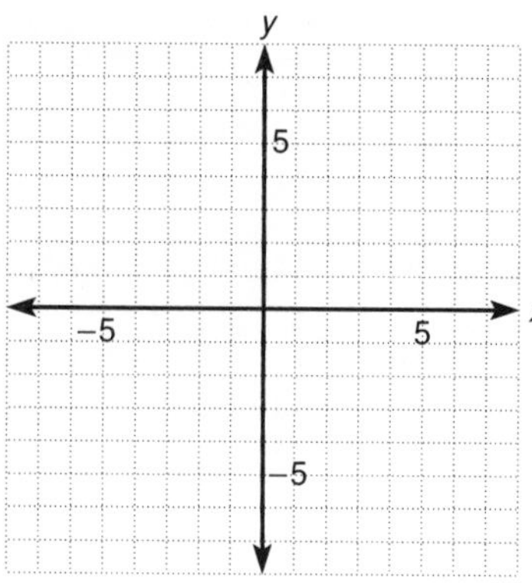

4. $x - y = 4$
$-3x + 3y = -12$

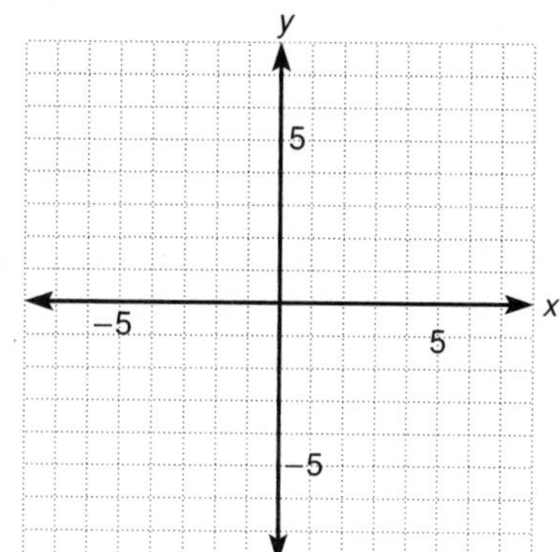

[8–2]

Directions Solve the following systems by addition. If a system is inconsistent or dependent, so state.

5. $x - 2y = 3$
$x + y = 3$

6. $2x + 3y = 1$
$-x + y = 2$

7. $x + 3y = 6$
$2x + 6y = -6$

8. $\frac{1}{2}x + \frac{1}{4}y = \frac{7}{4}$
$\frac{2}{3}x - \frac{1}{3}y = \frac{13}{3}$

9. $(0.3)x - (0.2)y = 1.1$
$(0.3)x + (0.2)y = 1.9$

10. $2x - y = 3$
$3x + y = 7$

[8–3]

Directions Solve the following systems by substitution. If a system is inconsistent or dependent, so state.

11. $x = y + 2$
$2x - 3y = 1$

12. $y = 2x - 1$
$6x - 4y = -5$

13. $x + y = 4$
$x - y = 2$

14. $x - y = 5$
$3x + 2y = 10$

15. $2x - y = 4$
$4x + 3y = 8$

16. $3y - x = 2$
$9y + 3x = 6$

Directions Solve the following systems of equations by either addition or substitution. If the system is inconsistent or dependent, so state.

17. $y = 3x + 1$
$y = -2x - 5$

18. $y - 2x = 7$
$2y + 2x = 5$

19. $3x - 5y = 2$
$2x + 3y = 4$

20. $4x - 3y = 1$
$8x - 6y = 0$

[8–4]

Directions Solve the following problems by setting up two linear equations with two unknowns.

21. The perimeter of a rectangle is 64 feet. Find the dimensions if three times the width is four less than the length.

22. Bruce made two investments totaling $18,000. On one investment, he made a 14% profit, but on the other investment, he took a 23% loss. If his net loss was $440, how much was in each investment?

23. Four times the number of teeth on a first gear is 6 less than the number of teeth on a second gear. If the total number of teeth on both gears is 66, how many teeth are on each gear?

24. A chemist wishes to make 120 milliliters (ml) of a 75% acid solution by mixing a 60% solution with an 80% solution. How many milliliters of each solution are necessary?

NAME

CLASS/SECTION DATE

Chaper 8 cumulative test

Directions Evaluate each of the following.

[3–4] **1.** -4^{-3}

[3–4] **2.** $\left(\frac{3}{4}\right)^{-1}$

[3–4] **3.** $\left(\frac{3}{5}+\frac{1}{8}\right)^{0}$

[3–4] **4.** $(-5)^{-2}$

[3–4] **5.** $5^{-1}+3^{-1}$

[1–8] **6.** Evaluate the expression $\frac{ab-bc}{a}$, when $a=\frac{1}{2}$, $b=\frac{2}{3}$, and $c=\frac{3}{4}$.

Directions Completely factor the following expressions.

[4–1] **7.** $3a^3+15a^2+27a$

[4–4] **8.** x^2-121

[4–5] **9.** $ax+ay-5x-5y$

[4–3] **10.** $3a^2-5ab-2b^2$

[4–4] **11.** $7x^3-7x$

[4–3] **12.** $5b^2-22b+8$

Directions Perform the indicated operations and simplify the results.

[6–1] **13.** $\frac{4x}{5y}\div\frac{24x^2}{15y^3}$

[6–2] **14.** $\frac{5}{x^2-9x}-\frac{3}{x}$

[3–3] **15.** $(-9x^2y^3z^3)^2$

[5–3] **16.** $\frac{36x^3y^2-56xy^3}{4xy}$

[6–1] **17.** $\frac{a^2-8a}{a^2-a-56}\cdot\frac{a^2-49}{7a}$

[3–3] **18.** $(5x-3y)^2$

[5–3] **19.** $(8y^2+10y-42)\div(4y-7)$

Directions Find the solution(s) of the following equations.

[6–5] **20.** $\frac{4a-1}{4}=\frac{5a+2}{7}$

[4–6] **21.** $x^2=-9x$

[6–5] **22.** $\frac{3}{4x} - 2 = \frac{5}{3x} + 1$

[4–6] **23.** $7x^2 + 4x = 3$

Directions Evaluate the following.

[1–6] **24.** $|-6|$

[1–6] **25.** $-\left|-\frac{1}{3}\right|$

[1–6] **26.** $\left|\frac{4}{5}\right|$

Directions Solve the following systems of equations by the appropriate method. If the system is inconsistent or dependent, so state.

[8–3] **27.** $3y - x = 2$
$8y + x = 20$

[8–3] **28.** $4x - y = 6$
$3x + 2y = -1$

[8–3] **29.** $5y - 2x = -12$
$y = -3x + 1$

[8–3] **30.** $x - 2y = -6$
$3x - 6y = 1$

[8–4] **31.** The sum of two numbers is 25. If one number is 1 more than three times the other, what are the numbers? (Solve by system of equations.)

[8–4] **32.** The sum of two numbers is 79. The difference between the two numbers is 5. Find the numbers. (Solve by system of equations.)

[4–7] **33.** The sum of the squares of two consecutive integers is 61. What are the numbers?

[4–7] **34.** The square of a number is equal to five times that number. Find the number.

[6–6] **35.** The sum of a number and twice its reciprocal is 3. Find the number.

[6–6] **36.** A tank can be filled in four hours by pipe *A* and in five hours by pipe *B*. How long will it take to fill the tank if both pipes are open?

[2–4] **37.** The length of a rectangle is 1 inch less than twice its width. If the perimeter is 40 inches, what are the dimensions of the rectangle?

CHAPTER

9

Roots and Radicals

Roger has a ladder that will extend to a length of 21 feet. For the ladder to be safe to climb on, it must be placed 7 feet away from the house. The roof is 20 feet above the ground. Will the ladder be able to reach the roof safely? If not, how far up will the ladder reach? (Leave your answer rounded to one decimal place.)

Proficiency check

[1–8] **1.** Evaluate the following expressions if $a = 3$, $b = 4$, and $c = 5$.
a. $a^2 + b^2$

b. $c^2 - a^2$

[3–2] **2.** Perform the indicated addition and subtraction.
a. $b^2 + b - 2b^2 + 3b$

b. $3xy^2 - 4x^2y^2 + 5x^2y^2 - 3xy^2$

[2–3] **3.** Find the solution of the following equations.
a. $2x + 5 = x + 8$

b. $4a^2 + 5a = (2a + 1)^2$

[3–3] **4.** Perform the indicated multiplication and simplify.
a. $3a(2a - 4)$

b. $5x^2y(3xy^3 - 4x^2y^2 + y^5)$

c. $(2a - b)(2a + b)$

d. $(4x + y)(x - 2y)$

9–1 Principal roots

Square root

In chapter 4, quadratic equations were solved by factoring, but many quadratic equations, such as

$$x^2 - 7 = 0 \text{ or } x^2 + 3x + 1 = 0,$$

will not factor over the set of rational numbers. We need to be able to solve equations that involve a squared variable. Therefore, we want a process that is the inverse of squaring a number.

In chapter 1, we discussed how to square a number. Recall the following method:

$$\text{If } x = 3, \quad \text{then } x^2 = (3)^2 = (3)(3) = 9.$$
$$\text{If } x = -3, \text{ then } x^2 = (-3)^2 = (-3)(-3) = 9.$$

Reversing the process, we ask the following question:

$$\text{If } x^2 = 9, \text{ then what number is } x \text{ equal to?}$$

This inverse operation is called *finding the square root of a number.*

> **Definition**
> For every pair of real numbers a and b, if $a^2 = b$, then a is called a square root of b.
>
> **Concept**
> A square root of a number is one of two equal factors of the number.

A_1 $\sqrt{4}$

From this discussion and the definition of square root, we can see that the answer to the question we asked,

If $x^2 = 9$, then what number is x equal to?

is 3 or -3 since $(3)^2 = 9$ and $(-3)^2 = 9$. To distinguish between the two square roots, we define the *principal square root* of a positive number to be positive. Thus, if $x = \sqrt{9}$, then $x = 3$ is the answer to our question and we say

$$\sqrt{9} = 3 \text{ (principal square root).}$$

A_2 $\sqrt{16}$

The parts of the principal square root are

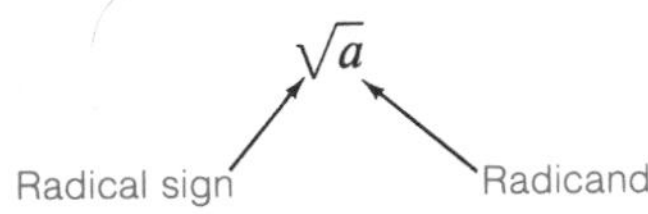

A_3 $\sqrt{64}$

The entire expression is called a *radical* and is read "the principal square root of a."

Example 9–1 A

Find the principal square root.

1. $\sqrt{16} = 4$, since $4 \cdot 4 = 4^2 = 16$.

You are now ready to do **A₁**.

2. $\sqrt{49} = 7$, since $7 \cdot 7 = 7^2 = 49$.

You are now ready to do **A₂**.

3. $\sqrt{25} = 5$, since $5 \cdot 5 = 5^2 = 25$.

You are now ready to do **A₃**.

4. $\sqrt{36} = 6$, since $6 \cdot 6 = 6^2 = 36$.

You are now ready to do **A₄**.

5. $\sqrt{0} = 0$, since $0 \cdot 0 = 0^2 = 0$.

You are now ready to do **A₅**.

A_4 $\sqrt{9}$

A_5 $\sqrt{1}$

> **Note**
> In the examples, 16, 49, 25, and 36 are called **perfect-square integers** because their square roots are integers. ■

Whenever we wish to express the negative value of the square root of a number, we use the $-\sqrt{}$ symbol. In our first example, $-\sqrt{9}$ would indicate that we want the negative square root value. That is, $-\sqrt{9} = -3$.

B_1 $-\sqrt{64}$

Example 9–1 B

Find the indicated root.

1. $-\sqrt{16} = -4$ Negative square root value

You are now ready to do **B₁**.

B₂ $-\sqrt{4}$

2. $-\sqrt{49} = -7$ Negative square root value

You are now ready to do **B_2**. ■

> **Summary of square roots**
>
> If a is any nonnegative number, then
>
> 1. $\sqrt{a}$ is the nonnegative square root of a.
> 2. $-\sqrt{a}$ is the negative square root of a.
> 3. $\sqrt{0} = 0$.

C₁ $\sqrt{5}$

Our first examples of finding the square root of a number have dealt only with perfect-square integers. We shall now try to find the $\sqrt{2}$. We could use 1.414 but when we square 1.414, we do not get 2 as an answer. We can show that no matter how many decimal places the answer is carried to, when the result is squared, it will be close to, but not equal to, 2. The $\sqrt{2}$ is called an **irrational number** because it has the property that it can never be expressed as a terminating or a repeating decimal number. Another number that is irrational is π, which is used in geometric formulas involving circles.

C₂ $\sqrt{19}$

Whenever you work with irrational numbers in a problem, you may have to approximate the number to as many decimal places as are needed in the problem by using a calculator or a table of values.

C₃ $\sqrt{20}$

Example 9–1 C

For the following irrational numbers, find the decimal approximation to 3 decimal places by using a calculator.

1. $\sqrt{3} \approx 1.732$

You are now ready to do **C_1**.

C₄ $-\sqrt{30}$

> **Note**
>
> "$\approx$" is read "is approximately equal to" and is used when our answer is not exact. Square roots of integers that are not perfect squares will be irrational.

2. $\sqrt{17} \approx 4.123$

You are now ready to do **C_2**.

3. $\sqrt{35} \approx 5.916$

C₅ $-\sqrt{77}$

You are now ready to do **C_3**.

4. $-\sqrt{41} \approx -6.403$

You are now ready to do **C_4**.

5. $\sqrt{50} \approx 7.071$

You are now ready to do **C_5**.

C₆ $\sqrt{99}$

6. $-\sqrt{80} \approx -8.944$

You are now ready to do **C_6**. ■

Not all real numbers have a rational or an irrational square root. Consider the following:

$$\sqrt{-4} = \text{what?}$$

We know that all real numbers are either positive, negative, or zero. If we square a real number, the product is never negative. Hence, there is no real number that when squared produces a negative answer. *The square root of a negative number does not exist in the set of real numbers.*

Example 9–1 D

Suppose an automotive engineer wishes to determine the diameter of the cylinder bore (D) required to produce H horsepower from N cylinders of an engine that is turning 1,000 rpm. The engineer will use the formula

$$D = \sqrt{\frac{H}{(0.4)\,N}}$$

What would be the bore diameter (in inches) required to produce 40 horsepower at 1,000 rpm from a 4-cylinder engine?

We substitute 40 for H and 4 for N.

$$D = \sqrt{\frac{(40)}{(0.4)(4)}} = \sqrt{\frac{40}{1.6}} = \sqrt{25} = 5$$

Therefore, we need a bore diameter of 5 inches. ■

*n*th roots (optional)

The concept of square root can be extended to find cube roots (third root of a number), fourth roots, fifth roots, and so on. A cube root is one of three equal factors of a number. The symbol that is used to express the principal cube root is $\sqrt[3]{}$. The 3 is called the **index** of the radical expression. The index denotes what root we are looking for. The principal fourth root would be indicated by $\sqrt[4]{}$. General notation for the principal nth root would be $\sqrt[n]{}$, where n is a natural number greater than 1.

> **The principal *n*th root**
>
> The principal nth root of number a, denoted by
>
> $$\sqrt[n]{a},$$
>
> is one of n equal factors such that $\sqrt[n]{a} = b$ and
>
> $$\overbrace{b \cdot b \cdot b \cdots b}^{n \text{ factors}} = b^n = a,$$
>
> *where* n *is a natural number greater than 1.*

The parts of the principal nth root are

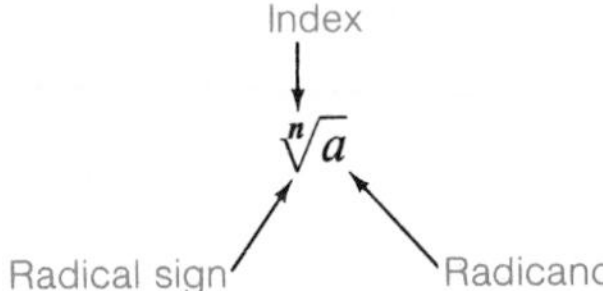

Note
If there is no index associated with a radical symbol, it is understood to be 2.

F_1 $\sqrt[3]{125}$

F_2 $\sqrt[3]{-8}$

F_3 $\sqrt[3]{64}$

F_4 $\sqrt[3]{-1}$

F_5 $\sqrt[3]{-64}$

F_6 $\sqrt[4]{11}$

F_7 $\sqrt[5]{-7}$

F_8 $\sqrt[3]{-5}$

F_9 $\sqrt{-25}$

Example 9–1 E

1. $\sqrt[4]{x}$ is read "the principal fourth root of x."
2. $\sqrt[7]{a}$ is read "the principal seventh root of a."
3. $\sqrt[3]{y}$ is read "the principal cube root of y."
4. $\sqrt[5]{32} = 2$, since $2 \cdot 2 \cdot 2 \cdot 2 \cdot 2 = 2^5 = 32$.
5. $\sqrt[3]{27} = 3$, since $3 \cdot 3 \cdot 3 = 3^3 = 27$.
6. $\sqrt[3]{-8} = -2$, since $(-2)(-2)(-2) = (-2)^3 = -8$. ■

If we exclude even roots of negative numbers, which do not exist in the set of real numbers, we can extend our idea of principal root to all other roots by saying: **the principal *n*th root** *of a number, denoted by* $\sqrt[n]{}$, *has the same sign as the number itself.*

Example 9–1 F

Find the indicated root.

1. $\sqrt[4]{16} = 2$, since $2 \cdot 2 \cdot 2 \cdot 2 = 2^4 = 16$.

You are now ready to do $\mathbf{F_1}$.

2. $\sqrt[3]{-27} = -3$, since $(-3)(-3)(-3) = (-3)^3 = -27$.

You are now ready to do $\mathbf{F_2}$.

3. $\sqrt[4]{81} = 3$, since $3 \cdot 3 \cdot 3 \cdot 3 = 3^4 = 81$.

You are now ready to do $\mathbf{F_3}$.

4. $\sqrt[5]{-32} = -2$, since $(-2)(-2)(-2)(-2)(-2) = (-2)^5 = -32$.

You are now ready to do $\mathbf{F_4}$.

5. $\sqrt[3]{-125} = -5$, since $(-5)(-5)(-5) = (-5)^3 = -125$.

You are now ready to do $\mathbf{F_5}$.

6. $\sqrt[3]{11} \approx 2.224$ (rounded to three decimal places).

You are now ready to do $\mathbf{F_6}$.

7. $\sqrt[3]{-30} \approx -3.107$ (rounded to three decimal places).

You are now ready to do $\mathbf{F_7}$.

8. $\sqrt[5]{-14} \approx -1.695$ (rounded to three decimal places).

You are now ready to do $\mathbf{F_8}$.

9. $\sqrt{-16}$ Does not exist in the set of real numbers.

You are now ready to do $\mathbf{F_9}$. ■

Answers to section 9–1 margin exercises

A_1 2 A_2 4 A_3 8 A_4 3 A_5 1 B_1 −8 B_2 −2 C_1 2.236 C_2 4.359 C_3 4.472 C_4 −5.477 C_5 −8.775 C_6 9.950 F_1 5 F_2 −2 F_3 4 F_4 −1 F_5 −4 F_6 1.821 F_7 −1.476 F_8 −1.710 F_9 does not exist in the set of real numbers

Mastery points

Can you

- Find the principal square root of a perfect-square integer?
- Find the principal root of a number?
- Find the decimal approximation from the table inside the front cover of the book or with a calculator for a root that is an irrational number?

Exercise 9–1

Directions Find the indicated root. See examples 9–1 A and B.

Example B₂ $-\sqrt{4}$

Solution $-\sqrt{4} = -2$ Since $2 \cdot 2 = 4$ and we want the negative value

1. $\sqrt{100}$
2. $\sqrt{36}$
3. $\sqrt{25}$
4. $\sqrt{64}$
5. $-\sqrt{144}$
6. $-\sqrt{81}$
7. $-\sqrt{121}$
8. $-\sqrt{16}$

Directions Find the decimal approximation of the indicated square root, to three decimal places, using a calculator. See example 9–1 C.

Examples C_3 $\sqrt{20}$

Solutions ≈ 4.472 Principal square root

C_5 $-\sqrt{77}$

≈ -8.775 Negative square root

9. $\sqrt{18}$
10. $\sqrt{24}$
11. $\sqrt{41}$
12. $\sqrt{47}$
13. $-\sqrt{52}$
14. $-\sqrt{10}$

Directions Solve the following problems. See example 9–1 D.

15. The current I (amperes) in a circuit is found by the formula $I = \sqrt{\dfrac{\text{watts}}{\text{ohms}}}$. What is the current of a circuit that has 3 ohms resistance and uses 1,728 watts?

16. What is the current of a circuit that has 2 ohms resistance and uses 450 watts? (Refer to exercise 15.)

17. The slant height, S, of a right circular cone is found by the formula $S = \sqrt{r^2 + h^2}$, where r is the radius of the base and h is the height of the cone. What is the slant height of a right circular cone whose base radius is 5 units and whose height is 12 units?

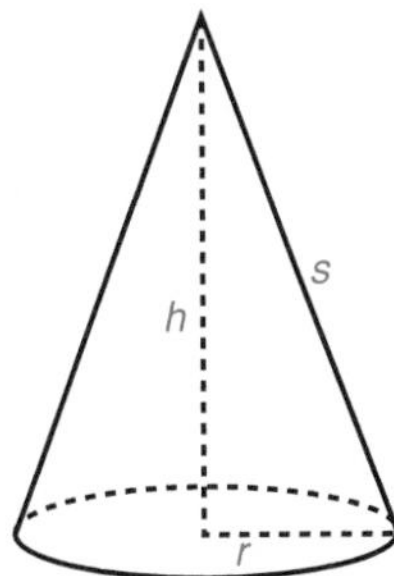

18. What is the slant height of a right circular cone whose base radius is 3 units and whose height is 4 units? (Refer to exercise 17.)

The following problems use an important property of right triangles called the **Pythagorean Theorem.**

In a right triangle, the square of the length of the hypotenuse (the side opposite the right angle) is equal to the sum of the squares of the lengths of the two legs (the sides that form the right angle). If c is the length of the hypotenuse and a and b are the lengths of the legs, this property can be stated as:

$c^2 = a^2 + b^2$ or $c = \sqrt{a^2 + b^2}$;
also as $a^2 = c^2 - b^2$ or $a = \sqrt{c^2 - b^2}$;
and as $b^2 = c^2 - a^2$ or $b = \sqrt{c^2 - a^2}$.

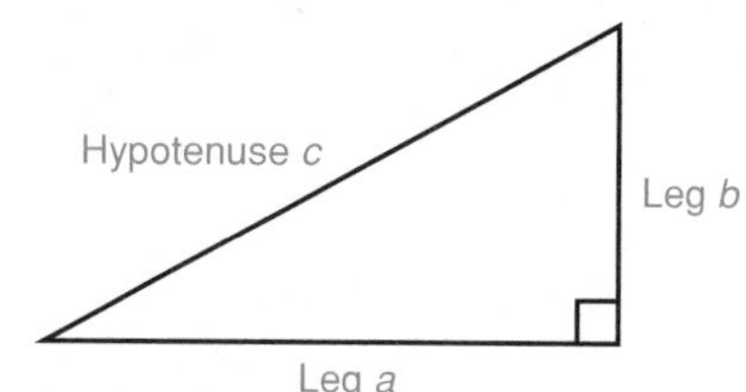

Examples a. Find the length of the hypotenuse of a right triangle whose legs are 6 centimeters and 8 centimeters.

Solutions a. We want to find c when $a = 6$ cm and $b = 8$ cm. By the Pythagorean Theorem,

$$\begin{aligned} c &= \sqrt{a^2 + b^2} \\ &= \sqrt{6^2 + 8^2} \\ &= \sqrt{36 + 64} \\ &= \sqrt{100} = 10. \end{aligned}$$

Hence, $c = 10$ cm.

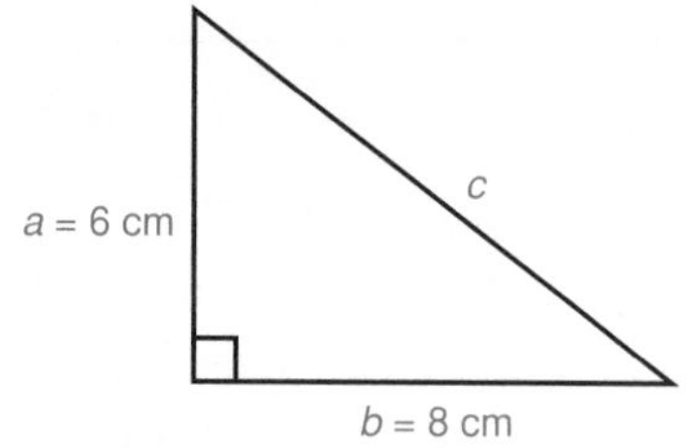

b. Find the second leg of a right triangle whose hypotenuse has length 13 inches and whose first leg is 5 inches long.

b. We want to find b given that $c = 13$ in. and $a = 5$ in. Using one of the forms of the theorem,

$$\begin{aligned} b &= \sqrt{c^2 - a^2} \\ &= \sqrt{13^2 - 5^2} \\ &= \sqrt{169 - 25} \\ &= \sqrt{144} = 12. \end{aligned}$$

Hence, $b = 12$ in.

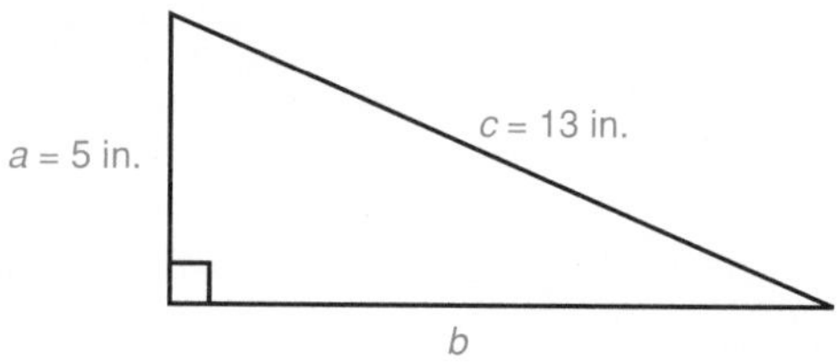

Directions In the following right triangles, find the length of the unknown side.

19. $a = 3$ m, $b = 4$ m

20. $a = 8$ ft, $c = 10$ ft

21. $a = 12$ in., $b = 5$ in.

22. $a = 15$ cm, $b = 8$ cm

23. $a = 6$ yd, $c = 10$ yd

24. $b = 16$ m, $c = 20$ m

25. $a = 12$ mm, $b = 16$ mm

26. $a = 10$ in., $b = 24$ in.

Optional
Directions Find the indicated root. See example 9–1 F.

Example F5 $\sqrt[3]{-64}$

Solution $\sqrt[3]{-64} = -4$ since $(-4)^3 = -64$

27. $\sqrt[3]{8}$

28. $\sqrt[3]{27}$

29. $\sqrt[3]{125}$

30. $\sqrt[3]{64}$

31. $\sqrt[3]{-27}$

32. $\sqrt[3]{-125}$ 33. $\sqrt[4]{16}$ **34.** $\sqrt[4]{81}$ **35.** $-\sqrt[4]{81}$ **36.** $-\sqrt[4]{625}$

37. $\sqrt[5]{32}$ **38.** $\sqrt[6]{64}$ **39.** $-\sqrt[5]{243}$ **40.** $\sqrt[5]{-243}$ **41.** $\sqrt[10]{1}$

42. $\sqrt[14]{1}$ 43. $\sqrt[9]{-1}$ **44.** $\sqrt[15]{-1}$

Directions Solve the following problems. See example 9–1 D.

45. The formula for finding the length of an edge, e, of a cube when the volume, v, is known is $e = \sqrt[3]{v}$. What is the length of the edge of a cube whose volume is 729 cubic units?

46. What is the length of the edge of a cube whose volume is 216 cubic units? (Refer to exercise 45.)

Review exercises

Directions Rewrite the following numbers in prime factor form. See section R–1.

1. 9 **2.** 12 **3.** 8 **4.** 40 **5.** 50 **6.** 81 **7.** 64 **8.** 16

9–2 Product property for radicals

Multiplying square roots

In this section, we are going to develop properties for simplifying radicals. Consider the following example:

$$\sqrt{4} \cdot \sqrt{25} = 2 \cdot 5 = 10.$$

We also observe that

$$\sqrt{4 \cdot 25} = \sqrt{100} = 10.$$

From our example, we can conclude that

$$\sqrt{4} \cdot \sqrt{25} = \sqrt{4 \cdot 25}.$$

We can generalize the product property for square roots as follows:

Product property for square roots

For all nonnegative real numbers a and b,

$$\sqrt{a} \cdot \sqrt{b} = \sqrt{ab}.$$

Concept

The product of two square roots equals the square root of their product.

A_1 $\sqrt{5}\sqrt{6}$

A_2 $\sqrt{7}\sqrt{10}$

A_3 $\sqrt{6}\sqrt{x}$

A_4 $\sqrt{2}\sqrt{a}\sqrt{b}$

B_1 $\sqrt{8}$

B_2 $\sqrt{40}$

Example 9–2 A

Perform the indicated operations. Assume that all variables represent nonnegative real numbers.

1. $\sqrt{3}\sqrt{5} = \sqrt{3 \cdot 5} = \sqrt{15}$

You are now ready to do **A_1**.

2. $\sqrt{6}\sqrt{7} = \sqrt{6 \cdot 7} = \sqrt{42}$

You are now ready to do **A_2**.

3. $\sqrt{3}\sqrt{a} = \sqrt{3a}$

You are now ready to do **A_3**.

4. $\sqrt{x}\sqrt{y}\sqrt{z} = \sqrt{xyz}$

You are now ready to do **A_4**. ■

The product of square roots is equal to the square root of the product

Simplifying square roots

An important use of the product property is in simplifying radicals. Consider the following example:

Since 12 can be factored into $4 \cdot 3$, by the product property, we can write

$$\sqrt{12} = \sqrt{4 \cdot 3} = \sqrt{4}\sqrt{3} = 2\sqrt{3}.$$

We are able to simplify the radical because the radicand contains a perfect-square integer factor, 4. In our example, $2\sqrt{3}$ is called the *simplified form* of $\sqrt{12}$.

Simplifying the principal square root

1. If the radicand is a perfect square, write the corresponding square root.
2. If possible, factor the radicand so that at least one factor is a perfect square. Write the corresponding square root as a coefficient of the radical.
3. The square root is in simplest form when the radicand has no perfect-square factors other than 1.

Example 9–2 B

Simplify the following expressions. Assume that all variables represent nonnegative real numbers.

1. $\sqrt{50} = \sqrt{25 \cdot 2}$ — 50 factors to $25 \cdot 2$

$= \sqrt{25}\sqrt{2}$ — $\sqrt{ab} = \sqrt{a} \cdot \sqrt{b}$

$= 5\sqrt{2}$ — $\sqrt{25} = 5$

You are now ready to do **B_1**.

2. $\sqrt{28} = \sqrt{4 \cdot 7}$ — 28 factors to $4 \cdot 7$

$= \sqrt{4}\sqrt{7}$ — $\sqrt{ab} = \sqrt{a} \cdot \sqrt{b}$

$= 2\sqrt{7}$ — $\sqrt{4} = 2$

You are now ready to do **B_2**.

3. $\sqrt{9a} = \sqrt{9 \cdot a}$
$= \sqrt{9}\sqrt{a}$ — $\sqrt{ab} = \sqrt{a} \cdot \sqrt{b}$
$= 3\sqrt{a}$ — $\sqrt{9} = 3$

You are now ready to do **B_3**.

B_3 $\sqrt{3x^2}$

4. $\sqrt{x^2y} = \sqrt{x^2 \cdot y}$
$= \sqrt{x^2}\sqrt{y}$ — $\sqrt{ab} = \sqrt{a} \cdot \sqrt{b}$
$= x\sqrt{y}$ — $\sqrt{x^2} = x$ (when x is a nonnegative number)

You are now ready to do **B_4**.

B_4 $\sqrt{ab^2}$

5. $\sqrt{a^3} = \sqrt{a^2 \cdot a}$ — a^3 can be written $a^2 \cdot a$
$= \sqrt{a^2}\sqrt{a}$ — $\sqrt{ab} = \sqrt{a} \cdot \sqrt{b}$
$= a\sqrt{a}$ — $\sqrt{a^2} = a$

You are now ready to do **B_5**.

B_5 $\sqrt{x^3}$

6. $\sqrt{y^5} = \sqrt{y^4 \cdot y}$ — y^5 can be written $y^4 \cdot y$
$= y^2\sqrt{y}$ — Divide 4 by 2 (the index) $\sqrt{y^4} = y^2$

You are now ready to do **B_6**.

B_6 $\sqrt{a^7}$

7. $\sqrt{a^3b^4} = \sqrt{a^2 \cdot a \cdot b^4}$ — a^3 can be written $a^2 \cdot a$
$= a\sqrt{a} \cdot b^2$ — $\sqrt{a^2} = a$ and $\sqrt{b^4} = b^2$
$= ab^2\sqrt{a}$ — Commutative property

You are now ready to do **B_7**.

B_7 $\sqrt{x^2y^3}$

8. $\sqrt{2}\sqrt{6} = \sqrt{2 \cdot 6}$ — $\sqrt{a} \cdot \sqrt{b} = \sqrt{ab}$
$= \sqrt{12}$ — Multiply in radicand
$= \sqrt{4 \cdot 3}$ — 12 can be written $4 \cdot 3$
$= 2\sqrt{3}$ — $\sqrt{4} = 2$

You are now ready to do **B_8**.

B_8 $\sqrt{3}\sqrt{12}$

9. $\sqrt{10}\sqrt{5} = \sqrt{10 \cdot 5}$ — $\sqrt{a} \cdot \sqrt{b} = \sqrt{ab}$
$= \sqrt{50}$ — Multiply in radicand
$= \sqrt{25 \cdot 2}$ — 50 can be written $25 \cdot 2$
$= 5\sqrt{2}$ — $\sqrt{25} = 5$

You are now ready to do **B_9**.

B_9 $\sqrt{14}\sqrt{7}$

10. $\sqrt{a^2 + b^2}$ Will not simplify because we are not able to factor the radicand. *The radicand must always be in a factored form before we can simplify.*

You are now ready to do **B_{10}**.

Note
$\sqrt{a^2 + b^2} \neq \sqrt{a^2} + \sqrt{b^2}$. For example, $\sqrt{9 + 16} \neq \sqrt{9} + \sqrt{16}$ because $\sqrt{9 + 16} = \sqrt{25} = 5$, whereas $\sqrt{9} + \sqrt{16} = 3 + 4 = 7$. ■

B_{10} $\sqrt{x^2 - y^2}$

Multiplying *n*th roots (optional)

C₁ $\sqrt[3]{6}\sqrt[3]{5}$

The product property for square roots can be extended to radicals with any index as follows:

> **Product property for *n*th roots**
> For all nonnegative real numbers a and b,
> $$\sqrt[n]{a}\sqrt[n]{b} = \sqrt[n]{ab},$$
> where n is a natural number greater than 1.
>
> **Concept**
> When we multiply two radicals *having the same index,* we multiply the radicands and put the product under a radical symbol with the common index.

C₂ $\sqrt[4]{2}\sqrt[4]{4}$

Example 9–2 C

C₃ $\sqrt[5]{3}\sqrt[5]{x^2}$

Perform the indicated operations. Assume that all variables represent nonnegative real numbers.

1. $\sqrt[3]{3}\sqrt[3]{2} = \sqrt[3]{3 \cdot 2} = \sqrt[3]{6}$

You are now ready to do **C₁**.

2. $\sqrt[5]{7} \cdot \sqrt[5]{9} = \sqrt[5]{7 \cdot 9} = \sqrt[5]{63}$

You are now ready to do **C₂**.

3. $\sqrt[4]{2}\sqrt[4]{a} = \sqrt[4]{2a}$

C₄ $\sqrt[3]{3}\sqrt[3]{x}\sqrt[3]{x}$

You are now ready to do **C₃**.

4. $\sqrt[3]{2}\sqrt[3]{x}\sqrt[3]{y} = \sqrt[3]{2xy}$

You are now ready to do **C₄**.

5. $\sqrt[3]{3}\sqrt[4]{5}$ These radicals cannot be multiplied together in this form since they do not have the same index.

You are now ready to do **C₅**. ■

C₅ $\sqrt[4]{x}\sqrt[3]{y}$

Simplifying *n*th roots (optional)

We simplify *n*th roots, where n is greater than 2, as we did square roots. As long as the radicand can be factored so that one or more factors is a

1. perfect cube when the index is 3,
2. perfect fourth-power when the index is 4,
3. perfect fifth-power when the index is 5, and so on,

the radical can be simplified. To do this, we use the property

$$\sqrt[n]{a^n} = a,$$

D₁ $\sqrt[3]{16}$

where a is a nonnegative real number.

Example 9–2 D

Simplify the following radical expressions. Assume that all variables represent nonnegative real numbers.

1. $\sqrt[3]{81} = \sqrt[3]{27 \cdot 3}$ $81 = 27 \cdot 3$

$= \sqrt[3]{27}\sqrt[3]{3}$ $\sqrt[3]{ab} = \sqrt[3]{a}\sqrt[3]{b}$

$= 3\sqrt[3]{3}$ $\sqrt[3]{27} = 3$ since $27 = 3^3$

You are now ready to do **D₁**.

2. $\sqrt[4]{32} = \sqrt[4]{16 \cdot 2}$ — $32 = 16 \cdot 2$

$= \sqrt[4]{16}\sqrt[4]{2}$ — $\sqrt[4]{ab} = \sqrt[4]{a}\sqrt[4]{b}$

$= 2\sqrt[4]{2}$ — $\sqrt[4]{16} = 2$ since $16 = 2^4$

D₂ $\sqrt[3]{32}$

You are now ready to do **D₂**.

3. $\sqrt[3]{x^5} = \sqrt[3]{x^3 \cdot x^2}$ — $x^5 = x^3 \cdot x^2$

$= \sqrt[3]{x^3}\sqrt[3]{x^2}$ — $\sqrt[3]{ab} = \sqrt[3]{a}\sqrt[3]{b}$

$= x\sqrt[3]{x^2}$ — $\sqrt[3]{x^3} = x$

D₃ $\sqrt[5]{x^7}$

You are now ready to do **D₃**.

4. $\sqrt[5]{y^{10}} = \sqrt[5]{y^5 \cdot y^5}$ — $y^{10} = y^5 \cdot y^5$

$= \sqrt[5]{y^5}\sqrt[5]{y^5}$ — $\sqrt[5]{ab} = \sqrt[5]{a}\sqrt[5]{b}$

$= y \cdot y$ — $\sqrt[5]{y^5} = y$

$= y^2$

Note
In example 4, the exponent 10 is evenly divisible by the index 5, and the radical is eliminated. When the exponent of a factor is evenly divisible by the index, that factor will no longer remain under the radical symbol.

D₄ $\sqrt[3]{a^6}$

You are now ready to do **D₄**.

5. $\sqrt[4]{x^7y^4} = \sqrt[4]{x^4 \cdot x^3 \cdot y^4}$ — $x^7 = x^4 \cdot x^3$

$= \sqrt[4]{x^4}\sqrt[4]{x^3}\sqrt[4]{y^4}$ — $\sqrt[4]{abc} = \sqrt[4]{a} \cdot \sqrt[4]{b} \cdot \sqrt[4]{c}$

$= x\sqrt[4]{x^3}\,y$ — $\sqrt[4]{a^4} = a$

$= xy\sqrt[4]{x^3}$ — Commutative property

D₅ $\sqrt[3]{a^3b^4}$

You are now ready to do **D₅**.

6. $\sqrt[3]{a^7b^2} = \sqrt[3]{a^3a^3ab^2}$ — $a^7 = a^3 \cdot a^3 \cdot a$

$= \sqrt[3]{a^3}\sqrt[3]{a^3}\sqrt[3]{ab^2}$ — $\sqrt[3]{abc} = \sqrt[3]{a}\sqrt[3]{b}\sqrt[3]{c}$

$= a \cdot a\sqrt[3]{ab^2}$ — $\sqrt[3]{a^3} = a$

$= a^2\sqrt[3]{ab^2}$ — Multiply

D₆ $\sqrt[4]{a^7b^3}$

Note
No simplification relative to b is possible because the exponent of b is less than the value of the index.

You are now ready to do **D₆**.

7. $\sqrt[3]{54x^3y^5} = \sqrt[3]{27 \cdot 2 \cdot x^3 \cdot y^3 \cdot y^2}$ — $54 = 27 \cdot 2$ and $y^5 = y^3 \cdot y^2$

$= \sqrt[3]{27}\sqrt[3]{x^3}\sqrt[3]{y^3}\sqrt[3]{2y^2}$ — $\sqrt[3]{abcd} = \sqrt[3]{a}\sqrt[3]{b}\sqrt[3]{c}\sqrt[3]{d}$

$= 3xy\sqrt[3]{2y^2}$ — $27 = 3^3$ and $\sqrt[3]{a^3} = a$

D₇ $\sqrt[3]{24a^3b^8}$

You are now ready to do **D₇**. ■

Observe from the preceding examples that we can simplify a radical if the radicand has a factor (or factors) whose exponent is equal to or greater than the index.

E_1 $\sqrt[5]{a^3}\sqrt[5]{a^3}$

Example 9–2 E

Perform the indicated multiplication and simplify. Assume that all variables represent nonnegative real numbers.

1. $\sqrt[3]{a^2}\sqrt[3]{a} = \sqrt[3]{a^2 \cdot a}$ — $\sqrt[3]{a}\sqrt[3]{b} = \sqrt[3]{a \cdot b}$

$= \sqrt[3]{a^3}$ — $a^2 \cdot a = a^3$

$= a$ — $\sqrt[3]{a^3} = a$

You are now ready to do E_1.

2. $\sqrt[4]{8a^2b^3}\sqrt[4]{4a^3b} = \sqrt[4]{8a^2b^3 \cdot 4a^3b}$ — $\sqrt[4]{a}\sqrt[4]{b} = \sqrt[4]{a \cdot b}$

$= \sqrt[4]{32a^5b^4}$ — Multiply in radicand

$= \sqrt[4]{16 \cdot 2 \cdot a^4 \cdot a \cdot b^4}$ — Factor in radicand

$= \sqrt[4]{16}\sqrt[4]{a^4}\sqrt[4]{b^4}\sqrt[4]{2a}$ — $\sqrt[4]{ab} = \sqrt[4]{a}\sqrt[4]{b}$

$= 2ab\sqrt[4]{2a}$ — Simplify radicals

You are now ready to do E_2. ■

E_2 $\sqrt[3]{18x^4y}\sqrt[3]{12xy^2}$

Note
A very common error in problems involving radicals is to forget to carry along the correct index for the radical symbol.

Answers to section 9–2 margin exercises

A_1 $\sqrt{30}$ **A_2** $\sqrt{70}$ **A_3** $\sqrt{6x}$ **A_4** $\sqrt{2ab}$ **B_1** $2\sqrt{2}$ **B_2** $2\sqrt{10}$ **B_3** $x\sqrt{3}$ **B_4** $b\sqrt{a}$ **B_5** $x\sqrt{x}$ **B_6** $a^3\sqrt{a}$ **B_7** $xy\sqrt{y}$ **B_8** 6 **B_9** $7\sqrt{2}$ **B_{10}** will not simplify **C_1** $\sqrt[3]{30}$ **C_2** $\sqrt[4]{8}$ **C_3** $\sqrt[5]{3x^2}$ **C_4** $\sqrt[3]{3x^2}$ **C_5** do not have same index, cannot be multiplied together in this form **D_1** $2\sqrt[3]{2}$ **D_2** $2\sqrt[3]{4}$ **D_3** $x\sqrt[5]{x^2}$ **D_4** a^2 **D_5** $ab\sqrt[3]{b}$ **D_6** $a\sqrt[4]{a^3b^3}$ **D_7** $2ab^2\sqrt[3]{3b^2}$ **E_1** $a\sqrt[5]{a}$ **E_2** $6xy\sqrt[3]{x^2}$

Mastery points

Can you
- Multiply radicals having the same index?
- Simplify radicals?

Exercise 9–2

Directions Assume that all variables in this exercise set represent nonnegative real numbers. Perform any indicated operations and simplify. See examples 9–2 A and B.

Examples **B_2** $\sqrt{40}$

Solutions

$\sqrt{40} = \sqrt{4 \cdot 10}$ — 40 factors to $4 \cdot 10$

$= \sqrt{4}\sqrt{10}$ — $\sqrt{ab} = \sqrt{a}\sqrt{b}$

$= 2\sqrt{10}$ — $\sqrt{4} = 2$

B_9 $\sqrt{14}\sqrt{7}$

$\sqrt{14}\sqrt{7} = \sqrt{14 \cdot 7}$ — $\sqrt{a}\sqrt{b} = \sqrt{ab}$

$= \sqrt{98}$ — $14 \cdot 7 = 98$

$= \sqrt{49 \cdot 2}$ — 98 factors to $49 \cdot 2$

$= \sqrt{49}\sqrt{2}$ — $\sqrt{ab} = \sqrt{a}\sqrt{b}$

$= 7\sqrt{2}$ — $\sqrt{49} = 7$

1. $\sqrt{16}$ **2.** $\sqrt{63}$ **3.** $\sqrt{28}$ **4.** $\sqrt{75}$

5. $\sqrt{a^7}$ **6.** $\sqrt{a^5}$ **7.** $\sqrt{4a^2b^3}$ **8.** $\sqrt{9ab^4c^3}$

9. $\sqrt{27a^3b^5}$

10. $\sqrt{24x^5yz^3}$

11. $\sqrt{6}\sqrt{3}$

12. $\sqrt{27}\sqrt{6}$

13. $\sqrt{15}\sqrt{15}$

14. $\sqrt{11}\sqrt{11}$

15. $\sqrt{6}\sqrt{10}$

16. $\sqrt{18}\sqrt{24}$

17. $\sqrt{25}\sqrt{15}$

18. $\sqrt{20}\sqrt{20}$

19. $\sqrt{5}\sqrt{15}$

20. $\sqrt{2a}\sqrt{3a}$

21. $\sqrt{5x}\sqrt{15x}$

22. $\sqrt{6x}\sqrt{14xy}$

23. $\sqrt{2a}\sqrt{24b^2}$

24. A square-shaped television picture tube has a surface area of 121 square inches. What is the length of the side of the tube? (*Hint:* Area of a square is found by squaring the length of a side. $A = s^2$.)

25. A room in the shape of a square is 169 square feet. What is the length of a side? (See exercise 24.)

26. The formula for approximating the velocity V in miles per hour of a car based on the length of its skid marks S (in feet) on wet pavement is given by $V = 2\sqrt{3S}$. If the skid marks are 75 feet long, what was the velocity?

27. The formula for approximating the velocity V in miles per hour of a car based on the length of its skid marks S (in feet) on dry pavement is given by $V = 2\sqrt{6S}$. If the skid marks are 24 feet long, what was the velocity?

Optional

Directions Assume that all variables in this exercise set represent only positive real numbers. Perform any indicated operations and simplify. See examples 9–2 C and D.

Example D_7 $\sqrt[3]{24a^3b^8}$

Solution

$= \sqrt[3]{8 \cdot 3 \cdot a^3 \cdot b^3 \cdot b^3 \cdot b^2}$ Factor cubes

$= \sqrt[3]{8}\sqrt[3]{a^3}\sqrt[3]{b^3}\sqrt[3]{b^3}\sqrt[3]{3}\sqrt[3]{b^2}$ $\sqrt[3]{ab} = \sqrt[3]{a}\sqrt[3]{b}$

$= 2abb\sqrt[3]{3b^2}$ $\sqrt[3]{a^3} = a$, $\sqrt[3]{b^3} = b$, and $\sqrt[3]{8} = 2$

$= 2ab^2\sqrt[3]{3b^2}$

28. $\sqrt[3]{48}$

29. $\sqrt[4]{32}$

30. $\sqrt[5]{64}$

31. $\sqrt[3]{24}$

32. $\sqrt[5]{a^7}$

33. $\sqrt[3]{b^8}$

34. $\sqrt[3]{x^9}$

35. $\sqrt[5]{y^{15}}$

36. $\sqrt[3]{a^{12}}$ 37. $\sqrt[3]{4a^2b^3}$ 38. $\sqrt[3]{8r^2s^8}$ 39. $\sqrt[3]{16a^4b^5}$

40. $\sqrt[5]{64x^{10}y^{14}}$ 41. $\sqrt[3]{81a^5b^{11}}$ 42. $\sqrt[3]{a^2}\sqrt[3]{a}$ 43. $\sqrt[3]{b^2}\sqrt[3]{b^2}$

44. $\sqrt[5]{b^4}\sqrt[5]{b^3}$ 45. $\sqrt[5]{a}\sqrt[5]{a^4}$ 46. $\sqrt[3]{5a^2b}\sqrt[3]{75a^2b^2}$ 47. $\sqrt[3]{3ab^2}\sqrt[3]{18a^2b^2}$

48. $\sqrt[4]{8a^3b}\sqrt[4]{4a^2b^2}$ 49. $\sqrt[4]{27a^2b^3}\sqrt[4]{9ab}$ 50. $\sqrt[3]{25x^5y^7}\sqrt[3]{15xy^3}$ 51. $\sqrt[3]{16a^{11}b^4}\sqrt[3]{12a^4b^6}$

52. $\sqrt[4]{8xy}\sqrt[4]{4x^3y^3}$

53. The moment of inertia for a rectangle is given by the formula $I = \frac{bh^3}{12}$. If we know the values of I and b, we can solve for h as follows: $h = \sqrt[3]{\frac{12I}{b}}$. Find h if $I = 2$ in.^{4} and $b = 3$ in.

54. Use exercise 53 to find h if $I = 27$ in.^{4} and $b = 4$ in.

55. The moment of inertia for a circle is given by the formula $I = \frac{\pi r^4}{4}$. If we know the value of I, we can solve for r as follows: $r = \sqrt[4]{\frac{4I}{\pi}}$. Find r if $I = 12.56$ in.^{4} and we use 3.14 for π.

56. Use exercise 55 to find r if $I = 63.585$ in.^{4}

Review exercises

Directions Reduce the following fractions and rational expressions to lowest terms. See sections R–1 and 5–2.

1. $\frac{49}{56}$ 2. $\frac{16x^3y^2}{-4xy}$ 3. $\frac{2y^2 - 50}{y^2 - 4y - 5}$

Directions Perform the indicated operations and simplify. See sections 9–1 and 9–2.

4. $\sqrt{5}\sqrt{5}$ 5. $\sqrt{3}\sqrt{3}$ 6. $\sqrt{2}\sqrt{8}$ 7. $\sqrt{12}\sqrt{3}$ 8. $\sqrt{x}\sqrt{x}$

9–3 Quotient property for radicals

The square root of a fraction

The following example will help us develop a property for division involving radicals.

$$\sqrt{\frac{4}{9}} = \sqrt{\left(\frac{2}{3}\right)^2} = \frac{2}{3}$$

We also observe that

$$\frac{\sqrt{4}}{\sqrt{9}} = \frac{2}{3}.$$

From our example, we can conclude that

$$\sqrt{\frac{4}{9}} = \frac{\sqrt{4}}{\sqrt{9}}.$$

We generalize this idea as follows:

Quotient property for square roots

For all nonnegative real numbers a and b, where $b \neq 0$,

$$\sqrt{\frac{a}{b}} = \frac{\sqrt{a}}{\sqrt{b}}$$

Concept

The square root of a fraction can be written as the square root of the numerator divided by the square root of the denominator.

Example 9–3 A

Simplify the following expressions. Assume that all variables represent positive real numbers.

Rewrite as the square root of the numerator over the square root of the denominator and simplify

1. $\sqrt{\frac{16}{25}} = \frac{\sqrt{16}}{\sqrt{25}} = \frac{4}{5}$

You are now ready to do **A$_1$**.

2. $\sqrt{\frac{36}{49}} = \frac{\sqrt{36}}{\sqrt{49}} = \frac{6}{7}$

You are now ready to do **A$_2$**.

3. $\sqrt{\frac{81}{100}} = \frac{\sqrt{81}}{\sqrt{100}} = \frac{9}{10}$

You are now ready to do **A$_3$**.

4. $\sqrt{\frac{x^4}{64}} = \frac{\sqrt{x^4}}{\sqrt{64}} = \frac{x^2}{8}$

You are now ready to do **A$_4$**.

5. $\sqrt{\frac{x^3}{y^4}} = \frac{\sqrt{x^3}}{\sqrt{y^4}} = \frac{x\sqrt{x}}{y^2}$

You are now ready to do **A$_5$**. ■

A$_1$ $\sqrt{\frac{4}{49}}$

A$_2$ $\sqrt{\frac{9}{16}}$

A$_3$ $\sqrt{\frac{1}{25}}$

A$_4$ $\sqrt{\frac{a^6}{36}}$

A$_5$ $\sqrt{\frac{2}{9}}$

B_1 $\frac{1}{\sqrt{3}}$

Rationalizing the denominator

When simplifying and evaluating radical expressions containing a radical in the denominator, it is easier if we can eliminate the radical in the denominator. For example,

$$\sqrt{\frac{4}{5}} = \frac{\sqrt{4}}{\sqrt{5}} = \frac{2}{\sqrt{5}}.$$

Since $\sqrt{5} \cdot \sqrt{5} = 5$, we can eliminate the radical $\sqrt{5}$ in the denominator by multiplying the numerator and the denominator of the fraction by $\sqrt{5}$.

$$\frac{2}{\sqrt{5}} \cdot \frac{\sqrt{5}}{\sqrt{5}} = \frac{2\sqrt{5}}{\sqrt{25}} = \frac{2\sqrt{5}}{5}$$

The process of changing the denominator from a radical to a rational number is called **rationalizing the denominator.**

Rationalizing the denominator

1. Multiply the numerator and the denominator by the square root that is in the denominator. The radicand in the denominator will be a perfect-square integer.
2. Simplify the radical expressions in the numerator and the denominator.
3. Reduce the resulting fraction if possible.

Example 9–3 B

Simplify the following expressions. Leave no radicals in the denominator. Assume that all variables represent positive real numbers.

B_2 $\frac{2}{\sqrt{11}}$

1. $\frac{5}{\sqrt{7}} = \frac{5}{\sqrt{7}} \cdot \frac{\sqrt{7}}{\sqrt{7}}$ Multiply numerator and denominator by $\sqrt{7}$

$= \frac{5\sqrt{7}}{\sqrt{49}}$ Multiply in numerator and denominator

$= \frac{5\sqrt{7}}{7}$ $\sqrt{49} = 7$

You are now ready to do **B_1**.

2. $\frac{3}{\sqrt{5}} = \frac{3}{\sqrt{5}} \cdot \frac{\sqrt{5}}{\sqrt{5}}$ Multiply numerator and denominator by $\sqrt{5}$

$= \frac{3\sqrt{5}}{\sqrt{25}}$ Multiply in numerator and denominator

$= \frac{3\sqrt{5}}{5}$ $\sqrt{25} = 5$

You are now ready to do **B_2**.

3. $\frac{4}{\sqrt{6}} = \frac{4}{\sqrt{6}} \cdot \frac{\sqrt{6}}{\sqrt{6}}$ Multiply numerator and denominator by $\sqrt{6}$

$= \frac{4\sqrt{6}}{\sqrt{36}}$ Multiply in numerator and denominator

$= \frac{4\sqrt{6}}{6}$ $\sqrt{36} = 6$

$= \frac{2\sqrt{6}}{3}$ Reduce (by 2) to lowest terms

B₃ $\frac{4}{\sqrt{6}}$

Note
In example 3, we were able to reduce the fraction as a final step. Always check to see that your answer is in the most reduced form.

B₄ $\frac{\sqrt{3}}{\sqrt{5}}$

You are now ready to do **B₃**.

4. $\frac{\sqrt{2}}{\sqrt{3}} = \frac{\sqrt{2}}{\sqrt{3}} \cdot \frac{\sqrt{3}}{\sqrt{3}}$ Multiply numerator and denominator by $\sqrt{3}$

$= \frac{\sqrt{6}}{\sqrt{9}}$ Multiply in numerator and denominator

$= \frac{\sqrt{6}}{3}$ $\sqrt{9} = 3$

You are now ready to do **B₄**.

B₅ $\frac{3\sqrt{7}}{\sqrt{5}}$

5. $\frac{2}{3\sqrt{5}} = \frac{2}{3\sqrt{5}} \cdot \frac{\sqrt{5}}{\sqrt{5}}$ Multiply numerator and denominator by $\sqrt{5}$

$= \frac{2\sqrt{5}}{3\sqrt{25}}$ Multiply in numerator and denominator

$= \frac{2\sqrt{5}}{3 \cdot 5}$ $\sqrt{25} = 5$

$= \frac{2\sqrt{5}}{15}$ Multiply in denominator

You are now ready to do **B₅**.

B₆ $\frac{a}{\sqrt{b}}$

6. $\frac{a}{\sqrt{a}} = \frac{a}{\sqrt{a}} \cdot \frac{\sqrt{a}}{\sqrt{a}}$ Multiply numerator and denominator by $\sqrt{a}$

$= \frac{a\sqrt{a}}{\sqrt{a^2}}$ Multiply in numerator and denominator

$= \frac{a\sqrt{a}}{a}$ $\sqrt{a^2} = a$

$= \sqrt{a}$ Reduce (by *a*) to lowest terms

You are now ready to do **B₆**.

7. $\sqrt{\frac{a^3}{b}} = \frac{\sqrt{a^3}}{\sqrt{b}}$ $\sqrt{\frac{a}{b}} = \frac{\sqrt{a}}{\sqrt{b}}$

$= \frac{a\sqrt{a}}{\sqrt{b}} \cdot \frac{\sqrt{b}}{\sqrt{b}}$ Multiply numerator and denominator by $\sqrt{b}$

$= \frac{a\sqrt{ab}}{\sqrt{b^2}}$ Multiply in numerator and denominator ($\sqrt{b}\sqrt{b} = \sqrt{b^2}$)

$= \frac{a\sqrt{ab}}{b}$ $\sqrt{b^2} = b$

B₇ $\sqrt{\frac{a}{b}}$

You are now ready to do **B₇**. ■

The *n*th root of a fraction (optional)

The quotient property for square roots can be extended to radicals with any index as follows:

Quotient property for *n*th roots

For all nonnegative real numbers a and b,

$$\sqrt[n]{\frac{a}{b}} = \frac{\sqrt[n]{a}}{\sqrt[n]{b}}, \text{ where } b \neq 0.$$

Concept

The *n*th root of a fraction can be written as the *n*th root of the numerator divided by the *n*th root of the denominator.

Example 9–3 C

Simplify the following expressions. Assume that all variables represent positive real numbers.

Rewrite as the *n*th root of the numerator over the *n*th root of the denominator and simplify

1. $\sqrt[3]{\frac{8}{27}} = \frac{\sqrt[3]{8}}{\sqrt[3]{27}} = \frac{2}{3}$

You are now ready to do **C_1**.

2. $\sqrt[5]{\frac{32}{a^5}} = \frac{\sqrt[5]{32}}{\sqrt[5]{a^5}} = \frac{2}{a}$

You are now ready to do **C_2**.

3. $\sqrt[7]{\frac{b^7}{c^{14}}} = \frac{\sqrt[7]{b^7}}{\sqrt[7]{c^{14}}} = \frac{b}{c^2}$

You are now ready to do **C_3**.

Note

As a general rule, *fractions are never left under a radical symbol.*

4. $\sqrt[3]{\frac{x^5}{y^6}} = \frac{\sqrt[3]{x^5}}{\sqrt[3]{y^6}} = \frac{x\sqrt[3]{x^2}}{y^2}$

You are now ready to do **C_4**.

5. $\sqrt[3]{\frac{8a^5b^6}{c^9}} = \frac{\sqrt[3]{8a^5b^6}}{\sqrt[3]{c^9}} = \frac{\sqrt[3]{2^3a^5b^6}}{\sqrt[3]{c^9}} = \frac{2ab^2\sqrt[3]{a^2}}{c^3}$

You are now ready to do **C_5**. ■

C_1 $\sqrt[3]{\frac{1}{27}}$

C_2 $\sqrt[4]{\frac{16}{y^8}}$

C_3 $\sqrt[5]{\frac{a^5b^3}{c^{10}}}$

C_4 $\sqrt[3]{\frac{a^4}{b^9}}$

C_5 $\sqrt[3]{\frac{27x^3y^2}{z^{12}}}$

Rationalizing the denominator (*n*th root) (optional)

The following example will help us develop a general rule for rationalizing a denominator that has a single term.

$$\sqrt[3]{\frac{1}{a}} = \frac{\sqrt[3]{1}}{\sqrt[3]{a}} = \frac{1}{\sqrt[3]{a}}$$

At this point, a radical still remains in the denominator. We must now determine what we can do to the fraction to remove the radical from the denominator.

Observations:

1. We can multiply the numerator and the denominator by the same number and form equivalent fractions.
2. If we multiply by a radical, the indices must be the same to carry out the multiplication.
3. To bring a factor out from under the radical symbol and not leave any of the factor behind, the index must divide evenly into the exponent.

With these observations in mind, we rationalize the fraction as follows:

$= \frac{1}{\sqrt[3]{a}} \cdot \frac{\sqrt[3]{\ }}{\sqrt[3]{\ }}$ Indices are the same

$= \frac{1}{\sqrt[3]{a}} \cdot \frac{\sqrt[3]{a^2}}{\sqrt[3]{a^2}}$ Multiply numerator and denominator by the same number

$= \frac{\sqrt[3]{a^2}}{\sqrt[3]{a^3}}$ The sum of the exponents of a in the denominator is equal to the index

$= \frac{\sqrt[3]{a^2}}{a}$. The index divides evenly into the exponent, the radical is eliminated

To rationalize an *n*th root denominator

1. We multiply the numerator and the denominator by a radical with the same index as the radical that we wish to eliminate from the denominator.
2. The exponent of each factor under the radical must be such that when we add it to the original exponent of the factor under the radical in the denominator, the sum will be equal to or divisible by the index of the radical.
3. Carry out the multiplication and reduce the fraction if possible.

D₁ $\frac{2}{\sqrt[3]{5}}$

D₂ $\frac{x}{\sqrt[3]{y^2}}$

Example 9–3 D

Simplify the following expressions. Leave no radicals in the denominator. Assume that all variables represent positive real numbers.

1. $\frac{1}{\sqrt[3]{7}} = \frac{1}{\sqrt[3]{7}} \cdot \frac{\sqrt[3]{7^2}}{\sqrt[3]{7^2}}$ Multiply numerator and denominator by $\sqrt[3]{7^2}$

$= \frac{\sqrt[3]{7^2}}{\sqrt[3]{7^3}}$ Multiply in numerator and denominator ($\sqrt[3]{7}\sqrt[3]{7^2} = \sqrt[3]{7^3}$)

$= \frac{\sqrt[3]{7^2}}{7}$ $\sqrt[3]{7^3} = 7$

$= \frac{\sqrt[3]{49}}{7}$ $7^2 = 49$

You are now ready to do **D₁**.

2. $\frac{a}{\sqrt[5]{b^2}} = \frac{a}{\sqrt[5]{b^2}} \cdot \frac{\sqrt[5]{b^3}}{\sqrt[5]{b^3}}$ Multiply numerator and denominator by $\sqrt[5]{b^3}$

$= \frac{a\sqrt[5]{b^3}}{\sqrt[5]{b^5}}$ Multiply in numerator and denominator ($\sqrt[5]{b^2}\sqrt[5]{b^3} = \sqrt[5]{b^5}$)

$= \frac{a\sqrt[5]{b^3}}{b}$ $\sqrt[5]{b^5} = b$

You are now ready to do **D₂**.

D₃ $\dfrac{1}{\sqrt[5]{b^2}}$

3. $\dfrac{x^2}{\sqrt[7]{y^4}} = \dfrac{x^2}{\sqrt[7]{y^4}} \cdot \dfrac{\sqrt[7]{y^3}}{\sqrt[7]{y^3}}$ Multiply numerator and denominator by $\sqrt[7]{y^3}$

$= \dfrac{x^2\sqrt[7]{y^3}}{\sqrt[7]{y^7}}$ $\sqrt[7]{y^4}\sqrt[7]{y^3} = \sqrt[7]{y^7}$

$= \dfrac{x^2\sqrt[7]{y^3}}{y}$ $\sqrt[7]{y^7} = y$

You are now ready to do **D₃**.

4. $\dfrac{x}{\sqrt[4]{x}} = \dfrac{x}{\sqrt[4]{x}} \cdot \dfrac{\sqrt[4]{x^3}}{\sqrt[4]{x^3}}$ Multiply numerator and denominator by $\sqrt[4]{x^3}$

D₄ $\dfrac{y}{\sqrt[5]{y^3}}$

$= \dfrac{x\sqrt[4]{x^3}}{\sqrt[4]{x^4}}$ $\sqrt[4]{x}\sqrt[4]{x^3} = \sqrt[4]{x^4}$

$= \dfrac{x\sqrt[4]{x^3}}{x}$ $\sqrt[4]{x^4} = x$

$= \sqrt[4]{x^3}$ Reduce (by x) to lowest terms

You are now ready to do **D₄**.

5. $\dfrac{\sqrt[5]{a^3}}{\sqrt[5]{b^2}} = \dfrac{\sqrt[5]{a^3}}{\sqrt[5]{b^2}} \cdot \dfrac{\sqrt[5]{b^3}}{\sqrt[5]{b^3}}$ Multiply numerator and denominator by $\sqrt[5]{b^3}$

D₅ $\dfrac{\sqrt[3]{a}}{\sqrt[3]{b}}$

$= \dfrac{\sqrt[5]{a^3b^3}}{\sqrt[5]{b^5}}$ $\sqrt[5]{b^2}\sqrt[5]{b^3} = \sqrt[5]{b^5}$

$= \dfrac{\sqrt[5]{a^3b^3}}{b}$ $\sqrt[5]{b^5} = b$

You are now ready to do **D₅**.

6. $\dfrac{a}{b\sqrt[6]{c}} = \dfrac{a}{b\sqrt[6]{c}} \cdot \dfrac{\sqrt[6]{c^5}}{\sqrt[6]{c^5}}$ Multiply numerator and denominator by $\sqrt[6]{c^5}$

$= \dfrac{a\sqrt[6]{c^5}}{b\sqrt[6]{c^6}}$ $\sqrt[6]{c}\sqrt[6]{c^5} = \sqrt[6]{c^6}$

$= \dfrac{a\sqrt[6]{c^5}}{bc}$ $\sqrt[6]{c^6} = c$

D₆ $\sqrt[3]{\dfrac{8a^5}{b^3}}$

You are now ready to do **D₆**.

7. $\dfrac{x}{\sqrt[7]{x^4y^6}} = \dfrac{x}{\sqrt[7]{x^4y^6}} \cdot \dfrac{\sqrt[7]{x^3y}}{\sqrt[7]{x^3y}}$ Multiply numerator and denominator by $\sqrt[7]{x^3y}$

$= \dfrac{x\sqrt[7]{x^3y}}{\sqrt[7]{x^7y^7}}$ $\sqrt[7]{x^4y^6}\sqrt[7]{x^3y} = \sqrt[7]{x^7y^7}$

$= \dfrac{x\sqrt[7]{x^3y}}{xy}$ $\sqrt[7]{x^7y^7} = xy$

$= \dfrac{\sqrt[7]{x^3y}}{y}$ Reduce (by x) to lowest terms

D₇ $\dfrac{a}{\sqrt[5]{b^2c}}$

You are now ready to do **D₇**.

Answers to section 9–3 margin exercises

A₁ $\frac{2}{7}$ **A₂** $\frac{3}{4}$ **A₃** $\frac{1}{5}$ **A₄** $\frac{a^3}{6}$ **A₅** $\frac{\sqrt{2}}{3}$ **B₁** $\frac{\sqrt{3}}{3}$ **B₂** $\frac{2\sqrt{11}}{11}$ **B₃** $\frac{2\sqrt{6}}{3}$
B₄ $\frac{\sqrt{15}}{5}$ **B₅** $\frac{3\sqrt{35}}{5}$ **B₆** $\frac{a\sqrt{b}}{b}$ **B₇** $\frac{\sqrt{ab}}{b}$ **C₁** $\frac{1}{3}$ **C₂** $\frac{2}{y^2}$ **C₃** $\frac{a\sqrt[5]{b^3}}{c^2}$ **C₄** $\frac{a\sqrt[3]{a}}{b^3}$
C₅ $\frac{3x\sqrt[3]{y^2}}{z^4}$ **D₁** $\frac{2\sqrt[3]{25}}{5}$ **D₂** $\frac{x\sqrt[3]{y}}{y}$ **D₃** $\frac{\sqrt[5]{b^3}}{b}$ **D₄** $\sqrt[5]{y^2}$ **D₅** $\frac{\sqrt[3]{ab^2}}{b}$ **D₆** $\frac{2a\sqrt[3]{a^2}}{b}$
D₇ $\frac{a\sqrt[5]{b^3c^4}}{bc}$

Mastery points

Can you

- Simplify radicals containing fractions?
- Rationalize denominators?

Exercise 9–3

Directions Assume that all variables represent positive real numbers. Simplify the following expressions. Leave no radicals in the denominator. See examples 9–3 A and B.

Examples [B3] $\dfrac{4}{\sqrt{6}}$

Solutions

$= \dfrac{4}{\sqrt{6}} \dfrac{\sqrt{6}}{\sqrt{6}}$ Multiply numerator and denominator by $\sqrt{6}$

$= \dfrac{4\sqrt{6}}{6}$ Multiply $\sqrt{6}\sqrt{6} = 6$

$= \dfrac{2\sqrt{6}}{3}$ Reduce to lowest terms

[B7] $\sqrt{\dfrac{a}{b}}$

$= \dfrac{\sqrt{a}}{\sqrt{b}}$

$= \dfrac{\sqrt{a}}{\sqrt{b}} \dfrac{\sqrt{b}}{\sqrt{b}}$ Multiply numerator and denominator by $\sqrt{b}$

$= \dfrac{\sqrt{ab}}{b}$ Multiply $\sqrt{a}\sqrt{b} = \sqrt{ab}$, $\sqrt{b} \cdot \sqrt{b} = b$

1. $\sqrt{\dfrac{9}{25}}$ **2.** $\sqrt{\dfrac{25}{36}}$ **3.** $\sqrt{\dfrac{25}{49}}$ **4.** $\sqrt{\dfrac{81}{100}}$ **5.** $\sqrt{\dfrac{3}{4}}$

6. $\sqrt{\dfrac{5}{9}}$ 7. $\sqrt{\dfrac{64}{a^2}}$ **8.** $\sqrt{\dfrac{y^4}{16}}$ **9.** $\sqrt{\dfrac{1}{2}}$ **10.** $\sqrt{\dfrac{1}{3}}$

11. $\sqrt{\dfrac{4}{7}}$ **12.** $\sqrt{\dfrac{9}{11}}$ **13.** $\sqrt{\dfrac{1}{15}}$ **14.** $\sqrt{\dfrac{1}{14}}$ **[15.]** $\sqrt{\dfrac{4}{75}}$

16. $\sqrt{\dfrac{5}{12}}$ 17. $\dfrac{2}{\sqrt{2}}$ **18.** $\dfrac{6}{\sqrt{3}}$ **19.** $\dfrac{10}{\sqrt{8}}$ **20.** $\dfrac{15}{\sqrt{27}}$

21. $\sqrt{\dfrac{x^2}{y}}$ **22.** $\sqrt{\dfrac{1}{a}}$ 23. $\sqrt{\dfrac{1}{x}}$ **24.** $\sqrt{\dfrac{a^2}{b^3}}$ **25.** $\dfrac{\sqrt{a^5}}{\sqrt{a}}$

Optional

Directions Assume that all variables in this exercise set represent only positive real numbers. Simplify the following expressions. Leave no radicals in the denominator. See examples 9–3 C and D.

Examples **D₃** $\frac{1}{\sqrt[5]{b^2}}$

D₆ $\sqrt[3]{\frac{8a^5}{b^3}}$

Solutions

$= \frac{1}{\sqrt[5]{b^2}} \cdot \frac{\sqrt[5]{b^3}}{\sqrt[5]{b^3}}$ Multiply numerator and denominator by $\sqrt[5]{b^3}$ since $b^2 \cdot b^3 = b^5$

$= \frac{\sqrt[5]{b^3}}{\sqrt[5]{b^5}}$

$= \frac{\sqrt[5]{b^3}}{b}$ $\sqrt[5]{b^5} = b$

$= \frac{\sqrt[3]{8a^5}}{\sqrt[3]{b^3}}$ $\sqrt[3]{\frac{a}{b}} = \frac{\sqrt[3]{a}}{\sqrt[3]{b}}$

$= \frac{\sqrt[3]{2^3a^5}}{b}$ $\sqrt[3]{b^3} = b; 8 = 2^3$

$= \frac{2a\sqrt[3]{a^2}}{b}$ $\sqrt[3]{2^3} = 2;\ \sqrt[3]{a^3} = a$

26. $\sqrt[3]{\frac{8}{27}}$

27. $\sqrt[3]{\frac{1}{8}}$

28. $\sqrt[4]{\frac{16}{81}}$

29. $\sqrt[3]{\frac{27}{125}}$

30. $\sqrt[3]{\frac{a^2}{b^2}}$

31. $\sqrt[3]{\frac{3a^6}{b^3}}$

32. $\sqrt[3]{\frac{x}{y^{12}}}$

33. $\sqrt[5]{\frac{a^4}{b^{10}}}$

34. $\sqrt[5]{\frac{32x^4}{y^5}}$

35. $\sqrt[4]{\frac{a^4b^9}{c^{11}}}$

36. $\sqrt[4]{\frac{a^9b^{13}}{c^8}}$

37. $\sqrt[5]{\frac{x^3y^2}{z^{15}}}$

38. $\sqrt[3]{\frac{8}{9}}$

39. $\sqrt[3]{\frac{4}{25}}$

40. $\sqrt[3]{\frac{27}{16}}$

41. $\sqrt[4]{\frac{16}{125}}$

42. $\sqrt[4]{\frac{3}{4}}$

43. $\sqrt[3]{\frac{x^3}{y^2}}$

44. $\sqrt[3]{\frac{x^6}{y}}$

45. $\frac{ab}{\sqrt[3]{a^2}}$

46. $\frac{xy}{\sqrt[5]{y^3}}$

47. $\sqrt[3]{\frac{a^3}{b^2c}}$

48. $\sqrt[3]{\frac{8}{xy^2}}$

49. $\sqrt[3]{\frac{a^2}{b^2c}}$

50. $\frac{a}{\sqrt[5]{a^2b^4}}$

51. $\frac{ab}{\sqrt[3]{ab^2}}$

52. $\frac{xy^2}{\sqrt[5]{x^4y}}$

53. If we wish to construct a sphere of specific volume, we can find the length of the radius necessary by the formula $r = \sqrt[3]{\frac{3V}{4\pi}}$. Find the radius necessary for a sphere to have a volume of 113.04 cubic units. (Use 3.14 for π.)

54. Use exercise 53 to find r if $V = 904.32$ cubic units. (Use 3.14 for π.)

Review exercises

Directions Combine in the following. See section 3–2.

1. $4x + 2x$
2. $9y - 5y$
3. $5ab + 3ab$
4. $xy + 4xy$

Directions Multiply the following. See section 3–3.

5. $(x + 3)(x - 3)$
6. $(x + y)(x - y)$
7. $(4x + 3y)(4x - 3y)$
8. $(3 - 2x)(3 + 2x)$

9–4 Sums and differences of radicals

Like radicals

We have learned that in addition and subtraction, we can only combine like terms. This same idea applies when we are dealing with radicals. *We can only add or subtract like radicals.*

For radicals to be like radicals, the following conditions must be true:

Like radicals

1. The radicals must have the same index.
2. The radicands must be the same.

For example $3\sqrt{5x}$ and $-2\sqrt{5x}$ are like radicals. $5\sqrt{7x}$ and $7\sqrt{5x}$ are not like radicals since the radicands are not the same. The radicals $\sqrt{5x}$ and $\sqrt[3]{5x}$ are not like since the indices are not the same.

Addition and subtraction involving square roots

Addition and subtraction of radicals follow the same procedure as addition and subtraction of algebraic expressions. That is, to add or subtract like radicals, apply the distributive property and add or subtract the numerical coefficients.

A_1 $3\sqrt{3} + 2\sqrt{3}$

A_2 $6\sqrt{11} - \sqrt{11}$

A_3 $5\sqrt{7} - 7\sqrt{7}$

A_4 $3\sqrt{6} + 2\sqrt{6} - \sqrt{6}$

A_5 $4\sqrt{x} + 3\sqrt{x}$

B_1 $4\sqrt{2} + \sqrt{18}$

B_2 $\sqrt{8} + \sqrt{50}$

B_3 $5\sqrt{2} + \sqrt{18}$

Example 9–4 A

Perform the indicated operations and simplify. Assume that all variables represent nonnegative real numbers.

1. $5\sqrt{2} + 3\sqrt{2} = (5 + 3)\sqrt{2} = 8\sqrt{2}$ — Apply distributive property

You are now ready to do **A₁**.

2. $4\sqrt{7} - 2\sqrt{7} = (4 - 2)\sqrt{7} = 2\sqrt{7}$ — Distributive property

You are now ready to do **A₂**.

3. $3\sqrt{11} - 8\sqrt{11} = (3 - 8)\sqrt{11} = -5\sqrt{11}$ — Combine numerical coefficients

You are now ready to do **A₃**.

4. $12\sqrt{3} - \sqrt{3} = (12 - 1)\sqrt{3} = 11\sqrt{3}$ — Subtract numerical coefficients

You are now ready to do **A₄**.

5. $2\sqrt{a} + 3\sqrt{a} = (2 + 3)\sqrt{a} = 5\sqrt{a}$ — Add numerical coefficients

You are now ready to do **A₅**. ■

Consider the example

$$\sqrt{27} + 4\sqrt{3}.$$

It appears that the indicated addition cannot be performed since we do not have like radicals. However, we should have observed that $\sqrt{27}$ can be simplified as

$$\sqrt{27} = \sqrt{9 \cdot 3} = 3\sqrt{3}.$$

Our problem then becomes

$$\sqrt{27} + 4\sqrt{3} = 3\sqrt{3} + 4\sqrt{3} = 7\sqrt{3},$$

and we are able to add the like radicals. Therefore, *whenever we are dealing with radicals, we must be certain that all radicals are in simplest form.*

Example 9–4 B

Perform the indicated operations. Assume that all variables represent nonnegative real numbers.

1. $6\sqrt{3} + \sqrt{12} = 6\sqrt{3} + \sqrt{4 \cdot 3}$ — Factor $12 = 4 \cdot 3$

$= 6\sqrt{3} + 2\sqrt{3}$ — $\sqrt{4} = 2$

$= (6 + 2)\sqrt{3}$ — Distributive property

$= 8\sqrt{3}$ — Add

You are now ready to do **B₁**.

2. $\sqrt{45} + \sqrt{20} = \sqrt{9 \cdot 5} + \sqrt{4 \cdot 5}$ — Factor $45 = 9 \cdot 5$ and $20 = 4 \cdot 5$

$= 3\sqrt{5} + 2\sqrt{5}$ — $\sqrt{4} = 2$; $\sqrt{9} = 3$

$= 5\sqrt{5}$ — Add coefficients

You are now ready to do **B₂**.

3. $\sqrt{32} + 5\sqrt{8} = \sqrt{16 \cdot 2} + 5\sqrt{4 \cdot 2}$ — Factor $32 = 16 \cdot 2$; $8 = 4 \cdot 2$

$= 4\sqrt{2} + 5 \cdot 2\sqrt{2}$ — $\sqrt{16} = 4$ and $\sqrt{4} = 2$

$= 4\sqrt{2} + 10\sqrt{2}$ — Multiply $5 \cdot 2 = 10$

$= 14\sqrt{2}$ — Add coefficients

You are now ready to do **B₃**.

4. $\sqrt{24} - \sqrt{27} = \sqrt{4 \cdot 6} - \sqrt{9 \cdot 3}$ — Factor $24 = 4 \cdot 6$; $27 = 9 \cdot 3$

$= 2\sqrt{6} - 3\sqrt{3}$ — $\sqrt{4} = 2$; $\sqrt{9} = 3$

Note
After simplifying the radicals, we are still unable to carry out the indicated subtraction since the radicals are not like radicals. No further simplification is possible.

You are now ready to do **B₄**.

5. $3\sqrt{3a} - \sqrt{12a} + 5\sqrt{48a}$

$= 3\sqrt{3a} - \sqrt{4 \cdot 3a} + 5\sqrt{16 \cdot 3a}$ — Factor $12a = 4 \cdot 3a$; $48a = 16 \cdot 3a$

$= 3\sqrt{3a} - 2\sqrt{3a} + 5 \cdot 4\sqrt{3a}$ — $\sqrt{4} = 2$; $\sqrt{16} = 4$

$= 3\sqrt{3a} - 2\sqrt{3a} + 20\sqrt{3a}$ — $5 \cdot 4 = 20$

$= 21\sqrt{3a}$ — Combine coefficients

You are now ready to do **B₅**. ■

To combine like radicals

1. Perform any simplification within the terms.
2. Use the distributive property to combine terms that have like radicals.

Addition and subtraction involving *n*th roots (optional)

Addition and subtraction of radicals other than square roots follow the same procedure as addition and subtraction of expressions containing square roots. That is, *once we have determined that we have like radicals, the operations of addition and subtraction are performed only with the numerical coefficients.*

Example 9–4 C

Perform the indicated operations and simplify. Assume that all variables represent nonnegative real numbers.

1. $\sqrt[3]{5} + 6\sqrt[3]{5} = (1 + 6)\sqrt[3]{5} = 7\sqrt[3]{5}$ — Combine coefficients

You are now ready to do **C₁**.

2. $4\sqrt[5]{x^2} + 3\sqrt[5]{x^2} = (4 + 3)\sqrt[5]{x^2} = 7\sqrt[5]{x^2}$ — Add coefficients

You are now ready to do **C₂**.

3. $7\sqrt[3]{a^2b} - 5\sqrt[3]{a^2b} = (7 - 5)\sqrt[3]{a^2b} = 2\sqrt[3]{a^2b}$ — Subtract coefficients

You are now ready to do **C₃**.

4. $4\sqrt[3]{81} - \sqrt[3]{24} = 4\sqrt[3]{27 \cdot 3} - \sqrt[3]{8 \cdot 3}$ — Factor $81 = 27 \cdot 3$; $24 = 8 \cdot 3$

$= 4 \cdot 3\sqrt[3]{3} - 2\sqrt[3]{3}$ — $\sqrt[3]{27} = 3$; $\sqrt[3]{8} = 2$

$= 12\sqrt[3]{3} - 2\sqrt[3]{3}$ — $4 \cdot 3 = 12$

$= 10\sqrt[3]{3}$ — Subtract coefficients

You are now ready to do **C₄**.

5. $\sqrt[3]{16x^2y} + \sqrt[3]{54x^2y} = \sqrt[3]{8 \cdot 2x^2y} + \sqrt[3]{27 \cdot 2x^2y}$ — Factor $16 = 8 \cdot 2$; $54 = 27 \cdot 2$

$= 2\sqrt[3]{2x^2y} + 3\sqrt[3]{2x^2y}$ — $\sqrt[3]{8} = 2$; $\sqrt[3]{27} = 3$

$= 5\sqrt[3]{2x^2y}$ — Add coefficients

You are now ready to do **C₅**. ■

B₄ $\sqrt{45} - \sqrt{12}$

B₅ $5\sqrt{5x} - \sqrt{20x} + 2\sqrt{80x}$

C₁ $\sqrt[4]{7} + 3\sqrt[4]{7}$

C₂ $7\sqrt[5]{a^3} + \sqrt[5]{a^3}$

C₃ $4\sqrt[3]{a^2b} + 3\sqrt[3]{a^2b}$

C₄ $2\sqrt[3]{24} - \sqrt[3]{81}$

C₅ $\sqrt[3]{8ab^2} + \sqrt[3]{27ab^2}$

Answers to section 9–4 margin exercises

A_1 $5\sqrt{3}$ **A_2** $5\sqrt{11}$ **A_3** $-2\sqrt{7}$ **A_4** $4\sqrt{6}$ **A_5** $7\sqrt{x}$ **B_1** $7\sqrt{2}$ **B_2** $7\sqrt{2}$ **B_3** $8\sqrt{2}$ **B_4** $3\sqrt{5} - 2\sqrt{3}$ **B_5** $11\sqrt{5x}$ **C_1** $4\sqrt[4]{7}$ **C_2** $8\sqrt[5]{a^3}$ **C_3** $7\sqrt[3]{a^2b}$ **C_4** $\sqrt[3]{3}$ **C_5** $5\sqrt[3]{ab^2}$

Mastery points
Can you • Identify like radicals? • Add and subtract like radicals?

Exercise 9–4

Directions Perform the indicated operations and simplify. Assume that all variables represent nonnegative real numbers. See examples 9–4 A and B.

Examples $\boxed{A_4}$ $3\sqrt{6} + 2\sqrt{6} - \sqrt{6}$

Solutions

$= (3 + 2 - 1)\sqrt{6}$ Distributive property

$= 4\sqrt{6}$ Combine coefficients

$\boxed{B_3}$ $5\sqrt{2} + \sqrt{18}$

$= 5\sqrt{2} + \sqrt{9 \cdot 2}$ Factor $18 = 9 \cdot 2$

$= 5\sqrt{2} + 3\sqrt{2}$ $\sqrt{9} = 3$

$= (5 + 3)\sqrt{2}$ Distributive property

$= 8\sqrt{2}$ Add coefficients

1. $5\sqrt{3} + 4\sqrt{3}$

2. $8\sqrt{7} - 2\sqrt{7}$

3. $6\sqrt{5} + 4\sqrt{5}$

4. $9\sqrt{6} - 6\sqrt{6}$

5. $2\sqrt{3} + 7\sqrt{3} - 3\sqrt{3}$

6. $5\sqrt{5} - 4\sqrt{5} + 6\sqrt{5}$

7. $\sqrt{7} + 5\sqrt{7} - 3\sqrt{7}$

8. $2\sqrt{10} + 11\sqrt{10} - 9\sqrt{10}$

9. $\sqrt{a} + 2\sqrt{a}$

10. $3\sqrt{x} + 4\sqrt{x}$

11. $5\sqrt{a} - 4\sqrt{a} + 7\sqrt{a}$

12. $6\sqrt{y} - \sqrt{y} + 4\sqrt{y}$

13. $5\sqrt{xy} + 2\sqrt{xy}$

$\boxed{\textbf{14.}}$ $3\sqrt{x} + 2\sqrt{y} - \sqrt{x}$

15. $5\sqrt{a} + 2\sqrt{ab} + 3\sqrt{a}$

16. $\sqrt{ab} + 2\sqrt{ab} + 3\sqrt{a}$

17. $5\sqrt{xy} - \sqrt{xy} + 3\sqrt{y}$

$\boxed{\textbf{18.}}$ $\sqrt{20} + 3\sqrt{5}$

19. $\sqrt{8} + 5\sqrt{2}$

20. $\sqrt{12} + \sqrt{75}$

21. $\sqrt{48} - \sqrt{27}$

22. $2\sqrt{3} + 3\sqrt{12}$

23. $5\sqrt{7} + 4\sqrt{63}$

24. $5\sqrt{3} + \sqrt{27} - \sqrt{12}$

25. $4\sqrt{2} - \sqrt{8} + \sqrt{50}$

26. $\sqrt{75} - 4\sqrt{3} + 2\sqrt{27}$

27. $\sqrt{12} + \sqrt{18} + \sqrt{50}$

28. $\sqrt{63} - \sqrt{28} + \sqrt{24}$

29. $\sqrt{50a} + \sqrt{8a}$

30. $\sqrt{32a} - \sqrt{18a}$

31. $3\sqrt{9x} - 5\sqrt{4x}$

32. $2\sqrt{4x^2y} + 3\sqrt{25x^2y}$

33. $2\sqrt{8a} + 4\sqrt{50a} - 7\sqrt{2a}$

34. $3\sqrt{48b} - 2\sqrt{12b} + \sqrt{3b}$

35. $\sqrt{50a} + 3\sqrt{12a} - \sqrt{18a}$

36. $4\sqrt{25x^2y} + 3\sqrt{81x^2y} - 2\sqrt{2y}$

37. We can find the height, h, of the given figure by finding b from the following formula: $b = \sqrt{c^2 - s^2}$. If $c = 10$ units and $s = 6$ units, find h.

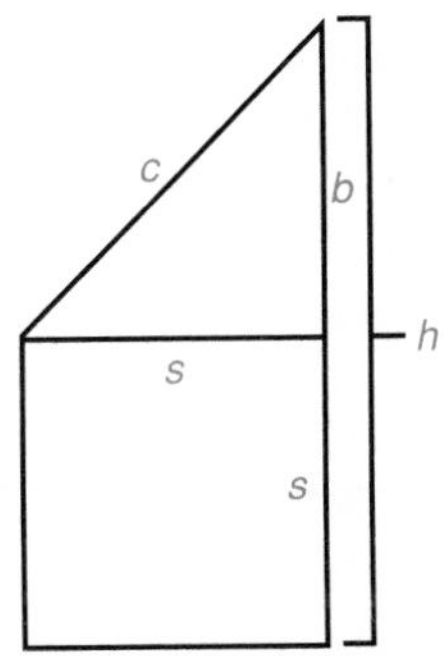

38. Use exercise 37 to find the height of the figure if $c = 13$ feet and $s = 5$ feet.

39. The figure is made up of 9 equal squares in which each square has an area of 7.29 square units. What are the dimensions of the figure?

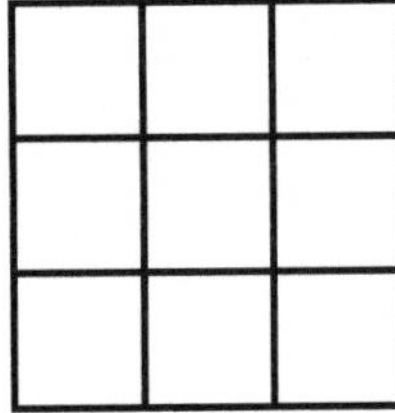

Optional

Directions Perform the indicated operations and simplify. Assume that all variables represent nonnegative real numbers. See example 9–4 C.

Example C₂ $7\sqrt[5]{a^3} + \sqrt[5]{a^3}$

Solution $= (7 + 1)\sqrt[5]{a^3}$ Distributive property

$= 8\sqrt[5]{a^3}$ Combine coefficients

40. $3\sqrt[3]{4} + 5\sqrt[3]{4}$

41. $7\sqrt[5]{2} - 4\sqrt[5]{2} + 3\sqrt[5]{2}$

42. $9\sqrt[4]{3} + 6\sqrt[4]{3} + 2\sqrt[4]{3}$

43. $\sqrt[3]{16} + \sqrt[3]{54}$

44. $\sqrt[3]{24} - \sqrt[3]{81}$

45. $\sqrt[3]{81} + 2\sqrt[3]{250}$

46. $\sqrt[3]{8a^2} + \sqrt[3]{27a^2}$

47. $\sqrt[4]{16x^3} + \sqrt[4]{81x^3}$

48. $\sqrt[4]{625a} - \sqrt[4]{81a}$

49. $\sqrt[3]{64x^2y} - \sqrt[3]{27x^2y}$

50. $\sqrt[3]{x^6y} + 2x^2\sqrt[3]{y}$

51. $3a\sqrt[3]{b^2} - \sqrt[3]{a^3b^2}$

Review exercises

Directions Multiply the following expressions. See section 3–3.

1. $3x(2x - y)$

2. $2a^2(a^2 - b^2)$

3. $(x - 1)(x - 1)$

4. $(y - 1)(y + 1)$

5. $(2x + 1)(2x - 1)$

6. $(x + 3y)(x + 2y)$

7. $(x - y)^2$

8. $(a + 2b)^2$

9–5 Further operations with radicals

Multiplication of radical expressions

In section 9–2, we learned the procedure for multiplying two radicals. We now combine those ideas along with the *distributive property,* $a(b + c) = ab + ac$, to perform multiplication of radical expressions containing more than one term.

Example 9–5 A

Perform the indicated operations and simplify. Assume that all variables represent nonnegative real numbers.

1. $\sqrt{2}(2 + \sqrt{3}) = \sqrt{2} \cdot 2 + \sqrt{2}\sqrt{3}$ — Distributive property
$= 2\sqrt{2} + \sqrt{6}$ — $\sqrt{2}\sqrt{3} = \sqrt{6}$

You are now ready to do **A₁**.

A₁ $\sqrt{5}(3 - \sqrt{2})$

2. $\sqrt{3}(3 + \sqrt{3}) = \sqrt{3} \cdot 3 + \sqrt{3}\sqrt{3}$ — Distributive property
$= 3\sqrt{3} + \sqrt{9}$ — $\sqrt{3}\sqrt{3} = \sqrt{9}$
$= 3\sqrt{3} + 3$ — $\sqrt{9} = 3$

You are now ready to do **A₂**.

A₂ $\sqrt{7}(\sqrt{7} + 4)$

3. $\sqrt{2}(\sqrt{3} + \sqrt{5}) = \sqrt{2}\sqrt{3} + \sqrt{2}\sqrt{5}$ — Distributive property
$= \sqrt{2 \cdot 3} + \sqrt{2 \cdot 5}$ — $\sqrt{a}\sqrt{b} = \sqrt{a \cdot b}$
$= \sqrt{6} + \sqrt{10}$ — Multiply in radicands

You are now ready to do **A₃**.

A₃ $\sqrt{2}(\sqrt{14} - \sqrt{6})$

4. $\sqrt{3}(\sqrt{6} + \sqrt{21}) = \sqrt{3}\sqrt{6} + \sqrt{3}\sqrt{21}$ — Distributive property
$= \sqrt{18} + \sqrt{63}$ — Multiply radicands
$= \sqrt{9 \cdot 2} + \sqrt{9 \cdot 7}$ — Factor $18 = 9 \cdot 2$; $63 = 9 \cdot 7$
$= 3\sqrt{2} + 3\sqrt{7}$ — Simplify radicals

You are now ready to do **A₄**.

A₄ $\sqrt{5}(\sqrt{15} + \sqrt{10})$

5. $(\sqrt{2} + \sqrt{3})(\sqrt{2} + 5\sqrt{3})$

Note
In this example, we are multiplying two binomials. Therefore, as we did in chapter 3, we will *multiply each term in the first parentheses by each term in the second parentheses.*

$= \sqrt{2}\sqrt{2} + \sqrt{2} \cdot 5\sqrt{3} + \sqrt{3}\sqrt{2} + \sqrt{3} \cdot 5\sqrt{3}$ — Distributive property
$= \sqrt{4} + 5\sqrt{6} + \sqrt{6} + 5 \cdot \sqrt{9}$ — Multiply radicands
$= 2 + 5\sqrt{6} + \sqrt{6} + 5 \cdot 3$ — $\sqrt{4} = 2$, $\sqrt{9} = 3$
$= 2 + 5\sqrt{6} + \sqrt{6} + 15$
$= 17 + 6\sqrt{6}$ — Combine like terms

You are now ready to do **A₅**.

A₅ $(\sqrt{2} + \sqrt{3})(\sqrt{2} - 2\sqrt{3})$

6. $(3 - \sqrt{2})(3 + \sqrt{2}) = 9 + 3\sqrt{2} - 3\sqrt{2} - \sqrt{4}$ — Distributive property
$= 9 + 3\sqrt{2} - 3\sqrt{2} - 2$ — Simplify radicals
$= 9 - 2$ — Combine like terms
$= 7$ — Subtract

We observe that when we simplified, there were no longer any radicals in the answer.

You are now ready to do **A₆**.

A₆ $(3 + \sqrt{5})(3 - \sqrt{5})$

7. $(\sqrt{a} - \sqrt{b})(\sqrt{a} + \sqrt{b})$
$= \sqrt{a}\sqrt{a} + \sqrt{a}\sqrt{b} - \sqrt{b}\sqrt{a} - \sqrt{b}\sqrt{b}$ — Distributive property
$= \sqrt{a^2} + \sqrt{ab} - \sqrt{ab} - \sqrt{b^2}$ — Multiply radicands
$= a + \sqrt{ab} - \sqrt{ab} - b$ — $\sqrt{a^2} = a$ and $\sqrt{b^2} = b$
$= a - b$ — Combine like terms

You are now ready to do **A₇**.

A₇ $(\sqrt{x} - \sqrt{y})(\sqrt{x} + \sqrt{y})$

A_8 $(\sqrt{7} - \sqrt{2})^2$

8. $(\sqrt{3} + 2\sqrt{2})^2$

$= (\sqrt{3} + 2\sqrt{2})(\sqrt{3} + 2\sqrt{2})$	
$= \sqrt{3}\sqrt{3} + \sqrt{3} \cdot 2\sqrt{2} + \sqrt{3} \cdot 2\sqrt{2} + 2\sqrt{2} \cdot 2\sqrt{2}$	Distributive property
$= \sqrt{9} + 2\sqrt{6} + 2\sqrt{6} + 4\sqrt{4}$	Multiply radicands
$= 3 + 2\sqrt{6} + 2\sqrt{6} + 4 \cdot 2$	Simplify radicals
$= 3 + 2\sqrt{6} + 2\sqrt{6} + 8$	Multiply
$= 11 + 4\sqrt{6}$	Combine like terms

You are now ready to do $\mathbf{A_8}$. ■

Conjugate factors

In example 9–5 A 6 and 7, the type of factors that we were multiplying are called **conjugate factors.** That is,

1. $(3 - \sqrt{2})$ and $(3 + \sqrt{2})$ are conjugate factors,
2. $(\sqrt{a} - \sqrt{b})$ and $(\sqrt{a} + \sqrt{b})$ are conjugate factors.

B_1 $3 + \sqrt{6}$

> **Definition of conjugates**
> The algebraic expressions $x + y$ and $x - y$ are conjugates of each other.

Example 9–5 B

Form the conjugates of the given expressions.

1. $\sqrt{7} + 2$ The conjugate is $\sqrt{7} - 2$.

You are now ready to do $\mathbf{B_1}$.

2. $\sqrt{11} - \sqrt{6}$ The conjugate is $\sqrt{11} + \sqrt{6}$.

You are now ready to do $\mathbf{B_2}$. ■

As we noted in example 9–5 A 6 and 7, the product of an expression and its conjugate produced an answer in which the radical sign was eliminated.

B_2 $6 - 3\sqrt{2}$

> **Product of conjugates**
> Given conjugates $x + y$ and $x - y$,
> $$(x + y)(x - y) = x^2 - y^2.$$

We use this to rationalize the denominator of a fraction in which the denominator has two terms where one or both terms contain a square root.

Rationalizing the denominator

To rationalize the denominator of a radical expression containing two terms, we use the fundamental principle of fractions as follows:

> **Rationalizing the denominator**
> To rationalize the denominator that has two terms where one or both terms contain a square root, multiply the numerator and the denominator by the conjugate of the denominator.

Example 9–5 C

Rationalize the denominators.

1. $\frac{2}{\sqrt{7}+2} = \frac{2}{\sqrt{7}+2} \cdot \frac{\sqrt{7}-2}{\sqrt{7}-2}$ — Multiply by the conjugate of the denominator

$= \frac{2(\sqrt{7}-2)}{(\sqrt{7})^2-(2)^2}$ — $(x+y)(x-y) = x^2 - y^2$

$= \frac{2\sqrt{7}-4}{7-4}$ — Simplify in numerator and denominator

$= \frac{2\sqrt{7}-4}{3}$ — Subtract in denominator

You are now ready to do **C_1**.

C_1 $\frac{3}{7+\sqrt{2}}$

2. $\frac{5}{\sqrt{11}-\sqrt{6}} = \frac{5}{\sqrt{11}-\sqrt{6}} \cdot \frac{\sqrt{11}+\sqrt{6}}{\sqrt{11}+\sqrt{6}}$ — Multiply by the conjugate of the denominator

$= \frac{5(\sqrt{11}+\sqrt{6})}{(\sqrt{11})^2-(\sqrt{6})^2}$ — $(x+y)(x-y) = x^2 - y^2$

$= \frac{5(\sqrt{11}+\sqrt{6})}{11-6}$ — Simplify radicals

$= \frac{5(\sqrt{11}+\sqrt{6})}{5}$ — Subtract in denominator

$= \sqrt{11}+\sqrt{6}$ — Reduce (by 5) to lowest terms

You are now ready to do **C_2**.

C_2 $\frac{4}{\sqrt{6}-\sqrt{2}}$

3. $\frac{\sqrt{3}}{5-2\sqrt{3}} = \frac{\sqrt{3}}{5-2\sqrt{3}} \cdot \frac{5+2\sqrt{3}}{5+2\sqrt{3}}$ — Multiply by the conjugate of the denominator

$= \frac{\sqrt{3}(5+2\sqrt{3})}{(5)^2-(2\sqrt{3})^2}$ — $(x+y)(x-y) = x^2 - y^2$

$= \frac{5\sqrt{3}+2\sqrt{9}}{5^2-2^2(\sqrt{3})^2}$ — Simplify radicals

$= \frac{5\sqrt{3}+2\cdot 3}{25-4\cdot 3}$ — Simplify radicals

$= \frac{5\sqrt{3}+6}{25-12}$ — Perform operations

$= \frac{5\sqrt{3}+6}{13}$ — Subtract in denominator

You are now ready to do **C_3**.

C_3 $\frac{\sqrt{5}}{4-\sqrt{5}}$

4. $\frac{6+\sqrt{2}}{\sqrt{2}-5} = \frac{(6+\sqrt{2})(\sqrt{2}+5)}{(\sqrt{2}-5)(\sqrt{2}+5)}$ — Multiply by the conjugate of the denominator

$= \frac{6\sqrt{2}+30+2+5\sqrt{2}}{2-25}$ — Multiply in numerator and denominator

$= \frac{11\sqrt{2}+32}{-23}$ — Subtract in denominator

$= -\frac{11\sqrt{2}+32}{23}$ or $\frac{-11\sqrt{2}-32}{23}$ — Standard form

You are now ready to do **C_4**. ■

C_4 $\frac{4-\sqrt{3}}{4+\sqrt{3}}$

Answers to section 9–5 margin exercises

A_1 $3\sqrt{5}-\sqrt{10}$ A_2 $7+4\sqrt{7}$ A_3 $2\sqrt{7}-2\sqrt{3}$ A_4 $5\sqrt{3}+5\sqrt{2}$ A_5 $-4-\sqrt{6}$ A_6 4 A_7 $x-y$ A_8 $9-2\sqrt{14}$ B_1 $3-\sqrt{6}$ B_2 $6+3\sqrt{2}$ C_1 $\frac{21-3\sqrt{2}}{47}$ C_2 $\sqrt{6}+\sqrt{2}$ C_3 $\frac{4\sqrt{5}+5}{11}$ C_4 $\frac{19-8\sqrt{3}}{13}$

Mastery points

Can you

- Multiply radical expressions containing more than one term?
- Form conjugate factors?
- Multiply conjugate factors?
- Rationalize a denominator that has two terms in which one or both terms contain a square root?

Exercise 9–5

Directions Assume that all variables represent positive real numbers. Perform the indicated operations and simplify. See example 9–5 A.

Example [A3] $\sqrt{2}(\sqrt{14} - \sqrt{6})$

Solution

$= \sqrt{2}\sqrt{14} - \sqrt{2}\sqrt{6}$ Distributive property
$= \sqrt{28} - \sqrt{12}$ Multiply radicands
$= \sqrt{4 \cdot 7} - \sqrt{4 \cdot 3}$ Factor radicands
$= 2\sqrt{7} - 2\sqrt{3}$ Simplify radicals

Example [A5] $(\sqrt{2} + \sqrt{3})(\sqrt{2} - 2\sqrt{3})$

Solution

$= \sqrt{2}\sqrt{2} - \sqrt{2} \cdot 2\sqrt{3} + \sqrt{3}\sqrt{2} - \sqrt{3} \cdot 2\sqrt{3}$ Distributive property
$= 2 - 2\sqrt{6} + \sqrt{6} - 2 \cdot 3$ Simplify radicals
$= 2 - 2\sqrt{6} + \sqrt{6} - 6$
$= -4 - \sqrt{6}$ Combine like terms

1. $3(\sqrt{2} + \sqrt{3})$

2. $5(2\sqrt{6} + \sqrt{2})$

3. $\sqrt{2}(\sqrt{3} + \sqrt{7})$

4. $\sqrt{5}(\sqrt{7} - \sqrt{3})$

[5.] $3\sqrt{2}(2\sqrt{3} - \sqrt{11})$

6. $\sqrt{6}(\sqrt{2} + \sqrt{3})$

7. $\sqrt{5}(\sqrt{15} - \sqrt{10})$

8. $\sqrt{14}(\sqrt{21} + \sqrt{10})$

9. $2\sqrt{7}(\sqrt{35} - 3\sqrt{14})$

10. $\sqrt{a}(\sqrt{ab} + \sqrt{b})$

11. $\sqrt{a}(3\sqrt{a} + \sqrt{b})$

12. $(5 + \sqrt{3})(4 - \sqrt{3})$

13. $(3 + \sqrt{2})(4 + \sqrt{2})$

14. $(5 - \sqrt{5})(5 - \sqrt{5})$

[15.] $(3 - 4\sqrt{a})(4 - 3\sqrt{a})$

16. $(7 + 2\sqrt{y})(6 + 5\sqrt{y})$

17. $(\sqrt{3} + \sqrt{2})(\sqrt{3} - \sqrt{2})$

18. $(\sqrt{7} + \sqrt{5})(\sqrt{7} - \sqrt{5})$

19. $(2 + \sqrt{6})(2 - \sqrt{6})$

20. $(5 - \sqrt{3})(5 + \sqrt{3})$

21. $(2 + \sqrt{5})^2$

22. $(3 - \sqrt{7})^2$

23. $(\sqrt{x} + \sqrt{y})^2$

24. $(\sqrt{a} - \sqrt{b})^2$

25. $(\sqrt{x} - \sqrt{y})(\sqrt{x} + \sqrt{y})$

26. $(2\sqrt{a} - \sqrt{b})(2\sqrt{a} + \sqrt{b})$

27. $(x\sqrt{y} + \sqrt{z})(x\sqrt{y} - \sqrt{z})$

28. $(a\sqrt{b} + c)(a\sqrt{b} - c)$

29. $(2\sqrt{x} + y)^2$

30. $(3\sqrt{a} + \sqrt{b})^2$

Directions Form the conjugate of the given expressions. See example 9–5 B.

Example B_2 $6 - 3\sqrt{2}$

Solution $6 + 3\sqrt{2}$ The conjugate

31. $11 - \sqrt{3}$

32. $5\sqrt{7} - \sqrt{2}$

33. $\sqrt{a} + 3\sqrt{b}$

34. $a\sqrt{b} + \sqrt{c}$

Directions Simplify the following expressions, leaving all denominators rationalized. See example 9–5 C.

Example C_1 $\dfrac{3}{7 + \sqrt{2}}$

Solution

$$= \frac{3}{7 + \sqrt{2}} \cdot \frac{7 - \sqrt{2}}{7 - \sqrt{2}}$$ Multiply by the conjugate of the denominator

$$= \frac{3(7 - \sqrt{2})}{(7)^2 - (\sqrt{2})^2}$$ $(x + y)(x - y) = x^2 - y^2$

$$= \frac{21 - 3\sqrt{2}}{49 - 2}$$ Simplify radicals

$$= \frac{21 - 3\sqrt{2}}{47}$$ Subtract

35. $\dfrac{1}{\sqrt{2} + 3}$

36. $\dfrac{1}{\sqrt{3} - 2}$

37. $\dfrac{7}{2 + \sqrt{7}}$

38. $\dfrac{6}{3 - \sqrt{6}}$

39. $\dfrac{3}{\sqrt{6} - \sqrt{3}}$

40. $\dfrac{1}{\sqrt{a} + b}$

41. $\dfrac{3}{2\sqrt{3} - \sqrt{5}}$

42. $\dfrac{4}{2\sqrt{3} - \sqrt{6}}$

43. $\dfrac{1 + \sqrt{5}}{1 - \sqrt{5}}$

44. $\dfrac{\sqrt{3} - \sqrt{7}}{\sqrt{3} + \sqrt{7}}$

45. $\dfrac{\sqrt{a} + b}{\sqrt{a} - b}$

Review exercises

Directions Perform the indicated operations. See sections 9–1 and 9–2.

1. $(\sqrt{7})^2$
2. $(\sqrt{x})^2$
3. $(\sqrt{x + 1})^2$

Directions Perform the indicated operations. See section 3–3.

4. $(x + 1)^2$
5. $(x - 2)^2$

Directions Find the solution set for the following equations. See section 4–6.

6. $x + 6 = x^2$
7. $x + 2 = x^2 - 9x + 18$
8. $x + 1 = x^2 + 2x + 1$

▣ 9–6 Equations involving radicals (optional)

Radical equations

An equation in which the unknown quantity appears under a radical symbol is called a **radical equation.** Examples of radical equations are

$$\sqrt{x} = 5; \quad \sqrt{x + 2} = 7; \quad \text{and} \quad \sqrt{x + 2} = x - 4.$$

In this section, we will consider radical equations containing only square roots.

Solving radical equations involves squaring both members of an equation to eliminate the square roots.

Squaring property of equality

If P and Q are polynomials and if

$$P = Q,$$

then all solutions of $P = Q$ are also solutions of the equation

$$P^2 = Q^2.$$

Concept

If each member of an equation is squared, the solution(s) of the original equation are solution(s) of the resulting equation.

A₁ $\sqrt{x} = 7$

This property implies that there *may be* solutions of the equation $P^2 = Q^2$ that are not solutions of the original equation $P = Q$. If such solutions exist, they are called *extraneous solutions* (roots). Thus, all apparent solutions must be checked in the original equation.

To solve a radical equation containing square roots

1. Restate the equation (if necessary) so that a radical is by itself in one member of the equation.
2. Square each member of the equation and combine like terms.
3. Repeat steps 1 and 2 if a radical remains in the equation.
4. Solve the resulting equation.
5. Check all solutions in the original equation.

Example 9–6 A

A₂ $\sqrt{x+5} = 6$

Find the solution set. Identify extraneous solutions if there are any.

1. $\sqrt{x} = 5$

$(\sqrt{x})^2 = (5)^2$ — Square both members

$x = 25$

Check:

$\sqrt{x} = 5$

$\sqrt{(25)} = 5$ — Substitute into original equation

$5 = 5$ — True

$\{25\}$ — Solution set

You are now ready to do **A₁**.

2. $\sqrt{x+2} = 7$

$(\sqrt{x+2})^2 = (7)^2$ — Square both members

$x + 2 = 49$

$x = 47$ — Subtract 2 from both members

Check:

$\sqrt{x+2} = 7$

$\sqrt{(47)+2} = 7$ — Substitute into original equation

$\sqrt{49} = 7$

$7 = 7$ — True

$\{47\}$ — Solution set

You are now ready to do **A₂**.

A₃ $\sqrt{x+6} = x$

3. $4 + \sqrt{x+2} = x$

$\sqrt{x+2} = x - 4$ Isolate the radical by subtracting 4

$(\sqrt{x+2})^2 = (x-4)^2$ Square both members

$x + 2 = x^2 - 8x + 16$ Don't forget the middle term when squaring $(x-4)^2$

$0 = x^2 - 9x + 14$ Subtract x and 2

$0 = (x-7)(x-2)$ Factor right member

$x - 7 = 0$ or $x - 2 = 0$ Set each factor equal to 0 and solve

$x = 7$ $\quad$ $x = 2$

Check:

$4 + \sqrt{x+2} = x$

$4 + \sqrt{(7)+2} = (7)$ Substitute 4

$4 + \sqrt{9} = 7$

$4 + 3 = 7$

$7 = 7$ True

$4 + \sqrt{x+2} = x$

$4 + \sqrt{(2)+2} = (2)$

$4 + \sqrt{4} = 2$

$4 + 2 = 2$

$6 = 2$ False

Therefore, 7 is the only solution to the equation. 2 is an *extraneous root.*

$\{7\}$ Solution set

You are now ready to do **A₃**.

4. $\sqrt{x+1} = x + 1$

$(\sqrt{x+1})^2 = (x+1)^2$ Square both members

$x + 1 = x^2 + 2x + 1$ Don't forget the middle term when squaring $(x+1)^2$

$0 = x^2 + x$ Subtract x and 1 from each member

$0 = x(x+1)$ Factor right member

$x = 0$ or $x + 1 = 0$ Set each factor equal to 0 and solve

Therefore, $x = 0$ $\quad$ $x = -1$.

A₄ $\sqrt{c+4} = c - 8$

Check:

For 0:

$\sqrt{x+1} = x + 1$

$\sqrt{(0)+1} = (0) + 1$ Substitute

$\sqrt{1} = 1$

$1 = 1$ True

For -1:

$\sqrt{x+1} = x + 1$

$\sqrt{(-1)+1} = (-1) + 1$

$\sqrt{0} = 0$

$0 = 0$ True

Therefore, 0 and -1 are solutions of the equation.

$\{-1, 0\}$ Solution set

You are now ready to do **A₄**.

5. $\sqrt{3x+4} = \sqrt{x+14}$

Note

There are two square roots in this problem, but we can eliminate both radical symbols by squaring both members.

$(\sqrt{3x+4})^2 = (\sqrt{x+14})^2$ Square both members

$3x + 4 = x + 14$ Subtract x from each member

$2x + 4 = 14$ Subtract 4 from each member

$2x = 10$ Divide each member by 2

$x = 5$

Check:

$$\sqrt{3x+4} = \sqrt{x+14}$$
$$\sqrt{3(5)+4} = \sqrt{(5)+14} \quad \text{Substitute into original equation}$$
$$\sqrt{15+4} = \sqrt{19}$$
$$\sqrt{19} = \sqrt{19} \quad \text{True}$$
$$\{5\} \quad \text{Solution set}$$

You are now ready to do **A₅**.

A₅ $\sqrt{2x+5} = \sqrt{x+8}$

6. $\sqrt{x+3} = -6$

$$(\sqrt{x+3})^2 = (-6)^2 \quad \text{Square both members}$$
$$x + 3 = 36 \quad \text{Subtract 3 from each member}$$
$$x = 33$$

Check:

$$\sqrt{x+3} = -6$$
$$\sqrt{(33)+3} = -6 \quad \text{Substitute into original equation}$$
$$\sqrt{36} = -6$$
$$6 = -6 \quad \text{False}$$

$x = 33$ does not check because $\sqrt{36} = 6$, not -6. We conclude that there is *no solution* to this equation. A set that contains no elements is called an **empty set** or a **null set.** It is denoted by { } or ∅.

{ } or ∅ — The solution set is empty

You are now ready to do **A₆**. ■

A₆ $\sqrt{a+7} = -4$

Answers to section 9–6 margin exercises

A₁ {49} **A₂** {31} **A₃** {3} **A₄** {12} **A₅** {3} **A₆** ∅

Mastery points
Can you • Solve equations containing radicals?

Exercise 9–6

Directions Find the solution set. See example 9–6 A.

Examples **A₂** $\sqrt{x+5} = 6$

Solutions

$$(\sqrt{x+5})^2 = (6)^2 \quad \text{Square each member}$$
$$x + 5 = 36 \quad \text{Solve for } x$$
$$x = 31$$

Check

$$\sqrt{31+5} = 6 \quad \text{Substitute}$$
$$\sqrt{36} = 6$$
$$6 = 6 \quad \text{True}$$
$$\{31\} \quad \text{Solution set}$$

A₅ $\sqrt{2x+5} = \sqrt{x+8}$

$$(\sqrt{2x+5})^2 = (\sqrt{x+8})^2$$
$$2x + 5 = x + 8$$
$$x + 5 = 8$$
$$x = 3$$

Check

$$\sqrt{2(3)+5} = \sqrt{(3)+8}$$
$$\sqrt{6+5} = \sqrt{11}$$
$$\sqrt{11} = \sqrt{11} \quad \text{True}$$
$$\{3\}$$

1. $\sqrt{x} = 4$

2. $\sqrt{x+5} = 4$

3. $\sqrt{x-3} = 5$

4. $\sqrt{2x+1} = 5$

5. $\sqrt{2x+6} = 6$

6. $\sqrt{x} + 4 = 7$

7. $\sqrt{x} + 7 = 5$

8. $\sqrt{x} + 8 = 4$

9. $\sqrt{2x + 1} = \sqrt{x + 5}$

10. $\sqrt{2x + 4} = \sqrt{3x - 2}$

11. $\sqrt{5x - 3} = \sqrt{2x + 9}$

12. $\sqrt{7x - 4} = \sqrt{3x + 20}$

13. $\sqrt{6x + 2} = \sqrt{3x - 4}$

14. $\sqrt{x}\sqrt{x + 2} = 0$

15. $\sqrt{x}\sqrt{x + 4} = 0$

16. $\sqrt{x}\sqrt{x - 6} = 4$

17. $\sqrt{x}\sqrt{x + 6} = 4$

18. $\sqrt{x + 3}\sqrt{x} = 2$

19. $\sqrt{x^2 + 1} = x + 2$

20. $\sqrt{x^2 + 3x} = x + 1$

21. $\sqrt{x^2 + 3x} = x - 3$

22. $\sqrt{x^2 + 12} = x + 2$

23. $\sqrt{x + 6} = x$

24. $\sqrt{5x + 6} = x$

25. $\sqrt{2x + 8} = x$

26. $\sqrt{4x + 12} = x$

27. $\sqrt{x - 4} = x - 6$

28. $\sqrt{x + 2} = x + 2$

29. $\sqrt{x + 4} + 8 = x$

30. $\sqrt{x} + 6 = x$

31. $\sqrt{x + 7} = 2x - 1$

32. $\sqrt{2x - 1} + 2x = 7$

Directions Find the unknown number in each of the following problems.

33. A certain number is equal to the square root of the sum of that number and 12.

34. The square root of the product of a number and 12 is equal to the number increased by 3.

35. The square root of the sum of a number and 11 is one less than the number.

36. The square root of the product of a number and 4 is three less than the number.

Review exercises

Directions Completely factor the following expressions. See sections 4–2 and 4–4.

1. $x^2 - 4$

2. $x^2 + 9x + 18$

3. $x^2 - 3x - 10$

4. $x^2 - 6x + 9$

Directions Simplify. See section 9–1.

5. $\sqrt{81}$

6. $\sqrt{49}$

7. $\sqrt{121}$

8. Solve the equation $x^2 = 64$. See section 4–6.

Chapter 9 lead-in problem

Roger has a ladder that will extend to a length of 21 feet. For the ladder to be safe to climb on, it must be placed 7 feet away from the house. The roof is 20 feet above the ground. Will the ladder be able to reach the roof safely? If not, how far up will the ladder reach? (Leave your answer rounded to one decimal place.)

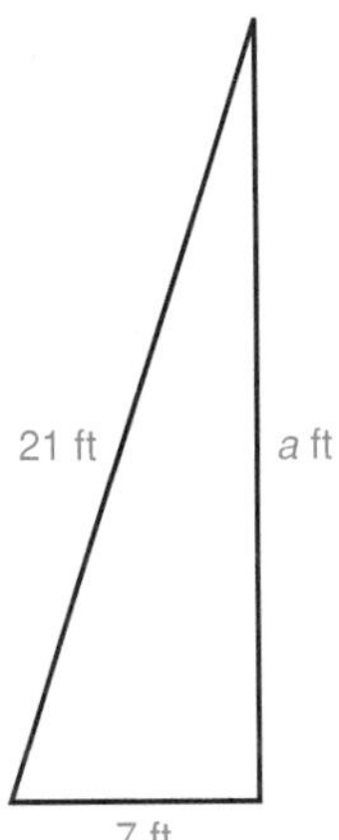

Solution

$a^2 + b^2 = c^2$	Pythagorean Theorem
$a^2 + (7)^2 = (21)^2$	Substitute 21 for c and 7 for b
$a^2 + 49 = 441$	Simplify
$a^2 = 392$	Isolate a^2
$a \approx 19.8$	Round the $\sqrt{392}$ to one decimal place

The ladder will not be able to safely reach the roof. The ladder's maximum safe reach is approximately 19.8 feet.

Chapter 9 summary

1. The principal square root of a positive number, denoted by $\sqrt{}$, is positive.
2. The **principal *n*th root** of a number, denoted by $\sqrt[n]{}$, has the same sign as the number itself.
3. When we multiply two radicals *having the same index,* we multiply the radicands and put the product under a radical symbol with the common index. $\sqrt{a}\sqrt{b} = \sqrt{ab}$ and $\sqrt[n]{a}\sqrt[n]{b} = \sqrt[n]{ab}$.
4. We can simplify a radical if the radicand has a factor(s) whose exponent is equal to or greater than the value of the index.
5. The *n*th root of a *fraction* can be written as the *n*th root of the numerator over the *n*th root of the denominator. $\sqrt{\frac{a}{b}} = \frac{\sqrt{a}}{\sqrt{b}}$ and $\sqrt[n]{\frac{a}{b}} = \frac{\sqrt[n]{a}}{\sqrt[n]{b}}$, where $b \neq 0$.
6. We eliminate radicals from the denominator of a fraction by **rationalizing** the denominator.
7. We can only add or subtract **like radicals.**
8. **Conjugate factors** are used to rationalize a denominator when the denominator has two terms where one or both terms contain a square root.
9. A set that contains no elements is called an **empty set** or a **null set,** which is denoted by $\emptyset$ or $\{\ \ \}$.
10. The **squaring property of equality** states that if both members of an equation are squared, all solutions of the original equation are among the solutions of the squared equation.
11. When solving equations where the unknown is under a radical symbol, we must check for **extraneous roots.**

Chapter 9 review

Directions Assume that all variables represent positive real numbers.

[9–1]

Directions Find the indicated root.

1. $\sqrt{81}$ **2.** $\sqrt{25}$ **3.** $-\sqrt{9}$ **4.** $-\sqrt{49}$

[9–2]

Directions Perform any indicated operations and simplify.

5. $\sqrt{40}$ **6.** $\sqrt{18a^2b^3}$ **7.** $\sqrt{2}\sqrt{14}$ **8.** $\sqrt{18}\sqrt{10}$

[9–3]

Directions Express the given radicals in simplest form with all denominators rationalized.

9. $\sqrt{\frac{16}{17}}$ **10.** $\sqrt{\frac{7}{18}}$ **11.** $\sqrt{\frac{a}{b}}$

12. $\sqrt{\frac{x}{y^3}}$ **13.** $\frac{a}{\sqrt{ab}}$ **14.** $\frac{2x}{\sqrt{xy}}$

[9–4]

Directions Perform the indicated operations and simplify.

15. $3\sqrt{7} + 4\sqrt{7}$ **16.** $\sqrt{18} + 5\sqrt{2}$ **17.** $3\sqrt{20} - \sqrt{45}$

18. $2\sqrt{75} - \sqrt{3} + 5\sqrt{27}$ **19.** $\sqrt{50a} - 2\sqrt{8a}$ **20.** $7\sqrt{9x} - 2\sqrt{4x}$

[9–5]

21. $\sqrt{3}(\sqrt{5} - \sqrt{7})$ **22.** $\sqrt{10}(\sqrt{14} + \sqrt{6})$ **23.** $(5 + \sqrt{7})(3 - \sqrt{7})$

24. $(6 - \sqrt{3})^2$

25. $(\sqrt{3} + \sqrt{5})^2$

26. $(2\sqrt{a} - \sqrt{b})(2\sqrt{a} + \sqrt{b})$

Directions Express the given radicals in simplest form with all denominators rationalized.

27. $\dfrac{1}{\sqrt{3} - 2}$

28. $\dfrac{2}{\sqrt{6} + 4}$

29. $\dfrac{1}{\sqrt{a} + b}$

30. $\dfrac{x}{\sqrt{xy} + x}$

31. $\dfrac{a}{a + \sqrt{b}}$

32. $\dfrac{\sqrt{2} + 3}{\sqrt{2} - 3}$

[9–6]

Directions Find the solution set.

33. $\sqrt{x} = 8$

34. $\sqrt{x - 4} = 7$

35. $\sqrt{5x - 3} = \sqrt{3x + 5}$

36. $\sqrt{7x + 4} = \sqrt{5x - 6}$

37. $\sqrt{x}\sqrt{x + 8} = 3$

38. $\sqrt{x^2 + 16} = x + 2$

39. $\sqrt{x + 6} = x + 4$

40. $\sqrt{x - 3} = x - 3$

NAME

Chapter 9 cumulative test

CLASS/SECTION DATE

Directions Perform the indicated operations and simplify. Assume that all variables represent positive real numbers and that no denominator is equal to zero.

[1–6] **1.** $3[4(6 - 2) + (-5 + 4)]$

[3–1] **2.** $x^3 \cdot x^2 \cdot x^2$

[3–4] **3.** $x^{12} \div x^6$

[3–2] **4.** $(3x^2 - 2x + 5) - (x^2 - 4x - 8)$

[3–3] **5.** $4a^2b^3(2a^2 - 3ab + 4b^2)$

[3–4] **6.** $\dfrac{8a^{-2}b^3c^0}{4a^{-5}b}$

[3–1] **7.** -6^2

[3–3] **8.** $(3a - b)^2$

[6–1] **9.** $\dfrac{a^2 - 9}{3a + 12} \cdot \dfrac{a + 4}{a^2 + 5a + 6}$

[9–4] **10.** $5\sqrt{12} + 2\sqrt{27}$

[9–1] **11.** $-\sqrt{25}$

[6–2] **12.** $\dfrac{2x}{x - 1} - \dfrac{x - 3}{x - 1}$

[9–5] **13.** $\dfrac{\sqrt{x}}{x - \sqrt{y}}$

[9–2] **14.** $\sqrt{81x^4y^6z}$

[3–3] **15.** $(5x - y)(5x + y)$

[3–2] **16.** $3x - [2x - (x - y) + 3y]$

Directions Factor completely.

[4–1] **17.** $6a^3b^4 - 2a^3b^5 + 8a^5b^3$

[4–4] **18.** $25c^2 - d^2$

[4–3] **19.** $2x^2 + 7x - 4$

[4–4] **20.** $y^4 - 4z^2$

[4–3] **21.** $6x^2 + 11x + 4$

[4–2] **22.** $x^2 + 3x - 28$

Directions Solve for x in problems 23–30.

[2–3] **23.** $2(4x - 3) = 5x - 7$

[4–6] **24.** $x^2 = 9$

[2–3] **25.** $3(x + 4) - 2(x - 3) = 12$

[6–4] **26.** $\frac{1}{4}x + 2 = \frac{1}{2}x - 1$

[2–6] **27.** $3x + 5 > x + 12$

[4–6] **28.** $2x^2 + 3x + 1 = 0$

[2–6] **29.** $-3 < 2x - 5 < 11$

[6–4] **30.** $\frac{3x + 1}{9} + \frac{1}{12} = \frac{2x - 1}{3}$

[7–3] **31.** Find the slope of the line passing through points (4,2) and (3,5).

[7–4] **32.** Write $8x - 2y = 4$ in slope-intercept form and determine the slope and y-intercept.

[8–2] **33.** Solve the system of equations.
$5x - y = 4$
$x + 3y = 2$

[2–4] **34.** One number is four times a second number and their sum is 70. Find the numbers.

[5–4] **35.** A punch machine can make 18 holes in 4 minutes. How many holes can the machine make in 5 hours?

[4–7] **36.** The product of two consecutive positive even integers is 288. Find the integers.

[2–4] **37.** The width of a rectangle is 6 feet less than its length. The perimeter of the rectangle is 96 feet. Find the dimensions.

CHAPTER

10

Solutions of Quadratic Equations

A rock is dropped from the top of the Washington Monument. If the monument is 555 feet tall, how long will it take the rock to strike the ground?

Proficiency check

[9–1] **1.** Simplify the following radical expressions.

a. $\sqrt{49}$

b. $\sqrt{40}$

[3–3] **2.** Find the following products.

a. $5x(x - 3)$

b. $(2y + 5)^2$

c. $(3x - 1)(2x + 7)$

[4–4] **3.** Factor the following expressions as binomial squares.

a. $x^2 - 24x + 144$

b. $x^2 - 5x + \frac{25}{4}$

c. $x^2 + \frac{2}{3}x + \frac{1}{9}$

[6–5] **4.** Clear the denominators of the following equations.

a. $x^2 - \frac{1}{3}x + \frac{2}{3} = 0$

b. $y^2 + \frac{3}{4}y + \frac{5}{2} = 0$

▣ 10–1 Solutions of quadratic equations by factoring or extracting the roots

In section 4–6, we solved quadratic equations of the form

$$ax^2 + bx + c = 0, a \neq 0,$$

by factoring. It was necessary that the quadratic expression $ax^2 + bx + c$ be factorable. Let us review the procedures used in solving quadratic equations by factoring.

To solve a quadratic equation by factoring

1. Write the equation in standard form

$$ax^2 + bx + c = 0,\ a \neq 0,$$

if the equation is not written in this form.
2. Factor the expression $ax^2 + bx + c$.
3. Set each of the resulting factors involving the variable equal to 0 and solve each equation for the variable.
4. Check your solutions in the original equation.

A_1 Solve by factoring.
$x^2 + 2x - 8 = 0$

Example 10–1 A

Find the solution set of each quadratic equation by factoring.

1. $x^2 - x - 12 = 0$

$(x - 4)(x + 3) = 0$ — Factor the left member

$x - 4 = 0$ or $x + 3 = 0$ — Set each factor equal to 0

$x = 4$ $\quad x = -3$ — Solve each equation for x

The solution set is $\{4,-3\}$.

You are now ready to do A_1.

A_2 Solve by factoring.
$4x^2 = 5x - 1$

2. $3y^2 = 7y + 6$

$3y^2 - 7y - 6 = 0$ — Write the equation in standard form

$(3y + 2)(y - 3) = 0$ — Factor left member

$3y + 2 = 0$ or $y - 3 = 0$ — Set each factor equal to 0

$3y = -2$ $\quad y = 3$ — Solve each equation for y

$y = -\frac{2}{3}$ $\quad y = 3$

The solution set is $\left\{-\frac{2}{3},3\right\}$.

You are now ready to do A_2.

3. $x^2 - \frac{5x}{2} = \frac{3}{2}$

$2x^2 - 5x = 3$ — Multiply each member by 2 to clear denominators

$2x^2 - 5x - 3 = 0$ — Write the equation in standard form

$(2x + 1)(x - 3) = 0$ — Factor the left member

$2x + 1 = 0$ or $x - 3 = 0$ — Set each factor equal to 0

$2x = -1$ $\quad x = 3$ — Solve each equation for x

$x = -\frac{1}{2}$ $\quad x = 3$

The solution set is $\left\{-\frac{1}{2},3\right\}$.

You are now ready to do A_3. ■

A_3 Solve by factoring.
$y^2 - \frac{1}{3}y - \frac{4}{3} = 0$

Extracting the roots

Given the quadratic equation $x^2 - 9 = 0$, factoring the left member and solving the resulting equations, we get

$$(x - 3)(x + 3) = 0$$
$$x - 3 = 0 \quad \text{or} \quad x + 3 = 0$$
$$x = 3 \quad \text{or} \quad x = -3.$$

The solutions of the equation are 3 and -3.

We can obtain the same result if we write the equation in the form

$$x^2 = 9.$$

Since 9 is positive, we can take the square root of each *member* of the equation. Then

$$x = \sqrt{9} = 3 \quad \text{or} \quad x = -\sqrt{9} = -3$$

and we obtain the same result. The solution set is $\{-3,3\}$. This development justifies the following method of solving a quadratic equation by **extracting the roots.**

Extracting the roots

If k is a non-negative number and $x^2 = k$, then

$$x = \sqrt{k} \quad \text{or} \quad x = -\sqrt{k}.$$

Example 10–1 B

Find the solution set of the following quadratic equations by extracting the roots.

1. $x^2 = 25$

$x = \sqrt{25} = 5$ or $x = -\sqrt{25} = -5$ — Extract the roots

The solution set is $\{-5,5\}$.

You are now ready to do **B_1**.

2. $y^2 = 18$

$y = \sqrt{18} = 3\sqrt{2}$ or $y = -\sqrt{18} = -3\sqrt{2}$ — Extract the roots ($\sqrt{18} = 3\sqrt{2}$)

The solution set is $\{-3\sqrt{2},3\sqrt{2}\}$.

You are now ready to do **B_2**.

3. $x^2 - 12 = 0$

$x^2 = 12$ — Add 12 to each member

$x = \sqrt{12} = 2\sqrt{3}$ or $x = -\sqrt{12} = -2\sqrt{3}$ — Extract the roots ($\sqrt{12} = 2\sqrt{3}$)

The solution set is $\{-2\sqrt{3},2\sqrt{3}\}$.

You are now ready to do **B_3**.

4. $z^2 = -9$

Since $\sqrt{-9}$ is not a real number, the equation $x^2 = -9$ has no real solutions. The solution set is $\emptyset$.

You are now ready to do **B_4**. ■

The equation $(x - 4)^2 = 49$ can be solved using extracting the roots. If $(x - 4)^2 = 49$, then

$$\begin{aligned} x - 4 &= \sqrt{49} = 7 & \text{or} \quad x - 4 &= -\sqrt{49} = -7 \\ x &= 4 + 7 & x &= 4 - 7 \\ x &= 11 & x &= -3 \end{aligned}$$

Add 4 to each member

The solution set is $\{-3,11\}$.

B_1 Solve by extracting the roots.
$x^2 = 36$

B_2 Solve by extracting the roots.
$y^2 = 8$

B_3 Solve by extracting the roots.
$x^2 - 24 = 0$

B_4 $y^2 = -10$

Example 10–1 C

Find the solution set of the following quadratic equations by extracting the roots.

1. $(x - 2)^2 = 4$

$x - 2 = \sqrt{4} = 2$ or $x - 2 = -\sqrt{4} = -2$ — Extract the roots

$x = 2 + 2 = 4$ $\quad$ $x = 2 - 2 = 0$ — Add 2 to each member

The solution set is $\{0,4\}$. Check the solutions in the original equation.

You are now ready to do **C_1**.

2. $(x + 3)^2 = 10$

$x + 3 = \sqrt{10}$ or $x + 3 = -\sqrt{10}$ — Extract the roots

$x = -3 + \sqrt{10}$ $\quad$ $x = -3 - \sqrt{10}$ — Subtract 3 from each member

The solution set is $\{-3 - \sqrt{10}, -3 + \sqrt{10}\}$.

You are now ready to do **C_2**.

3. $(2y - 1)^2 = 24$

$2y - 1 = \sqrt{24}$ or $2y - 1 = -\sqrt{24}$ — Extract the roots

$2y - 1 = 2\sqrt{6}$ $\quad$ $2y - 1 = -2\sqrt{6}$ — $(\sqrt{24} = 2\sqrt{6})$

$2y = 1 + 2\sqrt{6}$ $\quad$ $2y = 1 - 2\sqrt{6}$ — Add 1 to each member

$y = \dfrac{1 + 2\sqrt{6}}{2}$ $\quad$ $y = \dfrac{1 - 2\sqrt{6}}{2}$ — Divide each member by 2

The solution set is $\left\{\dfrac{1 - 2\sqrt{6}}{2}, \dfrac{1 + 2\sqrt{6}}{2}\right\}$.

You are now ready to do **C_3**. ■

Answers to section 10–1 margin exercises

A_1 $\{-4,2\}$ **A_2** $\left\{\frac{1}{4},1\right\}$ **A_3** $\left\{\frac{4}{3},-1\right\}$ **B_1** $\{-6,6\}$ **B_2** $\{-2\sqrt{2},2\sqrt{2}\}$ **B_3** $\{-2\sqrt{6},2\sqrt{6}\}$ **B_4** no real solutions, $\emptyset$ **C_1** $\{2,12\}$ **C_2** $\{-1 - \sqrt{7}, -1 + \sqrt{7}\}$ **C_3** $\left\{\frac{5 - 2\sqrt{5}}{3},\frac{5 + 2\sqrt{5}}{3}\right\}$

Mastery points

Can you

- Solve quadratic equations by factoring?
- Solve quadratic equations of the form $x^2 = k$ and $(ax + b)^2 = k$ by extracting the roots, $k \geq 0$?

C_1 $(x - 7)^2 = 25$

C_2 $(y + 1)^2 = 7$

C_3 $(3x - 5)^2 = 20$

Exercise 10–1

Directions Find the solution set of the following quadratic equations by factoring. See example 10–1 A.

Example [A2] $4x^2 = 5x - 1$

Solution

$$4x^2 - 5x + 1 = 0$$ Subtract $5x$ and add 1 to obtain the standard form of the equation

$$(4x - 1)(x - 1) = 0$$ Factor the left member

$$4x - 1 = 0 \quad \text{or} \quad x - 1 = 0$$ Set each equation equal to 0

$$4x = 1 \qquad x = 1$$

$$x = \frac{1}{4} \qquad x = 1$$

The solution set is $\left\{\frac{1}{4}, 1\right\}$.

1. $x^2 - 2x - 3 = 0$
2. $x^2 + 3x - 10 = 0$
3. $x^2 + 6x = -8$
4. $x^2 - 16 = 0$
5. $x^2 - 49 = 0$
6. [6.] $y^2 - 10y + 25 = 0$
7. $x^2 + 20x + 100 = 0$
8. $2x^2 - 9x - 5 = 0$
9. $4y^2 = 8y + 5$
10. $y - 4 = -5y^2$
11. [11.] $x^2 - \frac{3}{2}x - \frac{5}{2} = 0$
12. $x^2 - \frac{1}{5}x - \frac{4}{5} = 0$

Directions Find the solution set of each quadratic equation by extracting the roots. Express radicals in simplest form. See examples 10–1 B and C.

Example [C3] $(3x - 5)^2 = 20$

Solution

$$3x - 5 = \sqrt{20} \quad \text{or} \quad 3x - 5 = -\sqrt{20}$$ Extract the roots

$$3x - 5 = 2\sqrt{5} \qquad 3x - 5 = -2\sqrt{5}$$ 20 simplifies to $2\sqrt{5}$

$$3x = 5 + 2\sqrt{5} \qquad 3x = 5 - 2\sqrt{5}$$ Add 5 to each member

$$x = \frac{5 + 2\sqrt{5}}{3} \qquad x = \frac{5 - 2\sqrt{5}}{3}$$ Divide each member by 3

The solution set is $\left\{\frac{5 - 2\sqrt{5}}{3}, \frac{5 + 2\sqrt{5}}{3}\right\}$.

13. $x^2 = 4$
14. $x^2 = 81$
15. $y^2 = 11$
16. $x^2 = 5$
17. [17.] $a^2 = 20$
18. $x^2 = 28$
19. $p^2 - 32 = 0$
20. $x^2 - 40 = 0$

21. $4x^2 = 36$

22. $5x^2 = 75$

23. $3z^2 = 18$

24. $2x^2 - 100 = 0$

25. $4x^2 - 64 = 0$

26. $(x + 2)^2 = 4$

27. $(x + 6)^2 = 16$

28. $(x - 4)^2 = 25$

29. $(x + 3)^2 = 6$

30. $(x - 1)^2 = 7$

31. $(x - 9)^2 = 18$

32. $(x - 10)^2 = 27$

33. $(x + 8)^2 = 8$

34. $(x + 5)^2 = 32$

35. $(2x - 3)^2 = 16$

36. $(3x + 2)^2 = 24$

37. $(4y - 1)^2 = 45$

Directions Solve the following verbal problems by setting up a quadratic equation and extracting the roots.

Example A square has an area of 16 square inches. Find the length of each side.

Solution $A = s^2$, where A is the area and s is the length of a side. Then $16 = s^2$ or $s^2 = 16$,

$s^2 = 16$

$s = \sqrt{16}$ or $s = -\sqrt{16}$ Extract the roots

$s = 4$ $s = -4$

But a square cannot have a side -4 inches long, so $s = 4$ inches.

38. Find the length of each side of a square whose area is 25 square meters.

39. Given a square whose area is 45 square centimeters, how long is each side of the square?

40. A circle has an area of 12.56 square feet. Find the length of the radius r of the circle if $A \approx 3.14r^2$.

41. Find the length of the radius of a circle whose area is 50.24 square yards. (Refer to exercise 40 for the formula.)

Review exercises

Directions Multiply the following. See section 3–3.

1. $(x - 2)^2$

2. $(3z + 2)^2$

Directions Completely factor the following. See section 4–4.

3. $x^2 + 18x + 81$

4. $9y^2 + 30y + 25$

Directions Perform the indicated operations. See sections 6–1 and 6–2.

5. $\dfrac{3x}{x + 2} - \dfrac{x}{x^2 - 4}$

6. $\dfrac{x - 3}{x^2 - x - 2} \div \dfrac{x^2 - 9}{x + 1}$

10–2 Solutions of quadratic equations by completing the square

Building perfect square trinomials

The methods we have used to solve quadratic equations thus far have applied to special cases of the quadratic equation. The method that we call **completing the square** involves transforming the quadratic equation

$$ax^2 + bx + c = 0,\ a \neq 0,$$

into the form

$$(x + h)^2 = k.$$

This latter equation can then be solved by extracting the roots, as we did in section 10–1.

Consider the following perfect square trinomials and their equivalent binomial squares.

$$\begin{aligned} x^2 + 2x + 1 &= (x + 1)^2 \\ x^2 - 10x + 25 &= (x - 5)^2 \\ x^2 - 14x + 49 &= (x - 7)^2 \end{aligned}$$

In each of the perfect square trinomials in the left member,

a. the coefficient of x^2 is 1.
b. the third term, the constant, is the square of one-half of the coefficient of the variable x in the middle term.

We further observe that in the square of the binomial in the right member, the constant term in the binomial is one-half of the coefficient of the variable x in the middle term. That is,

1. In the trinomial $x^2 + 2x + 1$, the constant term, 1, is the square of one-half the coefficient of the middle term, 2.

$$\left[\frac{1}{2}(2)\right]^2 = (1)^2 = 1.$$

Constant term of the binomial

2. In the trinomial $x^2 - 10x + 25$, the constant term, 25, is the square of one-half of -10. Thus,

$$\left[\frac{1}{2}(-10)\right]^2 = (-5)^2 = 25.$$

Constant term of the binomial

3. In the trinomial $x^2 - 14x + 49$, the constant term, 49, is the square of one-half of -14. Thus,

$$\left[\frac{1}{2}(-14)\right]^2 = (-7)^2 = 49.$$

Constant term of the binomial

A_1 $x^2 + 14x$

Now we can use these observations to "build" perfect square trinomials by **completing the square** and obtain their equivalent binomial squares.

Example 10–2 A

Complete the square in each of the following expressions. Write the resulting expression as a binomial square.

1. $x^2 + 6x$

Since the coefficient of x is 6, the constant term is the square of one-half of 6.

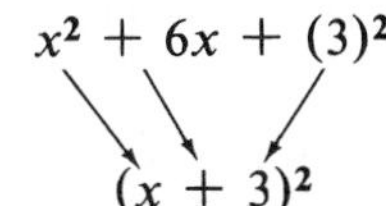

$x^2 + 6x + (3)^2$ $\qquad \left[\frac{1}{2}(6)\right]^2 = (3)^2$

Factors to $(x + 3)^2$

A_2 $x^2 - 26x$

Thus, $x^2 + 6x + 9 = (x + 3)^2$. $\qquad (3)^2 = 9$

You are now ready to do **A_1**.

2. $x^2 - 8x$

Since the coefficient of x is -8, the constant term is the square of one-half of -8.

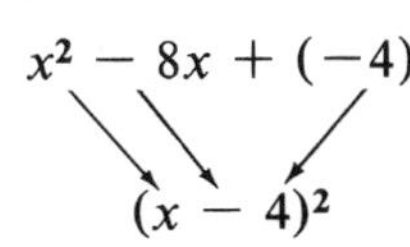

$x^2 - 8x + (-4)^2$ $\qquad \left[\frac{1}{2}(-8)\right]^2 = (-4)^2$

Factors to $(x - 4)^2$

Thus, $x^2 - 8x + 16 = (x - 4)^2$. $\qquad (-4)^2 = 16$

You are now ready to do **A_2**.

3. $y^2 - 3y$

Since the coefficient of y is -3, the constant term is the square of one-half of -3.

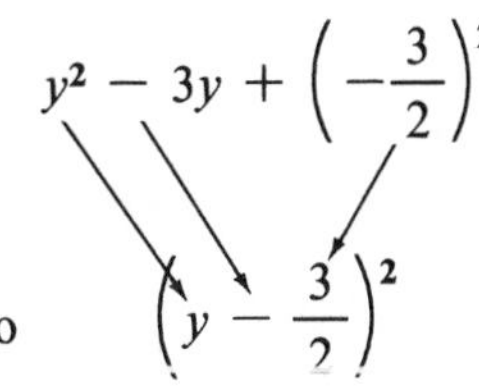

$y^2 - 3y + \left(-\frac{3}{2}\right)^2$ $\qquad \left[\frac{1}{2}(-3)\right]^2 = \left(-\frac{3}{2}\right)^2$

A_3 $x^2 - 5x$

Factors to $\left(y - \frac{3}{2}\right)^2$

Thus, $y^2 - 3y + \frac{9}{4} = \left(y - \frac{3}{2}\right)^2$. $\qquad \left(\frac{3}{2}\right)^2 = \frac{9}{4}$

You are now ready to do **A_3**. ■

Solutions by completing the square

The following examples show how we use the previous procedure to find the solution set of a quadratic equation by **completing the square.**

B_1 Solve by completing the square.
$x^2 + 3x - 18 = 0$

B_2 Solve by completing the square.
$x^2 - 8x + 4 = 0$

Example 10–2 B

Find the solution set by completing the square.

1. $x^2 - 2x - 8 = 0$

We first isolate the terms containing the variable in the left member.

$x^2 - 2x = 8$ — Add 8 to each member

Complete the square in the left member.

$\left[\frac{1}{2}(-2)\right]^2 = (-1)^2 = 1$ — Square one-half of the coefficient of x

$x^2 - 2x + 1 = 8 + 1$ — Add 1 to each member

$(x - 1)^2 = 9$ — Write left member as a binomial square where 1 is the constant and add in right member

$x - 1 = \sqrt{9} = 3$ or $x - 1 = -\sqrt{9} = -3$ — Extract the roots

$x = 1 + 3$ $\quad x = 1 - 3$ — Add 1 to each member

$x = 4$ $\quad x = -2$ — Combine in right member

The solution set is $\{-2,4\}$.

Check:

1. When $x = 4$,

$$x^2 - 2x - 8 = 0$$
$$(4)^2 - 2(4) - 8 = 0 \quad \text{Replace } x \text{ with } 4$$
$$16 - 8 - 8 = 0$$
$$0 = 0.$$

2. When $x = -2$,

$$x^2 - 2x - 8 = 0$$
$$(-2)^2 - 2(-2) - 8 = 0 \quad \text{Replace } x \text{ with } -2$$
$$4 + 4 - 8 = 0$$
$$0 = 0. \quad \text{(True)}$$

In future examples, we will not show a check but you should always do this.

You are now ready to do **B_1**.

2. $x^2 - 6x + 2 = 0$

Isolate the terms containing the variable in the left member.

$x^2 - 6x = -2$ — Subtract 2 from each member

Complete the square in the left member.

$\left[\frac{1}{2}(-6)\right]^2 = (-3)^2 = 9$ — Square one-half of the coefficient of x

$x^2 - 6x + 9 = -2 + 9$ — Add 9 to each member

$(x - 3)^2 = 7$ — Write left member as a binomial square; add in right member

$x - 3 = \sqrt{7}$ or $x - 3 = -\sqrt{7}$ — Extract the roots

$x = 3 + \sqrt{7}$ $\quad x = 3 - \sqrt{7}$ — Add 3 to each member

The solution set is $\{3 - \sqrt{7}, 3 + \sqrt{7}\}$.

You are now ready to do **B_2**.

3. $4x^2 + 3x = 8$

To complete the square using the method described, it is necessary for the coefficient of x^2 to be 1. To get this, we divide each term of the equation by 4 (the coefficient of the squared term).

B$_3$ $3x^2 + 4x = 6$

$$\frac{4x^2}{4} + \frac{3x}{4} = \frac{8}{4}$$ Divide each term by 4

$$x^2 + \frac{3}{4}x = 2$$ Reduce where possible

Complete the square in the left member.

$$\left[\frac{1}{2}\left(\frac{3}{4}\right)\right]^2 = \left(\frac{3}{8}\right)^2 = \frac{9}{16}$$ Square one-half of the coefficient of x

$$x^2 + \frac{3}{4}x + \frac{9}{16} = 2 + \frac{9}{16}$$ Add $\frac{9}{16}$ to each member

$$\left(x + \frac{3}{4}\right)^2 = \frac{41}{16}$$ Write the left member as a binomial square; add in the right member

$$x + \frac{3}{4} = \sqrt{\frac{41}{16}} = \frac{\sqrt{41}}{4} \quad \text{or} \quad x + \frac{3}{4} = -\sqrt{\frac{41}{16}} = -\frac{\sqrt{41}}{4}$$ Extract the roots

$$x = -\frac{3}{4} + \frac{\sqrt{41}}{4} \quad \text{or} \quad x = -\frac{3}{4} - \frac{\sqrt{41}}{4}$$ Subtract $\frac{3}{4}$ from each member

$$x = \frac{-3 + \sqrt{41}}{4} \quad \text{or} \quad x = \frac{-3 - \sqrt{41}}{4}$$ Add and subtract numerators

The solution set is $\left\{\frac{-3 - \sqrt{41}}{4}, \frac{-3 + \sqrt{41}}{4}\right\}$.

You are now ready to do **B**$_3$. ■

Solutions by completing the square

To find the solutions of the quadratic equation $ax^2 + bx + c = 0$, $a \neq 0$, by completing the square, we proceed as follows:

1. If $a = 1$, proceed to step 2. If $a \neq 1$, divide each member of the equation by a and simplify.
2. Write the equation with the variable terms in the left member and the constant in the right member.
3. Add to each member of the equation the square of one-half of the numerical coefficient of the linear term of the original equation.
4. Write the left member as a binomial square and combine in the right member.
5. Extract the roots and solve the resulting linear equations.
6. Check the solutions in the original equation.

Answers to section 10–2 margin exercises

A$_1$ $x^2 + 14x + 49 = (x + 7)^2$ **A**$_2$ $x^2 - 26x + 169 = (x - 13)^2$

A$_3$ $x^2 - 5x + \frac{25}{4} = \left(x - \frac{5}{2}\right)^2$ **B**$_1$ $\{-6,3\}$ **B**$_2$ $\{4 - 2\sqrt{3}, 4 + 2\sqrt{3}\}$

B$_3$ $\left\{\frac{-2 - \sqrt{22}}{3}, \frac{-2 + \sqrt{22}}{3}\right\}$

Mastery points

Can you

- Complete the square of a binomial in the form $x^2 + bx$?
- Find the solution set of a quadratic equation by completing the square?

Exercise 10–2

Directions Complete the square of each of the following binomials. State their equivalent binomial square. See example 10–2 A.

Example [A3] $x^2 - 5x$

Solution Since the coefficient of x is -5, the constant term is the square of one-half of -5.

$$x^2 - 5x + \left(-\frac{5}{2}\right)^2 \qquad \left[\frac{1}{2}(-5)\right]^2 = \left(-\frac{5}{2}\right)^2$$

Factors to $\left(x - \frac{5}{2}\right)^2$

Thus, $x^2 - 5x + \frac{25}{4} = \left(x - \frac{5}{2}\right)^2$. $\qquad \left(-\frac{5}{2}\right)^2 = \frac{25}{4}$

1. $x^2 + 10x$
2. $x^2 + 4x$
3. [3.] $z^2 - 12z$
4. $y^2 - 18y$
5. $x^2 + 24x$
6. $y^2 + 16y$
7. $y^2 - 20y$
8. $x^2 - 22x$
9. $x^2 + x$
10. $x^2 + 11x$
11. $x^2 - 7x$
12. $y^2 - 9y$
13. [13.] $x^2 + \frac{1}{2}x$
14. $z^2 + \frac{1}{4}z$
15. $z^2 - \frac{1}{5}z$
16. $x^2 - \frac{3}{8}x$

Directions Find the solution set by completing the square. See example 10–2 B.

Example **B₃** $3x^2 + 4x = 6$

Solution

$$\frac{3x^2}{3} + \frac{4x}{3} = \frac{6}{3}$$ Divide each member by the coefficient of x^2, 3

$$x^2 + \frac{4}{3}x = 2$$ Reduce in each term

$$\left[\frac{1}{2}\left(\frac{4}{3}\right)\right]^2 = \left(\frac{2}{3}\right)^2 = \frac{4}{9}$$ Square one-half of the coefficient of x

$$x^2 + \frac{4}{3}x + \frac{4}{9} = 2 + \frac{4}{9}$$ Add $\frac{4}{9}$ to each member

$$\left(x + \frac{2}{3}\right)^2 = \frac{22}{9}$$ Write left member as the square of a binomial and add in right member

$$x + \frac{2}{3} = \sqrt{\frac{22}{9}} = \frac{\sqrt{22}}{3} \text{ or } x + \frac{2}{3} = -\sqrt{\frac{22}{9}} = -\frac{\sqrt{22}}{3}$$ Extract the roots

$$x = -\frac{2}{3} + \frac{\sqrt{22}}{3} = \frac{-2 + \sqrt{22}}{3} \text{ or } x = -\frac{2}{3} - \frac{\sqrt{22}}{3} = \frac{-2 - \sqrt{22}}{3}$$ Subtract $\frac{2}{3}$ from each member

The solution set is $\left\{\frac{-2 + \sqrt{22}}{3}, \frac{-2 - \sqrt{22}}{3}\right\}$.

17. $x^2 + 8x + 7 = 0$

18. $x^2 + 12x + 11 = 0$

19. $z^2 - 4z - 12 = 0$

20. $y^2 - 10y + 9 = 0$

21. $x^2 - 4x = -3$

22. $x^2 + 14x = -13$

23. $u^2 - u - 1 = 0$

24. $y^2 + 3y - 1 = 0$

25. $x^2 + 21x + 10 = 0$

26. $x^2 + 8x = 3$

27. $x^2 + x - 3 = 0$

28. $3x^2 - 10x = -3$

29. $2y^2 + 7y + 3 = 0$

30. $3x^2 + 8x - 4 = 0$

31. $6x^2 - 13x = -6$

32. $6n^2 + n = 1$

33. $4 - x^2 = 2x$

34. $2 - y = 6y^2$

35. $(x + 3)(x - 2) = 1$ (*Hint:* Perform indicated operations.)

36. $(x - 5)(x - 3) = 4$

37. $(2x + 1)^2 = (x - 3)^2$

38. $(3y - 2)^2 = (y + 1)^2$

Directions Solve the following problems by completing the square.

Example A piece of lumber is divided into two pieces so that one piece is 5 inches longer than the other. If the product of their lengths is 104 square inches, what is the length of each piece?

Solution Let $x =$ the length of the shorter piece. Then $x + 5 =$ the length of the longer piece.

the product of the lengths	is	104 square inches
$x(x + 5)$	$=$	104

The equation is $x(x + 5) = 104$.
Then

$$x^2 + 5x = 104$$ Multiply in left member

$$\left[\frac{1}{2}(5)\right]^2 = \left(\frac{5}{2}\right)^2 = \frac{25}{4}$$ Square one-half of the coefficient of $5x$, which is 5

$$x^2 + 5x + \frac{25}{4} = 104 + \frac{25}{4}$$ Add $\frac{25}{4}$ to each member

$$\left(x + \frac{5}{2}\right)^2 = \frac{416}{4} + \frac{25}{4}$$ Write left member as the square of a binomial

$$\left(x + \frac{5}{2}\right)^2 = \frac{441}{4}.$$ Add in right member

$$x + \frac{5}{2} = \sqrt{\frac{441}{4}} \quad \text{or} \quad x + \frac{5}{2} = -\sqrt{\frac{441}{4}}$$ Extract the roots

$$x = -\frac{5}{2} + \frac{21}{2} \quad \text{or} \quad x = -\frac{5}{2} - \frac{21}{2}$$ $\sqrt{441} = 21$

$$x = \frac{-5 + 21}{2} = \frac{16}{2} = 8 \quad \text{or} \quad x = \frac{-5 - 21}{2} = \frac{-26}{2} = -13$$

The solutions are 8 or -13. Since we want the length of a piece of lumber, -13 is not an appropriate answer.

Thus,

$x = 8$ and $x + 5 = 13$.

The two pieces have lengths 8 inches and 13 inches.

39. A metal bar is to be divided into two pieces so that one piece is 4 inches shorter than the other. If the sum of the squares of the two lengths is 208 square inches, find the two lengths.

40. To find the total surface area of an automobile cylinder, we use the formula $A = 2\pi r^2 + 2\pi rh$, where π is approximately equal to the constant $\frac{22}{7}$. If the area A of the cylinder is approximately 88 square inches and the height h is 7 inches, find the approximate value of radius r. Round to one decimal place.

41. One surface of a rectangular solid has a width w that is 8 millimeters shorter than its length ℓ. If the area A of the surface is 105 square millimeters, what are its dimensions? (*Hint:* $A = \ell w$.)

42. The length of a rectangular-shaped piece of paper is 7 inches longer than its width. What are the dimensions of the paper if it has an area of 78 square inches?

43. The perimeter of a rectangle is 52 inches and its area is 153 square inches. What are its dimensions? (*Hint:* The formula for the perimeter of a rectangle is $P = 2\ell + 2w$. If we substitute 52 in place of P, we have $52 = 2\ell + 2w$. Divide each member of the equation by 2. Then $26 = \ell + w$. We can use this fact to establish the unknowns.)
Width of Rectangle: w
Length of Rectangle: $26 - w$
Equation: $153 = w(26 - w)$

44. The perimeter of a rectangle is 38 centimeters and its area A is 88 square centimeters. What are its dimensions? (See problem 43.)

45. The perimeter of a rectangle is 18 meters and its area is $19\frac{1}{4}$ square meters. What are its dimensions?

46. The area of a rectangular piece of sheet metal is 117 square inches. If the sum of the length ℓ and the width w is 22 inches, what are the dimensions of the metal plate?

47. A rectangular lot has an area of 84 square rods. If the sum of the length ℓ and the width w is 20 rods, what are the dimensions?

Review exercises

Directions Evaluate the following expressions for the given values. See sections 1–8 and 9–1.

1. $\sqrt{a + b}$; $a = 2$ and $b = 7$

2. $\sqrt{b^2 - 4ac}$; $a = -1$, $b = 5$, and $c = 5$

3. Solve the system of equations
$2x - y = 4$
$3x + 2y = 6$
by any method. See section 8–3.

4. Graph the equation $4x - 3y = -12$. See section 7–2.

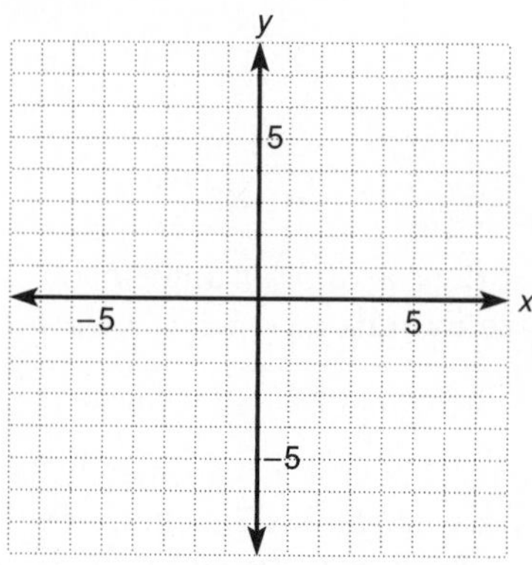

5. If 2 dozen oranges cost \$2.48, how many dozens of oranges can you buy for \$11.16? Set up a proportion. See section 5–4.

6. Find the solution set of the inequality $5 - 3x < 2x + 7$. Graph on the real number line. See section 2–4.

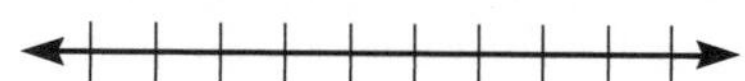

10–3 Solutions of quadratic equations by the quadratic formula

Identifying *a, b,* and *c* in a quadratic equation

We have found solution sets of quadratic equations of the form $ax^2 + bx + c = 0$ by factoring, extracting the roots, and by completing the square. Even though the solution set of *any* such quadratic equation can be found by completing the square, a general formula, which is called the **quadratic formula,** can be derived that will enable us to find the solution set in an easier fashion.

To use the quadratic formula, the equation must be written in standard form,

$$ax^2 + bx + c = 0, a > 0,$$

and we must be able to identify the coefficients a, b, and c of the standard quadratic form for any quadratic equation. In identifying a, b, and c, we note that

1. a is the coefficient of x^2,
2. b is the coefficient of x, and
3. c is the constant term.

Example 10–3 A

Write each equation in standard quadratic form and identify the values of a, b, and c.

1. $3x^2 - 2x + 1 = 0$
The equation is in standard form.

$3x^2 - 2x + 1 = 0$

Constant term, $c = 1$

Coefficient of x, $b = -2$

Coefficient of x^2, $a = 3$

You are now ready to do **A₁**.

A₁ $5x^2 - 3x + 4 = 0$

2. $3x^2 - 4 = x$
Equation must be written in standard form.

$3x^2 - x - 4 = 0$ Subtract x from each member

$a = 3,\ b = -1,\ c = -4$

You are now ready to do **A₂**.

A₂ $4x^2 - 5 = 7x$

3. $4x(x - 3) = 2x - 1$
The equation must be written in standard form.

$4x^2 - 12x = 2x - 1$ Multiply in left member

$4x^2 - 14x + 1 = 0$ Subtract $2x$ and add 1 to each member

$a = 4,\ b = -14,\ c = 1$

You are now ready to do **A₃**. ■

A₃ $3x(x - 1) = 4x - 2$

Solving equations using the quadratic formula

To derive the quadratic formula, we solve the equation $ax^2 + bx + c = 0$ by completing the square.

$ax^2 + bx + c = 0,\ a > 0$

$x^2 + \frac{b}{a}x + \frac{c}{a} = 0$ Divide each member of the equation by a

$x^2 + \frac{b}{a}x = -\frac{c}{a}$ Subtract $\frac{c}{a}$ from each member

$\left[\frac{1}{2}\left(\frac{b}{a}\right)\right]^2 = \left(\frac{b}{2a}\right)^2 = \frac{b^2}{4a^2}$ Find quantity needed to make a binomial square

$x^2 + \frac{b}{a}x + \frac{b^2}{4a^2} = -\frac{c}{a} + \frac{b^2}{4a^2}$ Add $\frac{b^2}{4a^2}$ to each member

$\left(x + \frac{b}{2a}\right)^2 = \frac{b^2}{4a^2} - \frac{c}{a}$ Write left member as a binomial square

$\left(x + \frac{b}{2a}\right)^2 = \frac{b^2}{4a^2} - \frac{4ac}{4a^2}$ Subtract fractions in right member

$\left(x + \frac{b}{2a}\right)^2 = \frac{b^2 - 4ac}{4a^2}$

$x + \frac{b}{2a} = \sqrt{\frac{b^2 - 4ac}{4a^2}}$ or $x + \frac{b}{2a} = -\sqrt{\frac{b^2 - 4ac}{4a^2}}$ Extract the roots

$= \frac{\sqrt{b^2 - 4ac}}{\sqrt{4a^2}}$ $= -\frac{\sqrt{b^2 - 4ac}}{\sqrt{4a^2}}$

$= \frac{\sqrt{b^2 - 4ac}}{2a}$ $= -\frac{\sqrt{b^2 - 4ac}}{2a}$

$x = \frac{-b}{2a} + \frac{\sqrt{b^2 - 4ac}}{2a}$ or
$x = \frac{-b}{2a} - \frac{\sqrt{b^2 - 4ac}}{2a}$ Subtract $\frac{b}{2a}$ from each member

$x = \frac{-b + \sqrt{b^2 - 4ac}}{2a}$ or $x = \frac{-b - \sqrt{b^2 - 4ac}}{2a}$ Subtract in right member

The results can be summarized by the **quadratic formula.**

Quadratic formula

$$x = \frac{-b \pm \sqrt{b^2 - 4ac}}{2a}.$$

Note

We read $\pm$ "plus or minus," which allows us to write the two solutions

$$x = \frac{-b + \sqrt{b^2 - 4ac}}{2a} \quad \text{or} \quad x = \frac{-b - \sqrt{b^2 - 4ac}}{2a}$$

as a single statement.

Caution When writing the quadratic formula, be sure that the fraction bar extends all the way beneath the numerator.

$$\frac{-b \pm \sqrt{b^2 - 4ac}}{2a}$$

Fraction bar

A common mistake is to write

$$-b \pm \frac{\sqrt{b^2 - 4ac}}{2a}.$$

To solve a quadratic equation by the quadratic formula

1. Write the equation in standard form, if it is not already in the form ($a > 0$).
2. Identify a (coefficient of x^2), b (coefficient of x), and c (the constant).
3. Substitute the values of a, b, and c into the quadratic formula.

$$x = \frac{-b \pm \sqrt{b^2 - 4ac}}{2a}$$

4. Simplify the resulting expression.

Example 10–3 B

Find the solution set using the quadratic formula.

1. $x^2 - 2x - 8 = 0$

The equation is already in standard form where $a = 1$, $b = -2$, and $c = -8$.

$$x = \frac{-(-2) \pm \sqrt{(-2)^2 - 4(1)(-8)}}{2(1)}$$

Replace a with 1, b with -2, and c with -8

$$= \frac{2 \pm \sqrt{4 - (-32)}}{2}$$

Simplify by performing indicated operations

$$= \frac{2 \pm \sqrt{36}}{2}$$

$$= \frac{2 \pm 6}{2}$$

$\sqrt{36} = 6$

$$x = \frac{2 + 6}{2} = \frac{8}{2} = 4 \quad \text{or} \quad x = \frac{2 - 6}{2} = \frac{-4}{2} = -2$$

The solution set is $\{4,-2\}$.

Note
The equation could have been solved by factoring since
$x^2 - 2x - 8 = (x - 4)(x + 2)$.

B₁ $x^2 - 3x - 4 = 0$

You are now ready to do **B₁**.

2. $x^2 = 2 - x$
Write the equation in standard form.

$x^2 + x - 2 = 0$ — Add x and subtract 4 from each member

$a = 1, b = 1$, and $c = -2$.

$$x = \frac{-1 \pm \sqrt{(1)^2 - 4(1)(-2)}}{2(1)}$$ Replace a with 1, b with 1, and c with -2

$$= \frac{-1 \pm \sqrt{1 + 8}}{2}$$ Simplify by performing operations

$$= \frac{-1 \pm 3}{2}$$

$$= \frac{-1 + 3}{2} = 1 \quad \text{or} \quad x = \frac{-1 - 3}{2} = -2$$

B₂ $x^2 = 3 - 2x$

The solution set is $\{-2,1\}$.

You are now ready to do **B₂**.

3. $x^2 + 2x - 2 = 0.$
The equation is already in standard form where $a = 1, b = 2$, and $c = -2$.

B₃ $x^2 + x - 1 = 0$

$$x = \frac{-2 \pm \sqrt{(2)^2 - 4(1)(-2)}}{2(1)}$$ Replace a with 1, b with 2, and c with -2

$$= \frac{-2 \pm \sqrt{4 + 8}}{2}$$ Simplify, perform operations

$$= \frac{-2 \pm \sqrt{12}}{2}$$

$$= \frac{-2 \pm 2\sqrt{3}}{2}$$ $\sqrt{12} = \sqrt{4 \cdot 3} = 2\sqrt{3}$

$$= \frac{2(1 \pm \sqrt{3})}{2}$$ Factor 2 from each term in the numerator

$$= -1 \pm \sqrt{3}$$ Reduce the fraction to lowest terms

The solution set is $\{-1 + \sqrt{3}, -1 - \sqrt{3}\}$.

You are now ready to do **B₃**.

B₄ $2x^2 - 2x - 3 = 0$

4. $3x^2 - x - 5 = 0$
The equation is already in standard form where $a = 3, b = -1$, and $c = -5$.

$$x = \frac{-(-1) \pm \sqrt{(-1)^2 - 4(3)(-5)}}{2(3)}$$ Replace a with 3, b with -1, and c with -5

$$= \frac{1 \pm \sqrt{1 + 60}}{6}$$ Simplify, perform operations

$$= \frac{1 \pm \sqrt{61}}{6}$$

The solution set is $\left\{\frac{1 - \sqrt{61}}{6}, \frac{1 + \sqrt{61}}{6}\right\}$.

You are now ready to do **B₄**.

B₅ $x^2 - 11 = 0$

5. $x^2 - 7 = 0$
The equation can be written $x^2 + 0x - 7 = 0$, which is then in standard form where $a = 1$, $b = 0$, and $c = -7$.

$$x = \frac{-0 \pm \sqrt{(0)^2 - 4(1)(-7)}}{2(1)}$$ Replace a with 1, b with 0, and c with -7

$$= \frac{\pm\sqrt{28}}{2}$$ Simplify, perform operations

$$= \pm\frac{2\sqrt{7}}{2}$$ $\sqrt{28} = \sqrt{4 \cdot 7} = 2\sqrt{7}$

$$= \pm\sqrt{7}$$ Reduce to lowest terms

The solution set is $\{\sqrt{7}, -\sqrt{7}\}$.

Note
In example 5, we could have solved the equation by extracting the roots.

$$x^2 - 7 = 0$$
$$x^2 = 7$$
$$x = \pm\sqrt{7}$$

You are now ready to do **B₅**.

6. $x^2 + x + 6 = 0$
The equation is already in standard form where $a = 1$, $b = 1$, and $c = 6$.

$$x = \frac{-1 \pm \sqrt{(1)^2 - 4(1)(6)}}{2(1)}$$ Replace a with 1, b with 1, and c with 6

$$= \frac{-1 \pm \sqrt{1 - 24}}{2}$$ Simplify

B₆ $x^2 + 4x + 7 = 0$

$$= \frac{-1 \pm \sqrt{-23}}{2}$$

Since $\sqrt{-23}$ is not a real number, the equation has no real solutions. In general, the equation $ax^2 + bx + c = 0$, $a \neq 0$, has no real solutions if $b^2 - 4ac$ is negative ($b^2 - 4ac < 0$).

You are now ready to do **B₆**. ■

Answers to section 10–3 margin exercises

A₁ $a = 5, b = -3, c = 4$ **A₂** $a = 4, b = -7, c = -5$ **A₃** $a = 3, b = -7, c = 2$ **B₁** $\{-1,4\}$ **B₂** $\{-3,1\}$ **B₃** $\left\{\frac{-1+\sqrt{5}}{2}, \frac{-1-\sqrt{5}}{2}\right\}$
B₄ $\left\{\frac{1-\sqrt{7}}{2}, \frac{1+\sqrt{7}}{2}\right\}$ **B₅** $\{-\sqrt{11}, \sqrt{11}\}$ **B₆** no real solutions, $\emptyset$

Mastery points

Can you

- Identify the values of *a*, *b*, and *c* in any quadratic equation?
- Use the quadratic formula

$$x = \frac{-b \pm \sqrt{b^2 - 4ac}}{2a}$$

to solve any quadratic equation?

Exercise 10–3

Directions Write each equation in standard form and identify the values of a, b, and c, where a is positive. See example 10–3 A.

Example **A₂** $4x^2 - 5 = 7x$

Solution We must first write the equation in standard form.

$4x^2 - 7x - 5 = 0$ Subtract $7x$ from each member

$a = 4, b = -7, c = -5$

1. $x^2 - 3x + 8 = 0$
2. $x^2 + x - 2 = 0$
3. $5y^2 - y + 6 = 0$
4. $2x^2 + 3x - 8 = 0$
5. $-6z^2 - 2z + 1 = 0$
6. $-3x^2 + x + 9 = 0$
7. $4x^2 = 2x - 1$
8. $y^2 = 5y + 3$
9. $x^2 = -3x$
10. $4x - 3x^2 = 0$
11. $5x^2 = 2$
12. $-8b^2 = -3$
13. $2x(x - 9) = 1$
14. $p(p + 3) = 4$
15. $(x + 3)(x - 1) = 6$
16. $(z - 4)(2z + 1) = -6$

Directions Find the real solutions, if they exist, using the quadratic formula, and state the solution set. See example 10–3 B.

Example **B₂** $x^2 = 3 - 2x$

Solution $x^2 + 2x - 3 = 0$ Add $2x$ to and subtract 3 from each member

$a = 1, b = 2$, and $c = -3$.

$$x = \frac{-(2) \pm \sqrt{(2)^2 - 4(1)(-3)}}{2(1)}$$ Replace a by 1, b by 2, and c by -3

$$= \frac{-2 \pm \sqrt{4 + 12}}{2}$$ Simplify, perform operations

$$= \frac{-2 \pm \sqrt{16}}{2}$$

$$x = \frac{-2 \pm 4}{2}$$ $\sqrt{16} = 4$

$$x = \frac{-2 + 4}{2} = \frac{2}{2} = 1 \quad \text{or} \quad x = \frac{-2 - 4}{2} = \frac{-6}{2} = -3$$

The solution set is $\{1, -3\}$.

Note
Since the solutions are rational numbers, this means the equation could be solved by factoring.

17. $y^2 + 6y + 9 = 0$

18. $x^2 - 3x + 2 = 0$

19. $2y^2 - 7y + 3 = 0$

20. $5x^2 - x - 4 = 0$

21. $x^2 - 9x + 4 = 0$

22. $a^2 - 5a - 6 = 0$

23. $a^2 + 1 = 8a$

24. $2x^2 = 7x - 6$

25. $3y^2 = 5y + 6$

26. $4t^2 = 8t - 3$

27. $x^2 - 25 = 0$

28. $2x^2 - 8 = 0$

29. $5x^2 - 10 = 0$

30. $3x^2 - 9x = 0$

31. $x^2 = 4x$

32. $y^2 + \frac{5}{2}y = -1$

33. $y^2 - y = \frac{3}{5}$

34. $a^2 + 2a = \frac{7}{4}$

35. $\frac{2}{3}x^2 - x = \frac{4}{3}$

36. $2x^2 - \frac{7}{2} + \frac{x}{2} = 0$

Directions Substitute into the given formulas and solve the resulting quadratic equation, using any method.

37. The distance s through which an object will fall in t seconds is $s = \frac{1}{2}gt^2$ feet, where $g = 32$ ft/sec².

a. Find t when $s = 64$.

b. Find t (correct to the tenth of a second) when $s = 96$.

c. Find t (correct to the tenth of a second) when $s = 120$.

38. Use the formula $s = vt + \frac{1}{2}at^2$ to solve the following, $t > 0$.

a. Find t when $s = 9$, $v = 3$, $a = 4$.

b. Find t when $s = 5$, $v = 4$, $a = 2$.

39. In a certain electric circuit, the relationship between i (in amperes), E (in volts), and R (in ohms) is given by $i^2R + iE = 8{,}000$.

a. Find i ($i > 0$) when $R = 2$ and $E = 80$.

b. Find i ($i > 0$) when $R = 4$ and $E = 60$.

40. If a certain projectile is fired vertically into the air, the distance in feet above the ground in t seconds is given by $s = 160t - 16t^2$.

a. Find t when $s = 0$.

b. Find t when $s = 384$.

c. Find t when $s = 160$.

41. The area of a triangle is 96 square inches. If the altitude is one-third the base, what are the lengths of the altitude and base? (Area $= \frac{1}{2}$ times base times altitude.)

42. A triangular-shaped plate has an altitude that is 5 inches longer than its base. If the area of the plate is 52 square inches, what is the length of the base, b, and the altitude, h, if the area of a triangle, A, is given by $A = \frac{1}{2}bh$?

43. The hypotenuse of a right triangle is 10 millimeters long. One leg is 2 millimeters longer than the other. What are the lengths of the two legs? (*Hint:* The hypotenuse is the longest side, and the other two sides are legs. $[\text{hypotenuse}]^2 = [\text{leg}]^2 + [\text{leg}]^2$)

44. Find the length of each side of a right triangle if the legs are 2 centimeters and 4 centimeters, respectively, shorter than the hypotenuse. (See exercise 43.)

45. Manufacturers often use quadratic equations to set up cost equations. The cost equation for manufacturing x units of a stereo component per week is $C = x^2 - 8x + 25$, where C is the cost of manufacturing x units (both measured in thousands). Find how many units x can be manufactured for a cost of \$13,000. (*Hint:* $C = 13$.)

46. Do problem 45 if the cost is \$10,000.

47. A manufacturer uses the profit equation $P = 3x^2 - 60x$ that yields the expected profit P in dollars made by selling x units of a particular article. To show a profit of \$132, how many units must be sold?

48. Do problem 47 if the manufacturer wishes to make a profit of \$900.

49. The area of a rectangle is 204 square feet. If the length is 5 feet longer than the width, find the dimensions of the rectangle. (*Hint:* Length · width = area.)

50. The length of a rectangular piece of cloth is 1 centimeter less than twice the width. What are the dimensions of the cloth if it has an area of 231 square centimeters?

Review exercises

Directions Graph the following equations by finding *three* ordered pair solutions and then graphing the points. See section 7–2.

1. $y = 4x - 3$

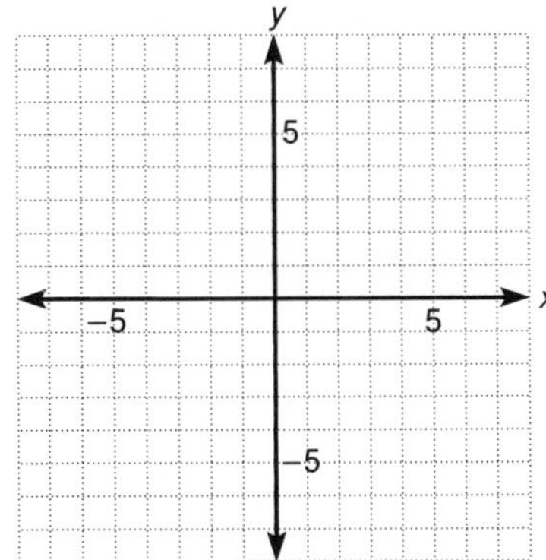

2. $y = 2 - 3x$

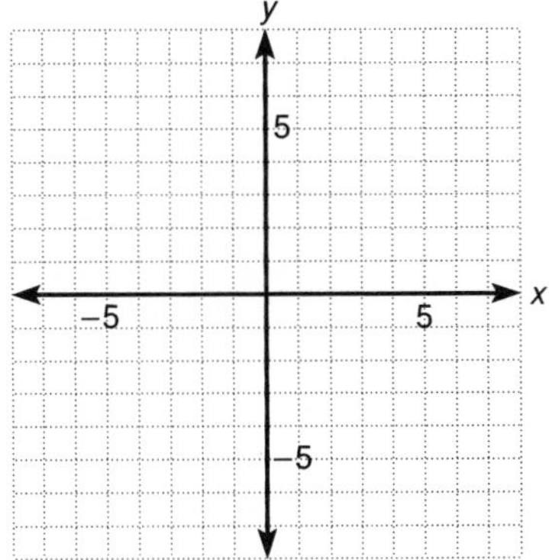

3. Graph the system of equations
$2x - y = 1$
$x + y = 3$
and find the simultaneous solution. See section 8–1.

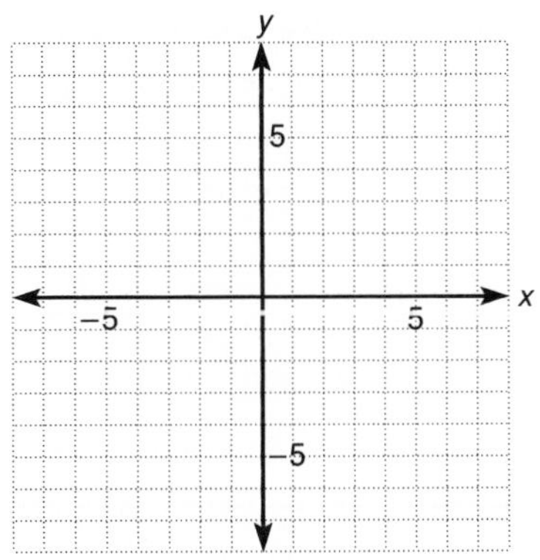

4. Find the equation of the line through the points $(1,-3)$ and $(4,5)$. See section 7–4.

Directions Perform the indicated operations. See sections 6–1 and 6–2.

5. $\dfrac{3x}{x-2} \cdot \dfrac{x^2 - x - 2}{4x^2}$

6. $\dfrac{x+2}{x^2-4} - \dfrac{x-1}{x^2-x-6}$

10–4 Graphing quadratic equations in two variables

In chapter 7, we graphed *linear* equations in two variables such as

$$2x - 3y = 12 \text{ and } y = 4x - 5.$$

The graphs of such equations were straight lines. In this section, we graph **quadratic equations in two variables** of the form

$$y = ax^2 + bx + c, a \neq 0$$

The graph of a quadratic (second-degree) equation is *not* a straight line. For this reason, we will need a number of points to plot the graph.

The parabola

The same procedures we used to graph linear equations can be used to graph quadratic equations. We choose a number of values of x and substitute them into the equation to find the corresponding values of y. Together they make up an ordered pair solution of the equation.

Consider the graph of the quadratic equation

$$y = x^2 + 2x - 8.$$

Suppose we let x take on the values -5, -4, -3, -2, -1, 0, 1, 2, and 3. The following table of related values shows the resulting ordered pairs and how they are found.

x	$y = x^2 + 2x - 8$	(x,y)
-5	$y = (-5)^2 + 2(-5) - 8 = 25 + (-10) - 8 = 7$	$(-5,7)$
-4	$y = (-4)^2 + 2(-4) - 8 = 16 + (-8) - 8 = 0$	$(-4,0)$
-3	$y = (-3)^2 + 2(-3) - 8 = 9 + (-6) - 8 = -5$	$(-3,-5)$
-2	$y = (-2)^2 + 2(-2) - 8 = 4 + (-4) - 8 = -8$	$(-2,-8)$
-1	$y = (-1)^2 + 2(-1) - 8 = 1 + (-2) - 8 = -9$	$(-1,-9)$
0	$y = (0)^2 + 2(0) - 8 = 0 + 0 - 8 = -8$	$(0,-8)$
1	$y = (1)^2 + 2(1) - 8 = 1 + 2 - 8 = -5$	$(1,-5)$
2	$y = (2)^2 + 2(2) - 8 = 4 + 4 - 8 = 0$	$(2,0)$
3	$y = (3)^2 + 2(3) - 8 = 9 + 6 - 8 = 7$	$(3,7)$

We now plot the points in the rectangular coordinate plane and draw a *smooth curve* through them to get the graph of the quadratic equation $y = x^2 + 2x - 8$. See figure 10–1.

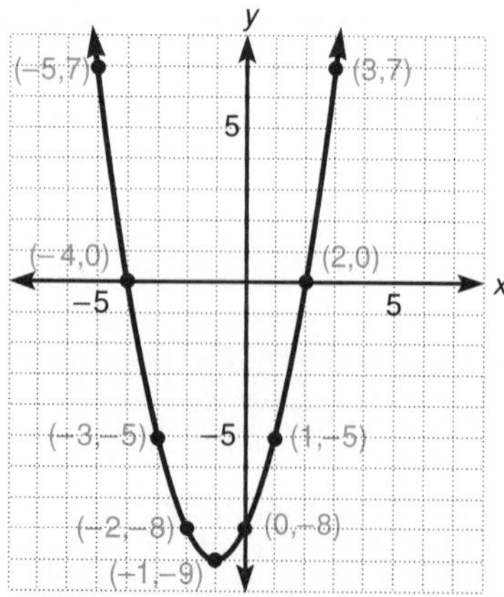

Figure 10–1

Note
We *do not* connect the points with straight line segments.

The curve thus obtained is called a **parabola.**

A_1 $y = x^2 - 9$

The *x*- and *y*-intercepts of a parabola

No matter how many points we plot, we cannot be sure that connecting all the points with a smooth curve will produce the correct graph and reveal all the important features of a curve. There are certain features of a parabola that we always wish to include in our graph, namely the x- and y-intercepts and the extreme (lowest or highest) point of the graph, called the *vertex* [the point $(-1,-9)$ in the figure 10–1 parabola].

We observe from our example that when the curve crosses the x-axis, the value of y is zero, and when the curve crosses the y-axis, the value of x is zero. This is the same observation that we made with linear equations, and we can generalize the idea of finding the x- and y-intercepts for any graph as follows:

1. To find the x-intercept(s), if there are any, we let $y = 0$ in the equation and solve for x.
2. To find the y-intercept, we let $x = 0$ in the equation and solve for y.

Example 10–4 A

Find the x- and y-intercepts.

1. $y = x^2 - 4$

a. Let $y = 0$.

$(0) = x^2 - 4$	Replace y with 0
$0 = (x - 2)(x + 2)$	Factor the right member
$x = 2$ or $x = -2$	Solve $x - 2 = 0$ and $x + 2 = 0$

The x-intercepts are the points $(-2,0)$ and $(2,0)$.

b. Let $x = 0$.

A_2 $y = x^2 + 4x + 4$

$y = (0)^2 - 4$	Replace x with 0
$y = -4$	

The y-intercept is the point $(0,-4)$.

You are now ready to do **A_1**.

2. $y = x^2 - 6x + 9$

a. Let $y = 0$.

$(0) = x^2 - 6x + 9$	Replace y with 0
$0 = (x - 3)(x - 3)$	Factor the right member
$x = 3$	Solve $x - 3 = 0$

The x-intercept is the point $(3,0)$.

b. Let $x = 0$.

$y = (0)^2 + 6(0) + 9$	Replace x with 0
$y = 9$	

The y-intercept is the point $(0,9)$.

You are now ready to do **A_2**.

3. $y = -x^2 + 2x + 3$

a. Let $y = 0$.

$(0) = -x^2 + 2x + 3$	Replace y with 0
$0 = x^2 - 2x - 3$	Multiply each member by -1 to obtain $a > 0$
$0 = (x - 3)(x + 1)$	Factor the right member
$x = 3$ or $x = -1$	Solve $x - 3 = 0$ and $x + 1 = 0$

The x-intercepts are the points $(3,0)$ and $(-1,0)$.

A₃ $y = -x^2 + 5x - 4$

b. Let $x = 0$.

$y = -(0)^2 + 2(0) + 3$ Replace x with 0
$y = 3$

The y-intercept is the point (0,3).

You are now ready to do **A₃**.

4. $y = x^2 + 1$

a. Let $y = 0$.

$0 = x^2 + 1$ Replace y with 0

Then $x^2 = -1$ and $x = \pm\sqrt{-1}$. Since $\sqrt{-1}$ is not a real number, there are no real solutions for x. Hence the graph has no x-intercepts.

b. Let $x = 0$.

$y = (0)^2 + 1$ Replace x with 0
$y = 1$

The y-intercept is the point (0,1).

Note
From these examples, we see that the y-intercept is always the constant c. If the quadratic equation is in standard form $y = ax^2 + bx + c$, the y-intercept will be the point $(0,c)$.

You are now ready to do **A₄**. ■

A₄ $y = x^2 + 5$

The vertex and the axis of symmetry of a parabola

We wish to find one remaining point of interest on the graph—the vertex. The vertex is the extreme point on the graph, that is, either the maximum or the minimum value that the second coordinate will attain. If our equation is in standard form, $y = ax^2 + bx + c$, we can show, but will not do so here, the x-coordinate of the vertex is given by $x = \frac{-b}{2a}$. Once we have determined the x-coordinate, we replace x with this value in our original equation and generate the corresponding y-value. Recall our original example: $y = x^2 + 2x - 8$. The value of a is 1 and b is 2. Therefore

$$x = \frac{-b}{2a} = \frac{-2}{2(1)} = \frac{-2}{2} = -1.$$

We then substitute this value for x in our original equation and we obtain

$$y = (-1)^2 + 2(-1) - 8 = 1 + (-2) - 8 = -9.$$

Hence, in this case, our vertex (the lowest, or minimum, point) is the point with coordinates $(-1,-9)$. This means no matter what value x takes, y is *never* less than -9.

Note
When the value of a, the coefficient of the quadratic term, is positive (as in this case), the parabola opens *upward* and the vertex is the *lowest* point of the graph. When a is negative, the parabola opens *downward* and the vertex is the *highest* point of the graph.

Examples 10–4 B

Find the vertex of each parabola.

1. $y = x^2 - 4$

$a = 1$ and $b = 0$. $\quad y = x^2 + 0x - 4$

$x = \frac{-b}{2a} = \frac{-0}{2(1)} = 0$ $\quad$ Replace a with 1 and b with 0

$y = (0)^2 - 4 = -4$ $\quad$ Replace x with 0 in $y = x^2 - 4$

The vertex is the point $(0,-4)$, the lowest point.

You are now ready to do **B₁**.

2. $y = x^2 - 6x + 9$

$a = 1$ and $b = -6$.

$x = \frac{-b}{2a} = \frac{-(-6)}{2(1)} = \frac{6}{2} = 3$ $\quad$ Replace a with 1 and b with -6

$y = (3)^2 - 6(3) + 9$ $\quad$ Replace x with 3 in $y = x^2 - 6x + 9$

$= 9 - 18 + 9$

$= 0$

The vertex is the point $(3,0)$, the lowest point.

You are now ready to do **B₂**.

3. $y = -x^2 + 2x + 3$

$a = -1$ and $b = 2$.

$x = \frac{-b}{2a} = \frac{-2}{2(-1)} = \frac{-2}{-2} = 1$ $\quad$ Replace a with -1 and b with 2

$y = -(1)^2 + 2(1) + 3$ $\quad$ Replace x with 1

$= -1 + 2 + 3$

$= 4$

The vertex is the point $(1,4)$, the highest point.

You are now ready to do **B₃**. ■

B₁ $y = x^2 - 9$

B₂ $y = x^2 + 4x + 4$

B₃ $y = -x^2 + 5x - 4$

If the vertex is the point, (h,k), the vertical line, $x = h$, which passes through the vertex, is called the **axis of symmetry** of the parabola. Since the parabola is a symmetric curve, if we fold the graph along the axis of symmetry, the left half of the curve will coincide with the right half of the curve. For this reason, we choose two values of x that are greater than h and two values of x that are less than h when finding our arbitrary points to graph.

To draw a reasonably accurate graph of the quadratic equation $y = ax^2 + bx + c$ in two variables, we take the following steps.

Graphing the quadratic equation $y = ax^2 + bx + c$ in two variables

1. Find the coordinates of the x- and y-intercepts.
   a. Let $x = 0$, solve for y-intercept.
   b. Let $y = 0$, solve for x-intercept(s).
2. Find the coordinates of the vertex.
   a. $x = \frac{-b}{2a}$.
   b. Replace x with $\frac{-b}{2a}$ in the original equation and solve for y.
3. Find the coordinates of four arbitrarily chosen points. Choose values of x such that, if (h,k) is the vertex of the parabola,
   a. two values are less than h and
   b. two values are greater than h.
4. Draw a smooth curve through the resulting points.

Examples 10–4 C

Graph the following quadratic equations. Determine the equation of the axis of symmetry.

1. $y = x^2 - 4$

In our previous examples, we found the x- and y-intercepts and the vertex. We need only determine four more points and we will be ready to graph the equation.

x	y	
2	0	x-intercepts
−2	0	
0	−4	y-intercept and vertex
−1	−3	Arbitrary points
1	−3	
−3	5	
3	5	

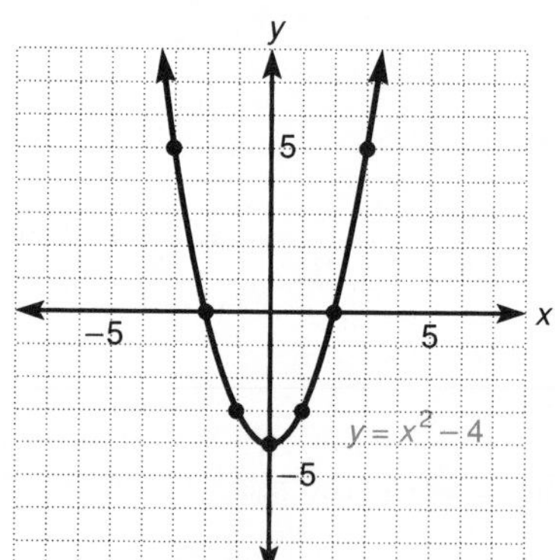

The axis of symmetry is the line $x = 0$ (y-axis).

You are now ready to do **C₁**.

C₁ $y = x^2 - 1$

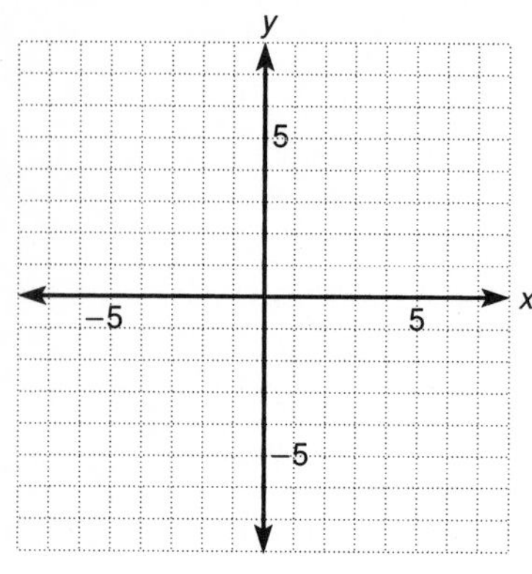

2. $y = x^2 - 6x + 9$

x	y	
3	0	x-intercept and vertex
0	9	y-intercept
1	4	Arbitrary points
2	1	
4	1	
5	4	
6	9	

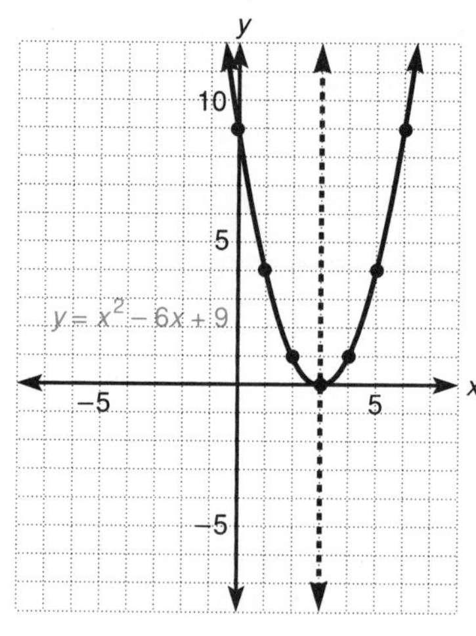

The axis of symmetry is the vertical line $x = 3$.

You are now ready to do **C₂**.

C₂ $y = x^2 + 4x + 4$

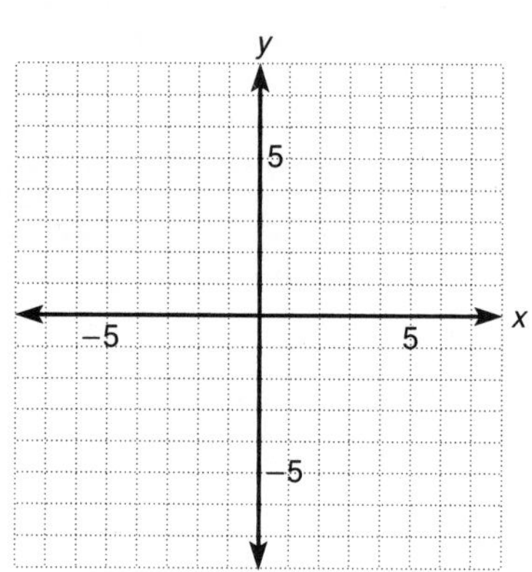

3. $y = -x^2 + 2x + 3$

x	y	
3	0	x-intercepts
−1	0	
0	3	y-intercept
1	4	Vertex
−2	−5	Arbitrary points
2	3	
4	−5	

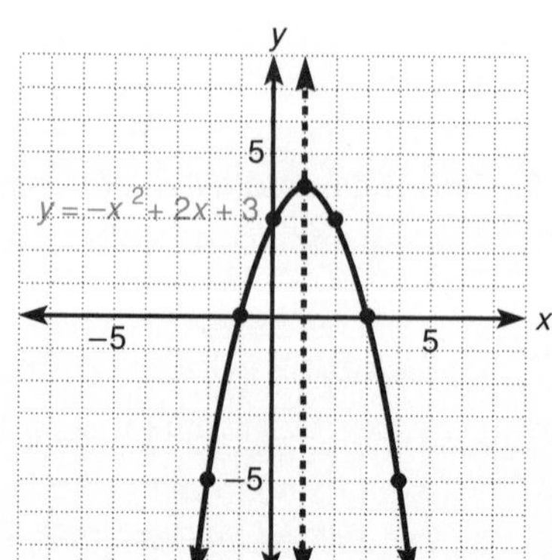

The axis of symmetry is the vertical line $x = 1$.

You are now ready to do **C₃**.

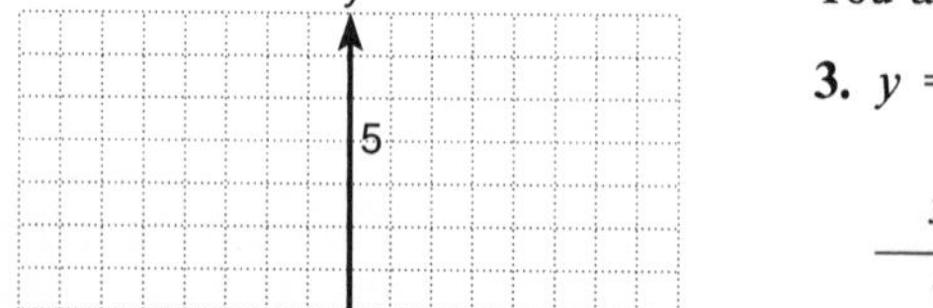

C₃ $y = -x^2 + 5x - 4$

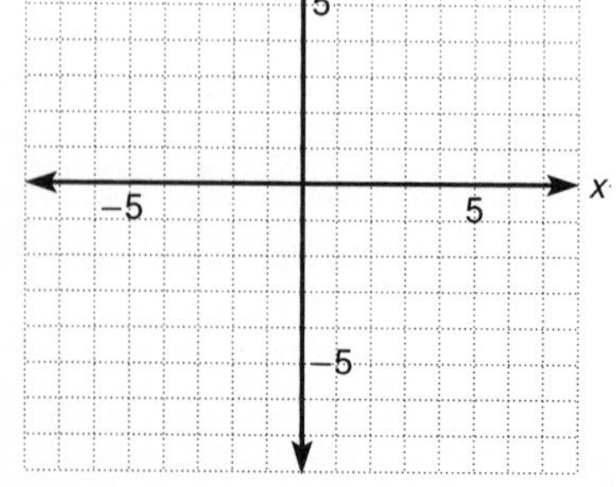

4. $y = x^2 + 1$

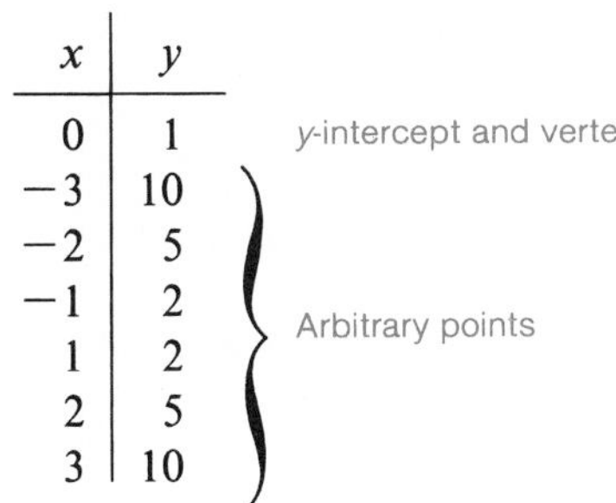

x	y	
0	1	y-intercept and vertex
−3	10	Arbitrary points
−2	5	
−1	2	
1	2	
2	5	
3	10	

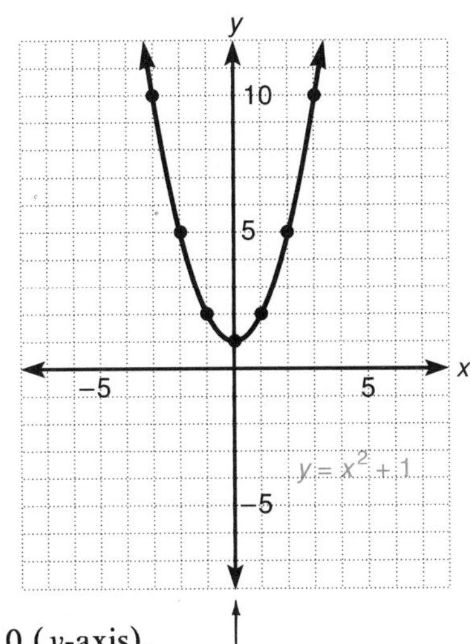

The axis of symmetry is the line $x = 0$ (y-axis).

You are now ready to do **C₄**.

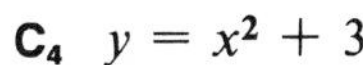

C₄ $y = x^2 + 3$

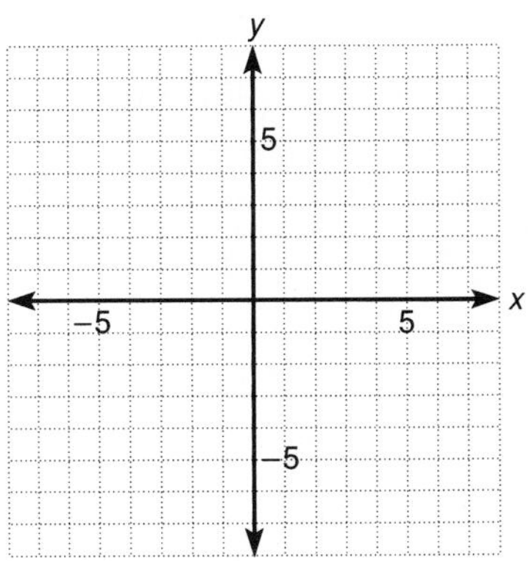

Quadratic equations are used in many physical situations. For example, if an object is thrown into the air, the graph of the distance the object travels versus the time it travels is a parabola.

Example 10–4 D

A projectile is fired vertically into the air. Its distance s in feet above the ground in t seconds is given by $s = 160t - 16t^2$. Find the highest point of the projectile (the vertex of the parabola) and the moment when the projectile will strike the ground. Graph the equation.

a. The vertex is the highest point (t,s),

$$s = -16t^2 + 160t,$$

$a = -16$, $b = 160$. The t value of the vertex is

$$t = \frac{-b}{2a} = \frac{-160}{2(-16)} = \frac{-160}{-32} = 5.$$

The height s will be

$$s = -16(5)^2 + 160(5) = -400 + 800 = 400 \text{ feet.}$$

The maximum height, $s = 400$ feet, is attained when $t = 5$ seconds.

b. The projectile will strike the ground when $s = 0$. Therefore we set $s = 0$ and solve for t.

$0 = -16t^2 + 160t$ — Replace s with 0

$\quad = -16t(t - 10)$ — Factor right member

$t = 0$ or 10 — Solve equations $-16t = 0$ and $t - 10 = 0$

The value $t = 0$ seconds represents when the projectile was fired. Hence the value $t = 10$ seconds represents the time when the object will strike the ground.

D₁ A projectile is fired vertically into the air. Its distance s in feet above the ground in t seconds is given by $s = 40t - 5t^2$. Find the highest point of the projectile, find when it will strike the ground, and graph the equation.

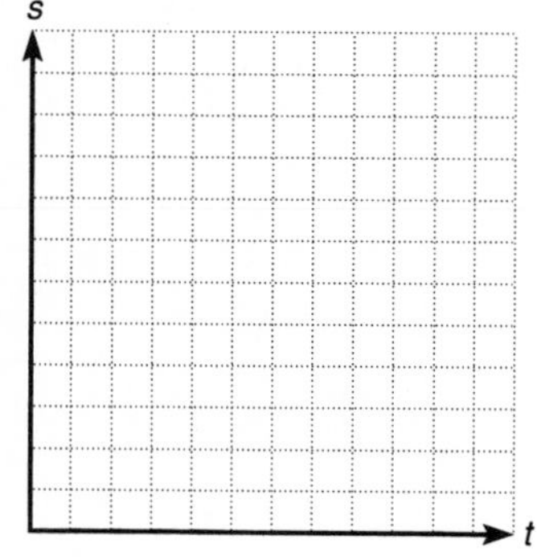

c. To graph the equation, we plot time, t, along the horizontal axis and distance, s, along the vertical axis.

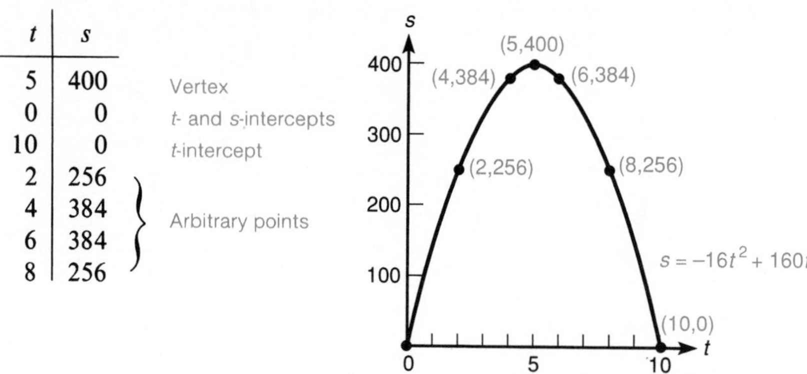

t	s	
5	400	Vertex
0	0	t- and s-intercepts
10	0	t-intercept
2	256	Arbitrary points
4	384	
6	384	
8	256	

Note
We have used different scales on the t- and s-axes, and we do not represent values on the graph for negative time or distance, since they do not have any meaning in this example.

You are now ready to do **D₁**. ■

Answers to section 10–4 margin exercises

A₁ x-intercepts, (3,0), (−3,0); y-intercept, (0,−9) **A₂** x-intercept, (−2,0); y-intercept, (0,4) **A₃** x-intercepts, (1,0), (4,0); y-intercept, (0,−4) **A₄** no x-intercept; y-intercept, (0,5) **B₁** (0,−9) **B₂** (−2,0) **B₃** $\left(\frac{5}{2}, \frac{9}{4}\right)$

C₁ axis of symmetry: $x = 0$ **C₂** axis of symmetry: $x = -2$

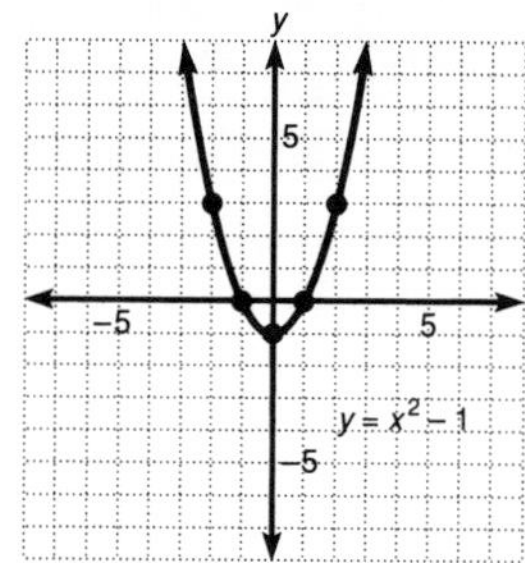

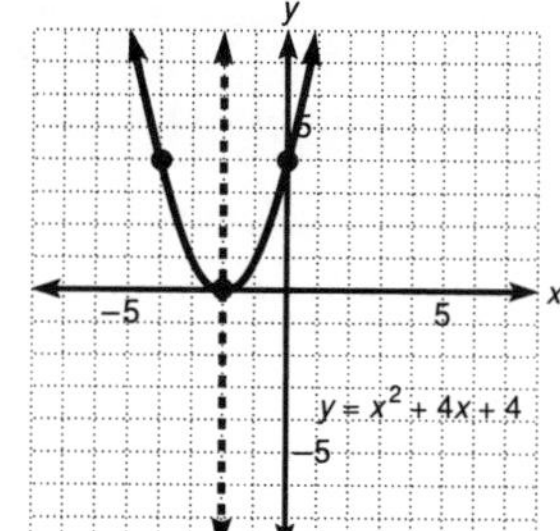

C₃ axis of symmetry: $x = \frac{5}{2}$ **C₄** axis of symmetry: $x = 0$

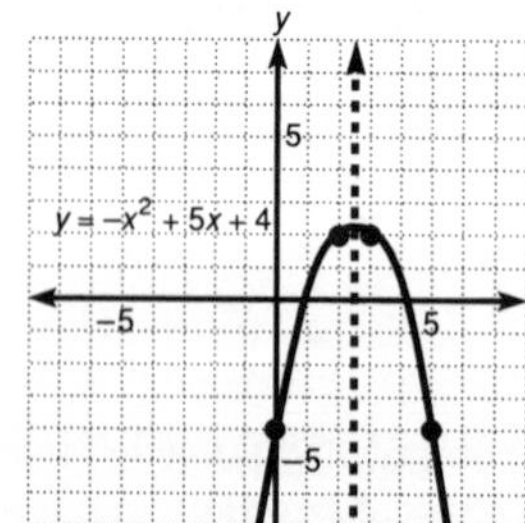

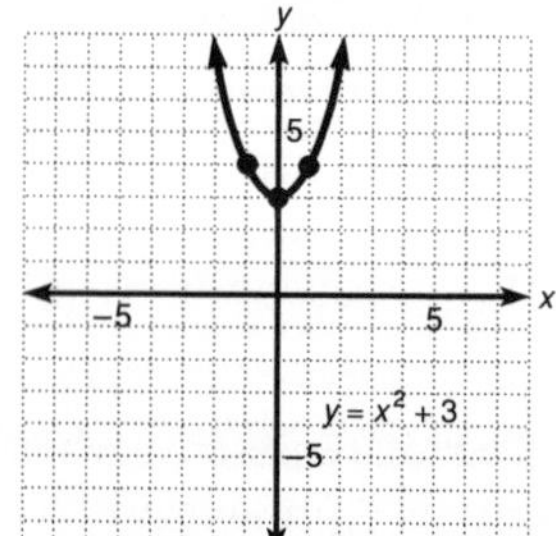

D_1 highest point 80 ft when $t = 4$ sec, strikes ground at $t = 8$ sec (*note:* each unit on the s-axis $= 10$ units)

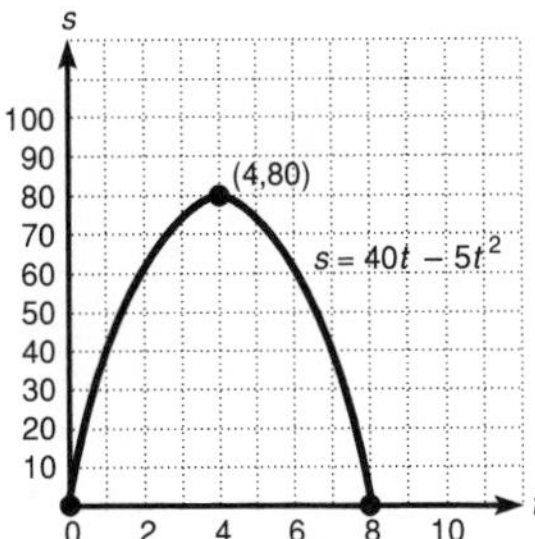

Mastery points

Can you

- Find the x- and y-intercepts in the graph of a quadratic equation?
- Find the coordinates of the vertex in the graph of a quadratic equation?
- Graph a quadratic function in two variables?
- Determine the equation of the axis of symmetry?

Exercise 10–4

Directions Find the x- and y-intercepts. If they do not exist, so state. See example 10–4 A.

Example $\boxed{A_3}$ $y = -x^2 + 5x - 4$

Solution a. Let $y = 0$.

$0 = -x^2 + 5x - 4$ Replace y with 0
$0 = x^2 - 5x + 4$ Multiply each member by -1
$0 = (x - 1)(x - 4)$ Factor the right member
$x = 1$ or $x = 4$ Solve equations $x - 1 = 0$ and $x - 4 = 0$

The x-intercepts are the points (1,0) and (4,0).

b. Let $x = 0$.

$y = -(0)^2 + 5(0) - 4$ Replace x by 0
$y = -4$

The y-intercept is the point $(0,-4)$.

1. $y = x^2 - 16$
2. $y = x^2 - 9$
3. $y = x^2 - 6x + 8$
4. $y = x^2 + 2x - 8$
5. $y = x^2 + 6x + 9$
6. $y = x^2 - 4x + 4$
7. $y = -x^2 + 8x - 16$
8. $y = -x^2 + 8x - 12$
9. $y = x^2 + 6$

10. $y = x^2 + 9$

11. $y = 2x^2 + 3x + 1$

12. $y = 2x^2 - 7x + 6$

13. $y = -2x^2 - x + 6$

14. $y = -3x^2 + 7x + 6$

Directions Find the vertex. Find the equation of the axis of symmetry. See example 10–4 B and C.

Example B_3 $y = -x^2 + 5x - 4$

Solution From the equation, $a = -1$ and $b = 5$.

$$x = \frac{-b}{2a} = \frac{-5}{2(-1)} = \frac{5}{2} \qquad \text{Replace } a \text{ with } -1 \text{ and } b \text{ with } 5$$

$$y = -\left(\frac{5}{2}\right)^2 + 5\left(\frac{5}{2}\right) - 4$$

$$= -\frac{25}{4} + \frac{25}{2} - 4$$

$$= \frac{9}{4}$$

The coordinates of the vertex are $\left(\frac{5}{2}, \frac{9}{4}\right)$.

The axis of symmetry is $x = \frac{5}{2}$.

15. $y = x^2 - 16$

16. $y = x^2 - 9$

17. $y = x^2 - 6x + 8$

18. $y = x^2 + 2x - 8$

19. $y = x^2 + 6x + 9$

20. $y = x^2 - 4x + 4$

21. $y = -x^2 + 8x - 16$

22. $y = -x^2 + 8x - 12$

23. $y = x^2 + 6$

24. $y = x^2 + 9$

25. $y = 2x^2 + 3x + 1$

26. $y = 2x^2 - 7x + 6$

27. $y = -2x^2 - x + 6$

28. $y = -3x^2 + 7x + 6$

Directions Graph the following equations using the x- and y-intercepts, the vertex, and four arbitrary points. See example 10–4 C.

Example $\boxed{C_3}$ $y = -x^2 + 5x - 4$

Solution

x	y	
1	0	x-intercepts
4	0	
0	-4	y-intercept
$\frac{5}{2}$	$\frac{9}{4}$	Vertex
-1	-10	Arbitrary points
2	2	
3	2	
5	-4	

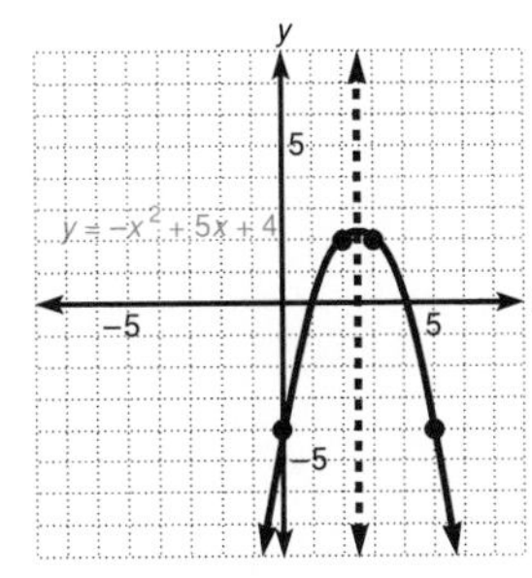

29. $y = 2x^2$

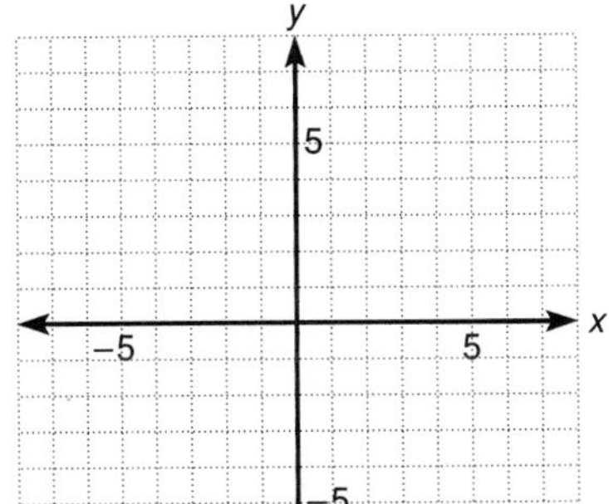

30. $y = -\frac{1}{2}x^2$

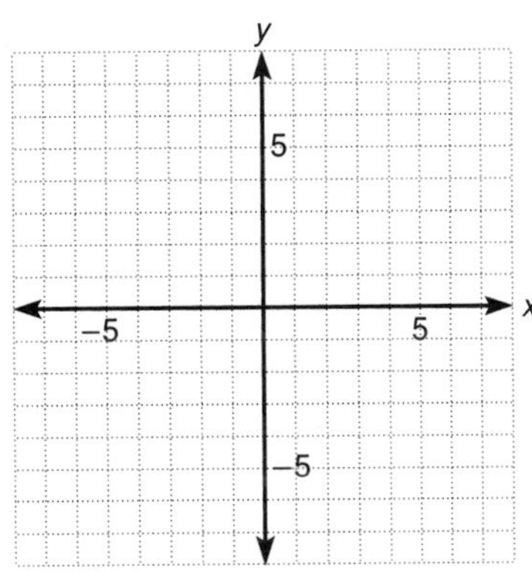

$\boxed{31.}$ $y = x^2 - 6x + 5$

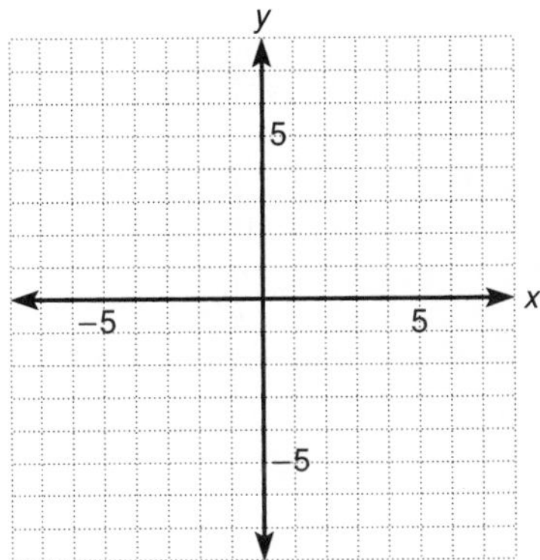

32. $y = x^2 + x - 6$

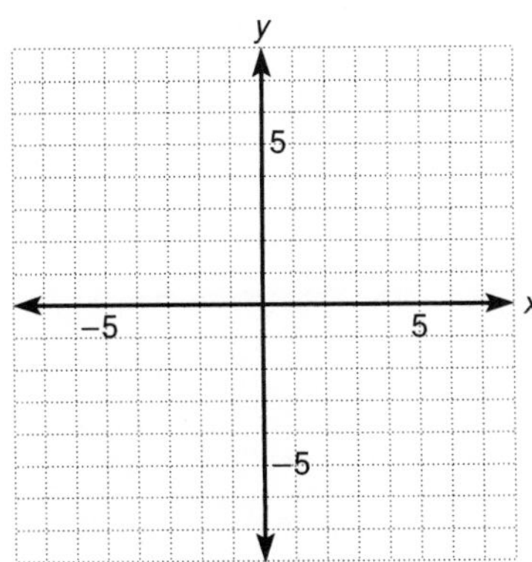

33. $y = x^2 + 2x + 1$

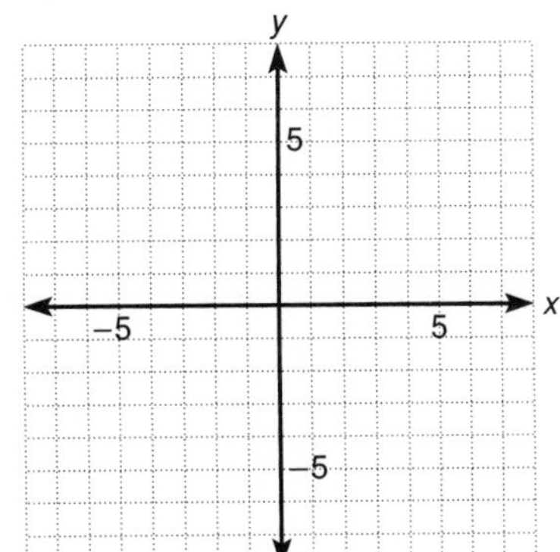

34. $y = x^2 - 4x + 4$

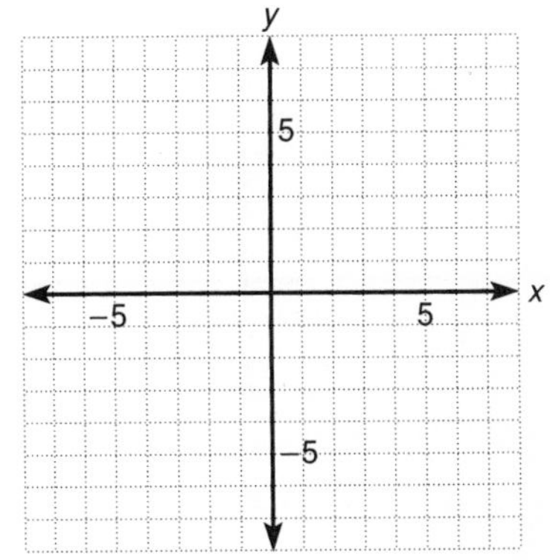

35. $y = -x^2 + 2x + 3$

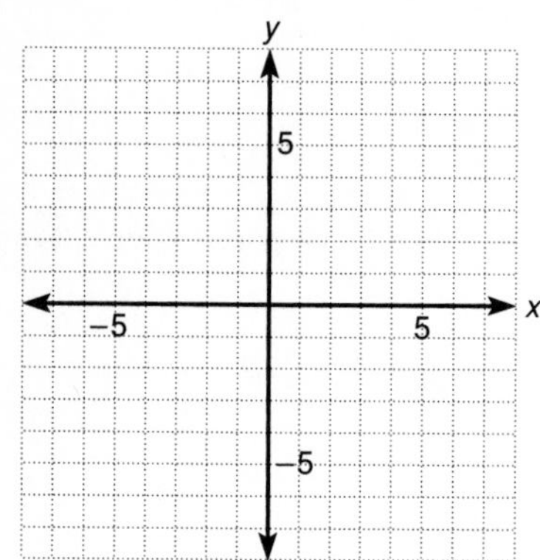

36. $y = -x^2 + 4x - 3$

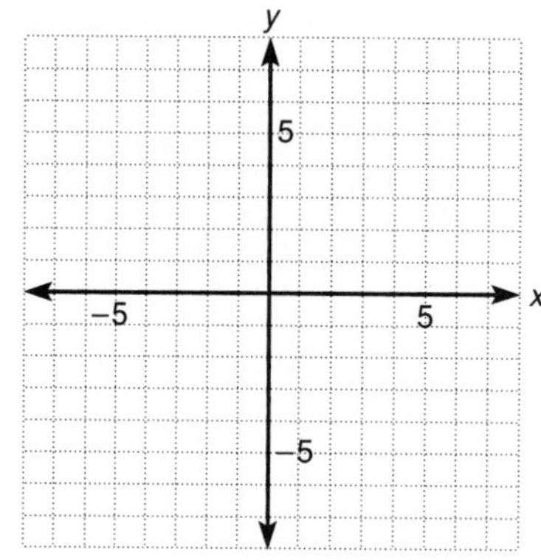

37. $y = x^2 + 6$

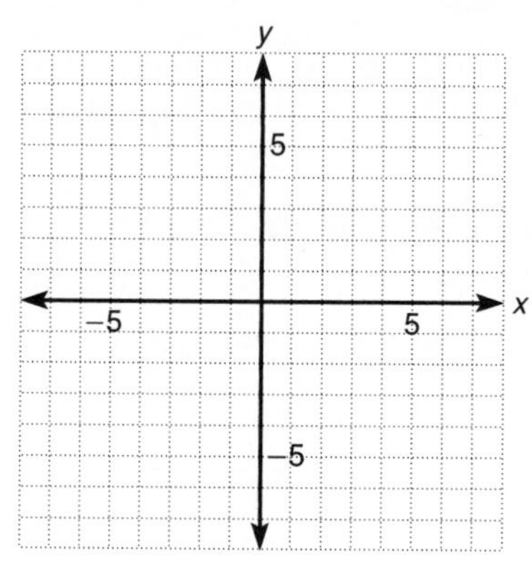

38. $y = x^2 + 2$

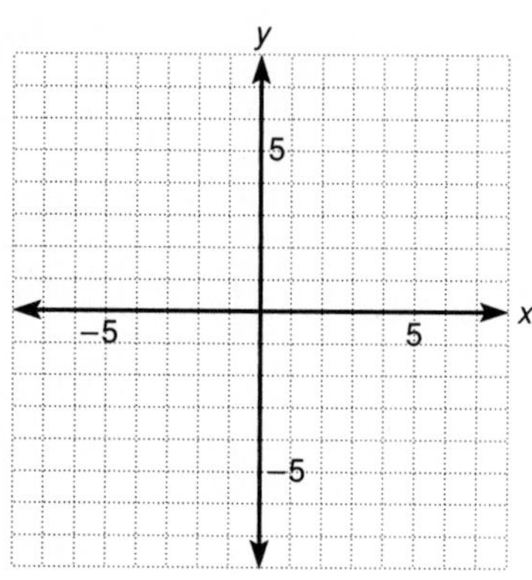

39. $y = 2x^2 + 3x + 1$

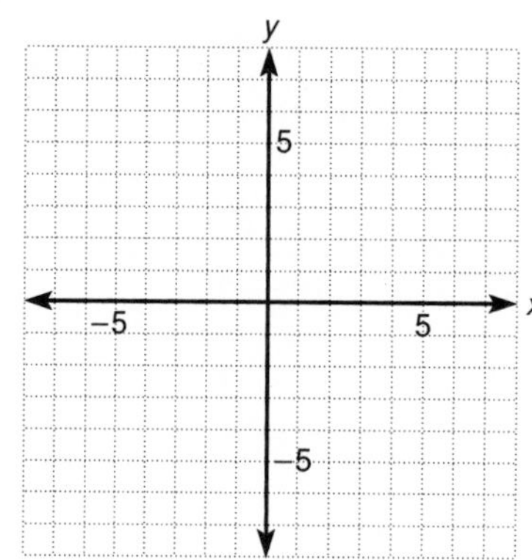

40. $y = 2x^2 - 5x + 2$

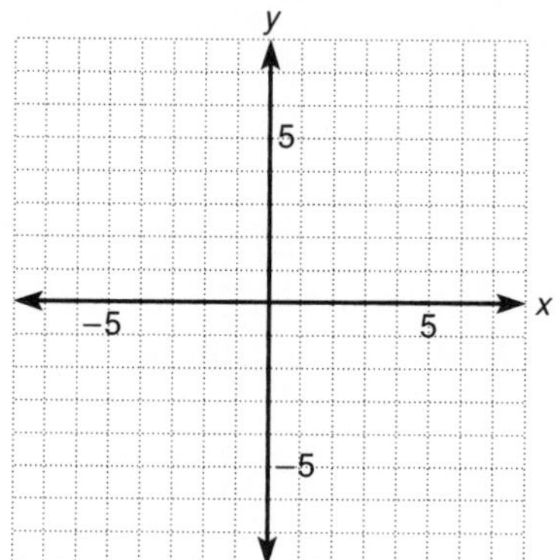

41. $y = -2x^2 - x + 6$

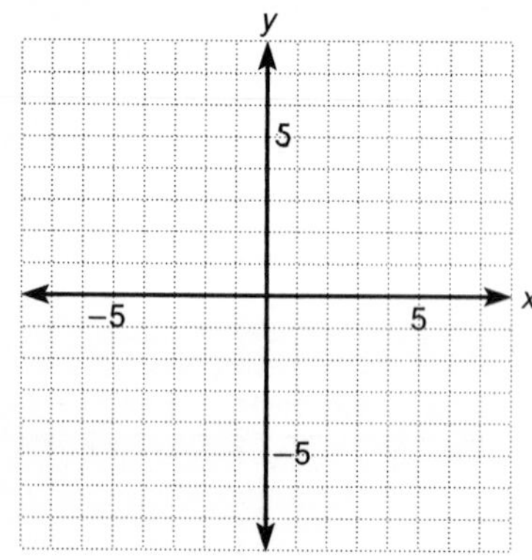

42. $y = -2x^2 - 3x + 5$

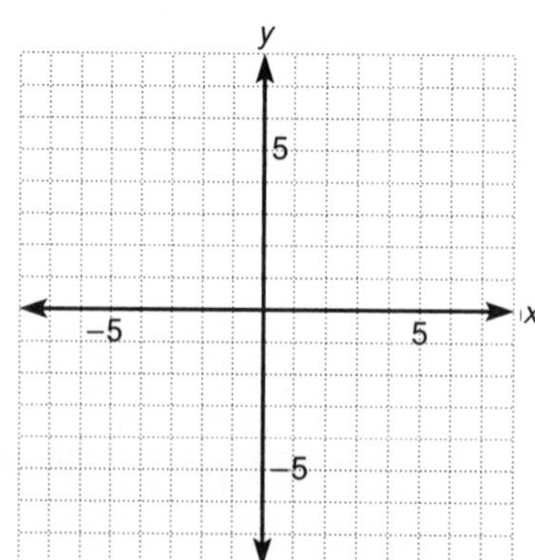

Directions Graph each equation in Quadrant 1 by plotting the variable for which the equation is solved along the vertical axis and by plotting the other variable along the horizontal axis. Graph the equation only in the regions for which the equation would have meaning. See example 10–4 D.

Example D₁ A projectile is fired vertically into the air. Its distance s in feet above the ground in t seconds is given by $s = 40t - 5t^2$. Find the highest point of the projectile and find when it will strike the ground. Graph the equation.

Solution $s = 40t - 5t^2 = -5t^2 + 40$

1. $a = -5$ and $b = 40$.

$$t = -\frac{b}{2a} = -\frac{40}{2(-5)} = 4$$

When $t = 4$, then

$$s = 40(4) - 5(4)^2 = 160 - 80 = 80.$$

The maximum height is 80 feet and is attained when $t = 4$ seconds.

2. The projectile will strike the ground when $s = 0$ feet.

$$\begin{aligned} 0 &= 40t - 5t^2 \\ 0 &= -5t^2 + 40t \\ &= -5t(t - 8) \\ t = 0 &\quad \text{or} \quad t = 8 \end{aligned}$$

The projectile will strike the ground at $t = 8$ seconds.

3.

t	s	
4	80	Vertex
0	0	t- and s-intercepts
8	0	t-intercept
1	35	Arbitrary points
2	60	
6	60	
7	35	

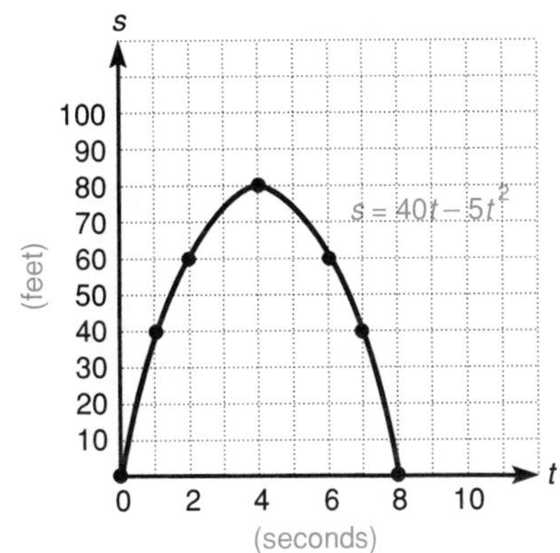

43. When a ball rolls down an inclined plane, it travels a distance $d = 6t + \frac{t^2}{2}$ feet in t seconds. Plot the graph showing how d depends on t. How long will it take the ball to travel 14 feet?

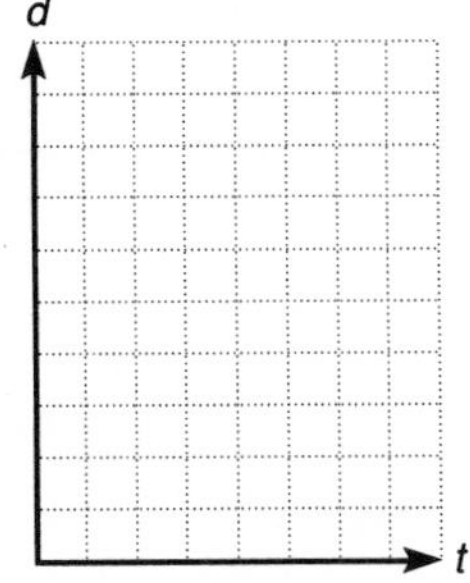

44. Referring to example 10–4D, if the initial velocity is 96 ft/sec, the equation is $s = 96t - 16t^2$. Find the maximum height and when the projectile will strike the ground.

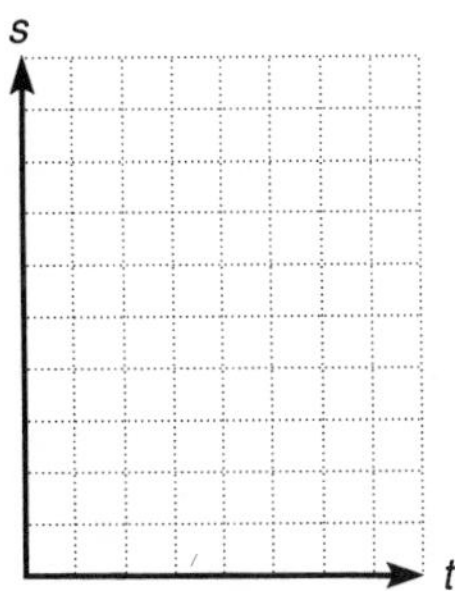

45. The output power P of a 100-volt electric generator is defined by $P = 100I - 5I^2$, where I is amperes. Plot the graph showing how P depends on I.

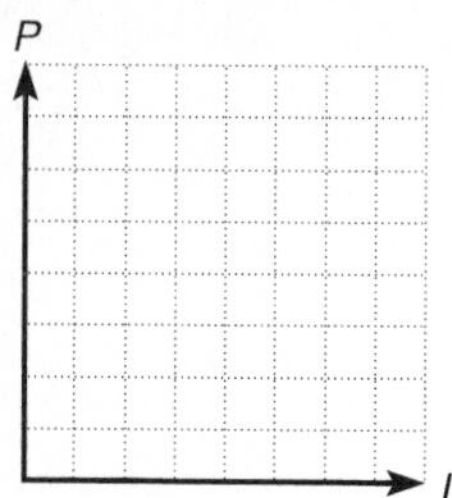

46. The distance s through which an object will fall in t seconds is $s = 16t^2$. Plot the graph showing the relation between s and t for the first 5 seconds.

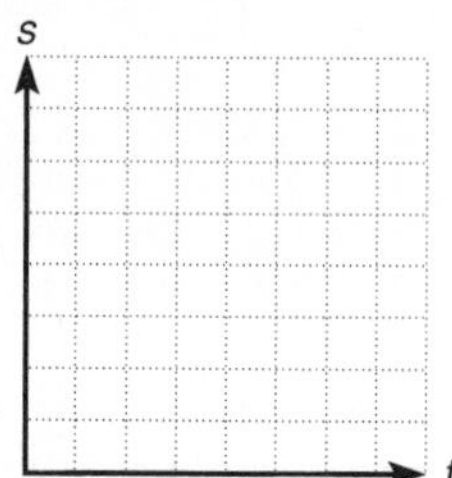

47. The current in a circuit flows according to the equation $i = 12 - 12t^2$, where i is the current and t is the time in seconds. Plot the graph of the relation given by the equation.

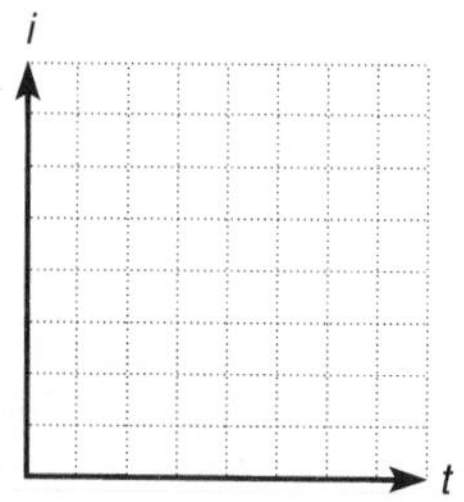

48. An object is dropped from the top of the Empire State Building (1,250 feet tall), and the distance that the object is from the ground is given by the equation $s = 1{,}250 - 16t^2$. Plot the graph showing how s depends on t and determine when the object will strike the ground. (t is time in seconds.)

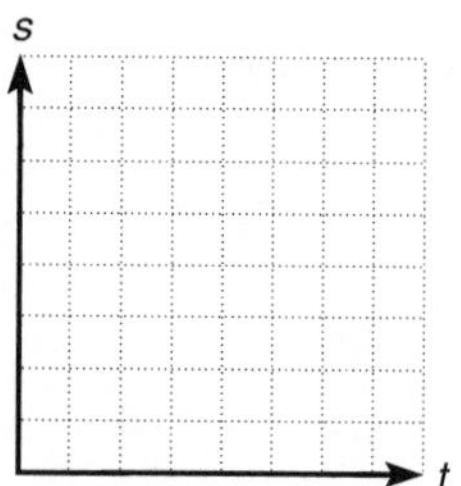

49. If a projectile is fired vertically into the air with an initial velocity of 80 feet per second, the distance in feet above the ground in t seconds is given by $s = 80t - 16t^2$. Find the object's maximum height and when the object will strike the ground. Plot the graph showing how s depends on t.

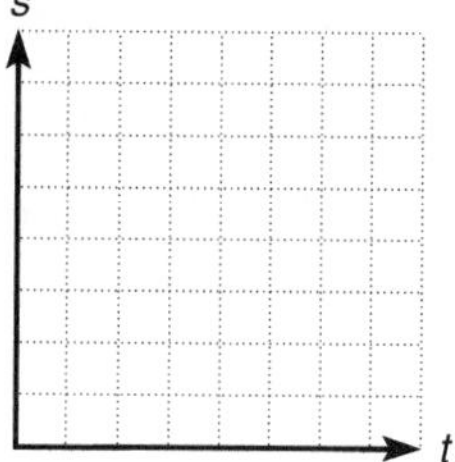

Chapter 10 lead-in problem

A rock is dropped from the top of the Washington Monument. If the monument is 555 feet tall, how long will it take the rock to strike the ground?

Solution

Use $s = 16t^2$, where s is the distance the rock fell and t is the time in seconds.

$555 = 16t^2$ — Replace s with 555

$t^2 = \frac{555}{16}$ — Divide each member by 16

$t = \sqrt{\frac{555}{16}} = \frac{\sqrt{555}}{4} \approx 5.9$ — Extract the roots

or $t = -\sqrt{\frac{555}{16}} = -\frac{\sqrt{555}}{4} \approx -5.9$

Reject the negative value since time t must be positive. Thus, the rock will strike the ground in approximately 5.9 seconds.

Chapter 10 summary

1. We can solve equations of the form $x^2 = k$ and $(ax + b)^2 = k$, $k \geq 0$, by **extracting the roots.**
2. If $x^2 = k$, then $x = \pm\sqrt{k}$, and if $(ax + b)^2 = k$, then $x = \frac{-b \pm \sqrt{k}}{a}$.
3. Any quadratic equation can be solved by **completing the square.**
4. Given the quadratic equation $ax^2 + bx + c = 0$, the **quadratic formula** states
$$x = \frac{-b \pm \sqrt{b^2 - 4ac}}{2a}.$$
5. We graph quadratic equations in two variables using the x- and y-intercepts, the vertex, and four arbitrary points in the plane.

Chapter 10 review

[10–1]

Directions Find the solution set of the following quadratic equations by extracting the roots.

1. $x^2 = 100$

2. $x^2 - 25 = 0$

3. $z^2 = 2$

4. $y^2 - 6 = 0$

5. $6x^2 = 24$

6. $8x^2 - 96 = 0$

7. $\frac{3}{4}x^2 = 12$

8. $\frac{2}{3}x^2 - 8 = 0$

9. $\frac{x^2}{3} - 8 = \frac{1}{4}$

[10–2]

Directions Find the solution set by completing the square.

10. $x^2 - 6x + 8 = 0$

11. $z^2 - 10z - 24 = 0$

12. $4 - x^2 = 5x$

13. $3y^2 - 6y - 5 = 0$

14. $2a^2 - 7a = -5$

15. $5 = 11y - y^2$

16. $4x^2 - 3 = 3x - 1$

17. $(x - 2)(x + 1) = 1$

18. $x(4x - 1) = 3$

19. $\frac{3}{5}x^2 + \frac{1}{5}x = 2$

20. The length of a rectangle is 2 meters more than 3 times the width. Its area is 16 square meters. What are its dimensions? (Solve by completing the square.)

[10–3]

Directions Find the solution set using the quadratic formula.

21. $x^2 - 2x - 5 = 0$

22. $x^2 - 8 = -4x$

23. $2y^2 - 3y = 5$

24. $3a^2 = 8 - 7a$

25. $2x^2 - 9 = 0$

26. $4x^2 = -7x$

27. $x^2 - \frac{2}{3}x = \frac{4}{3}$

28. $2x + \frac{3}{4} = \frac{3}{2}x^2$

29. A metal bar is to be divided into two pieces so that one piece is 3 inches longer than the other. If the sum of the squares of the two lengths is 117, find the two lengths. (Use the quadratic formula.)

[10–4]

Directions Graph the following quadratic equations using the x- and y-intercepts, the vertex, and four arbitrary points.

30. $y = x^2 - 5x + 6$

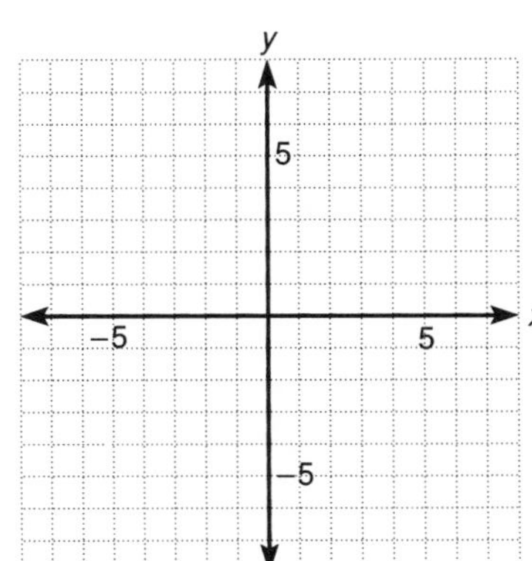

31. $y = -x^2 + 3x + 4$

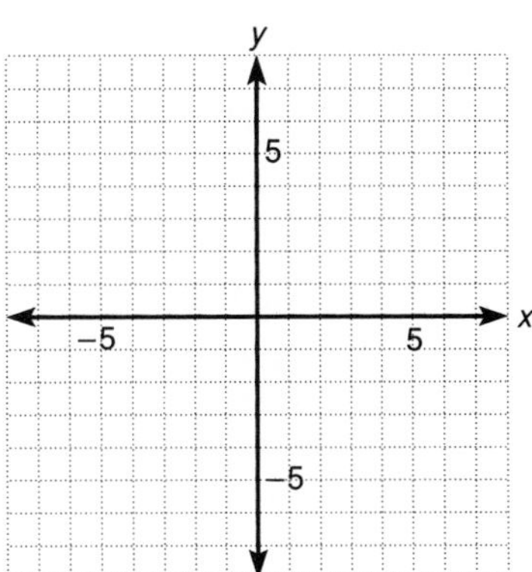

Final examination

[1–6] 1. Insert the proper inequality symbol, $<$ or $>$, to make the statement $|-5| \quad |4|$ true.

Directions Perform the indicated operations and simplify the expression.

[1–6] 2. $38 - 10 \div 5 + 3 \cdot 4 - 2^3 + \sqrt{4}$

[1–6] 3. $-4\,[9 - 3(9 - 4) + 6]$

[1–8] 4. Evaluate the expression $a - b(2c - d)$ when $a = -4$, $b = 3$, $c = 5$, and $d = -6$.

Directions Simplify the following and leave the answers with only positive exponents.

[3–4] 5. $x^5 \cdot x^{-3} \cdot x^4$

[3–4] 6. $\dfrac{2x^{-3}}{4x^2}$

[3–4] 7. $(3x^2y^3)(-4xy^2)$

[3–4] 8. $(3xy^{-2})^{-3}$

[3–1] 9. $(7x^3z^2)^0$

Directions Remove the grouping symbols and combine.

[3–2] **10.** $(4x^2 - y^2) - (2x^2 + y^2) + 5x^2 - 6y^2$

[3–2] **11.** $5x - (x - y) - 2x + y - (2x + 5y)$

Directions Perform the indicated operations and simplify.

[3–3] **12.** $(y + 9)(y - 9)$

[3–3] **13.** $(7z - 3w)^2$

[3–3] **14.** $(x + 4)(5x^2 - 3x + 1)$

[5–3] **15.** $\dfrac{5xy^2 - 3x^4y + x^2y^2}{xy}$

[5–3] **16.** $(8y^2 - 2y - 3) \div (2y - 1)$

Directions Find the solution set of the following equations.

[2–1] **17.** $2(x + 1) - 3(x - 3) = 4$

[4–6] **18.** $\dfrac{3x}{6} - 2 = \dfrac{5x}{4}$

[6–1] **19.** $x^2 - 11x - 12 = 0$

[6–3] **20.** $3 + \dfrac{2}{x^2} - \dfrac{7}{x} = 0$

[6–1] **21.** $8x^2 = 12x$

Directions Completely factor the following expressions.

[4–1] **22.** $3x^2 - 6xy + 9x$

[4–3] **23.** $a^2 - 4a - 21$

[4–3] **24.** $4x^2 - 12x + 5$

[4–4] **25.** $9a^2 - 64$

[4–4] **26.** $6ax - 2ay + 3bx - by$

[4–4] **27.** $x^2 - 10x + 25$

[4–6] **28.** The product of two consecutive integers is 132. Find the integers.

Directions Perform the indicated operations and reduce to lowest terms.

[6–1] **29.** $\dfrac{x^2 + 7x + 6}{x^2 - 4} \cdot \dfrac{x - 2}{x + 6}$

[6–1] **30.** $\dfrac{3x}{4x - 8} \div \dfrac{9x}{x^2 - 4x + 4}$

[6–2] **31.** $\dfrac{9}{x - 6} - \dfrac{5}{6 - x}$

[6–2] **32.** $\dfrac{x - 2}{x + 5} + \dfrac{x + 4}{x^2 - 25}$

[6–3] **33.** Simplify the complex fraction $\dfrac{5 + \dfrac{4}{y}}{4 - \dfrac{6}{y}}$.

[5–4] **34.** Find the value of x if $15 : 6 = 8 : x$.

[5–4] **35.** What is the ratio of 42 oz to 5 lb?

[7–4] **36.** Find the equation of the line passing through points $(-2,5)$ and $(1,-1)$.

[7–4] **37.** Given the equation $2x - 3y = 9$, find the slope m and the y-intercept b of the line.

[8–3] **38.** Solve the system of equations
$x - 2y = 3$
$2x - 3y = -5$.

[2–4] **39.** The perimeter of a rectangle is 34 feet. If the length is 2 more than twice the width, what are the dimensions of the rectangle?

Directions Simplify the following expressions by performing the indicated operations. Rationalize all denominators.

[9–4] **40.** $\sqrt{27} - \sqrt{48}$

[9–2] **41.** $\sqrt{3}(\sqrt{2} + \sqrt{3})$

[9–2] **42.** $(4 + \sqrt{3})(4 - \sqrt{3})$

[9–2] **43.** $(2 - \sqrt{7})^2$

[9–5] **44.** $\dfrac{3}{3 - \sqrt{5}}$

[9–1] **45.** $\sqrt[3]{-27}$

[9–2] **46.** $(3 \cdot \sqrt{2} + 2 \cdot \sqrt{3})(\sqrt{2} - 3 \cdot \sqrt{3})$

[9–6] **47.** Find the solution set of the equation $\sqrt{x+1} - 1 = x$.

[7–2] **48.** Sketch the graph of $3x + 2y = 12$ using the x- and y-intercepts.

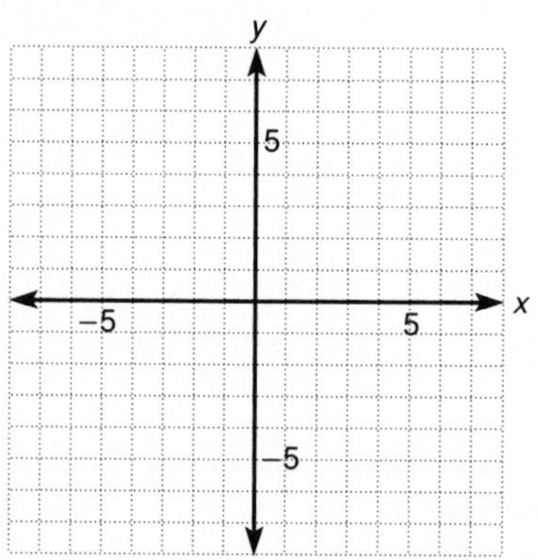

[10–4] **49.** Sketch the graph of $y = x^2 - 5x - 6$ using the vertex, x- and y-intercepts, and four arbitrary points.

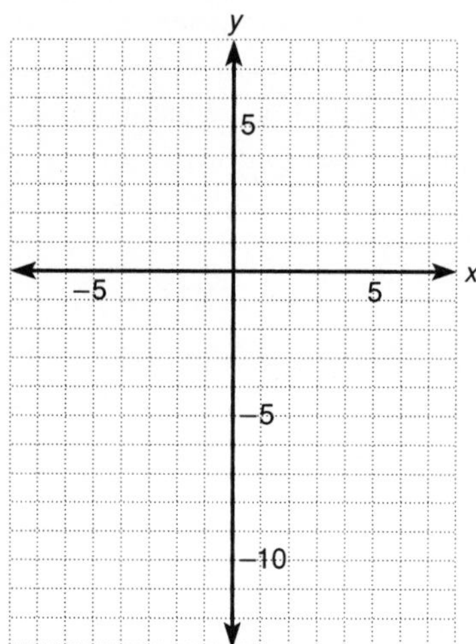

[11–3] **50.** Find the solution set of the quadratic equation $4x^2 - 7x = 3$ by any method.

Directions Solve the following inequalities.

[2–7] **51.** $4y - 3 < 9$

[2–7] **52.** $3x - 1 \geq x + 7$

[2–7] **53.** $-4 \leq 3x + 2 < 5$

Appendix Answers and Solutions

Chapter R

Exercise R–1

1. $\frac{1}{2}$ **2.** $\frac{1}{3}$ **3.** $\frac{5}{6}$ **5.** $\frac{8}{9}$ **6.** $\frac{2}{3}$ **7.** $\frac{7}{9}$ **9.** $\frac{1}{2}$ **10.** $\frac{3}{4}$ **11.** $\frac{17}{20}$ **13.** $\frac{1}{2}$ **14.** $\frac{5}{9}$ **15.** $\frac{49}{96}$ **17.** $\frac{7}{12}$ **18.** $\frac{9}{2}$ **19.** $\frac{15}{28}$ **21.** $\frac{2}{7}$
22. $\frac{32}{3}$ **23.** $\frac{25}{17}$ **25.** $\frac{51}{7}$ **26.** 22 **27.** $\frac{132}{7}$ or $18\frac{6}{7}$ **29.** 12 **30.** $\frac{10}{7}$ **31.** 12 **33.** $\frac{21}{32}$ **34.** $\frac{1}{24}$ **35.** $\frac{1}{5}$ **37.** $\frac{128}{315}$ **38.** $\frac{64}{45}$ **39.** 5
41. a. $187\frac{17}{48}$ in.^{3} **b.** $31\frac{39}{64}$ in.^{3} **42.** $4\frac{11}{28}$ in. **43.** 120 **45.** 126 **46.** 60 **47.** 144 **49.** 385 **50.** 60 **51.** 120 **53.** 60 **54.** 120
55. $\frac{2}{3}$ **57.** $\frac{7}{12}$ **58.** $\frac{2}{3}$ **59.** $\frac{3}{5}$ **61.** $\frac{13}{8}$ or $1\frac{5}{8}$ **62.** $\frac{23}{6}$ or $3\frac{5}{6}$ **63.** $\frac{17}{5}$ or $3\frac{2}{5}$ **65.** $\frac{16}{15}$ or $1\frac{1}{15}$ **66.** $\frac{1}{2}$ **67.** $\frac{7}{24}$ **69.** $\frac{149}{270}$ **70.** $\frac{4}{5}$
71. $\frac{11}{20}$ **73.** $\frac{57}{16}$ or $3\frac{9}{16}$ **74.** $\frac{41}{4}$ or $10\frac{1}{4}$ **75.** $\frac{5}{3}$ or $1\frac{2}{3}$ **77.** $86\frac{1}{2}$ ft **78.** $2\frac{1}{4}$ yd **79.** $10\frac{11}{12}$ lb

Solutions to trial exercise problems

7. $\frac{28}{36} = \frac{4 \cdot 7}{4 \cdot 9} = \frac{7}{9}$ **21.** $\frac{6}{7} \div 3 = \frac{6}{7} \cdot \frac{1}{3} = \frac{6 \cdot 1}{7 \cdot 3} = \frac{2 \cdot 3}{7 \cdot 3} = \frac{2}{7}$ **27.** $7\frac{1}{3} \cdot 2\frac{4}{7} = \frac{22}{3} \cdot \frac{18}{7} = \frac{22 \cdot 3 \cdot 3 \cdot 2}{3 \cdot 7} = \frac{22 \cdot 3 \cdot 2}{7} = \frac{132}{7}$

33. $\dfrac{\frac{7}{8}}{\frac{4}{3}} = \frac{7}{8} \div \frac{4}{3} = \frac{7}{8} \cdot \frac{3}{4} = \frac{7 \cdot 3}{8 \cdot 4} = \frac{21}{32}$ **35.** $\frac{4}{5} \cdot \frac{2}{3} \cdot \frac{3}{8} = \frac{4 \cdot 2 \cdot 3}{5 \cdot 3 \cdot 8} = \frac{1 \cdot (4 \cdot 2 \cdot 3)}{5 \cdot (4 \cdot 2 \cdot 3)} = \frac{1}{5}$ **42.** $61\frac{1}{2} \div 14 = \frac{123}{2} \cdot \frac{1}{14} = \frac{123}{28} = 4\frac{11}{28}$ in.

45. $6 = 2 \cdot 3$
$14 = 2 \cdot 7$ LCD is $2 \cdot 3 \cdot 3 \cdot 7 = 126$.
$18 = 2 \cdot 3 \cdot 3$

61. $1 + \frac{5}{8} = \frac{8}{8} + \frac{5}{8} = \frac{8 + 5}{8} = \frac{13}{8}$

71. $\frac{7}{15} + \frac{5}{6} - \frac{3}{4} = \frac{7}{15} \cdot \frac{4}{4} + \frac{5}{6} \cdot \frac{10}{10} - \frac{3}{4} \cdot \frac{15}{15} = \frac{28}{60} + \frac{50}{60} - \frac{45}{60}$
(LCD is 60) $= \frac{28 + 50 - 45}{60} = \frac{33}{60} = \frac{11}{20}$

77. $P = 2\ell + 2w = 2 \cdot 24\frac{1}{2} + 2 \cdot 18\frac{3}{4} = 2 \cdot \frac{49}{2} + 2 \cdot \frac{75}{4}$
$= 49 + \frac{75}{2} = \frac{98}{2} + \frac{75}{2} = \frac{98 + 75}{2} = \frac{173}{2}$
$= 86\frac{1}{2}$ ft

Exercise R–2

1. $\frac{2}{5}$ **2.** $\frac{4}{5}$ **3.** $\frac{3}{20}$ **5.** $\frac{1}{8}$ **6.** $\frac{31}{125}$ **7.** $\frac{7}{8}$ **9.** 19.019 **10.** 61.993 **11.** 540.2927 **13.** 13.5585 **14.** 13.369 **15.** 156.9876
17. 1.06964 **18.** 4,289.137 **19.** 9.699 **21.** 13.2227 **22.** 241.244 **23.** 23.2228 **25.** 42,630 **26.** 2,463.7 **27.** 56,076 **29.** 9.52816
30. 1,196.12 **31.** 0.428412 **33.** 0.9100081809 **34.** 0.00029472 **35.** 1.2 **37.** 40 **38.** 2.7 **39.** 102 **41.** 2,500 **42.** 52.4 **43.** 0.15
45. 0.65 **46.** 0.875 **47.** 0.125 **49.** $0.\overline{2}$ **50.** $0.\overline{5}$ **51.** 1.6 **53.** 13 cardinals **54.** \$12.91 **55.** 335.475 yd^2 **57.** 0.57 sec
58. 2,236.57 km **59.** 122.28 gal **61.** \$12.22 **62.** 1097.222 yd^2

Solutions to trial exercise problems

3. $0.15 = \frac{15}{100} = \frac{3 \cdot 5}{20 \cdot 5} = \frac{3}{20}$

13. $10.03 + 3.113 + 0.3342 + 0.0763 + 0.005 = 13.5585$

```
 10.0300
  3.1130
  0.3342
  0.0763
  0.0050
 -------
 13.5585
```

29. $(7.006)(1.36) = $

```
   7.006
    1.36
 -------
   42036
  21018
  7006
 -------
 9.52816
```

38. $21.681 \div 8.03 = 2.7$

```
          2.7
 8.03)21.681
      16 06
       5 621
       5 621
       -----
           0
```

43. $\frac{3}{20} = 20\overline{)3.000}$ = 0.15 (quotient .15)
20
100
100

49. $\frac{2}{9} = 9\overline{)2.000} = 0.\overline{2}$ (repeating) (quotient .222...)
18
20
18
20

54. 14.36 (89.9¢ = \$0.899)
0.899
12924
12924
11488
12.90964 ≈ \$12.91

Exercise R-3

1. $0.05 = \frac{1}{20}$ **2.** $0.01 = \frac{1}{100}$ **3.** $0.12 = \frac{3}{25}$ **5.** $1.35 = \frac{27}{20}$ or $1\frac{7}{20}$ **6.** $1.50 = \frac{3}{2}$ or $1\frac{1}{2}$ **7.** $3.25 = 3\frac{1}{4}$ or $\frac{13}{4}$ **9.** $\frac{4}{5}$, 80% **10.** $\frac{9}{10}$, 90% **11.** $\frac{27}{50}$, 54% **13.** $\frac{23}{20}$, 115% **14.** $\frac{12}{5}$, 240% **15.** 0.75, 75% **17.** 2 **18.** 3.6 **19.** 33.8 **21.** 550 **22.** 144 **23.** \$256.50 **25.** \$23 **26.** \$8.50 discount, \$25.50 discount price **27.** \$49,300 **29.** 0.9603 oz **30.** \$3,000 tax (S.S.); \$7,000 tax (fed) **31.** 30% **33.** $83\frac{1}{3}$% **34.** $133\frac{1}{3}$% **35.** 75% **37.** 300% **38.** 500% **39.** 40% **41.** 5% **42.** 48% plane, 52% boat **43.** 25% **45.** 35% **46.** 5% **47.** 25%

Solutions to trial exercise problems

3. 12% = 12.% = 0.12

$12\% = \frac{12}{100} = \frac{3 \cdot 4}{25 \cdot 4} = \frac{3}{25}$

11. 0.54 = 0.54. = 54%

$= \frac{54}{100} = \frac{27}{50}$

14. $2.40 = 2\frac{2}{5} = \frac{12}{5} = 240\%$

19. 26% of 130 = 0.26 × 130 = 130
0.26
780
260
33.80

26. discount = 25% of 34
= 0.25 × 34 = \$8.50
price = 34.00 − 8.50 = \$25.50

34. (what %) · 27 = 36

$\text{percent} = \frac{36}{27} = \frac{4}{3} = \frac{4}{3} \cdot \frac{100}{1}\% = \frac{400}{3}\% = 133\frac{1}{3}\%$

37. (what %) · 16 = 48

$\text{percent} = \frac{48}{16} = 3 = 3.00 = 300\%$

41. \$120 is what % of \$2,400
(what %) · 2,400 = 120

$\text{percent} = \frac{120}{2{,}400} = \frac{1}{20} = 0.05 = 5\%$

46. (what %) · \$480 = \$24

$\text{percent} = \frac{24}{480} = \frac{1}{20} = 0.05 = 5\%$

Chapter R review

1. $\frac{5}{7}$ **2.** $\frac{3}{4}$ **3.** $\frac{2}{3}$ **4.** $\frac{10}{7}$ or $1\frac{3}{7}$ **5.** $\frac{3}{5}$ **6.** $\frac{21}{20}$ or $1\frac{1}{20}$ **7.** $\frac{7}{8}$ **8.** $\frac{25}{8}$ or $3\frac{1}{8}$ **9.** $\frac{25}{3}$ or $8\frac{1}{3}$ **10.** $\frac{5}{8}$ acre **11.** $\frac{2}{5}$ cup **12.** $\frac{8}{7}$ or $1\frac{1}{7}$ **13.** $\frac{19}{24}$ **14.** $\frac{5}{6}$ **15.** $\frac{2}{9}$ **16.** $6\frac{17}{20}$ **17.** $\frac{11}{30}$ **18.** $\frac{7}{12}$ **19.** $\frac{7}{8}$ acre **20.** 263.51 **21.** 31.795 **22.** 1,355.09 **23.** 14.3 **24.** \$565.49 **25.** 7.86 acres **26.** ≈ 12.42 mpg **27.** 10 **28.** 68.4 **29.** 25 **30.** 78.72 **31.** 12.5% **32.** 225% **33.** \$10.65 tax, \$160.65 total cost **34.** 25%

Chapter 1

Proficiency check

1. $\frac{1}{6}$ **2.** 6 **3.** 4 **4.** $\frac{2}{3}$ **5.** $\frac{1}{12}$ **6.** 10.25 **7.** 37.41 **8.** 8.6 **9.** 19.11 **10.** 0.351

Exercise 1-1

1. −259° C, +100° C **2.** − \$10, +\$150 **3.** −39° C, +357° C **5.** +29,028 ft; −1,290 ft **6.** −14 pt, +8 pt **7.** $5 < 7$ **9.** $-2 > -4$ **10.** $-3 > -8$ **11.** $-9 < -6$ **13.** $-3 < 0$ **14.** $0 > -6$ **15.** $0 < 8$ **17.** 0 **18.** 5 **19.** 7 **21.** $\frac{3}{4}$ **22.** $1\frac{1}{2}$ **23.** 5.6 **25.** −2 **26.** $-2\frac{3}{4}$ **27.** $-\frac{5}{8}$ **29.** $|-6| > |-3|$ **30.** $|5| < |-7|$ **31.** $|0| < |-2|$ **33.** $|-8| > |-5|$ **34.** $|-9| > |7|$ **35.** $|-6| > |-2|$ **37.** $|-27|$ **38.** $|18|$ **39.** $|-9|$

Solutions to trial exercise problems

9. $-2 > -4$, since -2 lies to the right of -4. **13.** $-3 < 0$, since -3 lies to the left of 0. **25.** $-|-2| = -2$. The negative sign in front of the absolute value bar remains. **30.** $|5| = 5$ and $|-7| = 7$. Since 5 lies to the left of 7, then $|5| < |-7|$.

Review exercises

1. 14.3 **2.** $\frac{31}{4}$ or $7\frac{3}{4}$ **3.** $\frac{83}{6}$ or $13\frac{5}{6}$ **4.** 9.1 **5.** 7.25 **6.** $\frac{19}{12}$ or $1\frac{7}{12}$

Exercise 1-2

1. -13 **2.** -2 **3.** 5 **5.** -5 **6.** 4 **7.** -5 **9.** 0 **10.** 0 **11.** -13.6 **13.** -11.1 **14.** 7.5 **15.** $-\frac{1}{2}$ **17.** $\frac{1}{10}$ **18.** $-\frac{11}{4}$ or $-2\frac{3}{4}$ **19.** $-\frac{3}{4}$ **21.** 3 **22.** 0 **23.** 10 **25.** -44 **26.** -8 **27.** -22 **29.** -10 **30.** -27 **31.** 0 **33.** 11 **34.** 7 **35.** 15 **37.** \$32 **38.** 26° F **39.** 33 points gain **41.** 2 mb rise **42.** 28,800 ft **43.** \$86 **45.** 7° C **46.** 32-yd line

Solutions to trial exercise problems

11. $(-8.7) + (-4.9)$. The signs are the same. Add their absolute values and give the answer their common sign. $(-8.7) + (-4.9) = -13.6$
15. $\left(-\frac{1}{6}\right) + \left(-\frac{1}{3}\right)$. We change $-\frac{1}{3}$ to $-\frac{2}{6}$ and add the numerators prefixed with their common sign. $\left(-\frac{1}{6}\right) + \left(-\frac{1}{3}\right) = \left(-\frac{1}{6}\right) + \left(-\frac{2}{6}\right) = -\frac{3}{6} = -\frac{1}{2}$ **21.** $10 + (-5) + (-2) = 5 + (-2) = 3$. The numbers were added left to right.
23. $(-12) + (-10) + (+8) + (+24) = (-22) + (+8) + (+24) = (-14) + (+24) = 10$
34. the sum of ↓ increased by

$15 + (-18) \quad + 10 \quad = (-3) + 10 = 7$

38. Let t = the temperature at 1 P.M. To find the new temperature, we must *add* the rise in temperature to the original temperature.

temperature at 1 P.M. is temperature at 8 A.M. rose 39°

$t \quad = \quad -13 \quad + \quad 39$

$t = -13 + 39$

$t = 26$

The temperature at 1 P.M. was 26° F.

Review exercises

1. 7.3 **2.** $\frac{21}{4}$ or $5\frac{1}{4}$ **3.** $\frac{61}{10}$ or $6\frac{1}{10}$ **4.** 8.7 **5.** 4.68 **6.** 10.51

Exercise 1-3

1. -1 **2.** -8 **3.** 6 **5.** -12 **6.** 12 **7.** -5 **9.** -4 **10.** 4 **11.** 14 **13.** -6 **14.** -2 **15.** 7 **17.** $-\frac{1}{4}$ **18.** $-\frac{5}{12}$ **19.** $\frac{21}{8}$ or $2\frac{5}{8}$ **21.** -9.4 **22.** 120 **23.** -312 **25.** 301.8 **26.** -10 **27.** -24 **29.** -37 **30.** -10 **31.** -53 **33.** 16 **34.** 14 **35.** -3 **37.** 10 **38.** -28 **39.** -8 **41.** -7 **42.** 5 **43.** $-38°$ C **45.** $-\$372$ **46.** \$101, \$101 − \$23 = \$78 **47. a.** +31 °C **b.** +55° C **c.** −9° C **d.** +57° C **e.** −54° C **f.** −51° C **49.** -22 **50.** 15 **51.** -9 **53.** 60 **54.** 45 **55.** 19 **57.** \$8 **58.** \$23 **59.** 38° F **61.** 14 yr **62.** 268 ml **63.** \$245 **65.** 20,602 ft **66.** 14,729 ft **67.** \$19

Solutions to trial exercise problems

9. $(-8) - (-4) = (-8) + (4) = -4$ **13.** $(-6) + 0 = -6$. The sum of zero and a number is that number. **15.** $(+7) - 0 = 7$. A number minus zero is that number. **26.** $(-12) - (-10) - (8) = (-12) + (10) + (-8) = (-2) + (-8) = -10$ **38.** $12 + 3 - 16 - 10 - (12 + 5) = 12 + 3 - 16 - 10 - (17) = 15 - 16 - 10 - (17) = -1 - 10 - (17) = -11 - (17) = -28$
61. Let a = the age that Erin will be in the year 2000. We must find the *difference* between 2000 and 1986.

age in the year 2000 is the difference between 2000 and 1986

$a \quad = \quad 2000 \quad - \quad 1986$

$a = 2000 - 1986$

$a = 14$

Erin will be 14 years old in the year 2000.

Review exercises

1. 456 **2.** 381.81 **3.** 11.752 **4.** 1.495 **5.** 54.4 **6.** $\frac{1}{6}$ **7.** $\frac{9}{10}$

Exercise 1-4

1. 15 **2.** 0 **3.** -28 **5.** -60 **6.** 8 **7.** -36 **9.** 20 **10.** -120 **11.** -105 **13.** -4.32 **14.** 34.884 **15.** -13.769 **17.** -2.16 **18.** $-\frac{1}{5}$ **19.** $\frac{9}{16}$ **21.** $\frac{1}{4}$ **22.** $-\frac{3}{8}$ **23.** -120 **25.** 144 **26.** 1 **27.** 0 **29.** 0 **30.** $-5, 6$ **31.** $-4, 4$ **33.** $-1, 11$ **34.** $-24, 3$ **35.** $-4, 3$ **37.** 5, 7 **38.** $-3, -3$ **39.** $-1, 8$ **41.** $-3, 5$ **42.** $-3, 6$ **43.** 5, 5 **45.** $-\$6 \cdot 5 = -\$30$; $-\$30$ **46.** 1,050 people **47.** 56 students **49.** \$13.68 **50.** \$240 **51.** 525¢ = \$5.25 **53.** 700 gal

Solutions to trial exercise problems

11. $7 \cdot (-1)(-3)(-5) = (-7)(-3)(-5) = (21)(-5) = -105$; negative answer because there were an odd number of negative factors **18.** $\left(-\frac{1}{3}\right)\left(\frac{3}{5}\right) = -\frac{3}{15} = -\frac{1}{5}$ **27.** $(-2)(0)(3)(-4) = 0$. When zero is one of the factors, zero will be the answer. **30.** $-30, 1$. Since $(-5)(6) = (-30)$ and $(-5) + (6) = (1)$, then -5 and 6 are the integers. **31.** $-16, 0$. Since $(-4)(4) = (-16)$ and $(-4) + (4) = 0$, then -4 and 4 are the integers. **45.** Assets $(5)(-6)$, and his assets would change by (-30) dollars. **53.** Let $g =$ the number of gallons of milk sold in 4 weeks. Since there are 28 days in 4 weeks, we must *multiply* 28 by 25 to determine the amount of milk sold.

total gallons of milk sold	is	28 days	at	25 gallons per day
g	$=$	28	$\cdot$	25

$g = 28 \cdot 25$
$g = 700$

The grocery sold 700 gallons of milk.

Review exercises

1. 8 **2.** 24 **3.** $\frac{27}{4}$ or $6\frac{3}{4}$ **4.** 105 **5.** 3.8 **6.** 80.2

Exercise 1-5

1. 2 **2.** -3 **3.** -8 **5.** 2 **6.** -6 **7.** -8 **9.** undefined **10.** undefined **11.** 0 **13.** indeterminate **14.** 4 **15.** -7 **17.** -5 **18.** -8 **19.** -2 **21.** -4 **22.** 0 **23.** 0 **25.** -3 **26.** undefined **27.** undefined **29.** indeterminate **30.** indeterminate **31.** $-1°$ C **33.** 6 hr **34.** 41 mph **35.** 9 sec **37.** \$4 each **38.** 4 ft **39.** 25 mpg **41.** 4° per day **42.** 12 min **43.** 32 books

Solutions to trial exercise problems

11. $\frac{0}{(-9)} = 0$, since $(-9) \cdot 0 = 0$. **19.** $\frac{(-4)(-3)}{(-6)} = \frac{(12)}{(-6)} = -2$; odd number of negative factors **22.** $\frac{(-4)(0)}{(-8)} = \frac{0}{(-8)} = 0$, since $(-8) \cdot 0 = 0$. **26.** $\frac{(-2)(-4)}{(0)(4)} = \frac{(8)}{0} =$ undefined **29.** $\frac{(-6)(0)}{(-3)(0)} = \frac{0}{0} =$ indeterminate **33.** Number of hours $= \frac{\text{Number of miles}}{\text{Rate of travel in miles per hour}}$. Hence $\frac{282}{47} = 6$; 6 hours. **42.** Let $m =$ the number of minutes it took Alice to run 1 mile. Since there are 60 minutes in 1 hour, the race took 300 minutes + 12 minutes, which is 312 minutes. We must divide 312 minutes by 26 miles to determine the number of minutes per mile.

minutes per mile	is	number of minutes	divided by	number of miles
m	$=$	312	$\div$	26

$m = 312 \div 26 = 12$

Alice ran 1 mile every 12 minutes.

Review exercises

1. -6 **2.** -4 **3.** -8 **4.** 18 **5.** 0 **6.** -21

Exercise 1-6

1. 16 **2.** 625 **3.** -27 **5.** -36 **6.** -16 **7.** 4 **9.** 26 **10.** 7 **11.** 0 **13.** 3 **14.** 2 **15.** 6 **17.** $\frac{12}{7}$ or $1\frac{5}{7}$ **18.** 50 **19.** 121 **21.** $\frac{5}{24}$ **22.** $\frac{1}{2}$ **23.** 96 **25.** 3 **26.** -19 **27.** 38 **29.** 4 **30.** 7 **31.** 12 **33.** -15.99 **34.** 75.63 **35.** 38.47 **37.** 45 **38.** 48 **39.** 33 **41.** 4 **42.** $\frac{2}{13}$ **43.** $23\frac{1}{3}°$ C **45.** $\frac{110}{7} = 15\frac{5}{7}$ in.^{2} **46.** $\frac{1{,}936}{7} = 276\frac{4}{7}$ in.^{2} **47.** $\frac{288}{41} = 7\frac{1}{41}$ in. **49.** 8 pieces **50.** 3,750 words **51.** 1,728 points

Solutions to trial exercise problems

13. $0(5 + 2) + 3 = 0(7) + 3 = 0 + 3 = 3$ **27.** $4(2 - 5)^2 - 2(3 - 4) = 4(-3)^2 - 2(3 - 4) = 4(-3)^2 - 2(-1) = 4(9) - 2(-1) = 36 - 2(-1) = 36 - (-2) = 38$ **29.** $\frac{5(3 - 5)}{2} - \frac{27}{-3} = \frac{5(-2)}{2} - \frac{27}{-3} = \frac{-10}{2} - \frac{27}{-3} = (-5) - \frac{27}{-3} = (-5) - (-9) = 4$

37. $5[10 - 2(4 - 3) + 1] = 5[10 - 2(1) + 1] = 5[10 - 2 + 1] = 5[8 + 1] = 5[9] = 45$ **41.** $\left(\frac{6-3}{7-4}\right)\left(\frac{14+2\cdot 3}{5}\right) = \left(\frac{3}{3}\right)\left(\frac{14+6}{5}\right)$ $= \left(\frac{3}{3}\right)\left(\frac{20}{5}\right) = 1 \cdot 4 = 4$ **45.** $\frac{22}{7}\cdot 3^2 - \frac{22}{7}\cdot 2^2 = \frac{22}{7}\cdot 9 - \frac{22}{7}\cdot 4 = \frac{198}{7} - \frac{88}{7} = \frac{198-88}{7} = \frac{110}{7} = 15\frac{5}{7}$ in.^{2} **49.** Let p = the total number of pieces of lumber. *Dividing* the 16-foot board by 4 and the 12-foot board by 3 will give us the number of pieces of lumber from each board. If we *add* the number of pieces from the 16-foot board to the number of pieces from the 12-foot board, we will have the total number of pieces.

total number of pieces	is	number of pieces from the 16-foot board	combined with	number of pieces from the 12-foot board
p	=	$16 \div 4$	+	$12 \div 3$

$p = 16 \div 4 + 12 \div 3$
$= 4 + 4$ Priority 3
$= 8$ Priority 4

There will be 8 pieces of lumber.

Review exercises

1. 240 **2.** -15 **3.** 0 **4.** 4 **5.** $-\frac{27}{7}$ or $-3\frac{6}{7}$ **6.** undefined **7.** -40 **8.** 0

Exercise 1-7

1. 2 terms **2.** 1 term **3.** 3 terms **5.** 1 term **6.** 1 term **7.** 3 terms **9.** 2 terms **10.** 1 term **11.** 1 term **13.** 2 terms **14.** 3 terms **15.** 5 is the coefficient of x^2, 1 is the coefficient of x, -4 is the coefficient of z **17.** 1 is the coefficient of x, -1 is the coefficient of y, -3 is the coefficient of z **18.** -2 is the coefficient of a, -1 is the coefficient of b, 1 is the coefficient of c **19.** like **21.** like **22.** like **23.** unlike **25.** $14x$ **26.** $4a^2b$ **27.** $-3ab$ **29.** $7x^2 + 4x$ **30.** $4x^2y + 3xy + 5y$ **31.** $2a^3 + a^2b - 6ab^2 - b^3$ **33.** $13a - 5c - 2x^2$ **34.** $14a$ **35.** $-3a - 9b$ **37.** $3x + 8y$ **38.** $7a + b$ **39.** $2x + 3y$ **41.** $2a + b + 5c$ **42.** $x + y - z$ **43.** $2x + 4y$ **45.** $a + b$ **46.** $b - 3a$ **47.** $x - 7$ **49.** $\frac{x+y}{z}$ **50.** $x(y + z)$ **51.** $a - 5$ **53.** $\frac{1}{2}x - 2x$ **54.** let x = the number; $x - 12$ **55.** let x = the number; $3x + 1$ **57.** let x = the number; $\frac{x}{5}$ **58.** let x = the number; $2(x + 4)$ **59.** let x = the number; $\frac{x-6}{11}$

Solutions to trial exercise problems

10. $\frac{15x^2 + y}{8}$ has one term because the fraction bar is a grouping symbol. **33.** $3a + b + 2a - 5c - b - 2x^2 + 8a = (3a + 2a + 8a) + (b - b)$ $- 5c - 2x^2 = (3 + 2 + 8)a + (0) - 5c - 2x^2 = 13a - 5c - 2x^2$ **53.** $\frac{1}{2}$ of x, decreased by 2 times x would be $\frac{1}{2}x - 2x$. **55.** 3 times a number, increased by 1: If we let x represent the number, then we would have $3x + 1$.

Review exercises

1. -25 **2.** 64 **3.** -2 **4.** 15 **5.** 22 **6.** 23

Exercise 1-8

1. 9 **2.** 5 **3.** 5 **5.** 48 **6.** -60 **7.** 5 **9.** 62 **10.** 288 **11.** 288 **13.** 61 **14.** 35 **15.** 0 **17.** -1 **18.** 25 **19.** 1 **21.** -44 **22.** 10 **23.** 20 **25.** 0 **26.** 31 **27.** 43 **29.** $\frac{20}{3}$ or $6\frac{2}{3}$ **30.** 210 **31.** 160 **33.** 288 **34.** 60 **35.** 54 **37.** 2,140 **38.** 48 **39.** 114 **41.** $\frac{15{,}000}{857}$ or $17\frac{431}{857}$ **42.** $\frac{9}{7}$ or $1\frac{2}{7}$ **43.** $\frac{540}{13}$ or $41\frac{7}{13}$ rpm **45.** $\frac{400}{33}$ or $12\frac{4}{33}$ **46.** $\frac{1{,}280}{3}$ or $426\frac{2}{3}$ rpm **47.** $258 - n + m$ **49.** $\frac{c}{50}$ **50.** $x + 1$ **51.** $z + 2$ **53.** $12f + t$ **54.** $\frac{25}{h}$ **55.** $5n + 10d$ **57. a.** $p + 12$ **b.** $p - 5$ **58. a.** $3n$ **b.** $3n - 8$ **59.** $2d + 1{,}000$ **61.** $69x + 57y$ **62.** $9.95p + 12.99q$ **63.** $35(x - 7)$

Solutions to trial exercise problems

5. $(3a + 2b)(a - c) = [3(\ \ ) + 2(\ \ )][(\ \ ) - (\ \ )] = [3(2) + 2(3)][(2) - (-2)] = [6 + 6][4] = [12][4] = 48$
14. $(4a + b) - (3a - b)(c + 2d) = [4(\ \ ) + (\ \ )] - [3(\ \ ) - (\ \ )][(\ \ ) + 2(\ \ )] = [4(2) + (3)] - [3(2) - (3)][(-2) + 2(-3)]$ $= [8 + 3] - [6 - 3][(-2) + (-6)] = [11] - [3][-8] = [11] - [-24] = 35$ **31.** $I = prt$; $I = (\ \ )(\ \ )(\ \ ) = (1{,}000)(0.08)(2)$ $= (80)(2) = 160$ **39.** $A = \frac{I^2R - 120E^2}{R}$; $A = \frac{(\ \ )^2(\ \ ) - 120(\ \ )^2}{(\ \ )} = \frac{(12)^2(100) - 120(5)^2}{(100)} = \frac{(144)(100) - 120(25)}{100} = \frac{14{,}400 - 3{,}000}{100}$ $= \frac{11{,}400}{100} = 114$ **43.** $V = \frac{vn}{N}$; $V = \frac{(\ \ )(\ \ )}{(\ \ )} = \frac{(90)(30)}{(65)} = \frac{2{,}700}{65} = \frac{540}{13}$ or $41\frac{7}{13}$ **51.** If we use 11 as an example of an odd integer, the next greater odd integer would be 13. To get from 11 to 13 we must add 2. Therefore if z is an odd integer, then $z + 2$ is the next greater odd integer. **55.** n nickels is represented by $5n$ because there are 5 cents in each nickel. Therefore d dimes would be represented by $10d$. The total is represented by adding the cents from the nickels to the cents from the dimes, $5n + 10d$.

Review exercises

1. $8x$ **2.** $9y$ **3.** $5a + 4$ **4.** $-3a + 7b - 3$ **5.** $x + y$ **6.** $4a + 2c$

Chapter 1 review

1. < **2.** < **3.** > **4.** < **5.** > **6.** > **7.** −4 **8.** 3 **9.** −6 **10.** 1 **11.** −6 **12.** 15 **13.** −4 **14.** −9 **15.** 3 **16.** 15 **17.** −21 **18.** 12 **19.** 24 **20.** −144 **21.** 0 **22.** −7 **23.** 2 **24.** −6 **25.** undefined **26.** 0 **27.** indeterminate **28.** −1 **29.** −9, −4 **30. a.** 52,000 − 3,000 − 2,560 − 3,300 **b.** $43,140 **31. a.** +9, +8, −5, −6 **b.** greater by +6 **c.** 69 +(−11) = 58, 58° **32.** −64 **33.** −16 **34.** −27 **35.** 25 **36.** 98 **37.** −3 **38.** 20 **39.** 49 **40.** −9 **41.** 20 **42.** −100 **43.** 51 **44.** 30 **45.** $452 **46.** 3 terms **47.** 1 term **48.** 2 terms **49.** 2 terms **50.** 5, 1, −1 **51.** 1, 7, −1 **52.** −6, −4, 1 **53.** like **54.** unlike **55.** like **56.** $17x$ **57.** $17y$ **58.** $13a$ **59.** $10b$ **60.** $6z$ **61.** $-3c$ **62.** $8x + 23$ **63.** $14a - 5$ **64.** $-x - 4$ **65.** $3y + 5z$ **66.** $x + 2y$ **67.** $2a + 3b + 10c$ **68.** $5x$ **69.** $y - 7$ **70.** $z + 4$ **71.** let x = the number; $2x + 6$ **72.** 1 **73.** −1 **74.** 72 **75.** −4 **76.** 4 **77.** 7 **78. a.** 3 **b.** $\frac{189}{4}$ or $47\frac{1}{4}$ **79.** 1,040

Chapter 1 cumulative test

1. −3 **2.** 8.03 **3.** 2 **4.** −24 **5.** 25 **6.** 8 **7.** 0 **8.** 0 **9.** −44 **10.** −12 **11.** $\frac{5}{8}$ **12.** −36 **13.** 4 **14.** undefined **15.** −3 **16.** $\frac{4}{3}$ or $1\frac{1}{3}$ **17.** −6.48 **18.** $2a + 8$ **19.** 116 **20.** 40 **21.** $2x + 3y$ **22.** 19 **23. a.** −5 **b.** −14 **24. a.** $x + 6$ **b.** $y - 4$ **c.** $2n + 4$

Chapter 2

Proficiency check

1. −9 **2.** 4 **3.** 10 **4.** undefined **5.** 2 **6.** 4 **7.** 5 **8. a.** $5ab + 3ac$ **b.** $3xy$ **9. a.** $x + 7$ **b.** $x - 4$ **c.** $3x - 6$

Exercise 2–1

1. true **2.** true **3.** true **5.** true **6.** true **7.** false **9.** true **10.** true **11.** false **13.** $x = 16$ **14.** $y = 18$ **15.** $a = -3$ **17.** $y = -2$ **18.** $x = -2$ **19.** $x = -5$ **21.** $x = -6$ **22.** $a = 4$ **23.** $b = -7$ **25.** $x = 14$ **26.** $y = 7$ **27.** $b = -1$ **29.** $z = 4$ **30.** $x = 2$ **31.** $a = -5$ **33.** $a = 5$ **34.** $x = -6$ **35.** $b = 6$ **37.** $x = 6$ **38.** $x = -14$ **39.** $y = 8$ **41.** $x = -6$ **42.** $x = 0$ **43.** $a = 5$ **45.** $z = -7$ **46.** $x = 22$ **47.** $a = 12$ **49.** $x = 16$ **50.** $x = -29$ **51.** $b = 9$ **53.** 60 yr **54.** $735 **55.** $82.80 **57.** 13 dogs **58.** 33 yr

Solutions to trial exercise problems

10. $3x + 2 = 5x - 1; \frac{3}{2}$

$$\begin{aligned} 3\left(\frac{3}{2}\right) + 2 &= 5\left(\frac{3}{2}\right) - 1 \\ \frac{9}{2} + 2 &= \frac{15}{2} - 1 \\ \frac{9}{2} + \frac{4}{2} &= \frac{15}{2} - \frac{2}{2} \\ \frac{13}{2} &= \frac{13}{2} \quad \text{(true)} \end{aligned}$$

23.

$$\begin{aligned} b + 7 &= 0 \\ b + 7 - 7 &= 0 - 7 \\ b &= -7 \end{aligned}$$

Check: $(-7) + 7 = 0$

$0 = 0$ (true)

26.

$$\begin{aligned} -y - 6 &= -2y + 1 \\ -y + 2y - 6 &= -2y + 2y + 1 \\ y - 6 &= 1 \\ y - 6 + 6 &= 1 + 6 \\ y &= 7 \end{aligned}$$

Check: $-(7) - 6 = -2(7) + 1$

$-13 = -14 + 1$

$-13 = -13$ (true)

38.

$$\begin{aligned} 5(x + 2) &= 4(x - 1) \\ 5x + 10 &= 4x - 4 \\ 5x - 4x + 10 &= 4x - 4x - 4 \\ x + 10 &= -4 \\ x + 10 - 10 &= -4 - 10 \\ x &= -14 \end{aligned}$$

45.

$$\begin{aligned} 3(z + 7) - (8 + 2z) &= 6 \\ 3z + 21 - 8 - 2z &= 6 \\ z + 13 &= 6 \\ z + 13 - 13 &= 6 - 13 \\ z &= -7 \end{aligned}$$

55. Let b = the original balance.

original balance	makes a deposit	of $42.50	equals	new balance
b	+	42.50	=	125.30

$b + 42.50 = 125.30$

$b + 42.50 - 42.50 = 125.30 - 42.50$ Subtract 42.50 from both members.

$b = 82.80$

The original balance was $82.80.

Review exercises

1. 16 **2.** −12 **3.** 1 **4.** 1 **5.** 1 **6.** 1

Exercise 2-2

1. $x = 4$ **2.** $x = 6$ **3.** $x = 6$ **5.** $x = 16$ **6.** $x = 25$ **7.** $x = 35$ **9.** $x = 12$ **10.** $x = 6$ **11.** $x = -3$ **13.** $x = -4$ **14.** $x = -6$ **15.** $x = 7$ **17.** $x = -4$ **18.** $x = 11$ **19.** $x = \frac{7}{3}$ **21.** $x = \frac{3}{2}$ **22.** $x = -\frac{8}{3}$ **23.** $x = 0$ **25.** $x = 0$ **26.** $x = 0$ **27.** $x = 15$ **29.** $x = -14$ **30.** $x = 6$ **31.** $x = 4$ **33.** $x = -7$ **34.** $x = -5$ **35.** $x = 11$ **37.** $x = -26$ **38.** $x = \frac{56}{5}$ **39.** $x = \frac{112}{3}$ **41.** -9 **42.** -63 **43.** 64 **45.** \$4.50 per hour **46.** \$8.50 **47.** 64

Solutions to trial exercise problems

7.
$$\frac{1}{7}x = 5$$
$$7 \cdot \frac{1}{7}x = 7 \cdot 5$$
$$x = 35$$
Check: $\frac{1}{7}(35) = 5$
$5 = 5$ (true)

15.
$$-4x = -28$$
$$\frac{-4x}{-4} = \frac{-28}{-4}$$
$$x = 7$$
Check: $-4(7) = -28$
$-28 = -28$ (true)

23.
$$5x = 0$$
$$\frac{5x}{5} = \frac{0}{5}$$
$$x = 0$$
Check: $5(0) = 0$
$0 = 0$ (true)

27.
$$\frac{x}{3} = 5$$
$$3 \cdot \frac{x}{3} = 3 \cdot 5$$
$$x = 15$$
Check: $\frac{(15)}{3} = 5$
$5 = 5$ (true)

31.
$$2.6x = 10.4$$
$$\frac{2.6x}{2.6} = \frac{10.4}{2.6}$$
$$x = 4$$
Check: $2.6(4) = 10.4$
$10.4 = 10.4$ (true)

38.
$$\frac{5}{7}x = 8$$
$$\frac{7}{5} \cdot \frac{5}{7}x = \frac{7}{5} \cdot 8$$
$$x = \frac{56}{5}$$
Check: $\frac{5}{7}\left(\frac{56}{5}\right) = 8$
$8 = 8$ (true)

45. Let w = Nancy's hourly wage.

30 hours	at	hourly wage	is	\$135.00
30	$\cdot$	w	$=$	135

$$30w = 135$$
$$\frac{30w}{30} = \frac{135}{30} \quad \text{Divide both members by 30.}$$
$$w = 4.5$$
Nancy's hourly wage is \$4.50.

Review exercises

1. $5x - 2$ **2.** $2x + 1$ **3.** $12x + 2$ **4.** $3x - 5$ **5.** $10x - 1$ **6.** $5x + 1$

Exercise 2-3

1. $x = 2$ **2.** $x = \frac{11}{3}$ **3.** $x = -2$ **5.** $x = 36$ **6.** $x = 96$ **7.** $x = \frac{16}{3}$ **9.** $x = 4$ **10.** $x = 13$ **11.** $x = 0$ **13.** $x = 3$ **14.** $x = 3$ **15.** $x = 0$ **17.** $x = 1$ **18.** $x = \frac{5}{6}$ **19.** $x = \frac{8}{5}$ **21.** $x = -10$ **22.** $x = \frac{60}{7}$ **23.** $x = -\frac{9}{2}$ **25.** $x = 18$ **26.** $x = 32$ **27.** $x = -\frac{51}{8}$ **29.** $x = 12$ **30.** $x = 24$ **31.** $x = 3$ **33.** $x = \frac{10}{7}$ **34.** $x = -\frac{27}{2}$ **35.** $x = \frac{16}{11}$ **37.** $x = \frac{45}{16}$ **38.** $x = \frac{39}{8}$ **39.** $x = \frac{2}{5}$ **41.** $x = 3$ **42.** $x = 2$ **43.** $x = \frac{3}{2}$ **45. a.** $-\frac{70}{9}$ or $-7\frac{7}{9}$° C **b.** $-\frac{295}{9}$ or $-32\frac{7}{9}$° C **c.** $-\frac{50}{9}$ or $-16\frac{2}{3}$° C **46. a.** $K = \frac{9}{4}$ **b.** $K = 3$ **47.** $V = \frac{7}{3}$

Solutions to trial exercise problems

31.
$$\begin{aligned} 3(2x-1) &= 4x+3 \\ 6x-3 &= 4x+3 \\ 6x-4x-3 &= 4x-4x+3 \\ 2x-3 &= 3 \\ 2x-3+3 &= 3+3 \\ 2x &= 6 \\ \frac{2x}{2} &= \frac{6}{2} \\ x &= 3 \end{aligned}$$

35.
$$\begin{aligned} 8-2(3x+4) &= 5x-16 \\ 8-6x-8 &= 5x-16 \\ -6x &= 5x-16 \\ -6x+6x &= 5x+6x-16 \\ 0 &= 11x-16 \\ 0+16 &= 11x-16+16 \\ 16 &= 11x \\ \frac{16}{11} &= \frac{11x}{11} \\ \frac{16}{11} &= x \\ x &= \frac{16}{11} \end{aligned}$$

46b. $W = 243$, $T = -3$
$$\begin{aligned} W &= KT^4 \\ (243) &= K(-3)^4 \\ 243 &= K \cdot 81 \\ \frac{243}{81} &= \frac{K \cdot 81}{81} \\ 3 &= K \end{aligned}$$
Hence the value of K is 3.

Review exercises

1. $W = 108$ **2.** $S = 144$ **3.** $A = 88$ **4.** $I = 360$ **5.** $V = 280$ **6.** $V = 92$

Exercise 2-4

1. 22, 40 **2.** 19, 28 **3.** 35, 52 **5.** 28 **6.** 89 **7.** 7 **9.** 54 **10.** 22, 24, 26 **11.** 15, 17, 19 **13.** 12, 108 **14.** 10, 30, 4 **15.** 14, 7, 42 **17.** 5, 9 **18.** $\ell = 19$ ft, $w = 10$ ft **19.** $\ell = 19$ ft, $w = 16$ ft **21.** 4 ft, 8 ft **22.** 8 ft, 16 ft **23.** 31 ft, 19 ft **25.** \$13,000 at 8%; \$7,000 at 6% **26.** \$4,000 at $7\frac{1}{2}$%; \$14,000 at 9% **27.** \$8,000 at 10%; \$10,000 at 8% **29.** \$8,000 at 11%; \$17,000 at 18% **30.** \$7,700 at 13%; \$13,300 at 9% **31.** \$14,000

Solutions to trial exercise problems

5. Number: x Equation:
$$\begin{aligned} \frac{x}{4}+6 &= 13 \\ 4\left(\frac{x}{4}+6\right) &= 4 \cdot 13 \\ x+24 &= 52 \\ x &= 28 \end{aligned}$$

14. First: x Second: $3 \cdot x$ Third: $x-6$ Equation: $(x)+(3 \cdot x)+(x-6) = 44$
$$\begin{aligned} (x)+(3x)+(x-6) &= 44 \\ x+3x+x-6 &= 44 \\ 5x-6 &= 44 \\ 5x &= 50 \\ x &= 10 \end{aligned}$$
First is 10, second $(3x)$ is $3(10) = 30$, and the third $(x-6)$ is $(10)-6 = 4$.

21. Shorter piece: x Longer piece: $x+4$ Equation: $x+(x+4) = 12$
$$\begin{aligned} x+(x+4) &= 12 \\ x+x+4 &= 12 \\ 2x+4 &= 12 \\ 2x &= 8 \\ x &= 4 \end{aligned}$$
Shorter piece is 4 feet and the longer piece $(x+4)$ is $(4)+4 = 8$, 8 feet.

29. Number of dollars at 11% loss: x Number of dollars at 18% profit: $25{,}000-x$ Equation: $(25{,}000-x)(0.18)-x(0.11) = 2{,}180$
$$\begin{aligned} (25{,}000-x)(0.18)-x(0.11) &= 2{,}180 \\ (25{,}000)(0.18)-(0.18)x-(0.11)x &= 2{,}180 \\ 4{,}500-(0.29)x &= 2{,}180 \\ 4{,}500 &= (0.29)x+2{,}180 \\ 2{,}320 &= (0.29)x \\ 8{,}000 &= x \end{aligned}$$
Therefore \$8,000 was invested at the 11% loss and \$25,000 − 8,000 = \$17,000 was invested at 18% profit.

Review exercises

1. $I = 100$ **2.** $V = 84$ **3.** $F = 204$ **4.** $V = 108$ **5.** $A = 3{,}180$ **6.** $A = 16$ **7.** $S = 256$ **8.** $\ell = 40$

Exercise 2-5

1. $w = \dfrac{V}{\ell h}$ **2.** $\ell = \dfrac{V}{wh}$ **3.** $P = \dfrac{I}{rt}$ **5.** $m = \dfrac{F}{a}$ **6.** $R = \dfrac{E}{I}$ **7.** $V = \dfrac{K}{P}$ **9.** $R = \dfrac{W}{I^2}$ **10.** $w = \dfrac{A}{\ell}$ **11.** $w = \dfrac{P - 2\ell}{2}$

13. $a = P - b - c$ **14.** $b = \dfrac{2A}{h}$ **15.** $a = \dfrac{by + c + 3}{y}$ **17.** $k = V - gt$ **18.** $t = \dfrac{V - k}{g}$ **19.** $b = \dfrac{2A - ch}{h}$ **21.** $a = \ell - dn + d$

22. $d = \dfrac{\ell - a}{n - 1}$ **23.** $p = \dfrac{A}{1 + r}$ **25.** $f = \dfrac{T - g}{2}$ **26.** $r = \dfrac{12i}{pm}$ **27.** $q = \dfrac{D - R}{d}$ **29.** $c = \dfrac{W - b^2 - R}{2b}$ **30.** $p = \dfrac{A}{1 + rt}$

31. $r = \dfrac{A - p}{pt}$ **33.** $x = -6y$ **34.** $y = -\dfrac{x}{6}$ **35.** $g = \dfrac{2vt - 2S}{t^2}$ **37.** $g = \dfrac{2s - 2vt}{t^2}$ **38.** $v = \dfrac{2s - gt^2}{2t}$ **39.** $S = \dfrac{P + e + Cn}{n}$

41. $e = nS - Cn - P$

Solutions to trial exercise problems

18.
$$\begin{aligned} V &= k + gt, \text{ for } t \\ V &= k + gt \\ V - k &= gt \\ \frac{V - k}{g} &= t \\ t &= \frac{V - k}{g} \end{aligned}$$

22.
$$\begin{aligned} \ell &= a + (n - 1)d, \text{ for } d \\ \ell &= a + (n - 1)d \\ \ell - a &= (n - 1)d \\ \frac{\ell - a}{n - 1} &= d \\ d &= \frac{\ell - a}{n - 1} \end{aligned}$$

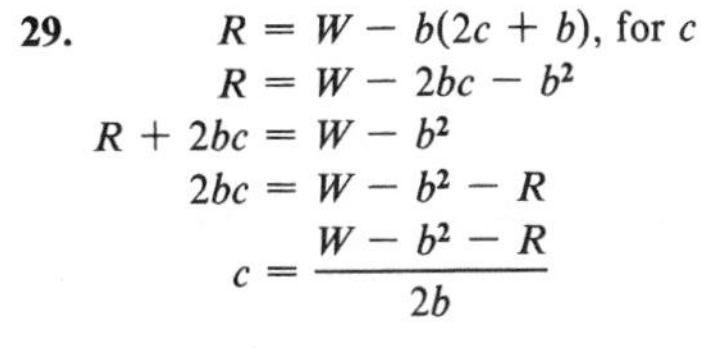

29.
$$\begin{aligned} R &= W - b(2c + b), \text{ for } c \\ R &= W - 2bc - b^2 \\ R + 2bc &= W - b^2 \\ 2bc &= W - b^2 - R \\ c &= \frac{W - b^2 - R}{2b} \end{aligned}$$

Review exercises

1. -25 **2.** 25 **3.** -81 **4.** -27 **5.** x^4 **6.** x^2 **7.** ab **8.** xy

Exercise 2-6

1. **2.** **3.**

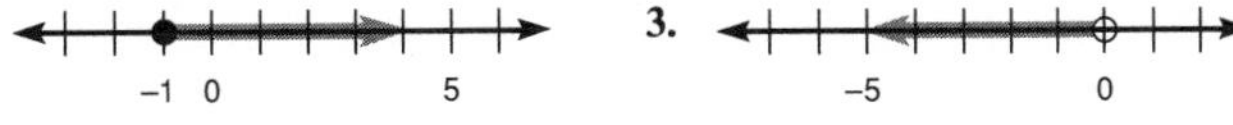

5. **6.**

7. **9.**

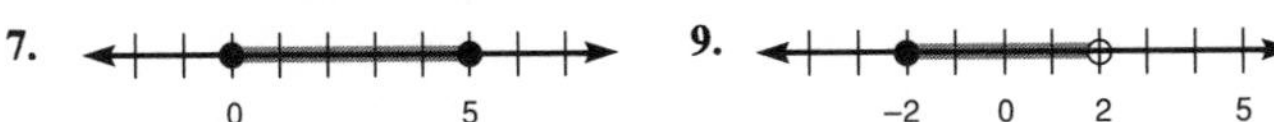

10. $x \geq 2$ **11.** $x < -5$ **13.** $x \leq -4$ **14.** $x \geq -1$

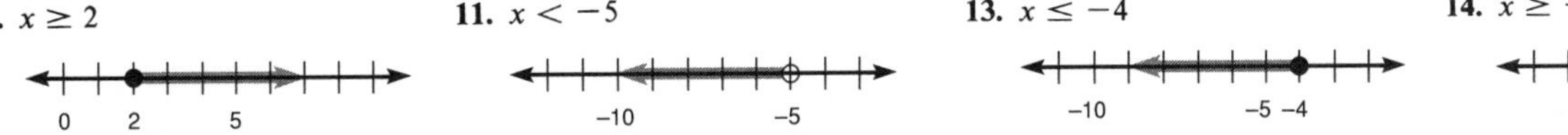

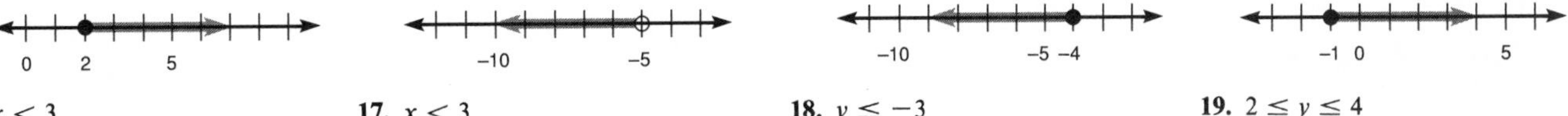

15. $x < 3$ **17.** $x < 3$ **18.** $y \leq -3$ **19.** $2 \leq y \leq 4$

21. $-4 \leq x < 5$ **22.** $3 < x \leq 6$

23. $x \geq 72$ **25.** $x \geq 8$ **26.** $P \geq 2C$ **27.** $2 \leq x \leq 7$ **29.** $x < 5$ **30.** $x \geq -3$ **31.** $x \geq 12$ **33.** $x \geq 9$

Solution to trial exercise problem

27. A company will hire at least 2 new employees, but not more than 7. Let x be the number of new employees. Then the inequality would be $x \geq 2$ and $x \leq 7$ which could also be written $2 \leq x$ and $x \leq 7$ which is written as $2 \leq x \leq 7$.

Review exercises

1. 1 **2.** 33 **3. a.** $x = -6$ **b.** $y = -\dfrac{5}{2}$ **c.** $y = \dfrac{156}{5}$ **4.** $S = 140$

Exercise 2-7

1. $x > 5$ **2.** $x \leq -3$ **3.** $x \geq 5$ **5.** $x < -4$

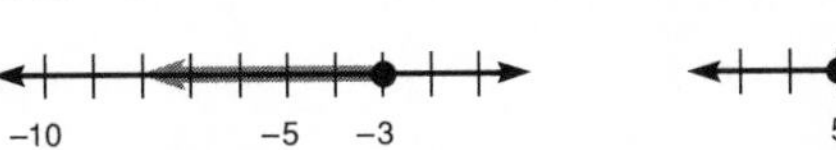

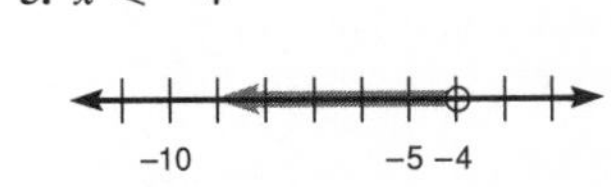

6. $x \geq 6$ **7.** $x > -3$ **9.** $x \geq 5$ **10.** $x < -15$

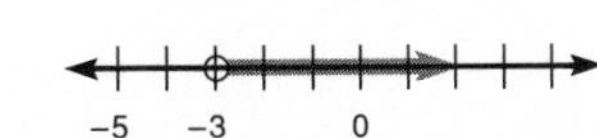

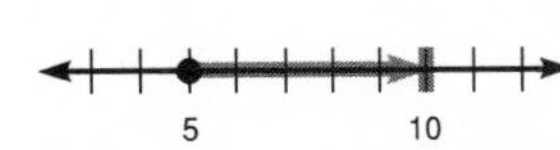

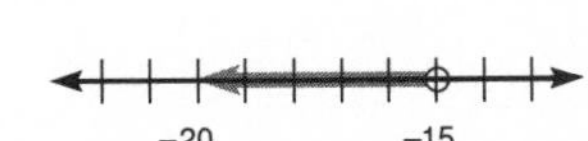

11. $x > -2\frac{1}{2}$

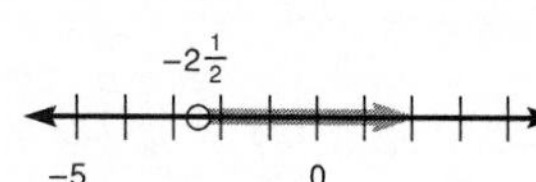

13. $x > 1\frac{3}{7}$

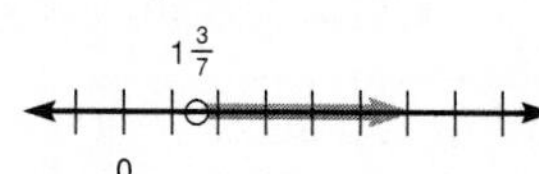

14. $y \geq -4$

15. $y \geq -1$

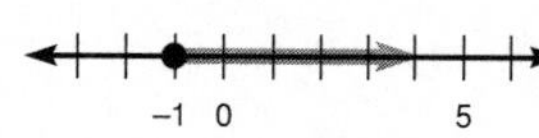

17. $x > -10$

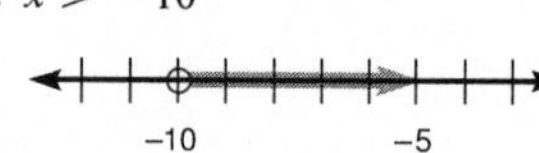

18. $x < 1\frac{5}{11}$

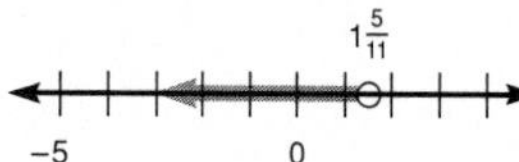

19. $x \geq 2\frac{1}{2}$

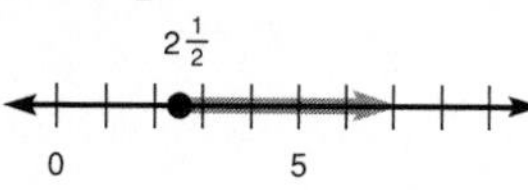

21. $-2 < x < \frac{1}{2}$

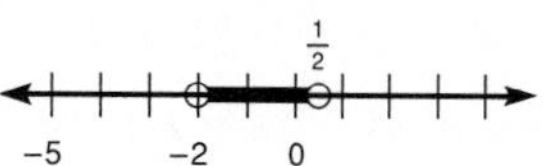

22. $-\frac{4}{5} \leq x \leq \frac{1}{5}$

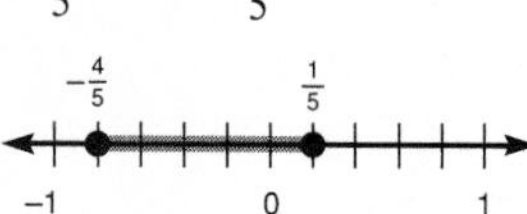

23. $-2 < x \leq 1\frac{1}{4}$

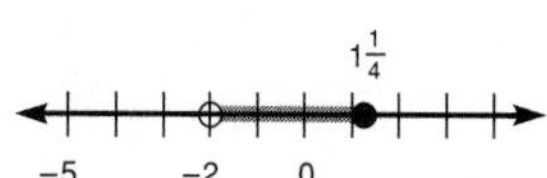

25. $-3 \leq x < 2$

26. $-1 \leq x < 7$

27. $-2 < x \leq \frac{1}{3}$

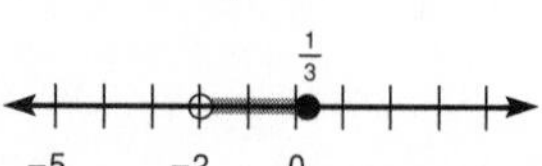

29. $x \leq 4$ **30.** $x \geq 3$ **31.** $x \geq 2$ **33.** $2 \leq x < 6$ **34.** $1 < x < 5$

35. $6 < x < 8$ **37.** $0 < x < 20$ **38.** $x > 60$ **39.** $x \geq 7$

Solutions to trial exercise problems

5.
$$\frac{3}{4}x < -3$$
$$\frac{4}{3} \cdot \frac{3}{4}x < -3 \cdot \frac{4}{3}$$
$$x < -4$$

7.
$$-4x < 12$$
$$\frac{-4x}{-4} > \frac{12}{-4}$$
$$x > -3$$

18.
$$8 - 2(3x + 4) > 5x - 16$$
$$8 - 6x - 8 > 5x - 16$$
$$-6x > 5x - 16$$
$$-6x + 6x > 5x + 6x - 16$$
$$0 > 11x - 16$$
$$0 + 16 > 11x - 16 + 16$$
$$16 > 11x$$
$$\frac{16}{11} > \frac{11x}{11}$$
$$1\frac{5}{11} > x$$
$$x < 1\frac{5}{11}$$

25.
$$-2 < -x \leq 3$$
$$-2 < -1 \cdot x \leq 3$$
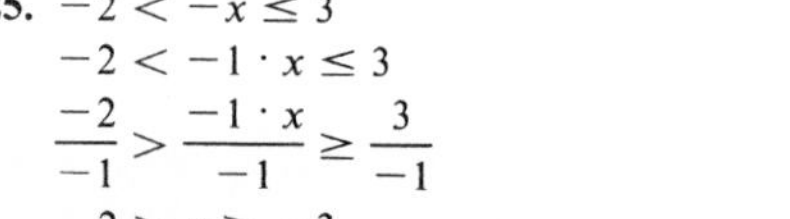
$$\frac{-2}{-1} > \frac{-1 \cdot x}{-1} \geq \frac{3}{-1}$$
$$2 > x \geq -3$$
$$-3 \leq x < 2$$

30. Let x be the number.

6 times a number		7 is added to	at least	25
$6 \cdot x$	+	7	$\geq$	25

$$6x + 7 \geq 25$$
$$6x \geq 18$$
$$x \geq 3$$

34. Two times a number plus 4 is greater than 6 but less than 14. Let x be the number. Then the inequality would be $2x + 4 > 6$ and $2x + 4 < 14$ which could also be written $6 < 2x + 4$ and $2x + 4 < 14$ which is written as $6 < 2x + 4 < 14$.

Solving: $6 - 4 < 2x + 4 - 4 < 14 - 4$
$$2 < 2x < 10$$
$$\frac{2}{2} < \frac{2x}{2} < \frac{10}{2}$$
$$1 < x < 5$$

37. The perimeter of a rectangle must be less than 100 feet. If the length is known to be 30 feet, find all numbers that the width could be. Let x represent the width of the rectangle. Then the inequality would be $2 \cdot 30 + 2 \cdot x < 100$.

Solving:
$$2 \cdot 30 + 2x < 100$$
$$60 + 2x < 100$$
$$2x < 40$$
$$x < 20$$

Since the width of a rectangle must be greater than zero, we have $0 < x < 20$. The width of the rectangle must be some real number greater than zero feet but less than 20 feet.

Review exercises

1. -31 **2.** $x + 7$ **3. a.** $y = -3x + 5$ **b.** $y = 4x - 6$ **4. a.** $\frac{1}{2}$ **b.** $\frac{5}{6}$

Chapter 2 review

1. true **2.** false **3.** false **4.** true **5.** $x = 7$ **6.** $x = 21$ **7.** $a = -11$ **8.** $b = -6$ **9.** $z = 4$ **10.** $x = 19$ **11.** $y = -2$ **12.** $x = 9$ **13.** $x = 3$ **14.** $x = 3$ **15.** $x = -7$ **16.** $x = -7$ **17.** $x = 12$ **18.** $x = 14$ **19.** $x = 15$ **20.** $x = 21$ **21.** $x = \frac{21}{4}$ **22.** $x = -18$ **23.** $x = -\frac{9}{2}$ **24.** $x = 35$ **25.** $x = 0$ **26.** $x = 4$ **27.** $a = 6$ **28.** $x = -8$ **29.** $x = 3$ **30.** $b = \frac{14}{3}$ **31.** $y = \frac{7}{3}$ **32.** $x = 3$ **33.** $a = \frac{1}{2}$ **34.** $x = -\frac{22}{3}$ **35.** $x = -\frac{1}{4}$ **36.** $a = \frac{7}{13}$ **37.** $x = -\frac{5}{2}$ **38.** $y = -14$ **39.** $x = -24$ **40.** $x = \frac{7}{4}$ **41.** $b = 0$ **42.** $x = \frac{1}{5}$ **43.** $c = -\frac{7}{4}$ **44.** $x = 2$ **45.** 41, 64 **46.** 36 **47.** 45 **48.** \$11,000 at 8%; \$9,000 at 7% **49.** \$12,000 at 12% profit; \$13,000 at 19% loss **50.** $a = \frac{F}{m}$ **51.** $I = \frac{E}{R}$ **52.** $P = \frac{k}{V}$ **53.** $g = V - k - t$ **54.** $c = \frac{2A - bh}{h}$ **55.** $x = \frac{4y}{3}$

56. $x > 4$ **57.** $x > -7$ 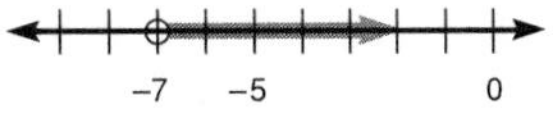 **58.** $x < 2$ **59.** $x > 4\frac{1}{2}$

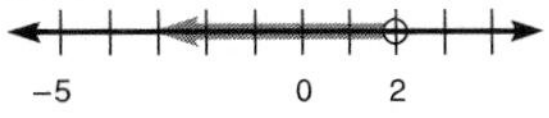

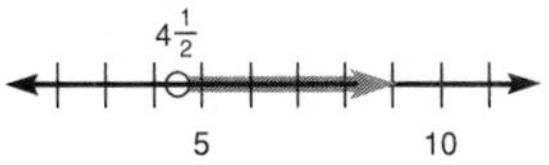

60. $x \leq \frac{2}{9}$ 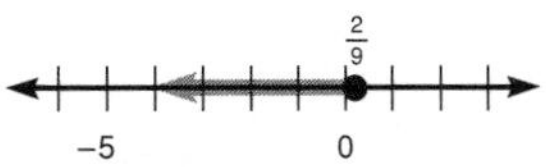 **61.** $-2\frac{1}{5} < x < \frac{3}{5}$ **62.** $-1 < x \leq \frac{1}{5}$ **63.** $\frac{1}{2} < x < 2\frac{1}{4}$

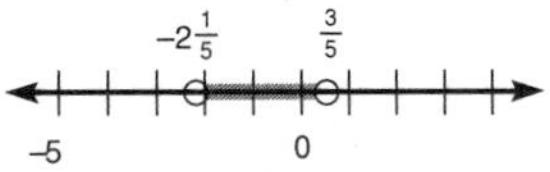

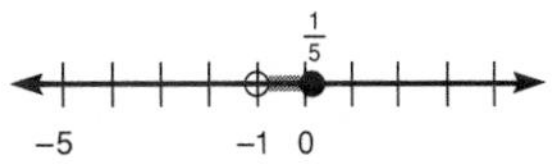

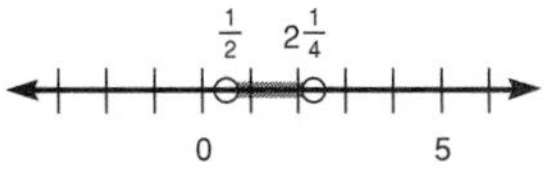

Chapter 2 cumulative test

1. -12 **2.** -25 **3.** 20 **4.** undefined **5.** 4 **6.** $a^3 + 2a^2 + a - 1$ **7.** 3 **8.** 6 **9.** $-5, 6$ **10.** $-6, -4$ **11.** $-15, -2$ **12.** 3, 16 **13.** $x = \frac{5}{3}$ **14.** $x = \frac{8}{5}$ **15.** $x = \frac{30}{11}$ **16.** $x = 4$ **17.** \$6,000 at 6%; \$4,000 at 5% **18.** 14, 16, 18 **19.** $x \leq 9$ **20.** $3 \leq y \leq 6$ **21.** $x < -3$ **22.** $x > 3$ **23.** $x \leq 6$

Chapter 3

Proficiency check

1. -25 **2.** 10 **3.** 1 **4.** -10 **5.** 36 **6.** 144 **7.** 64 **8.** -25 **9.** 234 **10.** $2x^2 + 3x$ **11.** $10ab + 2ac$

Exercise 3-1

1. a^5 **2.** b^4 **3.** $(-2)^4$ **5.** x^6 **6.** $(a + b)^2$ **7.** $(x - y)^3$ **9.** $y \cdot y \cdot y \cdot y \cdot y$ **10.** $(-2)(-2)(-2)$ **11.** $-(2 \cdot 2 \cdot 2 \cdot 2)$ **13.** $(x - y)(x - y)$ **14.** x^{11} **15.** a^{10} **17.** R^3 **18.** a^9 **19.** x^9 **21.** $5^5 = 3{,}125$ **22.** $4^7 = 16{,}384$ **23.** a^5b^5 **25.** $8a^3b^3c^3$ **26.** $64x^3y^3z^3$ **27.** a^8 **29.** y^4 **30.** b^{25} **31.** c^{27} **33.** $6x^4y^3$ **34.** a^7b^5 **35.** x^6y^5 **37.** a^9b^6 **38.** $x^{16}y^{12}z^4$ **39.** $8a^{15}b^6c^3$ **41.** $\frac{a^6}{b^6}$ **42.** $\frac{x^4}{y^4}$ **43.** $\frac{8}{27}$ **45.** $\frac{16x^4}{y^4}$ **46.** $\frac{27a^3}{b^3}$ **47.** $\frac{8x^6}{y^9}$ **49.** $\frac{4x^6y^6}{z^{10}}$ **50.** $\frac{a^{25}b^5c^{20}}{d^{10}e^5}$ **51.** $V = e \cdot e \cdot e$ **a.** $5^3 = 125$ cubic units **b.** $4^3 = 64$ cubic units **c.** $6^3 = 216$ cubic units **53.** πr^2 **54.** $\frac{4}{3}\pi r^3$ **55.** $n^3 + 6$ **57.** $2x^2 - y^3$ **58.** $a \cdot 10^8$ **59.** $\frac{p^3}{q^2}$

Solutions to trial exercise problems

17. $R^2 \cdot R = R^2 \cdot R^1 = R^{2+1} = R^3$ **21.** $5^2 \cdot 5^3 = 5^{2+3} = 5^5 = 3{,}125$ **33.** $(2xy^2)(3x^3y) = 2 \cdot 3 \cdot xx^3y^2y = 6x^{1+3}y^{2+1} = 6x^4y^3$ **51a.** $V = e^3$, then $V = (5)^3 = 5 \cdot 5 \cdot 5 = 25 \cdot 5 = 125$ cubic units **55.** The cube of Johnny's age is given as n^3. Since his mother is 6 years more than the cube of Johnny's age, we add 6, giving $n^3 + 6$.

Review exercises

1. $9a$ **2.** $8x$ **3.** $6ab$ **4.** $7xy$ **5.** $7a^2 + 5a$ **6.** $5x^2 + 5x$ **7.** $x^2y + 7xy^2$ **8.** $3ab^2 + 2a^2b$

Exercise 3–2

1. $9x$ **2.** $9y$ **3.** $13a + 2b$ **5.** $3x^2 + 11y^2$ **6.** $3a^2 + 3a$ **7.** $3x^2 - 3x$ **9.** $x^2y^2 - 2x^2y + 5xy$ **10.** $-4a^2b^2 + 8ab - 4a^2b^2$ **11.** $8x^2 + 2x + 1$ **13.** $-3x^2y + 15xy$ **14.** $-9x^2$ **15.** $4a^3 + a^2b + 6ab^2 - 5b^3$ **17.** $70a + 9b$ **18.** $xy + 32z$ **19.** $-5xy + 14yz + 9y^2z$ **21.** $-8b + 10$ **22.** $8x - 18y + 3z - 4$ **23.** $3a - 9b$ **25.** $3x^2 + 3z$ **26.** $4x - 3$ **27.** $2x$ **29.** $4x - 4a - 3b + 2y$ **30.** $4a + 3b$ **31.** $5a + 5b$ **33.** $-a - 2b$ **34.** $2x - 5a + 6y$ **35.** a

Solutions to trial exercise problems

19. $(8xy + 9y^2z) - (13xy - 14yz) = 8xy + 9y^2z - 13xy + 14yz = (8xy - 13xy) + 9y^2z + 14yz = (8 - 13)xy + 9y^2z + 14yz = -5xy + 9y^2z + 14yz$ **26.** $2x - [3x - (5x - 3)] = 2x - [3x - 5x + 3] = 2x - [-2x + 3] = 2x + 2x - 3 = 4x - 3$
33. $-[4a + 7b - (3a + 5b)] = -[4a + 7b - 3a - 5b] = -[a + 2b] = -a - 2b$

Review exercises

1. -15 **2.** 28 **3.** -40 **4.** -24 **5.** 0 **6.** 49 **7.** -16 **8.** -40

Exercise 3–3

1. trinomial **2.** binomial **3.** binomial **5.** binomial **6.** not a polynomial because a variable is used as a divisor (appears in the denominator) **7.** polynomial of 4 terms **9.** $30x^5$ **10.** $12a^5$ **11.** $14a^2b^2$ **13.** $12a^5b^3$ **14.** $5a^5b^9$ **15.** $-6a^3b^5$ **17.** $2a^3b - 2ab^2c + 2abc^2$ **18.** $24xy + 42xz$ **19.** $15ab^2 - 21ac^2$ **21.** $-15a^3b^2 + 5a^2b^3 - 20ab^4$ **22.** $24x^4 - 12x^3 + 18x^2$ **23.** $3a^3b - 6a^2b^2 - 3ab^3$ **25.** $10x^2y - 10xy^2 + 50xy$ **26.** $x^5y^3 + x^3y^5$ **27.** $x^2 + 7x + 12$ **29.** $y^2 - 13y + 36$ **30.** $z^2 - 4z - 77$ **31.** $a^2 + 2a + 1$ **33.** $R^2 - 6R + 9$ **34.** $R^2 - 4$ **35.** $a^2 - 9$ **37.** $6a^2 - 31a + 35$ **38.** $2y^2 - 7y + 6$ **39.** $4x^2 - 49$ **41.** $3k^2 - 17kw - 6w^2$ **42.** $5a^2 - 26abc - 24b^2c^2$ **43.** $a^2 + 12ab + 36b^2$ **45.** $4a^2 - 9b^2$ **46.** $16x^2 - y^2$ **47.** $a^3 + 2a^2b - 7ab^2 + 4b^3$ **49.** $6x^3 + 21x^2 - 5x + 28$ **50.** $x^3 - 3x^2y + 3xy^2 - y^3$ **51.** $a^3 + b^3$ **53.** $2x^3 + 5x^2y + xy^2 - 2y^3$ **54.** $2a^3 + 3a^2b - 10ab^2 - 3b^3$ **55.** $\pi R^2 - \pi r^2$

Solutions to trial exercise problems

25. $(2x)(x - y + 5)(5y) = [(2x)(x - y + 5)](5y) = [2x \cdot x - 2x \cdot y + 2x \cdot 5](5y) = [2x^2 - 2xy + 10x](5y) = 2x^2 \cdot 5y - 2xy \cdot 5y + 10x \cdot 5y = 10x^2y - 10xy^2 + 50xy$ **33.** $(R - 3)^2$ is a special product. $(R - 3)^2 = (R)^2 + [2 \cdot R \cdot (-3)] + (-3)^2 = R^2 - 6R + 9$ **34.** $(R + 2)(R - 2)$ is a special product. $(R + 2)(R - 2) = (R)^2 - (2)^2 = R^2 - 4$ **47.** $(a + 4b)(a^2 - 2ab + b^2) = a^3 - 2a^2b + ab^2 + 4a^2b - 8ab^2 + 4b^3 = a^3 + 2a^2b - 7ab^2 + 4b^3$

Review exercises

1. -5 **2.** 12 **3.** 3 **4.** -9 **5.** x^{12} **6.** a^{15} **7.** $27a^6b^3$ **8.** $\dfrac{8x^3}{y^6}$

Exercise 3–4

1. 1 **2.** 1 **3.** 5 **5.** $\dfrac{1}{S^2}$ **6.** $\dfrac{1}{R^5}$ **7.** $\dfrac{1}{8x^3}$ **9.** $\dfrac{4}{z^2}$ **10.** $\dfrac{9}{C^4}$ **11.** x^5 **13.** $\dfrac{y^3}{2}$ **14.** $\dfrac{x^2}{3}$ **15.** $\dfrac{2y^2}{x^4}$ **17.** $\dfrac{t^5}{r^2}$ **18.** $\dfrac{y^2}{x^3z^4}$ **19.** x^6 **21.** b^2 **22.** $\dfrac{1}{C^3}$ **23.** 9 **25.** $\dfrac{1}{64}$ **26.** x^5 **27.** y^4 **29.** $\dfrac{1}{y^6}$ **30.** $\dfrac{1}{b^3}$ **31.** a^3b^3 **33.** $\dfrac{1}{27a^3}$ **34.** $\dfrac{1}{5a^4b^2}$ **35.** x^3 **37.** $\dfrac{1}{a^6}$ **38.** $\dfrac{1}{R^7}$ **39.** $\dfrac{1}{(-5)^3} = -\dfrac{1}{125}$ **41.** 27 **42.** $\dfrac{1}{8}$ **43.** $\dfrac{1}{4a^4}$ **45.** $\dfrac{1}{b^6}$ **46.** a^6 **47.** $\dfrac{a^4}{b^6}$ **49.** $\dfrac{a^6}{4b^2}$ **50.** $\dfrac{y^6}{27x^{12}}$ **51.** $\dfrac{b^8}{a^5}$ **53.** $\dfrac{16}{y^5}$ **54.** $\dfrac{ab^4c^2}{8}$ **55.** $\dfrac{2bc^5}{5a^4}$ **57.** $\dfrac{2x}{3y^4}$ **58.** $\dfrac{y^2}{xz^4}$ **59.** $\dfrac{x^6z^{10}}{y^2}$ **61.** $\dfrac{16a^4}{b^{10}}$

Solutions to trial exercise problems

3. $5a^0 = 5 \cdot 1 = 5$ **9.** $4z^{-2} = 4 \cdot \dfrac{1}{z^2} = \dfrac{4}{z^2}$ **15.** $2x^{-4}y^2 = 2 \cdot \dfrac{1}{x^4} \cdot y^2 = \dfrac{2y^2}{x^4}$ **23.** $\dfrac{3^4}{3^2} = 3^{4-2} = 3^2 = 9$ **26.** $\dfrac{x^4x^3}{x^2} = \dfrac{x^{4+3}}{x^2} = \dfrac{x^7}{x^2} = x^{7-2} = x^5$

34. $\dfrac{5^2a^3b}{5^3a^7b^3} = 5^{2-3}a^{3-7}b^{1-3} = 5^{-1}a^{-4}b^{-2} = \dfrac{1}{5^1} \cdot \dfrac{1}{a^4} \cdot \dfrac{1}{b^2} = \dfrac{1}{5a^4b^2}$ **35.** $x^{-4}x^7 = x^{-4+7} = x^3$. *Alternative:* $x^{-4}x^7 = \dfrac{1}{x^4} \cdot x^7 = \dfrac{x^7}{x^4} = x^{7-4} = x^3$

39. $(-5)^{-3} = \dfrac{1}{(-5)^3} = -\dfrac{1}{125}$ (*Note:* The sign of the base, -5, is unchanged.) **43.** $(2a^2)^{-2} = \dfrac{1}{(2a^2)^2} = \dfrac{1}{2^2(a^2)^2} = \dfrac{1}{2^2a^4} = \dfrac{1}{4a^4}$

51. $\dfrac{a^{-2}b^3}{a^3b^{-5}} = \dfrac{\dfrac{1}{a^2} \cdot b^3}{a^3 \cdot \dfrac{1}{b^5}} = \dfrac{\dfrac{b^3}{a^2}}{\dfrac{a^3}{b^5}} = \dfrac{b^3}{a^2} \cdot \dfrac{b^5}{a^3} = \dfrac{b^{3+5}}{a^{2+3}} = \dfrac{b^8}{a^5}$ **54.** $\dfrac{4^{-1}a^{-2}b^3c^0}{2a^{-3}b^{-1}c^{-2}} = \dfrac{\dfrac{1}{4^1} \cdot \dfrac{1}{a^2} \cdot b^3 \cdot 1}{2 \cdot \dfrac{1}{a^3} \cdot \dfrac{1}{b^1} \cdot \dfrac{1}{c^2}} = \dfrac{\dfrac{b^3}{4a^2}}{\dfrac{2}{a^3bc^2}} = \dfrac{b^3}{4a^2} \cdot \dfrac{a^3bc^2}{2} = \dfrac{a^3b^{3+1}c^2}{2 \cdot 4a^2} = \dfrac{a^3b^4c^2}{8a^2} = \dfrac{b^4c^2}{8} \cdot a^{3-2}$
$= \dfrac{b^4c^2}{8} \cdot a^1 = \dfrac{ab^4c^2}{8}$

Review exercises

1. 35.34 **2.** 10.36 **3.** 16.72 **4.** 28.98 **5.** 18.81 **6.** 49.5

Exercise 3-5

1. 2.55×10^2 **2.** 6.5×10^7 **3.** 1.2345×10^4 **5.** 1.55×10^5 **6.** 1.436×10^1 **7.** 8.55076×10^2 **9.** 1.0076×10^6 **10.** 6.000736×10^6 **11.** 1.2×10^{-4} **13.** 8.1×10^{-6} **14.** 1.47×10^{-5} **15.** 7×10^{-4} **17.** 9.4×10^{-11} **18.** -4.56×10^2 **19.** -4.5×10^3 **21.** -5.85×10^6 **22.** -5.67×10^{-2} **23.** -4.578×10^1 **25.** -2.985×10^{-8} **26.** 2,070 **27.** 49,900,000 **29.** 7.23 **30.** 10,730 **31.** 0.0042 **33.** 0.00000147 **34.** 0.05 **35.** 0.000789 **37.** −0.00000000482 **38.** −261 **39.** −0.00000492 **41.** 1×10^{-9} **42.** 3×10^{10} **43.** 2×10^{12} **45.** 35,600,000 **46.** 9.5×10^{12} **47.** 0.00000000000000000000000093 **49.** 140,000 **50.** 33,000,000,000,000,000,000,000 **51.** 1.22304×10^{14} **53.** 3.63226×10^{-1} **54.** 2.64461×10^{10} **55.** 1.76979×10^{-7} **57.** 4.84481×10^8 **58.** 1.18×10^6 **59.** 1.4×10^3 **61.** 4.6×10^3 **62.** 1.2×10^0

Solution to trial exercise problem

58. $(177{,}000) \div (0.15) = \dfrac{1.77 \times 10^5}{1.5 \times 10^{-1}} = \dfrac{1.77}{1.5} \times 10^{5-(-1)} = \dfrac{1.77}{1.5} \times 10^6 = 1.18 \times 10^6$

Review exercises

1. $5x$ **2.** $3a^2$ **3.** $12ab$ **4.** $x^3 + 2x^2$ **5.** $6a^2 - 15a$ **6.** $3x^3y + 2x^2y^2 - 7x^2y$

Chapter 3 review

1. a^{12} **2.** a^{14} **3.** $4^5 = 1{,}024$ **4.** x^4y^4 **5.** a^{15} **6.** $8a^6b^9$ **7.** $3^{12}x^{16}y^{20} = 531{,}441x^{16}y^{20}$ **8.** $6x^3y^7$ **9.** $20a^4b^5$ **10.** $8x^{26}y^{25}$ **11.** $72a^{14}b^3$ **12.** $\dfrac{a^5}{b^5}$ **13.** $\dfrac{4y^2z^2}{x^2}$ **14.** $\dfrac{a^9b^3}{c^{12}}$ **15.** $\dfrac{9a^6b^4}{c^{10}}$ **16.** $\dfrac{32x^5y^{20}}{z^{30}}$ **17.** $5x$ **18.** $y - 7$ **19.** $z + 4$ **20.** let x = the number; $2x + 6$ **21.** $4x^2 - 3x + 3$ **22.** $-a^2 + a + 11$ **23.** $-6a^2$ **24.** $5x^3 - 4x^2 - 7xy^2 - 2y^3$ **25.** $-11ab + 11bc + 7b^2c$ **26.** $-2y - 4b + 1$ **27.** $5ab + 3ac - 4bc$ **28.** −5 **29.** $7x + y$ **30.** $2x + 5y$ **31.** $9a - 10b$ **32.** binomial **33.** binomial **34.** monomial **35.** not a polynomial, variable used as a divisor **36.** $10x^5y^5$ **37.** $-6a^6b^{10}$ **38.** $15x^2 - 10xy$ **39.** $-6a^4b + 9a^3b^2 - 12a^2b^3$ **40.** $30x^2y^2 - 10xy^3$ **41.** $x^2 - x - 12$ **42.** $x^2 + 10x + 25$ **43.** $a^2 - 49$ **44.** $15x^2 + 7xy - 2y^2$ **45.** $x^3 + x^2y - 5xy^2 - 2y^3$ **46.** $\dfrac{1}{b^2}$ **47.** $\dfrac{5}{a^2}$ **48.** a^4 **49.** $\dfrac{1}{x^3}$ **50.** 1 **51.** $\dfrac{5}{x^3y^2}$ **52.** a^3 **53.** $\dfrac{y^6}{4x^2}$ **54.** $\dfrac{xy^3z^3}{2}$ **55.** $\dfrac{2a^2c^3}{b^6}$ **56.** 1.84×10^3 **57.** 1.57×10^{-3} **58.** 1.07×10^8 **59.** 8.49×10^{11} **60.** -3.75×10^1 **61.** -5.43×10^{-3} **62.** 504,000 **63.** 0.00639 **64.** −596 **65.** −0.00886 **66.** 0.000000735 **67.** 812,000,000 **68.** 2.67672×10^5 **69.** 1.54818×10^{-8} **70.** 7.2×10^{-3} **71.** 1.25×10^{-7}

Chapter 3 cumulative test

1. −12 **2.** x^6 **3.** 20 **4.** $a + 3b$ **5.** 4 **6.** $4x^2 - 4xy + y^2$ **7.** 3 **8.** $8a^6b^3c^9$ **9.** 6 **10.** $4x^2y - 7xy^2$ **11.** $9a^2 - 4b^2$ **12.** −25 **13.** $\dfrac{8a^6}{b^3}$ **14.** undefined **15.** $6x^3y^4$ **16.** $a^3 + 2a^2 + a - 1$ **17.** $2x^2 - 5x - 12$ **18.** $-3x + 4y$ **19.** −5, 6 **20.** −6, −4 **21.** −15, −2 **22.** 3, 16 **23.** $x = \dfrac{5}{3}$ **24.** $x > \dfrac{8}{5}$ **25.** $x = \dfrac{30}{11}$ **26.** $-2 < x < 4$ **27.** \$6,000 at 6%; \$4,000 at 5% **28.** 14, 16, 18

Chapter 4

Proficiency check

1. $a^2 - 4ab + 4b^2$ **2.** a^6 **3.** $x^2 - 4y^2$ **4.** $6xy - 2xz$ **5.** $3a^2 - 7ab + 2b^2$ **6.** $15a^3b + 10a^4b^3 - 20a^2b^6$ **7.** $x^2 + 6xy + 9y^2$ **8.** $3x^2 - xy - 2y^2$ **9.** $8x^3 - y^3$ **10.** $a^4 - 25b^2c^2$

Exercise 4-1

1. $2(y + 3)$ **2.** $3(a - 4)$ **3.** $4(x^2 + 2y)$ **5.** $3(x^2y + 5z)$ **6.** $5(r^2 + 2rs - 4s)$ **7.** $7(a - 2b + 3c)$ **9.** $3(5xy - 6z + x^2)$ **10.** $3a(6b - 9 + c)$ **11.** $7(6xy - 3y^2 + 1)$ **13.** $2(4x - 5y + 6z - 9w)$ **14.** $3(5L^2 - 7W^2 + 12H)$ **15.** $5(a^2 - 12ab + 9b^2)$ **17.** $3xy(x + 2)$ **18.** $4x^2(2x + 1)$ **19.** $3x(x - y + 1)$ **21.** $6a(4a + 2 - a^2)$ **22.** $2x(x^3 - 3x + 4)$ **23.** $xy(y + z + 1)$ **25.** $7a(2ab - 3c^2 + 6bc)$ **26.** $5p(p + 2 - 3p^2)$ **27.** $x^2y(16x - 3y + 24y^2)$ **29.** $-3(2x + 3)$ **30.** $5(-a + 2b)$ **31.** $2(3x - 4z - 6w)$ **33.** $-4(a^3 + 9ab - 4ab^2 + 6b^3)$ **34.** $ab(-1 - a)$ **35.** $-a(3 - a^2b)$ **37.** $-x(1 - x + x^2)$ **38.** $-4x(x - 2 + 3x^2)$ **39.** $-xyz(1 - x + y - z)$ **41.** $(a + b)(x + y)$ **42.** $7(L + 2N)(3R - 5S)$ **43.** $5(2a + b)(3x + 2y)$ **45.** $9xy(a + 4b)$ **46.** $(2x - 1)(y + 32)$ **47.** $(b + 6)(8a - 1)$ **49.** $4xy(a - 2b)(3x + 2y)$ **50.** $(r + s)(t + u)$ **51.** $(a + b)(c + d)$ **53.** $(2a + b)(3x - 2y)$ **54.** $(2a - b)(x^2 + 3)$ **55.** $(5x - 3y)(4x + z)$ **57.** $(2c - y)(a + 3b)$ **58.** $(c - 2y)(2a + b)$ **59.** $(c + 4y)(2a + 3b)$ **61.** $(3x + y)(2a + b)$ **62.** $(a + 2b)(2x - d)$ **63.** $(x - 2d)(3a + b)$ **65.** $(a + 5)(2a^2 + 3)$ **66.** $(3a^2 + 5)(a - 2)$ **67.** $(4a^2 + 3)(2a - 1)$ **69.** $16t(35 - t)$ **70.** $\pi r(s + r)$ **71.** $\dfrac{wx}{48EI}(2x^3 - 3\ell x^2 - \ell^3)$

Solutions to trial exercise problems

11. $42xy - 21y^2 + 7 = 7 \cdot 6xy - 7 \cdot 3y^2 + 7 \cdot 1 = 7(6xy - 3y^2 + 1)$ **23.** $xy^2 + xyz + xy = xy \cdot y + xy \cdot z + xy \cdot 1 = xy(y + z + 1)$ **31.** $6x - 8z - 12w = 2(\quad); 2 \cdot 3x - 2 \cdot 4z - 2 \cdot 6w = 2(3x - 4z - 6w)$ **33.** $-4a^3 - 36ab + 16ab^2 - 24b^3 = -4(\quad)$; $(-4)a^3 + (-4)(9ab) + (-4)(-4ab^2) + (-4)(6b^3) = -4(a^3 + 9ab - 4ab^2 + 6b^3)$ **35.** $-3a + a^3b = -a(\quad); (-a) \cdot 3 + (-a)(-a^2b) = -a(3 - a^2b)$ **43.** $15x(2a + b) + 10y(2a + b) = 5(2a + b) \cdot 3x + 5(2a + b) \cdot 2y = 5(2a + b)(3x + 2y)$ **53.** $6ax - 2by + 3bx - 4ay = 6ax + 3bx - 4ay - 2by = (6ax + 3bx) + (-4ay - 2by) = 3x(2a + b) - 2y(2a + b) = (2a + b)(3x - 2y)$

71. $Y = \dfrac{2wx^4}{48EI} - \dfrac{3\ell wx^3}{48EI} - \dfrac{\ell^3wx}{48EI} = \dfrac{wx}{48EI} \cdot 2x^3 - \dfrac{wx}{48EI} \cdot 3\ell x^2 - \dfrac{wx}{48EI} \cdot \ell^3 = \dfrac{wx}{48EI}(2x^3 - 3\ell x^2 - \ell^3)$

Review exercises

1. 4, 5 **2.** 3, 4 **3.** −8, 2 **4.** 8, −2 **5.** 8, 2 **6.** −8, −2 **7.** 6, 6 **8.** 11, 1

Exercise 4–2

1. $(a + 6)(a + 3)$ **2.** $(c + 4)(c + 5)$ **3.** $(x + 12)(x - 1)$ **5.** $(y + 15)(y - 2)$ **6.** $(a + 7)(a + 2)$ **7.** $(x - 12)(x - 2)$ **9.** $(a + 8)(a - 3)$ **10.** $(y + 12)(y - 3)$ **11.** $(x + 6)(x + 2)$ **13.** $(a - 6)(a + 4)$ **14.** $(z - 9)(z + 4)$ **15.** $2(x + 5)(x - 2)$ **17.** $3(x - 8)(x + 2)$ **18.** will not factor, prime polynomial **19.** will not factor, prime polynomial **21.** $(y + 15)(y + 2)$ **22.** $(b + 8)(b + 5)$ **23.** $4(x + 2)(x - 3)$ **25.** $5(a - 5)(a + 2)$ **26.** $(xy - 7)(xy + 3)$ **27.** $(xy - 6)(xy + 3)$ **29.** $(xy + 12)(xy + 1)$ **30.** $4(ab - 7)(ab - 1)$ **31.** $3(xy + 3)(xy - 4)$ **33.** $(x + 2y)(x + y)$ **34.** $(a - 2b)(a + b)$ **35.** $(a - 3b)(a + b)$ **37.** $(a - 3b)(a + 2b)$ **38.** $(x + 4y)(x - 2y)$ **39.** $(x + 3y)(x - 5y)$

Solutions to trial exercise problems

17. $3x^2 - 18x - 48 = 3(x^2 - 6x - 16)$
m and *n* are −8 and 2. $= 3(x - 8)(x + 2)$

26. $x^2y^2 - 4xy - 21 = (xy)^2 - 4(xy) - 21$
m and *n* are −7 and 3. $= (xy - 7)(xy + 3)$

33. We need to find *m* and *n* that add to $3y$ and multiply to $2y^2$. The values are $2y$ and y. The factorization is $x^2 + 3xy + 2y^2 = (x + 2y)(x + y)$.

Review exercises

1. $x^2(a + b + c)$ **2.** $3x(x^2 + 4x - 2)$ **3.** $(3x + 5)(2x + 1)$ **4.** $(2x + 3)(3x - 2)$ **5.** $(4x + 1)(5x + 1)$ **6.** $(6x - 1)(2x + 3)$ **7.** $(x - 2)(3x - 5)$ **8.** $(7x - 3)(x - 9)$

Exercise 4–3

1. $(2x - 3)(x + 2)$ **2.** $(3x - 2)(x + 3)$ **3.** $(2x + 1)(x + 1)$ **5.** $(2R - 3)(R - 2)$ **6.** will not factor, prime polynomial **7.** $(5x + 3)(x - 2)$ **9.** $(3x - 1)(3x - 1) = (3x - 1)^2$ **10.** $(x - 2)(8x - 1)$ **11.** will not factor, prime polynomial **13.** $(2x + 3)(3x + 2)$ **14.** $(2r + 9)(r + 2)$ **15.** $(2x + 7)(2x + 3)$ **17.** will not factor, prime polynomial **18.** $(2x - 3)(2x + 1)$ **19.** $(3y - 8)(3y + 1)$ **21.** $(5x + 6)(2x - 1)$ **22.** $(5x + 2)(2x + 1)$ **23.** $(2x - 5)(x - 2)$ **25.** $2(2x + 3)(x + 2)$ **26.** $(R - 2)(5R + 1)$ **27.** $2(2x + 3)(x + 1)$ **29.** $(2x + 3)(3x - 1)$ **30.** $3(x + 2)(x + 2) = 3(x + 2)^2$ **31.** $2(x + 5)(x - 2)$ **33.** $(3x - 2)(2x + 3)$ **34.** $(3x - 4)(x - 5)$ **35.** $(2x + 3)(2x + 3) = (2x + 3)^2$ **37.** $(7x - 1)(x - 5)$ **38.** will not factor, prime polynomial **39.** $(3P + 1)(5P - 1)$ **41.** $2x(x - 5)(x + 2)$ **42.** $2(2x + 1)(x + 2)$ **43.** $a(2a + 1)(a + 7)$ **45.** $(2x - 5)(4x + 3)$ **46.** $(2x - 3)(4x - 3)$ **47.** $-16(t - 1)(t - 1) = -16(t - 1)^2$

Solutions to trial exercise problems

25. $4x^2 + 14x + 12 = 2(2x^2 + 7x + 6)$
m and *n* are 3 and 4. $= 2[(2x^2 + 3x) + (4x + 6)]$
$= 2[x(2x + 3) + 2(2x + 3)]$
$= 2(2x + 3)(x + 2)$

41. $2x^3 - 6x^2 - 20x = 2x(x^2 - 3x - 10)$
m and *n* are −5 and 2. $= 2x(x - 5)(x + 2)$

Review exercises

1. $x^2 - y^2$ **2.** $9a^2 - 4b^2$ **3.** $x^2 - 2xy + y^2$ **4.** $25a^2 - 16b^2$ **5.** $4a^2 + 4ab + b^2$ **6.** $16x^2 - 8xy + y^2$ **7.** $x^4 - 1$ **8.** $a^4 - 16$

Exercise 4–4

1. $(6)^2$ **2.** $(5)^2$ **3.** $(c)^2$ **5.** $(4x)^2$ **6.** $(7b)^2$ **7.** $(2z^2)^2$ **9.** $(x + 1)(x - 1)$ **10.** $(x + 5)(x - 5)$ **11.** $(a + 2)(a - 2)$ **13.** $(3 + E)(3 - E)$ **14.** $(7 + R)(7 - R)$ **15.** $(1 + k)(1 - k)$ **17.** $(3b + 4)(3b - 4)$ **18.** $(x + 4z)(x - 4z)$ **19.** $(b + 6c)(b - 6c)$ **21.** $(2a + 5b)(2a - 5b)$ **22.** $(a + 4b)(a - 4b)$ **23.** $(5p + 9)(5p - 9)$ **25.** $8(x + 2y)(x - 2y)$ **26.** $3(a + 3b)(a - 3b)$ **27.** $5(r + 5s)(r - 5s)$ **29.** $2(5 + x)(5 - x)$ **30.** $(xy + 2z)(xy - 2z)$ **31.** $(rs + 5t)(rs - 5t)$ **33.** $(x^2 - 3)(x^2 + 3)$ **34.** $(x^2 + 1)(x + 1)(x - 1)$ **35.** $(r^2 + 9)(r + 3)(r - 3)$ **37.** $(7x + 8y^2)(7x - 8y^2)$ **38.** $5(5p + 2v)(5p - 2v)$ **39.** $2(7xy + 5pc)(7xy - 5pc)$ **41.** $(c - 7)^2$ **42.** $(b + 4)^2$ **43.** $(a + 3)^2$ **45.** $(y - 3)^2$ **46.** $(a + 3b)^2$ **47.** $(2a - 3b)^2$ **49.** $(3c - 2d)^2$ **50.** $(3a - 5b)^2$ **51.** $\frac{V}{8I}(h + 2v_1)(h - 2v_1)$

Solutions to trial exercise problems

17. $9b^2 - 16 = (3b)^2 - (4)^2 = (3b + 4)(3b - 4)$ **25.** $8x^2 - 32y^2 = 8(x^2 - 4y^2) = 8[(x)^2 - (2y)^2] = 8(x + 2y)(x - 2y)$ **34.** $x^4 - 1 = (x^2)^2 - (1)^2 = (x^2 + 1)(x^2 - 1) = (x^2 + 1)[(x)^2 - (1)^2] = (x^2 + 1)(x + 1)(x - 1)$ **41.** $c^2 - 14c + 49 = (c)^2 - 2(c)(7) + (7)^2 = (c - 7)^2$

Review Exercises

1. $(x + 6)(x + 2)$ **2.** $(7a + 9)(7a - 9)$ **3.** $(x - 4y)(3a + b)$ **4.** $2x(x + 3)(x + 4)$ **5.** $(2a + 3)(5a + 3)$ **6.** $(2a - 5)^2$ **7.** $(xy + 5)(xy + 3)$ **8.** $(x + 2y)^2$

Exercise 4–5

1. $(n + 7)(n - 7)$ **2.** $(a + 5)(a + 1)$ **3.** $(7b + 1)(b + 5)$ **5.** $(xy + 4)(xy - 2)$ **6.** $(y + 10)(y + 1)$ **7.** $(6 + y)(6 - y)$ **9.** $10(a - b)^2$ **10.** $(ab + 2)(ab - 7)$ **11.** $4(a + 2b)(a - 2b)$ **13.** $(3a - b)(x + 2y)$ **14.** will not factor; prime polynomial **15.** $(3x + 5)(2x - 1)$ **17.** $(2m - n)(3a + 2b)$ **18.** $(5x + 3)(x - 7)$ **19.** $(7b - 5)(b + 3)$ **21.** $(4x - 3)(x + 5)$ **22.** $(5y + 6)(y + 2)$ **23.** $6(x^2 - 4xy - 8y^2)$ **25.** $3xy(x + 5y)(m - 4n)$ **26.** $(2x - 5y)^2$ **27.** $(3a - 5b)^2$ **29.** $3a(a^2 + 4)(a + 2)(a - 2)$ **30.** $3ab(a^2 - 3b^2)^2$ **31.** $3ab^3(a + b)^2$ **33.** $(3b + 7)(b - 13)$ **34.** $(b^2 + 9)(b + 3)(b - 3)$ **35.** $(3x + 2y)(a + 2b)$ **37.** $(6x - 1)(x + 2)$ **38.** $(6x + 1)(x - 3)$ **39.** $3x^2(x + 4)(x - 4)$

Solutions to trial exercise problems

25. $3x^2y(m-4n)+15xy^2(m-4n)=3xy(m-4n)(x+5y)$ common factor of $3xy(m-4n)$ **27.** $9a^2-30ab+25b^2=(3a)^2-2(3a)(5b)+(5b)^2=(3a-5b)^2$ **29.** $3a^5-48a=3a(a^4-16)=3a[(a^2)^2-(4)^2]=3a(a^2+4)(a^2-4)=3a(a^2+4)(a+2)(a-2)$

Review exercises

1. $x=-3$ **2.** $x=3$ **3.** $x=6$ **4.** $x=-\frac{3}{5}$ **5.** $x=-\frac{2}{3}$ **6.** $x=-\frac{1}{3}$ **7.** $x=\frac{1}{4}$ **8.** $x=0$

Exercise 4–6

1. $\{-5,5\}$ **2.** $\{-1,1\}$ **3.** $\{-6,0\}$ **5.** $\{0,7\}$ **6.** $\{-9,0\}$ **7.** $\left\{-\frac{3}{2},3\right\}$ **9.** $\left\{-\frac{2}{5},\frac{3}{4}\right\}$ **10.** $\left\{-\frac{1}{5},\frac{1}{5}\right\}$ **11.** $\left\{\frac{4}{3},\frac{8}{5}\right\}$ **13.** $\{-5,5\}$ **14.** $\{-8,8\}$ **15.** $\left\{-1,0,\frac{3}{2}\right\}$ **17.** $\left\{-\frac{3}{5},\frac{1}{4},10\right\}$ **18.** $\left\{-\frac{7}{2},\frac{1}{8},3\right\}$ **19.** $\{-4,0\}$ **21.** $\left\{0,\frac{5}{3}\right\}$ **22.** $\left\{-\frac{7}{4},0\right\}$ **23.** $\{-3,0\}$ **25.** $\left\{-\frac{3}{2},0\right\}$ **26.** $\left\{-\frac{3}{2},0\right\}$ **27.** $\{-5,5\}$ **29.** $\{-2,2\}$ **30.** $\{-3,3\}$ **31.** $\left\{-\frac{3}{2},\frac{3}{2}\right\}$ **33.** $\{-8,2\}$ **34.** $\{-1,4\}$ **35.** $\{-7\}$ **37.** $\{-7,2\}$ **38.** $\{-7,6\}$ **39.** $\{-2,-1\}$ **41.** $\{-1,12\}$ **42.** $\{-1,15\}$ **43.** $\{-4,8\}$ **45.** $\left\{-1,\frac{9}{2}\right\}$ **46.** $\left\{-1,\frac{3}{2}\right\}$ **47.** $\left\{\frac{1}{3},\frac{1}{2}\right\}$ **49.** $\left\{-\frac{3}{2},\frac{4}{3}\right\}$ **50.** $\left\{-\frac{1}{2},\frac{3}{2}\right\}$ **51.** $\left\{\frac{1}{3},\frac{3}{2}\right\}$ **53.** $\left\{-\frac{4}{3},\frac{5}{2}\right\}$ **54.** $\left\{-\frac{5}{3},-\frac{4}{3}\right\}$ **55.** $\{-1\}$ **57.** $\{-2,-1\}$ **58.** $\left\{-2,\frac{4}{3}\right\}$ **59.** $\{-2,-1\}$ **61.** $\{-2,9\}$ **62.** $\{-3,2\}$ **63.** $\left\{\frac{2}{3}\right\}$ **65.** $\{-1,5\}$ **66.** $\{-12,3\}$

Solutions to trial exercise problems

1. $(x+5)(x-5)=0$
$x+5=0$ or $x-5=0$
$x=-5$ $\quad x=5$
$\{-5,5\}$

11. $(4-3u)(8-5u)=0$
$4-3u=0$ or $8-5u=0$
$4=3u$ $\quad 8=5u$
$\frac{4}{3}=u$ $\quad \frac{8}{5}=u$
$\left\{\frac{4}{3},\frac{8}{5}\right\}$

30. $5y^2-45=0$
$5(y^2-9)=0$
$5(y+3)(y-3)=0$
$y+3=0$ or $y-3=0$
$y=-3$ $\quad y=3$
$\{-3,3\}$

42. $x^2-14x=15$
$x^2-14x-15=0$
$(x-15)(x+1)=0$
$x-15=0$ or $x+1=0$
$x=15$ $\quad x=-1$
$\{-1,15\}$

58. $3x(3x+2)=24$
$9x^2+6x=24$
$9x^2+6x-24=0$
$3(3x^2+2x-8)=0$
$3(3x-4)(x+2)=0$
$3x-4=0$ or $x+2=0$
$3x=4$ $\quad x=-2$
$x=\frac{4}{3}$ $\quad x=-2$
$\left\{-2,\frac{4}{3}\right\}$

7. $(3x-9)(2x+3)=0$
$3x-9=0$ or $2x+3=0$
$3x=9$ $\quad 2x=-3$
$x=3$ $\quad x=-\frac{3}{2}$
$\left\{-\frac{3}{2},3\right\}$

25. $10a^2=-15a$
$10a^2+15a=0$
$5a(2a+3)=0$
$5a=0$ or $2a+3=0$
$a=0$ $\quad 2a=-3$
$a=-\frac{3}{2}$
$\left\{-\frac{3}{2},0\right\}$

37. $b^2+5b-14=0$
$(b+7)(b-2)=0$
$b+7=0$ or $b-2=0$
$b=-7$ $\quad b=2$
$\{-7,2\}$

49. $6x^2+x-12=0$
$(3x-4)(2x+3)=0$
$3x-4=0$ or $2x+3=0$
$3x=4$ $\quad 2x=-3$
$x=\frac{4}{3}$ $\quad x=\frac{-3}{2}$
$\left\{\frac{-3}{2},\frac{4}{3}\right\}$

66. $x(x+7)=36-2x$
$x^2+7x=36-2x$
$x^2+9x-36=0$
$(x+12)(x-3)=0$
$x+12=0$ or $x-3=0$
$x=-12$ $\quad x=3$
$\{-12,3\}$

Review exercises

1. let x = the number; $x + 7$ **2.** let x = the number; $x - 11$ **3.** $6(x^2 + x)$ **4.** $\frac{x^2 + 2x}{8}$ **5.** 13 **6.** 6, 32 **7.** 22, 24, 26

Exercise 4–7

1. 11, 13 or $-13, -11$ **2.** 11, 12 or $-12, -11$ **3.** 14, 16 or $-16, -14$ **5.** 7, 13 or $-13, -7$ **6.** 9, 17 or $-17, -9$ **7.** $-2, 0$ or 4, 6 **9.** $-9, -4$ **10.** $-10, 7$ **11.** $-6, -\frac{7}{3}$ or 2, 7 **13.** $w = 4m$, $\ell = 6m$ **14.** $w = 3$ ft, $\ell = 7$ ft **15.** $w = 2$ ft, $\ell = 5$ ft **17.** 3 in., 6 in. or 4 in., 7 in. **18.** 6 in. and 10 in. **19. a.** 2 **b.** 1 **21. a.** 10 or 12 **b.** 12 or 20 **22. a.** 8 amperes or 12 amperes **b.** 5 amperes or 15 amperes **23. a.** 2 sec **b.** 4 sec **25.** 1 sec, 5 sec **26.** 6 sec **27.** 3 sec **29.** $h = 7$ in., $c = 8$ in. **30.** $h = 3$ ft **31.** $c = 4m$, $b = 8m$, altitude $= 4m$ **33.** $w = 7$ ft, $\ell = 8$ ft **34.** $w = 6$ in., $h = 3$ in. **35.** $w = 6$ ft, $\ell = 18$ ft

Solutions to trial exercise problems

7. Let x = the lesser integer.
Then $x + 2$ = the next consecutive even integer.
Then $x(x + 2) = 2[x + (x + 2)] + 4$
$x^2 + 2x = 2(2x + 2) + 4$
$x^2 + 2x = 4x + 4 + 4$
$x^2 + 2x = 4x + 8$
$x^2 - 2x - 8 = 0$
$(x - 4)(x + 2) = 0$
$x - 4 = 0$ or $x + 2 = 0$
$x = 4$ $\quad x = -2$
$x + 2 = 6$ $\quad x + 2 = 0$
The consecutive even integers are 4 and 6 or -2 and 0.

10. Let x = one integer.
Then $-3 - x$ = the other integer.
$x(-3 - x) = -70$
$-3x - x^2 = -70$
$0 = x^2 + 3x - 70 = (x + 10)(x - 7)$
$x + 10 = 0$ or $x - 7 = 0$
$x = -10$ $\quad x = 7$
$-3 - x = -3 - (-10) = 7$ or $-3 - x = -3 - 7 = -10$
The integers are -10 and 7.

15. Let w = the width. Let $\ell = w + 3$. From "the area of a rectangle is numerically equal to twice the length," we get
$w(w + 3) = 2(w + 3)$
$w^2 + 3w = 2w + 6$
$w^2 + w - 6 = 0$
$(w + 3)(w - 2) = 0$
$w + 3 = 0$ or $w - 2 = 0$
$w = -3$ $\quad w = 2$
(*Note:* A geometric figure cannot have a negative width, so we ignore $w = -3$.)
The width is 2 feet and the length is $w + 3 = 5$ feet.

22a. $P = 100I - 5I^2$, when $P = 480$.
$480 = 100I - 5I^2$
$5I^2 - 100I + 480 = 0$
$5(I^2 - 20I + 96) = 0$
$5(I - 8)(I - 12) = 0$
$I - 8 = 0$ or $I - 12 = 0$
$I = 8$ $\quad I = 12$
Therefore $I = 8$ amperes or $I = 12$ amperes.

25. $s = vt - 16t^2$, given $s = 80$ and $v = 96$.
$80 = 96t - 16t^2$
$16t^2 - 96t + 80 = 0$
$16(t^2 - 6t + 5) = 0$
$16(t - 5)(t - 1) = 0$
$t - 5 = 0$ or $t = 1$
$t = 5$ $\quad t = 1$
So $t = 1$ second on the way up, and $t = 5$ seconds on the way down.

30. Given $A = \frac{1}{2}h(b + c)$, $A = 21$ square feet, $c = 5$ feet, and using "b is 6 feet longer than the altitude h," we have $b = h + 6$.
Substitute $21 = \frac{1}{2}h[(h + 6) + 5]$
$21 = \frac{1}{2}h(h + 11)$.
Multiply both members by 2 to get $42 = h(h + 11)$.
Then $42 = h^2 + 11h$.
Add -42 to both members to get $0 = h^2 + 11h - 42$.
So $h^2 + 11h - 42 = 0$.
Factor the left member: $(h + 14)(h - 3) = 0$.
Then $h + 14 = 0$ or $h - 3 = 0$. So $h = -14$ or $h = 3$.
A trapezoid cannot have a negative altitude, so we ignore $h = -14$. The altitude of the trapezoid is 3 feet.

33. Given $V = \ell wh$, $V = 224$ cubic feet and $h = 4$ feet, from "the length is 1 foot longer than the width," $\ell = w + 1$.
Substituting, $224 = (w + 1) \cdot w \cdot 4$.
Multiplying the right member, $224 = 4w^2 + 4w$.
Add -224 to both members and interchange members.
$0 = 4w^2 + 4w - 224$
$4w^2 + 4w - 224 = 0$
Factor 4 from each term to get $4(w^2 + w - 56) = 0$.
Then $4(w + 8)(w - 7) = 0$, so $w + 8 = 0$ or $w - 7 = 0$.
So $w = -8$ or $w = 7$.
The width of a box cannot be negative, so we discard $w = -8$.
The width is then 7 feet and the length is $w + 1 = 8$ feet.

Review exercises

1. $x = \frac{2}{3}$ **2.** $a = \frac{5}{4}$ **3.** $\{-3,3\}$ **4.** $\{-4,-2\}$ **5.** 18 **6.** -27 **7.** 0 **8.** undefined

Chapter 4 review

1. $3(x + 3)$ **2.** $9x(x - 2)$ **3.** $-4y^2(y - 2)$ **4.** $7(a + 2b - 4c)$ **5.** $-5a(a + 3 - 6a^2)$ **6.** $3(a^2 - ab + b)$ **7.** $xy(x + z + yz)$ **8.** $a^3b(1 + b)$ **9.** $R^2(3R - 2 + 6R^2)$ **10.** $4y(y + 2 + 3y^2)$ **11.** $x^2(x^2 + 3x + 9)$ **12.** $4R^2S^2(4R - 3R^2S + 6)$ **13.** $5a^2b^2(2a^2b + 3 - 4a)$ **14.** $(a + b)(2 + x)$ **15.** $(x - 3z)(y + 4)$ **16.** $(3R + 1)(a + b)$ **17.** $(x - 3y)(2a - 3b)$ **18.** $(2x - y)(3a - b)$ **19.** $(4a + 3b)(x + 2y)$ **20.** $(x - 4)(a + 3b)$ **21.** $(x^2 + 4)(a - 2b)$ **22.** $(x - 7)(x - 2)$ **23.** $2a(a - 5)(a + 1)$ **24.** $(a + 2)(a + 12)$ **25.** $(x - 8)(x + 4)$ **26.** $(a + 2)(a - 18)$ **27.** $3(x - 5)(x + 2)$ **28.** $x(x - 3)(x + 2)$ **29.** $x(x - 7)(x + 3)$ **30.** $(ab + 3)(ab - 2)$ **31.** $(ab + 6)(ab + 4)$ **32.** $(ab - 6)(ab - 3)$ **33.** $(ab + 2)(ab - 10)$ **34.** $(2x + 1)(2x + 1) = (2x + 1)^2$ **35.** $9(r - 2)(r - 2) = 9(r - 2)^2$ **36.** $(4x - 1)(x - 1)$ **37.** $(3a + 5)(3a - 2)$ **38.** $(2a + 1)(4a - 3)$ **39.** $(4x + 3)(6x + 1)$ **40.** $(4a - 3)(2a - 3)$ **41.** $(2a + 3)(a + 6)$ **42.** $(2a + 3)(2a - 3)$ **43.** $(6b + c)(6b - c)$ **44.** $(5 + a)(5 - a)$ **45.** $4(2x + y)(2x - y)$ **46.** $(3x + y^2)(3x - y^2)$ **47.** $(x^2 + 4)(x + 2)(x - 2)$ **48.** $(y^2 + 9)(y + 3)(y - 3)$ **49.** $(b + 6)^2$ **50.** $(c - 5)^2$ **51.** $(2x - 3)^2$ **52.** $(3x - 2)^2$ **53.** $3x^3(4x - 1)$ **54.** $(a - 5)(a + 2)$ **55.** $(a - 5)(4a - 1)$ **56.** $(3y + 2)(3y - 2)$ **57.** $(3x - 2)(2a + 3b)$ **58.** $(b - 5)(b + 4)$ **59.** $(3x + 2)(3x + 5)$ **60.** $(a + 7)^2$ **61.** $3x^3(2x + 1)(2x - 1)$ **62.** $c(c + 5)(c + 4)$ **63.** $(4a - 1)^2$ **64.** $(b^2 + 1)(b + 1)(b - 1)$ **65.** $\{-3,1\}$ **66.** $\{0,8\}$ **67.** $\left\{-\frac{1}{5},\frac{7}{3}\right\}$ **68.** $\left\{\frac{1}{7},\frac{8}{5}\right\}$ **69.** $\left\{\frac{4}{3},9\right\}$ **70.** $\{-9,-4,0\}$ **71.** $\left\{-\frac{4}{5},\frac{4}{5}\right\}$ **72.** $\{-2,-1,3\}$ **73.** $\left\{0,\frac{9}{4}\right\}$ **74.** $\{-1,1\}$ **75.** $\{0,64\}$ **76.** $\{-5,5\}$ **77.** $\{-5,6\}$ **78.** $\{1\}$ **79.** $\left\{-3,-\frac{1}{4}\right\}$ **80.** $\left\{-\frac{2}{5},2\right\}$ **81.** $\{4\}$ **82.** $\{1,3\}$ **83.** $\left\{-1,\frac{3}{4}\right\}$ **84.** $\{-3,2\}$ **85.** 9,10 **86.** $w = 8$ ft, $\ell = 13$ ft **87.** 20 cattle **88.** 6 sec

Chapter 4 cumulative test

1. 33 **2.** $8a^6b^3$ **3.** $a^2 + 4ab + 4b^2$ **4.** a^6 **5.** 12 **6.** x^5y^4 **7.** $5x - 7y$ **8.** $9x^2 - 4y^2$ **9.** $\frac{8a^6}{b^3}$ **10.** $4x + 4y$ **11.** x^2 **12.** $x = \frac{9}{5}$ **13.** $x \geq 3$ **14.** $x = 7$ **15.** $\{2, 5\}$ **16.** $\{-3, 3\}$ **17.** $x < \frac{5}{2}$ **18.** $x = 3y$ **19.** $x = \frac{5y + 2}{3}$ **20.** $2ab(1 - 2ab - 4a^2b^4)$ **21.** $(2a + 3)^2$ **22.** $(5c + 3d)(5c - 3d)$ **23.** $(2a + 3)(2a - 5)$ **24.** $(x + 6)(x + 3)$ **25.** 14, 39 **26.** 11, 13 **27.** \$10,000 at 8%; \$5,000 at 6% **28.** $\ell = 11m, w = 6m$

Chapter 5

Proficiency check

1. a. $2^2 \cdot 7$ **b.** $2 \cdot 3^2 \cdot 5$ **2. a.** 72 **b.** 24 **3.** $\frac{6}{7}$ **4. a.** $\frac{3}{4}$ **b.** $\frac{7}{8}$ **c.** $\frac{3}{2}$ or $1\frac{1}{2}$ **d.** $\frac{69}{40}$ or $1\frac{29}{40}$ **5. a.** $(x - 3)(x + 3)$ **b.** $(y - 1)^2$ **c.** $3(x + 5)(x - 1)$ **6. a.** $\{-1,6\}$ **b.** $\left\{-7,\frac{1}{2}\right\}$

Exercise 5-1

1. $\frac{1}{3}$ **2.** $\frac{7}{12}$ **3.** $-\frac{7}{4}$ **5.** 4 **6.** $\frac{40}{9}$ **7.** 0 **9.** 0 **10.** -3 **11.** undefined **13.** $-\frac{10}{3}$ **14.** $\frac{33}{40}$ **15.** $x \neq 0$, all real numbers except 0 **17.** $x \neq 2$, all real numbers except 2 **18.** $x \neq 5$, all real numbers except 5 **19.** $x \neq -7$, all real numbers except -7 **21.** $x \neq \frac{1}{2}$, all real numbers except $\frac{1}{2}$ **22.** $a \neq \frac{3}{4}$, all real numbers except $\frac{3}{4}$ **23.** $p \neq \frac{5}{2}$, all real numbers except $\frac{5}{2}$ **25.** $x \neq -5$, all real numbers except -5 **26.** $b \neq -\frac{7}{3}$, all real numbers except $-\frac{7}{3}$ **27.** $x \neq -6, x \neq 3$, all real numbers except -6, 3 **29.** all real numbers **30.** all real numbers **31.** $s \neq \frac{3}{2}, s \neq -1$, all real numbers except $\frac{3}{2}$, -1 **33.** $x \neq -4, x \neq 4$, all real numbers except 4, -4 **34.** $x \neq -\frac{2}{3}, x \neq \frac{2}{3}$, all real numbers except $-\frac{2}{3}, \frac{2}{3}$ **35.** $x \neq -5, x \neq 5$, all real numbers except 5, -5 **37.** $x \neq -3, x \neq -1$, all real numbers except -3, -1 **38.** $y \neq -2, y \neq 2$, all real numbers except 2, -2 **39.** $z \neq -8, z \neq 8$, all real numbers except 8, -8

Solutions to trial exercise problems

6. $\frac{-5b^3}{5 - 2b}$; $b = -2$

$$\frac{-5b^3}{5 - 2b} = \frac{-5(-2)^3}{5 - 2(-2)} = \frac{-5(-8)}{5 + 4} = \frac{40}{9}$$

23. $\frac{p - 3}{5 - 2p}$ Set $5 - 2p = 0$. Then

$$2p = 5$$
$$p = \frac{5}{2}.$$

The domain is all real numbers except $\frac{5}{2}$.

21. $\frac{x + 1}{2x - 1}$ Set $2x - 1 = 0$, then $2x = 1$ and $x = \frac{1}{2}$.

The domain is all real numbers except $\frac{1}{2}$.

29. $\frac{2x^2}{x^2 + 9}$ Since $x^2 + 9 \neq 0$ for any real number, the domain is all real numbers.

31. $\dfrac{5s^2+7}{2s^2-s-3}$ Set $2s^2 - s - 3 = 0$ and factor. We have $(2s-3)(s+1) = 0$. Then

$$\begin{array}{lcl} 2s - 3 = 0 & \text{or} & s + 1 = 0 \\ 2s = 3 & & s = -1 \\ s = \dfrac{3}{2} & & s = -1 \end{array}$$

The domain is all real numbers except -1 and $\dfrac{3}{2}$.

Review exercises

1. distributive property **2.** -50 **3.** 5 **4.** $\dfrac{5}{9}$ **5.** $-\dfrac{1}{15}$ **6.** $(2x+1)(x-5)$ **7.** $4(y-5)(y-5) = 4(y-5)^2$

Exercise 5-2

1. $\dfrac{3}{4}$ **2.** $\dfrac{15}{29}$ **3.** $\dfrac{2x}{5}$ **5.** $\dfrac{4x}{3}$ **6.** $\dfrac{3b^2}{4}$ **7.** $\dfrac{-4}{3x^2}$ **9.** $\dfrac{4a}{5b}$ **10.** $\dfrac{3ax}{7}$ **11.** $\dfrac{5}{4}$ **13.** $\dfrac{6}{x+3}$ **14.** $\dfrac{-2}{x-6}$ **15.** $\dfrac{3}{5}$ **17.** $\dfrac{1}{2}$ **18.** $\dfrac{2}{3}$
19. $\dfrac{1}{a-b}$ **21.** $\dfrac{3}{4(y+1)}$ **22.** $-2(y+x)$ **23.** $\dfrac{n-m}{m+n}$ **25.** $\dfrac{x-3}{x+3}$ **26.** $\dfrac{y-7}{y+6}$ **27.** $\dfrac{x-5}{x-3}$ **29.** $\dfrac{2y+3}{4y-1}$ **30.** $\dfrac{3x-1}{x+5}$
31. $\dfrac{3x-2}{2x+1}$ **33.** $\dfrac{-(x-y)}{y+x}$ or $\dfrac{y-x}{y+x}$ **34.** $-\dfrac{2}{3}$ **35.** -8 **37.** $\dfrac{-1}{4+x}$ **38.** $\dfrac{-1}{2y+1}$ **39.** -1

Solutions to trial exercise problems

10. $\dfrac{15a^2x^3}{35ax^2} = \dfrac{3\cdot 5\cdot a\cdot a\cdot x\cdot x\cdot x}{7\cdot 5\cdot a\cdot x\cdot x} = \dfrac{3\cdot a\cdot x\cdot(5\cdot a\cdot x\cdot x)}{7\cdot(5\cdot a\cdot x\cdot x)} = \dfrac{3ax}{7}$ **19.** $\dfrac{a+b}{a^2-b^2} = \dfrac{a+b}{(a+b)(a-b)} = \dfrac{1}{a-b}$

23. $\dfrac{n^2-m^2}{(m+n)^2} = \dfrac{(n+m)(n-m)}{(m+n)(m+n)} = \dfrac{n-m}{m+n}$ **29.** $\dfrac{2y^2-3y-9}{4y^2-13y+3} = \dfrac{(2y+3)(y-3)}{(4y-1)(y-3)} = \dfrac{2y+3}{4y-1}$

37. $\dfrac{x-3}{12-x-x^2} = \dfrac{x-3}{(3-x)(4+x)} = \dfrac{-1(3-x)}{(3-x)(4+x)} = \dfrac{-1}{x+4}$

Review exercises

1. 3.14×10^{-4} **2.** $-\dfrac{11}{7}$ **3.** 25 **4.** 5 ft, 11 ft **5.** 1 **6.** $27y^3$ **7.** $-8x^9y^6$

Exercise 5-3

1. $4x^2$ **2.** $-5x^3$ **3.** $-5x^3yz$ **5.** $3(a-b)$ **6.** $2x-3$ **7.** $x-1$ **9.** $3x^2-2x+\dfrac{3}{4}$ **10.** $5a^2-3a+4-\dfrac{2}{a}$ **11.** $-4a^2+2a$
13. $-x+y+2y^2$ **14.** $2ab^2-3ab-4$ **15.** $10xy^2+7-6y^2$ **17.** $a-c$ **18.** $a-b$ **19.** $x+9+\dfrac{28}{x-2}$ **21.** $y+2+\dfrac{4}{y+3}$
22. $x-9$ **23.** $y-6+\dfrac{4}{y-5}$ **25.** $2a+1$ **26.** $3a-4-\dfrac{4}{3a-4}$ **27.** $9a^2+3a+1$ **29.** $x^3+2x^2+4x+8+\dfrac{2}{x-2}$
30. x^2+2x+3 **31.** $2a^2+7a+22+\dfrac{122}{a-5}$ **33.** $3x^3+4x^2+5x+4-\dfrac{7}{2x-3}$ **34.** $-3a-8$ **35.** $x^2-x-1+\dfrac{2x+7}{x^2-x+4}$
37. $y^2+3y+2-\dfrac{5y}{y^2-y+1}$ **38.** $y^2-2y+9+\dfrac{-26y+42}{y^2+2y-5}$ **39.** width $= x+2$ **41.** $6x^3+5x^2-21x+10$ **42.** $-6x^4+15x^3$ $+4x^2-22x+30$

Solutions to trial exercise problems

3. $\dfrac{-65x^4y^2z}{13xy} = \dfrac{-13\cdot 5\cdot x\cdot x\cdot x\cdot x\cdot y\cdot y\cdot z}{13\cdot x\cdot y} = -5x^3yz$

10. $\dfrac{15a^3-9a^2+12a-6}{3a} = \dfrac{15a^3}{3a} - \dfrac{9a^2}{3a} + \dfrac{12a}{3a} - \dfrac{6}{3a} = 5a^2-3a+4-\dfrac{2}{a}$

17. $\dfrac{a(b-1)-c(b-1)}{b-1} = \dfrac{a(b-1)}{(b-1)} - \dfrac{c(b-1)}{(b-1)} = a-c$

23. $(y^2-11y+34) \div (y-5)$

$$\begin{array}{r} y - 6 \\ y-5\overline{)\,y^2 - 11y + 34} \\ \underline{y^2 - 5y } \\ -6y + 34 \\ \underline{-6y + 30} \\ 4 \end{array} \quad = y - 6 + \dfrac{4}{y-5}$$

27. $(27a^3 - 1) \div (3a - 1)$
(*Note:* Insert zeros to hold positions where terms are missing.)

$$\begin{array}{r} 9a^2 + 3a + 1 \\ 3a - 1\overline{)27a^3 + 0a^2 + 0a - 1} \\ \underline{27a^3 - 9a^2} \quad\quad\quad\quad \\ 9a^2 + 0a \quad\quad \\ \underline{9a^2 - 3a} \quad\quad \\ 3a - 1 \\ \underline{3a - 1} \\ 0 \end{array}$$

Answer: $9a^2 + 3a + 1$.

39. The length times the width is $x^2 + 6x + 8$. If we know the length to be $x + 4$, then the width is found by

$$\begin{array}{r} x + 2 \\ x + 4\overline{)x^2 + 6x + 8} \\ \underline{x^2 + 4x} \quad\quad \\ 2x + 8 \\ \underline{2x + 8} \\ 0 \end{array}$$

Width $= x + 2$.

Review exercises

1. $\left\{-2, -\frac{1}{4}\right\}$ **2.** $w = 6$ ft, $\ell = 7$ ft **3.** $16x^2 - 24x + 9$ **4.** $x^3 + 3x^2 + x - 2$ **5.** $25y^2 - 1$ **6.** $\frac{3y + 1}{2y + 3}$

Exercise 5–4

1. $\frac{12}{7}$, 12:7 **2.** $\frac{8}{19}$, 8:19 **3.** $\frac{8}{3}$, 8:3 **5.** $\frac{8}{15}$, 8:15 **6.** $\frac{9}{4}$, 9:4 **7.** $\frac{5}{2}$, 5:2 **9.** $\frac{1}{4}$, 1:4 **10.** $\frac{3}{7}$ **11.** $\frac{7}{1}$ **13.** $\frac{3}{2}$ **14.** $\frac{5}{12}$ in.
15. $\frac{1}{21}$ **17.** $\frac{32}{1}$ **18.** $\frac{1}{26}$ **19.** $\frac{10 \text{ cm}}{1 \text{ in.}^3}$ **21.** $\frac{3 \text{ kg}}{1 \text{ m}^3}$ **22.** $\frac{60 \text{ mi}}{1 \text{ hr}}$ **23.** $\frac{1}{3}$ **25.** $\frac{15}{17}$ **26.** $\frac{13}{14}$ **27.** $\frac{5}{12}, \frac{12}{5}$ **29.** $\frac{11}{5}$ **30.** $\frac{21}{2}$ **31.** $\frac{7}{50}$
33. $\frac{9}{4}$ **34.** $x = 20$ **35.** $p = 6$ **37.** $R = \frac{9}{5}$ or $1\frac{4}{5}$ **38.** $x = 3$ **39.** $a = \frac{12}{19}$ **41.** 7 weeks **42.** 36 grams **43.** 390 units of weight
45. $R = 6{,}826\frac{2}{3}$ ohms **46.** 320 min or $5\frac{1}{3}$ hr **47.** $\ell = 45$ in. **49.** 21 ft **50.** 270 min or 4 hr 30 min

Solutions to trial exercise problems

5. Write 32 to 60 as $\frac{32}{60}$ or 32:60.
Reduce by 4. $\frac{32}{60} = \frac{8}{15}$ or 8:15.

14. Since there are $3 \times 12 = 36$ inches in 3 feet, we have 15 to 36 written $\frac{15}{36} = \frac{5}{12}$ or 5:12.

25. $ME = \frac{\text{output}}{\text{input}} = \frac{375 \text{ h}}{425 \text{ h}} = \frac{15}{17}$
Therefore the mechanical efficiency is $\frac{15}{17}$.

41. Let x = how many weeks man must work to earn \$1,260.
Then $\frac{1 \text{ week}}{180} = \frac{x \text{ weeks}}{1{,}260}$
$180x = 1{,}260$
$x = 7$.
The man works 7 weeks to earn \$1,260.

9. $2\frac{1}{2}$ to 10 is written $\frac{5}{2}$ to $10 = \frac{\frac{5}{2}}{10}$ or $\frac{5}{2}$:10.
But $\frac{\frac{5}{2}}{10} = \frac{5}{2} \cdot \frac{1}{10} = \frac{1}{4}$. Therefore, $2\frac{1}{2}$ to $10 = \frac{1}{4}$ or 1:4.

21. 105 kg to 35 m³ is written $\frac{105 \text{ kg}}{35 \text{ m}^3} = \frac{3 \text{ kg}}{1 \text{ m}^3}$ (reduce by 35).
Thus, 105 kg to 35 m³ = 3 kg/m³.

34. $\frac{36}{x} = \frac{9}{5}$, then $9 \cdot x = 36 \cdot 5$
$9x = 180$
$x = \frac{180}{9} = 20$
Therefore $\frac{36}{20} = \frac{9}{5}$

47. Let ℓ = the length of the enlargement.
Then $\frac{10 \text{ in.}}{8 \text{ in.}} = \frac{\ell \text{ in.}}{36 \text{ in.}}$ and $8 \cdot \ell = 10 \cdot 36$
$8\ell = 360$
$\ell = \frac{360}{8} = 45$
Therefore the enlargement will be 45 inches long.

Review exercises

1. $\frac{19}{15}$ **2.** $\frac{1}{4}$ **3.** $\frac{4}{7}$ **4.** 4 **5.** $y = -\frac{9}{5}$ **6.** $w = \frac{P - 2\ell}{2}$ **7.** 11, 13; −13, −11

Chapter 5 review

1. 9 **2.** undefined **3.** 6 **4.** $\frac{2}{3}$ **5.** $\frac{5}{6}$ **6.** all real numbers except 0 **7.** all real numbers except -7 **8.** all real numbers except 9 **9.** all real numbers except $-\frac{2}{3}$ **10.** all real numbers except $\frac{3}{5}$ **11.** all real numbers except 3, -4 **12.** all real numbers except 1, -1 **13.** $\frac{3b}{a}$ **14.** $\frac{3xz}{2y^2}$ **15.** $\frac{x-7}{x+7}$ **16.** $\frac{x+3}{x+7}$ **17.** $\frac{6}{5}$ **18.** $-1(x+y)$ **19.** $\frac{3p-2}{5p+1}$ **20.** $\frac{R-4}{3R-1}$ **21.** $\frac{5-n}{2+n}$ **22.** $-8x^2$ **23.** $2a-3+5a^2$ **24.** $5x-3y^3+xy$ **25.** $2a+3b-6ab^6$ **26.** $4a+1-\frac{2}{2a-1}$ **27.** $3a-2+\frac{1}{a-5}$ **28.** $x-7$ **29.** $5x^2-x-4$ **30.** $\frac{3}{7}$ **31.** $\frac{9}{4}$ **32.** $\frac{2}{5}$ **33.** $\frac{30 \text{ mi}}{1 \text{ gal}}$ **34.** $\frac{2{,}193}{881}$ **35.** $\frac{7}{3}$ **36.** $x = 32$ **37.** $a = 3.6$ **38.** $y = \frac{54}{5}$ or $10\frac{4}{5}$ **39.** $p = \frac{2}{5}$ **40.** 35 ft **41.** 12 qt antifreeze, 4 qt water

Chapter 5 cumulative test

1. 1,756 **2.** undefined **3.** -36 **4.** $5a+3b$ **5.** $9x^2-12x+4$ **6.** $25y^2-4$ **7.** $4a^2-21ab-18b^2$ **8.** $x^3-3x^2y+3xy^2-y^3$ **9.** -33 **10.** $x=-2$ **11.** $x=8$ **12.** $x=2$ **13.** $n = \frac{\ell - a + d}{d}$ **14.** $(x-y)(m+n)$ **15.** $(3a+4)(a+1)$ **16.** $(2x-5)(2x-5) = (2x-5)^2$ **17.** $(2z+3)(2z-3)$ **18.** $(6+y)(6-y)$ **19.** $(x+3)(x-15)$ **20.** $3(2x-3)(x+1)$ **21.** $\{7,-2\}$ **22.** $\left\{\frac{3}{2},-3\right\}$ **23.** $\frac{z^3}{64y^3}$ **24.** a^3 **25.** $8a^3$ **26.** $x=24$ **27.** $\frac{13}{6}$ **28.** $x-6+\frac{1}{x-2}$ **29.** $\frac{4}{3}$ **30.** $\frac{9b}{7a^2}$ **31.** $\frac{a-6}{a-7}$ **32.** $\frac{8}{5(x+y)}$ **33.** $\frac{y+4}{y+5}$ **34.** $\frac{x-3y}{3x+2y}$ **35.** $21\frac{1}{3}$ in. **36.** width $= 12\frac{6}{7}$ ft

Chapter 6

Proficiency check

1. a. $\frac{41}{24}$ or $1\frac{17}{24}$ **b.** $\frac{23}{12}$ or $1\frac{11}{12}$ **c.** $\frac{3}{4}$ **d.** 6 **2. a.** $\frac{8}{15}$ **b.** $\frac{4}{2y-1}$ **3. a.** $x = \frac{8}{3}$ **b.** $y = \frac{7}{3}$

Exercise 6–1

1. $\frac{3}{5}$ **2.** $\frac{1}{2}$ **3.** $\frac{5}{6}$ **5.** $\frac{x}{4y}$ **6.** $\frac{3a}{16}$ **7.** $\frac{3x}{4}$ **9.** $\frac{4a}{3}$ **10.** $\frac{20b}{7a}$ **11.** 10 **13.** $\frac{35x}{4}$ **14.** $\frac{23x}{2}$ **15.** $\frac{4n^2}{5m}$ **17.** $\frac{7c}{2b}$ **18.** $\frac{15axy}{2}$ **19.** $\frac{2a}{5b^2x}$ **21.** $-\frac{3}{4}$ **22.** $-\frac{18}{5}$ **23.** $-\frac{15}{4}$ **25.** $\frac{4}{a-5}$ **26.** $\frac{3}{4(z+4)}$ **27.** $\frac{18x-36}{x+2}$ **29.** r^2-5r+4 **30.** $\frac{2a-1}{a^2}$ **31.** $\frac{9m}{2(m+1)}$ **33.** $\frac{a^2+9a+14}{a^2-a-132}$ **34.** $\frac{a-3}{a-5}$ **35.** $\frac{x^2-2x-3}{x^2+x-2}$ **37.** 1 **38.** $\frac{2x-3}{x-3}$ **39.** $\frac{m}{2m+1}$ **41.** $3x+4$ **42.** $\frac{1}{2m^2-3m-2}$

Solutions to trial exercise problems

6. $\frac{7a}{12b} \cdot \frac{9b}{28} = \frac{7a \cdot 9b}{12b \cdot 28} = \frac{7 \cdot a \cdot 3 \cdot 3 \cdot b}{2 \cdot 2 \cdot 3 \cdot b \cdot 2 \cdot 2 \cdot 7} = \frac{3 \cdot a \cdot (7 \cdot 3 \cdot b)}{2 \cdot 2 \cdot 2 \cdot 2 \cdot (7 \cdot 3 \cdot b)} = \frac{3a}{16}$ **15.** $\frac{28m}{15n} \div \frac{7m^2}{3n^3} = \frac{28m \cdot 3n^3}{15n \cdot 7m^2} = \frac{4n^2}{5m}$

25. $\frac{4a+12}{a-5} \div (a+3) = \frac{4(a+3)}{a-5} \cdot \frac{1}{a+3} = \frac{4}{a-5}$ **29.** $\frac{r^2-16}{r+1} \div \frac{r+4}{r^2-1} = \frac{(r^2-16)(r^2-1)}{(r+1)(r+4)} = \frac{(r-4)(r+4)(r+1)(r-1)}{(r+1)(r+4)} = r^2-5r+4$ **34.** $\frac{a^2-5a+6}{a^2-9a+20} \cdot \frac{a^2-5a+4}{a^2-3a+2} = \frac{(a-3)(a-2)\cdot(a-4)(a-1)}{(a-4)(a-5)\cdot(a-2)(a-1)} = \frac{a-3}{a-5}$

37. $\frac{6r^2-r-7}{12r^2+16r-35} \div \frac{r^2-r-2}{2r^2+r-10} = \frac{(6r^2-r-7)(2r^2+r-10)}{(12r^2+16r-35)(r^2-r-2)} = \frac{(6r-7)(r+1)(2r+5)(r-2)}{(6r-7)(2r+5)(r-2)(r+1)} = 1$

41. $(3x^2-2x-8) \div \frac{x^2-4}{x+2} = \frac{(3x+4)(x-2)}{1} \cdot \frac{x+2}{(x+2)(x-2)} = 3x+4$

Review exercises

1. $\frac{19}{12}$ **2.** $\frac{11}{24}$ **3.** $2(x+5)(x-5)$ **4.** $(x+11)(x-2)$ **5.** $(x+4)^2$ **6.** $x = \frac{24}{5}$ or $4\frac{4}{5}$ **7.** $y = 15$ **8.** 7.89×10^{-5}

Exercise 6–2

1. $\frac{8}{x}$ **2.** $\frac{18}{y^2}$ **3.** $\frac{7}{p}$ **5.** $\frac{14x}{x+2}$ **6.** $\frac{11y}{y-1}$ **7.** $-\frac{2}{x}$ **9.** $\frac{5x+8}{x^2-1}$ **10.** $\frac{-2b+5}{b+3}$ **11.** $-\frac{1}{7}$ **13.** $\frac{9}{z}$ **14.** $-\frac{3}{y}$ **15.** $-\frac{7}{x-2}$ **17.** $\frac{9y}{y-6}$ **18.** $\frac{3z}{z-3}$ **19.** $\frac{4-x}{x-5}$ **21.** $\frac{3y+2}{2y-3}$ **22.** $\frac{-3z+6}{4z-3}$ **23.** $\frac{x-4}{5-2x}$ or $\frac{4-x}{2x-5}$ **25.** $18x$ **26.** $24a$ **27.** $48x^2$ **29.** $140y^3$

30. $63z^4$ **31.** $64a^4$ **33.** $180a^3$ **34.** $2(2x-1)$ **35.** $3(x-4)$ **37.** $18y^3(y-4)$ **38.** $32z^2(z-2)$ **39.** $a(a+1)(a-1)$ **41.** $8(a+2)(a+1)$ **42.** $9(p-2)(p-5)$ **43.** $(a+2)(a-2)(a-3)$ **45.** $(a+6)(a-6)(a+2)(a-2)(a-3)$ **46.** $(p+3)(p-3)(p-2)^2$ **47.** $2(x+7)(x-7)$

Solutions to trial exercise problems

5. $\frac{5x}{x+2}+\frac{9x}{x+2}=\frac{14x}{x+2}$ **7.** $\frac{x-1}{2x}-\frac{x+3}{2x}=\frac{(x-1)-(x+3)}{2x}=\frac{x-1-x-3}{2x}=\frac{-4}{2x}=-\frac{2}{x}$

18. $\frac{4z}{z-3}+\frac{z}{3-z}=\frac{4z}{z-3}+\frac{z}{-1(z-3)}=\frac{4z}{z-3}+\frac{-z}{z-3}=\frac{4z+(-z)}{z-3}=\frac{3z}{z-3}$

21. $\frac{2y-5}{2y-3}-\frac{y+1}{3-2y}=\frac{2y-5}{2y-3}-\frac{y+7}{-(2y-3)}=\frac{2y-5}{2y-3}+\frac{y+7}{2y-3}$

$=\frac{(2y-5)+(y+7)}{2y-3}=\frac{2y-5+y+7}{2y-3}$

$=\frac{3y+2}{2y-3}$

33. $10a^2=2\cdot5\cdot a^2$
$12a^2=2^2\cdot3\cdot a^3$
$9a=3^2\cdot a$
LCD is $2^2\cdot3^2\cdot5\cdot a^3=180a^3$.

45. $a^2-36=(a+6)(a-6)$
$a^2-5a+6=(a-2)(a-3)$
$a^2-4a-12=(a-6)(a+2)$
LCD is $(a+6)(a-6)(a+2)(a-2)(a-3)$.

47. $x^2-49=(x+7)(x-7)$
$7-x=-1(x-7)$
$2x+14=2(x+7)$
LCD $=2(x+7)(x-7)$

Review exercises

1. 1.5,363 **2.** $66\frac{2}{3}\%$ **3.** commutative property of addition **4.** $5(y+2)(y-2)$ **5.** $(x+10)(x+10)=(x+10)^2$ **6.** $(3y-4)(y+1)$ **7.** $\frac{11}{8}$ or $1\frac{3}{8}$ **8.** $\frac{1}{18}$

Exercise 6–3

1. $\frac{2x+9}{12}$ **2.** $\frac{13z}{30}$ **3.** $\frac{23}{6x}$ **5.** $\frac{11}{3}$ **6.** $\frac{9x+7}{(x-1)(x+3)}$ **7.** $\frac{15y-12}{(y+4)(y-5)}$ **9.** $\frac{9x+40}{x+8}$ **10.** $\frac{10y}{y-1}$ **11.** $\frac{10}{y-2}$ **13.** $\frac{7x+62}{4(x+2)(x-2)}$ **14.** $\frac{8y-19}{(y+3)(y-3)}$ **15.** $\frac{x(x+4)}{(x-1)(x+1)}$ **17.** $\frac{9x+22}{(x+2)(x-3)(x+3)}$ **18.** $\frac{11x+46}{(x-6)(x+2)(x+6)}$ **19.** $\frac{7y^2-13y}{(y-3)(y-3)(y+1)}$ **21.** $\frac{2y^2-9y+1}{(y-5)(y+2)(y-3)}$ **22.** $\frac{6x^2-10x-9}{(x+5)(x+1)(x-6)}$ **23.** $\frac{2y-15}{18}$ **25.** $\frac{25}{42y}$ **26.** $-\frac{19}{36z}$ **27.** $\frac{19a+39}{60}$ **29.** $\frac{4x+25}{18x}$ **30.** $\frac{18y-2}{15y}$ **31.** $\frac{-5x-17}{(2x-3)(x-5)}$ **33.** $\frac{17}{7(y+2)}$ **34.** $-\frac{6}{5(x-3)}$ **35.** $\frac{9x+66}{x+8}$ **37.** $\frac{-25x-9}{3x+1}$ **38.** $\frac{-46y+40}{5y-4}$ **39.** $\frac{-3(2a-1)}{(a-3)(a-2)(a+2)}$ **41.** $\frac{12(y-1)}{(y-6)(y+4)(y-3)}$ **42.** $\frac{-5p^2+24p-8}{(p-4)(p-5)}$ **43.** $\frac{-3a^2+11a-3}{(a-2)(a-3)}$ **45.** $\frac{6a(a-5)}{(a+5)(a-3)(2a+1)}$ **46.** $\frac{y^2+27y-20}{10(y+5)(y-5)}$ **47.** $\frac{bc+ac+ab}{abc}$ **49.** $\frac{3}{m}$ **50.** $\frac{9}{h}$ **51.** $\frac{h}{36}$ **53.** $\frac{48}{m}$ **54.** $\ell=\frac{54}{w}$ **55.** $w=\frac{A}{23}$ **57.** $b=\frac{2A}{9}$ **58.** $r=\frac{25}{h}$ **59.** $t=\frac{d}{55}$

Solutions to trial exercise problems

6. $\frac{4}{x-1}+\frac{5}{x+3}=\frac{4(x+3)+5(x-1)}{(x-1)(x+3)}=\frac{4x+12+5x-5}{(x-1)(x+3)}=\frac{9x+7}{(x-1)(x+3)}$ **9.** $5+\frac{4x}{x+8}=\frac{5(x+8)}{x+8}+\frac{4x}{x+8}$

$=\frac{5x+40}{x+8}+\frac{4x}{x+8}=\frac{5x+40+4x}{x+8}=\frac{9x+40}{x+8}$ **13.** $\frac{12}{x^2-4}+\frac{7}{4x-8}=\frac{12}{(x+2)(x-2)}+\frac{7}{4(x-2)}$

$=\frac{12\cdot4}{4(x+2)(x-2)}+\frac{7(x+2)}{4(x+2)(x-2)}=\frac{48+7x+14}{4(x+2)(x-2)}=\frac{7x+62}{4(x+2)(x-2)}$ **19.** $\frac{2y}{y^2-6y+9}+\frac{5y}{y^2-2y-3}$

$=\frac{2y}{(y-3)^2}+\frac{5y}{(y-3)(y+1)}=\frac{2y(y+1)}{(y-3)^2(y+1)}+\frac{5y(y-3)}{(y-3)^2(y+1)}=\frac{2y^2+2y+5y^2-15y}{(y-3)^2(y+1)}=\frac{7y^2-13y}{(y-3)^2(y+1)}$

25. $\frac{9}{14y}-\frac{1}{21y}=\frac{9\cdot3}{2\cdot3\cdot7\cdot y}-\frac{1\cdot2}{2\cdot3\cdot7\cdot y}=\frac{27}{42y}-\frac{2}{42y}=\frac{27-2}{42y}=\frac{25}{42y}$

27. $\frac{5a+3}{12}-\frac{a-4}{10}=\frac{5a+3}{12}\cdot\frac{5}{5}-\frac{a-4}{10}\cdot\frac{6}{6}=\frac{5(5a+3)}{60}-\frac{6(a-4)}{60}=\frac{(25a+15)-(6a-24)}{60}=\frac{25a+15-6a+24}{60}=\frac{19a+39}{60}$

37. $\frac{2x}{3x+1}-9=\frac{2x}{3x+1}-\frac{9(3x+1)}{3x+1}=\frac{2x-(27x+9)}{3x+1}=\frac{2x-27x-9}{3x+1}=\frac{-25x-9}{3x+1}$

42. $\frac{2p}{p^2-9p+20}-\frac{5p-2}{p-5}=\frac{2p}{(p-5)(p-4)}-\frac{5p-2}{p-5}=\frac{2p}{(p-5)(p-4)}-\frac{(5p-2)(p-4)}{(p-5)(p-4)}=\frac{2p-(5p^2-22p+8)}{(p-5)(p-4)}$

$=\frac{2p-5p^2+22p-8}{(p-5)(p-4)}=\frac{-5p^2+24p-8}{(p-5)(p-4)}$ **47.** $\frac{1}{a}+\frac{1}{b}+\frac{1}{c}=\frac{1}{a}\cdot\frac{bc}{bc}+\frac{1}{b}\cdot\frac{ac}{ac}+\frac{1}{c}\cdot\frac{ab}{ab}=\frac{bc}{abc}+\frac{ac}{abc}+\frac{ab}{abc}=\frac{bc+ac+ab}{abc}$

53. Let n be the number.

$m \cdot n = 48$

$n = \frac{48}{m}$

57. Using $A = \frac{1}{2}bh$ and $h = 9$ rods,

$A = \frac{1}{2} \cdot b \cdot 9$

$2A = 9b$

$b = \frac{2A}{9}$

Review exercises

1. $(x - 7)^2$ **2.** $(2x - 1)(x - 5)$ **3.** $4(x + 2)(x - 2)$ **4.** $x^2 - 81$ **5.** $16x^2 + 24x + 9$ **6.** $2x^2 - 15x - 8$ **7.** 48 **8.** $12x^2$ **9.** $(x - 3)^2(x + 3)$ **10.** $\frac{13}{2x}$ **11.** $\frac{2x + 1}{(x - 2)(x - 1)}$

Exercise 6–4

1. $\frac{5}{6}$ **2.** $\frac{21}{20}$ **3.** $\frac{3}{2}$ **5.** $\frac{8}{9}$ **6.** $\frac{34}{13}$ **7.** $\frac{5}{2}$ **9.** $\frac{23}{30}$ **10.** $\frac{73}{24}$ **11.** -1 **13.** $\frac{4x + 1}{4x - 3}$ **14.** $\frac{6y - 5}{6y + 3}$ **15.** $\frac{1 + 3a}{2 - 4a}$ **17.** $\frac{3 + 4a^2}{5a^2 - 3a}$ **18.** $\frac{5x^2 - 5x^3}{6x^3 + 4}$ **19.** $\frac{ab - 3}{ab + 4}$ **21.** $\frac{y + x}{y - x}$ **22.** $\frac{3y^2 - 4x^2y}{5xy^2 + 2x^2}$ **23.** xy **25.** $\frac{xy}{y - x}$ **26.** $\frac{-xy}{x + y}$ **27.** $\frac{ab}{2a - b}$ **29.** $\frac{y - x}{x^2y^2}$ **30.** $-\frac{y}{x}$ **31.** $\frac{-(a^2 + b^2)}{(a^2 - b^2)^2}$ **33.** $\frac{5 - 4xy}{x^3y^3}$ **34.** $\frac{2b + 3}{a^3b^4}$ **35.** $\frac{2x + 41}{14x + 7}$ **37.** $\frac{15b - 91}{6}$ **38.** $\frac{-5}{x + 31}$ or $\frac{5}{-x - 31}$ **39.** $\frac{7x^2 - 8x - 87}{-x + 69}$ **41.** $\frac{T_1}{T_2 - T_1}$ **42.** $\frac{(L_1 - M)(L_2 + M)}{L_2 + L_1}$

Solutions to trial exercise problems

7. $$\frac{7}{2 + \frac{4}{5}} = \frac{7 \cdot 5}{\left(2 + \frac{4}{5}\right) \cdot 5} = \frac{7 \cdot 5}{2 \cdot 5 + \frac{4}{5} \cdot 5} = \frac{35}{10 + 4} = \frac{35}{14} = \frac{5}{2}$$

11. $$\frac{\frac{6}{7} - \frac{5}{14}}{\frac{3}{14} - \frac{5}{7}} = \frac{\left(\frac{6}{7} - \frac{5}{14}\right) \cdot 14}{\left(\frac{3}{14} - \frac{5}{7}\right) \cdot 14} = \frac{\frac{6}{7} \cdot 14 - \frac{5}{14} \cdot 14}{\frac{3}{14} \cdot 14 - \frac{5}{7} \cdot 14} = \frac{12 - 5}{3 - 10} = \frac{7}{-7} = -1$$

15. $$\frac{\frac{1}{a} + 3}{\frac{2}{a} - 4} = \frac{\left(\frac{1}{a} + 3\right) \cdot a}{\left(\frac{2}{a} - 4\right) \cdot a} = \frac{\frac{1}{a} \cdot a + 3 \cdot a}{\frac{2}{a} \cdot a - 4 \cdot a} = \frac{1 + 3a}{2 - 4a}$$

22. $$\frac{\frac{3}{x^2} - \frac{4}{y}}{\frac{5}{x} + \frac{2}{y^2}} = \frac{\left(\frac{3}{x^2} - \frac{4}{y}\right) \cdot x^2y^2}{\left(\frac{5}{x} + \frac{2}{y^2}\right) \cdot x^2y^2} = \frac{\frac{3}{x^2} \cdot x^2y^2 - \frac{4}{y} \cdot x^2y^2}{\frac{5}{x} \cdot x^2y^2 + \frac{2}{y^2} \cdot x^2y^2} = \frac{3y^2 - 4x^2y}{5xy^2 + 2x^2}$$

30. $$\frac{\frac{1}{x + y} - \frac{1}{x - y}}{\frac{1}{x + y} + \frac{1}{x - y}} = \frac{\left(\frac{1}{x + y} - \frac{1}{x - y}\right) \cdot (x + y)(x - y)}{\left(\frac{1}{x + y} + \frac{1}{x - y}\right) \cdot (x + y)(x - y)} = \frac{\frac{1}{x + y} \cdot (x + y)(x - y) - \frac{1}{x - y} \cdot (x + y)(x - y)}{\frac{1}{x + y} \cdot (x + y)(x - y) + \frac{1}{x - y} \cdot (x + y)(x - y)}$$
$$= \frac{(x - y) - (x + y)}{(x - y) + (x + y)} = \frac{x - y - x - y}{x - y + x + y} = \frac{-2y}{2x} = \frac{-y}{x}$$

37. $$\frac{\frac{7}{b - 7} + \frac{8}{b - 5}}{\frac{6}{b^2 - 12b + 35}} = \frac{\left(\frac{7}{b - 7} + \frac{8}{b - 5}\right) \cdot (b - 5)(b - 7)}{\frac{6}{(b - 5)(b - 7)} \cdot (b - 5)(b - 7)}$$ The LCM is $(b - 5)(b - 7)$.
$$= \frac{\frac{7}{b - 7} \cdot (b - 5)(b - 7) + \frac{8}{b - 5} \cdot (b - 5)(b - 7)}{6} = \frac{7(b - 5) + 8(b - 7)}{6} = \frac{7b - 35 + 8b - 56}{6} = \frac{15b - 91}{6}$$

Review exercises

1. $\frac{6}{7}$ **2.** $\frac{x - 7}{x + 2}$ **3.** $2x^3 + 3x^2 + x - 21$ **4.** $x = 3$ **5.** $y = -2$ **6.** $x = -3, x = 1$ **7.** All real numbers except -7 **8.** All real numbers except $-2, 2$

Exercise 6-5

1. $y = 4$ **2.** $x = \frac{20}{3}$ **3.** $x = 35$ **5.** $a = \frac{10}{9}$ **6.** $x = 8$ **7.** $x = 11$ **9.** $x = -\frac{5}{8}, (x \neq 0)$ **10.** $b = -3, (b \neq 0)$ **11.** $y = -\frac{5}{27}, (y \neq 0)$ **13.** $b = 1, (b \neq 0)$ **14.** $x = \frac{11}{27}, (x \neq 0)$ **15.** $a = \frac{11}{5}, (a \neq 0)$ **17.** $x = 36, (x \neq -4,4)$ **18.** $x = \frac{15}{26}, \left(x \neq -\frac{1}{2}, 3\right)$ **19.** no solution, $(x \neq 3)$ **21.** $b = -\frac{13}{7}, (b \neq -2,2)$ **22.** $x = 18, (x \neq -3,3)$ **23.** $a = 40, (a \neq -5,5)$ **25.** $x = -\frac{19}{3}, (x \neq -5,-3,2)$ **26.** $a = -\frac{34}{7}, (a \neq -4,2,4)$ **27.** $x = -\frac{2}{3}$ **29.** $b = -3, b = \frac{3}{2}$ **30.** $x = -4, x = \frac{2}{5}$ **31.** $x = -\frac{1}{2}, x = \frac{4}{3}$ **33.** $x = \frac{2y}{3y-1}$ **34.** $I = \frac{5E}{8+6E}$ **35.** $c_1 = \frac{cc_2}{c_2 - c}$ **37.** $a = \frac{8b}{b-8}$ **38.** $a = \frac{3b-5}{4}$ **39.** $r = \frac{I}{pt}$ **41.** $s = \frac{pD}{2t}$ **42.** $f = \frac{Fa}{A}$ **43.** $L_t = kL_0t + L_0, L_0 = \frac{L_t}{kt+1}$ **45.** $R_1 = \frac{RR_2}{R_2 - R}$ **46.** $T_1 = \frac{T_2}{1-E}$

Solutions to trial exercise problems

3. $\frac{x}{6} - 5 = \frac{5}{6}$ Multiply by 6 to get

The LCM is 6.

$$\frac{x}{6}\cdot 6 - 5\cdot 6 = \frac{5}{6}\cdot 6$$
$$x\cdot 1 - 30 = 5\cdot 1$$
$$x - 30 = 5$$
$$x = 35$$

11. $\frac{4}{6y} + 5 = \frac{1}{9y} + 2$ Multiply by $18y$ to get

The LCM is $18y$.

$$\frac{4}{6y}\cdot 18y + 5\cdot 18y = \frac{1}{9y}\cdot 18y + 2\cdot 18y$$
$$4\cdot 3 + 90y = 1\cdot 2 + 36y$$
$$12 + 90y = 2 + 36y$$
$$90y = -10 + 36y$$
$$54y = -10$$
$$y = \frac{-10}{54} = \frac{-5}{27}, (y \neq 0)$$

23. $\frac{5}{a^2 - 25} + \frac{3}{a-5} = \frac{4}{a+5}$

Multiply each term by $(a+5)(a-5)$.

$$5 + 3(a+5) = 4(a-5)$$
$$5 + 3a + 15 = 4a - 20$$
$$3a + 20 = 4a - 20$$
$$a = 40, (a \neq -5,5)$$

27. $3x^2 + 4x + \frac{4}{3} = 0$ Multiply by 3 to obtain

$9x^2 + 12x + 4 = 0$ Factor the left member.

$$(3x+2)^2 = 0$$
$$3x + 2 = 0$$
$$3x = -2$$
$$x = -\frac{2}{3}$$

35. $$\frac{1}{c} = \frac{1}{c_1} + \frac{1}{c_2}$$

$\frac{1}{c}\cdot cc_1c_2 = \frac{1}{c_1}\cdot cc_1c_2 + \frac{1}{c_2}\cdot cc_1c_2$ Multiply by cc_1c_2.

$c_1c_2 = cc_2 + cc_1$ Reduce in each item

$c_1c_2 - cc_1 = cc_2$ Add $-cc_1$ to both members.

$(c_2 - c)c_1 = cc_2$ Factor c_1 in the left member.

$c_1 = \frac{cc_2}{c_2 - c}$ Divide both members by $c_2 - c$.

43. Given $k = \frac{L_t - L_0}{L_0t}$. Multiply both members by L_0t to get $kL_0t = L_t - L_0$.

a. To find L_t, add L_0 to both members to get $L_t = kL_0t + L_0$.

b. To find L_0, use $L_t = kL_0t + L_0$, factor L_0 in the right member to get $L_t = (kt+1)L_0$. Divide both members by $kt + 1$.

Then $\frac{L_t}{kt+1} = L_0$ or $L_0 = \frac{L_t}{kt+1}$.

Review exercises

1. 14 **2.** $\frac{17}{3}$ **3.** 4 **4.** $y = -5x + 4$ **5.** $y = \frac{6-2x}{3}$ **6.** $y = \frac{x-8}{4}$ **7.** $\frac{3y}{x^2}$ **8.** $\frac{y^4}{x^5}$

Exercise 6-6

1. $29\frac{1}{6}$ min **2.** $2\frac{8}{11}$ hr **3.** $2\frac{14}{29}$ hr **5.** Dick takes 12 hr **6.** smaller pipe takes 90 min **7.** $3\frac{1}{3}$ hr **9.** 10 hr **10.** $2\frac{2}{29}$ min **11.** 110 mi at 55 mph, 210 mi at 60 mph **13.** car B at 50 mph, car A at 40 mph **14.** 65 mph **15.** $\frac{6}{7}$ mph **17.** 220 mi **18.** 2,000 mi **19.** $\frac{5}{9}$ **21.** 3, 12 **22.** 5, 20 **23.** 6 **25.** 4 **26.** $\frac{1}{11}$ **27.** $3\frac{3}{7}$ ohms **29.** $1\frac{29}{31}$ ohms **30.** 20 ohms **31.** 15 ohms

Solutions to trial exercise problems

1. Let x = the number of minutes required for both boys to mow the lawn. Then, since 1 hour 10 minutes = 70 minutes,

$$\frac{1}{50} + \frac{1}{70} = \frac{1}{x}.$$

Multiply by the LCM of 50, 70, and x, that is, $350x$.

$$350x \cdot \frac{1}{50} + 350x \cdot \frac{1}{70} = 350x \cdot \frac{1}{x}$$
$$7x + 5x = 350$$
$$12x = 350$$
$$x = \frac{350}{12} = 29\frac{1}{6}$$

Together Jim and Kenny could mow the lawn in $29\frac{1}{6}$ minutes.

13. Let x = the average speed of car A.
Then $x + 10$ = the average speed of car B.
Using $t = \frac{d}{r}$, let t_s = time of car A, t_f = time of car B,
then $t_A = t_B$.
Now $t_A = \frac{120}{x}$ and $t_B = \frac{150}{x + 10}$, so

$$\frac{120}{x} = \frac{150}{x + 10}.$$

Multiply both members by the LCM of x and $x + 10$, that is, $x(x + 10)$.

$$x(x + 10) \cdot \frac{120}{x} = x(x + 10) \cdot \frac{150}{x + 10}$$
$$(x + 10)120 = 150x$$
$$120x + 1{,}200 = 150x$$
$$1{,}200 = 30x$$
$$40 = x$$

So $x + 10 = 50$. Therefore car B averaged 50 mph and car A averaged 40 mph.

27. Let R = the total resistance of the circuit. Then

$$\frac{1}{6} + \frac{1}{8} = \frac{1}{R}.$$

Multiply by the LCM of 6, 8, and R, that is, $24R$.

$$24R \cdot \frac{1}{6} + 24R \cdot \frac{1}{8} = 24R \cdot \frac{1}{R}$$
$$4R + 3R = 24$$
$$7R = 24$$
$$R = \frac{24}{7}$$

Therefore the total resistance in the parallel circuit is $\frac{24}{7}$ or $3\frac{3}{7}$ ohms.

5. Let x = the time required for Dick to paint the house alone.
Then $\frac{1}{6} + \frac{1}{x} = \frac{1}{4}$.
Multiply both members by the LCM of 4, 6, and x, that is, $12x$.

$$12x \cdot \frac{1}{6} + 12x \cdot \frac{1}{x} = 12x \cdot \frac{1}{4}$$
$$2x + 12 = 3x$$
$$12 = x$$

Therefore Dick would take 12 hours to paint the house alone.

21. Let x = the lesser of the two numbers then
$4x$ = the greater of the two numbers.
Their reciprocals are then $\frac{1}{x}$ and $\frac{1}{4x}$ and we get the equation

$$\frac{1}{x} + \frac{1}{4x} = \frac{5}{12}.$$

Multiply both members by the LCM of x, $4x$, and 12, that is, $12x$.

$$12x \cdot \frac{1}{x} + 12x \cdot \frac{1}{4x} = 12x \cdot \frac{5}{12}$$
$$12 + 3 = 5x$$
$$15 = 5x$$

then
$$x = 3$$
$$4x = 12$$

Therefore the two numbers are 3 and 12.

(*Note:* To check, show $\frac{1}{3} + \frac{1}{12} = \frac{5}{12}$

$$\frac{4}{12} + \frac{1}{12} = \frac{5}{12}$$
$$\frac{5}{12} = \frac{5}{12}\Big)$$

30. Let R_1 = the resistance in the unknown branch.
Then $\frac{1}{R_1} + \frac{1}{30} = \frac{1}{12}$.
Multiply by the LCM of R_1, 12, and 30, that is, $60R_1$.

$$60R_1 \cdot \frac{1}{R_1} + 60R_1 \cdot \frac{1}{30} = 60R_1 \cdot \frac{1}{12}$$
$$60 + 2R_1 = 5R_1$$
$$60 = 3R_1$$
$$20 = R_1.$$

Therefore the other branch has resistance of 20 ohms.

Review exercises

1. $y = 2$ **2.** $y = \frac{3x + 6}{2}$ **3.** $8(y + 2)(y - 2)$ **4.** $(x + 10)(x + 10) = (x + 10)^2$ **5.** $(3y + 2)(y - 2)$ **6.** $\frac{5x^2 + 7x}{(x - 1)(x + 3)}$
7. $\frac{-2y^2 - 23y}{(2y + 1)(y - 5)}$

Chapter 6 review

1. $\frac{9a}{b}$ **2.** $x - 2$ **3.** $\frac{1}{(y - 1)^2}$ **4.** $\frac{-1}{3(x + 5)}$ **5.** $\frac{2a}{3}$ **6.** $\frac{9}{2ab}$ **7.** $\frac{1}{(x - 2)(x + 6)}$ **8.** $\frac{1}{x - 8}$ **9.** $\frac{3(a + 1)}{4(a - 1)}$ **10.** $\frac{15ab}{42a^2b^2}, \frac{16}{42a^2b^2}$
11. $\frac{4y^2 + 20y}{(y + 3)(y - 5)(y + 5)}, \frac{9y^2 + 27y}{(y + 3)(y - 5)(y + 5)}$ **12.** $\frac{(2x - 1)(x + 1)(3x - 5)}{x(x + 1)^2(3x - 5)}, \frac{x(x + 3)(3x - 5)}{x(x + 1)^2(3x - 5)}, \frac{x^2(x + 1)}{x(x + 1)^2(3x - 5)}$
13. $\frac{23}{48a}$ **14.** $\frac{47x - 6}{(3x + 1)(4x - 3)}$ **15.** $\frac{80a + 48b - 15ab}{20a^2b^2}$ **16.** $\frac{-10x^2 - 3}{x^2 + 1}$ **17.** $\frac{13y^2 - 89y}{(y - 9)(y + 2)(y - 2)}$ **18.** $\frac{4(2x^2 - 10x - 45)}{x(x - 5)(x + 4)}$
19. $\frac{16}{63}$ **20.** 1 **21.** $\frac{4 + 3x}{2 - 5x}$ **22.** $y - x$ **23.** $\frac{a^3 - 2a^2b^2 - 3ab^2}{ab - 3b^2}$ **24.** $x = -96$ **25.** $a = \frac{13}{24}$ **26.** $y = -\frac{39}{14}$ **27.** $x = 0, x = 12$

28. $x = -5, x = 3$ **29.** $x = \frac{a+b}{3}$ **30.** $y = \frac{4a-3b}{a}$ **31.** $L = \frac{Wp-2E}{EF}$ **32.** $m = \frac{rF}{V^2+rg}$ **33.** $5\frac{1}{3}$ hr, 16 hr **34.** $1\frac{5}{7}$ mph

35. $\frac{2}{3}$ or 1

Chapter 6 cumulative test

1. $-5\frac{1}{12}$ **2.** $\frac{3}{4}$ **3.** $\frac{43}{30}$ **4.** $\frac{8}{5}$ **5.** x^{11} **6.** $\frac{1}{y^9}$ **7.** $\frac{25x^4}{y^6}$ **8.** $10x^3 - 4x^2 + 11x - 9$ **9.** $x = -\frac{26}{7}$ **10.** $x = \frac{81}{4}$ **11.** $y = -\frac{3}{2}$, $y = 2$ **12.** $2(x+3)(x-3)$ **13.** $3x^2(2x^3 - 12x + 3)$ **14.** $(2x+5)(2x+3)$ **15.** $3(1+2x^3)(1-2x^3)$ **16.** $49x^2 - 84x + 36$ **17.** $25 - \frac{1}{4}x^2$ **18.** $6x^3 - 19x^2 + 37x - 33$ **19.** $8x^4 - 22x^2 + 15$ **20.** $x = 20$ **21.** $2{,}400\,\frac{\text{ft-lb}}{\text{min}}$ **22.** $\frac{4a^2}{5b^2}$ **23.** $\frac{y^2+10y+21}{y^2-8y+12}$ **24.** $y^2 - 5y + 6$ **25.** $\frac{(x-y)(x-1)}{y}$ **26.** $\frac{2y+4x}{x^2y^2}$ **27.** $\frac{3x+9y}{(x-y)(x+y)}$ **28.** $\frac{9}{a-2}$ **29.** $\frac{13x+56}{(x+7)(x-7)(x+2)}$ **30.** $\frac{-x(x+6)}{(x+3)(x-2)(x-6)}$ **31.** $\frac{3y-1}{4y+5}$ **32.** $\frac{y+x}{3x-4y}$ **33.** $\frac{x^2-11x+28}{x+5}$ **34.** $x = 2$ **35.** $x = -\frac{1}{3}, x = 6$ **36.** $q = \frac{fp}{p-f}$ **37.** $2\frac{2}{5}$ days **38.** $\frac{8}{17}$

Chapter 7

Proficiency check

1. a. $y = -4x + 5$ **b.** $y = \frac{3x+4}{2}$ **c.** $y = -\frac{-x-9}{3}$ **2. a.** $y = 10$ **b.** $y = -8$ **c.** $y = 4$ **3.** $y = -10$ **4.** $x = -1$

Exercise 7-1

1. yes, yes, no **2.** no, yes, yes **3.** no, yes, yes **5.** yes, no, no **6.** yes, yes, no **7.** yes, no, yes **9.** yes, no, yes **10.** yes, no, yes **11.** no, yes, yes **13.** (1,5), (−2,−4), (0,2) **14.** (−1,−7), (2,5), (0,−3) **15.** (3,−5), (−2,10), (0,4) **17.** (1,−4), (−1,1), $\left(0,-\frac{3}{2}\right)$ **18.** $\left(\frac{1}{4},-\frac{1}{6}\right)$, (−4,−3), $\left(0,-\frac{1}{3}\right)$ **19.** (1,5), (−6,5), (0,5) **21.** (4,−1), (−5,2), (1,0) **22.** (3,2), (−6,−4), (0,0) **23.** (−7,−1), (−7,3), (−7,0) **25.** (−2,3), (2,−7), $\left(-\frac{4}{5},0\right)$ **26. a.** (205,430) **b.** (340,700) **c.** (690,1400) **27. a.** (2,236) **b.** (12,216) **c.** (0,240) **29. a.** (2,26) **b.** (1,23) **c.** (4,32) **30. a.** (0,20) **b.** (5,35) **c.** (3,29) **31. a.** (3,165) **b.** (8,440) **c.** $\left(\frac{26}{5},286\right)$ **33.** III **34.** IV **35.** I **37.** II **38.** IV **39.** III **41.** (0,4), (−4,0), (−2,2), (2,6) **42.** (0,1), $\left(-\frac{1}{2},0\right)$, (2,5), (−1,−1)

43. (0,−4), (−1,−7), $\left(-\frac{1}{3},-5\right)$, (2,2) **45.** (0,3), (−3,6), (3,0), $\left(\frac{5}{2},\frac{1}{2}\right)$ **46.** (0,3), (3,−3), (−2,7), $\left(\frac{3}{2},0\right)$

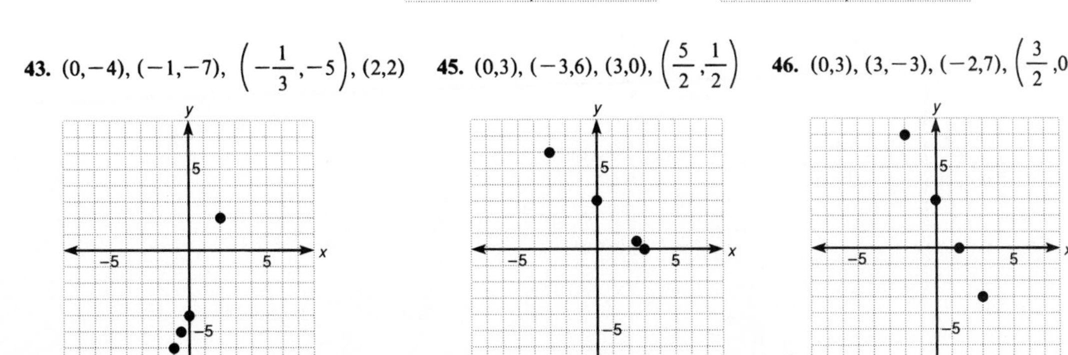

47. (0,4), (−3,7), (2,2), (3,1) **49.** 0 **50.** II **51.** 0

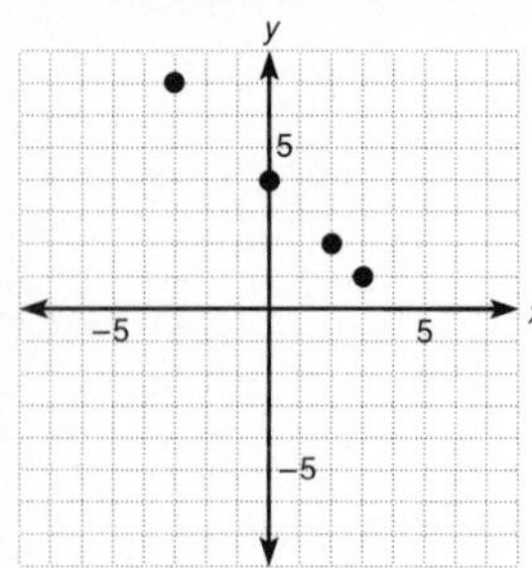

Solutions to trial exercise problems

1. $y = 3x - 1$; (1,2), (−1,−4), (2,3)
Solution:

a. (1,2)	**b.** (−1,−4)	**c.** (2,3)
$2 = 3(1) - 1$	$-4 = 3(-1) - 1$	$3 = 3(2) - 1$
$2 = 3 - 1$	$-4 = -3 - 1$	$3 = 6 - 1$
$2 = 2$ (true)	$-4 = -4$ (true)	$3 = 5$ (false)

Therefore (1,2) and (−1,−4) are solutions and (2,3) is not a solution.

9. $x = -4$; (−4,1), (4,2), (−4,−4)
Solution:
Since we can write $x = -4$ as $x = 0 \cdot y - 4$, then $x = -4$ for *any* value of y. Therefore (−4,1) and (−4,−4) are solutions but (4,2) is not since, substituting 4 for x, $4 = -4$ is false.

19. $y = 5$; $x = 1$, $x = -6$, $x = 0$
Solution:
We write $y = 5$ as $y = 0 \cdot x + 5$, so for *every* value of x, $y = 5$. Therefore (1,5), (−6,5), (0,5).

21. $x = -3y + 1$; $y = -1$, $y = 2$, $y = 0$
Solution:
When $y = -1$, $x = -3(-1) + 1 = 3 + 1 = 4$ (4,−1)
When $y = 2$, $x = -3(2) + 1 = -6 + 1 = -5$ (−5,2)
When $y = 0$, $x = -3(0) + 1 = 0 + 1 = 1$ (1,0)

26. Given $c = 2x + 20$, when

a. $c = 430$, then $(430) = 2x + 20$	**b.** $c = 700$, then $(700) = 2x + 20$	**c.** $c = 1{,}400$, then $(1{,}400) = 2x + 20$
$410 = 2x$	$680 = 2x$	$1{,}380 = 2x$
$x = 205$	$x = 340$	$x = 690$
(205,430)	(340,700)	(690,1400)

41. When $x = 0$, $y = 0 + 4 = 4$ (0,4)
When $x = -4$, $y = -4 + 4 = 0$ (−4,0)
When $x = -2$, $y = -2 + 4 = 2$ (−2,2)
When $x = 2$, $y = 2 + 4 = 6$ (2,6)

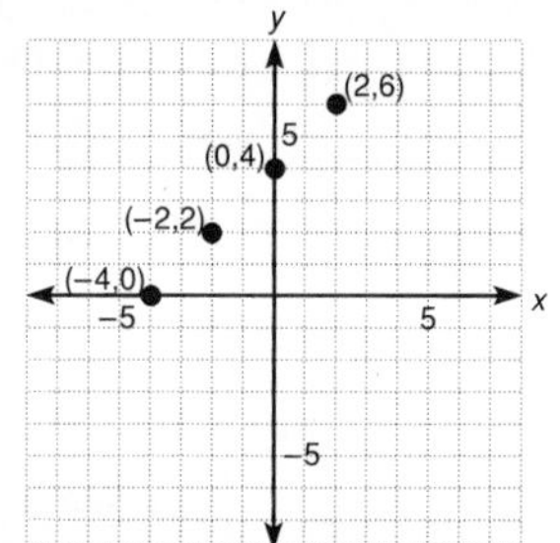

Review exercises

1. $2x(x + 2)$ **2.** $\frac{x + 3}{2x + 1}$ **3.** $\frac{x + 10}{(x - 2)(x + 1)}$ **4.** −8 **5.** x^3 **6.** 0

Exercise 7–2

1. (−1,−1), (−2,−3), (1,3) **2.** (0,3), (−1,2), (−4,−1) **3.** (3,0), (0,2), (−3,4)

5.
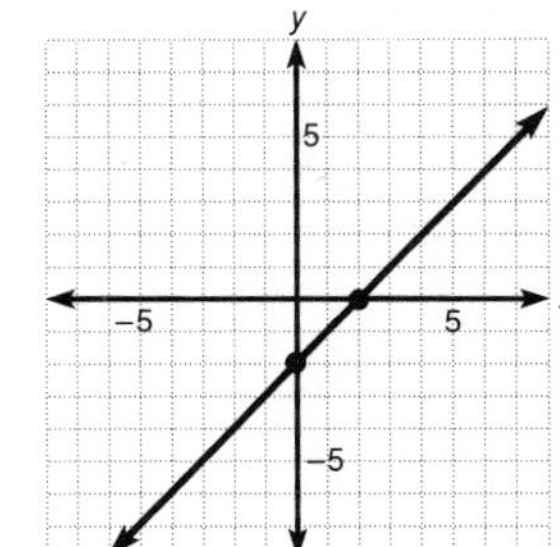

6.
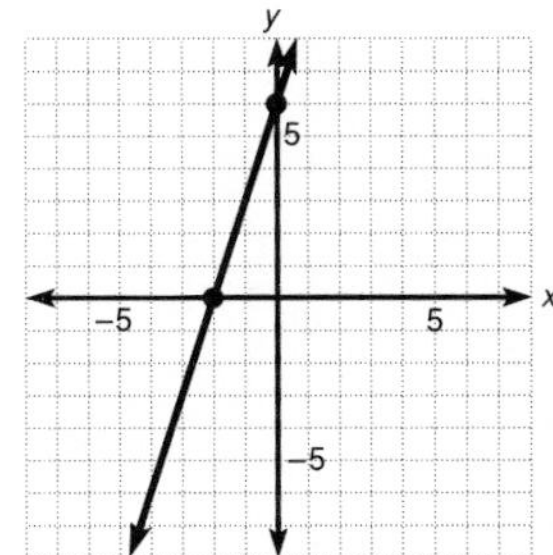

7.
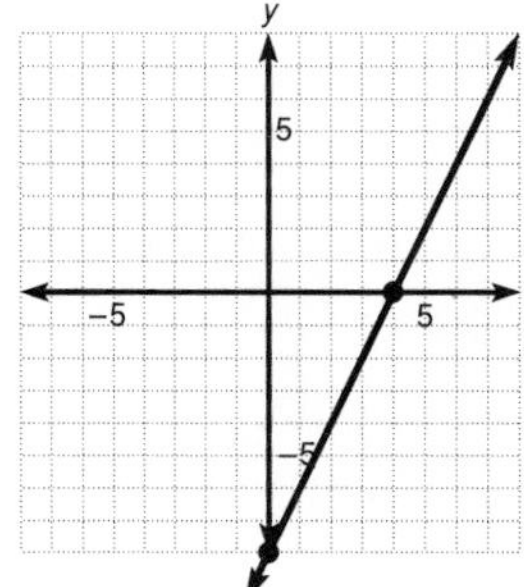

9.
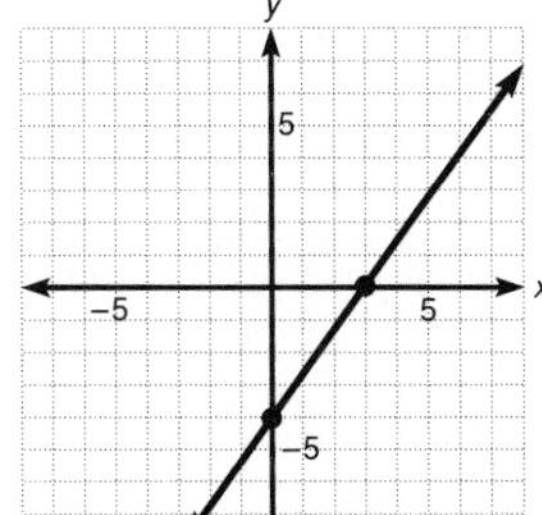

10.
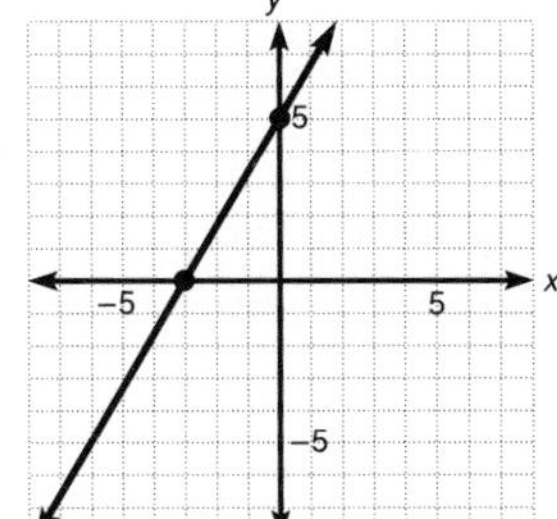

11.
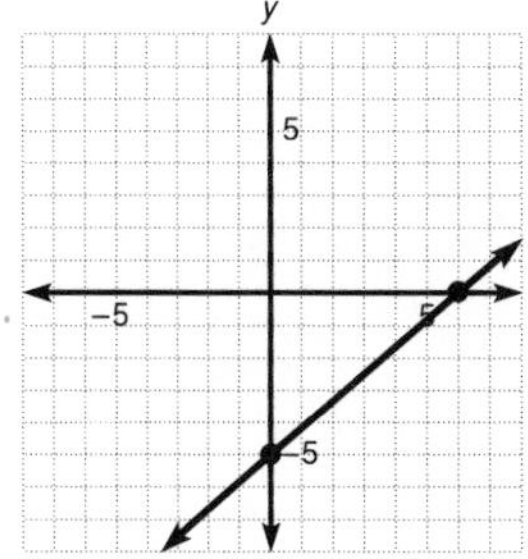

13.
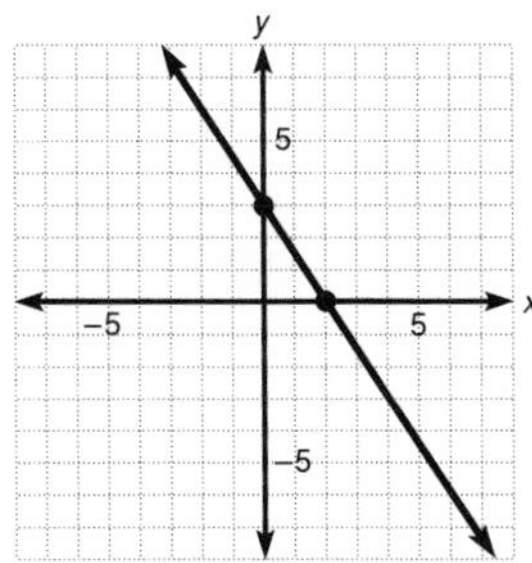

14.
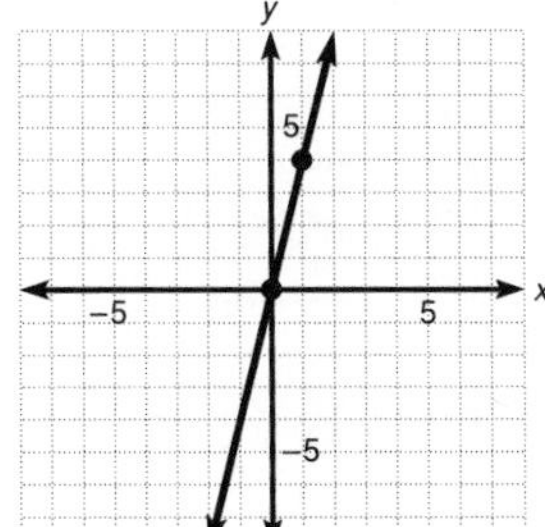

15.
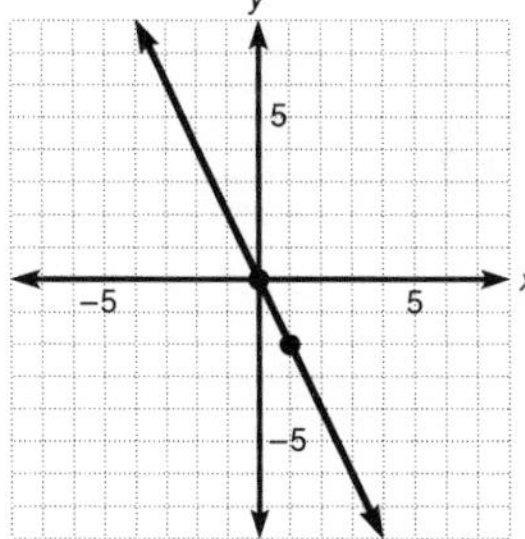

17.
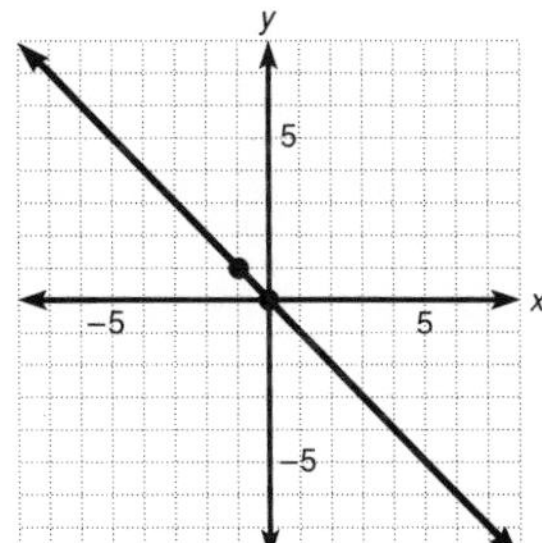

18.
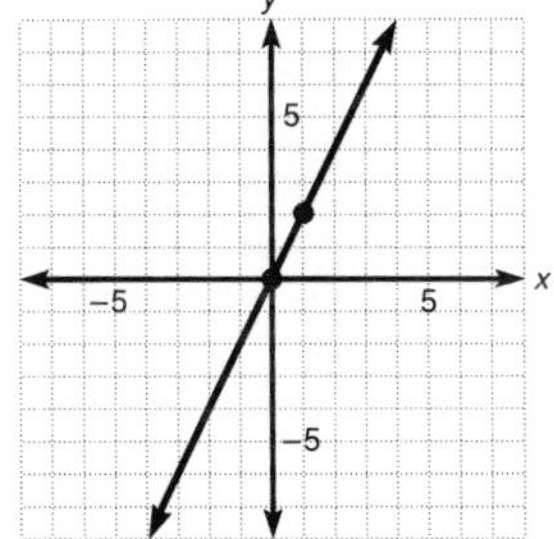

19.
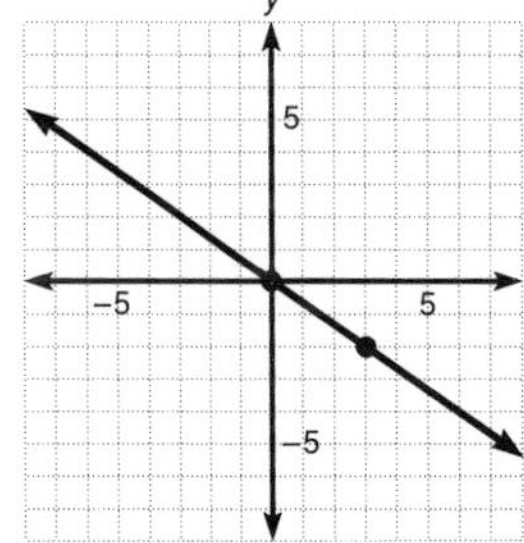

21.
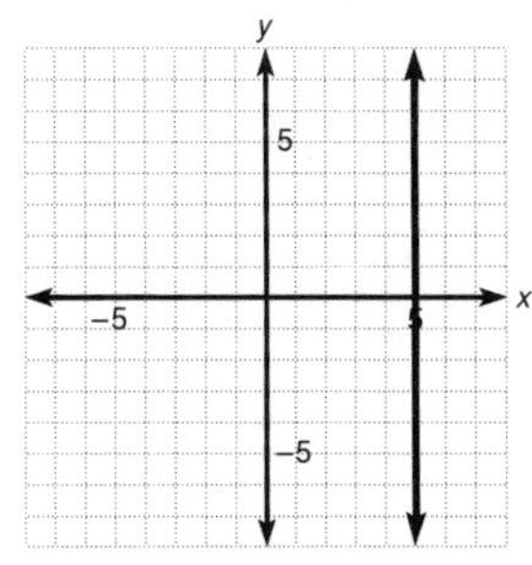

22.
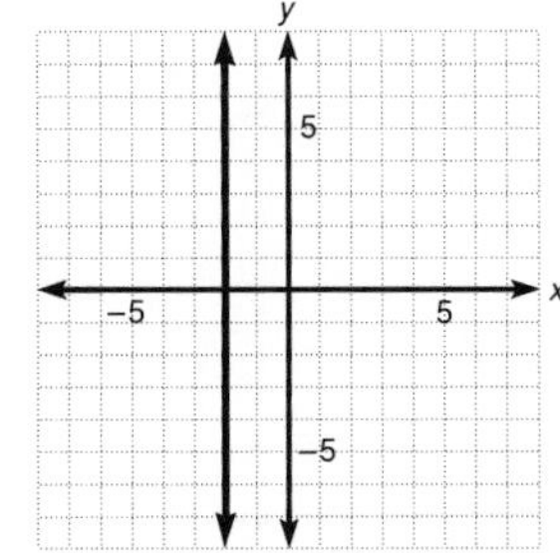

23.
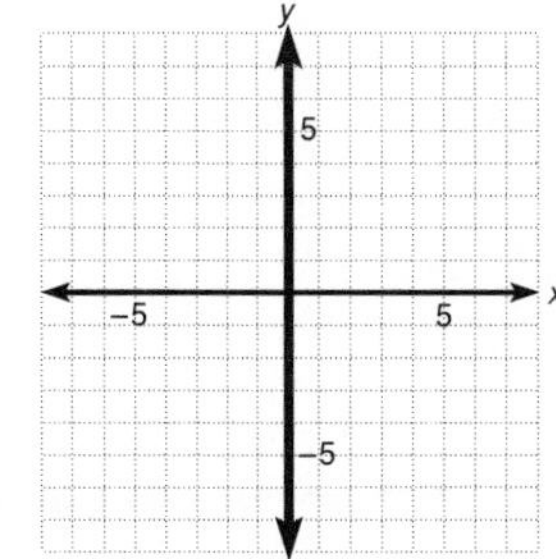

25.

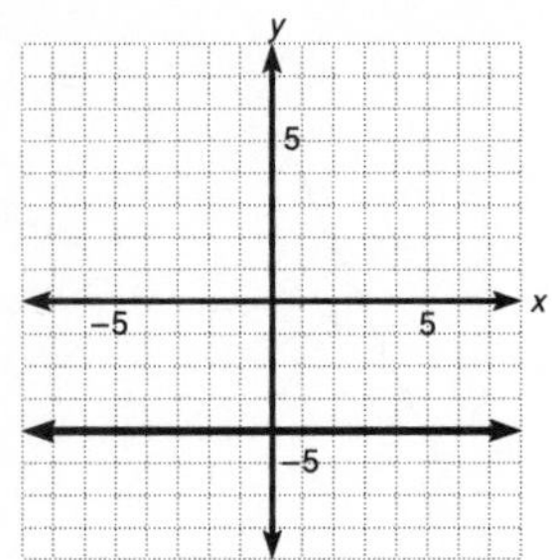

26.

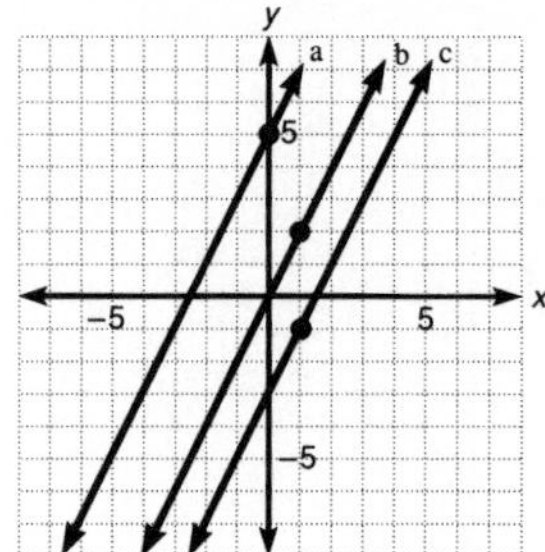

27.

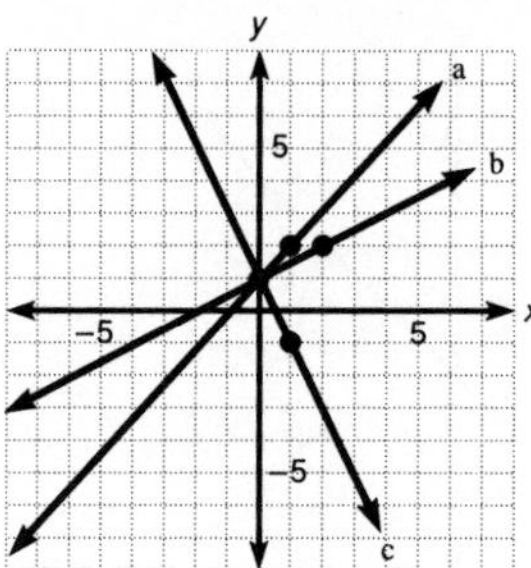

29.

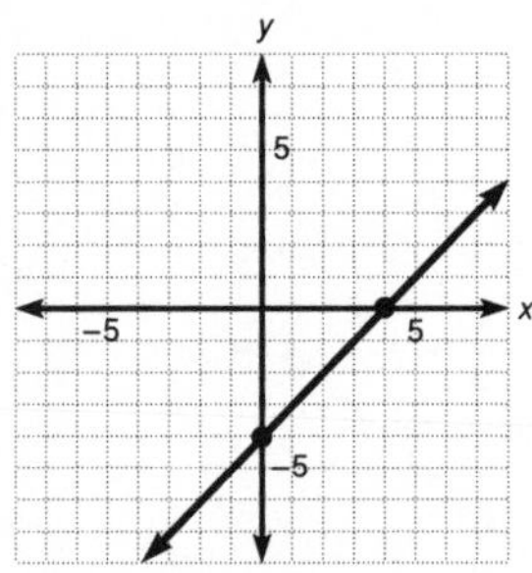

$x = y + 4$

30.

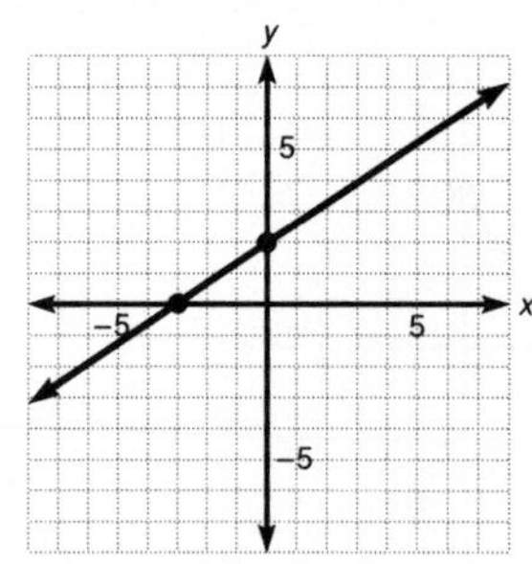

$3y - 2x = 6$

31.

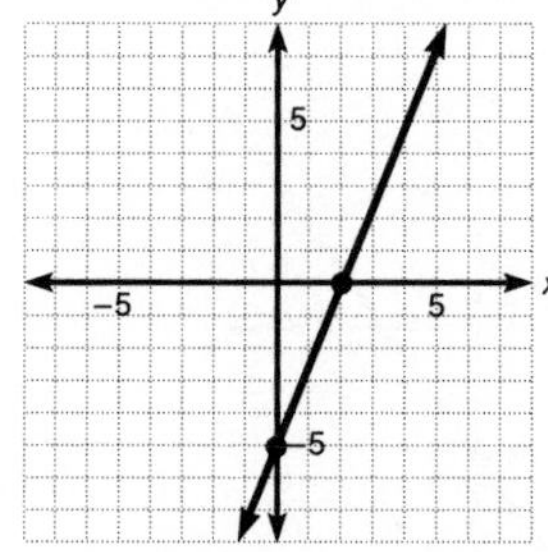

$5x - 2y = 10$

33.

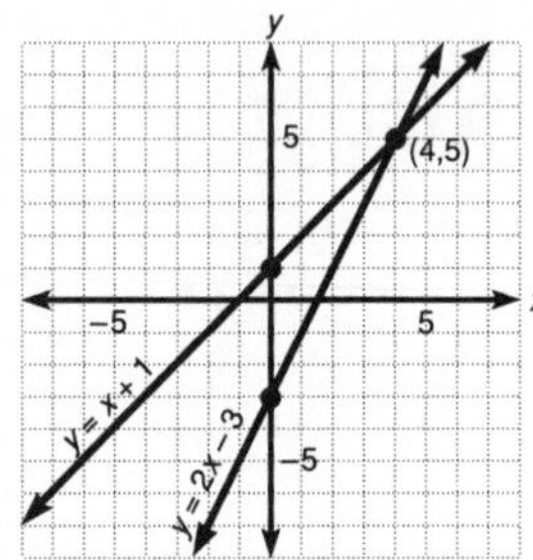

34.

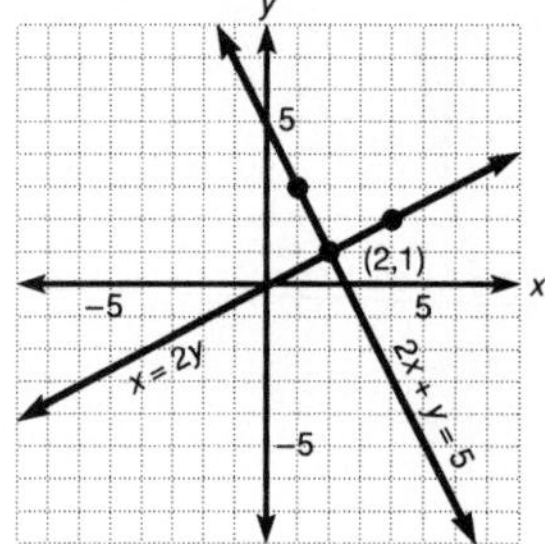

Solutions to trial exercise problems

6. $y = 3x + 6$

x	y	
0	6	y-intercept
−2	0	x-intercept
−1	3	checkpoint

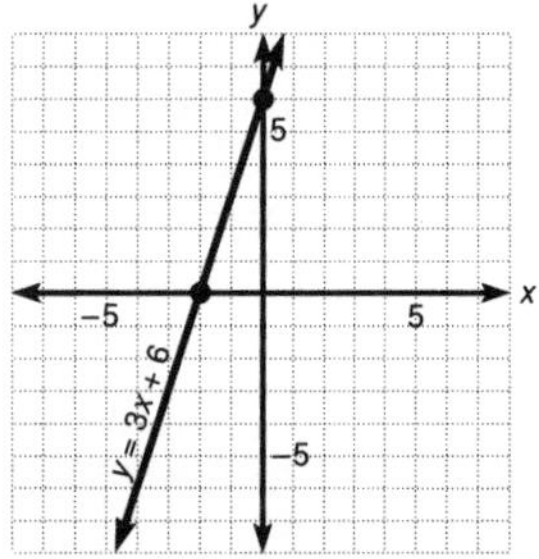

9. $4x - 3y = 12$

x	y	
0	−4	y-intercept
3	0	x-intercept
1	$\frac{-8}{3}$	checkpoint

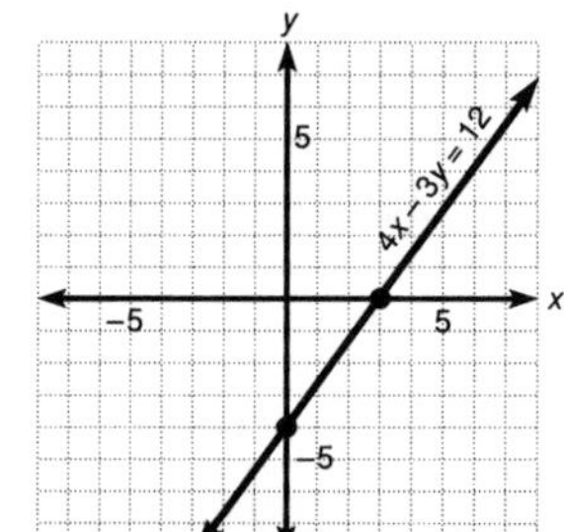

29. $x = y + 4$

x	y	
0	−4	y-intercept
4	0	x-intercept
1	−3	checkpoint

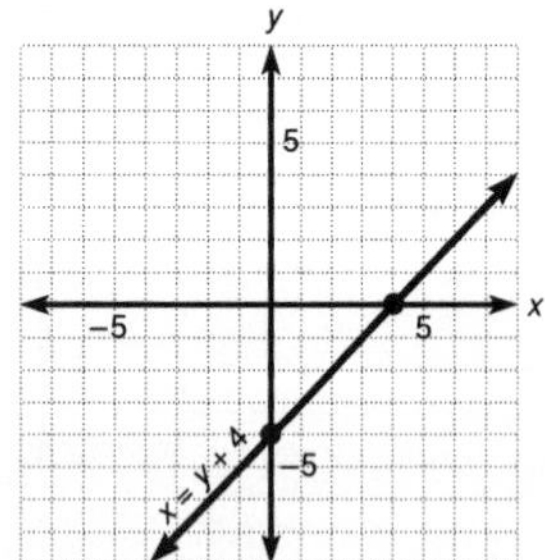

Review exercises

1. $\frac{6}{5}$ **2.** $\frac{1}{x + 4}$ **3.** $\frac{x - 4}{x + 5}$ **4.** $-\frac{1}{5}$ **5.** $y = -3x + 6$ **6.** -4 or 4

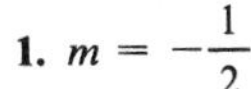

Exercise 7–3

1. $m = -\frac{1}{2}$ **2.** $m = \frac{1}{6}$ **3.** $m = \frac{2}{3}$

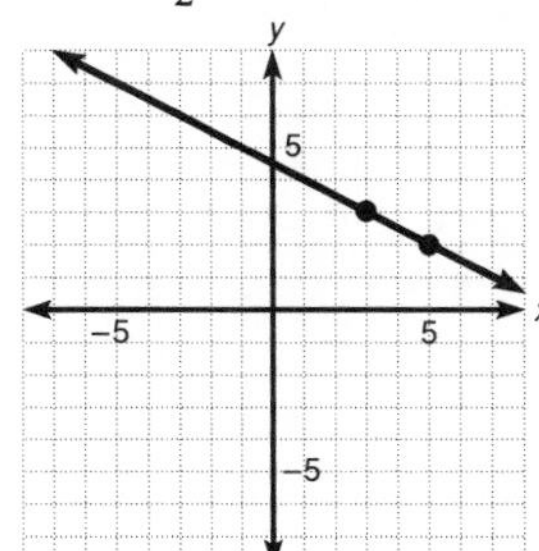

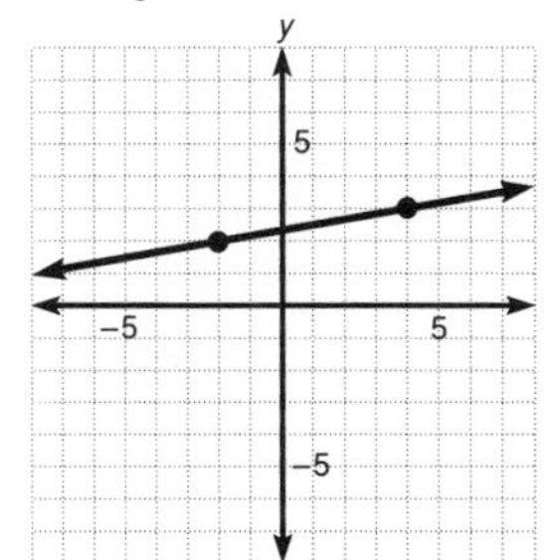

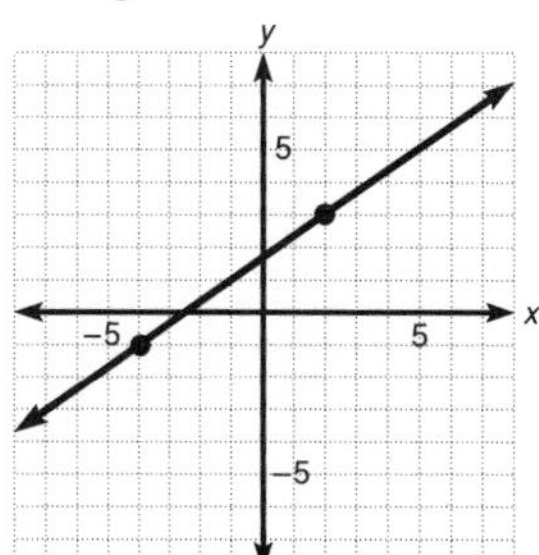

5. $m = 0$ **6.** $m = 0$ **7.** m is undefined

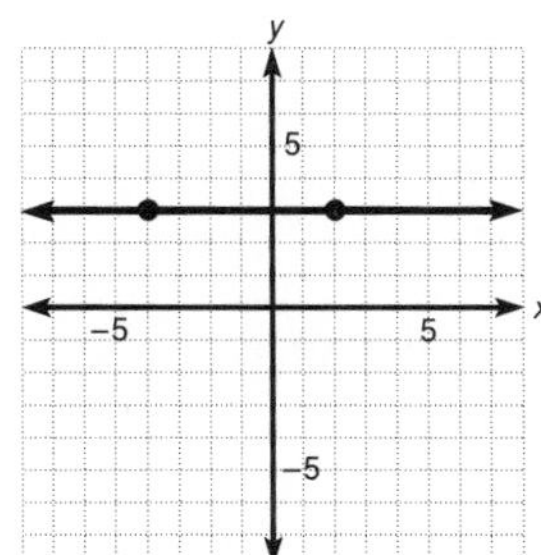

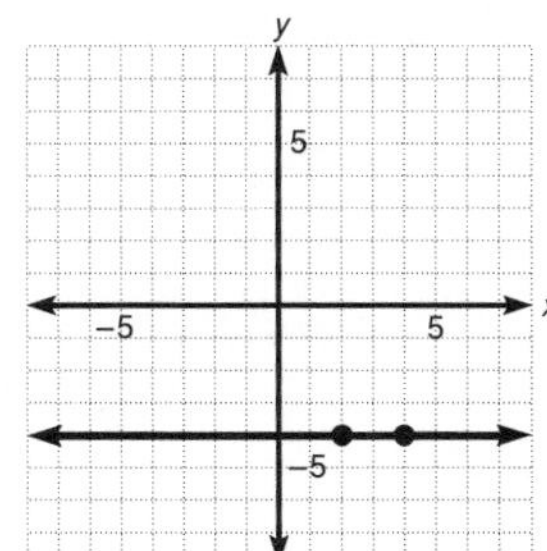

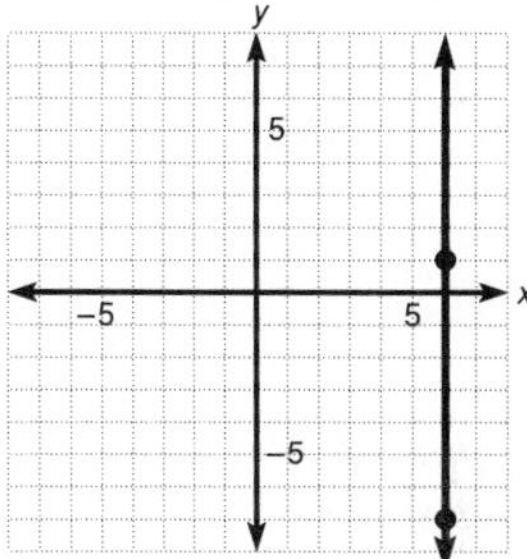

9. $m = \frac{2}{3}$ **10.** $m = -\frac{4}{3}$ **11.** m is undefined **13.** $m = \frac{6}{5}$ **14.** $m = -\frac{3}{4}$ **15.** m is undefined **17.** $m = \frac{1}{7}$ **18.** $m = 1$ **19.** $m = 0$ **21.** $m = \frac{10}{11}$ **22.** $m = \frac{5}{8}$ **23.** pitch $= \frac{2}{3}$ **25.** $m = \frac{2}{3}$ **26.** $m = \frac{4}{5}$ **27.** $m = 4$ **29.** $m = \frac{15}{2}$ **30.** $m = \frac{7{,}000}{1} = 7{,}000$

31.

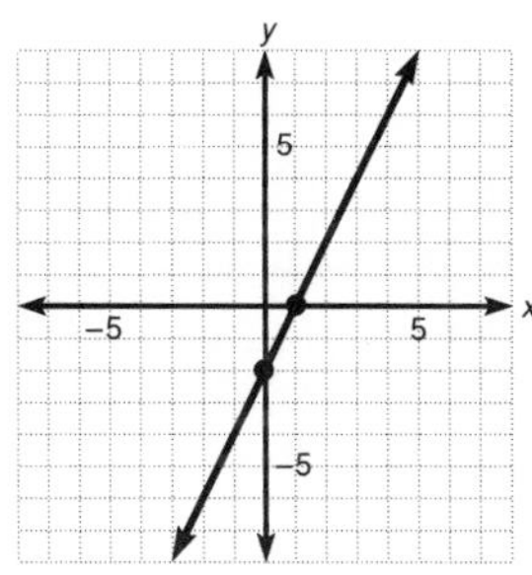

$m = 2$

33.

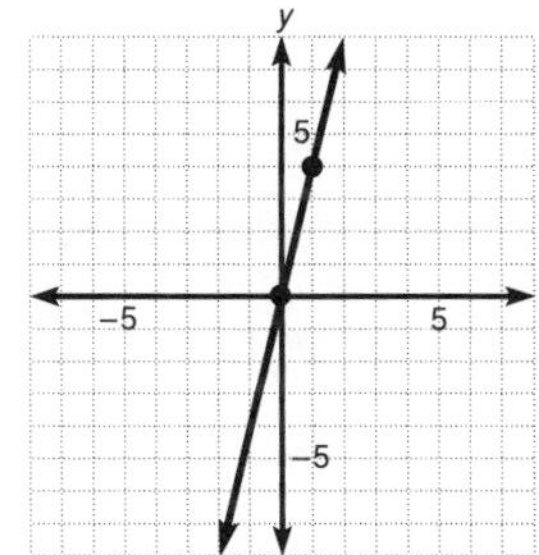

$m = 4$

34.

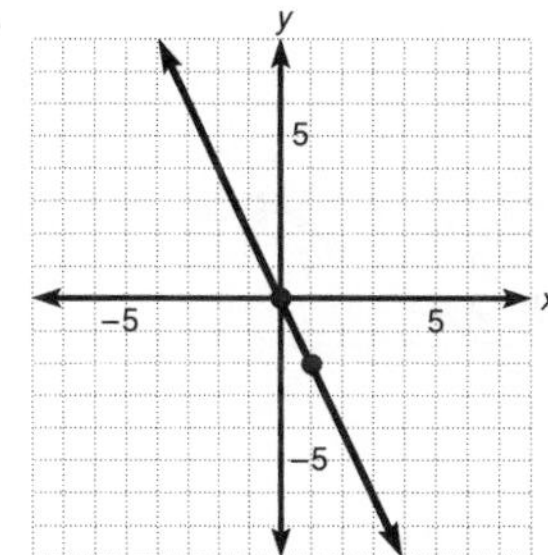

$m = -2$

Solutions to trial exercise problems

1. $(5,2), (3,3); m = \frac{3-2}{3-5} = \frac{1}{-2} = -\frac{1}{2}$

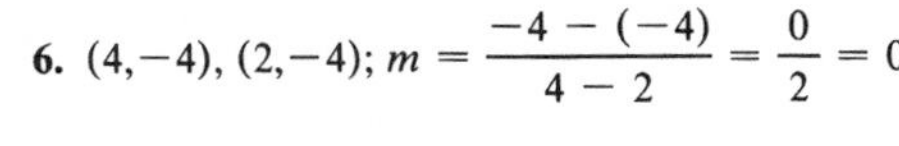

6. $(4,-4), (2,-4); m = \frac{-4-(-4)}{4-2} = \frac{0}{2} = 0$

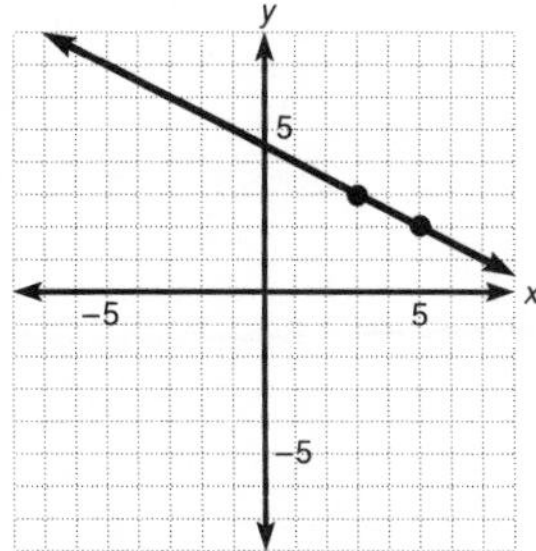

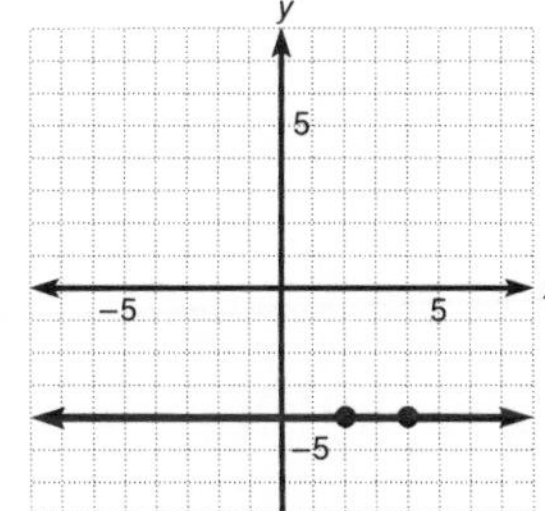

15. (0,7), (0,−8); $m = \dfrac{7-(-8)}{0-0} = \dfrac{15}{0}$ slope is undefined **23.** $m = \dfrac{8}{12} = \dfrac{2}{3}$ **27.** $m = \dfrac{1{,}000}{250} = \dfrac{4}{1} = 4$

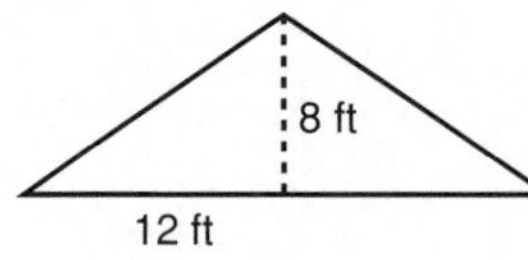

Review exercises

1. −9 **2.** −13 **3.** $-\dfrac{1}{8}$ **4.** $\dfrac{b^5}{a^5}$ **5.** x **6.** 13 **7.** $y = -3x - 1$ **8.** $y = \dfrac{3x-6}{3}$

Exercise 7–4

1. $x - 3y = 4$ **2.** $3x - y = 4$ **3.** $2x - y = -5$ **5.** $2x - 3y = -9$ **6.** $x + 2y = -12$ **7.** $8x - 5y = -4$ **9.** $2x - y = -7$ **10.** $4x - 7y = -39$ **11.** $5x + 8y = -15$ **13.** $y = 3$ **14.** $x = 1$ **15.** $x + 2y = 7$ **17.** $x + 2y = -2$ **18.** $7x + 3y = -8$ **19.** $x = 5$ **21.** $x + 7y = 0$ **22.** $2x + y = -7$ **23.** $y = -x + 2$, $m = -1$, (0,2)

25. $y = -3x - 2$, $m = -3$, (0,−2) **26.** $y = 4x + 5$, $m = 4$, (0,5) **27.** $y = -\dfrac{2}{5}x + 2$, $m = -\dfrac{2}{5}$, (0,2) **29.** $y = \dfrac{8}{9}x - \dfrac{1}{9}$, $m = \dfrac{8}{9}$, $\left(0, -\dfrac{1}{9}\right)$ **30.** $y = \dfrac{7}{4}x - \dfrac{5}{4}$, $m = \dfrac{7}{4}$, $\left(0, -\dfrac{5}{4}\right)$

31.

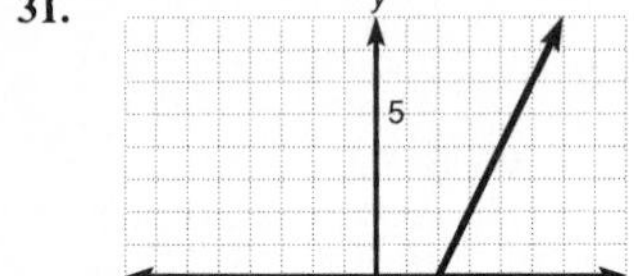

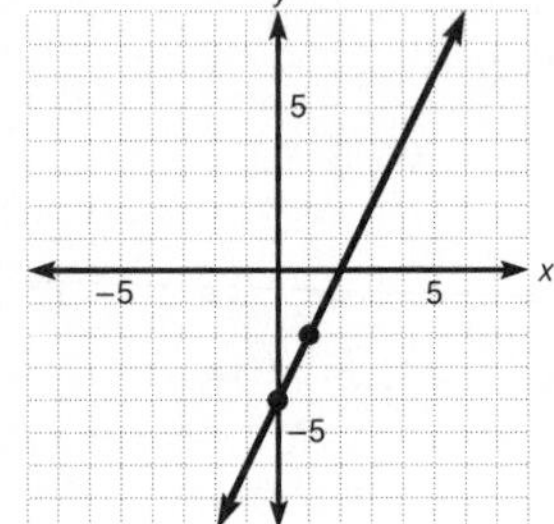

33.

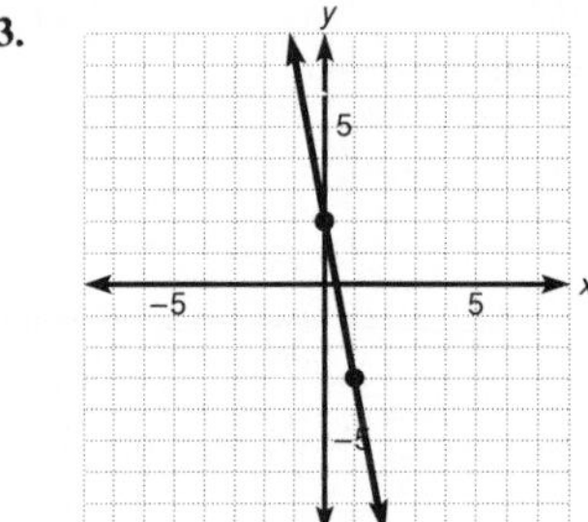

34.

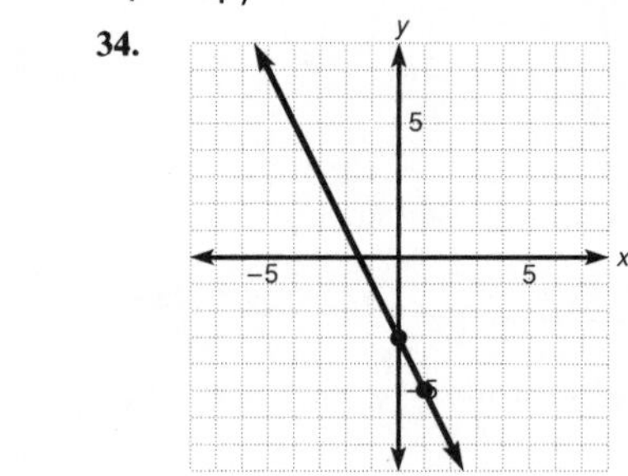

35.

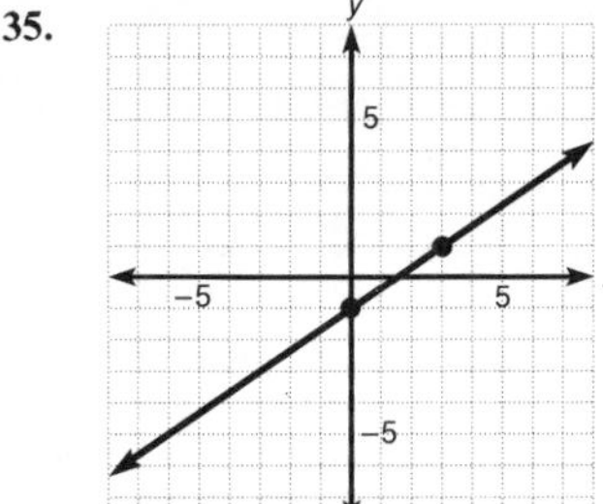

37.

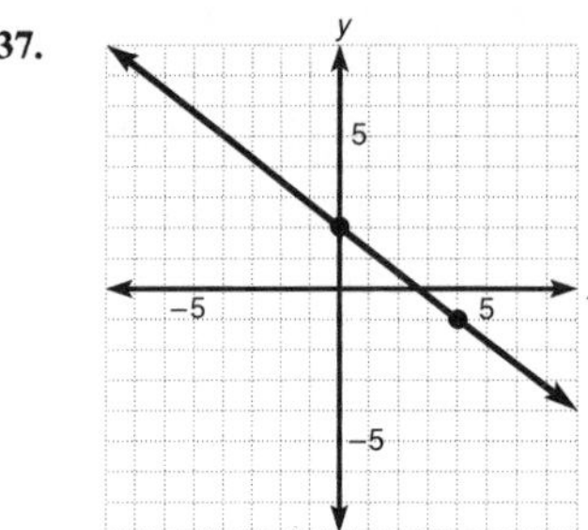

38.

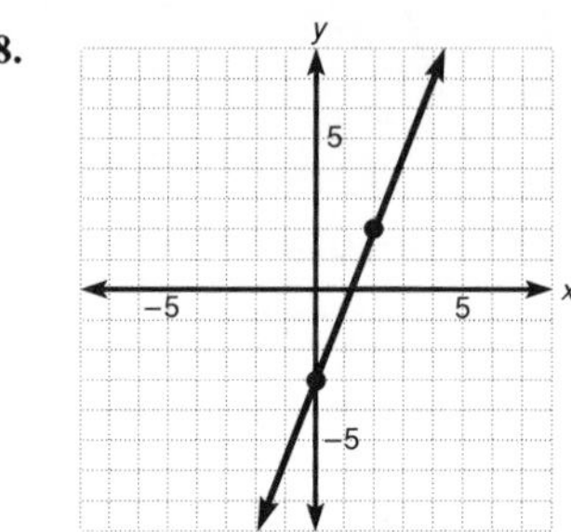

39.

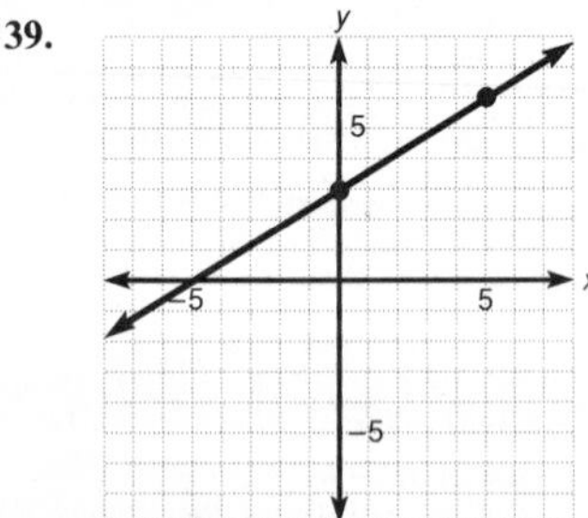

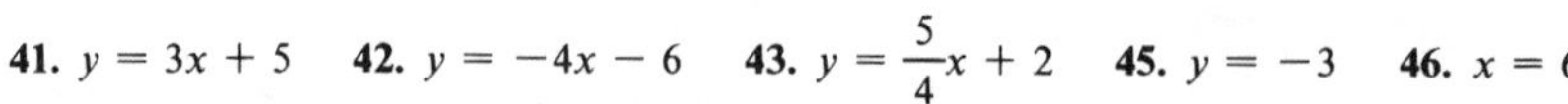

41. $y = 3x + 5$ **42.** $y = -4x - 6$ **43.** $y = \dfrac{5}{4}x + 2$ **45.** $y = -3$ **46.** $x = 6$

47. $m_1 = -1$, $m_2 = -1$, parallel

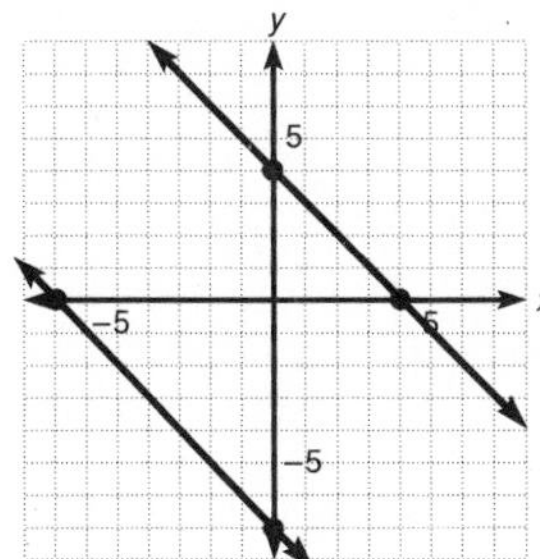

49. $m_1 = -\frac{1}{2}$, $m_2 = 2$, perpendicular

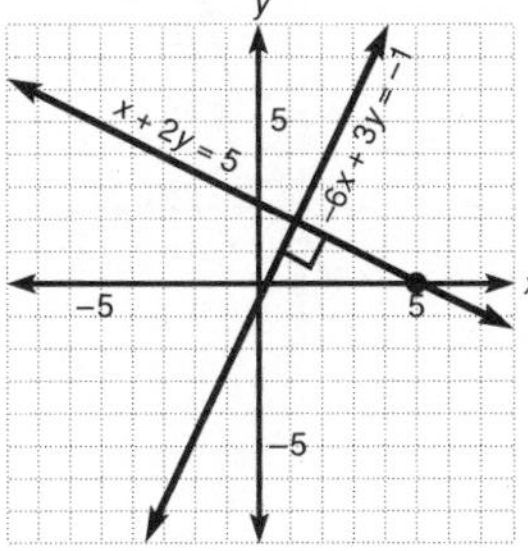

50. $m_1 = 3$, $m_2 = -3$, neither

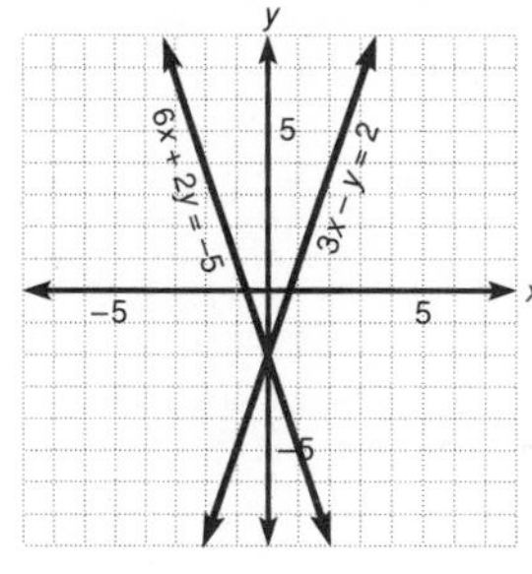

51. $m_1 = 4$, $m_2 = 4$, parallel

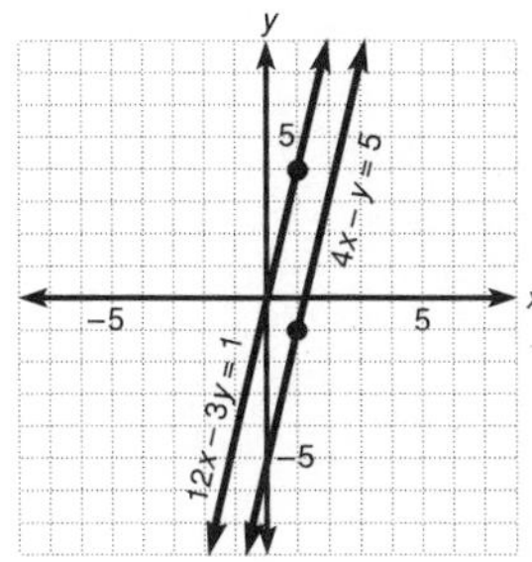

53. $m_1 = -5$, $m_2 = \frac{-10}{3}$, neither

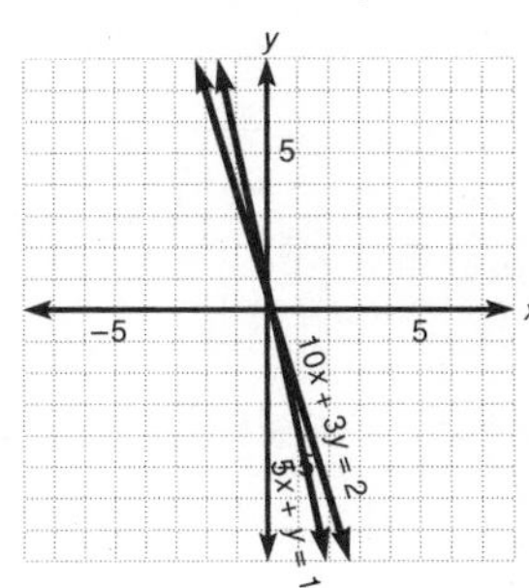

54. $m_1 = -\frac{2}{3}$, $m_2 = -\frac{2}{3}$, parallel

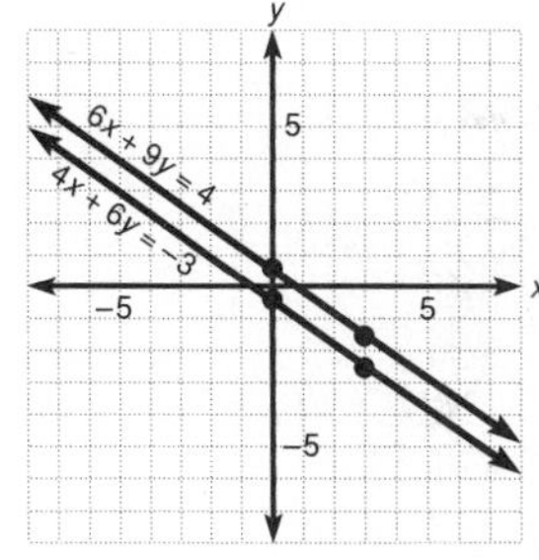

Solutions to trial exercise problems

6.
$$y = -\frac{1}{2}x - 6$$
$2y = -x - 12$ Multiply by 2.
$x + 2y = -12$ Add x to each member.

21. (7,−1) and (0,0)
$$m = \frac{-1 - 0}{7 - 0} = -\frac{1}{7}$$
Using $y - y_1 = m(x - x_1)$ and point (0,0),
$$y - 0 = -\frac{1}{7}(x - 0)$$
$$y = -\frac{1}{7}x$$
$$7y = -x$$
$$x + 7y = 0$$

31. $y = 2x - 4$;
$m = 2$ and $b = -4$
$\left(\textit{Note: } m = \frac{2}{1} = \frac{\text{rise}}{\text{run}}\right)$

11. $(-3,0)$; $m = -\frac{5}{8}$
$$y - 0 = -\frac{5}{8}[x - (-3)]$$
$$8y = -5(x + 3)$$
$$8y = -5x - 15$$
$$5x + 8y = -15$$

27. $2x + 5y = 10$
$$5y = -2x + 10$$
$$y = \frac{-2x + 10}{5} \qquad m = -\frac{2}{5}$$
$$y = -\frac{2}{5}x + 2 \qquad b = 2 \quad (0,2)$$

37. $3x + 4y = 8$
$$4y = -3x + 8$$
$$y = -\frac{3}{4}x + 2$$
$$m = -\frac{3}{4}, b = 2$$

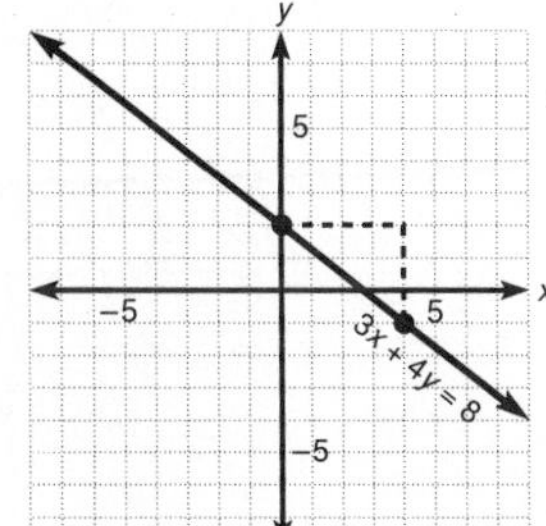

49. $x + 2y = 5$
$-6x + 3y = -1$

Now $x + 2y = 5$ | $-6x + 3y = -1$
$2y = -x + 5$ | $3y = 6x - 1$
$y = -\frac{1}{2}x + \frac{5}{2}$ | $y = 2x - \frac{1}{3}$

$m_1 = -\frac{1}{2}$ $m_2 = 2$

The lines are *perpendicular* since $m_1 m_2 = -\frac{1}{2} \cdot 2 = -1$.

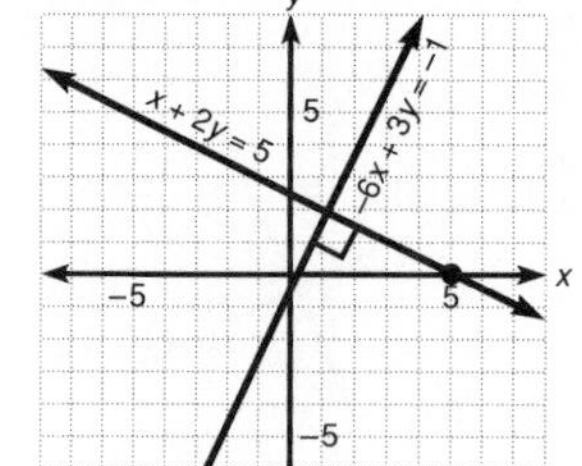

Review exercises

1. $41\frac{1}{2}$ ft, $58\frac{1}{2}$ ft **2.** $0, -3, 9, \frac{9}{3}, \frac{0}{4}$ **3.** $y = -3$ **4.** $y = \frac{1}{7}$ **5.** $x = 10$ **6.** $(3x - 2)(x + 2)$ **7.** prime, not factorable
8. $8(y + 2x)(y - 2x)$

Exercise 7–5

1.
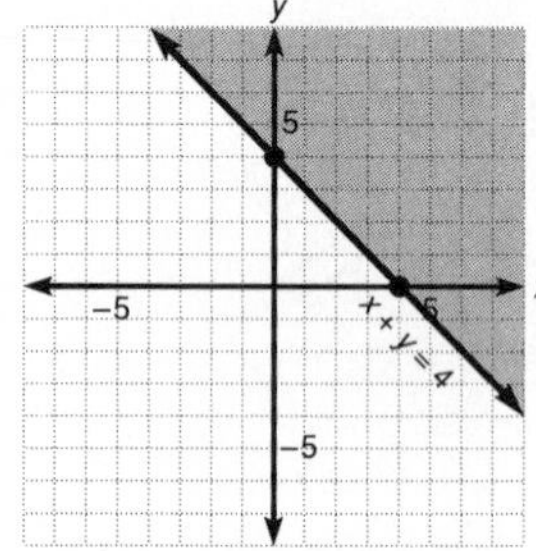

2.
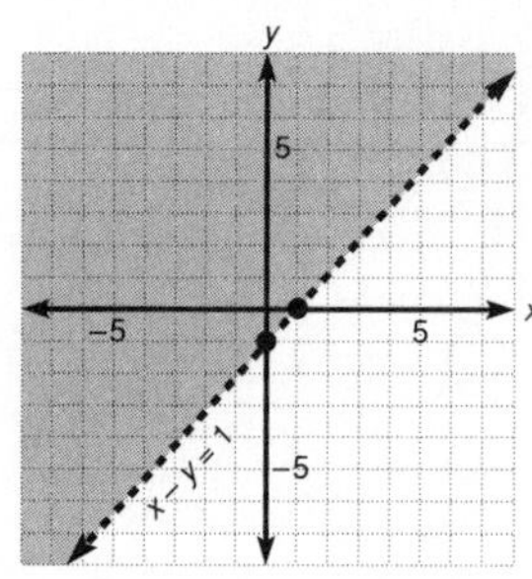

3.
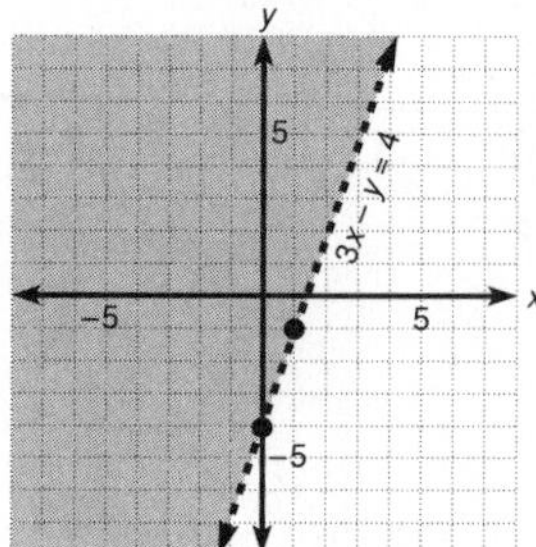

5.
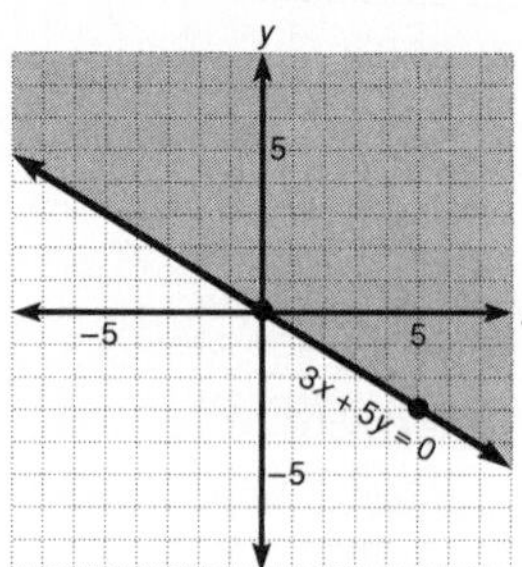

6.
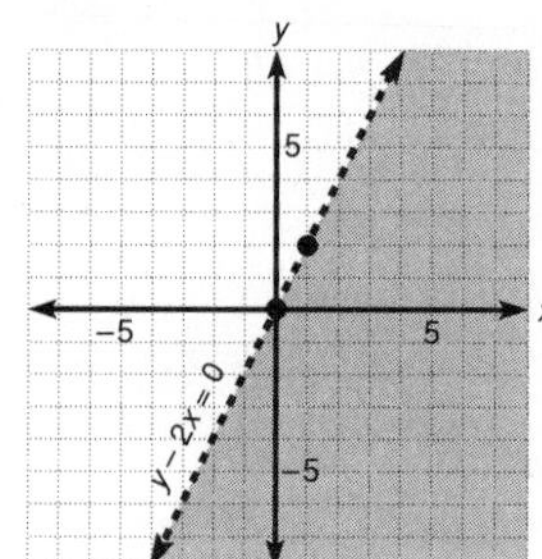

7.
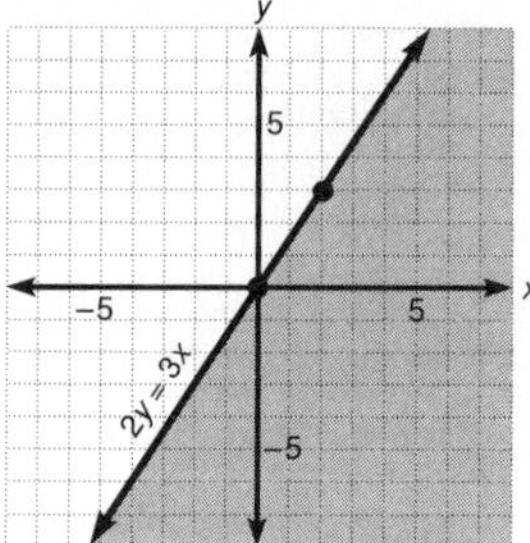

9.
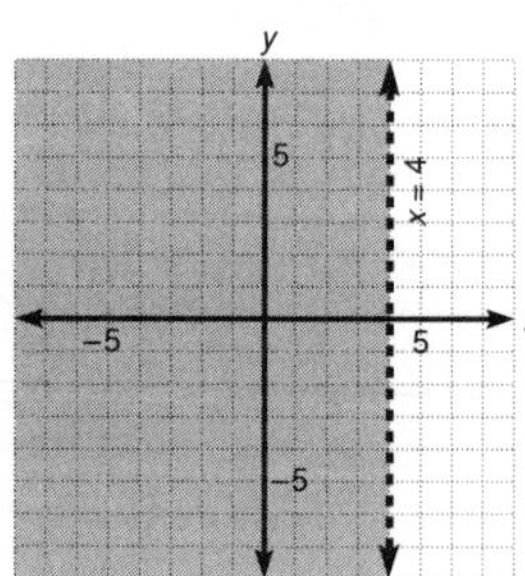

10.
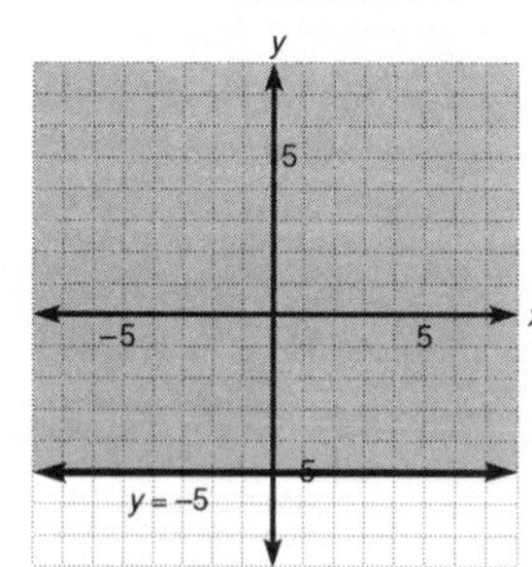

11.
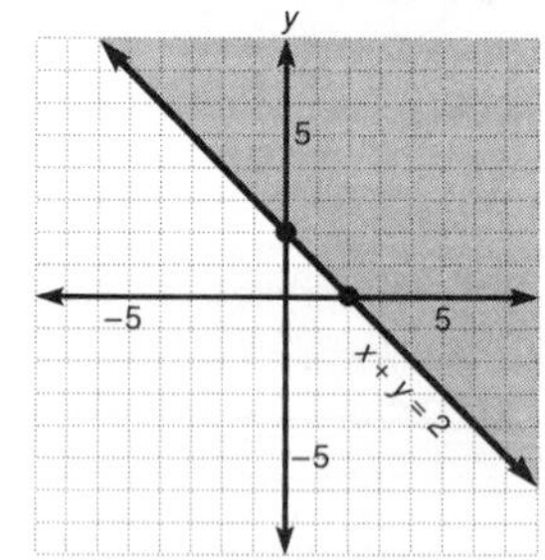

13.
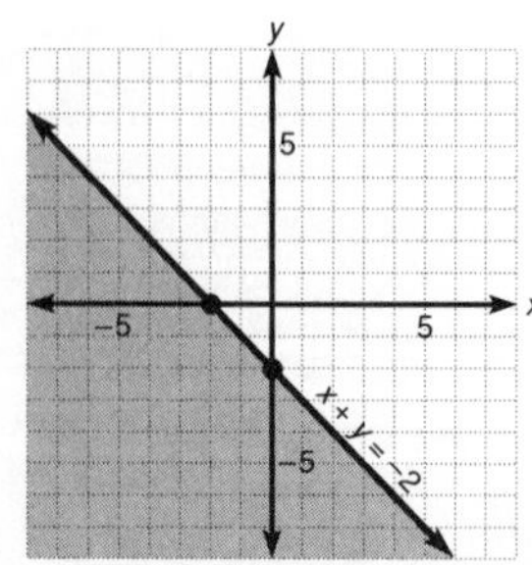

14.
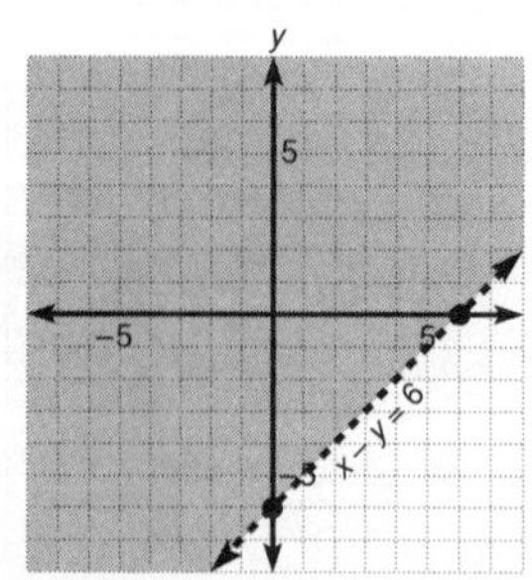

15.
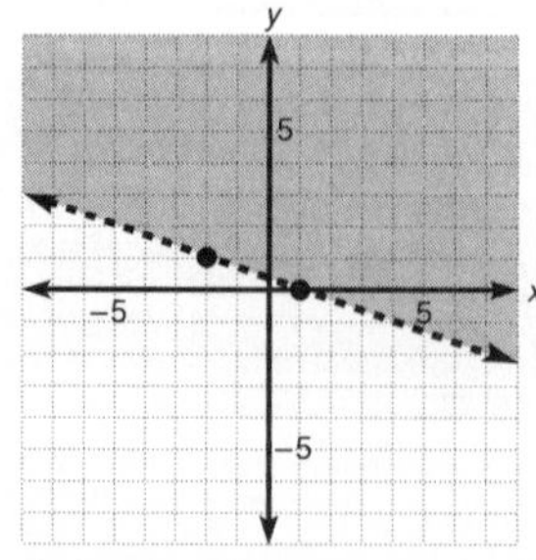

17. 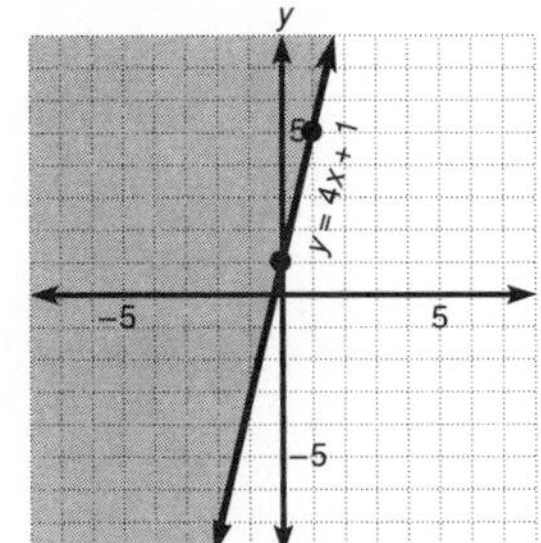

18. 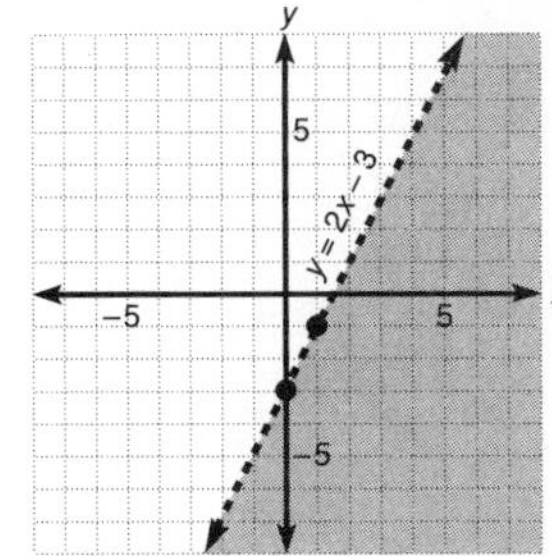

19. 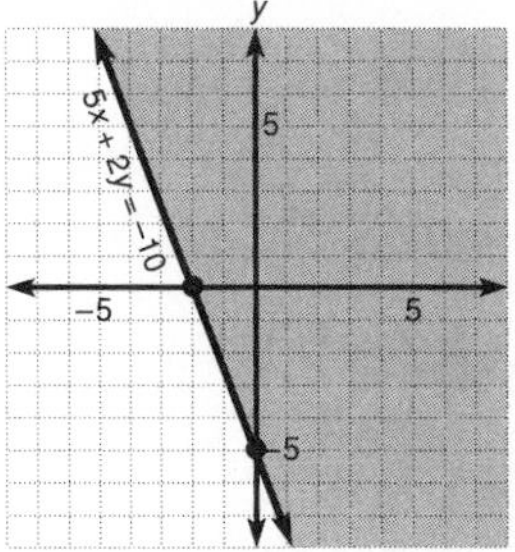

21. 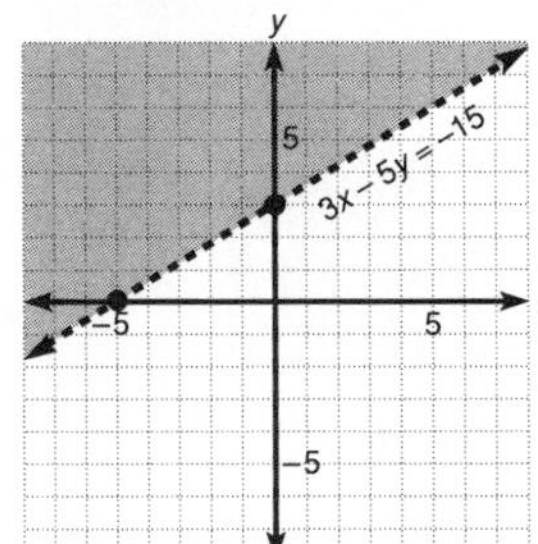

22. 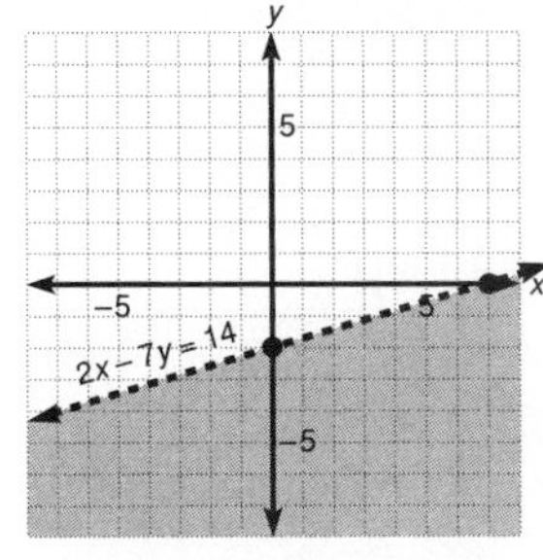

23. 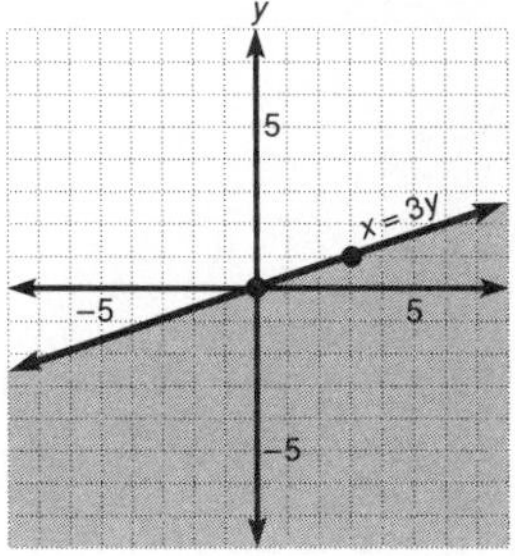

25. 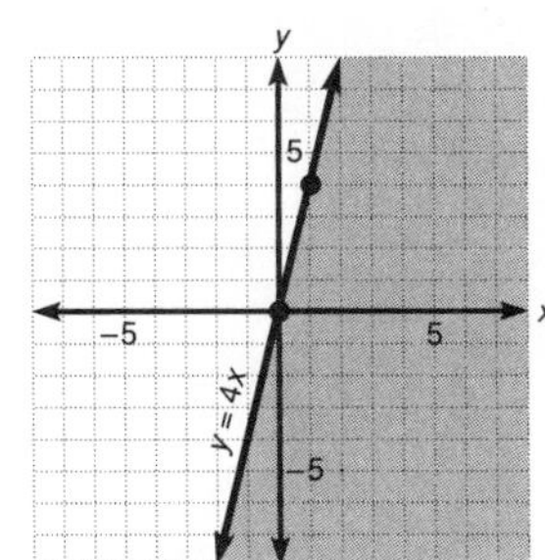

26. 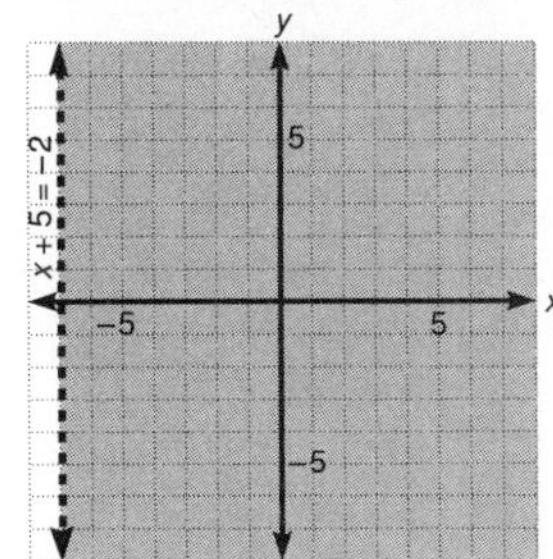

27. 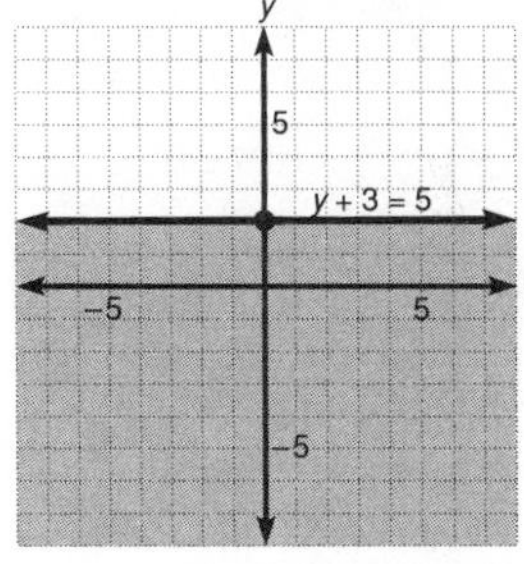

29. 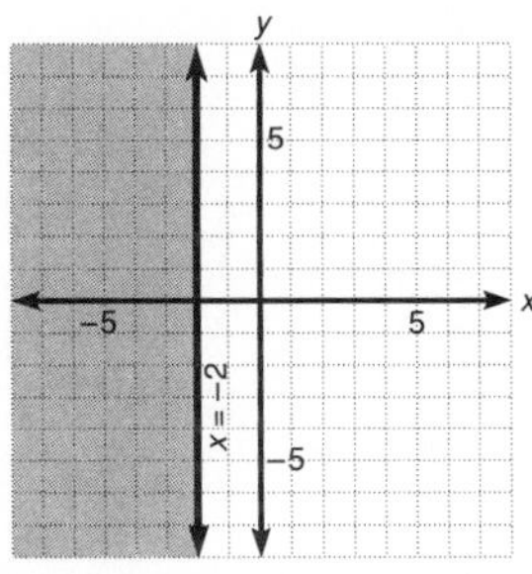

30. 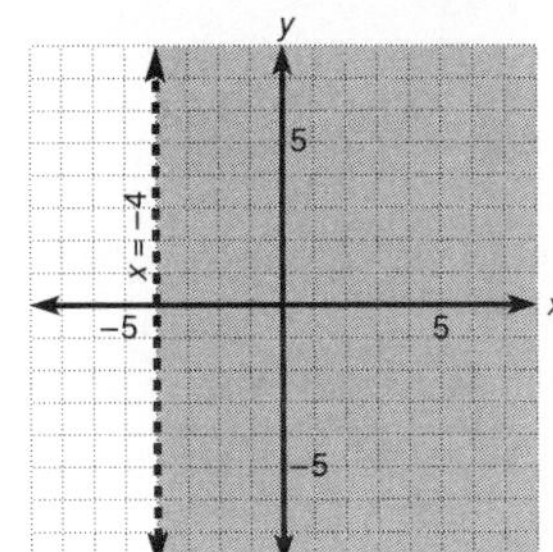

31. 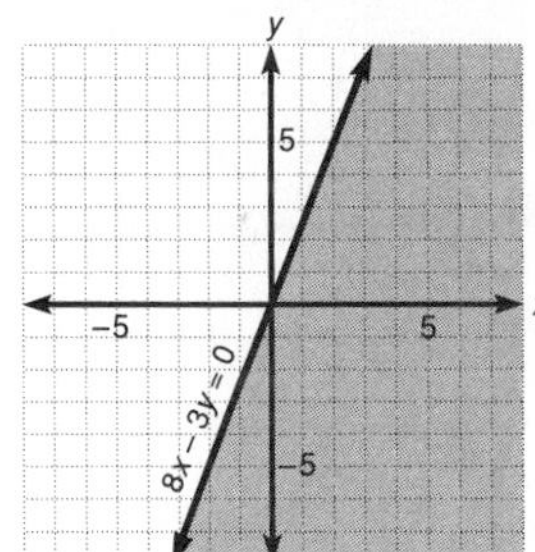

Solutions to trial exercise problems

3. $3x - y \le 4$
Using (0,0), $3(0) - (0) \le 4$
$0 - 0 \le 4$
0 (true)
Shade half-plane that does contain the origin.

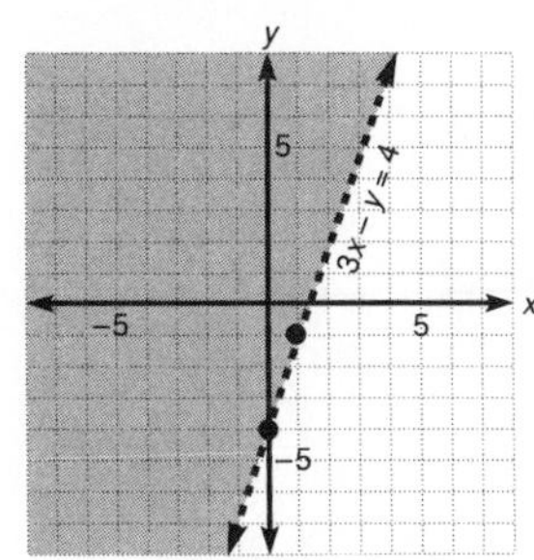

7. $2y \le 3x$
Using (1,1), $2(1) \le 3(1)$
$2 \le 3$ (true)
Shade half-plane that contains (1,1).

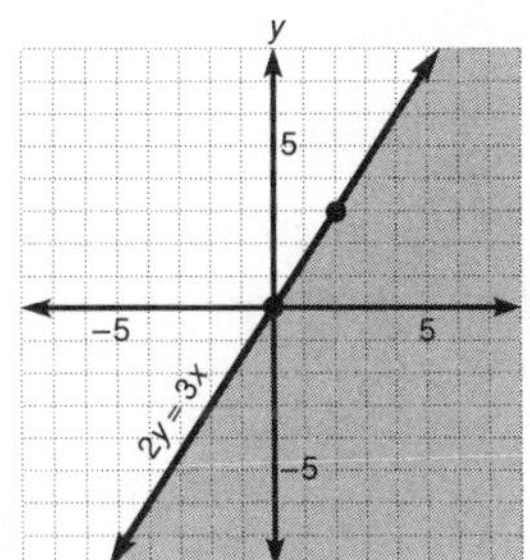

9. $x < 4$
Using (0,0),
$0 < 4$ (true)
Shade half-plane containing the origin.

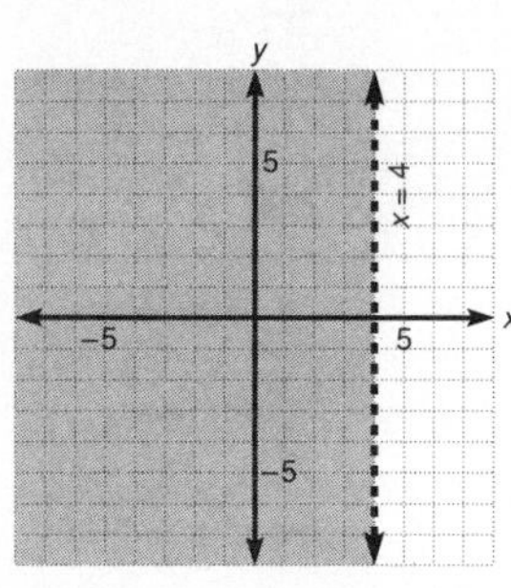

11. $x + y \geq 2$
Graph $x + y = 2$ in a solid line.
Using (0,0),
$0 + 0 \geq 2$
$0 \geq 2$ (false)
Shade half-plane that does not contain (0,0).

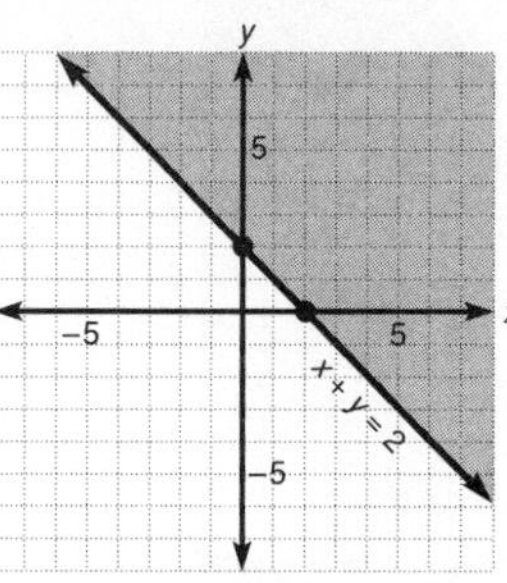

22. $2x - 7y > 14$
Graph $2x - 7y = 14$ in a dashed line.
Using (0,0),
$2(0) - 7(0) > 14$
$0 > 14$ (false)
Shade half-plane that does not contain (0,0).

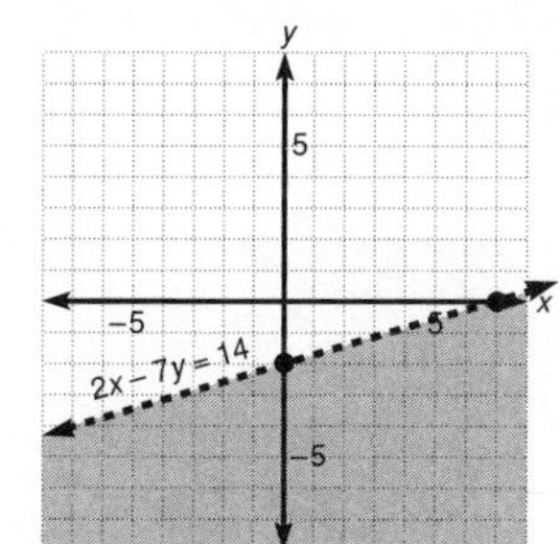

Review exercises

1.

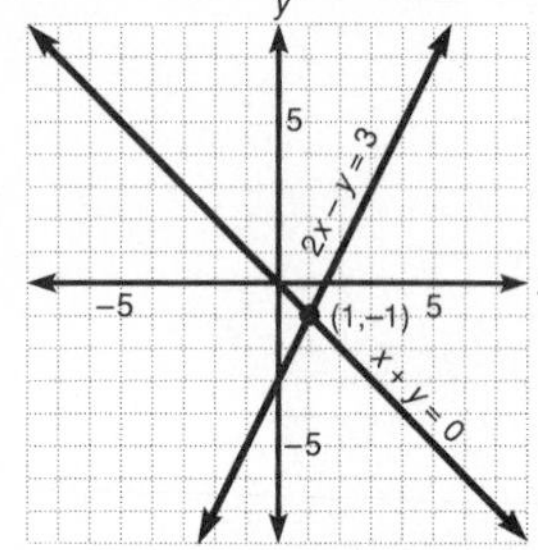

2.

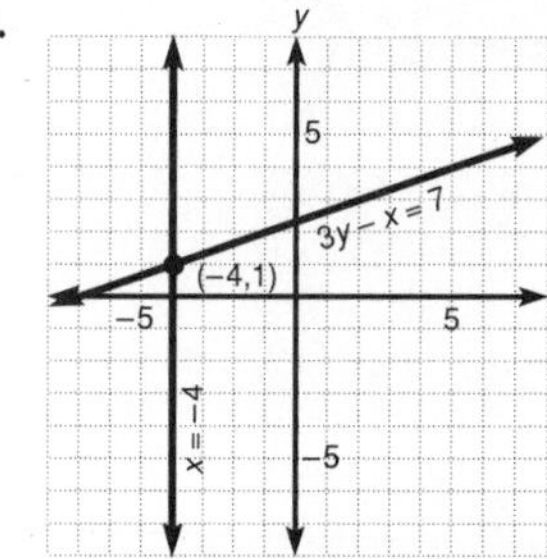

3. $y = \frac{5}{2}$ **4.** $x = 13$ **5.** $x + 3y = 7$ **6.** $3x - 4y = 8$ **7.** $x = -3$ **8.** $y = -3$

Chapter 7 review

1. $(-1,1), (0,4), (4,16)$ **2.** $(-2,-1), \left(0,\frac{1}{3}\right), (1,1)$ **3.** $(-7,-3), (0,-3), (5,-3)$ **4.** $(-3,15), (0,0), (3,-15)$ **5.** $(7,-2), (1,0), (-14,5)$

6. $\left(\frac{9}{4},-1\right), \left(\frac{7}{4},0\right), \left(\frac{1}{4},3\right)$ **7.** $(1,-8), (1,0), (1,2)$ **8.** $(-2,-3), (0,0), \left(\frac{2}{3},1\right)$ **9–14.**

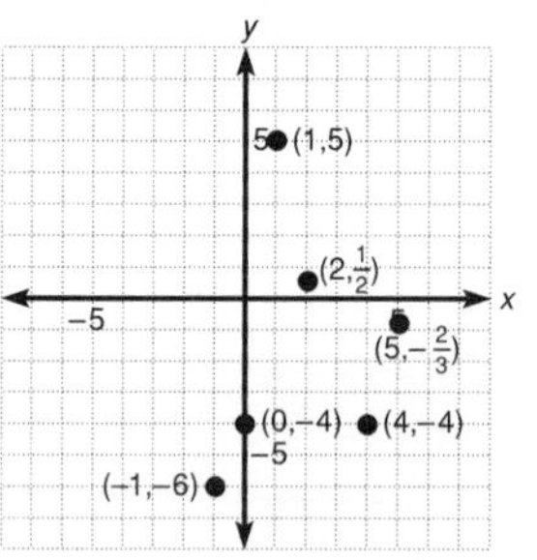

15. $A(-1,-2)$ **16.** $B(1,1)$ **17.** $C(5,1)$ **18.** $D(0,3)$ **19.** $E(-2,1)$ **20.** $F(3,-4)$

21. $(2,6), (0,4), (-1,3), (-2,2)$

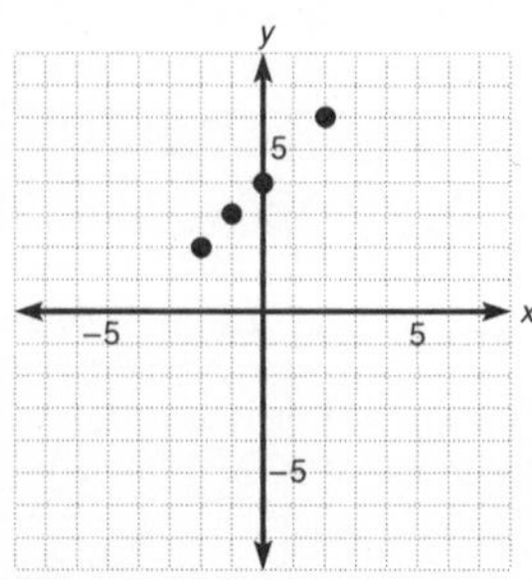

22. $(-1,7), \left(\frac{5}{2},0\right), (0,5), (3,-1)$

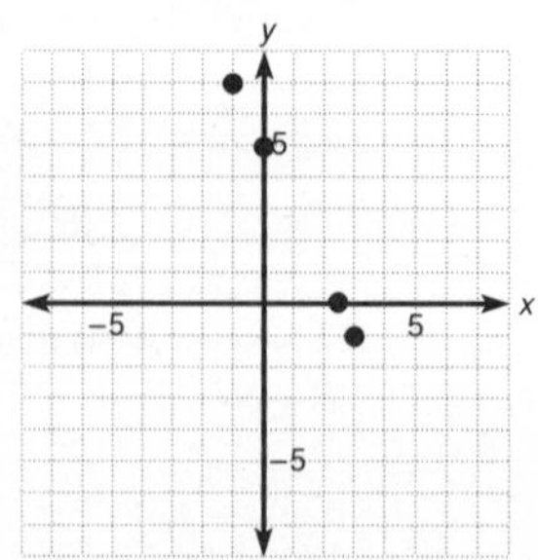

23. $\left(-\frac{5}{3},0\right)$, $(0,5)$ **24.** $(0,0)$, $(0,0)$ **25.** $\left(\frac{2}{3},0\right)$, $(0,-2)$ **26.** $(8,0)$, $(0,-2)$

27.

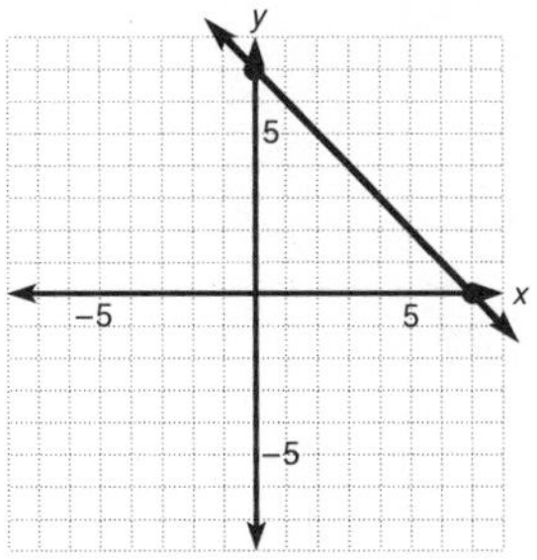

x-intercept, $(7,0)$; y-intercept, $(0,7)$

28.

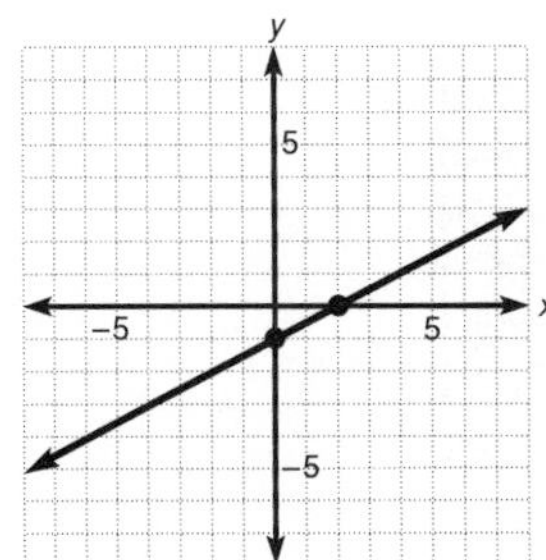

x-intercept, $(2,0)$; y-intercept, $(0,-1)$

29.

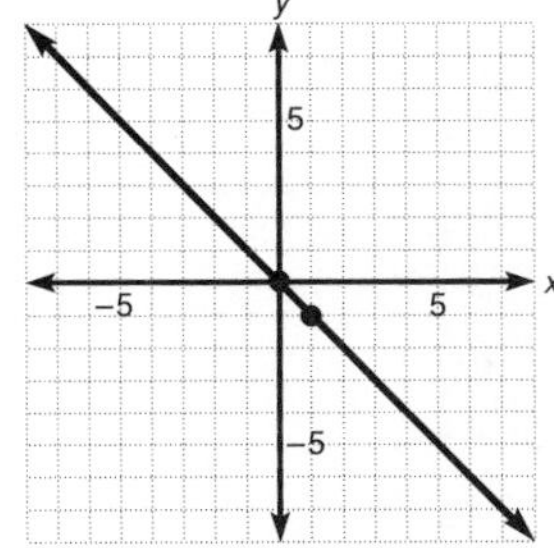

x-intercept, $(0,0)$; y-intercept, $(0,0)$

30.

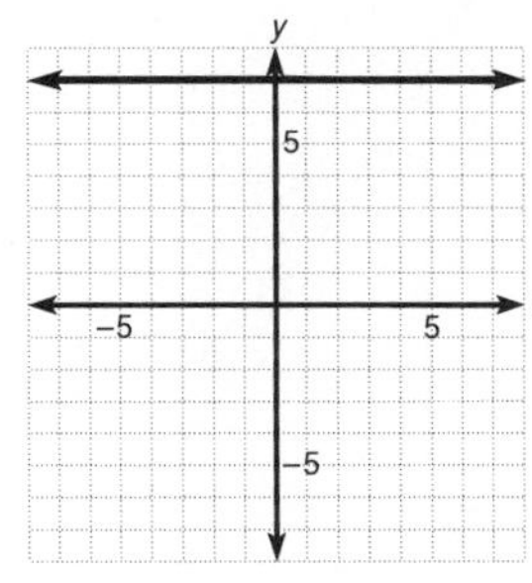

y-intercept, $(0,7)$

31.

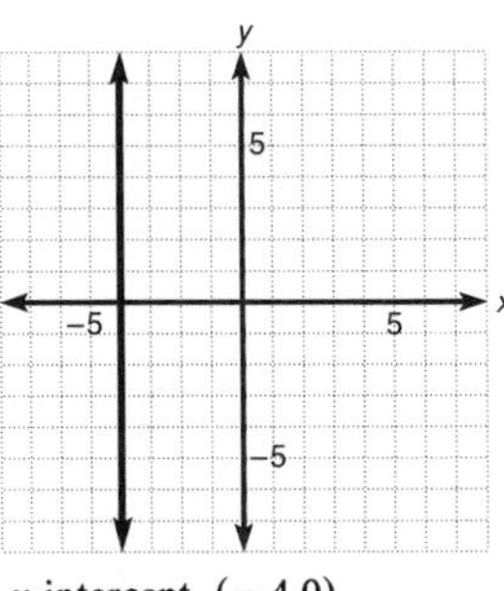

x-intercept, $(-4,0)$

32.

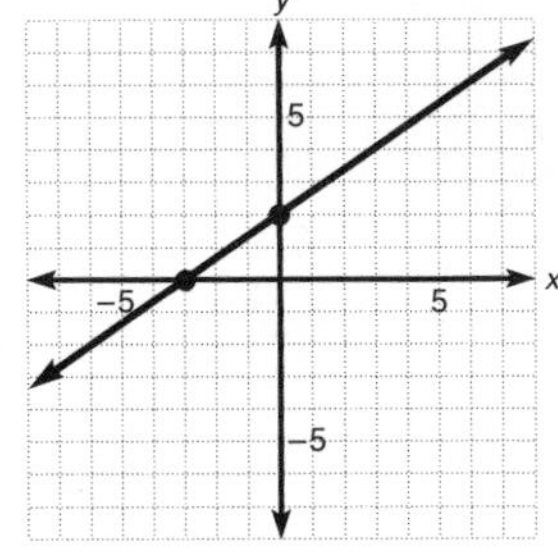

x-intercept, $(-3,0)$; y-intercept, $(0,2)$

33.

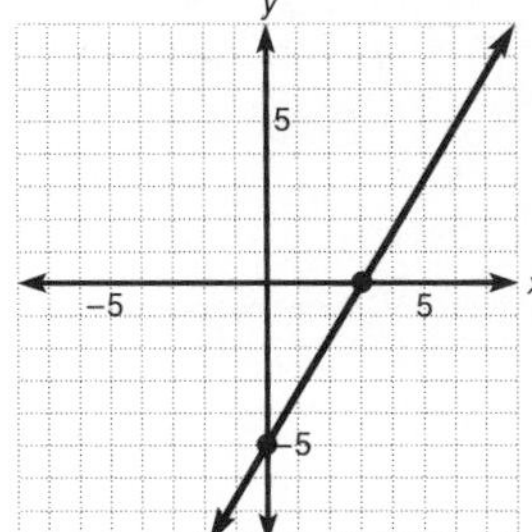

x-intercept, $(3,0)$; y-intercept, $(0,-5)$

34. $m = -\frac{3}{5}$ **35.** undefined **36.** $y = \frac{3}{4}x - 2$, $m = \frac{3}{4}$, $(0,-2)$ **37.** $y = -\frac{4}{3}x + \frac{2}{3}$, $m = -\frac{4}{3}$, $\left(0,\frac{2}{3}\right)$

38. $y = 4x - 3$ **39.** $4x + y = 21$ **40.** $x - 3y = -12$ **41.** $x - 8y = -11$ **42.** $4x - 3y = -12$

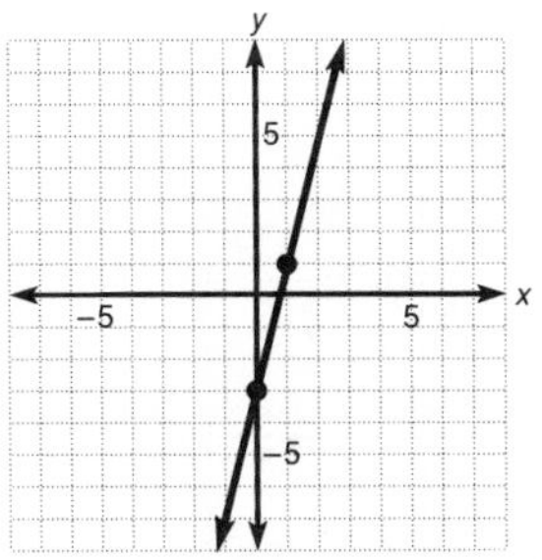

43.

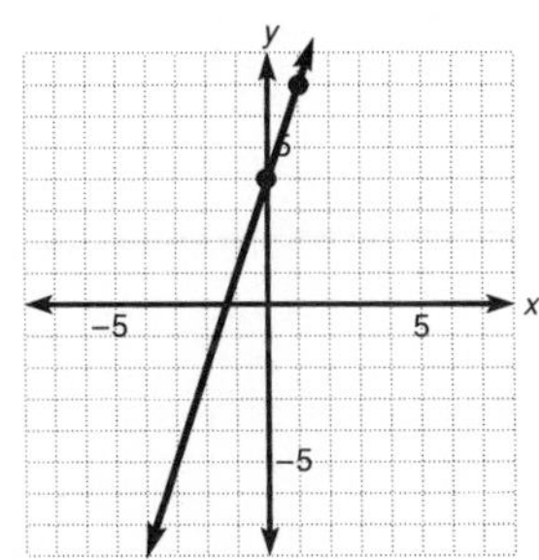

44.

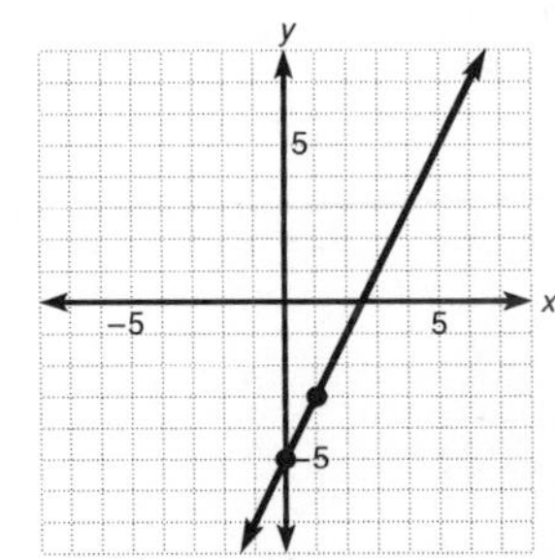

45. perpendicular **46.** parallel **47.** neither

48. 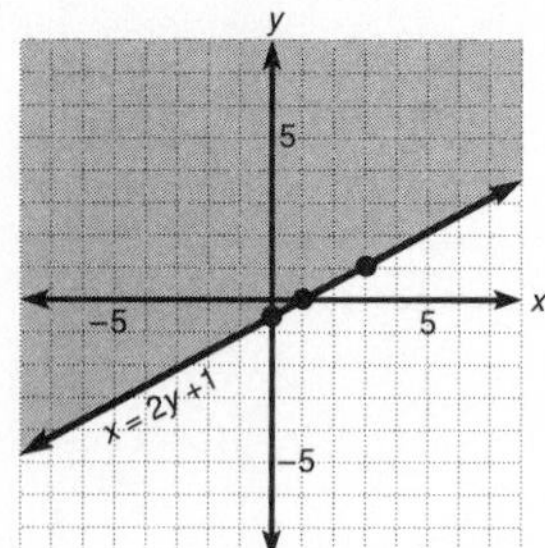

49. 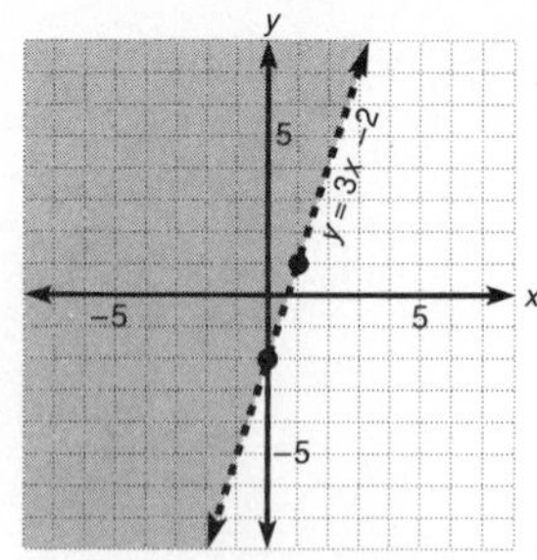

50. 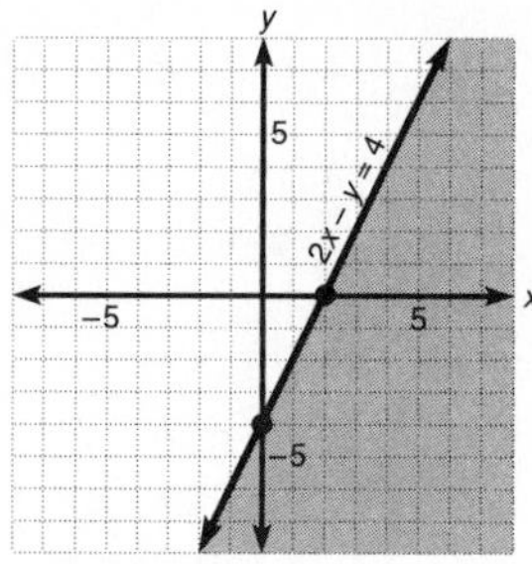

51. 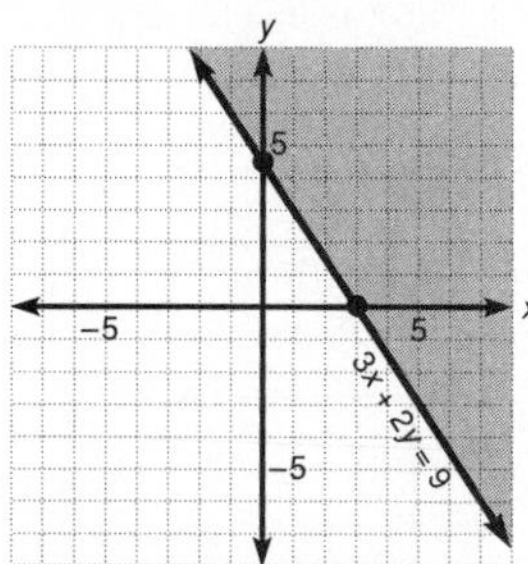

52. 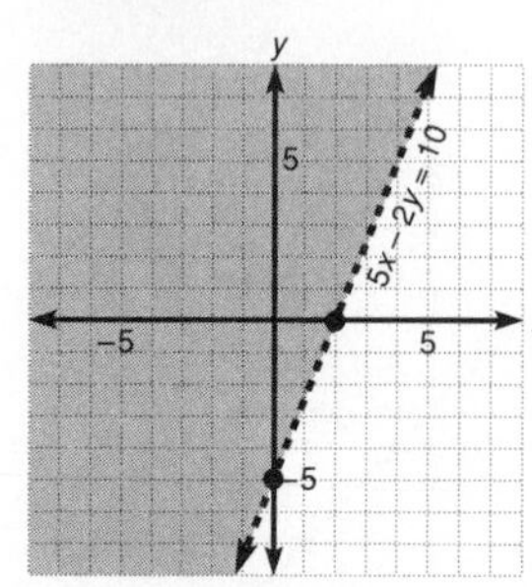

53. 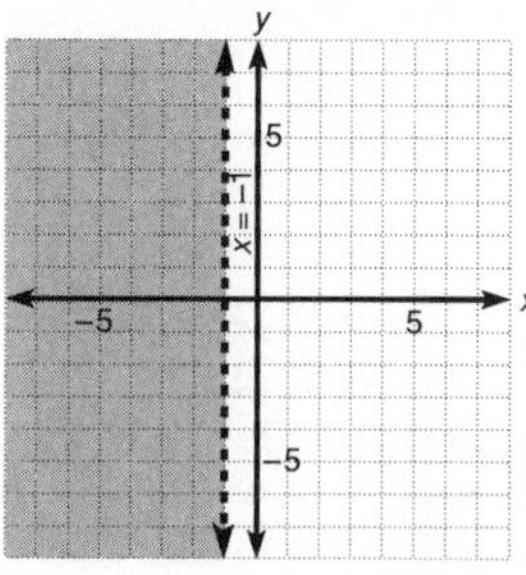

54. 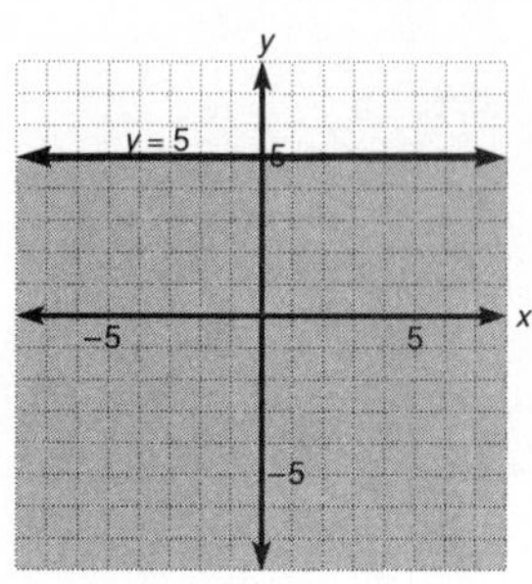

55. 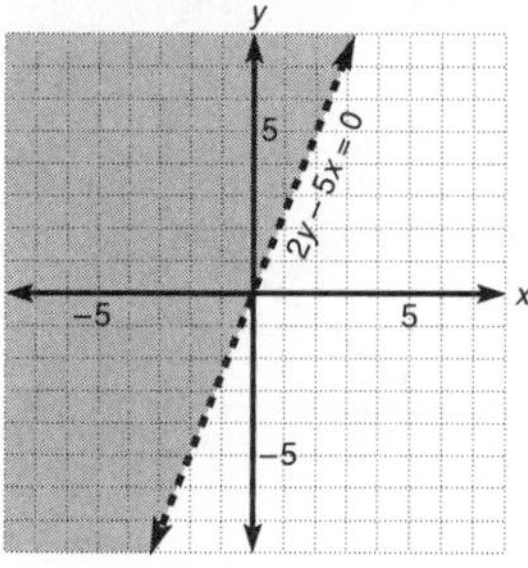

Chapter 7 cumulative test

1. 25 **2.** $36 - 27x$ **3.** $x = \frac{8}{3}$ **4.** $x = \frac{60}{17}$ **5.** $y = -\frac{5}{3}$ **6.** $x = -\frac{2}{3}, x = 2$ **7.** $(7x + 1)(x - 1)$ **8.** $y^6(y^2 + y - 1)$
9. $16(a + b)(a - b)$ **10.** $t(t - 7)(t - 1)$ **11.** $-7(5y + 4z)$ **12.** $16y^2 - 24xy + 9x^2$ **13.** $20x^2 - 3x - 56$
14. $25 - \frac{9}{16}y^2$ **15.** $x^3 - 3x^2y + 3xy^2 - y^3$ **16.** $15y^5 + 18y^4 + 32y^3 + 66y^2 - 7y + 56$ **17.** $\frac{5x^2 + 32x}{(x + 6)(x - 7)(x + 7)}$
18. $\frac{a^2 - 2a + 1}{(a + 5)(a - 2)}$ or $\frac{(a - 1)^2}{(a + 5)(a - 2)}$ **19.** $\frac{6}{y + 3}$ **20.** $\frac{1}{x^9}$ **21.** $\frac{1}{8^8}$ **22.** $-\frac{125}{a^9}$ **23.** 7.76×10^{-6} **24.** $3x^2 - 8x + 20 - \frac{45}{x + 2}$
25. $\frac{2x^2 - x + 9}{3x + 4}$

26. 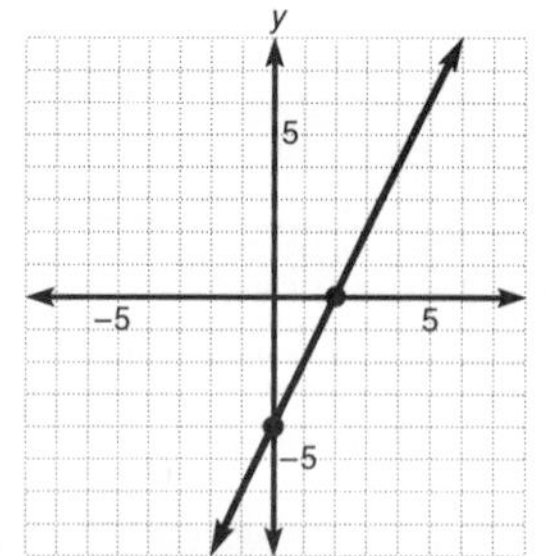

27. 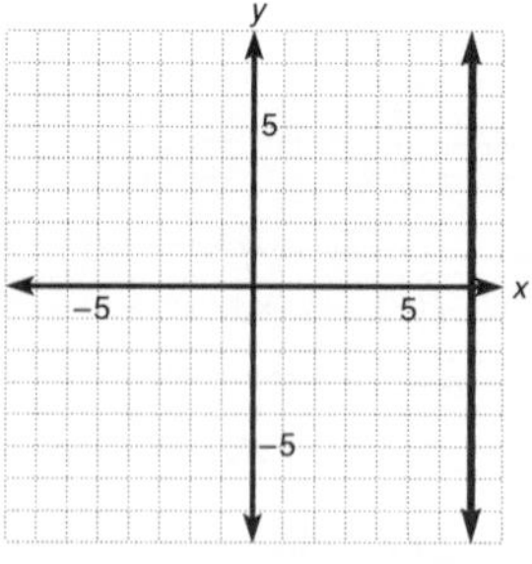

28. $m = \frac{7}{3}$ **29.** $3x - 4y = -13$ **30.** $3x + 5y = 27$ **31.** parallel **32.** neither **33.** 136 **34.** 12 **35.** \$1,900 at 6%; \$1,100 at 5%

36. 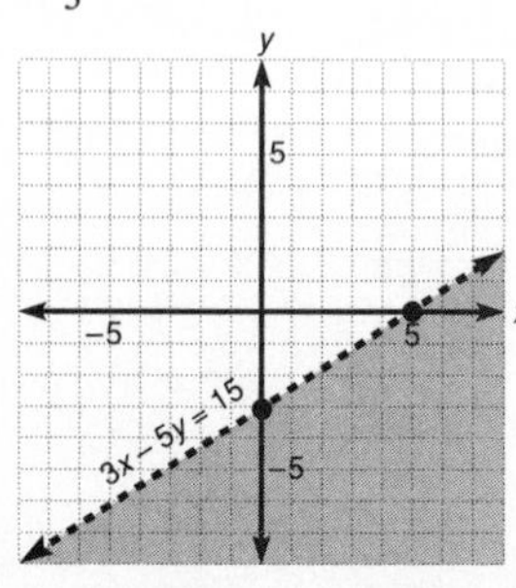

37. 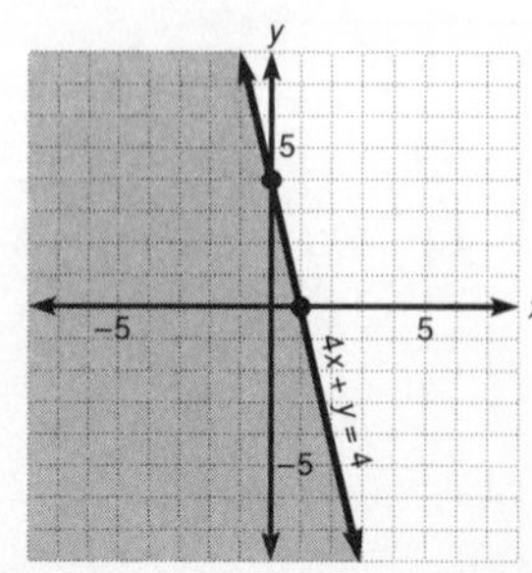

Chapter 8

Proficiency check

1. a. $x = 1$ **b.** $y = 4$ **2.**

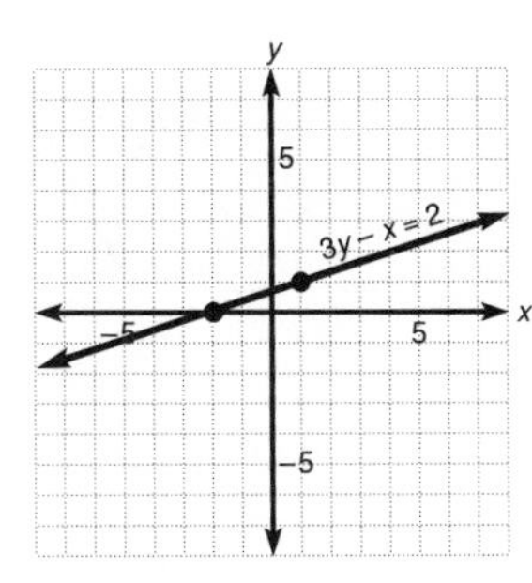

a. $3y - x = 2$

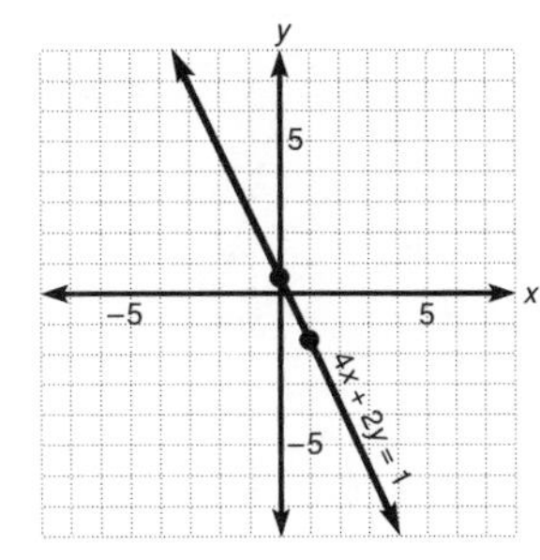

b. $4x + 2y = 1$

3. a. $9x - 6y = 3$ **b.** $-2y + 10x = 4$

4. $x = -4$ **5.** $y = \frac{7}{4}$

Exercise 8–1

1. yes **2.** yes **3.** yes **5.** yes **6.** not a solution **7.** not a solution **9.** yes **10.** not a solution **11.** not a solution

13.

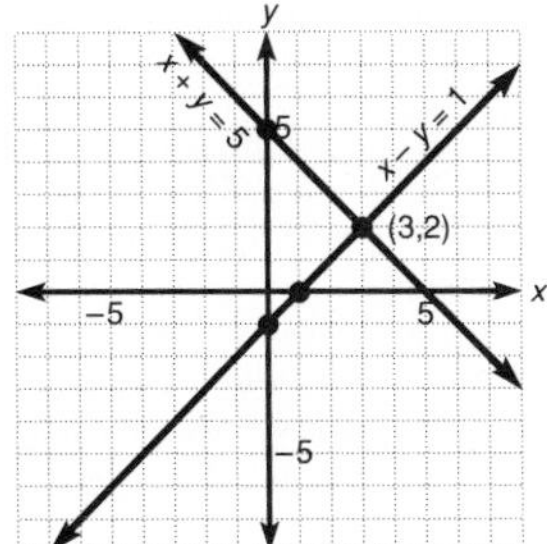

14.

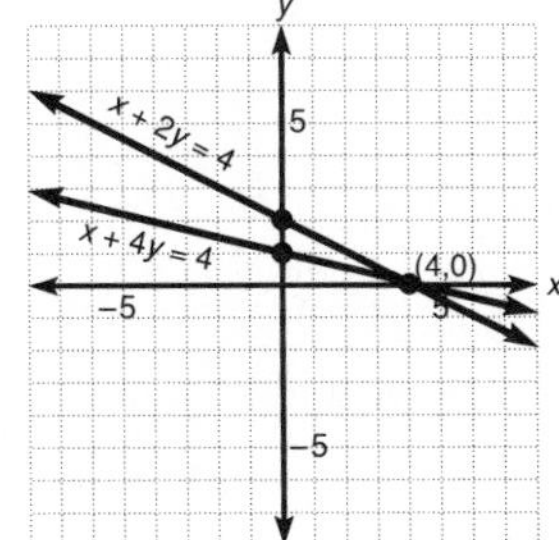

15.

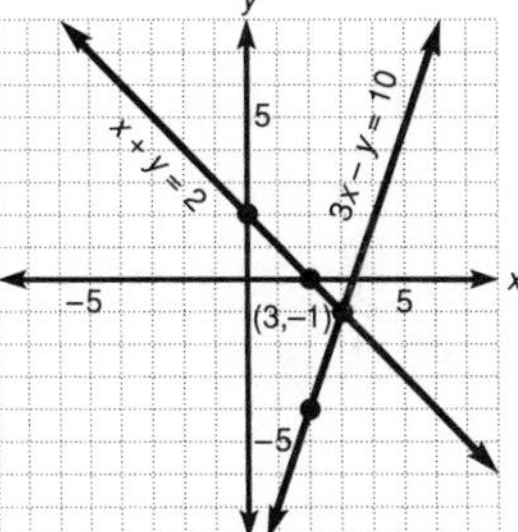

17.

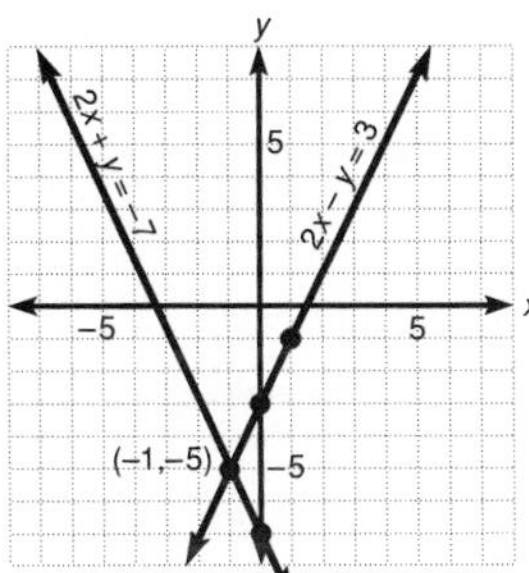

18.

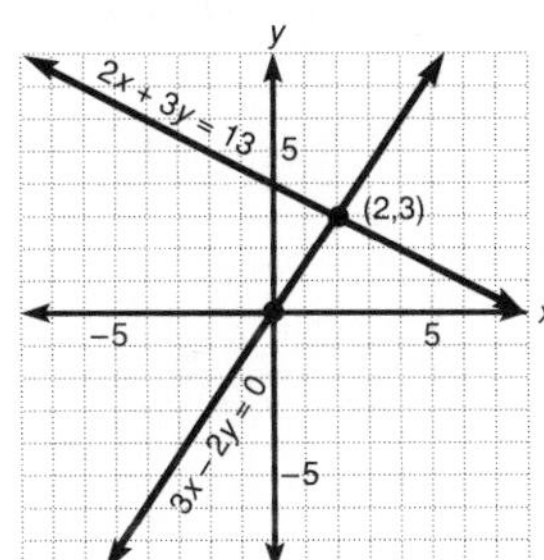

19.

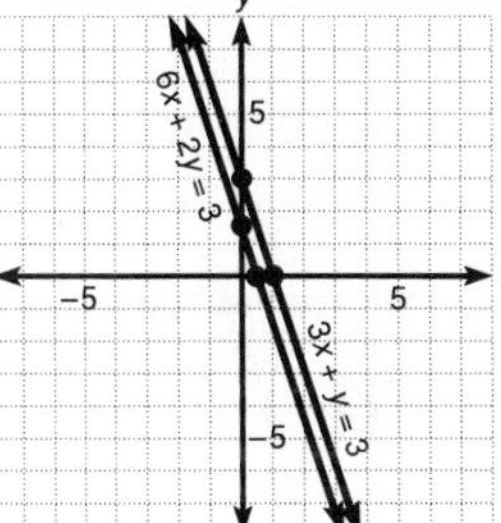

21.

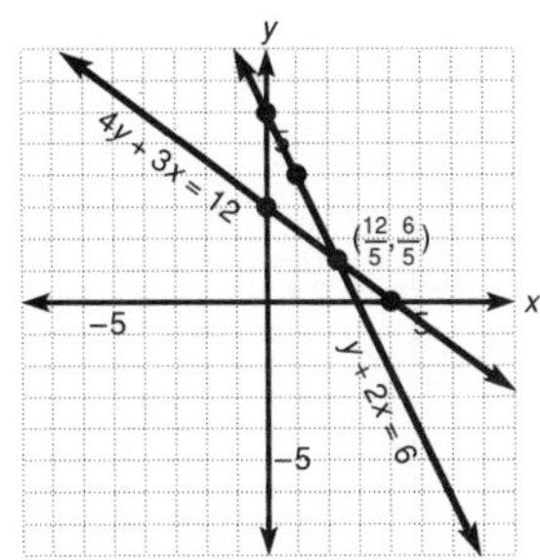

22.

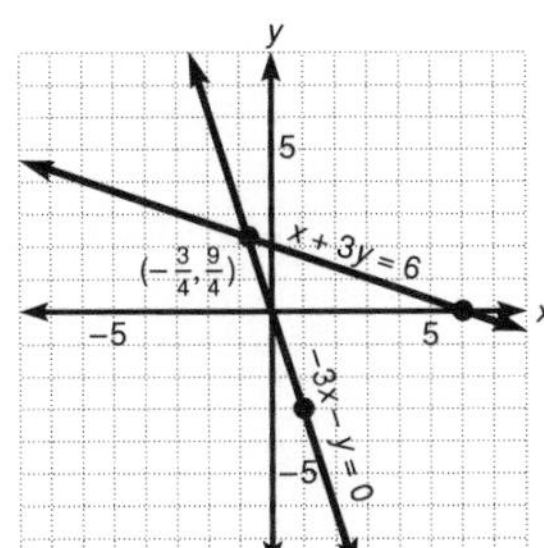

23.

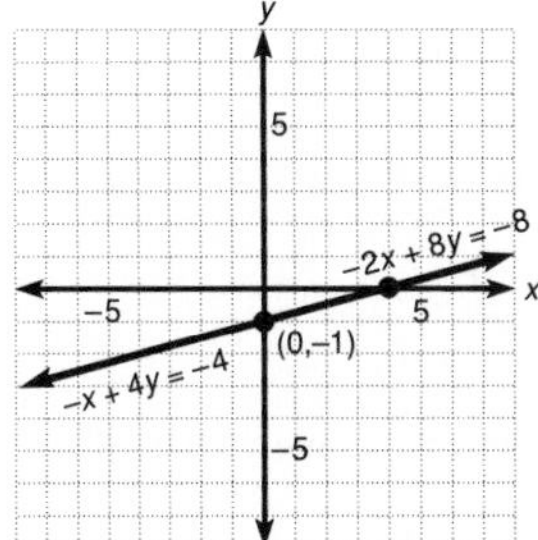

dependent, infinitely many solutions

25.

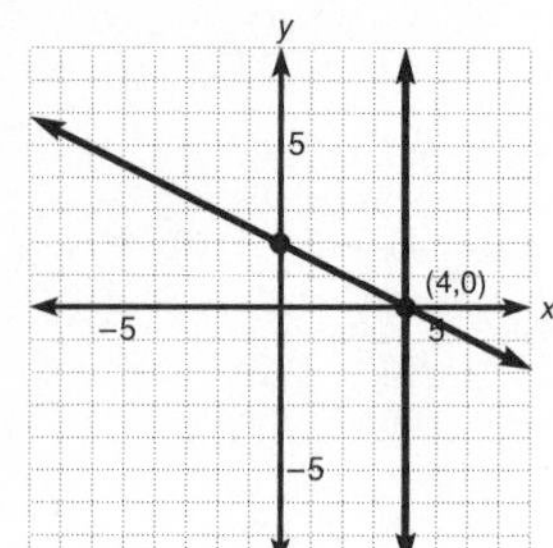

26.

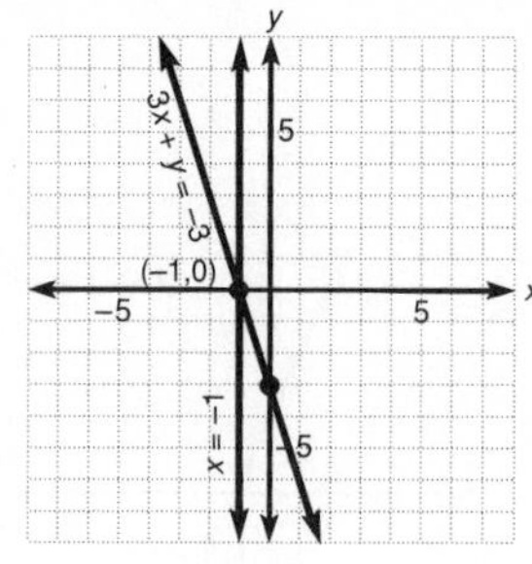

27.

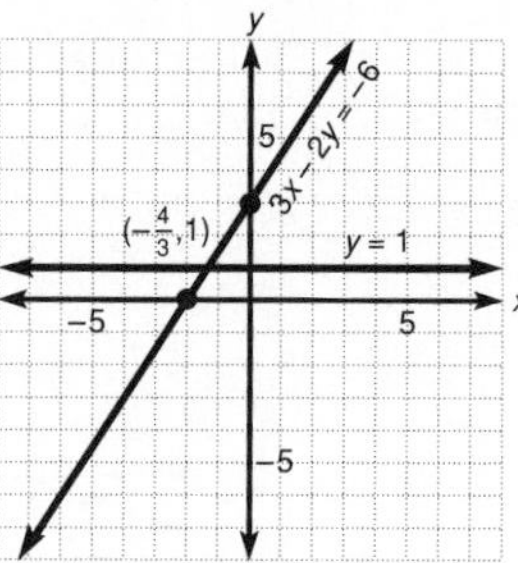

29.

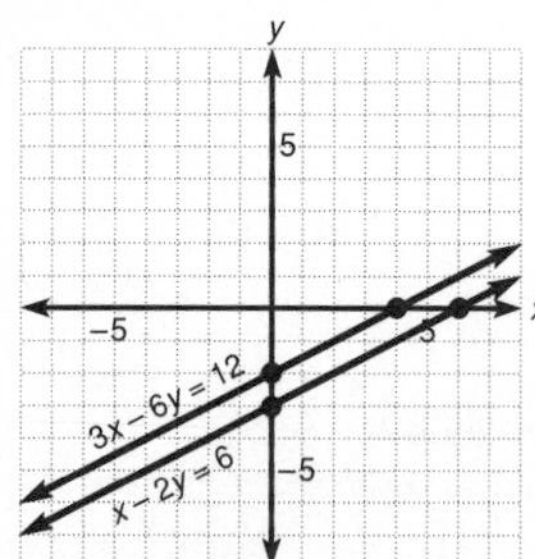

parallel, no solution, inconsistent

30.

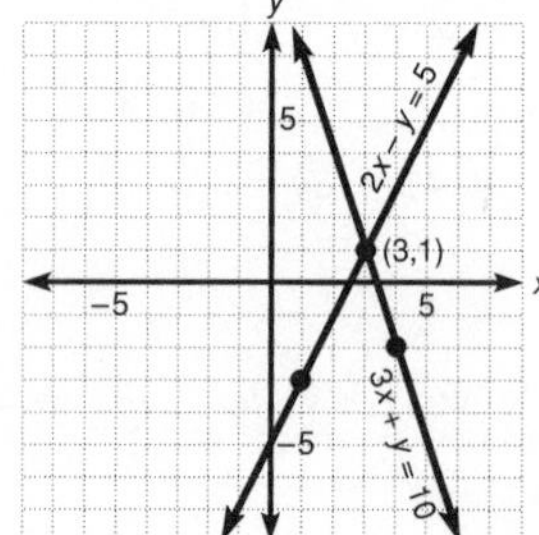

Solutions to trial exercise problems

5. $2x + y = 2$
$6x - y = 22$ $(3,-4)$
Let $x = 3$ and $y = -4$.

$2(3) + (-4) = 2$
$6 - 4 = 2$
$2 = 2$ (true)

$6(3) - (-4) = 22$
$18 + 4 = 22$
$22 = 22$ (true)

Therefore $(3,-4)$ is a simultaneous solution.

10. $y = 4x - 3$
$y = -1$ $(-1,-1)$
Let $x = -1$ and $y = -1$.

$-1 = 4(-1) - 3$
$-1 = -4 - 3$
$-1 = -7$ (false)

$y = -1$
$-1 = -1$ (true)

Therefore $(-1,-1)$ is *not* a simultaneous solution.

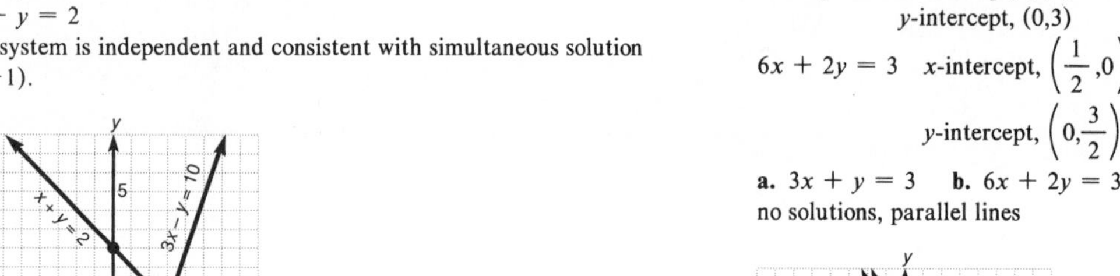

15. $3x - y = 10$
$x + y = 2$
The system is independent and consistent with simultaneous solution $(3,-1)$.

19. $3x + y = 3$ x-intercept, $(1,0)$
y-intercept, $(0,3)$
$6x + 2y = 3$ x-intercept, $\left(\frac{1}{2},0\right)$
y-intercept, $\left(0,\frac{3}{2}\right)$

a. $3x + y = 3$ **b.** $6x + 2y = 3$
no solutions, parallel lines

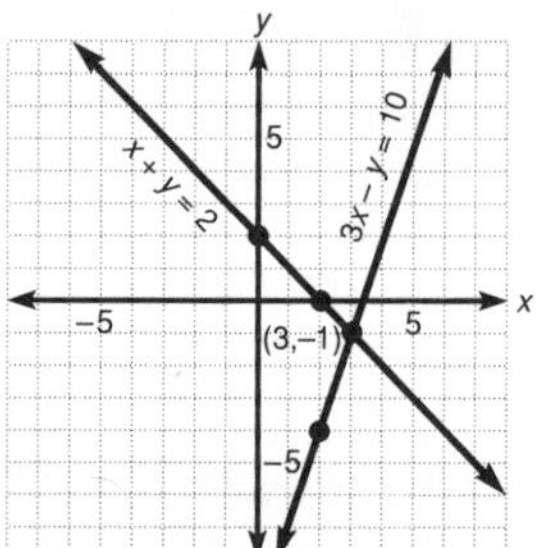

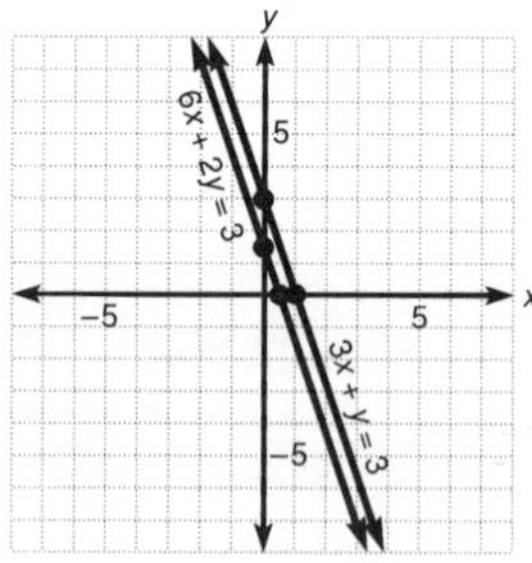

23. $-x + 4y = -4$ x-intercept, $(4,0)$
y-intercept, $(0,-1)$
$-2x + 8y = -8$ x-intercept, $(4,0)$
y-intercept, $(0,-1)$

a. $-x + 4y = -4$ **b.** $-2x + 8y = -8$
Dependent, infinitely many solutions

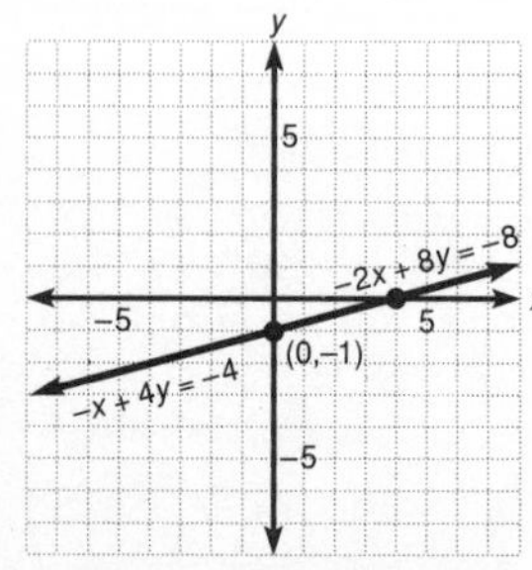

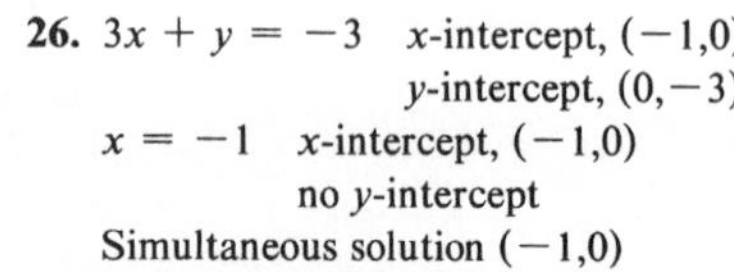

26. $3x + y = -3$ x-intercept, $(-1,0)$
y-intercept, $(0,-3)$
$x = -1$ x-intercept, $(-1,0)$
no y-intercept
Simultaneous solution $(-1,0)$

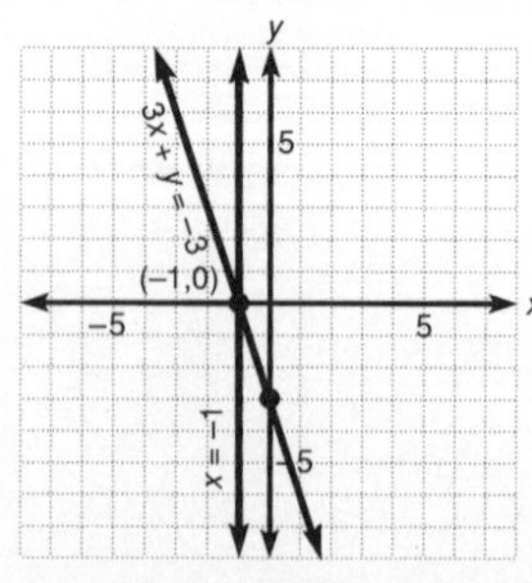

Review exercises

1. $x = \frac{4}{5}$ **2.** $3x^2 - 10x + 30 - \frac{89}{x+3}$ **3.** $y \le 5$

[number line: shaded to the left of a closed dot at 5; labels 0, 5]

4. $-3 < x \le 3$

[number line: open dot at −3, closed dot at 3, shaded between; labels −5, −3, 0, 3]

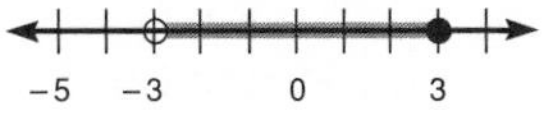

5. x^4 **6.** $x^5 - 2x^4 + x^3$

7. $4x^2 - 4xy + y^2$

Exercise 8–2

1. (3,2) **2.** (3,−1) **3.** (2,3) **5.** $\left(3,\frac{5}{4}\right)$ **6.** (4,−2) **7.** $\left(2,-\frac{2}{3}\right)$ **9.** (3,0) **10.** (−1,3) **11.** (1,1) **13.** $\left(-\frac{3}{4},2\right)$ **14.** (1,−7) **15.** (0,−2) **17.** (−2,3) **18.** no solution, inconsistent **19.** (0,0) **21.** inconsistent, no solution **22.** dependent, infinitely many solutions **23.** $\left(\frac{4}{5},\frac{9}{5}\right)$ **25.** inconsistent, no solution **26.** inconsistent, no solution **27.** dependent, infinitely many solutions **29.** (3,1) **30.** (7,3) **31.** $y = 5x$ **33.** $y = x + 20$ **34.** $3x + 3(x + 20) = 500$ **35.** $x + y = 14{,}000$

Solutions to trial exercise problems

5. $x = 8 - 4y$

$x - 4y = -2$

$x + 4y = 8$

$\underline{x - 4y = -2}$

$2x = 6$ Add terms.

$x = 3$

Use $x = 8 - 4y$

$3 = 8 - 4y$ Replace x with 3.

$-5 = -4y$

$y = \frac{5}{4}$

Simultaneous solution is $\left(3,\frac{5}{4}\right)$.

9. $x - y = 3$ Multiply by 3. $3x - 3y = 9$

$2x + 3y = 6$ $\quad\underline{2x + 3y = 6}$

$5x = 15$ Add terms.

$x = 3$

Use $x - y = 3$

$3 - y = 3$ Replace x with 3.

$-y = 0$

$y = 0$

The simultaneous solution is (3,0).

13. $4x + 7y = 11$ Multiply by −2. $-8x - 14y = -22$

$8x - 3y = -12$ $\quad\underline{8x - 3y = -12}$

$-17y = -34$ Add terms.

$y = 2$

Use $4x + 7y = 11$

$4x + 7(2) = 11$ Replace y with 2.

$4x + 14 = 11$

$4x = -3$

$x = -\frac{3}{4}$

The simultaneous solution is $\left(-\frac{3}{4},2\right)$.

18. $-3x + y = -3$

$\underline{3x - y = -1}$

$0 = -4$ Add terms.

A false statement, so there are no simultaneous solutions. The system is inconsistent.

23. $\frac{1}{2}x + \frac{1}{3}y = 1$ Multiply by 6. $3x + 2y = 6$

$\frac{2}{3}x - \frac{1}{4}y = \frac{1}{12}$ Multiply by 12. $8x - 3y = 1$

(*Note:* We have just cleared denominators.)

$3x + 2y = 6$ Multiply by 3. $9x + 6y = 18$

$8x - 3y = 1$ Multiply by 2. $\underline{16x - 6y = 2}$

$25x = 20$

$x = \frac{20}{25} = \frac{4}{5}$

Using either original equation

$\frac{1}{2}x + \frac{1}{3}y = 1$

$\frac{1}{2}\left(\frac{4}{5}\right) + \frac{1}{3}y = 1$ Replace x with $\frac{4}{5}$.

$\frac{2}{5} + \frac{1}{3}y = 1$

$\frac{1}{3}y = \frac{3}{5}$ Subtract $\frac{2}{5}$ from each member.

$y = \frac{9}{5}$ Multiply each member by 3.

The simultaneous solution is $\left(\frac{4}{5},\frac{9}{5}\right)$.

29. $x + (0.4)y = 3.4$ Multiply by 10. $10x + 4y = 34$
$(0.6)x - (1.4)y = 0.4$ Multiply by 10. $6x - 14y = 4$
(*Note:* The coefficients are now integers.)
$10x + 4y = 34$ Multiply by 3. $30x + 12y = 102$
$6x - 14y = 4$ Multiply by -5. $-30x + 70y = -20$
$82y = 82$
$y = 1$

Substitute 1 for y in $x + 0.4y = 3.4$.
$x + (0.4)(1) = 3.4$
$x + 0.4 = 3.4$
$x = 3$
The simultaneous solution is (3,1).

31. x = width
y = length
"length is five times the width"
thus $y = 5x$

Review exercises

1. $x = \frac{1}{3}$ **2.** $62\frac{1}{2}\%$ **3.** 150 **4.** $4(2x + y)(2x - y)$ **5.** $(3x - 2)^2$ **6.** $(5y + 4)(y - 2)$ **7.** $x = 1$

Exercise 8–3

1. $(-3,-9)$ **2.** $(-1,3)$ **3.** $(-2,-1)$ **5.** (6,8) **6.** (3,0) **7.** (2,0) **9.** $(-1,3)$ **10.** $(5,-5)$ **11.** (4,5) **13.** (5,8) **14.** (4,1) **15.** $\left(-\frac{3}{5},\frac{21}{5}\right)$ **17.** dependent, infinitely many solutions **18.** $(-1,0)$ **19.** $(4,-1)$ **21.** $\left(\frac{28}{3},2\right)$ **22.** $(-3,-2)$ **23.** $(-1,-1)$ **25.** inconsistent, no solution **26.** (4,0) **27.** (1,1) **29.** $\left(0,\frac{1}{2}\right)$ **30.** $(1,-1)$ **31.** $(13,-2)$ **33.** $\left(-\frac{76}{13},\frac{60}{13}\right)$ **34.** $\left(\frac{5}{3},0\right)$ **35.** (9,4) **37.** $\left(\frac{17}{14},\frac{2}{7}\right)$ **38.** $\left(-2,\frac{5}{2}\right)$ **39.** $x = 2y$ **41.** $x + y = 80$ **42.** $190x + 250y = 8{,}400$

Solutions to trial exercise problems

5. $3x - y = 10$
$y = x + 2$
$3x - (x + 2) = 10$ Replace y with $x + 2$.
$3x - x - 2 = 10$
$2x = 12$
$x = 6$
In $y = x + 2$
$y = (6) + 2$ Replace x with 6.
$y = 8$
The simultaneous solution is (6,8).

15. $2x + y = 3$
$3x - y = -6$
$y = -2x + 3$ Solve $2x + y = 3$ for y.
$3x - (-2x + 3) = -6$ Replace y with $-2x + 3$ in $3x - y = -6$.
$3x + 2x - 3 = -6$
$5x = -3$
$x = -\frac{3}{5}$
$y = -2\left(-\frac{3}{5}\right) + 3$ Replace x with $-\frac{3}{5}$ in $y = -2x + 3$.
$= \frac{6}{5} + 3$
$= \frac{6}{5} + \frac{15}{5}$
$= \frac{21}{5}$
The simultaneous solution is $\left(-\frac{3}{5},\frac{21}{5}\right)$.

7. $5x + y = 10$
$x = 2 - 3y$
$5(2 - 3y) + y = 10$ Replace x with $2 - 3y$.
$10 - 15y + y = 10$
$-14y = 0$
$y = 0$
$x = 2 - 3(0)$ Replace y with 0.
$x = 2$
The simultaneous solution is (2,0).

33. $\frac{y}{3} - \frac{x}{4} = 3$ Multiply by 12. $4y - 3x = 36$
$\frac{x}{2} + \frac{y}{5} = -2$ Multiply by 10. $2y + 5x = -20$
$4y - 3x = 36$
$2y + 5x = -20$ Multiply by -2.
$4y - 3x = 36$
$-4y - 10x = 40$
$-13x = 76$
$x = -\frac{76}{13}$
In $\frac{x}{2} + \frac{y}{5} = -2$
$\frac{-\frac{76}{13}}{2} + \frac{y}{5} = -2$ Replace x with -2.
$-\frac{38}{13} + \frac{y}{5} = -2$
$\frac{y}{5} = \frac{12}{13}$
$y = \frac{60}{13}$
The simultaneous solution is $\left(-\frac{76}{13},\frac{60}{13}\right)$.

Review exercises

1. 16 ft, 26 ft **2.** $w = 4$ yd, $\ell = 9$ yd **3.** $b = \frac{2A - hc}{h}$ **4.** $m = \frac{2}{9}$ **5.** $x = \frac{5}{8}$ **6.** $-1 < x \leq 1$

Exercise 8–4

1. $w = 4$ m $\ell = 14$ m **2.** $w = 8$ ft, $\ell = 12$ ft **3.** $w = 14$ m, $\ell = 36$ m **5.** $w = 11$ ft, $\ell = 20$ ft **6.** \$7,000 at 6%; \$13,000 at 8% **7.** \$4,000 at $7\frac{1}{2}$%; \$14,000 at 9% **9.** \$8,000 at 9%; \$22,000 at 7% **10.** \$18,000 at 18%; \$7,000 at 11% **11.** \$7,700 at 13%; \$3,300 at 9% **13.** 7 ft, 12 ft **14.** 8 ft, 16 ft **15.** 28 amps, 52 amps **17.** 38 teeth, 26 teeth **18.** 49 teeth, 34 teeth **19.** 47 volts, 79 volts **21.** 19 ohms, 5 ohms **22.** 21 ohms, 46 ohms **23.** 28 suits at \$125, 12 suits at \$185 **25.** 40 cc of 10%, 80 cc of 4% **26.** $666\frac{2}{3}$ liters of 4%, $333\frac{1}{3}$ liters of 2.5% **27.** 3 oz of 60%, 9 oz of 80% **29.** $87\frac{1}{2}$% **30.** 10 liters of 60%, 20 liters of 30% **31.** $5\frac{5}{7}$ cl of 38%, $94\frac{2}{7}$ cl of 3% **33.** $m = -2, b = 5, y = -2x + 5$ **34.** $y = -3x + 4$ **35.** $y = -2x - 1$ **37.** 75 mph and 25 mph **38.** boat at 10 mph, current at 2 mph **39.** Jim at 3 mph, Jane at $2\frac{1}{2}$ mph

Solutions to trial exercise problems

1. The perimeter P of a rectangle, by formula, is found by $P = 2\ell + 2w$, where ℓ is the length and w is the width of the rectangle. From "the perimeter of a rectangle is 36 meters," we get $2\ell + 2w = 36$. From "the length is 2 meters more than three times the width," we get $\ell = 3w + 2$.

We solve the system $2\ell + 2w = 36$,
$\ell = 3w + 2$.

Using substitution, substitute $3w + 2$ for ℓ in the first equation.

$2(3w + 2) + 2w = 36$ Then $\ell = 3w + 2$
$6w + 4 + 2w = 36$ $\ell = 3(4) + 2$
$8w + 4 = 36$ $\ell = 12 + 2$
$8w = 32$ $\ell = 14$
$w = 4$

The solution of the system is $(\ell,w) = (14,4)$. The rectangle has length $\ell = 14$ m and width $w = 4$ m.

6. Let x = the amount invested at 8% interest and y = the amount invested at 6% interest. From "Phil has \$20,000, part of which he invests at 8% interest and the rest at 6%," we get $x + y = 20{,}000$. From "if his total income from the two investments was \$1,460," we get $0.08x + 0.06y = 1{,}460$. Multiply by 100 to clear decimal points: $8x + 6y = 146{,}000$.

We solve the system $x + y = 20{,}000$
$8x + 6y = 146{,}000$.

Multiply the first equation by -6: $(-6)x + (-6)y = -6(20{,}000)$
$-6x - 6y = -120{,}000$
$8x + 6y = 146{,}000$
Add. $2x = 26{,}000$
$x = 13{,}000$

Substitute 13,000 for x in $x + y = 20{,}000$: $13{,}000 + y = 20{,}000$, $y = 7{,}000$. Phil invested \$13,000 at 8% and \$7,000 at 6% interest.

Check: (0.08)13,000 = \$1,040.00
(0.06)7,000 = \$ 420.00
Add to get income. = \$1,460.00

13. Let x = the length of the longer piece of pipe and y = the length of the shorter piece of pipe. From "a piece of pipe is 19 feet long," we get $x + y = 19$. From "one piece is 5 feet longer than the other piece," we get $x = y + 5$.

Solve the system: $x + y = 19$
$x = y + 5$.

Use substitution: Substitute $y + 5$ for x in $x + y = 19$.

$(y + 5) + y = 19$
$2y + 5 = 19$
$2y = 14$
$y = 7$

Substitute 7 for y in $x + y = 19$.

$x + 7 = 19$
$x = 12$

The pipe is cut into pieces 12 feet and 7 feet long.

33. Using $y = mx + b$, substitute
(a) 2 for x and 1 for y $1 = 2m + b$
(b) -1 for x and 7 for y $7 = -m + b$

$2m + b = 1$ $2m + b = 1$
$-m + b = 7$ Multiply by 2. $-2m + 2b = 14$
$3b = 15$
$b = 5$

$m = -2, b = 5,$
$y = -2x + 5$

Using $2m + b = 1$
$2m + 5 = 1$ Replace b with 5.
$2m = -4$
$m = -2$

25. Let x = the number of cubic centimeters (cc) of the 10% solution and y = the number of cc of the 4% solution.

Then $x + y = 120$ and $(0.10)x + (0.04)y = (0.06)120$.

Multiply the second equation by 100: $10x + 4y = 6(120)$, so $10x + 4y = 720$. Solve the system.

$x + y = 120$ Multiply by -4. $-4x - 4y = -480$
$10x + 4y = 720$ $10x + 4y = 720$
Add. $6x = 240$
$x = 40$

Substitute 40 for x in $x + y = 120$.

$40 + y = 120$
$y = 80$

Therefore the mechanic must have 40 cc of 10% solution and 80 cc of 4% solution.

37. Let x = the speed of the faster car and y = the speed of the slower car. Then using "if they drive toward each other they will meet in 1 hour," $t = 1$ for each car, so $x + y = 100$. Using "if they drive in the same direction they will meet in 2 hours," $t = 2$ for each car and the faster car travels 100 miles farther, so $2x - 2y = 100$.
We now have the system $x + y = 100$
$2x - 2y = 100$.
Multiply the first equation by 2.

$$\begin{aligned} 2x + 2y &= 200 \\ \underline{2x - 2y} &= \underline{100} \\ 4x \quad\quad &= 300 \\ x &= 75 \end{aligned}$$

Then since $x + y = 100$, $75 + y = 100$, $y = 25$. The average speeds are 75 mph and 25 mph.

38. Let x = the speed of the boat in still water and y = the speed of the current. Using $d = rt$ and (a) "a boat can travel 24 miles downstream in 2 hours," we get $2x + 2y = 24$; using $d = rt$ and (b) "and 16 miles upstream in the same length of time," we get $2x - 2y = 16$.
We have the system of equations $2x + 2y = 24$

$$\begin{aligned} \underline{2x - 2y} &= \underline{16} \\ 4x \quad\quad &= 40 \\ x &= 10. \end{aligned}$$

Then substituting 10 for x, $2(10) + 2y = 24$

$$\begin{aligned} 20 + 2y &= 24 \\ 2y &= 4 \\ y &= 2 \end{aligned}$$

Therefore the boat travels at 10 mph in still water and the current is traveling at 2 mph.

Review exercises

1. $-64x^6y^9$ **2.** $\frac{y}{x^3}$ **3.** $\frac{7}{12}$ **4.** $x^2 - 5x + 4$ **5.** $12x^4 + 8x^3 - 12x^2$ **6.** $9y^2 - 4$ **7.** $16x^2 - 40xy + 25y^2$ **8.** $x = -1$ **9.** $x = 5$ or $x = -2$

Chapter 8 review

1.

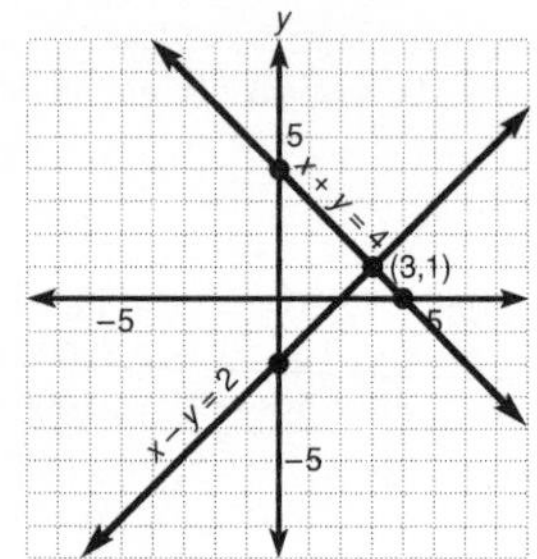

(3,1)

2.

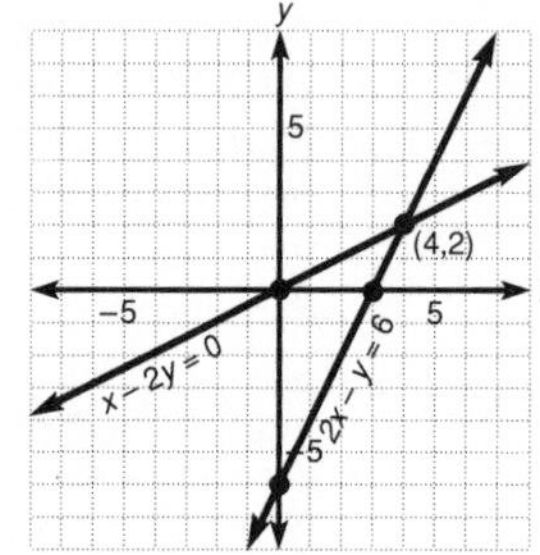

(4,2)

3.

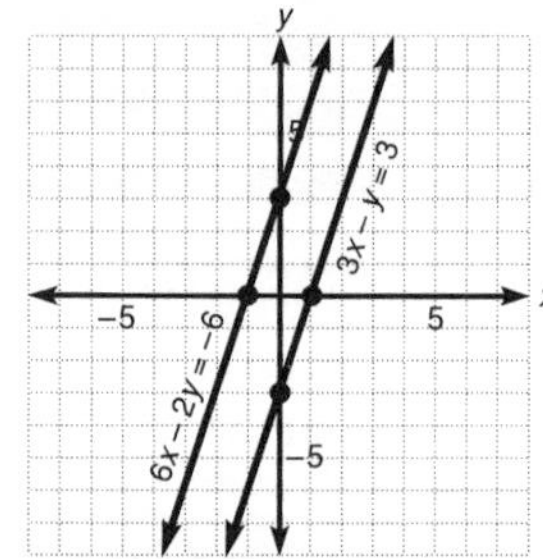

inconsistent, no solution

4.

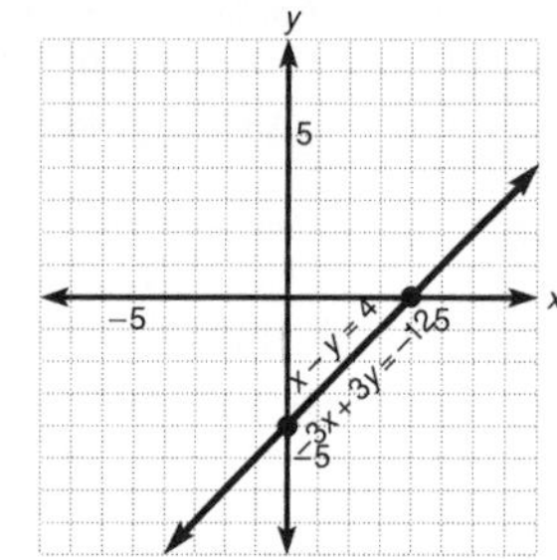

dependent, infinitely many solutions

5. (3,0) **6.** (−1,1) **7.** inconsistent, no solution **8.** (5,−3) **9.** (5,2) **10.** (2,1) **11.** (5,3) **12.** $\left(\frac{9}{2},8\right)$ **13.** (3,1) **14.** (4,−1) **15.** (2,0) **16.** dependent, infinitely many solutions **17.** $\left(-\frac{6}{5}, -\frac{13}{5}\right)$ **18.** $\left(-\frac{3}{2},4\right)$ **19.** $\left(\frac{26}{19}, \frac{8}{19}\right)$ **20.** inconsistent, no solution **21.** $w = 7$ ft, $\ell = 25$ ft **22.** $8,000 at 23%; $10,000 at 14% **23.** 12 teeth, 54 teeth **24.** 90 ml of 80%, 30 ml of 60%

Chapter 8 cumulative test

1. $-\frac{1}{64}$ **2.** $\frac{4}{3}$ **3.** 1 **4.** $\frac{1}{25}$ **5.** $\frac{8}{15}$ **6.** $-\frac{1}{3}$ **7.** $3a(a^2 + 5a + 9)$ **8.** $(x + 11)(x - 11)$ **9.** $(a - 5)(x + y)$ **10.** $(3a + b)(a - 2b)$ **11.** $7x(x + 1)(x - 1)$ **12.** $(5b - 2)(b - 4)$ **13.** $\frac{y^2}{2x}$ **14.** $\frac{32 - 3x}{x(x - 9)}$ **15.** $81x^4y^6z^6$ **16.** $9x^2y - 14y^2$ **17.** $\frac{a - 7}{7}$ **18.** $25x^2 - 30xy + 9y^2$ **19.** $2y + 6$ **20.** $a = \frac{15}{8}$ **21.** $x = 0, x = -9$ **22.** $x = -\frac{11}{36}$ **23.** $x = \frac{3}{7}, x = -1$ **24.** 6 **25.** $-\frac{1}{3}$ **26.** $\frac{4}{5}$ **27.** (4,2) **28.** (1,−2) **29.** (−2,1) **30.** inconsistent, no solution **31.** 19 and 6 **32.** 37 and 42 **33.** 5 and 6 or −6 and −5 **34.** 0 or 5 **35.** 2 or 1 **36.** $2\frac{2}{9}$ hr **37.** $w = 7$ in., $\ell = 13$ in

Chapter 9

Proficiency check

1. a. 25 **b.** 16 **2. a.** $-b^2 + 4b$ **b.** x^2y^2 **3. a.** $x = 3$ **b.** $a = 1$ **4. a.** $6a^2 - 12a$ **b.** $15x^3y^4 - 20x^4y^3 + 5x^2y^6$ **c.** $4a^2 - b^2$ **d.** $4x^2 - 7xy - 2y^2$

Exercise 9–1

1. 10 **2.** 6 **3.** 5 **5.** −12 **6.** −9 **7.** −11 **9.** 4.243 **10.** 4.899 **11.** 6.403 **13.** −7.211 **14.** −3.162 **15.** 24 amps **17.** 13 units **18.** 5 units **19.** $c = 5m$ **21.** $c = 13$ in. **22.** $c = 17$ cm **23.** $b = 8$ yd **25.** $c = 20$ mm **26.** $c = 26$ in **27.** 2 **29.** 5 **30.** 4 **31.** −3 **33.** 2 **34.** 3 **35.** −3 **37.** 2 **38.** 2 **39.** −3 **41.** 1 **42.** 1 **43.** −1 **45.** 9 units **46.** 6 units

Solutions to trial exercise problems

15. $I = \sqrt{\frac{\text{watts}}{\text{ohms}}} = \sqrt{\frac{(\ )}{(\ )}} = \sqrt{\frac{1{,}728}{3}} = \sqrt{576} = 24$. Answer: 24 amperes. **27.** $\sqrt[3]{8} = 2$, since $2 \cdot 2 \cdot 2 = 2^3 = 8$.
35. $-\sqrt[4]{81} = -3$, since $3 \cdot 3 \cdot 3 \cdot 3 = 3^4 = 81$ and the negative sign indicates that we want the negative root.
41. $\sqrt[10]{1} = 1$, since $1^{10} = 1$. 1 raised to any power is 1 and the nth root of 1 is 1.

Review exercises

1. 3^2 **2.** $2^2 \cdot 3$ **3.** 2^3 **4.** $2^3 \cdot 5$ **5.** $2 \cdot 5^2$ **6.** 3^4 **7.** 2^6 **8.** 2^4

Exercise 9–2

1. 4 **2.** $3\sqrt{7}$ **3.** $2\sqrt{7}$ **5.** $a^3\sqrt{a}$ **6.** $a^2\sqrt{a}$ **7.** $2ab\sqrt{b}$ **9.** $3ab^2\sqrt{3ab}$ **10.** $2x^2z\sqrt{6xyz}$ **11.** $3\sqrt{2}$ **13.** 15 **14.** 11 **15.** $2\sqrt{15}$ **17.** $5\sqrt{15}$ **18.** 20 **19.** $5\sqrt{3}$ **21.** $5x\sqrt{3}$ **22.** $2x\sqrt{21y}$ **23.** $4b\sqrt{3a}$ **25.** 13 ft **26.** 30 mph **27.** 24 mph **29.** $2\sqrt[4]{2}$ **30.** $2\sqrt[5]{2}$ **31.** $2\sqrt[3]{3}$ **33.** $b^2\sqrt[3]{b^2}$ **34.** x^3 **35.** y^3 **37.** $b\sqrt[3]{4a^2}$ **38.** $2s^2\sqrt[3]{r^2s^2}$ **39.** $2ab\sqrt[3]{2ab^2}$ **41.** $3ab^3\sqrt[3]{3a^2b^2}$ **42.** a **43.** $b\sqrt[3]{b}$ **45.** a **46.** $5ab\sqrt[3]{3a}$ **47.** $3ab\sqrt[3]{2b}$ **49.** $3b\sqrt[4]{3a^3}$ **50.** $5x^2y^3\sqrt[3]{3y}$ **51.** $4a^5b^3\sqrt[3]{3b}$ **53.** 2 in. **54.** $3\sqrt[3]{3}$ in. **55.** 2 in.

Solutions to trial exercise problems

7. $\sqrt{4a^2b^3} = \sqrt{4 \cdot a^2 \cdot b^2 \cdot b} = \sqrt{4}\sqrt{a^2}\sqrt{b^2}\sqrt{b} = 2ab\sqrt{b}$ **11.** $\sqrt{6}\sqrt{3} = \sqrt{18} = \sqrt{9 \cdot 2} = \sqrt{9}\sqrt{2} = 3\sqrt{2}$
22. $\sqrt{6x}\sqrt{14xy} = \sqrt{84x^2y} = \sqrt{4 \cdot 21x^2y} = \sqrt{4}\sqrt{x^2}\sqrt{21y} = 2x\sqrt{21y}$ **34.** $\sqrt[3]{x^9} = \sqrt[3]{x^3 \cdot x^3 \cdot x^3} = \sqrt[3]{x^3}\sqrt[3]{x^3}\sqrt[3]{x^3} = x \cdot x \cdot x = x^3$
46. $\sqrt[3]{5a^2b}\sqrt[3]{75a^2b^2} = \sqrt[3]{375a^4b^3} = \sqrt[3]{125 \cdot 3 \cdot a^3 \cdot a \cdot b^3} = \sqrt[3]{125}\sqrt[3]{a^3}\sqrt[3]{b^3}\sqrt[3]{3a} = 5ab\sqrt[3]{3a}$
53. $h = \sqrt[3]{\frac{12I}{b}} = \sqrt[3]{\frac{12(\ )}{(\ )}} = \sqrt[3]{\frac{12(2)}{(3)}} = \sqrt[3]{\frac{24}{3}} = \sqrt[3]{8} = \sqrt[3]{2^3} = 2$. Answer: $h = 2$ inches.

Review exercises

1. $\frac{7}{8}$ **2.** $-4x^2y$ **3.** $\frac{2y + 10}{y + 1}$ **4.** 5 **5.** 3 **6.** 4 **7.** 6 **8.** x

Exercise 9–3

1. $\frac{3}{5}$ **2.** $\frac{5}{6}$ **3.** $\frac{5}{7}$ **5.** $\frac{\sqrt{3}}{2}$ **6.** $\frac{\sqrt{5}}{3}$ **7.** $\frac{8}{a}$ **9.** $\frac{\sqrt{2}}{2}$ **10.** $\frac{\sqrt{3}}{3}$ **11.** $\frac{2\sqrt{7}}{7}$ **13.** $\frac{\sqrt{15}}{15}$ **14.** $\frac{\sqrt{14}}{14}$ **15.** $\frac{2\sqrt{3}}{15}$ **17.** $\sqrt{2}$ **18.** $2\sqrt{3}$ **19.** $\frac{5\sqrt{2}}{2}$ **21.** $\frac{x\sqrt{y}}{y}$ **22.** $\frac{\sqrt{a}}{a}$ **23.** $\frac{\sqrt{x}}{x}$ **25.** a^2 **26.** $\frac{2}{3}$ **27.** $\frac{1}{2}$ **29.** $\frac{3}{5}$ **30.** $\frac{\sqrt[3]{a^2b}}{b}$ **31.** $\frac{a^2\sqrt[3]{3}}{b}$ **33.** $\frac{\sqrt[5]{a^4}}{b^2}$ **34.** $\frac{2\sqrt[5]{x^4}}{y}$ **35.** $\frac{ab^2\sqrt[4]{bc}}{c^3}$ **37.** $\frac{\sqrt[5]{x^3y^2}}{z^3}$ **38.** $\frac{2\sqrt[3]{3}}{3}$ **39.** $\frac{\sqrt[3]{20}}{5}$ **41.** $\frac{2\sqrt[4]{5}}{5}$ **42.** $\frac{\sqrt[4]{12}}{2}$ **43.** $\frac{x\sqrt[3]{y}}{y}$ **45.** $b\sqrt[3]{a}$ **46.** $x\sqrt[5]{y^2}$ **47.** $\frac{a\sqrt[3]{bc^2}}{bc}$ **49.** $\frac{\sqrt[3]{a^2bc^2}}{bc}$ **50.** $\frac{\sqrt[5]{a^3b}}{b}$ **51.** $\sqrt[3]{a^2b}$ **53.** 3 units **54.** 6 units

Solutions to trial exercise problems

15. $\sqrt{\frac{4}{75}} = \frac{\sqrt{4}}{\sqrt{75}} = \frac{\sqrt{2^2}}{\sqrt{3 \cdot 5^2}} = \frac{2}{5\sqrt{3}} \cdot \frac{\sqrt{3}}{\sqrt{3}} = \frac{2\sqrt{3}}{5 \cdot 3} = \frac{2\sqrt{3}}{15}$ **31.** $\sqrt[3]{\frac{3a^6}{b^3}} = \frac{\sqrt[3]{3a^6}}{\sqrt[3]{b^3}} = \frac{a^2\sqrt[3]{3}}{b}$ **35.** $\sqrt[4]{\frac{a^4b^9}{c^{11}}} = \frac{\sqrt[4]{a^4b^9}}{\sqrt[4]{c^{11}}} = \frac{ab^2\sqrt[4]{b}}{c^2\sqrt[4]{c^3}} \cdot \frac{\sqrt[4]{c^1}}{\sqrt[4]{c^1}}$
$= \frac{ab^2\sqrt[4]{bc}}{c^2\sqrt[4]{c^4}} = \frac{ab^2\sqrt[4]{bc}}{c^2 \cdot c} = \frac{ab^2\sqrt[4]{bc}}{c^3}$

41. $\sqrt[4]{\frac{16}{125}} = \frac{\sqrt[4]{16}}{\sqrt[4]{125}} = \frac{\sqrt[4]{2^4}}{\sqrt[4]{5^3}} = \frac{2}{\sqrt[4]{5^3}} \cdot \frac{\sqrt[4]{5^1}}{\sqrt[4]{5^1}} = \frac{2\sqrt[4]{5^1}}{\sqrt[4]{5^4}} = \frac{2\sqrt[4]{5}}{5}$ **45.** $\frac{ab}{\sqrt[3]{a^2}} \cdot \frac{\sqrt[3]{a^1}}{\sqrt[3]{a^1}} = \frac{ab\sqrt[3]{a}}{\sqrt[3]{a^3}} = \frac{ab\sqrt[3]{a}}{a} = b\sqrt[3]{a}$

47. $\sqrt[3]{\frac{a^3}{b^2c}} = \frac{\sqrt[3]{a^3}}{\sqrt[3]{b^2c}} = \frac{a}{\sqrt[3]{b^2c}} \cdot \frac{\sqrt[3]{b^1c^2}}{\sqrt[3]{b^1c^2}} = \frac{a\sqrt[3]{bc^2}}{\sqrt[3]{b^3c^3}} = \frac{a\sqrt[3]{bc^2}}{bc}$ **53.** $r = \sqrt[3]{\frac{3V}{4\pi}} = \sqrt[3]{\frac{3(\ )}{4(\ )}} = \sqrt[3]{\frac{3(113.04)}{4(3.14)}} = \sqrt[3]{\frac{339.12}{12.56}} = \sqrt[3]{27} = \sqrt[3]{3^3} = 3$.
Answer: 3 units.

Review exercises

1. $6x$ **2.** $4y$ **3.** $8ab$ **4.** $5xy$ **5.** $x^2 - 9$ **6.** $x^2 - y^2$ **7.** $16x^2 - 9y^2$ **8.** $9 - 4x^2$

Exercise 9–4

1. $9\sqrt{3}$ **2.** $6\sqrt{7}$ **3.** $10\sqrt{5}$ **5.** $6\sqrt{3}$ **6.** $7\sqrt{5}$ **7.** $3\sqrt{7}$ **9.** $3\sqrt{a}$ **10.** $7\sqrt{x}$ **11.** $8\sqrt{a}$ **13.** $7\sqrt{xy}$ **14.** $2\sqrt{x} + 2\sqrt{y}$ **15.** $8\sqrt{a} + 2\sqrt{ab}$ **17.** $4\sqrt{xy} + 3\sqrt{y}$ **18.** $5\sqrt{5}$ **19.** $7\sqrt{2}$ **21.** $\sqrt{3}$ **22.** $8\sqrt{3}$ **23.** $17\sqrt{7}$ **25.** $7\sqrt{2}$ **26.** $7\sqrt{3}$ **27.** $2\sqrt{3} + 8\sqrt{2}$ **29.** $7\sqrt{2a}$ **30.** $\sqrt{2a}$ **31.** $-\sqrt{x}$ **33.** $17\sqrt{2a}$ **34.** $9\sqrt{3b}$ **35.** $2\sqrt{2a} + 6\sqrt{3a}$ **37.** 14 units **38.** 17 ft **39.** 8.1 units by 8.1 units **41.** $6\sqrt[5]{2}$ **42.** $17\sqrt[4]{3}$ **43.** $5\sqrt[3]{2}$ **45.** $3\sqrt[3]{3} + 10\sqrt[3]{2}$ **46.** $5\sqrt[3]{a^2}$ **47.** $5\sqrt[4]{x^3}$ **49.** $\sqrt[3]{x^2y}$ **50.** $3x^2\sqrt[3]{y}$ **51.** $2a\sqrt[3]{b^2}$

Solutions to trial exercise problems

14. $3\sqrt{x} + 2\sqrt{y} - \sqrt{x} = 3\sqrt{x} - \sqrt{x} + 2\sqrt{y} = 2\sqrt{x} + 2\sqrt{y}$ **18.** $\sqrt{20} + 3\sqrt{5} = \sqrt{2^2 \cdot 5} + 3\sqrt{5} = 2\sqrt{5} + 3\sqrt{5} = 5\sqrt{5}$ **29.** $\sqrt{50a} + \sqrt{8a} = \sqrt{2 \cdot 5^2 \cdot a} + \sqrt{2^3 \cdot a} = 5\sqrt{2a} + 2\sqrt{2a} = 7\sqrt{2a}$ **37.** $h = b + s$, where $s = 6$ units and $b = \sqrt{c^2 - s^2} = \sqrt{(10)^2 - (6)^2}$ $= \sqrt{100 - 36} = \sqrt{64} = 8$. Then $h = b + s = (8) + (6) = 14$. Answer: 14 units. **43.** $\sqrt[3]{16} + \sqrt[3]{54} = \sqrt[3]{2^4} + \sqrt[3]{2 \cdot 3^3} = 2\sqrt[3]{2} + 3\sqrt[3]{2} = 5\sqrt[3]{2}$ **50.** $\sqrt[3]{x^6y} + 2x^2\sqrt[3]{y} = x^2\sqrt[3]{y} + 2x^2\sqrt[3]{y} = (1 + 2)x^2\sqrt[3]{y} = 3x^2\sqrt[3]{y}$

Review exercises

1. $6x^2 - 3xy$ **2.** $2a^4 - 2a^2b^2$ **3.** $x^2 - 2x + 1$ **4.** $y^2 - 1$ **5.** $4x^2 - 1$ **6.** $x^2 + 5xy + 6y^2$ **7.** $x^2 - 2xy + y^2$ **8.** $a^2 + 4ab + 4b^2$

Exercise 9–5

1. $3\sqrt{2} + 3\sqrt{3}$ **2.** $10\sqrt{6} + 5\sqrt{2}$ **3.** $\sqrt{6} + \sqrt{14}$ **5.** $6\sqrt{6} - 3\sqrt{22}$ **6.** $2\sqrt{3} + 3\sqrt{2}$ **7.** $5\sqrt{3} - 5\sqrt{2}$ **9.** $14\sqrt{5} - 42\sqrt{2}$ **10.** $a\sqrt{b} + \sqrt{ab}$ **11.** $3a + \sqrt{ab}$ **13.** $14 + 7\sqrt{2}$ **14.** $30 - 10\sqrt{5}$ **15.** $12 - 25\sqrt{a} + 12a$ **17.** 1 **18.** 2 **19.** -2 **21.** $9 + 4\sqrt{5}$ **22.** $16 - 6\sqrt{7}$ **23.** $x + 2\sqrt{xy} + y$ **25.** $x - y$ **26.** $4a - b$ **27.** $x^2y - z$ **29.** $4x + 4y\sqrt{x} + y^2$ **30.** $9a + 6\sqrt{ab} + b$ **31.** $11 + \sqrt{3}$ **33.** $\sqrt{a} - 3\sqrt{b}$ **34.** $a\sqrt{b} - \sqrt{c}$ **35.** $-\dfrac{\sqrt{2} - 3}{7}$ or $\dfrac{-\sqrt{2} + 3}{7}$ **37.** $-\dfrac{14 - 7\sqrt{7}}{3}$ or $\dfrac{7\sqrt{7} - 14}{3}$ **38.** $6 + 2\sqrt{6}$ **39.** $\sqrt{6} + \sqrt{3}$ **41.** $\dfrac{6\sqrt{3} + 3\sqrt{5}}{7}$ **42.** $\dfrac{4\sqrt{3} + 2\sqrt{6}}{3}$ **43.** $-\dfrac{3 + \sqrt{5}}{2}$ or $\dfrac{-3 - \sqrt{5}}{2}$ **45.** $\dfrac{a + 2b\sqrt{a} + b^2}{a - b^2}$

Solutions to trial exercise problems

5. $3\sqrt{2}(2\sqrt{3} - \sqrt{11}) = 3\sqrt{2} \cdot 2\sqrt{3} - 3\sqrt{2} \cdot \sqrt{11} = 6\sqrt{6} - 3\sqrt{22}$ **15.** $(3 - 4\sqrt{a})(4 - 3\sqrt{a}) = 3 \cdot 4 - 3 \cdot 3\sqrt{a} - 4\sqrt{a} \cdot 4 + 4\sqrt{a} \cdot 3\sqrt{a}$ $= 12 - 9\sqrt{a} - 16\sqrt{a} + 12 \cdot a = 12 - 25\sqrt{a} + 12a$ **17.** $(\sqrt{3} + \sqrt{2})(\sqrt{3} - \sqrt{2})$ Conjugates, therefore $= (\sqrt{3})^2 - (\sqrt{2})^2 = 3 - 2 = 1$. **21.** $(2 + \sqrt{5})^2 = (2 + \sqrt{5})(2 + \sqrt{5}) = 2 \cdot 2 + 2\sqrt{5} + 2\sqrt{5} + \sqrt{5}\sqrt{5} = 4 + 4\sqrt{5} + 5 = 9 + 4\sqrt{5}$ **26.** $(2\sqrt{a} - \sqrt{b})(2\sqrt{a} + \sqrt{b})$ Conjugates, therefore $= (2\sqrt{a})^2 - (\sqrt{b})^2 = 2^2(\sqrt{a})^2 - b = 4a - b$. **38.** $\dfrac{6}{3 - \sqrt{6}} = \dfrac{6}{3 - \sqrt{6}} \cdot \dfrac{3 + \sqrt{6}}{3 + \sqrt{6}} = \dfrac{6(3 + \sqrt{6})}{(3)^2 - (\sqrt{6})^2} = \dfrac{6(3 + \sqrt{6})}{9 - 6}$ $= \dfrac{6(3 + \sqrt{6})}{3} = 2(3 + \sqrt{6}) = 6 + 2\sqrt{6}$ **43.** $\dfrac{1 + \sqrt{5}}{1 - \sqrt{5}} = \dfrac{1 + \sqrt{5}}{1 - \sqrt{5}} \cdot \dfrac{1 + \sqrt{5}}{1 + \sqrt{5}} = \dfrac{1 \cdot 1 + 1 \cdot \sqrt{5} + 1 \cdot \sqrt{5} + \sqrt{5} \cdot \sqrt{5}}{(1)^2 - (\sqrt{5})^2}$ $= \dfrac{1 + 2\sqrt{5} + 5}{1 - 5} = \dfrac{6 + 2\sqrt{5}}{-4} = \dfrac{2(3 + \sqrt{5})}{-4} = \dfrac{-(3 + \sqrt{5})}{2} = \dfrac{-3 - \sqrt{5}}{2}$

Review exercises

1. 7 **2.** x **3.** $x + 1$ **4.** $x^2 + 2x + 1$ **5.** $x^2 - 4x + 4$ **6.** $\{-2,3\}$ **7.** $\{2,8\}$ **8.** $\{-1,0\}$

Exercise 9–6

1. $\{16\}$ **2.** $\{11\}$ **3.** $\{28\}$ **5.** $\{15\}$ **6.** $\{9\}$ **7.** $\emptyset$ **9.** $\{4\}$ **10.** $\{6\}$ **11.** $\{4\}$ **13.** $\emptyset$ **14.** $\{0\}$ **15.** $\{0\}$ **17.** $\{2\}$ **18.** $\{1\}$ **19.** $\left\{-\dfrac{3}{4}\right\}$ **21.** $\emptyset$ **22.** $\{2\}$ **23.** $\{3\}$ **25.** $\{4\}$ **26.** $\{6\}$ **27.** $\{8\}$ **29.** $\{12\}$ **30.** $\{9\}$ **31.** $\{2\}$ **33.** 4 **34.** 3 **35.** 5

Solutions to trial exercise problems

7.
$\sqrt{x} + 7 = 5$
$\sqrt{x} = -2$
$(\sqrt{x})^2 = (-2)^2$
$x = 4$
Check:
$\sqrt{4} + 7 = 5$
$2 + 7 = 5$
$9 = 5$ (false)
Therefore no solution and the solution set is $\emptyset$.

9.
$\sqrt{2x + 1} = \sqrt{x + 5}$
$(\sqrt{2x + 1})^2 = (\sqrt{x + 5})^2$
$2x + 1 = x + 5$
$x + 1 = 5$
$x = 4$
Check:
$\sqrt{2(4) + 1} = \sqrt{(4) + 5}$
$\sqrt{8 + 1} = \sqrt{9}$
$\sqrt{9} = \sqrt{9}$
$3 = 3$ (true)
$\{4\}$

14.
$\sqrt{x}\sqrt{x + 2} = 0$
$\sqrt{x(x + 2)} = 0$
$\sqrt{x^2 + 2x} = 0$
$(\sqrt{x^2 + 2x})^2 = (0)^2$
$x^2 + 2x = 0$
$x(x + 2) = 0$
$x = 0$ or $x + 2 = 0$
$x = 0$ $\quad x = -2$
Check: $\sqrt{(0)}\sqrt{(0) + 2} = 0$
$0 \cdot \sqrt{2} = 0$
$0 = 0$ (true)
$\sqrt{(-2)}\sqrt{(-2) + 2} = 0$
$\sqrt{-2} \cdot \sqrt{0} = 0$
Since $\sqrt{-2}$ does not have meaning in the set of real numbers, -2 is not a solution. Therefore, 0 is the only solution, $\{0\}$.

19. $\sqrt{x^2+1} = x+2$
$(\sqrt{x^2+1})^2 = (x+2)^2$
$x^2+1 = (x+2)(x+2)$
$x^2+1 = x^2+2x+2x+4$
$x^2+1 = x^2+4x+4$
$1 = 4x+4$
$-3 = 4x$
$-\frac{3}{4} = x$
Check:
$\sqrt{\left(-\frac{3}{4}\right)^2+1} = \left(-\frac{3}{4}\right)+2$
$\sqrt{\frac{9}{16}+1} = -\frac{3}{4}+\frac{8}{4}$
$\sqrt{\frac{9}{16}+\frac{16}{16}} = \frac{5}{4}$
$\sqrt{\frac{25}{16}} = \frac{5}{4}$
$\frac{\sqrt{25}}{\sqrt{16}} = \frac{5}{4}$
$\frac{5}{4} = \frac{5}{4}$ (true)
$\left\{-\frac{3}{4}\right\}$

23. $\sqrt{x+6} = x$
$(\sqrt{x+6})^2 = (x)^2$
$x+6 = x^2$
$0 = x^2-x-6$
$0 = (x-3)(x+2)$
$x-3=0$ or $x+2=0$
$x=3$ $x=-2$
Check:
$\sqrt{(3)+6} = (3)$
$\sqrt{9} = 3$
$3 = 3$ (true)
$\sqrt{(-2)+6} = (-2)$
$\sqrt{4} = -2$
$2 = -2$ (false)
$\{3\}$

27. $\sqrt{x-4} = x-6$
$(\sqrt{x-4})^2 = (x-6)^2$
$x-4 = (x-6)(x-6)$
$x-4 = x^2-6x-6x+36$
$x-4 = x^2-12x+36$
$0 = x^2-13x+40$
$0 = (x-8)(x-5)$
$x-8=0$ or $x-5=0$
$x=8$ $x=5$
Check:
$\sqrt{(8)-4} = (8)-6$
$\sqrt{4} = 2$
$2 = 2$ (true)
$\sqrt{(5)-4} = (5)-6$
$\sqrt{1} = -1$
$1 = -1$ (false)
$\{8\}$

33. Let x = the number.
$\sqrt{x+12} = x$
$(\sqrt{x+12})^2 = (x)^2$
$x+12 = x^2$
$0 = x^2-x-12$
$0 = (x-4)(x+3)$
$x-4=0$ or $x+3=0$
$x=4$ $x=-3$
Check:
$\sqrt{(4)+12} = (4)$
$\sqrt{16} = 4$
$4 = 4$ (true)
$\sqrt{(-3)+12} = (-3)$
$\sqrt{9} = -3$
$3 = -3$ (false)
Hence the number is 4.

Review exercises

1. $(x+2)(x-2)$ **2.** $(x+6)(x+3)$ **3.** $(x+2)(x-5)$ **4.** $(x-3)^2$ **5.** 9 **6.** 7 **7.** 11 **8.** $\{-8,8\}$

Chapter 9 review

1. 9 **2.** 5 **3.** −3 **4.** −7 **5.** $2\sqrt{10}$ **6.** $3ab\sqrt{2b}$ **7.** $2\sqrt{7}$ **8.** $6\sqrt{5}$ **9.** $\frac{4\sqrt{17}}{17}$ **10.** $\frac{\sqrt{14}}{6}$ **11.** $\frac{\sqrt{ab}}{b}$ **12.** $\frac{\sqrt{xy}}{y^2}$ **13.** $\frac{\sqrt{ab}}{b}$ **14.** $\frac{2\sqrt{xy}}{y}$ **15.** $7\sqrt{7}$ **16.** $8\sqrt{2}$ **17.** $3\sqrt{5}$ **18.** $24\sqrt{3}$ **19.** $\sqrt{2a}$ **20.** $17\sqrt{x}$ **21.** $\sqrt{15}-\sqrt{21}$ **22.** $2\sqrt{35}+2\sqrt{15}$ **23.** $8-2\sqrt{7}$ **24.** $39-12\sqrt{3}$ **25.** $8+2\sqrt{15}$ **26.** $4a-b$ **27.** $-\sqrt{3}-2$ **28.** $-\frac{\sqrt{6}-4}{5}$ or $\frac{4-\sqrt{6}}{5}$ **29.** $\frac{\sqrt{a}-b}{a-b^2}$ **30.** $\frac{\sqrt{xy}-x}{y-x}$ **31.** $\frac{a^2-a\sqrt{b}}{a^2-b}$ **32.** $-\frac{11+6\sqrt{2}}{7}$ or $\frac{-11-6\sqrt{2}}{7}$ **33.** $\{64\}$ **34.** $\{53\}$ **35.** $\{4\}$ **37.** $\{1\}$ **38.** $\{3\}$ **39.** $\{-2\}$ **40.** $\{3,4\}$

Chapter 9 cumulative test

1. 45 **2.** x^7 **3.** x^6 **4.** $2x^2+2x+13$ **5.** $8a^4b^3-12a^3b^4+16a^2b^5$ **6.** $2a^3b^2$ **7.** −36 **8.** $9a^2-6ab+b^2$ **9.** $\frac{a-3}{3(a+2)}$ **10.** $16\sqrt{3}$ **11.** −5 **12.** $\frac{x+3}{x-1}$ **13.** $\frac{x\sqrt{x}+\sqrt{xy}}{x^2-y}$ **14.** $9x^2y^3\sqrt{z}$ **15.** $25x^2-y^2$ **16.** $2x-4y$ **17.** $2a^3b^3(3b-b^2+4a^2)$ **18.** $(5c+d)(5c-d)$ **19.** $(2x-1)(x+4)$ **20.** $(y^2+2z)(y^2-2z)$ **21.** $(3x+4)(2x+1)$ **22.** $(x+7)(x-4)$ **23.** $x=-\frac{1}{3}$ **24.** $x=-3$ or $x=3$ **25.** $x=-6$ **26.** $x=12$ **27.** $x>\frac{7}{2}$ **28.** $x=-1$ or $x=-\frac{1}{2}$ **29.** $1<x<8$ **30.** $x=\frac{19}{12}$ **31.** −3 **32.** $y=4x-2$, $m=4, b=-2$ **33.** $\left(\frac{7}{8},\frac{3}{8}\right)$ **34.** 14, 56 **35.** 1,350 **36.** 16, 18 **37.** $\ell = 27$ ft, $w = 21$ ft

Chapter 10

Proficiency check

1. a. 7 **b.** $2\sqrt{10}$ **2. a.** $5x^2 - 15x$ **b.** $4y^2 + 20y + 25$ **c.** $6x^2 + 19x - 7$ **3. a.** $(x - 12)^2$ **b.** $\left(x - \frac{5}{2}\right)^2$ **c.** $\left(x + \frac{1}{3}\right)^2$
4. a. $3x^2 - x + 2$ **b.** $4y^2 + 3y + 10 = 0$

Exercise 10-1

1. $\{-1,3\}$ **2.** $\{-5,2\}$ **3.** $\{-4,-2\}$ **5.** $\{-7,7\}$ **6.** $\{5\}$ **7.** $\{-10\}$ **9.** $\left\{-\frac{1}{2},\frac{5}{2}\right\}$ **10.** $\left\{-1,\frac{4}{5}\right\}$ **11.** $\left\{-1,\frac{5}{2}\right\}$ **13.** $\{-2,2\}$ **14.** $\{-9,9\}$
15. $\{-\sqrt{11},\sqrt{11}\}$ **17.** $\{-2\sqrt{5},2\sqrt{5}\}$ **18.** $\{-2\sqrt{7},2\sqrt{7}\}$ **19.** $\{-4\sqrt{2},4\sqrt{2}\}$ **21.** $\{-3,3\}$ **22.** $\{-\sqrt{15},\sqrt{15}\}$ **23.** $\{-\sqrt{6},\sqrt{6}\}$ **25.** $\{-4,4\}$
26. $\{-4,0\}$ **27.** $\{-10,-2\}$ **29.** $\{-3 - \sqrt{6},-3 + \sqrt{6}\}$ **30.** $\{1 - \sqrt{7},1 + \sqrt{7}\}$ **31.** $\{9 - 3\sqrt{2},9 + 3\sqrt{2}\}$ **33.** $\{-8 - 2\sqrt{2},-8 + 2\sqrt{2}\}$
34. $\{-5 - 4\sqrt{2},-5 + 4\sqrt{2}\}$ **35.** $\left\{-\frac{1}{2},\frac{7}{2}\right\}$ **37.** $\{-9,9\}$ **38.** $5m$ **39.** $3\sqrt{5}$ cm **41.** 4 yd

Solutions to trial exercise problems

6. $y^2 - 10y + 25 = 0$
$(y - 5)^2 = 0$ Factor left member.
$y - 5 = 0$ Set factor equal to 0.
$y = 5$
The solution set is $\{5\}$.

11. $x^2 - \frac{3}{2}x - \frac{5}{2} = 0$
$2x^2 - 3x - 5 = 0$ Multiply by 2.
$(2x - 5)(x + 1) = 0$ Factor the left member.
$2x - 5 = 0$ or $x + 1 = 0$ Set each factor equal to 0.
$x = \frac{5}{2}$ $\quad x = -1$
The solution set is $\left\{-1,\frac{5}{2}\right\}$.

17. $a^2 = 20$
Extract the roots.
$a = \sqrt{20}$ or $a = -\sqrt{20}$
$= \sqrt{4 \cdot 5}$ or $a = -\sqrt{4 \cdot 5}$
$= 2\sqrt{5}$ or $a = -2\sqrt{5}$
The solution set is $\{-2\sqrt{5},2\sqrt{5}\}$.

26. $(x + 2)^2 = 4$
Extract the roots.
$x + 2 = 2$ or $x + 2 = -2$
Add -2 to each member.
So $x = -2 + 2$ or $x = -2 - 2$
$x = 0$ $\quad x = -4$
The solution set is $\{-4,0\}$.

22. $5x^2 = 75$
Divide each member by 5.
$x^2 = 15$
Extract the roots.
$x = \sqrt{15}$ or $x = -\sqrt{15}$
The solution set is $\{-\sqrt{15},\sqrt{15}\}$.

31. $(x - 9)^2 = 18$
Extract the roots.
$x - 9 = \sqrt{18} = 3\sqrt{2}$ or $x - 9 = -\sqrt{18} = -3\sqrt{2}$
Add 9 to each member.
$x = 9 + 3\sqrt{2}$ or $x = 9 - 3\sqrt{2}$
The solution set is $\{9 - 3\sqrt{2},9 + 3\sqrt{2}\}$.

Review exercises

1. $x^2 - 4x + 4$ **2.** $9z^2 + 12z + 4$ **3.** $(x + 9)^2$ **4.** $(3y + 5)^2$ **5.** $\frac{3x^2 - 7x}{(x + 2)(x - 2)}$ **6.** $\frac{1}{(x - 2)(x + 3)}$

Exercise 10-2

1. $x^2 + 10x + 25 = (x + 5)^2$ **2.** $x^2 + 4x + 4 = (x + 2)^2$ **3.** $z^2 - 12z + 36 = (z - 6)^2$ **5.** $x^2 + 24x + 144 = (x + 12)^2$
6. $y^2 + 16y + 64 = (y + 8)^2$ **7.** $y^2 - 20y + 100 = (y - 10)^2$ **9.** $x^2 + x + \frac{1}{4} = \left(x + \frac{1}{2}\right)^2$ **10.** $x^2 + 11x + \frac{121}{4} = \left(x + \frac{11}{2}\right)^2$
11. $x^2 - 7x + \frac{49}{4} = \left(x - \frac{7}{2}\right)^2$ **13.** $x^2 + \frac{1}{2}x + \frac{1}{16} = \left(x + \frac{1}{4}\right)^2$ **14.** $z^2 + \frac{1}{4}z + \frac{1}{64} = \left(z + \frac{1}{8}\right)^2$ **15.** $z^2 - \frac{1}{5}z + \frac{1}{100} = \left(z - \frac{1}{10}\right)^2$
17. $\{-7,-1\}$ **18.** $\{-11,-1\}$ **19.** $\{-2,6\}$ **21.** $\{1,3\}$ **22.** $\{-13,-1\}$ **23.** $\left\{\frac{1 - \sqrt{5}}{2},\frac{1 + \sqrt{5}}{2}\right\}$ **25.** $\left\{\frac{-21 - \sqrt{401}}{2},\frac{-21 + \sqrt{401}}{2}\right\}$
26. $\{-4 - \sqrt{19},-4 + \sqrt{19}\}$ **27.** $\left\{\frac{-1 - \sqrt{13}}{2},\frac{-1 + \sqrt{13}}{2}\right\}$ **29.** $\left\{-3,-\frac{1}{2}\right\}$ **30.** $\left\{\frac{-4 - 2\sqrt{7}}{3},\frac{-4 + 2\sqrt{7}}{3}\right\}$ **31.** $\left\{\frac{2}{3},\frac{3}{2}\right\}$
33. $\{-1 - \sqrt{5}, -1 + \sqrt{5}\}$ **34.** $\left\{\frac{-2}{3},\frac{1}{2}\right\}$ **35.** $\left\{\frac{-1 - \sqrt{29}}{2},\frac{-1 + \sqrt{29}}{2}\right\}$ **37.** $\left\{-4,\frac{2}{3}\right\}$ **38.** $\left\{\frac{1}{4},\frac{3}{2}\right\}$ **39.** 12 in. and 8 in.
41. 15 mm and 7 mm **42.** 13 in. and 6 in. **43.** 17 in. and 9 in. **45.** $5\frac{1}{2}$ m and $3\frac{1}{2}$ m **46.** 13 in. and 9 in. **47.** 14 rods and 6 rods

Solutions to trial exercise problems

3. $z^2 - 12z$

Square one-half of the coefficient of z, -12.

$\left[\frac{1}{2}(-12)\right]^2 = (-6)^2 = 36$

Then $z^2 - 12z + 36 = (z - 6)^2$.

13. $x^2 + \frac{1}{2}x$

Square one-half of the coefficient of x, $\frac{1}{2}$.

$\left[\frac{1}{2}\left(\frac{1}{2}\right)\right]^2 = \left(\frac{1}{4}\right)^2 = \frac{1}{16}$

So $x^2 + \frac{1}{2}x + \frac{1}{16} = \left(x + \frac{1}{4}\right)^2$.

23. $u^2 - u - 1 = 0$

Add 1 to each member.

$u^2 - u = 1$

Add $\left[\frac{1}{2}(-1)\right]^2 = \left(-\frac{1}{2}\right)^2 = \frac{1}{4}$ to each member.

$u^2 - u + \frac{1}{4} = 1 + \frac{1}{4}$

Then $\left(u - \frac{1}{2}\right)^2 = \frac{5}{4}$. Then

$u - \frac{1}{2} = \pm\sqrt{\frac{5}{4}} = \pm\frac{\sqrt{5}}{2}$,

so $u = \frac{1}{2} \pm \frac{\sqrt{5}}{2} = \frac{1 \pm \sqrt{5}}{2}$.

Then $u = \frac{1 + \sqrt{5}}{2}$ or $u = \frac{1 - \sqrt{5}}{2}$.

$\left\{\frac{1 + \sqrt{5}}{2}, \frac{1 - \sqrt{5}}{2}\right\}$

26.
$x^2 + 8x = 3$

$x^2 + 8x + 16 = 3 + 16$ Complete the square.

$(x + 4)^2 = 19$

$x + 4 = \pm\sqrt{19}$ Extract the roots.

$x = -4 + \sqrt{19}, x = -4 - \sqrt{19}$

$\{-4 - \sqrt{19}, -4 + \sqrt{19}\}$

35. $(x + 3)(x - 2) = 1$

Perform the indicated multiplication in the left member.

$x^2 + x - 6 = 1$

Add 6 to each member to get $x^2 + x = 7$.

Add $\left[\frac{1}{2}(1)\right]^2 = \left(\frac{1}{2}\right)^2 = \frac{1}{4}$ to each member.

Thus $x^2 + x + \frac{1}{4} = 7 + \frac{1}{4}$

$\left(x + \frac{1}{2}\right)^2 = \frac{29}{4}$.

Then $x + \frac{1}{2} = \pm\sqrt{\frac{29}{4}} = \pm\frac{\sqrt{29}}{2}$

so $x = -\frac{1}{2} \pm \frac{\sqrt{29}}{2} = \frac{-1 \pm \sqrt{29}}{2}$

then $x = \frac{-1 + \sqrt{29}}{2}$ or $x = \frac{-1 - \sqrt{29}}{2}$.

$\left\{\frac{-1 + \sqrt{29}}{2}, \frac{-1 - \sqrt{29}}{2}\right\}$

41. By "a rectangular solid has a width w that is 8 millimeters shorter than its length ℓ," we get ℓ = the length of the part and $\ell - 8$ = the width of the part. Then given area $A = 105$ square millimeters, and using $A = \ell w$, $\ell(\ell - 8) = 105$, then $\ell^2 - 8\ell = 105$.

Add $\left[\frac{1}{2}(-8)\right]^2 = (-4)^2 = 16$ to both members.

$\ell^2 - 8\ell + 16 = 105 + 16$

$(\ell - 4)^2 = 121$

$\ell - 4 = \pm\sqrt{121} = \pm 11$

so $\ell - 4 = 11$ or $\ell - 4 = -11$.

Then

$\ell = 4 + 11$ or $\ell = 4 - 11$.

$\ell = 15$ $\ell = -7$

Since a rectangle must have positive length, -7 is ruled out. So the length $\ell = 15$ millimeters and the width $\ell - 8 = 7$ millimeters.

Review exercises

1. 3 **2.** $3\sqrt{5}$ **3.** (2,0) **4.**

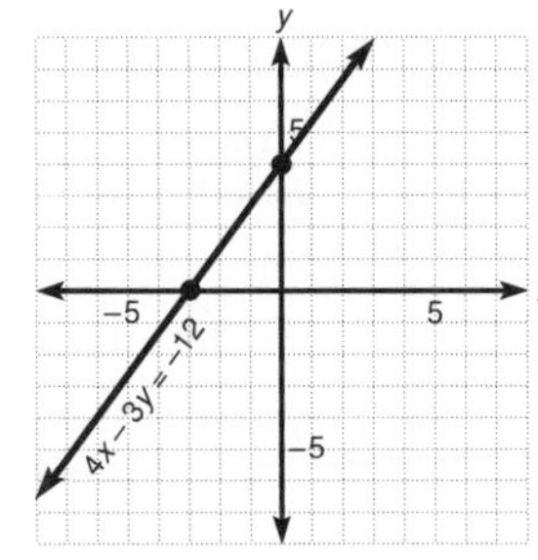

5. 9 dozen **6.** $\left\{x \mid x > -\frac{2}{5}\right\}$

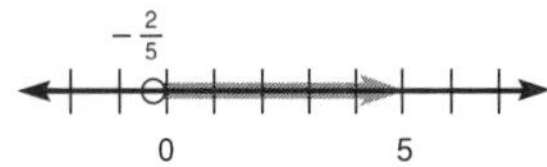

Exercise 10–3

1. $a = 1, b = -3, c = 8$ **2.** $a = 1, b = 1, c = -2$ **3.** $a = 5, b = -1, c = 6$ **5.** $a = 6, b = 2, c = -1$ **6.** $a = 3, b = -1, c = -9$ **7.** $a = 4, b = -2, c = 1$ **9.** $a = 1, b = 3, c = 0$ **10.** $a = 3, b = -4, c = 0$ **11.** $a = 5, b = 0, c = -2$ **13.** $a = 2, b = -18, c = -1$ **14.** $a = 1, b = 3, c = -4$ **15.** $a = 1, b = 2, c = -9$ **17.** $\{-3\}$ **18.** $\{2, 1\}$ **19.** $\left\{3, \frac{1}{2}\right\}$ **21.** $\left\{\frac{9 - \sqrt{65}}{2}, \frac{9 + \sqrt{65}}{2}\right\}$ **22.** $\{6, -1\}$ **23.** $\{4 - \sqrt{15}, 4 + \sqrt{15}\}$ **25.** $\left\{\frac{5 - \sqrt{97}}{6}, \frac{5 + \sqrt{97}}{6}\right\}$ **26.** $\left\{\frac{3}{2}, \frac{1}{2}\right\}$ **27.** $\{-5, 5\}$ **29.** $\{-\sqrt{2}, \sqrt{2}\}$ **30.** $\{0, 3\}$

31. $\{0, 4\}$ **33.** $\left\{\frac{5-\sqrt{85}}{10}, \frac{5+\sqrt{85}}{10}\right\}$ **34.** $\left\{\frac{-2+\sqrt{11}}{2}, \frac{-2-\sqrt{11}}{2}\right\}$ **35.** $\left\{\frac{3+\sqrt{41}}{4}, \frac{3-\sqrt{41}}{4}\right\}$ **37. a.** $t = 2$ sec **b.** $t = \sqrt{6} \approx 2.5$ sec **c.** $t = \frac{\sqrt{30}}{2} \approx 2.7$ sec **38. a.** $t = \frac{3}{2}$ sec **b.** $t = 1$ sec **39. a.** $-20 + 20\sqrt{11} \approx 46.33$ amps **b.** $\frac{-15 + 5\sqrt{329}}{2} \approx 37.85$ amps **41.** $h = 8$ in., $b = 24$ in. **42.** $b = 8$ in., $h = 13$ in. **43.** 6 mm and 8 mm **45.** 6,000 units or 2,000 units **46.** 5,000 units or 3,000 units **47.** 22 **49.** $\ell = 17$ ft, $w = 12$ ft **50.** $w = 11$ cm, $\ell = 21$ cm

Solutions to trial exercise problems

5. $-6z^2 - 2z + 1 = 0$
$6z^2 + 2z - 1 = 0$ Multiply by -1 (standard form).
$a = 6, b = 2, c = -1$.

9. $x^2 = -3x$
Add $3x$ to each member. Then
$x^2 + 3x = 0$ and
$a = 1, b = 3, c = 0$.

13. $2x(x - 9) = 1$
Perform the indicated multiplication.
$2x^2 - 18x = 1$
Add -1 to each member.
$2x^2 - 18x - 1 = 0$ so
$a = 2, b = -18, c = -1$.

17. $y^2 + 6y + 9 = 0$
Now $a = 1$, $b = 6$, and $c = 9$ so
$$y = \frac{-6 \pm \sqrt{(6)^2 - 4(1)(9)}}{2(1)} = \frac{-6 \pm \sqrt{36 - 36}}{2} = \frac{-6 \pm \sqrt{0}}{2} = \frac{-6}{2} = -3$$
The solution set is $\{-3\}$.

26. $4t^2 = 8t - 3$
Add $3 - 8t$ to each member.
$4t^2 - 8t + 3 = 0$
So $a = 4, b = -8, c = 3$,
$$\text{and } t = \frac{-(-8) \pm \sqrt{(-8)^2 - 4(4)(3)}}{2(4)} = \frac{8 \pm \sqrt{64 - 48}}{8} = \frac{8 \pm \sqrt{16}}{8}$$
$$\text{so } t = \frac{8 \pm 4}{8}$$
Then $t = \frac{8+4}{8} = \frac{12}{8} = \frac{3}{2}$ or $t = \frac{8-4}{8} = \frac{4}{8} = \frac{1}{2}$.
The solution set is $\left\{\frac{1}{2}, \frac{3}{2}\right\}$.

31. $x^2 = 4x$
Add $-4x$ to each member and write the equation as
$x^2 - 4x + 0 = 0$.
So $a = 1, b = -4, c = 0$,
$$\text{and } x = \frac{-(-4) \pm \sqrt{(-4)^2 - 4(1)(0)}}{2(1)} = \frac{4 \pm \sqrt{16}}{2} = \frac{4 \pm 4}{2}$$
Then $x = \frac{4+4}{2} = \frac{8}{2} = 4$ or $x = \frac{4-4}{2} = \frac{0}{2} = 0$.
The solution set is $\{0,4\}$.

33. $y^2 - y = \frac{3}{5}$
$5y^2 - 5y = 3$ Multiply by 5.
$5y^2 - 5y - 3 = 0$ Standard form
$a = 5, b = -5, c = -3$.
$$y = \frac{-(-5) \pm \sqrt{(-5)^2 - 4(5)(-3)}}{2(5)} = \frac{5 \pm \sqrt{25 + 60}}{10} = \frac{5 \pm \sqrt{85}}{10}$$
$$y = \frac{5 + \sqrt{85}}{10} \text{ or } \frac{5 - \sqrt{85}}{10}$$
The solution set is $\left\{\frac{5-\sqrt{85}}{10}, \frac{5+\sqrt{85}}{10}\right\}$.

37a. $s = \frac{1}{2}gt^2$
$g = 32$ and $s = 64$
$64 = \frac{1}{2}(32)t^2$
$64 = 16t^2$
$t^2 = 4$
$t = \pm 2$
Object will fall 64 ft in 2 sec.
(Reject $t = -2$ since time is positive.)

43. $x^2 + (x + 2)^2 = 10^2$ Pythagorean theorem.
$x^2 + x^2 + 4x + 4 = 100$ Multiply.
$2x^2 + 4x - 96 = 0$
$2(x^2 + 2x - 48) = 0$
$2(x + 8)(x - 6) = 0$
$x + 8 = 0$ or $x - 6 = 0$
$x = -8$ $\quad x = 6$
Reject -8 since we want the length of a leg.
$x = 6$
$x + 2 = 8$
The legs are 6 mm and 8 mm in length.

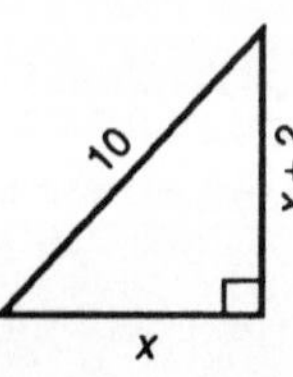

Review exercises

1.

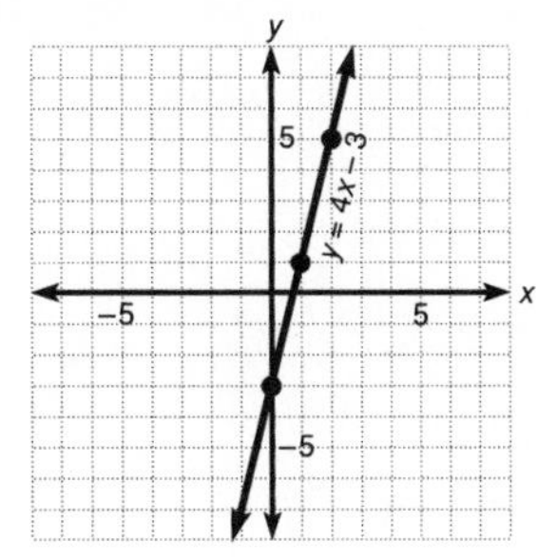

2.

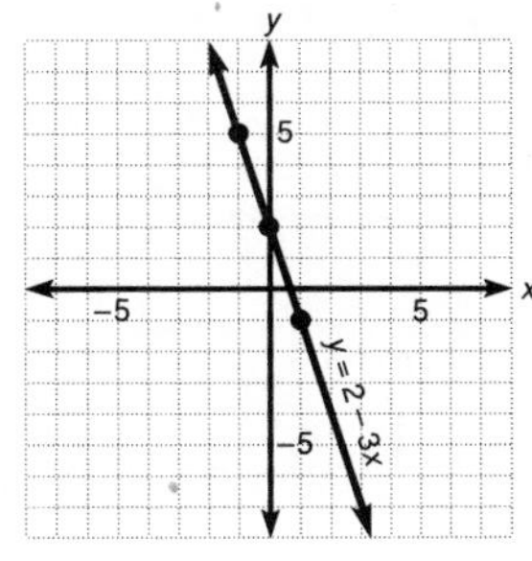

3.

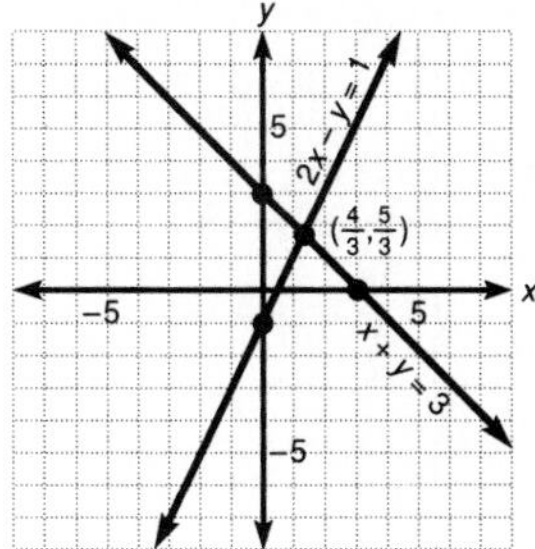

4. $8x - 3y = 17$ **5.** $\dfrac{3(x + 1)}{4x}$ **6.** $\dfrac{2(x - 4)}{(x + 2)(x - 2)(x - 3)}$

Exercise 10–4

1. (4,0), (−4,0), (0,−16) **2.** (3,0), (−3,0), (0,−9) **3.** (4,0), (2,0), (0,8) **5.** (−3,0), (0,9) **6.** (2,0), (0,4) **7.** (4,0), (0,−16)
9. no x-intercept, (0,6) **10.** no x-intercept, (0,9) **11.** $\left(-\frac{1}{2},0\right)$, (−1,0), (0,1) **13.** (−2,0), $\left(\frac{3}{2},0\right)$, (0,6) **14.** (3,0), $\left(-\frac{2}{3},0\right)$, (0,6)
15. (0,−16), $x = 0$ **17.** (3,−1), $x = 3$ **18.** (−1,−9), $x = -1$ **19.** (−3,0), $x = -3$ **21.** (4,0), $x = 4$ **22.** (4,4), $x = 4$
23. (0,6), $x = 0$ **25.** $\left(-\frac{3}{4},-\frac{1}{8}\right)$, $x = \frac{-3}{4}$ **26.** $\left(\frac{7}{4},-\frac{1}{8}\right)$, $x = \frac{7}{4}$ **27.** $\left(-\frac{1}{4},\frac{49}{8}\right)$, $x = -\frac{1}{4}$

29.

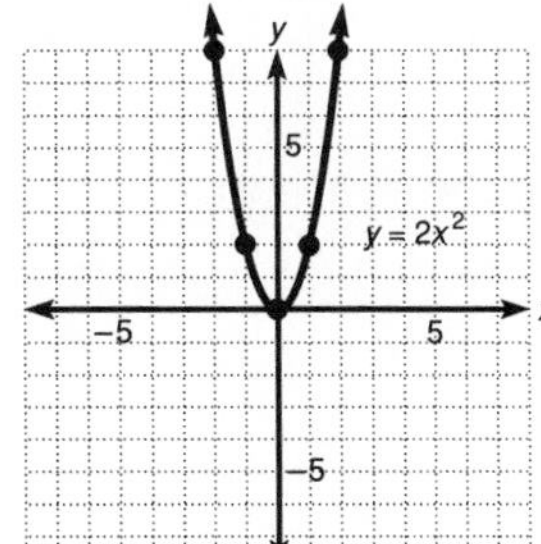

x-intercept, y-intercept, vertex, (0,0)

30.

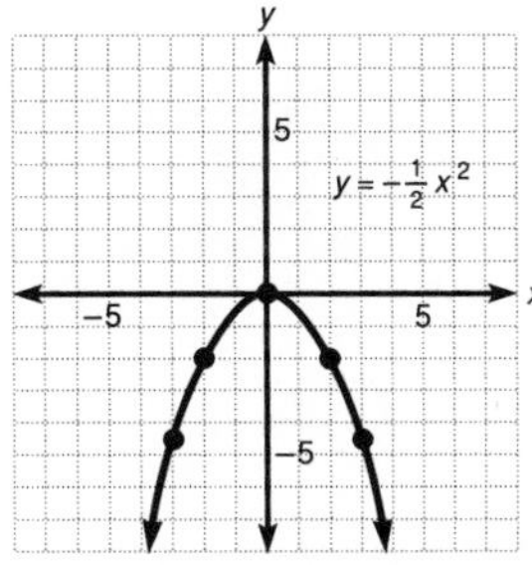

x-intercept, y-intercept, vertex, (0,0)

31.

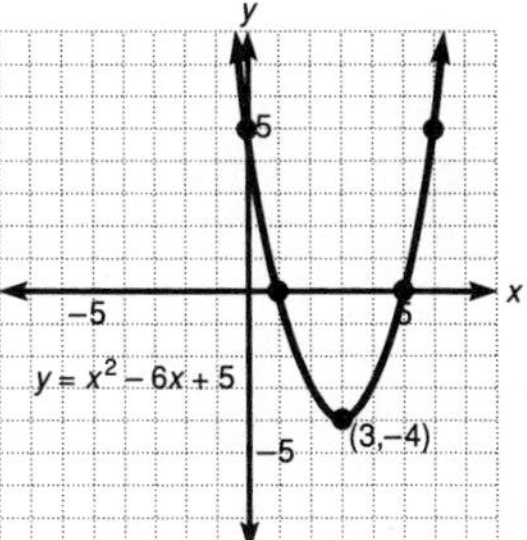

x-intercepts, (5,0), (1,0); y-intercept, (0,5); vertex, (3,−4)

33.

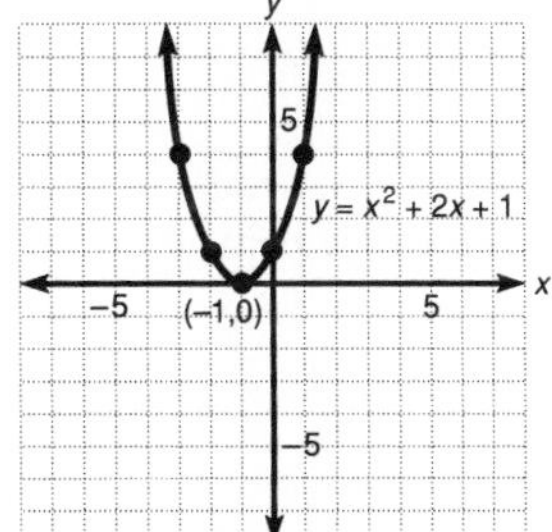

x-intercept, (−1,0); y-intercept, (1,0); vertex, (−1,0)

34.

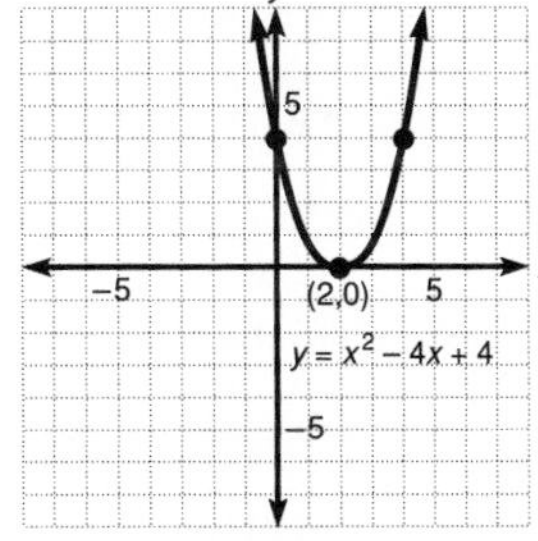

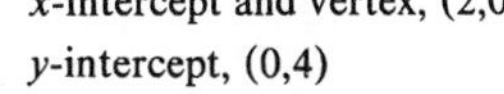

x-intercept and vertex, (2,0); y-intercept, (0,4)

35.

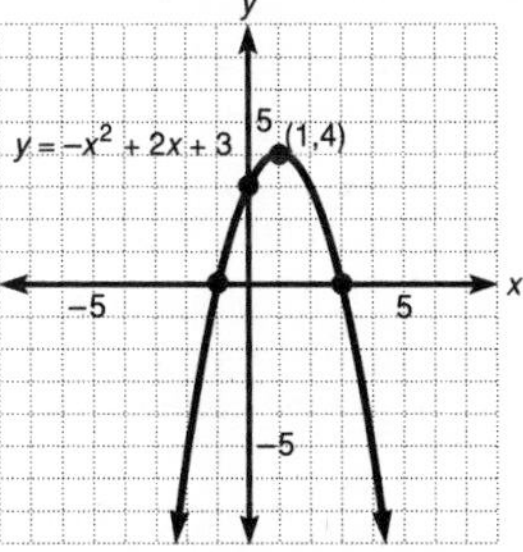

x-intercepts, (3,0), (−1,0); y-intercept, (0,3); vertex, (1,4)

37.

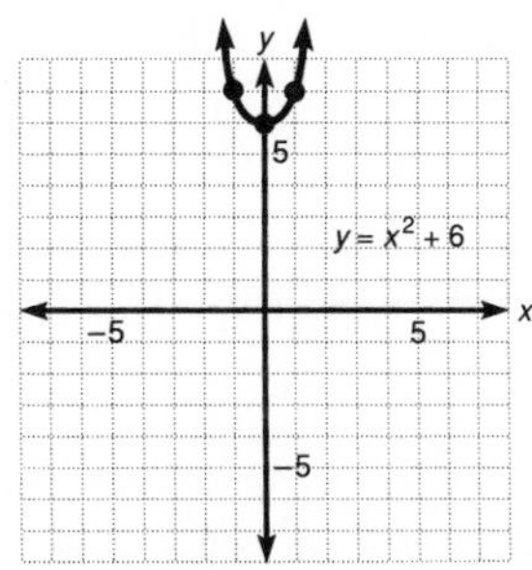

no x-intercept; y-intercept and vertex, (0,6)

38.

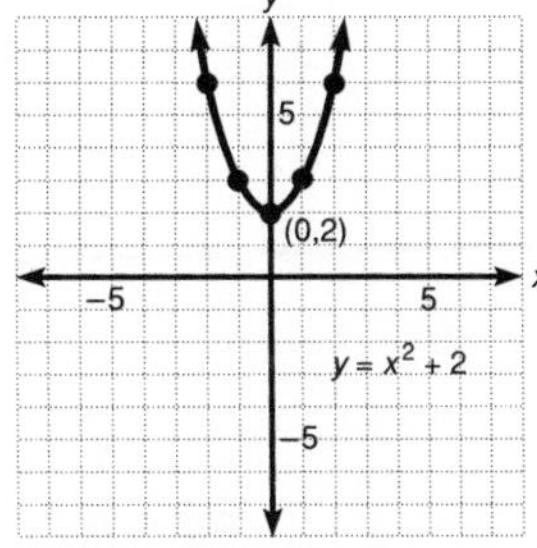

no x-intercept;

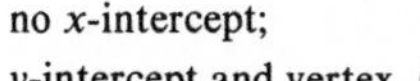

y-intercept and vertex, (0,2)

39.

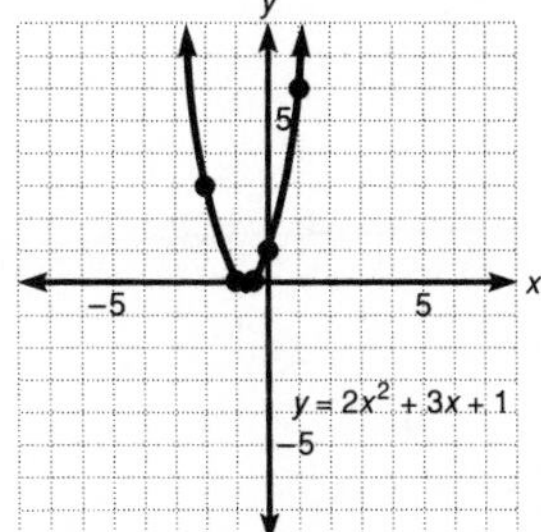

x-intercepts, $\left(-\frac{1}{2},0\right)$, (−1,0); y-intercept, (0,1); vertex, $\left(-\frac{3}{4},-\frac{1}{8}\right)$

41.

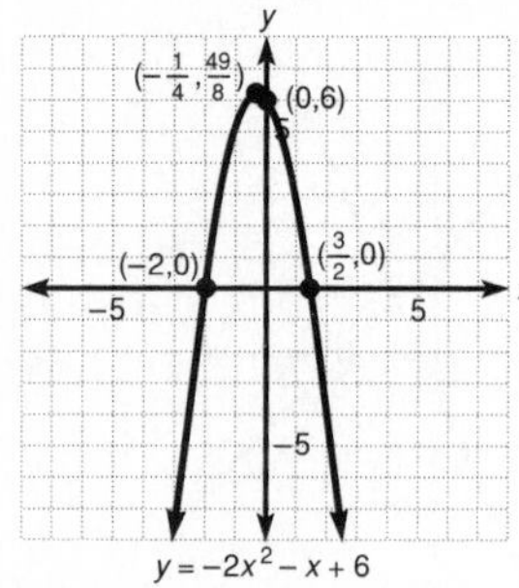

x-intercepts, $(-2,0)$, $\left(\frac{3}{2},0\right)$;

y-intercept, $(0,6)$; vertex, $\left(-\frac{1}{4},\frac{49}{8}\right)$

42.

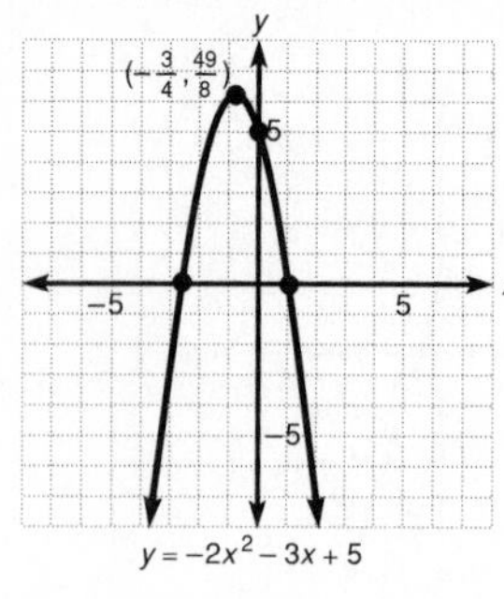

x-intercepts, $(1,0)$, $\left(-\frac{5}{2},0\right)$;

y-intercept, $(0,5)$; vertex, $\left(-\frac{3}{4},\frac{49}{8}\right)$

43.

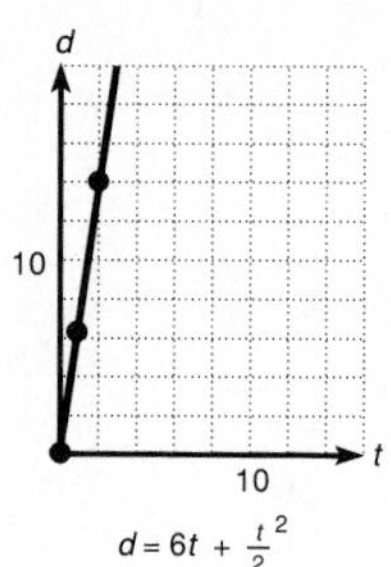

$t = 2$ sec

45.

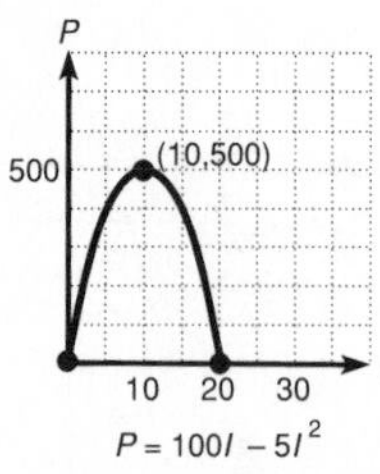

I-intercepts, $(0,0)$, $(20,0)$;

P-intercept, $(0,0)$; vertex, $(10,500)$

46.

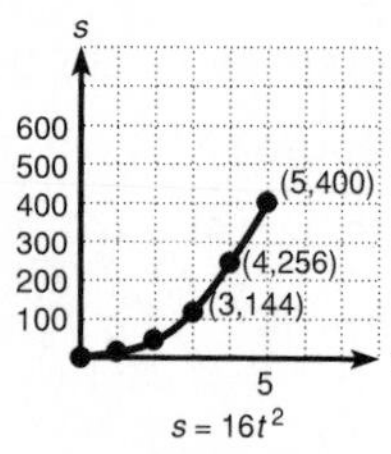

t-intercept, s-intercept, and vertex, $(0,0)$

47.

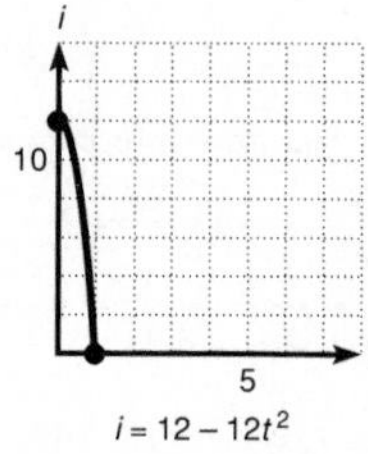

t-intercepts, $(-1,0)$, $(1,0)$;

i-intercept and vertex, $(0,12)$

49.

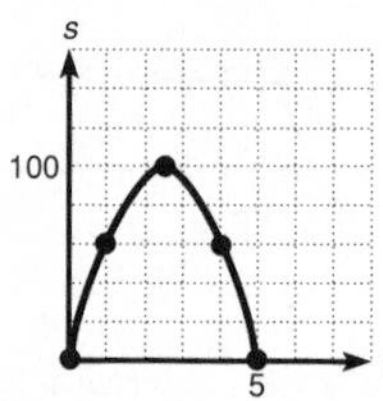

$h = 100$ ft when $t = 2.5$ sec,
will strike the ground at $t = 5$ sec

Solutions to trial exercise problems

3. $y = x^2 - 6x + 8$
Let $x = 0$, then $y = 0^2 - 6(0) + 8 = 8$. $(0,8)$
Let $y = 0$, then $0 = x^2 - 6x + 8$. Factor the right member.
$0 = (x - 4)(x - 2)$; $x - 4 = 0$ or $x - 2 = 0$
so $x = 4$ or $x = 2$ $(4,0)$, $(2,0)$
The y-intercept is 8 and the x-intercepts are 4 and 2.

11. $y = 2x^2 + 3x + 1$
Let $x = 0$, then $y = 2(0)^2 + 3(0) + 1 = 1$. $(0,1)$
Let $y = 0$, then $0 = 2x^2 + 3x + 1$. Factor the right member.
$0 = (2x + 1)(x + 1)$
then $2x + 1 = 0$ or $x + 1 = 0$
so $x = -\frac{1}{2}$ or $x = -1$ $\left(-\frac{1}{2},0\right)$, $(-1,0)$
The y-intercept is 1 and the x-intercepts are $-\frac{1}{2}$ and -1.

17. $y = x^2 - 6x + 8$
Now $a = 1$ and $b = -6$
so $x = \frac{-b}{2a} = -\frac{-6}{2(1)} = 3$,
then $y = (3)^2 - 6(3) + 8$
$= 9 - 18 + 8$
$= -1$
The vertex is at $(3,-1)$. Axis of symmetry is $x = 3$.

25. $y = 2x^2 + 3x + 1$
Now $a = 2$ and $b = 3$ so $x = \frac{-b}{2a} = -\frac{3}{2(2)} = -\frac{3}{4}$. Then

$$y = 2\left(-\frac{3}{4}\right)^2 + 3\left(-\frac{3}{4}\right) + 1$$
$$= 2\left(\frac{9}{16}\right) - \frac{9}{4} + 1$$
$$= \frac{9}{8} - \frac{18}{8} + 1$$
$$= -\frac{9}{8} + 1 = -\frac{1}{8}$$

The vertex is at $\left(-\frac{3}{4},-\frac{1}{8}\right)$. Axis of symmetry is $x = -\frac{3}{4}$.

31. $y = x^2 - 6x + 5$

x	y	
0	5	y-intercept
5	0	x-intercepts
1	0	
3	-4	vertex
2	-3	arbitrary points
4	-3	
6	5	

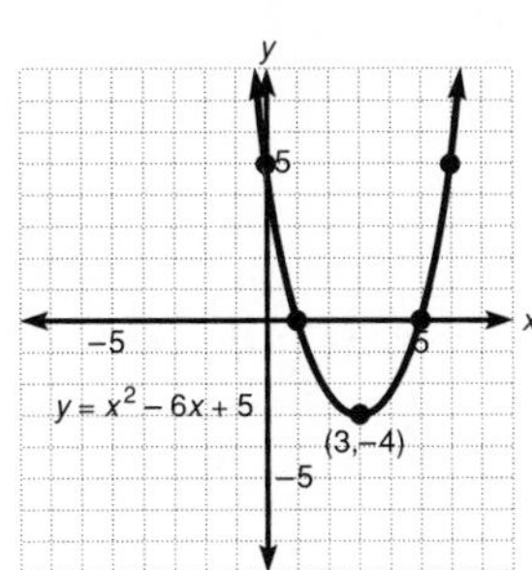

39. $y = 2x^2 + 3x + 1$

x	y	
0	1	y-intercept
$-\frac{1}{2}$	0	x-intercepts
-1	0	
$-\frac{3}{4}$	$-\frac{1}{8}$	vertex
1	6	arbitrary points
-2	3	
-3	10	

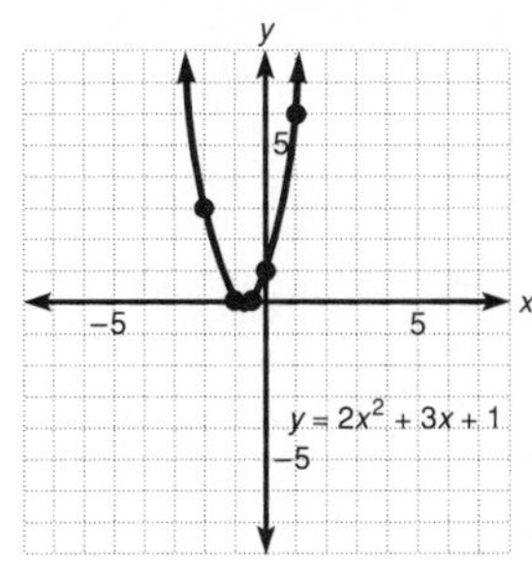

43. $d = 6t + \frac{t^2}{2}$ (*Note:* We must choose $t \geq 0$.)

$$d = 6t + \frac{t^2}{2}$$
$$14 = 6t + \frac{t^2}{2}$$
$$28 = 12t + t^2$$
$$t^2 + 12t - 28 = 0$$
$$(t + 14)(t - 2) = 0$$
$$t = -14 \text{ or } t = 2$$

Reject -14.

$$t = 2 \text{ sec and } d = 6(2) + \frac{2^2}{2}$$
$$= 12 + 2$$
$$= 14 \text{ feet}$$

t	d
0	0
1	$\frac{13}{2}$ or $6\frac{1}{2}$
2	14
3	$\frac{45}{2}$ or $22\frac{1}{2}$
4	32

$t = 2$ seconds when $d = 14$ feet

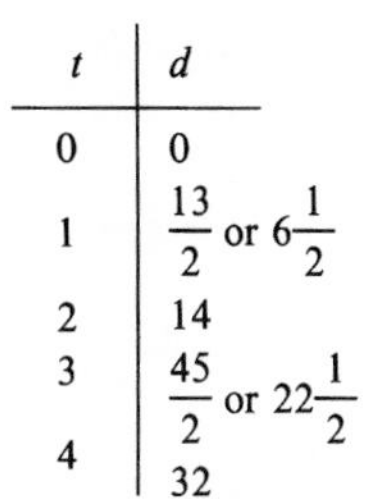

It takes 2 seconds to travel 14 feet.

Chapter 10 review

1. $\{-10, 10\}$ 2. $\{-5, 5\}$ 3. $\{-\sqrt{2}, \sqrt{2}\}$ 4. $\{-\sqrt{6}, \sqrt{6}\}$ 5. $\{-2, 2\}$ 6. $\{-2\sqrt{3}, 2\sqrt{3}\}$ 7. $\{-4, 4\}$ 8. $\{-2\sqrt{3}, 2\sqrt{3}\}$

9. $\left\{-\frac{3\sqrt{11}}{2}, \frac{3\sqrt{11}}{2}\right\}$ 10. $\{2,4\}$ 11. $\{-2,12\}$ 12. $\left\{\frac{-5 - \sqrt{41}}{2}, \frac{-5 + \sqrt{41}}{2}\right\}$ 13. $\frac{3 - 2\sqrt{6}}{3}, \frac{3 + 2\sqrt{6}}{3}$ 14. $\left\{1, \frac{5}{2}\right\}$

15. $\left\{\frac{11 + \sqrt{101}}{2}, \frac{11 - \sqrt{101}}{2}\right\}$ 16. $\left\{\frac{3 + \sqrt{41}}{8}, \frac{3 - \sqrt{41}}{8}\right\}$ 17. $\left\{\frac{1 - \sqrt{13}}{2}, \frac{1 + \sqrt{13}}{2}\right\}$ 18. $\left\{-\frac{3}{4}, 1\right\}$ 19. $\left\{\frac{5}{3}, -2\right\}$

20. $\ell = 8\ m, w = 2\ m$ 21. $\{1 - \sqrt{6}, 1 + \sqrt{6}\}$ 22. $\{-2 - 2\sqrt{3}, -2 + 2\sqrt{3}\}$ 23. $\left\{-1, \frac{5}{2}\right\}$ 24. $\left\{\frac{-7 - \sqrt{145}}{6}, \frac{-7 + \sqrt{145}}{6}\right\}$

25. $\left\{\frac{-3\sqrt{2}}{2}, \frac{3\sqrt{2}}{2}\right\}$ 26. $\left\{-\frac{7}{4}, 0\right\}$ 27. $\left\{\frac{1 + \sqrt{13}}{3}, \frac{1 - \sqrt{13}}{3}\right\}$ 28. $\left\{\frac{4 - \sqrt{34}}{6}, \frac{4 + \sqrt{34}}{6}\right\}$ 29. 6 in., 9 in.

30.

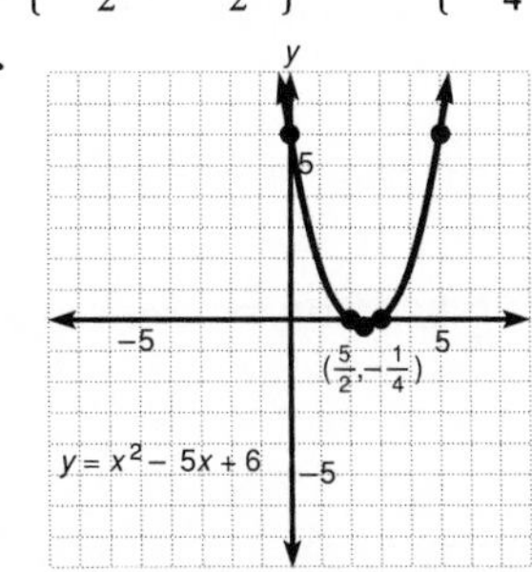

x-intercepts, (3,0), (2,0);

y-intercept, (0,6); vertex, $\left(2\frac{1}{2}, -\frac{1}{4}\right)$

31.

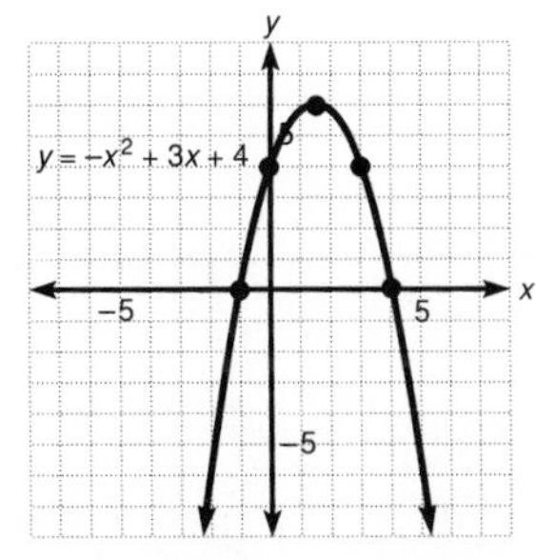

x-intercepts, $(-1,0)$, (4,0);

y-intercept, (0,4); vertex, $\left(\frac{3}{2}, \frac{25}{4}\right)$

Final examination

1. $|-5| > |4|$ **2.** 42 **3.** 0 **4.** -52 **5.** x^6 **6.** $\frac{1}{2x^5}$ **7.** $-12x^3y^5$ **8.** $\frac{y^6}{27x^3}$ **9.** 1 **10.** $7x^2 - 8y^2$ **11.** $-3y$ **12.** $y^2 - 81$ **13.** $49z^2 - 42wz + 9w^2$ **14.** $5x^3 + 17x^2 - 11x + 4$ **15.** $5y - 3x^3 + xy$ **16.** $4y + 1 - \frac{2}{2y - 1}$ **17.** $\{7\}$ **18.** $\left\{-\frac{8}{3}\right\}$ **19.** $\{-1,12\}$ **20.** $\left\{\frac{1}{3},2\right\}$ **21.** $\left\{0,\frac{3}{2}\right\}$ **22.** $3x(x - 2y + 3)$ **23.** $(a - 7)(a + 3)$ **24.** $(2x - 5)(2x - 1)$ **25.** $(3a + 8)(3a - 8)$ **26.** $(2a + b)(3x - y)$ **27.** $(x - 5)^2$ **28.** $-12, -11$ or $11, 12$ **29.** $\frac{x + 1}{x + 2}$ **30.** $\frac{x - 2}{12}$ **31.** $\frac{14}{x - 6}$ **32.** $\frac{x^2 - 6x + 14}{(x + 5)(x - 5)}$ **33.** $\frac{5y + 4}{4y - 6}$ **34.** $x = \frac{16}{5}$ **35.** $\frac{21}{40}$ **36.** $2x + y = 1$ **37.** $m = \frac{2}{3}, b = -3$ **38.** $(-19,-11)$ **39.** $\ell = 12$ ft, $w = 5$ ft **40.** $-\sqrt{3}$ **41.** $\sqrt{6} + 3$ **42.** 13 **43.** $11 - 4\sqrt{7}$ **44.** $\frac{9 + 3\sqrt{5}}{4}$ **45.** -3 **46.** $-12 - 7 \cdot \sqrt{6}$ **47.** $\{0, -1\}$ **48.**

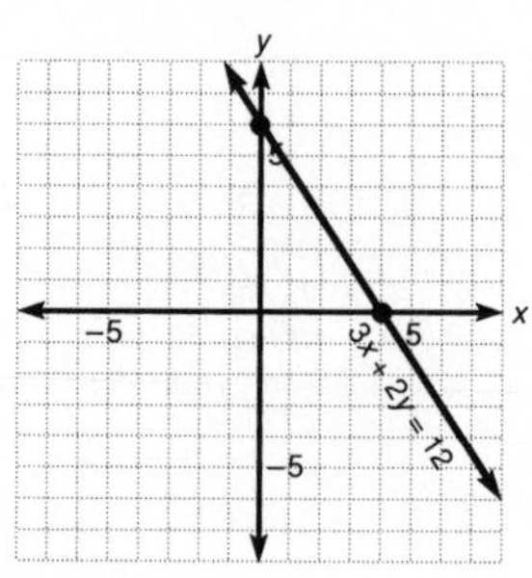

x-intercept, (4,0);
y-intercept, (0,6)

49.

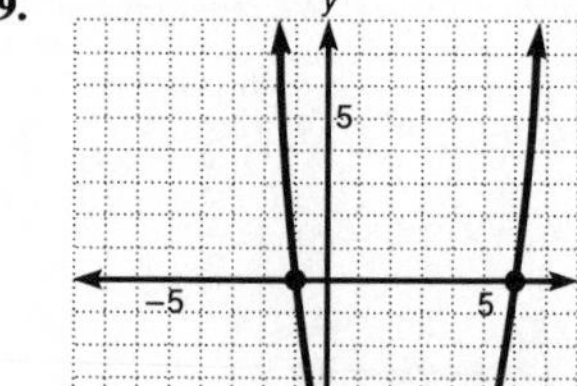

x-intercepts, $(-1,0)$, $(6,0)$;
y-intercept, $(0,-6)$; vertex, $\left(\frac{5}{2}, -\frac{49}{4}\right)$

50. $\left\{\frac{7 - \sqrt{97}}{8},\frac{7 + \sqrt{97}}{8}\right\}$ **51.** $y < 3$ **52.** $x \geq 4$ **53.** $-2 \leq x < 1$

Index

Symbols

Symbol	Means or Is Read	Section Number
$\emptyset$	Empty set or null set	9–6
$\approx$	Is approximately equal to	1–1
$<$	Less than	1–1
$>$	Greater than	1–1
$\leq$	Less than or equal to	2–6
$\geq$	Greater than or equal to	2–6
$\lvert x \rvert$	Absolute value of x	1–1
a^n	The nth power of a	3–1
a^0	a to the zero power ($a^0 = 1, a \neq 0$)	3–4
a^{-n}	a to the negative n power $\left(a^{-n} = \frac{1}{a^n}, a \neq 0\right)$	3–4
$\{\ \}$	Solution set	4–6
$a:b$	Ratio of a to b	5–4
(x,y)	Ordered pair	7–1
m	Slope of a line	7–3
$(ax + by = c, (a > 0)$	Standard form of a line	7–3
$y - y_1 = m(x - x_1)$	Point-slope form of a line	7–3
$y = mx + b$	Slope-intercept form of a line	7–3
$\sqrt[n]{a}$	The principal nth root of a	9–1
$\pm$	Plus or minus	10–3
$\frac{-b \pm \sqrt{b^2 - 4ac}}{2a}$	Quadratic formula	10–3
$y = ax^2 + bx + c, (a \neq 0)$	Standard form of the equation of a parabola	10–4